PBO

SMALL CRAFT
ALMANAC
2002

EDITOR
Edward Lee-Elliott

THE UNITED KINGDOM & IRELAND
AND DENMARK TO GIBRALTAR

PBO
SMALL CRAFT
ALMANAC
2 0 0 2

Editor: Edward Lee-Elliott
Consultant editors: Brian Goulder, Basil D'Oliveira & Gary Rowitt

The Editors would like to thank the many official bodies who have kindly provided essential information in the preparation of this Almanac. They include the UK Hydrographic Office, Trinity House, Northern Lighthouse Board, Irish Lights, HM Nautical Almanac Office, HM Stationery Office, HM Customs, Meteorological Office, Maritime and Coastguard Agency.

Information from the Admiralty List of Lights, Admiralty Tide Tables, and the Admiralty List of Radio Signals is reproduced with the permission of the UK Hydrographic Office and the Controller of HMSO. Extracts from the following are published by permission of the Controller of HM Stationery Office: International Code of Signals, 1969; Meteorological Office Weather Services for Shipping. Phases of the Moon and Sun/Moon rising and setting times are derived from the current edition of the Nautical Almanac, and are included by permission of HM Nautical Almanac Office. UK and Foreign tidal predictions are supplied by the UK Hydrographic Office, Taunton TA1 2DN. Acknowledgment is also made to the following authorities for permission to use tidal predictions stated: SHOM, France: Dunkerque, Dieppe, Le Havre, Cherbourg, St Malo, Brest, Pointe de Grave, authorisation (No. 769/99). Rijkswaterstaat, The Netherlands: Vlissingen, and Hoek van Holland. BSH, Hamburg and Rostock: Helgoland, Wilhelmshaven and Cuxhaven (BSH 8095·02/99-Z1102). Marina Institute Hidrográfico, Portugal: Lisboa. **Warning:** The UK Hydrographic Office has not verified the reproduced data and does not accept any liability for the accuracy of reproduction or any modifications made thereafter.

Important note
This Almanac is intended as an aid to navigation only. The information contained within should not solely be relied on for navigational use, rather it should be used in conjunction with official hydrographic data. Whilst every care has been taken in compiling the information contained in this Almanac, the publishers, editors and their agents accept no responsibility for any errors or omissions, or for any accidents or mishaps which may arise from its use.

Correspondence
Letters on nautical matters should be addressed to: The Editor, Macmillan Reeds Almanacs, The Book Barn, Westbourne, Hampshire, PO10 8RS.

Production control: Chris Stevens
Cartography & production: Jamie Russell, Chris Stevens, Garold West
Cover design: Garold West
Cover photography: David Harding

Nautical Data Limited, The Book Barn, Westbourne, Hampshire, PO10 8RS, UK
Tel: +44 (0)1243 389352
Fax: +44 (0)1243 379136
www.nauticaldata.com

CONTENTS

Conversion Tables

Sq inches to sq millimetres	645.2	1	0.002	Sq millimetres to sq inches
multiply by **645.20**				multiply by **0.0016**
Inches to millimetres	25.40	1	0.04	Millimetres to inches
multiply by **25.40**				multiply by **0.0394**
Sq feet to square metres	0.09	1	10.76	Sq metres to sq feet
multiply by **0.093**				multiply by **10.7640**
Inches to centimetres	2.54	1	0.39	Centimetres to inches
multiply by **2.54**				multiply by **0.3937**
Feet to metres	0.31	1	3.28	Metres to feet
multiply by **0.305**				multiply by **3.2810**
Nautical miles to kilometres	1.85	1	0.54	Kilometres to nautical miles
multiply by **1.852**				multiply by **0.5400**
Miles to kilometres	1.61	1	0.62	Kilometres to miles
multiply by **1.609**				multiply by **0.6214**
Miles to nautical miles	0.87	1	1.15	Nautical miles to miles
multiply by **0.8684**				multiply by **1.1515**
HP to metric HP	1.01	1	0.99	Metric HP to HP
multiply by **1.014**				multiply by **0.9862**
Pounds per sq inch to kg per sq centimetre	0.07	1	4.22	Kg per sq centimetre to pounds per sq inch
multiply by **0.0703**				multiply by **14.2200**
HP to kilowatts	0.75	1	1.34	Kilowatts to HP
multiply by **0.746**				multiply by **1.341**
Cu inches to cu centimetres	16.39	1	0.06	Cu centimetres to cu inches
multiply by **16.39**				multiply by **0.0610**
Gallons to litres	4.54	1	0.22	Litres to gallons
multiply by **4.540**				multiply by **0.2200**
Pints to litres	0.57	1	1.76	Litres to pints
multiply by **0.5680**				multiply by **1.7600**
Pounds to kilogrammes	0.45	1	2.21	Kilogrammes to pounds
multiply by **0.4536**				multiply by **2.2050**

SECTION 1 - TIDES

CONTENTS

Tidal curves & prediction tables

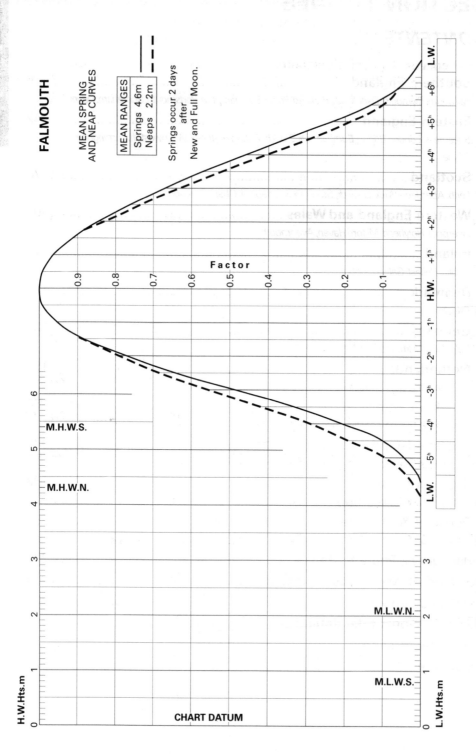

FALMOUTH

MEAN SPRING AND NEAP CURVES

MEAN RANGES	
Springs	4.6m
Neaps	2.2m

Springs occur 2 days after New and Full Moon.

Factor

H.W.Hts.m

M.H.W.S.
M.H.W.N.

CHART DATUM

L.W.Hts.m

M.L.W.N.
M.L.W.S.

TIME ZONE (UTC)
For Summer Time add ONE hour in **non-shaded areas**

ENGLAND – FALMOUTH

LAT 50°09′N   LONG 5°03′W

TIMES AND HEIGHTS OF HIGH AND LOW WATERS

YEAR **2002**

JANUARY

Day	Time m	Time m	Time m	Time m
1 TU	0035 0.9	0621 5.4	1302 5.2	1849 5.2
16 W	0112 1.2	0643 5.2	1335 1.2	1905 4.9
2 W	0120 0.9	0708 5.5	1348 0.9	1936 5.1
17 TH	0144 1.3	0717 5.1	1406 1.3	1938 4.8
3 TH	0205 1.0	0755 5.4	1434 0.9	2025 5.1
18 F	0212 1.4	0753 5.0	1434 1.4	2013 4.7
4 F	0250 1.1	0842 5.3	1521 1.1	2114 4.9
19 SA	0239 1.5	0828 4.9	1502 1.5	2050 4.6
5 SA	0337 1.3	0933 5.1	1609 1.3	2208 4.6
20 SU	0307 1.6	0905 4.7	1533 1.7	2128 4.4
6 SU	0428 1.5	1028 4.9	1704 1.5	2308 4.6
21 M	0341 1.8	0944 4.5	1612 1.8	2213 4.3
7 M	0527 1.7	1133 4.7	1809 1.7	
22 TU	0428 2.0	1033 4.4	1709 2.0	2311 4.2
8 TU	0016 4.5	0639 1.8	1242 4.6	1923 1.7
23 W	0540 2.2	1137 4.3	1826 2.1	
9 W	0124 4.5	0757 1.8	1350 4.6	2036 1.7
24 TH	0022 4.2	0704 2.1	1252 4.3	1940 1.9
10 TH	0227 4.6	0906 1.6	1452 4.7	2138 1.5
25 F	0141 4.4	0817 1.9	1412 4.4	2048 1.7
11 F	0322 4.8	1004 1.5	1547 4.8	2230 1.4
26 SA	0248 4.6	0922 1.6	1516 4.6	2149 1.5
12 SA	0411 5.0	1055 1.3	1635 4.9	2316 1.3
27 SU	0344 4.9	1021 1.3	1611 4.9	2245 1.2
13 SU ●	0454 5.1	1140 1.2	1716 5.0	2358 1.2
28 M	0434 5.2	1115 1.0	1702 5.1	2337 0.9
14 M	0531 5.2	1222 1.1	1755 5.0	
29 TU	0520 5.4	1206 0.7	1751 5.2	
15 TU	0037 1.1	0608 5.2	1300 1.1	1831 4.9
30 W	0026 0.7	0608 5.5	1255 0.5	1840 5.3
31 TH	0113 0.6	0658 5.6	1341 0.4	1928 5.3

FEBRUARY

Day	Time m	Time m	Time m	Time m
1 F	0157 0.6	0746 5.6	1425 0.5	2013 5.3
16 SA	0151 1.1	0733 5.1	1409 1.1	1951 4.8
2 SA	0239 0.7	0831 5.5	1506 0.7	2058 5.1
17 SU	0213 1.3	0805 4.9	1431 1.3	2021 4.7
3 SU	0320 0.9	0917 5.3	1547 1.0	2142 4.9
18 M	0236 1.4	0833 4.8	1455 1.4	2049 4.6
4 M	0402 1.2	1003 5.0	1631 1.4	2231 4.6
19 TU	0303 1.5	0901 4.6	1526 1.6	2121 4.4
5 TU	0450 1.5	1056 4.6	1722 1.6	2332 4.4
20 W	0340 1.7	0940 4.4	1608 1.8	2211 4.3
6 W	0550 1.8	1204 4.4	1829 1.9	
21 TH	0433 2.0	1041 4.2	1715 2.0	2323 4.2
7 TH	0045 4.3	0712 2.0	1321 4.3	2001 2.0
22 F	0607 2.1	1202 4.1	1856 2.1	
8 F	0159 4.3	0844 1.9	1432 4.3	2120 1.8
23 SA	0049 4.2	0743 2.0	1337 4.2	2019 1.9
9 SA	0301 4.5	0952 1.6	1531 4.5	2218 1.6
24 SU	0217 4.5	0859 1.6	1457 4.5	2130 1.5
10 SU	0354 4.8	1044 1.4	1620 4.7	2304 1.4
25 M	0322 4.9	1005 1.3	1556 4.8	2231 1.1
11 M	0437 5.0	1128 1.2	1701 4.8	2346 1.2
26 TU	0415 5.2	1102 0.8	1646 5.1	2324 0.7
12 TU ●	0514 5.1	1208 1.0	1737 4.9	
27 W ○	0504 5.5	1153 0.4	1734 5.3	
13 W	0023 1.0	0550 5.2	1245 0.9	1813 5.0
28 TH	0013 0.4	0552 5.7	1240 0.2	1823 5.4
14 TH	0057 1.0	0626 5.2	1317 0.9	1846 5.0
15 F	0126 1.0	0700 5.2	1345 1.0	1919 4.9

MARCH

Day	Time m	Time m	Time m	Time m
1 F	0059 0.2	0641 5.7	1325 0.2	1909 5.5
16 SA	0101 0.9	0637 5.2	1317 0.9	1854 5.0
2 SA	0141 0.2	0727 5.7	1406 0.2	1953 5.4
17 SU	0125 1.0	0710 5.1	1340 1.0	1924 5.0
3 SU	0220 0.3	0811 5.6	1444 0.4	2033 5.3
18 M	0147 1.1	0738 5.0	1402 1.1	1951 4.8
4 M	0258 0.6	0853 5.3	1521 0.8	2111 5.0
19 TU	0209 1.2	0804 4.8	1426 1.3	2016 4.7
5 TU	0336 1.1	0933 4.9	1559 1.3	2149 4.7
20 W	0236 1.4	0830 4.6	1454 1.5	2046 4.6
6 W	0418 1.5	1017 4.5	1644 1.7	2237 4.3
21 TH	0310 1.5	0909 4.4	1533 1.7	2134 4.4
7 TH	0512 1.9	1127 4.1	1744 2.1	
22 F	0400 1.8	1013 4.2	1633 2.0	2246 4.2
8 F	0005 4.1	0630 2.2	1300 4.0	1919 2.3
23 SA	0528 2.1	1136 4.0	1822 2.2	
9 SA	0134 4.1	0828 2.1	1415 4.1	2105 2.1
24 SU	0015 4.2	0718 2.0	1314 4.2	1956 1.9
10 SU	0241 4.4	0938 1.7	1513 4.3	2201 1.7
25 M	0150 4.5	0841 1.6	1440 4.5	2112 1.5
11 M	0332 4.7	1027 1.5	1601 4.6	2246 1.4
26 TU	0301 4.9	0948 1.2	1538 4.9	2214 1.1
12 TU	0415 4.9	1109 1.1	1640 4.8	2325 1.1
27 W	0356 5.2	1044 0.7	1628 5.2	2306 0.6
13 W	0452 5.1	1147 0.9	1714 4.9	
28 TH ○	0444 5.5	1133 0.3	1713 5.4	2353 0.3
14 TH ●	0001 0.9	0526 5.2	1222 0.8	1749 5.0
29 F	0530 5.7	1220 0.2	1800 5.5	
15 F	0034 0.9	0602 5.2	1252 0.8	1822 5.0
30 SA	0038 0.2	0619 5.8	1302 0.1	1845 5.6
31 SU	0119 0.2	0705 5.7	1342 0.2	1926 5.5

APRIL

Day	Time m	Time m	Time m	Time m
1 M	0158 0.3	0747 5.5	1419 0.5	2004 5.3
16 TU	0122 1.0	0714 4.9	1337 1.1	1925 5.0
2 TU	0234 0.6	0826 5.2	1455 0.9	2038 5.0
17 W	0148 1.1	0742 4.8	1404 1.3	1953 4.8
3 W	0311 1.1	0902 4.8	1531 1.4	2108 4.7
18 TH	0218 1.3	0815 4.6	1435 1.5	2029 4.7
4 TH	0352 1.5	0940 4.4	1614 1.8	2146 4.4
19 F	0255 1.5	0859 4.5	1517 1.7	2120 4.5
5 F	0444 1.9	1042 4.0	1712 2.2	2301 4.1
20 SA	0348 1.8	1000 4.2	1620 2.0	2227 4.3
6 SA	0558 2.2	1237 3.9	1838 2.4	
21 SU	0517 2.0	1122 4.1	1802 2.1	2352 4.3
7 SU	0104 4.1	0800 2.2	1351 4.0	2034 2.2
22 M	0657 1.9	1258 4.2	1934 1.9	
8 M	0213 4.3	0911 1.8	1448 4.3	2132 1.8
23 TU	0126 4.5	0819 1.5	1417 4.5	2049 1.5
9 TU	0304 4.6	0958 1.5	1533 4.6	2216 1.5
24 W	0237 4.9	0925 1.1	1515 4.9	2150 1.1
10 W	0346 4.8	1039 1.2	1611 4.8	2255 1.2
25 TH	0332 5.2	1020 0.7	1604 5.2	2243 0.7
11 TH	0424 5.0	1116 1.0	1646 5.0	2331 1.0
26 F	0422 5.5	1109 0.3	1650 5.4	2330 0.4
12 F ●	0459 5.1	1149 0.9	1719 5.0	
27 SA ○	0509 5.6	1155 0.2	1734 5.5	
13 SA	0002 0.9	0534 5.1	1219 0.8	1754 5.1
28 SU	0014 0.2	0555 5.6	1238 0.2	1819 5.5
14 SU	0031 0.9	0610 5.1	1246 0.9	1827 5.1
29 M	0056 0.3	0640 5.5	1318 0.4	1900 5.5
15 M	0057 0.9	0644 5.1	1312 1.0	1858 5.0
30 TU	0135 0.5	0722 5.4	1355 0.7	1936 5.3

Chart Datum: 2·91 metres below Ordnance Datum (Newlyn)

TIME ZONE (UTC)
For Summer Time add ONE hour in **non-shaded areas**

ENGLAND – FALMOUTH

LAT 50°09′N   LONG 5°03′W

TIMES AND HEIGHTS OF HIGH AND LOW WATERS

YEAR **2002**

MAY

Day	Time	m	Time	m
1 W	0213	0.8	16 TH 0136	1.1
	0801	5.0	0730	4.8
	1432	1.1	1353	1.3
	2007	5.0	1940	5.0
2 TH	0251	1.2	17 F 0213	1.3
	0836	4.7	0809	4.7
	1509	1.5	1430	1.4
	2037	4.7	2022	4.8
3 F	0332	1.5	18 SA 0256	1.5
	0912	4.3	0857	4.5
	1552	1.9	1518	1.6
	2115	4.4	2113	4.7
4 SA	0423	1.9	19 SU 0353	1.6
	1008	4.0	0956	4.3
	1647	2.2	1623	1.8
	2215	4.2	2216	4.5
5 SU	0529	2.2	20 M 0510	1.7
	1200	3.9	1111	4.3
	1759	2.3	1745	1.9
			2335	4.5
6 M	0017	4.1	21 TU 0634	1.6
	0656	2.1	1236	4.4
	1314	4.0	1907	1.7
	1929	2.2		
7 TU	0131	4.3	22 W 0058	4.6
	0820	1.9	0750	1.5
	1410	4.2	1348	4.6
	2042	1.9	2020	1.5
8 W	0224	4.5	23 TH 0208	4.9
	0913	1.6	0856	1.2
	1455	4.5	1447	4.9
	2132	1.6	2122	1.2
9 TH	0309	4.7	24 F 0306	5.1
	0956	1.4	0953	0.9
	1534	4.7	1539	5.1
	2214	1.4	2216	0.9
10 F	0349	4.9	25 SA 0357	5.3
	1035	1.2	1044	0.6
	1612	4.9	1626	5.3
	2252	1.2	2306	0.6
11 SA	0428	5.0	26 SU 0446	5.4
	1110	1.0	1131	0.5
	1648	5.0	1710	5.4
	2326	1.0	○ 2351	0.5
12 SU	0506	5.0	27 M 0532	5.4
	1143	1.0	1215	0.6
	1724	5.1	1754	5.4
	● 2359	1.0		
13 M	0543	5.0	28 TU 0035	0.6
	1216	1.0	0618	5.3
	1800	5.1	1256	0.7
			1835	5.3
14 TU	0031	1.0	29 W 0116	0.7
	0621	5.0	0702	5.1
	1248	1.0	1335	0.9
	1834	5.1	1912	5.2
15 W	0103	1.0	30 TH 0156	1.0
	0655	4.9	0740	4.9
	1319	1.1	1413	1.2
	1906	5.0	1945	5.0
			31 F 0235	1.3
			0817	4.6
			1451	1.5
			2017	4.8

JUNE

Day	Time	m	Time	m
1 SA	0315	1.5	16 SU 0302	1.2
	0854	4.4	0858	4.7
	1532	1.8	1522	1.5
	2056	4.6	2109	4.9
2 SU	0401	1.8	17 M 0355	1.4
	0941	4.2	0952	4.6
	1620	2.0	1617	1.5
	2147	4.4	2207	4.8
3 M	0455	2.0	18 TU 0455	1.5
	1050	4.0	1057	4.5
	1718	2.2	1722	1.6
	2255	4.2	2314	4.7
4 TU	0558	2.0	19 W 0604	1.5
	1210	4.0	1207	4.5
	1824	2.2	1833	1.6
5 W	0019	4.2	20 TH 0027	4.7
	0703	1.9	0715	1.5
	1313	4.2	1315	4.6
	1930	2.0	1945	1.5
6 TH	0127	4.3	21 F 0138	4.7
	0805	1.7	0824	1.4
	1405	4.4	1416	4.7
	2030	1.8	2052	1.4
7 F	0221	4.5	22 SA 0240	4.8
	0858	1.5	0926	1.2
	1451	4.6	1513	4.9
	2122	1.5	2152	1.2
8 SA	0309	4.7	23 SU 0336	5.0
	0945	1.4	1021	1.0
	1535	4.8	1603	5.1
	2208	1.4	2245	1.0
9 SU	0355	4.8	24 M 0427	5.0
	1028	1.2	1110	0.9
	1617	4.9	1650	5.2
	2250	1.2	○ 2333	0.9
10 M	0438	4.9	25 TU 0514	5.1
	1109	1.1	1156	0.9
	1657	5.0	1733	5.2
	● 2330	1.1		
11 TU	0518	4.9	26 W 0019	0.9
	1149	1.1	0600	5.0
	1736	5.1	1240	0.9
			1815	5.2
12 W	0010	1.0	27 TH 0102	0.9
	0600	5.0	0643	4.9
	1229	1.1	1320	1.1
	1816	5.1	1852	5.2
13 TH	0051	1.0	28 F 0142	1.0
	0642	4.9	0723	4.8
	1309	1.1	1358	1.2
	1854	5.1	1927	5.0
14 F	0132	1.0	29 SA 0220	1.2
	0724	4.9	0759	4.7
	1350	1.2	1434	1.4
	1935	5.1	2001	4.9
15 SA	0215	1.1	30 SU 0257	1.4
	0809	4.8	0834	4.5
	1434	1.3	1510	1.5
	2020	5.0	2038	4.7

JULY

Day	Time	m	Time	m
1 M	0333	1.5	16 TU 0343	1.0
	0913	4.4	0940	4.8
	1547	1.8	1601	1.3
	2120	4.6	2152	5.0
2 TU	0414	1.7	17 W 0432	1.2
	0959	4.2	1033	4.7
	1630	1.9	1653	1.5
	2208	4.4	2249	4.8
3 W	0502	1.9	18 TH 0529	1.5
	1055	4.1	1135	4.5
	1724	2.0	1755	1.6
	2306	4.3	2355	4.6
4 TH	0559	1.9	19 F 0636	1.6
	1159	4.1	1242	4.5
	1827	2.1	1908	1.7
5 F	0014	4.3	20 SA 0108	4.5
	0700	1.9	0751	1.6
	1304	4.2	1349	4.5
	1930	2.0	2025	1.6
6 SA	0125	4.3	21 SU 0218	4.5
	0801	1.7	0903	1.5
	1405	4.4	1451	4.7
	2030	1.8	2134	1.5
7 SU	0228	4.4	22 M 0319	4.6
	0858	1.6	1005	1.4
	1459	4.6	1546	4.9
	2127	1.5	2232	1.3
8 M	0322	4.6	23 TU 0413	4.8
	0951	1.4	1057	1.2
	1548	4.8	1635	5.0
	2219	1.4	2322	1.1
9 TU	0412	4.8	24 W 0500	4.9
	1041	1.3	1144	1.1
	1633	5.0	1716	5.1
	2308	1.2	○	
10 W	0459	4.9	25 TH 0007	1.0
	1129	1.1	0544	4.9
	1716	5.1	1227	1.0
	● 2355	1.0	1757	5.2
11 TH	0544	5.0	26 F 0050	0.9
	1217	1.0	0625	4.9
	1800	5.2	1306	1.0
			1834	5.2
12 F	0042	0.9	27 SA 0128	1.0
	0632	5.0	0702	4.8
	1303	0.9	1341	1.1
	1845	5.3	1908	5.1
13 SA	0128	0.8	28 SU 0201	1.1
	0719	5.0	0735	4.8
	1347	0.9	1413	1.2
	1930	5.3	1941	5.0
14 SU	0213	0.8	29 M 0232	1.2
	0805	5.0	0808	4.7
	1431	1.0	1441	1.4
	2016	5.3	2016	4.9
15 M	0258	0.9	30 TU 0259	1.4
	0852	4.9	0842	4.6
	1515	1.1	1508	1.5
	2103	5.2	2050	4.7
			31 W 0327	1.5
			0919	4.4
			1536	1.7
			2126	4.5

AUGUST

Day	Time	m	Time	m
1 TH	0400	1.7	16 F 0452	1.5
	0959	4.3	1059	4.5
	1613	1.9	1719	1.7
	2208	4.4	2324	4.4
2 F	0447	1.9	17 SA 0555	1.8
	1051	4.2	1211	4.3
	1713	2.1	1834	2.0
	2304	4.2		
3 SA	0557	2.0	18 SU 0046	4.2
	1157	4.1	0722	2.0
	1835	2.1	1328	4.3
			2009	2.0
4 SU	0018	4.1	19 M 0206	4.3
	0712	2.0	0852	1.9
	1314	4.2	1437	4.5
	1949	2.0	2126	1.7
5 M	0146	4.2	20 TU 0311	4.4
	0821	1.8	0956	1.6
	1425	4.5	1533	4.7
	2055	1.7	2223	1.5
6 TU	0256	4.5	21 W 0402	4.6
	0923	1.5	1046	1.4
	1522	4.7	1620	5.0
	2155	1.5	2311	1.2
7 W	0352	4.7	22 TH 0446	4.8
	1021	1.3	1130	1.1
	1612	5.0	1700	5.1
	2251	1.1	○ 2353	1.0
8 TH	0441	4.9	23 F 0524	4.9
	1114	1.1	1211	1.0
	1658	5.2	1735	5.2
	● 2342	0.8		
9 F	0528	5.1	24 SA 0032	0.9
	1204	0.8	0601	5.0
	1745	5.4	1247	0.9
			1810	5.2
10 SA	0031	0.6	25 SU 0106	0.9
	0617	5.2	0635	5.0
	1252	0.6	1318	1.0
	1832	5.5	1844	5.2
11 SU	0117	0.5	26 M 0135	1.0
	0705	5.2	0707	4.9
	1336	0.6	1345	1.1
	1918	5.6	1916	5.1
12 M	0201	0.4	27 TU 0200	1.1
	0750	5.2	0737	4.9
	1418	0.6	1408	1.3
	2003	5.5	1948	5.0
13 TU	0242	0.6	28 W 0221	1.3
	0834	5.2	0808	4.7
	1458	0.8	1427	1.4
	2047	5.3	2017	4.8
14 W	0322	0.8	29 TH 0242	1.5
	0918	5.0	0838	4.6
	1538	1.0	1449	1.5
	2131	5.1	2044	4.6
15 TH	0404	1.2	30 F 0307	1.6
	1004	4.8	0910	4.4
	1623	1.4	1519	1.8
	2219	4.8	2119	4.4
			31 SA 0342	1.8
			0953	4.2
			1604	2.0
			2211	4.2

ENGLAND – FALMOUTH

LAT 50°09′N LONG 5°03′W

TIMES AND HEIGHTS OF HIGH AND LOW WATERS

YEAR **2002**

SEPTEMBER

Day	Time m	Day	Time m
1 SU	0439 2.1 / 1058 4.1 / 1732 2.3 / 2328 4.1	**16** M	0033 4.0 / 0700 2.3 / 1311 4.2 / 2004 2.2
2 M	0628 2.2 / 1221 4.2 / 1916 2.2	**17** TU	0157 4.1 / 0844 2.1 / 1422 4.4 / 2118 1.8
3 TU	0107 4.1 / 0753 2.0 / 1354 4.4 / 2032 1.8	**18** W	0300 4.4 / 0942 1.7 / 1517 4.7 / 2208 1.5
4 W	0238 4.4 / 0903 1.7 / 1501 4.8 / 2138 1.5	**19** TH	0348 4.7 / 1028 1.4 / 1600 5.0 / 2251 1.2
5 TH	0335 4.7 / 1004 1.3 / 1552 5.1 / 2235 1.0	**20** F	0427 4.9 / 1109 1.2 / 1638 5.2 / 2330 1.0
6 F	0424 5.0 / 1058 0.9 / 1639 5.4 / 2326 0.6	**21** SA	0501 5.0 / 1146 1.0 / 1711 5.3 ○
7 SA	0510 5.3 / 1147 0.6 / 1724 5.6 ●	**22** SU	0005 0.9 / 0532 5.1 / 1220 0.9 / 1744 5.3
8 SU	0013 0.4 / 0556 5.4 / 1234 0.4 / 1812 5.7	**23** M	0037 0.9 / 0617 5.1 / 1249 1.0 / 1817 5.3
9 M	0058 0.2 / 0642 5.5 / 1317 0.3 / 1858 5.7	**24** TU	0103 1.0 / 0636 5.1 / 1313 1.1 / 1848 5.2
10 TU	0140 0.3 / 0726 5.5 / 1357 0.4 / 1941 5.6	**25** W	0125 1.1 / 0707 5.0 / 1334 1.2 / 1918 5.0
11 W	0219 0.5 / 0808 5.3 / 1435 0.7 / 2024 5.4	**26** TH	0145 1.2 / 0735 4.9 / 1353 1.4 / 1946 4.9
12 TH	0257 0.8 / 0850 5.1 / 1513 1.0 / 2105 5.1	**27** F	0206 1.4 / 0802 4.8 / 1416 1.5 / 2010 4.7
13 F	0335 1.3 / 0931 4.8 / 1555 1.5 / 2148 4.6	**28** SA	0230 1.6 / 0831 4.6 / 1446 1.7 / 2044 4.5
14 SA	0419 1.7 / 1020 4.5 / 1648 1.9 / 2251 4.2	**29** SU	0304 1.8 / 0915 4.4 / 1529 2.0 / 2140 4.2
15 SU	0519 2.1 / 1141 4.2 / 1806 2.2	**30** M	0355 2.2 / 1021 4.2 / 1644 2.3 / 2259 4.1

OCTOBER

Day	Time m	Day	Time m
1 TU	0547 2.4 / 1145 4.2 / 1850 2.3	**16** W	0138 4.1 / 0819 2.3 / 1358 4.4 / 2053 1.9
2 W	0040 4.1 / 0729 2.2 / 1323 4.4 / 2012 1.9	**17** TH	0237 4.4 / 0915 1.9 / 1450 4.7 / 2141 1.5
3 TH	0218 4.4 / 0844 1.7 / 1437 4.8 / 2119 1.4	**18** F	0321 4.7 / 0959 1.5 / 1533 5.0 / 2221 1.3
4 F	0315 4.8 / 0945 1.3 / 1530 5.2 / 2214 0.9	**19** SA	0358 4.9 / 1038 1.3 / 1609 5.1 / 2258 1.1
5 SA	0403 5.2 / 1038 0.9 / 1617 5.5 / 2304 0.5	**20** SU	0432 5.1 / 1114 1.1 / 1642 5.2 / 2332 1.0
6 SU	0447 5.4 / 1126 0.5 / 1703 5.7 ● / 2350 0.3	**21** M	0503 5.2 / 1147 1.0 / 1715 5.3 ○
7 M	0530 5.6 / 1211 0.3 / 1748 5.8	**22** TU	0002 1.0 / 0534 5.2 / 1216 1.0 / 1749 5.2
8 TU	0034 0.2 / 0617 5.6 / 1253 0.3 / 1834 5.8	**23** W	0028 1.0 / 0607 5.2 / 1242 1.1 / 1822 5.2
9 W	0115 0.3 / 0700 5.6 / 1333 0.4 / 1918 5.6	**24** TH	0053 1.1 / 0639 5.2 / 1305 1.2 / 1852 5.1
10 TH	0154 0.6 / 0741 5.5 / 1412 0.7 / 2000 5.3	**25** F	0116 1.3 / 0708 5.1 / 1329 1.4 / 1921 4.9
11 F	0231 1.0 / 0820 5.2 / 1450 1.2 / 2039 5.0	**26** SA	0140 1.5 / 0736 4.9 / 1356 1.5 / 1951 4.7
12 SA	0308 1.5 / 0858 4.9 / 1532 1.6 / 2120 4.5	**27** SU	0208 1.6 / 0809 4.8 / 1429 1.7 / 2030 4.5
13 SU	0352 1.9 / 0941 4.5 / 1625 2.0 / 2221 4.1	**28** M	0245 1.9 / 0856 4.6 / 1514 2.0 / 2127 4.3
14 M	0452 2.3 / 1104 4.2 / 1742 2.4	**29** TU	0338 2.2 / 0959 4.4 / 1631 2.2 / 2240 4.1
15 TU	0018 4.0 / 0631 2.5 / 1249 4.2 / 1945 2.3	**30** W	0519 2.4 / 1118 4.4 / 1823 2.3
		31 TH	0016 4.2 / 0702 2.2 / 1250 4.5 / 1946 1.8

NOVEMBER

Day	Time m	Day	Time m
1 F	0149 4.5 / 0818 1.8 / 1407 4.9 / 2053 1.4	**16** SA	0243 4.6 / 0918 1.7 / 1455 4.8 / 2141 1.5
2 SA	0249 4.9 / 0920 1.4 / 1504 5.2 / 2149 1.0	**17** SU	0322 4.8 / 0959 1.5 / 1534 5.0 / 2219 1.3
3 SU	0338 5.2 / 1013 1.0 / 1554 5.5 / 2239 0.6	**18** M	0357 5.0 / 1037 1.4 / 1611 5.1 / 2254 1.2
4 M	0423 5.5 / 1101 0.6 / 1641 5.7 ● / 2326 0.4	**19** TU	0433 5.1 / 1112 1.2 / 1647 5.1 / 2326 1.2
5 TU	0508 5.6 / 1147 0.5 / 1725 5.7	**20** W	0507 5.2 / 1144 1.2 / 1723 5.2 ○ / 2356 1.2
6 W	0009 0.4 / 0551 5.7 / 1231 0.5 / 1812 5.7	**21** TH	0542 5.2 / 1215 1.2 / 1759 5.1
7 TH	0051 0.5 / 0635 5.6 / 1312 0.6 / 1856 5.5	**22** F	0027 1.2 / 0616 5.2 / 1245 1.3 / 1834 5.0
8 F	0131 0.8 / 0716 5.5 / 1352 0.9 / 1938 5.2	**23** SA	0057 1.3 / 0648 5.1 / 1316 1.4 / 1907 4.9
9 SA	0209 1.2 / 0755 5.2 / 1432 1.3 / 2019 4.9	**24** SU	0128 1.5 / 0722 5.1 / 1350 1.5 / 1942 4.8
10 SU	0248 1.5 / 0832 4.9 / 1515 1.6 / 2100 4.5	**25** M	0202 1.5 / 0800 4.9 / 1429 1.6 / 2026 4.6
11 M	0332 2.0 / 0913 4.6 / 1606 2.0 / 2155 4.2	**26** TU	0244 1.8 / 0848 4.8 / 1518 1.8 / 2120 4.4
12 TU	0427 2.3 / 1016 4.4 / 1713 2.3 / 2342 4.0	**27** W	0339 2.0 / 0945 4.7 / 1626 1.9 / 2226 4.3
13 W	0543 2.5 / 1205 4.3 / 1846 2.3	**28** TH	0457 2.1 / 1056 4.6 / 1751 1.9 / 2348 4.3
14 TH	0059 4.1 / 0722 2.4 / 1316 4.4 / 2006 2.1	**29** F	0625 2.1 / 1215 4.7 / 1911 1.7
15 F	0157 4.3 / 0829 2.1 / 1411 4.6 / 2058 1.7	**30** SA	0109 4.5 / 0743 1.8 / 1330 4.8 / 2021 1.5

DECEMBER

Day	Time m	Day	Time m
1 SU	0215 4.8 / 0849 1.5 / 1434 5.1 / 2121 1.2	**16** M	0237 4.6 / 0909 1.8 / 1452 4.7 / 2131 1.6
2 M	0310 5.1 / 0946 1.2 / 1528 5.3 / 2214 0.9	**17** TU	0320 4.8 / 0955 1.6 / 1538 4.8 / 2213 1.5
3 TU	0359 5.3 / 1038 0.9 / 1619 5.4 / 2303 0.8	**18** W	0402 5.0 / 1036 1.5 / 1621 4.9 / 2252 1.4
4 W	0445 5.5 / 1126 0.8 / 1707 5.5 / 2349 0.7	**19** TH	0442 5.1 / 1115 1.3 / 1702 5.0 ○ / 2331 1.3
5 TH	0530 5.6 / 1211 0.7 / 1754 5.4	**20** F	0520 5.2 / 1154 1.2 / 1743 5.0
6 F	0032 0.8 / 0615 5.5 / 1256 0.8 / 1839 5.3	**21** SA	0009 1.2 / 0559 5.2 / 1233 1.2 / 1822 5.0
7 SA	0114 1.0 / 0658 5.4 / 1338 1.0 / 1923 5.1	**22** SU	0047 1.2 / 0638 5.2 / 1312 1.2 / 1902 5.0
8 SU	0154 1.3 / 0737 5.2 / 1420 1.3 / 2004 4.8	**23** M	0125 1.3 / 0717 5.2 / 1352 1.3 / 1941 4.9
9 M	0234 1.5 / 0815 5.0 / 1502 1.5 / 2043 4.6	**24** TU	0205 1.4 / 0758 5.1 / 1434 1.4 / 2026 4.8
10 TU	0315 1.8 / 0854 4.8 / 1546 1.8 / 2128 4.3	**25** W	0248 1.5 / 0843 5.0 / 1520 1.5 / 2114 4.7
11 W	0401 2.1 / 0941 4.6 / 1636 2.0 / 2226 4.2	**26** TH	0336 1.6 / 0934 4.9 / 1613 1.6 / 2210 4.6
12 TH	0456 2.3 / 1042 4.4 / 1736 2.2 / 2344 4.1	**27** F	0433 1.7 / 1032 4.8 / 1715 1.6 / 2315 4.5
13 F	0601 2.3 / 1200 4.3 / 1843 2.2	**28** SA	0542 1.8 / 1141 4.7 / 1827 1.7
14 SA	0052 4.2 / 0712 2.2 / 1307 4.4 / 1948 2.0	**29** SU	0026 4.5 / 0700 1.8 / 1253 4.7 / 1942 1.6
15 SU	0148 4.4 / 0816 2.0 / 1403 4.5 / 2044 1.8	**30** M	0138 4.6 / 0815 1.6 / 1403 4.8 / 2051 1.5
		31 TU	0242 4.8 / 0921 1.5 / 1507 4.9 / 2152 1.3

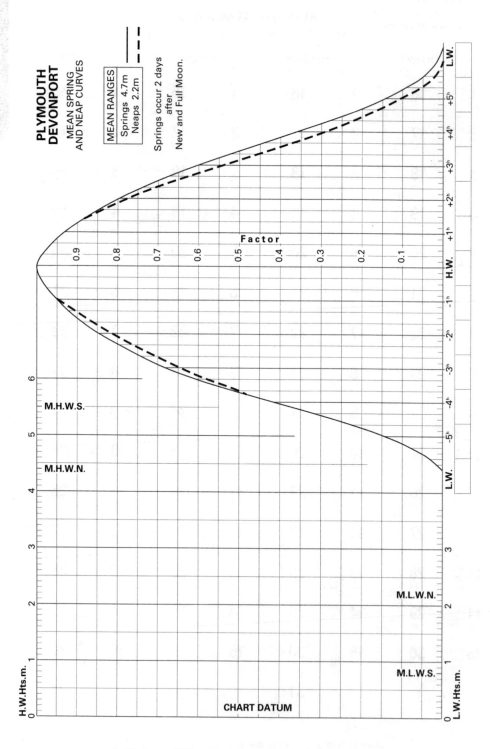

PLYMOUTH DEVONPORT

MEAN SPRING AND NEAP CURVES

MEAN RANGES
Springs 4.7m
Neaps 2.2m

Springs occur 2 days after New and Full Moon.

Factor

0.9 0.8 0.7 0.6 0.5 0.4 0.3 0.2 0.1

L.W.

+5ʰ +4ʰ +3ʰ +2ʰ +1ʰ H.W. -1ʰ -2ʰ -3ʰ -4ʰ -5ʰ L.W.

M.H.W.S.

M.H.W.N.

M.L.W.N.

M.L.W.S.

H.W.Hts.m.

L.W.Hts.m.

CHART DATUM

TIME ZONE (UTC)
For Summer Time add ONE hour in **non-shaded areas**

ENGLAND – PLYMOUTH

LAT 50°22'N   LONG 4°11'W

TIMES AND HEIGHTS OF HIGH AND LOW WATERS

YEAR **2002**

JANUARY

	Time	m		Time	m
1 TU	0045 / 0654 / 1312 / 1922	0.9 / 5.5 / 0.8 / 5.3	**16** W	0122 / 0716 / 1345 / 1937	1.2 / 5.3 / 1.2 / 5.0
2 W	0130 / 0740 / 1358 / 2008	0.9 / 5.6 / 0.8 / 5.2	**17** TH	0154 / 0749 / 1416 / 2010	1.3 / 5.2 / 1.3 / 4.9
3 TH	0215 / 0826 / 1444 / 2055	1.0 / 5.5 / 0.9 / 5.2	**18** F	0222 / 0824 / 1444 / 2044	1.4 / 5.1 / 1.4 / 4.8
4 F	0300 / 0912 / 1531 / 2143	1.1 / 5.4 / 1.1 / 5.0	**19** SA	0249 / 0858 / 1512 / 2119	1.6 / 5.0 / 1.6 / 4.6
5 SA	0347 / 1001 / 1619 / 2235	1.3 / 5.2 / 1.3 / 4.8	**20** SU	0317 / 0934 / 1543 / 2156	1.7 / 4.8 / 1.8 / 4.5
6 SU	0438 / 1055 / 1714 / 2334	1.5 / 5.0 / 1.5 / 4.7	**21** M	0351 / 1012 / 1622 / 2240	1.9 / 4.6 / 1.9 / 4.4
7 M	0537 / 1158 / 1819	1.8 / 4.8 / 1.7	**22** TU	0438 / 1100 / 1719 / 2337	2.1 / 4.5 / 2.1 / 4.3
8 TU	0042 / 0649 / 1309 / 1933	4.6 / 1.9 / 4.7 / 1.8	**23** W	0550 / 1202 / 1836	2.2 / 4.4 / 2.1
9 W	0152 / 0807 / 1419 / 2046	4.6 / 1.9 / 4.7 / 1.8	**24** TH	0049 / 0714 / 1319 / 1950	4.3 / 2.2 / 4.4 / 2.0
10 TH	0257 / 0916 / 1523 / 2148	4.7 / 1.7 / 4.8 / 1.6	**25** F	0209 / 0827 / 1441 / 2058	4.4 / 2.0 / 4.5 / 1.8
11 F	0354 / 1014 / 1619 / 2240	4.9 / 1.5 / 4.9 / 1.4	**26** SA	0319 / 0932 / 1548 / 2159	4.7 / 1.7 / 4.7 / 1.5
12 SA	0444 / 1105 / 1708 / 2326	5.1 / 1.3 / 5.0 / 1.2	**27** SU	0416 / 1031 / 1644 / 2255	5.0 / 1.3 / 5.0 / 1.2
13 SU ●	0528 / 1150 / 1751	5.2 / 1.1 / 5.1	**28** M ○	0507 / 1125 / 1736 / 2347	5.3 / 1.0 / 5.2 / 0.9
14 M	0008 / 0606 / 1232 / 1829	1.2 / 5.3 / 1.1 / 5.1	**29** TU	0555 / 1216 / 1825	5.5 / 0.7 / 5.3
15 TU	0047 / 0642 / 1312 / 1904	1.1 / 5.3 / 1.1 / 5.0	**30** W	0036 / 0642 / 1305 / 1913	0.7 / 5.6 / 0.5 / 5.4
			31 TH	0123 / 0730 / 1351 / 2000	0.6 / 5.7 / 0.4 / 5.4

FEBRUARY

	Time	m		Time	m
1 F	0207 / 0817 / 1435 / 2044	0.6 / 5.7 / 0.5 / 5.4	**16** SA	0201 / 0805 / 1419 / 2022	1.1 / 5.2 / 1.1 / 4.9
2 SA	0249 / 0901 / 1516 / 2127	0.7 / 5.6 / 0.7 / 5.2	**17** SU	0223 / 0836 / 1441 / 2051	1.2 / 5.0 / 1.3 / 4.8
3 SU	0330 / 0945 / 1557 / 2210	0.9 / 5.4 / 1.0 / 5.0	**18** M	0246 / 0903 / 1505 / 2118	1.4 / 4.9 / 1.4 / 4.7
4 M	0412 / 1030 / 1641 / 2258	1.2 / 5.1 / 1.3 / 4.7	**19** TU	0313 / 0930 / 1536 / 2149	1.6 / 4.7 / 1.6 / 4.5
5 TU	0500 / 1122 / 1732 / 2357	1.6 / 4.7 / 1.7 / 4.5	**20** W	0350 / 1008 / 1618 / 2238	1.8 / 4.5 / 1.9 / 4.4
6 W	0600 / 1230 / 1839	1.9 / 4.5 / 2.0	**21** TH	0443 / 1108 / 1725 / 2348	2.1 / 4.3 / 2.1 / 4.2
7 TH	0112 / 0722 / 1349 / 2011	4.4 / 2.1 / 4.3 / 2.1	**22** F	0617 / 1228 / 1906	2.2 / 4.2 / 2.2
8 F	0228 / 0854 / 1502 / 2130	4.4 / 2.0 / 4.4 / 1.9	**23** SA	0116 / 0753 / 1405 / 2029	4.3 / 2.1 / 4.3 / 2.0
9 SA	0332 / 1002 / 1603 / 2228	4.6 / 1.7 / 4.6 / 1.6	**24** SU	0247 / 0909 / 1528 / 2140	4.6 / 1.7 / 4.6 / 1.6
10 SU	0426 / 1054 / 1653 / 2314	4.9 / 1.4 / 4.8 / 1.4	**25** M	0354 / 1015 / 1628 / 2241	4.9 / 1.3 / 4.9 / 1.1
11 M	0510 / 1138 / 1735 / 2356	5.1 / 1.2 / 4.9 / 1.2	**26** TU	0448 / 1112 / 1720 / 2334	5.3 / 0.8 / 5.2 / 0.7
12 TU ●	0549 / 1218 / 1812	5.2 / 1.0 / 5.0	**27** W ○	0538 / 1203 / 1809	5.6 / 0.4 / 5.4
13 W	0033 / 0624 / 1255 / 1846	1.0 / 5.3 / 0.9 / 5.1	**28** TH	0023 / 0626 / 1250 / 1856	0.4 / 5.8 / 0.2 / 5.5
14 TH	0107 / 0659 / 1327 / 1919	1.0 / 5.3 / 0.9 / 5.1			
15 F	0136 / 0732 / 1355 / 1951	1.0 / 5.3 / 1.0 / 5.0			

MARCH

	Time	m		Time	m
1 F	0109 / 0714 / 1335 / 1941	0.2 / 5.8 / 0.1 / 5.6	**16** SA	0111 / 0710 / 1327 / 1927	0.9 / 5.3 / 0.9 / 5.1
2 SA	0151 / 0759 / 1416 / 2024	0.2 / 5.8 / 0.2 / 5.5	**17** SU	0135 / 0742 / 1350 / 1956	1.0 / 5.2 / 1.0 / 5.0
3 SU	0230 / 0842 / 1454 / 2103	0.3 / 5.7 / 0.4 / 5.4	**18** M	0157 / 0810 / 1412 / 2022	1.1 / 5.1 / 1.1 / 4.9
4 M	0308 / 0922 / 1531 / 2140	0.6 / 5.4 / 0.8 / 5.1	**19** TU	0219 / 0835 / 1436 / 2046	1.2 / 4.9 / 1.3 / 4.8
5 TU	0346 / 1001 / 1609 / 2217	1.0 / 5.0 / 1.3 / 4.8	**20** W	0246 / 0900 / 1504 / 2115	1.4 / 4.7 / 1.5 / 4.7
6 W	0428 / 1044 / 1654 / 2304	1.5 / 4.6 / 1.8 / 4.4	**21** TH	0320 / 0938 / 1543 / 2202	1.6 / 4.5 / 1.8 / 4.5
7 TH	0522 / 1152 / 1754	2.0 / 4.2 / 2.2	**22** F	0410 / 1040 / 1643 / 2313	1.9 / 4.3 / 2.1 / 4.3
8 F	0031 / 0640 / 1327 / 1929	4.2 / 2.3 / 4.1 / 2.4	**23** SA	0538 / 1201 / 1832	2.2 / 4.1 / 2.3
9 SA	0202 / 0838 / 1444 / 2115	4.2 / 2.2 / 4.2 / 2.2	**24** SU	0041 / 0728 / 1342 / 2006	4.3 / 2.1 / 4.2 / 2.0
10 SU	0311 / 0948 / 1545 / 2211	4.5 / 1.8 / 4.4 / 1.8	**25** M	0219 / 0851 / 1510 / 2122	4.6 / 1.7 / 4.6 / 1.6
11 M	0404 / 1037 / 1634 / 2256	4.8 / 1.4 / 4.7 / 1.4	**26** TU	0332 / 0958 / 1610 / 2224	5.0 / 1.1 / 5.0 / 1.1
12 TU	0448 / 1119 / 1713 / 2335	5.0 / 1.1 / 4.9 / 1.1	**27** W	0428 / 1054 / 1701 / 2316	5.3 / 0.7 / 5.3 / 0.6
13 W ○	0526 / 1157 / 1749	5.2 / 0.9 / 5.0	**28** TH ●	0518 / 1143 / 1748	5.6 / 0.3 / 5.5
14 TH ●	0011 / 0601 / 1230 / 1823	0.9 / 5.3 / 0.8 / 5.1	**29** F	0003 / 0605 / 1230 / 1834	0.3 / 5.8 / 0.1 / 5.6
15 F	0044 / 0636 / 1302 / 1855	0.9 / 5.3 / 0.8 / 5.1	**30** SA	0048 / 0652 / 1312 / 1918	0.1 / 5.8 / 0.0 / 5.7
			31 SU	0129 / 0737 / 1352 / 1958	0.1 / 5.8 / 0.2 / 5.6

APRIL

	Time	m		Time	m
1 M	0208 / 0818 / 1429 / 2035	0.3 / 5.6 / 0.5 / 5.4	**16** TU	0132 / 0746 / 1347 / 1957	1.0 / 5.0 / 1.1 / 5.1
2 TU	0244 / 0856 / 1505 / 2108	0.6 / 5.3 / 0.9 / 5.1	**17** W	0158 / 0814 / 1414 / 2024	1.1 / 4.9 / 1.3 / 4.9
3 W	0321 / 0931 / 1541 / 2137	1.1 / 4.9 / 1.4 / 4.8	**18** TH	0228 / 0845 / 1445 / 2059	1.3 / 4.7 / 1.5 / 4.8
4 TH	0402 / 1008 / 1624 / 2214	1.6 / 4.5 / 1.9 / 4.5	**19** F	0305 / 0928 / 1527 / 2148	1.6 / 4.5 / 1.8 / 4.6
5 F	0454 / 1109 / 1722 / 2327	2.0 / 4.1 / 2.3 / 4.2	**20** SA	0358 / 1028 / 1630 / 2254	1.9 / 4.3 / 2.1 / 4.4
6 SA	0608 / 1304 / 1848	2.3 / 4.0 / 2.5	**21** SU	0527 / 1147 / 1812	2.1 / 4.2 / 2.2
7 SU	0132 / 0810 / 1420 / 2044	4.2 / 2.3 / 4.1 / 2.3	**22** M	0018 / 0707 / 1325 / 1944	4.4 / 1.9 / 4.3 / 2.0
8 M	0242 / 0921 / 1519 / 2142	4.4 / 1.9 / 4.4 / 1.9	**23** TU	0154 / 0829 / 1447 / 2059	4.6 / 1.6 / 4.6 / 1.5
9 TU	0335 / 1008 / 1605 / 2226	4.7 / 1.5 / 4.7 / 1.5	**24** W	0307 / 0935 / 1547 / 2200	5.0 / 1.1 / 5.0 / 1.1
10 W	0418 / 1049 / 1644 / 2305	4.9 / 1.2 / 4.9 / 1.2	**25** TH	0404 / 1030 / 1637 / 2253	5.3 / 0.7 / 5.3 / 0.6
11 TH	0457 / 1126 / 1720 / 2341	5.1 / 1.0 / 5.0 / 1.0	**26** F	0455 / 1119 / 1724 / 2340	5.6 / 0.3 / 5.5 / 0.4
12 F	0533 / 1159 / 1754	5.2 / 0.8 / 5.1	**27** SA ○	0543 / 1205 / 1809	5.7 / 0.2 / 5.6
13 SA	0012 / 0609 / 1229 / 1828	0.9 / 5.2 / 0.8 / 5.2	**28** SU	0024 / 0629 / 1248 / 1852	0.2 / 5.7 / 0.2 / 5.6
14 SU	0041 / 0644 / 1256 / 1900	0.9 / 5.2 / 0.9 / 5.2	**29** M	0106 / 0713 / 1328 / 1932	0.3 / 5.6 / 0.4 / 5.5
15 M	0107 / 0717 / 1322 / 1930	0.9 / 5.2 / 1.0 / 5.1	**30** TU	0145 / 0754 / 1405 / 2008	0.5 / 5.4 / 0.7 / 5.4

ENGLAND – PLYMOUTH

LAT 50°22′N   LONG 4°11′W

TIMES AND HEIGHTS OF HIGH AND LOW WATERS

TIME ZONE (UTC)
For Summer Time add ONE hour in **non-shaded areas**

YEAR 2002

(● = new moon, O = full moon)

MAY

Day		Time	m	Time	m	Time	m	Time	m
1	W	0223	0.8	0832	5.1	1442	1.1	2038	5.1
2	TH	0301	1.2	0906	4.8	1519	1.5	2107	4.8
3	F	0342	1.6	0941	4.4	1602	2.0	2144	4.5
4	SA	0433	2.0	1035	4.1	1657	2.3	2242	4.3
5	SU	0539	2.2	1226	4.0	1809	2.4		
6	M	0043	4.2	0706	2.2	1342	4.1	1939	2.3
7	TU	0159	4.3	0830	2.0	1439	4.3	2052	2.0
8	W	0254	4.6	0923	1.6	1526	4.6	2142	1.7
9	TH	0340	4.8	1006	1.4	1606	4.8	2224	1.4
10	F	0421	5.0	1045	1.1	1645	5.0	2302	1.2
11	SA	0501	5.1	1120	1.0	1722	5.1	2336	1.0
12	SU ●	0540	5.1	1153	1.0	1759	5.2		
13	M	0009	1.0	0617	5.1	1226	1.0	1834	5.2
14	TU	0041	1.0	0654	5.1	1258	1.0	1907	5.2
15	W	0113	1.0	0728	5.0	1329	1.1	1938	5.1
16	TH	0146	1.1	0802	4.9	1403	1.3	2012	5.1
17	F	0223	1.3	0840	4.8	1440	1.5	2052	4.9
18	SA	0306	1.5	0926	4.6	1528	1.7	2142	4.8
19	SU	0403	1.7	1024	4.4	1633	1.9	2243	4.6
20	M	0520	1.8	1137	4.4	1755	2.0		
21	TU	0000	4.6	0644	1.7	1303	4.4	1917	1.8
22	W	0125	4.7	0800	1.5	1417	4.7	2030	1.5
23	TH	0237	5.0	0906	1.2	1518	5.0	2132	1.2
24	F	0337	5.2	1003	0.8	1611	5.2	2226	0.9
25	SA	0430	5.4	1054	0.6	1659	5.4	2316	0.6
26	SU O	0520	5.5	1141	0.5	1745	5.5		
27	M	0001	0.5	0607	5.4	1225	0.5	1828	5.5
28	TU	0045	0.6	0651	5.4	1306	0.7	1908	5.4
29	W	0126	0.7	0734	5.2	1345	0.9	1944	5.3
30	TH	0206	1.0	0812	5.0	1423	1.2	2016	5.1
31	F	0245	1.3	0847	4.7	1501	1.6	2047	4.9

JUNE

Day		Time	m	Time	m	Time	m	Time	m
1	SA	0325	1.6	0923	4.5	1542	1.9	2125	4.7
2	SU	0411	1.9	1009	4.2	1630	2.1	2215	4.5
3	M	0505	2.1	1116	4.1	1728	2.3	2321	4.3
4	TU	0608	2.1	1236	4.1	1834	2.3		
5	W	0046	4.3	0713	2.0	1341	4.3	1940	2.1
6	TH	0155	4.4	0815	1.8	1434	4.5	2040	1.9
7	F	0251	4.6	0908	1.6	1522	4.7	2132	1.6
8	SA	0340	4.8	0955	1.4	1607	4.9	2218	1.4
9	SU	0427	4.9	1038	1.2	1650	5.0	2300	1.2
10	M ●	0511	5.0	1119	1.1	1731	5.1	2340	1.1
11	TU	0553	5.0	1159	1.1	1811	5.2		
12	W	0020	1.0	0634	5.0	1239	1.1	1849	5.2
13	TH	0101	1.0	0715	5.0	1319	1.1	1927	5.2
14	F	0142	1.0	0756	5.0	1400	1.2	2007	5.2
15	SA	0225	1.1	0840	4.9	1444	1.3	2050	5.1
16	SU	0312	1.2	0927	4.8	1532	1.4	2138	5.0
17	M	0405	1.4	1020	4.7	1627	1.6	2234	4.9
18	TU	0505	1.5	1123	4.6	1732	1.7	2340	4.8
19	W	0614	1.5	1233	4.6	1843	1.7		
20	TH	0054	4.8	0725	1.5	1343	4.7	1955	1.6
21	F	0206	4.8	0834	1.4	1446	4.8	2102	1.4
22	SA	0310	4.9	0936	1.2	1544	5.0	2202	1.2
23	SU	0408	5.1	1031	1.0	1636	5.2	2255	1.0
24	M O	0500	5.1	1124	0.9	1724	5.3	2343	0.9
25	TU	0549	5.2	1206	0.9	1808	5.3		
26	W	0029	0.8	0634	5.1	1250	0.9	1848	5.4
27	TH	0112	0.9	0716	5.0	1330	1.1	1925	5.2
28	F	0152	1.0	0755	4.9	1408	1.2	1959	5.1
29	SA	0230	1.2	0830	4.7	1444	1.4	2032	5.0
30	SU	0307	1.4	0904	4.6	1520	1.6	2108	4.8

JULY

Day		Time	m	Time	m	Time	m	Time	m
1	M	0343	1.6	0942	4.5	1557	1.8	2148	4.7
2	TU	0424	1.8	1027	4.3	1640	2.0	2235	4.5
3	W	0512	2.0	1121	4.2	1734	2.1	2332	4.4
4	TH	0609	2.0	1225	4.2	1837	2.2		
5	F	0040	4.4	0710	2.0	1332	4.3	1940	2.1
6	SA	0153	4.4	0811	1.8	1434	4.5	2040	1.9
7	SU	0258	4.5	0908	1.7	1530	4.7	2137	1.6
8	M	0354	4.7	1001	1.4	1620	4.9	2229	1.4
9	TU	0445	4.9	1051	1.3	1706	5.1	2318	1.2
10	W ●	0533	5.0	1139	1.1	1751	5.2		
11	TH	0005	1.0	0618	5.1	1227	1.0	1834	5.3
12	F	0052	0.8	0705	5.1	1313	0.9	1918	5.4
13	SA	0138	0.8	0751	5.1	1357	0.9	2002	5.4
14	SU	0223	0.8	0836	5.1	1441	0.9	2046	5.4
15	M	0308	0.9	0921	5.0	1525	1.1	2132	5.3
16	TU	0353	1.0	1008	4.9	1611	1.2	2220	5.1
17	W	0442	1.2	1100	4.7	1703	1.5	2315	4.9
18	TH	0539	1.5	1200	4.6	1805	1.7		
19	F	0021	4.7	0646	1.7	1309	4.6	1918	1.8
20	SA	0136	4.6	0801	1.7	1418	4.6	2035	1.7
21	SU	0248	4.6	0913	1.6	1522	4.8	2144	1.6
22	M	0351	4.7	1015	1.4	1618	5.0	2242	1.3
23	TU	0446	4.9	1107	1.2	1708	5.1	2332	1.1
24	W O	0534	5.0	1154	1.1	1751	5.2		
25	TH	0017	1.0	0618	5.0	1237	1.0	1831	5.3
26	F	0100	0.9	0658	5.0	1316	1.0	1907	5.3
27	SA	0138	1.0	0734	4.9	1351	1.1	1940	5.2
28	SU	0211	1.1	0807	4.9	1423	1.2	2013	5.1
29	M	0242	1.2	0839	4.8	1451	1.4	2046	5.0
30	TU	0309	1.4	0912	4.7	1518	1.6	2119	4.8
31	W	0337	1.6	1021	4.4	1546	1.8	2154	4.6

AUGUST

Day		Time	m	Time	m	Time	m	Time	m
1	TH	0410	1.8	1027	4.4	1623	2.0	2235	4.5
2	F	0457	2.0	1117	4.3	1723	2.2	2330	4.3
3	SA	0607	2.1	1223	4.2	1845	2.2		
4	SU	0045	4.2	0722	2.1	1342	4.3	1959	2.1
5	M	0215	4.3	0831	1.9	1455	4.6	2105	1.8
6	TU	0327	4.6	0933	1.6	1554	4.8	2205	1.5
7	W	0424	4.8	1031	1.3	1645	5.1	2301	1.1
8	TH ●	0515	5.0	1124	1.0	1732	5.3	2352	0.8
9	F	0603	5.2	1214	0.8	1819	5.5		
10	SA	0041	0.6	0650	5.3	1302	0.6	1905	5.6
11	SU	0127	0.5	0737	5.3	1346	0.6	1950	5.6
12	M	0211	0.5	0821	5.3	1428	0.6	2034	5.6
13	TU	0252	0.6	0904	5.3	1508	0.8	2116	5.4
14	W	0332	0.8	0946	5.1	1548	1.0	2159	5.2
15	TH	0414	1.2	1031	4.9	1633	1.4	2246	4.8
16	F	0502	1.6	1125	4.6	1729	1.8	2349	4.5
17	SA	0605	1.9	1237	4.4	1844	2.1		
18	SU	0113	4.3	0732	2.1	1356	4.4	2019	2.1
19	M	0235	4.4	0902	2.0	1507	4.6	2136	1.8
20	TU	0342	4.5	1006	1.7	1605	4.8	2233	1.5
21	W	0435	4.7	1056	1.4	1653	5.1	2321	1.2
22	TH O	0520	4.9	1140	1.1	1734	5.2		
23	F	0003	1.0	0559	5.0	1221	1.0	1810	5.3
24	SA	0042	0.9	0635	5.1	1257	0.9	1844	5.3
25	SU	0116	0.9	0708	5.1	1328	1.0	1917	5.3
26	M	0145	1.0	0739	5.0	1355	1.1	1948	5.2
27	TU	0210	1.1	0809	5.0	1418	1.2	2019	5.1
28	W	0231	1.3	0839	4.8	1437	1.4	2047	4.9
29	TH	0252	1.5	0908	4.7	1459	1.6	2114	4.7
30	F	0317	1.7	0939	4.5	1529	1.9	2147	4.5
31	SA	0352	1.9	1021	4.4	1614	2.1	2238	4.3

TIME ZONE (UTC)
For Summer Time add ONE hour in **non-shaded areas**

ENGLAND – PLYMOUTH

LAT 50°22'N   LONG 4°11'W

TIMES AND HEIGHTS OF HIGH AND LOW WATERS

YEAR **2002**

SEPTEMBER

Day	Time	m	Day	Time	m
1 SU	0449	2.2	**16** M	0100	4.1
	1124	4.2		0710	2.4
	1742	2.4		1339	4.3
	2353	4.2		2014	2.3
2 M	0638	2.3	**17** TU	0226	4.2
	1248	4.3		0854	2.2
	1926	2.3		1452	4.5
				2128	1.9
3 TU	0135	4.2	**18** W	0331	4.5
	0803	2.1		0952	1.8
	1423	4.5		1549	4.8
	2042	1.9		2218	1.5
4 W	0308	4.5	**19** TH	0420	4.8
	0913	1.8		1038	1.4
	1532	4.9		1633	5.1
	2148	1.5		2301	1.2
5 TH	0407	4.8	**20** F	0500	5.0
	1014	1.3		1119	1.1
	1624	5.2		1711	5.3
	2245	1.0		2340	1.0
6 F	0457	5.1	**21** SA	0535	5.1
	1108	0.9		1156	1.0
	1712	5.5		1746	5.4 ○
	2336	0.6			
7 SA	0544	5.4	**22** SU	0015	0.8
	1157	0.6		0607	5.2
	1759	5.7 ●		1230	0.9
				1818	5.4
8 SU	0023	0.4	**23** M	0047	0.9
	0630	5.5		0639	5.2
	1244	0.4		1259	1.0
	1845	5.8		1850	5.4
9 M	0108	0.2	**24** TU	0113	0.9
	0715	5.6		0709	5.2
	1327	0.3		1323	1.1
	1930	5.8		1921	5.3
10 TU	0150	0.3	**25** W	0135	1.1
	0758	5.6		0739	5.1
	1407	0.4		1344	1.2
	2013	5.7		1950	5.1
11 W	0229	0.5	**26** TH	0155	1.2
	0839	5.4		0807	5.0
	1445	0.7		1403	1.4
	2054	5.5		2017	5.0
12 TH	0307	0.8	**27** F	0216	1.4
	0919	5.2		0833	4.9
	1523	1.0		1426	1.6
	2134	5.1		2041	4.8
13 F	0345	1.3	**28** SA	0240	1.6
	0959	4.9		0901	4.7
	1605	1.5		1456	1.8
	2216	4.7		2114	4.6
14 SA	0429	1.8	**29** SU	0314	1.9
	1047	4.6		0944	4.5
	1658	1.9		1539	2.1
	2317	4.3		2208	4.3
15 SU	0529	2.2	**30** M	0405	2.3
	1206	4.3		1048	4.3
	1816	2.3		1654	2.4
				2325	4.1

OCTOBER

Day	Time	m	Day	Time	m
1 TU	0557	2.5	**16** W	0206	4.2
	1210	4.3		0829	2.4
	1900	2.4		1427	4.5
				2103	2.0
2 W	0107	4.2	**17** TH	0307	4.5
	0739	2.3		0925	2.0
	1351	4.5		1521	4.8
	2022	1.9		2151	1.6
3 TH	0248	4.5	**18** F	0353	4.8
	0854	1.8		1009	1.6
	1507	4.9		1605	5.1
	2129	1.4		2231	1.3
4 F	0347	4.9	**19** SA	0431	5.0
	0955	1.3		1048	1.3
	1602	5.3		1642	5.2
	2224	0.9		2308	1.1
5 SA	0436	5.3	**20** SU	0505	5.2
	1048	0.9		1124	1.1
	1650	5.6		1716	5.3
	2314	0.5		2342	1.0
6 SU	0521	5.5	**21** M	0537	5.3
	1136	0.5		1157	1.0
	1737	5.8 ●		1750	5.4 ○
7 M	0000	0.3	**22** TU	0012	1.0
	0605	5.7		0609	5.3
	1221	0.3		1226	1.0
	1822	5.9		1823	5.3
8 TU	0044	0.2	**23** W	0038	1.0
	0650	5.7		0641	5.3
	1303	0.3		1252	1.1
	1907	5.9		1855	5.3
9 W	0125	0.3	**24** TH	0103	1.1
	0732	5.7		0712	5.3
	1343	0.4		1315	1.2
	1950	5.7		1925	5.2
10 TH	0204	0.6	**25** F	0126	1.3
	0813	5.5		0740	5.1
	1422	0.7		1339	1.4
	2031	5.4		1953	5.0
11 F	0241	1.0	**26** SA	0150	1.5
	0850	5.1		0808	5.0
	1500	1.2		1406	1.6
	2109	5.0		2022	4.8
12 SA	0318	1.5	**27** SU	0218	1.7
	0927	5.0		0840	4.8
	1542	1.7		1439	1.8
	2148	4.6		2100	4.6
13 SU	0402	2.0	**28** M	0255	2.0
	1009	4.6		0925	4.7
	1635	2.0		1524	2.1
	2248	4.2		2155	4.4
14 M	0502	2.4	**29** TU	0348	2.3
	1130	4.3		1027	4.5
	1752	2.5		1641	2.4
				2307	4.2
15 TU	0044	4.1	**30** W	0529	2.5
	0641	2.6		1144	4.5
	1316	4.3		1833	2.3
	1955	2.4			
			31 TH	0042	4.3
				0712	2.3
				1317	4.6
				1956	1.9

NOVEMBER

Day	Time	m	Day	Time	m
1 F	0218	4.6	**16** SA	0313	4.7
	0828	1.9		0928	1.8
	1436	5.0		1526	4.9
	2103	1.4		2151	1.6
2 SA	0320	5.0	**17** SU	0354	4.9
	0930	1.4		1009	1.5
	1535	5.3		1606	5.1
	2159	1.0		2229	1.3
3 SU	0410	5.3	**18** M	0430	5.1
	1023	1.0		1047	1.3
	1626	5.6		1644	5.2
	2249	0.6		2304	1.2
4 M	0456	5.6	**19** TU	0506	5.2
	1111	0.6		1122	1.2
	● 1714	5.8		1721	5.2
	2336	0.4		2336	1.1
5 TU	0542	5.7	**20** W	0541	5.3
	1157	0.5		1154	1.2
	1800	5.8		W 1758	5.2
6 W	0019	0.4	**21** TH	0006	1.2
	0625	5.8		0616	5.3
	1241	0.5		1225	1.2
	1845	5.7		1833	5.2
7 TH	0101	0.5	**22** F	0037	1.2
	0708	5.7		0649	5.3
	1322	0.6		1255	1.3
	1929	5.6		1907	5.1
8 F	0141	0.8	**23** SA	0107	1.3
	0748	5.6		0721	5.2
	1402	0.9		1326	1.4
	2010	5.3		1939	5.0
9 SA	0219	1.2	**24** SU	0138	1.4
	0826	5.3		0754	5.1
	1442	1.3		1400	1.5
	2049	5.0		2014	4.9
10 SU	0258	1.6	**25** M	0212	1.6
	0902	5.0		0831	5.0
	1525	1.7		1439	1.7
	2129	4.6		2056	4.7
11 M	0342	2.1	**26** TU	0254	1.9
	0942	4.7		0917	4.9
	1616	2.1		1528	1.9
	2213	4.3		2148	4.5
12 TU	0437	2.4	**27** W	0349	2.1
	1043	4.5		1013	4.8
	1723	2.4		1636	2.0
				2253	4.4
13 W	0007	4.1	**28** TH	0507	2.2
	0553	2.6		1122	4.7
	1231	4.4		1801	1.9
	1856	2.4			
14 TH	0126	4.2	**29** F	0013	4.4
	0732	2.5		0635	2.1
	1344	4.5		1241	4.8
	2016	2.2		1921	1.8
15 F	0226	4.4	**30** SA	0137	4.6
	0839	2.2		0753	1.9
	1440	4.7		1358	4.9
	2108	1.8		2031	1.5

DECEMBER

Day	Time	m	Day	Time	m
1 SU	0244	4.9	**16** M	0307	4.7
	0859	1.5		0919	1.9
	1504	5.2		1523	4.8
	2131	1.2		2141	1.7
2 M	0341	5.2	**17** TU	0352	4.9
	0956	1.2		1005	1.7
	1600	5.4		1610	4.9
	2224	0.9		2223	1.5
3 TU	0432	5.4	**18** W	0435	5.1
	1048	0.9		1046	1.5
	1652	5.5		1654	5.0
	2313	0.8		2302	1.3
4 W	0519	5.6	**19** TH	0516	5.2
	1136	0.7		1125	1.3
	● 1741	5.6		1736	5.1
	2359	0.7		○ 2341	1.3
5 TH	0605	5.6	**20** F	0555	5.3
	1221	0.7		1204	1.2
	1828	5.5		1817	5.1
6 F	0042	0.8	**21** SA	0019	1.2
	0648	5.6		0633	5.3
	1306	0.8		1243	1.2
	1912	5.4		1855	5.1
7 SA	0124	1.0	**22** SU	0057	1.2
	0730	5.5		0711	5.3
	1348	1.0		1322	1.2
	1955	5.2		1934	5.0
8 SU	0204	1.3	**23** M	0135	1.3
	0809	5.3		0749	5.3
	1430	1.3		1402	1.3
	2035	4.9		2013	5.0
9 M	0244	1.6	**24** TU	0215	1.4
	0845	5.1		0829	5.2
	1512	1.6		1444	1.4
	2113	4.7		2056	4.9
10 TU	0325	1.9	**25** W	0258	1.5
	0923	4.8		0913	5.1
	1556	1.9		1530	1.5
	2156	4.4		2143	4.8
11 W	0411	2.2	**26** TH	0346	1.7
	1009	4.5		1002	5.0
	1646	2.1		1623	1.6
	2253	4.3		2237	4.7
12 TH	0506	2.4	**27** F	0443	1.8
	1109	4.5		1059	4.9
	1746	2.3		1725	1.7
				2341	4.6
13 F	0009	4.2	**28** SA	0552	1.9
	0611	2.4		1206	4.8
	1226	4.4		1837	1.8
	1853	2.2			
14 SA	0119	4.3	**29** SU	0053	4.6
	0722	2.3		0710	1.9
	1335	4.5		1320	4.8
	1958	2.1		1952	1.7
15 SU	0217	4.5	**30** M	0206	4.7
	0826	2.1		0825	1.7
	1432	4.6		1432	4.9
	2054	1.9		2101	1.5
			31 TU	0312	4.9
				0931	1.5
				1538	5.0
				2202	1.3

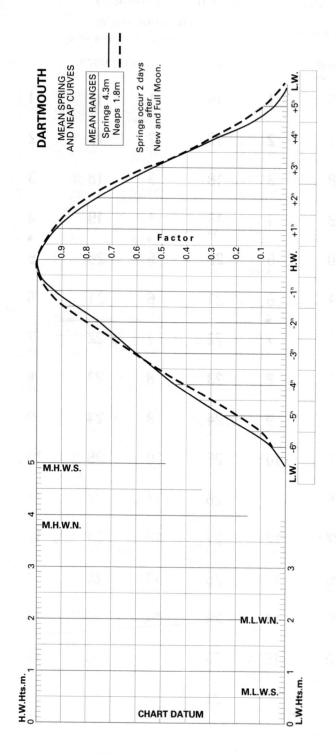

DARTMOUTH

MEAN SPRING AND NEAP CURVES

MEAN RANGES
Springs 4.3m
Neaps 1.8m

Springs occur 2 days after New and Full Moon.

TIME ZONE (UTC)
For Summer Time add ONE hour in **non-shaded areas**

ENGLAND - DARTMOUTH

YEAR **2002**

LAT 50°21'N   LONG 3°34'W

TIMES AND HEIGHTS OF HIGH AND LOW WATERS

JANUARY

Day	Time m	Time m	Time m	Time m
1 TU	0045 0.7	0718 4.9	1312 0.7	1945 4.7
2 W	0129 0.7	0803 5.0	1357 0.7	2030 4.6
3 TH	0214 0.8	0848 4.9	1442 0.7	2116 4.6
4 F	0258 0.9	0933 4.8	1528 0.9	2203 4.4
5 SA	0341 1.1	1020 4.6	1616 1.1	2253 4.2
6 SU	0434 1.4	1113 4.4	1710 1.4	2351 4.1
7 M	0532 1.6	1214 4.2	1814 1.6	
8 TU	0057 4.0	0645 1.7	1324 4.1	1929 1.6
9 W	0209 4.0	0803 1.7	1437 4.1	2043 1.6
10 TH	0316 4.1	0913 1.5	1543 4.4	2146 1.4
11 F	0415 4.3	1012 1.3	1641 4.3	2239 1.2
12 SA	0504 4.5	1104 1.1	1731 4.4	2325 1.1
13 SU	0552 4.6	1149 1.0	1816 4.5	●
14 M	0007 1.0	0631 4.7	1232 0.9	1854 4.5
15 TU	0047 0.9	0706 4.7	1310 0.9	1928 4.4
16 W	0122 1.0	0739 4.7	1344 1.0	2000 4.4
17 TH	0153 1.1	0811 4.6	1415 1.1	2032 4.3
18 F	0221 1.2	0846 4.5	1442 1.2	2105 4.2
19 SA	0247 1.4	0919 4.4	1510 1.4	2139 4.1
20 SU	0315 1.5	0954 4.2	1540 1.6	2215 3.9
21 M	0348 1.7	1031 4.0	1619 1.7	2258 3.8
22 TU	0434 1.9	1118 3.9	1715 1.9	2354 3.7
23 W	0545 2.1	1218 3.8	1832 2.0	
24 TH	0104 3.7	0710 2.0	1335 3.8	1946 1.8
25 F	0226 3.9	0823 1.8	1459 3.9	2055 1.6
26 SA	0339 4.1	0930 1.6	1609 4.1	2157 1.3
27 SU	0438 4.4	1030 1.1	1706 4.4	2254 1.0
28 M	0530 4.7	1124 0.8	1800 4.6	2346 0.7 ○
29 TU	0620 4.9	1215 0.5	1850 4.7	
30 W	0036 0.5	0706 5.0	1305 0.3	1937 4.8
31 TH	0123 0.4	0753 5.1	1350 0.2	2022 4.8

FEBRUARY

Day	Time m	Time m	Time m	Time m
1 F	0206 0.4	0839 5.1	1433 0.3	2105 4.8
2 SA	0247 0.5	0922 5.0	1514 0.5	2147 4.6
3 SU	0327 0.7	1004 4.8	1554 0.8	2229 4.4
4 M	0409 1.0	1048 4.5	1637 1.2	2316 4.1
5 TU	0456 1.4	1139 4.1	1727 1.5	
6 W	0013 3.9	0555 1.7	1245 3.9	1835 1.8
7 TH	0127 3.8	0718 1.9	1406 3.8	2007 1.9
8 F	0246 3.8	0851 1.8	1521 3.8	2128 1.7
9 SA	0352 4.0	1000 1.5	1624 4.0	2226 1.5
10 SU	0448 4.3	1053 1.2	1716 4.2	2313 1.2
11 M	0533 4.5	1137 1.0	1759 4.3	2355 1.0
12 TU	0614 4.6	1217 0.8	1837 4.4	●
13 W	0033 0.8	0649 4.7	1255 0.7	1910 4.5
14 TH	0107 0.8	0723 4.7	1327 0.7	1942 4.5
15 F	0135 0.8	0755 4.7	1354 0.8	2013 4.4
16 SA	0200 0.9	0827 4.6	1418 0.9	2044 4.3
17 SU	0222 1.1	0857 4.4	1439 1.1	2112 4.2
18 M	0244 1.2	0924 4.3	1503 1.2	2138 4.1
19 TU	0311 1.4	0950 4.1	1533 1.5	2208 3.9
20 W	0347 1.6	1027 3.9	1615 1.7	2256 3.8
21 TH	0439 1.9	1126 3.7	1721 1.9	
22 F	0004 3.7	0612 2.0	1244 3.6	1902 2.0
23 SA	0132 3.7	0749 1.9	1422 3.7	2025 1.8
24 SU	0306 4.0	0906 1.5	1548 4.0	2138 1.4
25 M	0415 4.4	1013 1.1	1650 4.4	2240 0.9
26 TU	0511 4.7	1111 0.6	1744 4.6	2333 0.5
27 W	0602 5.0	1202 0.2	1834 4.8	○
28 TH	0022 0.2	0651 5.2	1250 0.0	1920 4.9

MARCH

Day	Time m	Time m	Time m	Time m
1 F	0109 0.0	0738 5.2	1334 -0.1	2004 5.0
2 SA	0150 0.0	0821 5.2	1415 0.0	2046 4.9
3 SU	0228 0.1	0903 5.1	1452 0.2	2124 4.8
4 M	0306 0.4	0942 4.8	1528 0.6	2200 4.5
5 TU	0343 0.9	1020 4.4	1606 1.1	2236 4.2
6 W	0425 1.3	1102 4.0	1650 1.6	2322 3.8
7 TH	0518 1.8	1208 3.6	1749 2.0	
8 F	0046 3.6	0636 2.1	1343 3.5	1925 2.2
9 SA	0219 3.6	0835 2.0	1502 3.6	2112 2.0
10 SU	0330 3.9	0946 1.6	1606 3.8	2209 1.6
11 M	0425 4.2	1036 1.3	1656 4.1	2255 1.2
12 TU	0511 4.4	1118 0.9	1736 4.3	2334 0.9
13 W	0550 4.6	1156 0.7	1814 4.4	
14 TH	0010 0.7	0626 4.7	1232 0.6	1848 4.5 ●
15 F	0044 0.7	0700 4.7	1302 0.6	1919 4.5
16 SA	0111 0.7	0734 4.7	1327 0.7	1950 4.5
17 SU	0134 0.8	0805 4.6	1349 0.8	2018 4.5
18 M	0156 0.9	0832 4.5	1411 0.9	2044 4.3
19 TU	0218 1.0	0856 4.3	1434 1.1	2107 4.2
20 W	0244 1.1	0921 4.1	1502 1.3	2135 4.1
21 TH	0318 1.4	0958 3.9	1540 1.6	2221 3.9
22 F	0407 1.7	1058 3.7	1639 1.9	2331 3.7
23 SA	0533 2.0	1217 3.5	1828 2.1	
24 SU	0056 3.7	0724 1.9	1358 3.7	2002 1.8
25 M	0237 4.0	0848 1.5	1529 4.0	2119 1.4
26 TU	0352 4.4	0956 1.0	1631 4.4	2222 0.9
27 W	0450 4.7	1053 0.5	1724 4.7	2315 0.4
28 TH	0542 5.0	1142 0.1	1813 4.9	○
29 F	0002 0.1	0630 5.2	1230 -0.1	1858 5.0 ●
30 SA	0048 -0.1	0716 5.3	1312 -0.2	1941 5.1
31 SU	0129 -0.1	0800 5.2	1351 0.0	2020 5.0

APRIL

Day	Time m	Time m	Time m	Time m
1 M	0207 0.1	0840 5.0	1428 0.3	2056 4.8
2 TU	0242 0.4	0917 4.7	1503 0.7	2129 4.5
3 W	0319 0.9	0951 4.3	1538 1.2	2157 4.2
4 TH	0359 1.4	1027 3.9	1621 1.7	2233 3.9
5 F	0450 1.8	1127 3.5	1718 2.1	2344 3.6
6 SA	0603 2.1	1319 3.4	1844 2.3	
7 SU	0148 3.6	0806 2.1	1438 3.5	2041 2.1
8 M	0300 3.8	0918 1.7	1539 3.8	2140 1.7
9 TU	0355 4.1	0951 1.3	1626 4.1	2224 1.3
10 W	0440 4.3	1048 1.0	1706 4.3	2304 1.0
11 TH	0520 4.5	1125 0.8	1744 4.5	2340 0.8
12 F	0557 4.6	1158 0.7	1819 4.5	
13 SA	0011 0.7	0634 4.6	1228 0.6	1853 4.6
14 SU	0041 0.7	0708 4.6	1256 0.7	1924 4.6
15 M	0107 0.7	0740 4.6	1322 0.8	1953 4.5
16 TU	0131 0.8	0808 4.4	1346 0.9	2019 4.5
17 W	0157 0.9	0836 4.3	1413 1.1	2046 4.3
18 TH	0227 1.1	0906 4.1	1443 1.3	2120 4.2
19 F	0303 1.4	0948 3.9	1525 1.6	2207 4.0
20 SA	0355 1.7	1047 3.7	1626 1.9	2312 3.8
21 SU	0523 1.9	1203 3.6	1807 2.0	
22 M	0034 3.8	0703 1.8	1341 3.7	1940 1.8
23 TU	0211 4.0	0825 1.4	1506 4.0	2056 1.3
24 W	0326 4.4	0933 0.9	1608 4.4	2158 0.9
25 TH	0425 4.7	1029 0.5	1659 4.7	2252 0.5
26 F	0518 5.0	1118 0.1	1748 4.9	2339 0.2
27 SA	0607 5.1	1204 0.0	1834 5.0	○
28 SU	0023 0.0	0654 5.1	1248 0.0	1916 5.0
29 M	0106 0.1	0737 5.0	1328 0.2	1955 5.0
30 TU	0144 0.3	0816 4.8	1404 0.5	2030 4.8

Chart Datum: 2·62 metres below Ordnance Datum (Newlyn)

TIME ZONE (UTC)
For Summer Time add ONE hour in **non-shaded areas**

ENGLAND - DARTMOUTH

LAT 50°21'N   LONG 3°34'W

TIMES AND HEIGHTS OF HIGH AND LOW WATERS

YEAR **2002**

MAY

Day	Time	m	Time	m		Day	Time	m	Time	m
1 W	0222	0.6	0853	4.5		**16** TH	0145	0.9	0824	4.3
	1440	0.9	2059	4.5			1402	1.1	2034	4.5
2 TH	0259	1.0	0927	4.2		**17** F	0222	1.1	0901	4.2
	1517	1.3	2128	4.2			1438	1.3	2113	4.3
3 F	0339	1.4	1001	3.8		**18** SA	0304	1.3	0946	4.0
	1559	1.8	2204	3.9			1526	1.5	2202	4.2
4 SA	0429	1.8	1053	3.5		**19** SU	0400	1.5	1043	3.8
	1653	2.1	2300	3.7			1629	1.7	2301	4.0
5 SU	0534	2.1	1242	3.4		**20** M	0516	1.6	1154	3.8
	1804	2.2					1750	1.8		
6 M	0058	3.6	0702	2.0		**21** TU	0016	4.0	0640	1.5
	1358	3.5	1935	2.1			1318	3.9	1913	1.6
7 TU	0216	3.8	0827	1.8		**22** W	0141	4.1	0756	1.3
	1457	3.7	2049	1.8			1435	4.1	2027	1.3
8 W	0313	4.0	0920	1.5		**23** TH	0255	4.4	0903	1.0
	1546	4.0	2140	1.5			1538	4.4	2130	1.0
9 TH	0400	4.2	1004	1.2		**24** F	0357	4.6	1001	0.7
	1627	4.2	2222	1.2			1632	4.6	2224	0.7
10 F	0443	4.4	1044	1.0		**25** SA	0452	4.8	1053	0.4
	1708	4.4	2301	1.0			1722	4.8	2315	0.4
11 SA	0524	4.5	1119	0.8		**26** SU	0544	4.9	1140	0.3
	1746	4.5	2335	0.8			1810	4.9	O	
12 SU	0604	4.5	1152	0.8		**27** M	0000	0.3	0632	4.9
	1824	4.6 ●					1224	0.4	1853	4.9
13 M	0008	0.8	0642	4.5		**28** TU	0045	0.4	0715	4.8
	1225	0.8	1858	4.6			1306	0.5	1932	4.8
14 TU	0041	0.8	0718	4.5		**29** W	0126	0.5	0757	4.6
	1258	0.8	1931	4.6			1344	0.7	2007	4.7
15 W	0113	0.8	0751	4.4		**30** TH	0205	0.8	0834	4.4
	1329	0.9	2001	4.5			1422	1.0	2038	4.5
						31 F	0243	1.1	0908	4.1
							1459	1.4	2108	4.3

JUNE

Day	Time	m	Time	m		Day	Time	m	Time	m
1 SA	0323	1.4	0943	3.9		**16** SU	0310	1.0	0947	4.2
	1539	1.7	2145	4.1			1529	1.3	2158	4.4
2 SU	0408	1.7	1028	3.7		**17** M	0402	1.2	1039	4.1
	1626	1.9	2234	3.9			1624	1.4	2252	4.3
3 M	0501	1.9	1133	3.5		**18** TU	0501	1.3	1140	4.0
	1724	2.1	2338	3.7			1727	1.5	2357	4.2
4 TU	0603	1.9	1251	3.5		**19** W	0609	1.4	1248	4.0
	1830	2.1					1839	1.5		
5 W	0101	3.7	0709	1.8		**20** TH	0109	4.2	0721	1.3
	1357	3.7	1936	1.9			1359	4.1	1951	1.4
6 TH	0212	3.8	0811	1.6		**21** F	0223	4.2	0831	1.2
	1452	3.9	2037	1.7			1505	4.2	2059	1.2
7 F	0310	4.0	0905	1.4		**22** SA	0329	4.3	0934	1.0
	1542	4.1	2130	1.4			1604	4.4	2200	1.0
8 SA	0400	4.2	0953	1.2		**23** SU	0429	4.5	1030	0.8
	1628	4.3	2216	1.2			1658	4.6	2254	0.8
9 SU	0449	4.3	1037	1.0		**24** M	0523	4.5	1119	0.7
	1713	4.4	2259	1.0			1748	4.7	O 2342	0.7
10 M	0534	4.4	1118	0.9		**25** TU	0614	4.6	1205	0.7
	1755	4.5	● 2339	0.9			1833	4.7		
11 TU	0618	4.4	1158	0.9		**26** W	0028	0.7	0658	4.5
	1836	4.6					1250	0.7	1912	4.7
12 W	0019	0.8	0658	4.5		**27** TH	0112	0.7	0739	4.4
	1239	0.9	1913	4.6			1329	0.9	1948	4.7
13 TH	0101	0.8	0738	4.4		**28** F	0151	0.8	0817	4.3
	1319	0.9	1950	4.6			1407	1.0	2021	4.5
14 F	0141	0.8	0818	4.4		**29** SA	0228	1.0	0851	4.2
	1359	1.0	2029	4.6			1442	1.2	2053	4.4
15 SA	0224	0.9	0901	4.3		**30** SU	0305	1.2	0925	4.0
	1442	1.1	2111	4.5			1518	1.4	2129	4.2

JULY

Day	Time	m	Time	m		Day	Time	m	Time	m
1 M	0340	1.4	1002	3.9		**16** TU	0350	0.8	1027	4.3
	1554	1.7	2207	4.1			1608	1.1	2239	4.3
2 TU	0421	1.6	1046	3.7		**17** W	0438	1.0	1118	4.2
	1636	1.8	2253	3.9			1659	1.3	2332	4.3
3 W	0508	1.8	1138	3.6		**18** TH	0534	1.3	1216	4.0
	1729	1.9	2349	3.8			1800	1.5		
4 TH	0604	1.8	1241	3.6		**19** F	0037	4.1	0642	1.5
	1833	2.0					1324	4.0	1914	1.6
5 F	0055	3.8	0706	1.8		**20** SA	0152	4.0	0757	1.5
	1348	3.7	1936	1.9			1436	4.0	2032	1.5
6 SA	0210	3.8	0807	1.6		**21** SU	0307	4.0	0910	1.4
	1452	3.9	2037	1.7			1542	4.2	2142	1.4
7 SU	0317	3.9	0905	1.5		**22** M	0412	4.1	1013	1.2
	1550	4.1	2135	1.4			1640	4.4	2241	1.1
8 M	0415	4.1	0959	1.2		**23** TU	0509	4.3	1106	1.0
	1642	4.3	2227	1.2			1731	4.5	2331	0.9
9 TU	0508	4.4	1050	1.1		**24** W	0558	4.4	1153	0.9
	1729	4.5	2317	1.0			1816	4.6	O	
10 W	0557	4.4	1138	0.9		**25** TH	0016	0.8	0643	4.4
	1816	4.6 ●					1237	0.8	1855	4.7
11 TH	0004	0.8	0643	4.5		**26** F	0100	0.7	0722	4.4
	1226	0.8	1858	4.7			1316	0.8	1931	4.7
12 F	0052	0.7	0729	4.5		**27** SA	0137	0.8	0757	4.3
	1313	0.7	1941	4.8			1350	0.9	2003	4.6
13 SA	0137	0.6	0813	4.5		**28** SU	0210	0.9	0829	4.3
	1356	0.7	2024	4.8			1422	1.0	2035	4.5
14 SU	0222	0.6	0857	4.5		**29** M	0240	1.0	0900	4.2
	1439	0.8	2107	4.8			1449	1.2	2107	4.4
15 M	0306	0.7	0941	4.4		**30** TU	0307	1.2	0933	4.1
	1523	0.9	2152	4.7			1516	1.4	2139	4.2
						31 W	0334	1.4	1006	3.9
							1543	1.6	2213	4.0

AUGUST

Day	Time	m	Time	m		Day	Time	m	Time	m
1 TH	0407	1.6	1046	3.8		**16** F	0458	1.4	1142	4.0
	1620	1.8	2253	3.9			1725	1.6		
2 F	0453	1.8	1134	3.7		**17** SA	0005	3.9	0600	1.7
	1719	2.0	2347	3.7			1252	3.8	1840	1.9
3 SA	0602	1.9	1239	3.6		**18** SU	0128	3.7	0728	1.9
	1841	2.0					1413	3.8	2015	1.9
4 SU	0100	3.6	0718	1.9		**19** M	0253	3.8	0859	1.8
	1358	3.7	1955	1.9			1526	4.0	2134	1.6
5 M	0233	3.7	0828	1.7		**20** TU	0402	3.9	1004	1.5
	1514	4.0	2102	1.6			1626	4.2	2232	1.3
6 TU	0347	4.0	0931	1.4		**21** W	0457	4.1	1055	1.2
	1615	4.2	2203	1.3			1716	4.5	2320	1.0
7 W	0446	4.2	1030	1.1		**22** TH	0544	4.3	1139	0.9
	1708	4.5	2300	0.9			1758	4.6	O	
8 TH	0539	4.4	1123	0.9		**23** F	0002	0.8	0624	4.4
	1756	4.7	● 2351	0.6			1220	0.8	1835	4.7
9 F	0628	4.6	1213	0.6		**24** SA	0042	0.7	0659	4.5
	1844	4.9					1257	0.7	1908	4.7
10 SA	0041	0.4	0714	4.7		**25** SU	0116	0.7	0732	4.5
	1302	0.4	1929	5.0			1328	0.8	1940	4.7
11 SU	0127	0.3	0800	4.7		**26** M	0144	0.8	0802	4.4
	1345	0.4	2012	5.1			1354	0.9	2010	4.6
12 M	0210	0.2	0843	4.7		**27** TU	0209	0.9	0831	4.4
	1427	0.4	2055	5.0			1417	1.1	2041	4.5
13 TU	0250	0.4	0925	4.7		**28** W	0229	1.1	0900	4.2
	1506	0.6	2136	4.8			1435	1.2	2108	4.3
14 W	0329	0.6	1005	4.6		**29** TH	0250	1.3	0929	4.1
	1545	0.8	2218	4.6			1457	1.4	2135	4.1
15 TH	0411	1.0	1049	4.3		**30** F	0315	1.6	0959	3.9
	1629	1.2	2304	4.3			1527	1.7	2206	3.9
						31 SA	0349	1.7	1040	3.8
							1611	1.9	2256	3.7

Chart Datum: 2·62 metres below Ordnance Datum (Newlyn)
Register for your **FREE** weekly weather email service from Macmillan Reeds
》 at **www.nauticaldata.com – NOW!**
weekend weather reports sent to your email address, every Thursday 《

ENGLAND - DARTMOUTH

LAT 50°21′N   LONG 3°34′W

TIMES AND HEIGHTS OF HIGH AND LOW WATERS

TIME ZONE (UTC)
For Summer Time add ONE hour in **non-shaded areas**

YEAR 2002

SEPTEMBER

Day	Time m	Time m	Time m	Time m		Day	Time m	Time m	Time m	Time m
1 SU	0445 2.0	1141 3.6	1737 2.2			16 M	0115 3.5	0706 2.2	1355 3.7	2010 2.1
2 M	0009 3.6	0634 2.1	1303 3.7	1922 2.1		17 TU	0244 3.6	0851 2.0	1511 3.9	2125 1.7
3 TU	0151 3.6	0759 1.9	1441 3.9	2039 1.7		18 W	0351 3.9	0950 1.6	1610 4.2	2216 1.3
4 W	0327 3.9	0910 1.6	1552 4.3	2146 1.3		19 TH	0442 4.2	1037 1.2	1655 4.5	2300 1.0
5 TH	0428 4.2	1012 1.1	1646 4.6	2244 1.1		20 F	0523 4.4	1118 1.0	1734 4.7	2339 0.8
6 F	0520 4.5	1107 0.7	1735 4.9	2335 0.4		21 SA	0559 4.6	1155 0.8	1811 4.8 ○	
7 SA	0608 4.8	1156 0.4	1824 5.1 ●			22 SU	0014 0.7	0632 4.6	1230 0.7	1843 4.8
8 SU	0022 0.2	0654 4.9	1244 0.2	1909 5.2		23 M	0047 0.7	0703 4.6	1259 0.6	1914 4.8
9 M	0108 0.0	0738 5.0	1327 0.1	1953 5.2		24 TU	0113 0.8	0733 4.6	1323 0.9	1944 4.7
10 TU	0149 0.1	0820 5.0	1406 0.2	2035 5.1		25 W	0134 0.9	0802 4.5	1343 1.0	2012 4.5
11 W	0228 0.3	0900 4.8	1443 0.5	2115 4.9		26 TH	0154 1.0	0829 4.4	1402 1.2	2039 4.4
12 TH	0305 0.6	0939 4.6	1521 0.8	2154 4.6		27 F	0215 1.2	0854 4.3	1425 1.4	2102 4.2
13 F	0342 1.1	1018 4.3	1602 1.3	2235 4.1		28 SA	0238 1.5	0922 4.1	1454 1.6	2135 4.0
14 SA	0426 1.6	1105 4.0	1654 1.8	2334 3.7		29 SU	0312 1.7	1004 3.9	1536 1.9	2227 3.7
15 SU	0525 2.0	1222 3.7	1811 2.1			30 M	0402 2.1	1106 3.7	1650 2.2	2342 3.6

OCTOBER

Day	Time m	Time m	Time m	Time m		Day	Time m	Time m	Time m	Time m
1 TU	0552 2.3	1226 3.7	1856 2.2			16 W	0223 3.6	0825 2.2	1445 3.9	2100 1.8
2 W	0122 3.6	0735 2.1	1408 3.9	2018 1.8		17 TH	0326 3.9	0922 1.8	1541 4.2	2149 1.4
3 TH	0307 3.9	0851 1.6	1526 4.3	2126 1.2		18 F	0414 4.2	0851 1.6	1626 4.5	2230 1.1
4 F	0408 4.3	0953 1.1	1623 4.7	2222 0.7		19 SA	0453 4.4	1047 1.1	1704 4.6	2307 0.9
5 SA	0458 4.7	1047 0.7	1713 5.0	2313 0.3		20 SU	0528 4.6	1123 0.9	1740 4.7	2341 0.8
6 SU	0545 4.9	1135 0.3	1801 5.2	2359 0.1 ●		21 M	0601 4.7	1156 0.8	1815 4.8 ○	
7 M	0630 5.1	1220 0.1	1847 5.3			22 TU	0011 0.8	0634 4.7	1225 0.8	1848 4.7
8 TU	0044 0.0	0714 5.1	1303 0.1	1931 5.3		23 W	0038 0.9	0705 4.7	1252 0.9	1919 4.7
9 W	0125 0.1	0755 5.1	1342 0.2	2012 5.1		24 TH	0103 0.9	0738 4.6	1315 1.0	1948 4.6
10 TH	0203 0.4	0835 5.0	1421 0.5	2052 4.8		25 F	0126 1.1	0803 4.6	1338 1.2	2015 4.4
11 F	0239 0.8	0911 4.7	1458 1.0	2130 4.5		26 SA	0149 1.3	0911 4.7	1405 1.4	2044 4.2
12 SA	0316 1.3	0947 4.4	1539 1.5	2207 4.0		27 SU	0217 1.5	0901 4.3	1437 1.6	2121 4.0
13 SU	0359 1.8	1028 4.0	1631 1.9	2306 3.6		28 M	0253 1.8	0945 4.1	1522 1.9	2214 3.8
14 M	0458 2.2	1147 3.7	1747 2.3			29 TU	0345 2.1	1046 3.9	1637 2.1	2325 3.6
15 TU	0059 3.5	0637 2.4	1332 3.7	1951 2.2		30 W	0525 2.3	1201 3.9	1829 2.1	
						31 TH	0057 3.7	0708 2.1	1333 4.0	1952 1.7

NOVEMBER

Day	Time m	Time m	Time m	Time m		Day	Time m	Time m	Time m	Time m
1 F	0236 4.0	0824 1.7	1454 4.4	2100 1.2		16 SA	0332 4.1	0925 1.6	1546 4.3	2149 1.4
2 SA	0340 4.4	0928 1.2	1555 4.7	2157 0.8		17 SU	0415 4.3	1007 1.4	1627 4.5	2227 1.1
3 SU	0431 4.7	1021 0.8	1648 5.0	2248 0.4		18 M	0452 4.5	1046 1.2	1706 4.6	2303 1.0
4 M	0519 5.0	1110 0.4	1737 5.2	2335 0.2 ●		19 TU	0529 4.6	1121 1.0	1745 4.6	2335 1.0
5 TU	0606 5.1	1156 0.3	1825 5.2			20 W	0605 4.7	1153 1.0	1823 4.7 ○	
6 W	0018 0.2	0650 5.2	1241 0.3	1909 5.2		21 TH	0005 1.0	0641 4.7	1224 1.0	1857 4.6
7 TH	0101 0.3	0732 5.1	1323 0.4	1952 5.0		22 F	0037 1.0	0713 4.7	1255 1.1	1931 4.5
8 F	0140 0.6	0810 5.0	1401 0.7	2032 4.7		23 SA	0107 1.1	0744 4.6	1326 1.2	2002 4.4
9 SA	0218 1.0	0848 4.7	1440 1.1	2110 4.4		24 SU	0137 1.3	0816 4.6	1359 1.3	2036 4.3
10 SU	0256 1.4	0923 4.4	1523 1.5	2149 4.0		25 M	0211 1.4	0852 4.4	1437 1.5	2117 4.1
11 M	0339 1.9	1002 4.1	1613 1.9	2242 3.7		26 TU	0252 1.7	0937 4.3	1526 1.7	2207 3.9
12 TU	0433 2.2	1101 3.9	1719 2.2			27 W	0346 1.9	1032 4.2	1632 1.8	2311 3.8
13 W	0023 3.5	0548 2.4	1246 3.8	1852 2.2		28 TH	0503 2.0	1139 4.1	1756 1.8	
14 TH	0142 3.6	0728 2.3	1400 3.9	2012 2.0		29 F	0029 3.8	0631 2.0	1256 4.2	1917 1.6
15 F	0244 3.8	0836 2.0	1458 4.1	2105 1.6		30 SA	0153 4.0	0749 1.7	1415 4.3	2028 1.3

DECEMBER

Day	Time m	Time m	Time m	Time m		Day	Time m	Time m	Time m	Time m
1 SU	0302 4.3	0856 1.3	1523 4.6	2129 1.0		16 M	0326 4.1	0916 1.7	1543 4.2	2139 1.5
2 M	0401 4.6	0954 1.0	1621 4.8	2222 0.7		17 TU	0413 4.3	1003 1.5	1631 4.3	2221 1.3
3 TU	0454 4.8	1047 0.7	1715 4.9	2312 0.6		18 W	0457 4.5	1045 1.3	1717 4.4	2301 1.2
4 W	0543 5.0	1135 0.6	1805 5.0	2358 0.5 ●		19 TH	0540 4.6	1124 1.1	1800 4.5	2340 1.1 ○
5 TH	0630 5.1	1220 0.5	1853 4.9			20 F	0620 4.7	1203 1.0	1842 4.5	
6 F	0042 0.6	0712 5.0	1306 0.6	1936 4.8		21 SA	0018 1.0	0657 4.7	1243 1.0	1919 4.5
7 SA	0124 0.8	0753 4.9	1347 0.8	2017 4.6		22 SU	0057 1.0	0735 4.7	1322 1.0	1957 4.5
8 SU	0203 1.1	0831 4.7	1428 1.1	2056 4.3		23 M	0134 1.1	0811 4.7	1401 1.1	2035 4.4
9 M	0242 1.4	0906 4.5	1510 1.4	2134 4.1		24 TU	0214 1.2	0851 4.6	1442 1.2	2117 4.3
10 TU	0323 1.7	0943 4.3	1553 1.7	2215 3.8		25 W	0256 1.3	0934 4.5	1527 1.3	2203 4.2
11 W	0408 2.0	1028 4.1	1642 1.9	2311 3.7		26 TH	0343 1.5	1021 4.4	1620 1.4	2255 4.1
12 TH	0502 2.2	1127 3.9	1741 2.1			27 F	0439 1.6	1117 4.3	1721 1.5	2358 4.0
13 F	0025 3.6	0606 2.2	1242 3.8	1849 2.1		28 SA	0547 1.7	1222 4.2	1833 1.6	
14 SA	0135 3.7	0718 2.1	1351 3.9	1954 1.9		29 SU	0108 4.0	0706 1.7	1336 4.2	1948 1.5
15 SU	0235 3.9	0822 1.9	1450 4.0	2051 1.7		30 M	0223 4.1	0821 1.5	1450 4.3	2058 1.3
						31 TU	0331 4.3	0929 1.3	1558 4.4	2200 1.1

Chart Datum: 2·62 metres below Ordnance Datum (Newlyn)

17

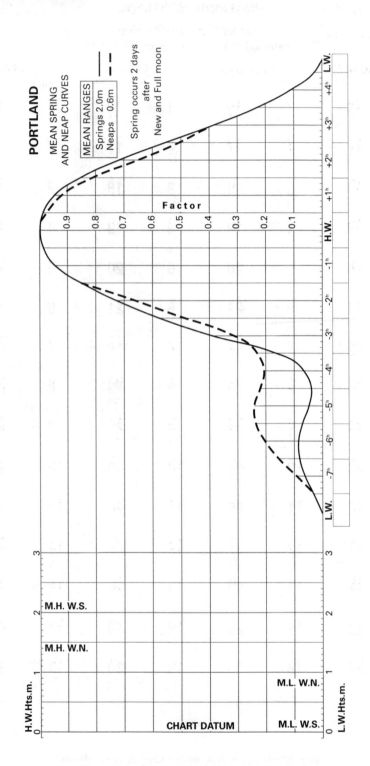

PORTLAND

MEAN SPRING AND NEAP CURVES

MEAN RANGES	
Springs 2.0m	
Neaps 0.6m	- - -

Spring occurs 2 days after New and Full moon

Factor

0.9 0.8 0.7 0.6 0.5 0.4 0.3 0.2 0.1

L.W. +4ʰ +3ʰ +2ʰ +1ʰ H.W. -1ʰ -2ʰ -3ʰ -4ʰ -5ʰ -6ʰ -7ʰ L.W.

H.W.Hts.m.

M.H. W.S.

M.H. W.N.

CHART DATUM

M.L. W.N.

M.L. W.S.

L.W.Hts.m.

TIME ZONE (UTC)
For Summer Time add ONE hour in **non-shaded areas**

YEAR **2002**

ENGLAND – PORTLAND

LAT 50°34'N   LONG 2°26'W

TIMES AND HEIGHTS OF HIGH AND LOW WATERS

Note - Double LWs occur at Portland. The predictions are for the first LW. The second LW occurs from 3 to 4 Hrs later and may, at Springs, on occasions be lower than the first.

JANUARY

Time	m		Time	m
1 0026	0.2		**16** 0107	0.3
0750	2.2		0814	2.0
TU 1251	0.3		W 1336	0.3
2022	2.0		2034	1.8
2 0112	0.2		**17** 0142	0.3
0833	2.2		0843	2.0
W 1338	0.3		TH 1411	0.3
2105	1.9		2102	1.7
3 0158	0.3		**18** 0212	0.4
0915	2.1		0911	1.8
TH 1425	0.3		F 1441	0.4
2148	1.9		2131	1.6
4 0244	0.4		**19** 0235	0.4
0958	2.0		0940	1.7
F 1515	0.4		SA 1502	0.4
2232	1.8		2201	1.5
5 0333	0.5		**20** 0256	0.5
1043	1.9		1009	1.6
SA 1610	0.4		SU 1526	0.5
2321	1.7		2234	1.4
6 0428	0.6		**21** 0325	0.6
1134	1.8		1040	1.5
SU 1710	0.5		M 1601	0.6
			2315	1.3
7 0019	1.6		**22** 0408	0.6
0531	0.7		1123	1.4
M 1234	1.7		TU 1654	0.6
1816	0.6			
8 0128	1.6		**23** 0014	1.3
0644	0.7		0514	0.7
TU 1345	1.6		W 1233	1.3
1925	0.6		1808	0.6
9 0243	1.6		**24** 0138	1.4
0800	0.7		0644	0.7
W 1501	1.6		TH 1408	1.3
2031	0.6		1928	0.6
10 0351	1.7		**25** 0303	1.5
0909	0.7		0811	0.6
TH 1611	1.6		F 1534	1.4
2130	0.5		2041	0.5
11 0450	1.8		**26** 0412	1.7
1006	0.6		0920	0.6
F 1711	1.7		SA 1643	1.6
2222	0.5		2143	0.4
12 0541	1.9		**27** 0511	1.8
1054	0.5		1017	0.5
SA 1804	1.7		SU 1744	1.7
2307	0.4		2239	0.3
13 0627	2.0		**28** 0606	2.0
1137	0.4		1109	0.3
SU 1851	1.8		M 1840	1.9
● 2349	0.4		○ 2330	0.2
14 0708	2.0		**29** 0658	2.2
1218	0.4		1158	0.2
M 1932	1.8		TU 1931	2.0
15 0029	0.3		**30** 0018	0.1
0743	2.1		0746	2.3
TU 1258	0.3		W 1246	0.1
2005	1.8		2018	2.1
			31 0105	0.1
			0831	2.3
			TH 1331	0.1
			2101	2.1

FEBRUARY

Time	m		Time	m
1 0149	0.1		**16** 0156	0.2
0912	2.3		0859	1.9
F 1416	0.1		SA 1417	0.2
2140	2.0		2116	1.7
2 0233	0.1		**17** 0218	0.2
0952	2.2		0926	1.8
SA 1501	0.1		SU 1435	0.2
2218	1.9		2140	1.6
3 0315	0.2		**18** 0236	0.3
1030	2.0		0951	1.6
SU 1547	0.2		M 1454	0.3
2257	1.8		2203	1.5
4 0400	0.4		**19** 0259	0.4
1110	1.9		1014	1.5
M 1635	0.4		TU 1521	0.4
2340	1.6		2232	1.4
5 0451	0.5		**20** 0330	0.5
1155	1.6		1044	1.4
TU 1731	0.5		W 1600	0.4
			2313	1.4
6 0033	1.5		**21** 0418	0.6
0554	0.7		1133	1.3
W 1253	1.5		TH 1701	0.6
1838	0.6			
7 0150	1.4		**22** 0019	1.3
0720	0.8		0538	0.7
TH 1418	1.4		F 1259	1.2
1959	0.7		1837	0.6
8 0320	1.5		**23** 0157	1.4
0857	0.7		0735	0.7
F 1551	1.4		SA 1458	1.3
2114	0.7		2018	0.6
9 0430	1.6		**24** 0337	1.5
1000	0.6		0908	0.6
SA 1701	1.5		SU 1627	1.5
2208	0.6		2132	0.5
10 0525	1.7		**25** 0450	1.8
1045	0.5		1009	0.4
SU 1755	1.6		M 1733	1.7
2253	0.5		2229	0.3
11 0613	1.9		**26** 0552	2.0
1124	0.4		1101	0.2
M 1841	1.7		TU 1830	1.9
2333	0.4		2319	0.1
12 0654	2.0		**27** 0646	2.2
1203	0.3		1148	0.1
TU 1921	1.8		W 1920	2.1
			○	
13 0013	0.3		**28** 0006	0.0
0730	2.0		0733	2.3
W 1241	0.2		TH 1234	-0.1
1954	1.8		2004	2.2
14 0051	0.2			
0802	2.1			
TH 1318	0.1			
2023	1.8			
15 0126	0.2			
0831	2.0			
F 1351	0.1			
2049	1.8			

MARCH

Time	m		Time	m
1 0051	-0.1		**16** 0103	0.1
0817	2.4		0811	2.0
F 1317	-0.1		SA 1325	0.0
2044	2.2		2029	1.9
2 0133	-0.1		**17** 0133	0.1
0857	2.4		0840	2.0
SA 1359	-0.1		SU 1350	0.1
2122	2.1		2055	1.8
3 0214	-0.1		**18** 0155	0.1
0934	2.2		0907	1.8
SU 1440	0.0		M 1409	0.2
2156	2.0		2117	1.7
4 0253	0.1		**19** 0214	0.2
1009	2.0		0930	1.7
M 1520	0.1		TU 1428	0.2
2230	1.8		2137	1.6
5 0332	0.3		**20** 0235	0.3
1044	1.8		0952	1.5
TU 1600	0.3		W 1451	0.3
2305	1.6		2202	1.5
6 0416	0.5		**21** 0303	0.4
1122	1.5		1020	1.4
W 1647	0.6		TH 1524	0.4
2348	1.5		2238	1.4
7 0514	0.7		**22** 0345	0.5
1211	1.3		1106	1.3
TH 1751	0.7		F 1616	0.6
			2336	1.4
8 0054	1.4		**23** 0502	0.7
0649	0.8		1228	1.2
F 1338	1.2		SA 1808	0.7
1926	0.8			
9 0250	1.4		**24** 0109	1.4
0856	0.7		0721	0.7
SA 1545	1.3		SU 1436	1.3
2057	0.7		2006	0.7
10 0411	1.5		**25** 0304	1.5
0951	0.6		0857	0.5
SU 1652	1.4		M 1613	1.5
2150	0.6		2119	0.5
11 0506	1.7		**26** 0428	1.7
1028	0.5		0956	0.3
M 1741	1.6		TU 1718	1.7
2231	0.5		2214	0.3
12 0552	1.8		**27** 0531	2.0
1103	0.3		1045	0.1
TU 1823	1.7		W 1812	2.0
2310	0.3		2303	0.1
13 0632	1.9		**28** 0625	2.2
1130	0.2		1131	-0.1
W 1900	1.8		TH 1859	2.2
2349	0.2		○ 2348	0.0
14 0709	2.0		**29** 0713	2.4
1216	0.1		1215	-0.2
TH 1933	1.9		F 1942	2.3
●				
15 0027	0.1		**30** 0031	-0.1
0741	2.1		0756	2.4
F 1252	0.0		SA 1257	-0.2
2002	1.9		2022	2.3
			31 0113	-0.1
			0836	2.4
			SU 1337	-0.2
			2058	2.2

APRIL

Time	m		Time	m
1 0152	-0.1		**16** 0129	0.2
0912	2.2		0845	1.8
M 1416	0.0		TU 1342	0.2
2132	2.1		2053	1.8
2 0229	0.1		**17** 0152	0.2
0946	2.0		0910	1.7
TU 1452	0.2		W 1406	0.3
2204	1.9		2115	1.7
3 0307	0.3		**18** 0217	0.3
1018	1.7		0935	1.5
W 1528	0.4		TH 1432	0.4
2235	1.6		2141	1.5
4 0348	0.5		**19** 0249	0.4
1054	1.5		1008	1.4
TH 1607	0.6		F 1507	0.5
2312	1.5		2218	1.5
5 0444	0.7		**20** 0335	0.5
1142	1.3		1059	1.3
F 1706	0.8		SA 1603	0.7
			2317	1.5
6 0008	1.4		**21** 0501	0.7
0620	0.8		1223	1.3
SA 1313	1.2		SU 1803	0.8
1846	0.9			
7 0210	1.3		**22** 0047	1.4
0838	0.7		0707	0.7
SU 1532	1.3		M 1422	1.4
2026	0.8		1948	0.7
8 0340	1.5		**23** 0237	1.6
0925	0.6		0833	0.5
M 1629	1.4		TU 1549	1.6
2119	0.7		2058	0.5
9 0433	1.6		**24** 0400	1.8
0958	0.5		0932	0.3
TU 1712	1.6		W 1651	1.8
2201	0.5		2152	0.3
10 0518	1.8		**25** 0503	2.0
1032	0.3		1022	0.1
W 1751	1.7		TH 1744	2.0
2241	0.4		2241	0.2
11 0559	1.9		**26** 0558	2.2
1108	0.2		1108	0.0
TH 1828	1.9		F 1832	2.2
2320	0.2		2326	0.0
12 0637	2.0		**27** 0648	2.3
1145	0.1		1152	-0.1
F 1902	2.0		SA 1916	2.3
● 2358	0.2		○	
13 0713	2.0		**28** 0009	0.0
1220	0.1		0732	2.3
SA 1934	2.0		SU 1234	-0.1
			1956	2.3
14 0033	0.1		**29** 0051	0.0
0746	2.0		0813	2.3
SU 1253	0.1		M 1314	0.0
2003	2.0		2034	2.2
15 0104	0.1		**30** 0130	0.1
0817	2.0		0851	2.1
M 1319	0.1		TU 1352	0.1
2030	1.9		2109	2.1

Chart Datum: 0·93 metres below Ordnance Datum (Newlyn)

TIME ZONE (UTC)
For Summer Time add ONE hour in **non-shaded areas**

YEAR **2002**

ENGLAND – PORTLAND

LAT 50°34'N   LONG 2°26'W

TIMES AND HEIGHTS OF HIGH AND LOW WATERS

Note - Double LWs occur at Portland. The predictions are for the first LW. The second LW occurs from 3 to 4 Hrs later and may, at Springs, on occasions be lower than the first.

MAY

Day	Time	m	Time	m	Day	Time	m	Time	m
1 W	0208 0.2	0925 1.9	1427 0.3	2139 1.9	16 TH	0136 0.3	0856 1.8	1354 0.3	2102 1.8
2 TH	0247 0.3	0957 1.7	1502 0.5	2208 1.7	17 F	0210 0.3	0928 1.6	1429 0.4	2133 1.7
3 F	0329 0.5	1031 1.4	1539 0.7	2241 1.5	18 SA	0250 0.4	1007 1.5	1514 0.6	2215 1.6
4 SA	0423 0.7	1118 1.3	1630 0.8	2330 1.4	19 SU	0346 0.5	1103 1.4	1621 0.7	2314 1.6
5 SU	0544 0.8	1236 1.2	1801 0.9		20 M	0506 0.6	1223 1.4	1752 0.7	
6 M	0050 1.4	0728 0.7	1448 1.3	1932 0.9	21 TU	0036 1.5	0639 0.6	1358 1.5	1919 0.7
7 TU	0240 1.4	0832 0.6	1546 1.4	2036 0.8	22 W	0209 1.6	0759 0.5	1515 1.6	2029 0.6
8 W	0342 1.5	0913 0.5	1628 1.6	2123 0.6	23 TH	0327 1.8	0901 0.3	1618 1.8	2126 0.4
9 TH	0430 1.7	0952 0.4	1708 1.7	2206 0.5	24 F	0432 1.9	0954 0.2	1713 2.0	2216 0.3
10 F	0515 1.8	1030 0.3	1746 1.9	2247 0.3	25 SA	0530 2.0	1043 0.1	1804 2.1	2304 0.2
11 SA	0558 1.9	1108 0.2	1824 2.0	2325 0.3	26 SU	0622 2.1	1129 0.1	1850 2.2	○2349 0.2
12 SU ●	0639 2.0	1144 0.2	1901 2.0		27 M	0712 2.1	1210 0.1	1934 2.2	
13 M	0001 0.2	0718 2.0	1218 0.2	1935 2.0	28 TU	0032 0.2	0753 2.1	1254 0.2	2013 2.2
14 TU	0034 0.2	0754 1.9	1250 0.2	2007 2.0	29 W	0113 0.2	0833 2.0	1332 0.3	2049 2.1
15 W	0104 0.2	0826 1.9	1321 0.3	2034 1.9	30 TH	0153 0.3	0908 1.8	1409 0.4	2120 1.9
					31 F	0233 0.4	0940 1.6	1445 0.5	2148 1.7

JUNE

Day	Time	m	Time	m	Day	Time	m	Time	m
1 SA	0315 0.5	1013 1.5	1521 0.7	2218 1.6	16 SU	0257 0.4	1015 1.7	1524 0.5	2223 1.8
2 SU	0401 0.6	1054 1.3	1604 0.8	2259 1.5	17 M	0351 0.4	1107 1.6	1621 0.6	2316 1.7
3 M	0501 0.7	1150 1.3	1708 0.9	2356 1.4	18 TU	0455 0.5	1210 1.5	1728 0.6	
4 TU	0615 0.7	1305 1.3	1832 0.9		19 W	0021 1.6	0607 0.5	1323 1.6	1841 0.7
5 W	0111 1.4	0725 0.6	1426 1.4	1943 0.8	20 TH	0136 1.6	0720 0.5	1437 1.6	1952 0.6
6 TH	0227 1.4	0820 0.6	1527 1.5	2039 0.7	21 F	0251 1.7	0827 0.4	1544 1.7	2057 0.6
7 F	0332 1.5	0906 0.5	1617 1.6	2127 0.6	22 SA	0401 1.7	0928 0.4	1644 1.9	2154 0.5
8 SA	0428 1.6	0949 0.4	1703 1.8	2210 0.5	23 SU	0504 1.8	1022 0.3	1739 2.0	2246 0.4
9 SU	0519 1.6	1029 0.3	1748 1.9	2250 0.4	24 M	0602 1.9	1111 0.3	1830 2.1	○2334 0.3
10 M	0607 1.8	1108 0.3	1831 2.0	●2329 0.3	25 TU	0654 1.9	1156 0.3	1916 2.1	
11 TU	0652 1.9	1148 0.2	1911 2.0		26 W	0019 0.3	0740 1.9	1239 0.3	1957 2.1
12 W	0008 0.3	0735 1.9	1228 0.3	1949 2.0	27 TH	0102 0.3	0821 1.9	1319 0.3	2034 2.0
13 TH	0047 0.3	0815 1.9	1309 0.3	2026 2.0	28 F	0142 0.3	0856 1.8	1356 0.4	2105 1.9
14 F	0127 0.3	0853 1.8	1351 0.3	2101 1.9	29 SA	0221 0.3	0926 1.7	1432 0.5	2132 1.8
15 SA	0210 0.3	0931 1.7	1435 0.4	2139 1.9	30 SU	0259 0.4	0954 1.6	1505 0.5	2201 1.7

JULY

Day	Time	m	Time	m	Day	Time	m	Time	m
1 M	0336 0.5	1027 1.4	1537 0.6	2233 1.6	16 TU	0342 0.3	1057 1.7	1605 0.4	2308 1.8
2 TU	0413 0.5	1108 1.4	1611 0.7	2313 1.5	17 W	0435 0.4	1145 1.6	1659 0.5	2358 1.7
3 W	0457 0.6	1200 1.3	1704 0.8		18 TH	0534 0.5	1244 1.6	1803 0.6	
4 TH	0006 1.4	0557 0.6	1306 1.3	1823 0.8	19 F	0058 1.6	0642 0.5	1356 1.5	1915 0.7
5 F	0117 1.4	0706 0.6	1418 1.4	1939 0.8	20 SA	0214 1.5	0756 0.6	1514 1.6	2033 0.7
6 SA	0234 1.4	0808 0.6	1525 1.5	2040 0.7	21 SU	0336 1.6	0909 0.5	1623 1.7	2143 0.6
7 SU	0343 1.5	0902 0.5	1623 1.7	2132 0.6	22 M	0448 1.6	1009 0.5	1723 1.8	2238 0.5
8 M	0444 1.6	0952 0.4	1716 1.8	2220 0.5	23 TU	0551 1.7	1059 0.4	1816 1.9	2325 0.4
9 TU	0540 1.7	1041 0.3	1806 1.9	2306 0.4	24 W	0644 1.8	1144 0.4	1903 2.0	○
10 W	0633 1.8	1128 0.3	1854 2.0	●2352 0.3	25 TH	0008 0.3	0730 1.8	1225 0.3	1944 2.1
11 TH	0723 1.9	1215 0.2	1940 2.1		26 F	0048 0.3	0809 1.9	1303 0.3	2020 2.1
12 F	0037 0.3	0809 1.9	1301 0.2	2023 2.1	27 SA	0127 0.2	0842 1.8	1340 0.3	2049 2.0
13 SA	0122 0.2	0853 1.9	1346 0.2	2104 2.1	28 SU	0204 0.2	0908 1.8	1414 0.3	2114 1.9
14 SU	0207 0.2	0934 1.9	1431 0.3	2144 2.0	29 M	0238 0.3	0932 1.7	1444 0.4	2141 1.8
15 M	0254 0.2	1014 1.8	1517 0.3	2224 1.9	30 TU	0306 0.3	0959 1.6	1507 0.5	2208 1.6
					31 W	0327 0.4	1029 1.5	1527 0.5	2235 1.5

AUGUST

Day	Time	m	Time	m	Day	Time	m	Time	m
1 TH	0351 0.5	1104 1.4	1558 0.6	2306 1.4	16 F	0501 0.5	1205 1.6	1728 0.6	
2 F	0429 0.5	1152 1.3	1650 0.7	2355 1.3	17 SA	0022 1.5	0606 0.6	1316 1.5	1847 0.8
3 SA	0529 0.6	1302 1.3	1810 0.8		18 SU	0142 1.4	0734 0.7	1452 1.4	2030 0.8
4 SU	0120 1.3	0652 0.6	1430 1.4	1946 0.8	19 M	0328 1.4	0902 0.7	1612 1.6	2143 0.7
5 M	0301 1.4	0819 0.6	1547 1.6	2104 0.7	20 TU	0447 1.5	1001 0.6	1713 1.8	2232 0.6
6 TU	0418 1.5	0928 0.5	1650 1.7	2202 0.5	21 W	0545 1.6	1046 0.5	1803 1.9	2312 0.4
7 W	0522 1.7	1024 0.4	1747 1.9	2253 0.4	22 TH	0633 1.8	1126 0.4	1847 2.0	○2350 0.3
8 TH	0620 1.8	1115 0.3	1840 2.1	●2341 0.3	23 F	0714 1.9	1203 0.3	1926 2.1	
9 F	0713 2.0	1203 0.2	1929 2.2		24 SA	0027 0.2	0749 1.9	1241 0.2	1958 2.1
10 SA	0027 0.1	0800 2.1	1249 0.1	2014 2.3	25 SU	0104 0.2	0818 1.9	1317 0.2	2026 2.1
11 SU	0112 0.1	0842 2.1	1333 0.1	2055 2.3	26 M	0139 0.1	0842 1.9	1350 0.2	2051 2.1
12 M	0156 0.0	0921 2.1	1416 0.1	2134 2.2	27 TU	0210 0.2	0905 1.8	1417 0.3	2116 1.9
13 TU	0239 0.1	0958 2.0	1458 0.2	2211 2.1	28 W	0232 0.3	0929 1.7	1435 0.4	2140 1.7
14 W	0323 0.2	1035 1.9	1542 0.3	2248 1.9	29 TH	0246 0.3	0952 1.6	1451 0.5	2201 1.5
15 TH	0409 0.3	1116 1.7	1629 0.5	2330 1.7	30 F	0305 0.4	1017 1.5	1514 0.5	2224 1.4
					31 SA	0335 0.5	1052 1.4	1553 0.6	2301 1.3

Chart Datum: 0·93 metres below Ordnance Datum (Newlyn)

TIME ZONE (UTC)
For Summer Time add ONE hour in **non-shaded areas**

YEAR **2002**

ENGLAND – PORTLAND

LAT 50°34′N LONG 2°26′W

TIMES AND HEIGHTS OF HIGH AND LOW WATERS

Note - Double LWs occur at Portland. The predictions are for the first LW. The second LW occurs from 3 to 4 Hrs later and may, at Springs, on occasions be lower than the first.

SEPTEMBER

Day	Time	m	Time	m		Day	Time	m	Time	m
1 SU	0423	0.6	1149	1.3		16 M	0132	1.3	0717	0.9
	1705	0.8					1441	1.5	2040	0.8
2 M	0012	1.2	0554	0.7		17 TU	0341	1.4	0857	0.8
	1322	1.4	1911	0.8			1601	1.6	2138	0.7
3 TU	0224	1.3	0756	0.7		18 W	0444	1.5	0947	0.7
	1511	1.5	2050	0.7			1654	1.8	2215	0.6
4 W	0403	1.5	0915	0.6		19 TH	0529	1.7	1024	0.6
	1627	1.7	2150	0.5			1739	1.9	2247	0.4
5 TH	0509	1.7	1011	0.4		20 F	0609	1.8	1059	0.5
	1728	2.0	2239	0.3			1819	2.0	2322	0.3
6 F	0605	1.9	1100	0.3		21 SA	0646	1.9	1135	0.3
	1822	2.2	2325	0.3			1856	2.1	○ 2357	0.2
7 SA ●	0655	2.1	1146	0.1		22 SU	0718	2.0	1212	0.2
	1911	2.3					1928	2.1		
8 SU	0010	0.0	0740	2.2		23 M	0033	0.1	0746	2.0
	1230	0.0	1955	2.4			1249	0.2	1956	2.1
9 M	0053	-0.1	0821	2.3		24 TU	0107	0.1	0811	2.0
	1313	0.0	2035	2.4			1321	0.1	2023	2.0
10 TU	0136	-0.1	0859	2.2		25 W	0135	0.2	0835	1.9
	1354	0.0	2113	2.3			1347	0.3	2049	1.9
11 W	0217	0.0	0934	2.1		26 TH	0155	0.3	0858	1.8
	1435	0.1	2148	2.1			1403	0.4	2112	1.7
12 TH	0257	0.2	1009	1.9		27 F	0209	0.4	0918	1.7
	1515	0.3	2224	1.9			1419	0.4	2132	1.6
13 F	0338	0.4	1045	1.7		28 SA	0227	0.4	0940	1.6
	1600	0.5	2302	1.7			1440	0.5	2155	1.4
14 SA	0425	0.6	1129	1.6		29 SU	0251	0.5	1012	1.5
	1659	0.7	2352	1.4			1514	0.6	2231	1.3
15 SU	0530	0.8	1238	1.4		30 M	0331	0.7	1104	1.4
	1834	0.9					1621	0.8	2344	1.3

OCTOBER

Day	Time	m	Time	m		Day	Time	m	Time	m
1 TU	0508	0.9	1231	1.4		16 W	0334	1.4	0834	1.0
	1900	0.8					1533	1.6	2113	0.7
2 W	0206	1.3	0744	0.8		17 TH	0421	1.6	0918	0.8
	1435	1.5	2035	0.7			1621	1.7	2142	0.6
3 TH	0350	1.5	0859	0.7		18 F	0459	1.7	0952	0.7
	1601	1.8	2130	0.5			1702	1.9	2212	0.4
4 F	0451	1.8	0952	0.6		19 SA	0534	1.9	1026	0.5
	1702	2.0	2218	0.3			1741	2.0	2246	0.3
5 SA	0543	2.0	1039	0.3		20 SU	0608	2.0	1103	0.4
	1756	2.2	2303	0.1			1816	2.0	2322	0.2
6 SU	0630	2.2	1124	0.1		21 M	0640	2.1	1141	0.3
	1844	2.4	● 2346	0.0			1850	2.1	○ 2358	0.2
7 M	0713	2.3	1207	0.0		22 TU	0710	2.1	1217	0.3
	1929	2.4					1922	2.1		
8 TU	0029	-0.1	0754	2.4		23 W	0030	0.2	0738	2.1
	1249	0.0	2010	2.4			1249	0.3	1953	2.0
9 W	0110	0.0	0832	2.3		24 TH	0058	0.2	0805	2.0
	1330	0.1	2048	2.3			1314	0.3	2022	1.9
10 TH	0150	0.1	0907	2.2		25 F	0120	0.3	0829	2.0
	1409	0.2	2124	2.1			1334	0.4	2046	1.8
11 F	0228	0.3	0941	2.0		26 SA	0139	0.4	0851	1.9
	1449	0.4	2159	1.8			1354	0.5	2110	1.6
12 SA	0305	0.5	1015	1.8		27 SU	0200	0.5	0915	1.7
	1535	0.6	2236	1.6			1420	0.6	2138	1.5
13 SU	0346	0.7	1054	1.6		28 M	0227	0.6	0947	1.6
	1636	0.8	2327	1.4			1459	0.7	2221	1.4
14 M	0448	0.9	1157	1.5		29 TU	0308	0.8	1038	1.5
	1822	0.9					1616	0.8	2337	1.3
15 TU	0150	1.3	0640	1.0		30 W	0458	0.9	1202	1.5
	1419	1.5	2028	0.8			1839	0.9		
						31 TH	0150	1.4	0719	0.9
							1400	1.6	2005	0.7

NOVEMBER

Day	Time	m	Time	m		Day	Time	m	Time	m
1 F	0324	1.6	0833	0.7		16 SA	0416	1.7	0910	0.8
	1528	1.8	2102	0.5			1614	1.7	2130	0.5
2 SA	0422	1.8	0926	0.5		17 SU	0450	1.8	0949	0.6
	1630	2.0	2150	0.3			1653	1.8	2207	0.4
3 SU	0513	2.1	1014	0.4		18 M	0524	1.9	1029	0.5
	1725	2.2	2236	0.1			1733	1.9	2244	0.3
4 M ●	0600	2.2	1059	0.2		19 TU	0559	2.0	1107	0.4
	1815	2.3	2320	0.0			1812	2.0	2320	0.3
5 TU	0644	2.3	1142	0.1		20 W	0634	2.1	1143	0.4
	1902	2.3					1851	2.0	○ 2354	0.3
6 W	0003	0.0	0726	2.4		21 TH	0708	2.1	1215	0.4
	1225	0.1	1945	2.3			1927	1.9		
7 TH	0044	0.1	0805	2.3		22 F	0025	0.3	0740	2.1
	1307	0.2	2025	2.2			1245	0.4	2000	1.9
8 F	0124	0.2	0843	2.2		23 SA	0054	0.4	0809	2.0
	1347	0.3	2103	2.0			1314	0.4	2030	1.8
9 SA	0201	0.4	0917	2.0		24 SU	0124	0.5	0835	1.9
	1429	0.5	2138	1.8			1344	0.5	2059	1.7
10 SU	0238	0.6	0949	1.8		25 M	0155	0.5	0905	1.8
	1515	0.6	2215	1.5			1420	0.6	2134	1.6
11 M	0317	0.8	1024	1.7		26 TU	0231	0.7	0942	1.7
	1615	0.8	2304	1.4			1509	0.6	2222	1.5
12 TU	0410	1.0	1113	1.5		27 W	0323	0.8	1033	1.6
	1738	0.9					1625	0.7	2333	1.4
13 W	0101	1.3	0539	1.1		28 TH	0456	0.9	1147	1.6
	1459	0.7	1922	0.8			1802	0.7		
14 TH	0250	1.4	0721	1.0		29 F	0113	1.5	0637	0.9
	1440	1.5	2018	0.7			1322	1.6	1922	0.6
15 F	0339	1.5	0826	0.9		30 SA	0241	1.6	0754	0.7
	1532	1.6	2054	0.6			1448	1.7	2025	0.5

DECEMBER

Day	Time	m	Time	m		Day	Time	m	Time	m
1 SU	0345	1.8	0854	0.6		16 M	0356	1.6	0909	0.7
	1556	1.9	2119	0.4			1603	1.6	2126	0.5
2 M	0440	2.0	0946	0.5		17 TU	0439	1.8	0954	0.6
	1654	2.0	2208	0.3			1653	1.7	2206	0.4
3 TU	0530	2.1	1035	0.4		18 W	0522	1.9	1034	0.5
	1748	2.1	2256	0.2			1740	1.8	2246	0.4
4 W ●	0618	2.2	1122	0.3		19 TH	0604	2.0	1113	0.5
	1839	2.1	2341	0.2			1826	1.9	○ 2325	0.3
5 TH	0703	2.3	1207	0.3		20 F	0645	2.1	1150	0.5
	1926	2.1					1910	1.9		
6 F	0024	0.2	0745	2.3		21 SA	0003	0.3	0724	2.1
	1251	0.3	2009	2.0			1228	0.4	1950	1.9
7 SA	0105	0.3	0825	2.2		22 SU	0043	0.4	0800	2.1
	1334	0.4	2049	1.9			1306	0.4	2028	1.8
8 SU	0144	0.4	0901	2.1		23 M	0122	0.4	0835	2.0
	1416	0.5	2125	1.7			1345	0.4	2104	1.8
9 M	0222	0.6	0932	1.9		24 TU	0202	0.4	0910	1.9
	1500	0.6	2159	1.6			1428	0.4	2142	1.7
10 TU	0300	0.7	1003	1.7		25 W	0245	0.5	0950	1.8
	1549	0.7	2237	1.4			1517	0.5	2226	1.6
11 W	0341	0.8	1041	1.6		26 TH	0335	0.6	1036	1.7
	1648	0.7	2328	1.3			1615	0.5	2320	1.5
12 TH	0439	0.9	1133	1.5		27 F	0436	0.7	1134	1.7
	1756	0.8					1724	0.6		
13 F	0039	1.3	0601	1.0		28 SA	0028	1.5	0549	0.7
	1243	1.4	1901	0.7			1243	1.6	1835	0.6
14 SA	0206	1.4	0718	0.9		29 SU	0146	1.6	0706	0.7
	1400	1.5	1956	0.6			1402	1.6	1944	0.5
15 SU	0308	1.5	0820	0.8		30 M	0302	1.7	0818	0.7
	1507	1.5	2043	0.6			1519	1.7	2048	0.5
						31 TU	0409	1.8	0922	0.6
							1628	1.8	2147	0.4

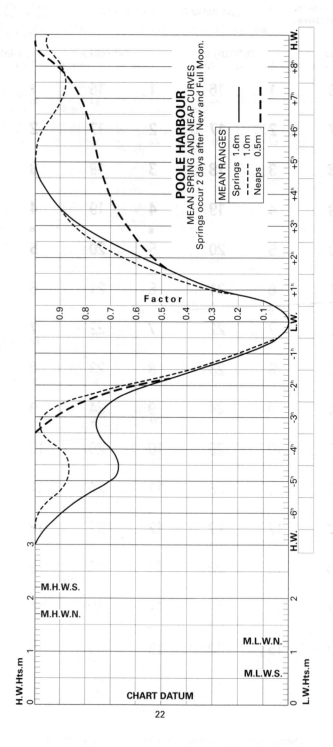

POOLE HARBOUR
MEAN SPRING AND NEAP CURVES
Springs occur 2 days after New and Full Moon.

MEAN RANGES	
Springs	1.6m
	1.0m
Neaps	0.5m

Factor

0.9 0.8 0.7 0.6 0.5 0.4 0.3 0.2 0.1

H.W. +8ʰ +7ʰ +6ʰ +5ʰ +4ʰ +3ʰ +2ʰ +1ʰ L.W. -1ʰ -2ʰ -3ʰ -4ʰ -5ʰ -6ʰ H.W.

H.W.Hts.m

M.H.W.S.
M.H.W.N.

M.L.W.N.
M.L.W.S.

CHART DATUM

L.W.Hts.m

22

TIME ZONE (UTC)
For Summer Time add ONE hour in **non-shaded areas**

YEAR 2002

ENGLAND – POOLE HARBOUR

LAT 50°42'N   LONG 1°59'W

TIMES AND HEIGHTS OF HIGH AND LOW WATERS

Note - HW times are not shown because they cannot be predicted with reasonable accuracy. Approximate times can be gained using LW times and the Tidal Curves at the start of this section.

JANUARY

Day	Time	m	Day	Time	m
1 TU	0519 / 1747	2.2 0.7 / 2.2 0.6	16 W	0558 / 1819	2.1 0.8 / 2.0 0.7
2 W	0607 / 1834	2.3 0.7 / 2.2 0.6	17 TH	0632 / 1851	2.1 0.9 / 2.0 0.8
3 TH	0656 / 1923	2.2 0.7 / 2.1 0.6	18 F	0705 / 1922	2.0 0.9 / 2.0 0.8
4 F	0747 / 2014	2.2 0.8 / 2.1 0.7	19 SA	0738 / 1955	2.0 1.0 / 1.9 0.9
5 SA	0841 / 2108	2.1 0.9 / 2.0	20 SU	0813 / 2031	2.0 1.1 / 1.8 1.0
6 SU	0941 / 2207	2.1 0.9 / 1.9 0.9	21 M	0856 / 2116	1.9 1.2 / 1.8 1.1
7 M	1046 / 2313	2.0 1.0 / 1.9	22 TU	0950 / 2215	1.8 1.3 / 1.7 1.2
8 TU	1157	2.0 1.0 (1.8)	23 W	1100 / 2329	1.8 1.3 / 1.6 1.2
9 W	0023 / 1307	1.0 2.0 / 1.0 1.9	24 TH	1221	1.8 1.2 (1.7)
10 TH	0131 / 1408	1.0 2.0 / 0.9 1.9	25 F	0047 / 1330	1.2 1.9 / 1.1 1.8
11 F	0229 / 1501	0.9 2.1 / 0.9 2.0	26 SA	0151 / 1425	1.0 2.0 / 0.9 1.9
12 SA	0319 / 1547	0.9 2.1 / 0.8 2.0	27 SU	0245 / 1515	0.9 2.1 / 0.8 2.1
13 SU ●	0403 / 1630	0.8 2.1 / 0.7 2.1	28 M ○	0335 / 1604	0.8 2.1 / 0.6 2.2
14 M	0444 / 1709	0.8 2.1 / 0.7	29 TU	0424 / 1652	0.7 2.2 / 0.5 2.3
15 TU	0522 / 1745	2.1 0.8 / 2.1 0.7	30 W	0512 / 1739	0.6 2.3 / 0.4
			31 TH	0559 / 1825	2.3 0.6 / 2.3 0.4

FEBRUARY

Day	Time	m	Day	Time	m
1 F	0645 / 1911	2.3 0.6 / 2.3 0.4	16 SA	0640 / 1855	2.1 0.8 / 2.0 0.7
2 SA	0732 / 1956	2.3 0.6 / 2.1 0.6	17 SU	0706 / 1922	2.0 0.8 / 2.0 0.8
3 SU	0820 / 2043	2.2 0.7 / 2.1 0.7	18 M	0736 / 1953	2.0 0.9 / 1.9 0.9
4 M	0910 / 2135	2.1 0.8 / 1.9 0.8	19 TU	0811 / 2031	1.9 1.0 / 1.8 1.0
5 TU	1009 / 2236	2.0 0.9 / 1.8 1.0	20 W	0856 / 2122	1.8 1.1 / 1.8 1.2
6 W	1120 / 2350	1.9 1.1 / 1.7 1.1	21 TH	0958 / 2236	1.8 1.2 / 1.6 1.3
7 TH	1240	1.8 1.1 (1.7)	22 F	1129	1.7 1.3 (1.6)
8 F	0110 / 1351	1.2 1.8 / 1.0 1.8	23 SA	0014 / 1304	1.3 1.8 / 1.2 1.8
9 SA	0216 / 1448	1.0 2.0 / 0.9 1.9	24 SU	0135 / 1409	1.1 1.9 / 0.9 1.9
10 SU	0309 / 1534	0.9 2.1 / 0.8 2.0	25 M	0234 / 1502	0.9 2.0 / 0.7 2.1
11 M	0352 / 1614	0.8 2.1 / 0.7 2.1	26 TU	0325 / 1551	0.7 2.1 / 0.6 2.2
12 TU ●	0431 / 1652	0.8 2.2 / 0.6 2.1	27 W ○	0413 / 1638	0.6 2.2 / 0.4 2.3
13 W	0507 / 1727	0.7 2.2 / 0.7 2.0	28 TH	0500 / 1724	0.4 2.3 / 0.3 2.3
14 TH	0540 / 1759	2.1 0.7 / 2.0 0.7			
15 F	0611 / 1828	2.1 0.6 / 2.0 0.7			

MARCH

Day	Time	m	Day	Time	m
1 F	0545 / 1809	2.4 0.4 / 2.3 0.3	16 SA	0547 / 1802	2.1 0.6 / 2.0 0.6
2 SA	0629 / 1852	2.4 0.4 / 2.3 0.4	17 SU	0613 / 1827	2.1 0.7 / 2.0 0.7
3 SU	0711 / 1934	2.3 0.4 / 2.2 0.4	18 M	0638 / 1853	2.0 0.7 / 2.0 0.7
4 M	0754 / 2016	2.2 0.6 / 2.1 0.6	19 TU	0705 / 1923	2.0 0.8 / 2.0 0.8
5 TU	0839 / 2103	2.1 0.7 / 2.0 0.8	20 W	0739 / 1959	1.9 0.8 / 1.9 0.9
6 W	0932 / 2203	1.9 0.9 / 1.8 1.0	21 TH	0821 / 2049	1.9 1.0 / 1.8 1.1
7 TH	1043 / 2323	1.8 1.2 / 1.7 1.2	22 F	0920 / 2204	1.8 1.2 / 1.7 1.3
8 F	1213	1.6 1.2 (1.6)	23 SA	1055 / 2354	1.6 1.2 / 1.6 1.3
9 SA	0052 / 1333	1.2 1.8 / 1.2 1.8	24 SU	1243	1.7 1.2 (1.8)
10 SU	0205 / 1431	1.1 1.8 / 1.0 1.9	25 M	0121 / 1352	1.1 1.8 / 0.9 1.9
11 M	0255 / 1515	1.0 1.9 / 0.9 2.0	26 TU	0220 / 1446	0.9 2.0 / 0.7 2.0
12 TU	0336 / 1553	0.8 2.0 / 0.7 2.0	27 W	0310 / 1533	0.7 2.1 / 0.5 2.3
13 W	0412 / 1629	0.7 2.0 / 0.7 2.1	28 TH ○	0357 / 1619	0.5 2.2 / 0.4 2.3
14 TH ●	0446 / 1703	0.7 2.0 / 0.6	29 F	0442 / 1704	0.4 2.3 / 0.3
15 F	0518 / 1734	2.1 0.6 / 2.0 0.6	30 SA	0525 / 1747	2.4 0.3 / 2.3 0.3
			31 SU	0608 / 1828	2.4 0.3 / 2.3 0.4

APRIL

Day	Time	m	Day	Time	m
1 M	0649 / 1909	2.3 0.4 / 2.3 0.5	16 TU	0612 / 1828	2.1 0.7 / 2.0 0.7
2 TU	0729 / 1949	2.2 0.6 / 2.1 0.7	17 W	0642 / 1900	2.0 0.7 / 2.0 0.8
3 W	0811 / 2035	2.1 0.7 / 2.0 0.9	18 TH	0718 / 1940	2.0 0.8 / 1.9 0.9
4 TH	0900 / 2133	1.9 0.8 / 1.8 1.1	19 F	0802 / 2033	1.9 0.9 / 1.8 1.1
5 F	1009 / 2255	1.7 1.2 / 1.7 1.3	20 SA	0904 / 2151	1.8 1.1 / 1.8 1.2
6 SA	1142	1.6 1.2 (1.6)	21 SU	1037 / 2332	1.7 1.2 / 1.7 1.2
7 SU	0027 / 1306	1.3 1.6 / 1.2 1.8	22 M	1216	1.7 1.0 (1.8)
8 M	0140 / 1404	1.2 1.7 / 0.9 1.9	23 TU	0056 / 1327	1.1 1.8 / 0.9 2.0
9 TU	0230 / 1446	1.0 2.0 / 0.9 2.0	24 W	0157 / 1421	0.9 2.0 / 0.7 2.1
10 W	0309 / 1524	0.8 1.9 / 0.7 2.0	25 TH	0248 / 1509	0.7 2.1 / 0.6 2.3
11 TH	0344 / 1559	0.7 1.9 / 0.7 2.1	26 F	0335 / 1555	0.5 2.1 / 0.4 2.3
12 F ●	0418 / 1633	0.7 2.0 / 0.6 2.1	27 SA ○	0420 / 1640	0.4 2.3 / 0.4 2.4
13 SA	0451 / 1705	0.6 2.0 / 0.6 2.3	28 SU	0504 / 1723	0.4 2.3 / 0.4
14 SU	0520 / 1733	2.1 0.6 / 2.0 0.6	29 M	0546 / 1804	2.3 0.4 / 2.3 0.4
15 M	0546 / 1800	2.1 0.6 / 2.0 0.7	30 TU	0627 / 1845	2.3 0.4 / 2.2 0.6

Chart Datum: 1·40 metres below Ordnance Datum (Newlyn)

ENGLAND – POOLE HARBOUR

LAT 50°42′N   LONG 1°59′W

TIMES AND HEIGHTS OF HIGH AND LOW WATERS

TIME ZONE (UTC)
For Summer Time add ONE hour in **non-shaded areas**

YEAR **2002**

Note - HW times are not shown because they cannot be predicted with reasonable accuracy. Approximate times can be gained using LW times and the Tidal Curves at the start of this section.

MAY

Day	Time	m / m	Time	m / m
1 W	0707	2.2 / 0.6	1926	2.1 / 0.8
2 TH	0748	2.0 / 0.8	2011	2.0 / 0.9
3 F	0836	1.9 / 0.9	2107	1.8 / 1.2
4 SA	0938	1.7 / 1.1	2220	1.7 / 1.3
5 SU	1059	1.6 / 1.2	2344	1.7 / 1.3
6 M	1220	1.6 / 1.2		1.8
7 TU	0057	1.2 / 1.6	1321	1.1 / 1.9
8 W	0150	1.0 / 1.8	1406	1.0 / 1.9
9 TH	0231	0.9 / 2.0	1446	0.8 / 2.0
10 F	0308	0.8 / 1.9	1523	0.8 / 2.0
11 SA	0344	0.7 / 1.9	1558	0.7 / 2.0
12 SU ●	0418	0.7 / 2.0	1632	0.7 / 2.1
13 M	0450	0.7 / 2.0	1704	0.7
14 TU	0521	2.1 / 0.7	1735	2.0 / 0.7
15 W	0552	2.1 / 0.7	1809	2.0 / 0.8
16 TH	0628	2.0 / 0.7	1848	2.0 / 0.8
17 F	0709	2.0 / 0.8	1934	2.0 / 0.9
18 SA	0759	1.9 / 0.9	2031	1.9 / 1.0
19 SU	0902	1.8 / 1.0	2143	1.9 / 1.1
20 M	1020	1.8 / 1.0	2304	1.8 / 1.1
21 TU	1141	1.8 / 1.0		1.9
22 W	0021	1.0 / 1.9	1252	0.9 / 2.0
23 TH	0125	0.8 / 2.0	1350	0.7 / 2.1
24 F	0220	0.7 / 2.1	1442	0.6 / 2.2
25 SA	0310	0.6 / 2.1	1530	0.6 / 2.3
26 SU ○	0358	0.5 / 2.2	1616	0.5 / 2.3
27 M	0443	0.5 / 2.2	1701	0.6
28 TU	0527	2.3 / 0.5	1743	2.2 / 0.6
29 W	0608	2.2 / 0.6	1825	2.1 / 0.7
30 TH	0649	2.1 / 0.7	1906	2.1 / 0.8
31 F	0729	2.0 / 0.8	1950	2.0 / 0.9

JUNE

Day	Time	m / m	Time	m / m
1 SA	0813	1.9 / 0.9	2039	1.9 / 1.1
2 SU	0904	1.8 / 1.0	2137	1.8 / 1.2
3 M	1006	1.6 / 1.2	2246	1.8 / 1.3
4 TU	1116	1.6 / 1.2	2357	1.8 / 1.3
5 W	1222	1.6 / 1.2		1.8
6 TH	0057	1.2 / 1.6	1315	1.0 / 1.9
7 F	0145	1.0 / 1.8	1401	1.0 / 1.9
8 SA	0227	1.0 / 1.8	1442	0.9 / 2.0
9 SU	0307	0.9 / 1.9	1522	0.8 / 2.0
10 M ●	0345	0.8 / 2.0	1600	0.8 / 2.1
11 TU	0422	0.7 / 2.0	1638	0.8 / 2.1
12 W	0500	0.7 / 2.1	1718	0.7
13 TH	0540	2.1 / 0.7	1759	2.1 / 0.7
14 F	0622	2.1 / 0.7	1843	2.1 / 0.8
15 SA	0708	2.0 / 0.7	1932	2.1 / 0.8
16 SU	0759	2.0 / 0.8	2027	2.0 / 0.9
17 M	0856	1.9 / 1.0	2128	2.0 / 0.9
18 TU	0958	1.9 / 1.0	2234	2.0 / 1.0
19 W	1105	1.9 / 1.0	2344	2.0 / 1.0
20 TH	1213	1.9 / 1.0		2.0
21 F	0052	1.9 / 1.2	1318	0.8 / 2.1
22 SA	0154	2.0 / 1.0	1417	0.8 / 2.1
23 SU	0249	0.7 / 2.0	1509	0.7 / 2.1
24 M ○	0339	0.7 / 2.1	1558	0.7 / 2.2
25 TU	0427	0.6 / 2.0	1644	0.7 / 2.1
26 W	0511	0.6 / 2.0	1727	0.7
27 TH	0553	2.1 / 0.7	1808	2.1 / 0.8
28 F	0632	2.1 / 0.7	1847	2.1 / 0.8
29 SA	0710	2.0 / 0.8	1927	2.0 / 0.9
30 SU	0747	1.9 / 0.9	2008	2.0 / 1.0

JULY

Day	Time	m / m	Time	m / m
1 M	0827	1.8 / 0.9	2052	1.9 / 1.1
2 TU	0912	1.8 / 1.0	2143	1.8 / 1.2
3 W	1004	1.7 / 1.2	2243	1.8 / 1.2
4 TH	1106	1.6 / 1.2	2350	1.8 / 1.2
5 F	1213	1.6 / 1.2		1.8
6 SA	0052	1.2 / 1.7	1312	1.1 / 1.9
7 SU	0145	1.0 / 1.8	1403	1.0 / 1.9
8 M	0232	1.0 / 1.9	1450	0.9 / 2.0
9 TU	0317	0.8 / 2.0	1535	0.8 / 2.1
10 W ●	0401	0.7 / 2.1	1620	0.8 / 2.1
11 TH	0445	0.6 / 2.1	1705	0.7
12 F	0530	0.6 / 2.1	1750	0.7
13 SA	0616	0.6 / 2.2	1837	2.2 / 0.7
14 SU	0702	0.6 / 2.2	1925	2.2 / 0.7
15 M	0750	0.6 / 2.1	2014	2.1 / 0.7
16 TU	0840	2.0 / 0.7	2107	2.1 / 0.8
17 W	0933	2.0 / 0.8	2205	2.0 / 0.9
18 TH	1033	1.9 / 0.9	2311	2.0 / 0.9
19 F	1140	1.8 / 1.0		1.9
20 SA	0023	1.0 / 1.8	1253	1.0 / 1.9
21 SU	0133	0.9 / 1.9	1359	1.0 / 2.0
22 M	0234	0.9 / 1.9	1457	0.9 / 2.0
23 TU	0327	0.8 / 2.0	1547	0.8 / 2.1
24 W ○	0414	0.7 / 2.1	1631	0.8 / 2.1
25 TH	0457	0.7 / 2.1	1713	0.8 / 2.1
26 F	0535	0.7 / 2.1	1750	0.8
27 SA	0612	2.0 / 0.7	1826	2.1 / 0.8
28 SU	0646	2.0 / 0.7	1901	2.0 / 0.8
29 M	0718	2.0 / 0.8	1934	2.0 / 0.9
30 TU	0749	1.9 / 0.9	2008	2.0 / 1.0
31 W	0823	1.8 / 0.9	2046	1.9 / 1.1

AUGUST

Day	Time	m / m	Time	m / m
1 TH	0902	1.8 / 1.1	2133	1.8 / 1.2
2 F	0954	1.7 / 1.2	2235	1.8 / 1.3
3 SA	1103	1.6 / 1.3	2355	1.8 / 1.3
4 SU	1225	1.6 / 1.3		1.8
5 M	0110	1.2 / 1.8	1334	1.2 / 1.9
6 TU	0208	1.0 / 1.9	1430	1.0 / 2.0
7 W	0258	0.8 / 2.0	1519	0.9 / 2.1
8 TH ●	0345	0.7 / 2.1	1606	0.8 / 2.1
9 F	0431	0.6 / 2.2	1652	0.7 / 2.2
10 SA	0517	0.5 / 2.3	1738	0.6
11 SU	0602	0.4 / 2.3	1823	0.6
12 M	0647	2.3 / 0.4	1908	2.3 / 0.6
13 TU	0732	2.3 / 0.5	1954	2.3 / 0.6
14 W	0817	2.1 / 0.7	2042	2.1 / 0.7
15 TH	0906	2.0 / 0.9	2136	2.0 / 0.9
16 F	1003	1.9 / 0.9	2241	1.9
17 SA	1114	1.8 / 1.1		1.8
18 SU	0001	1.1 / 1.8	1236	1.2 / 1.8
19 M	0121	1.1 / 1.9	1351	1.1 / 1.9
20 TU	0226	1.0 / 1.9	1449	1.0 / 2.0
21 W	0317	0.8 / 1.9	1536	0.9 / 2.0
22 TH ○	0359	0.7 / 2.1	1617	0.7 / 2.1
23 F	0438	0.7 / 2.1	1654	0.7 / 2.1
24 SA	0514	0.6 / 2.1	1729	0.7
25 SU	0547	2.0 / 0.6	1802	2.1 / 0.7
26 M	0618	2.0 / 0.7	1832	2.1 / 0.8
27 TU	0646	2.0 / 0.7	1859	2.0 / 0.8
28 W	0712	2.0 / 0.8	1927	2.0 / 0.9
29 TH	0740	1.9 / 0.9	2000	1.9 / 0.9
30 F	0815	1.8 / 1.0	2040	1.8 / 1.1
31 SA	0901	1.8 / 1.1	2136	1.8 / 1.3

Chart Datum: 1·40 metres below Ordnance Datum (Newlyn)

ENGLAND – POOLE HARBOUR

LAT 50°42′N   LONG 1°59′W

TIMES AND HEIGHTS OF HIGH AND LOW WATERS

YEAR **2002**

Note - HW times are not shown because they cannot be predicted with reasonable accuracy. Approximate times can be gained using LW times and the Tidal Curves at the start of this section.

SEPTEMBER

Day	Time	m	Day	Time	m
1 SU	1009 / 2303	1.6 1.3 / 1.7 1.3	**16** M	1224	1.7 1.3 / 1.8
2 M	1151	1.6 1.4 / 1.7	**17** TU	0110 / 1342	1.2 1.8 / 1.2 1.8
3 TU	0044 / 1317	1.2 1.8 / 1.3 2.0	**18** W	0214 / 1437	1.0 2.0 / 1.0 2.0
4 W	0151 / 1415	1.0 1.9 / 2.0	**19** TH	0300 / 1519	0.9 2.1 / 0.9 2.0
5 TH	0243 / 1504	0.8 2.0 / 0.9 2.1	**20** F	0338 / 1555	0.8 2.1 / 0.8 2.1
6 F	0329 / 1550	0.7 2.2 / 0.7 2.2	**21** SA ○	0414 / 1630	0.7 2.1 / 0.7 2.1
7 SA ●	0414 / 1635	0.5 2.3 / 0.6 2.3	**22** SU	0447 / 1703	0.6 2.1 / 0.7 2.1
8 SU	0459 / 1719	0.4 2.3 / 0.4	**23** M	0520 / 1734	0.6 2.1 / 0.7 2.1
9 M	0542 / 1803	2.3 0.4 / 2.4 0.4	**24** TU	0549 / 1801	2.1 0.7 / 2.1 0.7
10 TU	0625 / 1846	2.3 0.4 / 2.4 0.5	**25** W	0614 / 1826	2.1 0.7 / 2.1 0.8
11 W	0708 / 1930	2.3 0.5 / 2.3 0.6	**26** TH	0638 / 1852	2.0 0.8 / 2.0 0.8
12 TH	0751 / 2015	2.1 0.6 / 2.1 0.7	**27** F	0705 / 1922	2.0 0.9 / 2.0 0.9
13 F	0838 / 2107	2.0 0.8 / 2.0 0.9	**28** SA	0738 / 2001	1.9 1.0 / 1.9 1.1
14 SA	0936 / 2214	1.9 1.0 / 1.9 1.1	**29** SU	0822 / 2055	1.8 1.2 / 1.8 1.3
15 SU	1054 / 2342	1.8 1.8 / 1.8 1.2	**30** M	0932 / 2226	1.7 1.4 / 1.7 1.3

OCTOBER

Day	Time	m	Day	Time	m
1 TU	1126	1.6 1.4 / 1.7	**16** W	0045 / 1320	1.2 1.9 / 1.2 1.8
2 W	0020 / 1257	1.3 1.8 / 1.3 1.8	**17** TH	0149 / 1412	1.1 2.0 / 1.1 1.9
3 TH	0130 / 1356	1.0 1.9 / 1.0 2.0	**18** F	0232 / 1451	0.9 2.1 / 0.9 2.0
4 F	0222 / 1444	0.8 2.1 / 0.8 2.1	**19** SA	0309 / 1526	0.8 2.1 / 0.8 2.1
5 SA	0307 / 1528	0.6 2.3 / 0.6 2.3	**20** SU	0343 / 1600	0.7 2.1 / 0.7 2.1
6 SU ●	0351 / 1612	0.5 2.4 / 0.5 2.3	**21** M ○	0416 / 1632	0.7 2.4 / 0.7 2.1
7 M	0435 / 1656	0.4 2.4 / 0.4 2.4	**22** TU	0448 / 1703	0.7 2.4 / 0.7
8 TU	0518 / 1740	0.4 2.4 / 0.4	**23** W	0517 / 1731	0.7 2.1 / 0.7
9 W	0600 / 1822	2.4 0.4 / 2.4 0.5	**24** TH	0544 / 1756	0.8 2.1 / 0.8
10 TH	0642 / 1904	2.3 0.6 / 2.3 0.6	**25** F	0609 / 1824	0.8 2.1 / 0.8
11 F	0725 / 1949	2.2 0.7 / 2.1 0.8	**26** SA	0638 / 1856	0.9 2.0 / 0.9
12 SA	0813 / 2039	2.0 0.9 / 2.0 1.0	**27** SU	0714 / 1937	1.0 2.0 / 1.0
13 SU	0912 / 2147	1.9 1.2 / 1.8 1.2	**28** M	0801 / 2033	1.2 1.9 / 1.2
14 M	1032 / 2317	1.8 1.3 / 1.7 1.3	**29** TU	0913 / 2200	1.4 1.8 / 1.3
15 TU	1203	1.8 1.3 / 1.7	**30** W	1057 / 2342	1.4 1.7 / 1.2
			31 TH	1225	1.8 1.3 / 1.8

NOVEMBER

Day	Time	m	Day	Time	m
1 F	0056 / 1327	1.0 2.0 / 1.0 2.0	**16** SA	0151 / 1415	1.0 2.0 / 1.0 1.9
2 SA	0152 / 1417	0.8 2.1 / 0.8 2.1	**17** SU	0230 / 1452	0.9 2.1 / 0.9 2.0
3 SU	0239 / 1503	0.7 2.3 / 0.7 2.3	**18** M	0306 / 1527	0.7 2.3 / 0.8 2.0
4 M ●	0325 / 1548	0.5 2.4 / 0.5 2.3	**19** TU	0342 / 1601	0.6 2.1 / 0.8 2.0
5 TU	0409 / 1633	0.4 2.4 / 0.4 2.4	**20** W ○	0416 / 1634	0.6 2.1 / 0.8 2.1
6 W	0453 / 1717	0.4 2.4 / 0.5	**21** TH	0447 / 1704	0.7 2.1 / 0.8
7 TH	0536 / 1800	2.4 / 2.4 0.6	**22** F	0517 / 1734	0.8 2.1 / 0.8
8 F	0619 / 1843	2.3 0.7 / 2.3 0.7	**23** SA	0548 / 1807	0.9 2.1 / 0.8
9 SA	0703 / 1928	2.2 / 2.1	**24** SU	0623 / 1844	0.9 2.1 / 0.9 2.0
10 SU	0751 / 2017	1.0 2.1 / 1.0	**25** M	0704 / 1929	2.0 / 2.0 0.9
11 M	0848 / 2118	1.2 1.9 / 1.2	**26** TU	0756 / 2026	1.9 / 1.9 1.0
12 TU	1000 / 2235	1.8 1.7 / 1.3	**27** W	0902 / 2138	1.2 1.8 / 1.1
13 W	1123 / 2357	1.8 1.4 / 1.3	**28** TH	1023 / 2258	1.3 1.8 / 1.1
14 TH	1238	1.8 1.7	**29** F	1142	1.9 1.7
15 F	0103 / 1333	1.2 1.9 / 1.2 1.8	**30** SA	0011 / 1250	1.0 2.0 / 1.0 2.0

DECEMBER

Day	Time	m	Day	Time	m
1 SU	0114 / 1347	0.9 2.1 / 0.9 2.1	**16** M	0144 / 1413	1.1 2.0 / 1.0 1.9
2 M	0209 / 1438	0.7 2.3 / 0.7 2.1	**17** TU	0228 / 1453	1.0 2.0 / 0.9 1.9
3 TU	0258 / 1527	0.7 2.3 / 0.8 2.3	**18** W	0308 / 1531	0.9 2.1 / 0.9 2.1
4 W ●	0346 / 1614	0.6 2.4 / 0.6 2.3	**19** TH ○	0346 / 1608	0.9 2.1 / 0.9 2.1
5 TH	0433 / 1701	0.6 2.4 / 0.6	**20** F	0423 / 1645	0.8 2.1 / 0.8 2.1
6 F	0518 / 1745	2.3 0.7 / 2.3 0.6	**21** SA	0459 / 1721	0.8 2.1 / 0.7
7 SA	0602 / 1828	2.3 0.7 / 2.2 0.8	**22** SU	0536 / 1800	2.1 0.8 / 2.1 0.7
8 SU	0646 / 1911	2.2 0.8 / 2.1 0.8	**23** M	0617 / 1841	2.1 0.8 / 2.1
9 M	0731 / 1956	2.1 1.0 / 2.0 0.9	**24** TU	0701 / 1927	0.9 2.0 / 2.0
10 TU	0821 / 2045	1.9 1.1 / 1.0	**25** W	0751 / 2019	0.9 2.0 / 0.8
11 W	0918 / 2143	1.8 1.3 / 1.2	**26** TH	0848 / 2116	1.0 2.0 / 0.9
12 TH	1025 / 2249	1.6 1.3 / 1.2	**27** F	0951 / 2219	1.0 2.0 / 0.9
13 F	1136 / 2356	1.6 1.8 / 1.3	**28** SA	1101 / 2328	1.1 2.0 / 1.0
14 SA	1239	1.9 1.3	**29** SU	1212	2.0 1.9
15 SU	0055 / 1330	1.2 1.9 / 1.2 1.8	**30** M	0037 / 1319	0.9 2.0 / 0.9 1.9
			31 TU	0142 / 1419	0.8 2.1 / 0.8 2.0

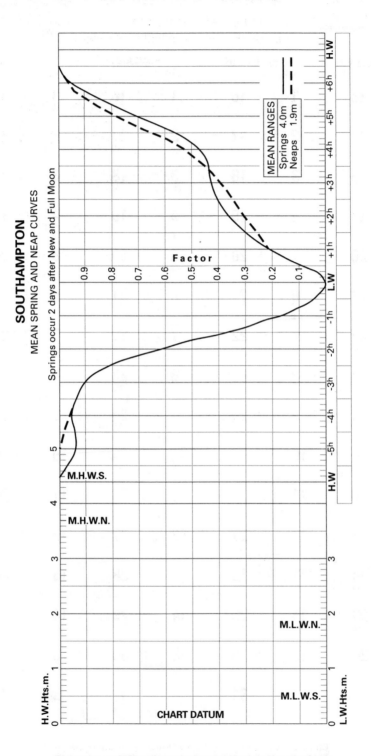

SOUTHAMPTON

MEAN SPRING AND NEAP CURVES

Springs occur 2 days after New and Full Moon

MEAN RANGES
Springs 4.0m
Neaps 1.9m

Factor

0.9 0.8 0.7 0.6 0.5 0.4 0.3 0.2 0.1

H.W +6h +5h +4h +3h +2h +1h L.W -1h -2h -3h -4h -5h H.W

M.H.W.S.
M.H.W.N.
M.L.W.N.
M.L.W.S.

H.W.Hts.m.
L.W.Hts.m.

CHART DATUM

TIME ZONE (UTC)
For Summer Time add ONE hour in **non-shaded areas**

YEAR **2002**

ENGLAND – SOUTHAMPTON

LAT 50°54′N   LONG 1°24′W

TIMES AND HEIGHTS OF HIGH AND LOW WATERS

Note - Double HWs occur at Southampton. The predictions are for the first HW.

JANUARY

Day	Time	m		Day	Time	m
1 TU	0528	0.8		16 W	0013	4.4
	1150	4.7			0606	1.0
	1755	0.6			1224	4.4
					1824	0.8
2 W	0018	4.6		17 TH	0048	4.3
	0613	0.8			0641	1.0
	1236	4.7			1259	4.3
	1840	0.6			1855	0.9
3 TH	0105	4.6		18 F	0123	4.3
	0700	0.9			0713	1.2
	1324	4.6			1335	4.2
	1927	0.7			1925	1.1
4 F	0155	4.5		19 SA	0159	4.2
	0750	1.0			0745	1.3
	1415	4.4			1411	4.1
	2017	0.9			1957	1.2
5 SA	0249	4.4		20 SU	0237	4.1
	0844	1.2			0820	1.5
	1510	4.3			1450	3.9
	2111	1.1			2034	1.5
6 SU	0348	4.2		21 M	0319	3.9
	0944	1.4			0903	1.7
	1612	4.1			1534	3.8
	2212	1.3			2120	1.7
7 M	0453	4.1		22 TU	0409	3.8
	1050	1.5			0958	1.9
	1720	4.0			1630	3.6
	2320	1.4			2221	1.8
8 TU	0602	4.1		23 W	0511	3.8
	1200	1.5			1109	1.9
	1831	3.9			1740	3.6
					2337	1.9
9 W	0029	1.5		24 TH	0622	3.8
	0709	4.1			1225	1.8
	1308	1.5			1858	3.7
	1940	4.0				
10 TH	0135	1.4		25 F	0052	1.8
	0810	4.2			0731	3.9
	1409	1.3			1333	1.6
	2041	4.1			2006	3.9
11 F	0232	1.3		26 SA	0157	1.5
	0904	4.3			0830	4.1
	1503	1.1			1431	1.3
	2133	4.2			2102	4.1
12 SA	0323	1.2		27 SU	0253	1.3
	0951	4.3			0921	4.3
	1550	1.0			1523	1.0
	2219	4.3			2151	4.3
13 SU	0408	1.0		28 M	0344	1.0
	1033	4.4			1008	4.5
	1634	0.8			1612	0.7
	● 2259	4.3			○ 2237	4.5
14 M	0451	1.0		29 TU	0432	0.7
	1112	4.4			1054	4.7
	1714	0.8			1700	0.4
	2337	4.4			2322	4.7
15 TU	0530	0.9		30 W	0519	0.6
	1148	4.4			1138	4.8
	1751	0.7			1746	0.3
				31 TH	0007	4.7
					0605	0.5
					1224	4.8
					1831	0.3

FEBRUARY

Day	Time	m		Day	Time	m
1 F	0053	4.7		16 SA	0055	4.3
	0650	0.5			0648	0.9
	1310	4.7			1307	4.2
	1915	0.3			1859	0.8
2 SA	0139	4.6		17 SU	0127	4.2
	0735	0.6			0714	1.0
	1356	4.6			1339	4.1
	1959	0.5			1925	1.0
3 SU	0226	4.5		18 M	0159	4.1
	0821	0.8			0742	1.2
	1445	4.4			1412	4.0
	2045	0.8			1955	1.2
4 M	0317	4.3		19 TU	0233	4.0
	0911	1.1			0816	1.4
	1537	4.1			1448	3.9
	2136	1.1			2032	1.4
5 TU	0413	4.1		20 W	0313	3.9
	1008	1.4			0900	1.6
	1638	3.9			1534	3.7
	2237	1.5			2121	1.7
6 W	0519	3.9		21 TH	0407	3.7
	1119	1.6			1002	1.8
	1753	3.7			1640	3.6
	2353	1.7			2235	1.9
7 TH	0637	3.8		22 F	0522	3.7
	1239	1.7			1130	1.9
	1918	3.7			1809	3.6
8 F	0113	1.7		23 SA	0011	1.9
	0753	3.9			0649	3.7
	1352	1.5			1300	1.7
	2031	3.8			1935	3.7
9 SA	0220	1.5		24 SU	0133	1.7
	0854	4.0			0804	4.0
	1451	1.3			1410	1.3
	2127	4.0			2042	4.0
10 SU	0313	1.3		25 M	0236	1.3
	0943	4.2			0903	4.2
	1538	1.1			1507	0.9
	2211	4.3			2134	4.3
11 M	0357	1.1		26 TU	0330	0.9
	1024	4.3			0952	4.5
	1619	0.9			1559	0.5
	2249	4.3			2221	4.6
12 TU	0437	0.9		27 W	0420	0.6
	1059	4.3			1038	4.7
	1657	0.7			1646	0.2
	● 2322	4.3			○ 2306	4.8
13 W	0515	0.8		28 TH	0507	0.3
	1132	4.4			1123	4.8
	1733	0.6			1732	0.0
	2353	4.4			2350	4.8
14 TH	0549	0.7				
	1203	4.3				
	1805	0.6				
15 F	0024	4.3				
	0620	0.8				
	1235	4.3				
	1833	0.7				

MARCH

Day	Time	m		Day	Time	m
1 F	0552	0.2		16 SA	0555	0.6
	1206	4.9			1208	4.3
	1815	0.0			1808	0.6
2 SA	0033	4.8		17 SU	0025	4.3
	0634	0.2			0621	0.7
	1250	4.8			1238	4.3
	1856	0.1			1832	0.7
3 SU	0117	4.8		18 M	0055	4.3
	0715	0.3			0645	0.8
	1334	4.7			1309	4.2
	1936	0.3			1856	0.9
4 M	0200	4.6		19 TU	0125	4.2
	0756	0.6			0711	0.9
	1418	4.4			1340	4.1
	2017	0.7			1924	1.1
5 TU	0245	4.3		20 W	0157	4.1
	0839	0.9			0743	1.1
	1506	4.1			1415	4.0
	2101	1.1			1959	1.3
6 W	0335	4.0		21 TH	0234	4.0
	0929	1.3			0824	1.4
	1602	3.8			1458	3.8
	2158	1.6			2046	1.6
7 TH	0438	3.7		22 F	0324	3.8
	1038	1.7			0921	1.7
	1719	3.6			1603	3.7
	2320	1.9			2156	1.9
8 F	0604	3.6		23 SA	0439	3.6
	1211	1.8			1048	1.8
	1900	3.6			1735	3.6
					2341	2.0
9 SA	0057	1.9		24 SU	0615	3.7
	0736	3.7			1231	1.7
	1337	1.7			1910	3.8
	2021	3.8				
10 SU	0211	1.7		25 M	0113	1.7
	0842	3.9			0739	3.9
	1436	1.4			1349	1.3
	2115	4.0			2020	4.1
11 M	0301	1.4		26 TU	0219	1.3
	0930	4.1			0842	4.2
	1521	1.1			1448	0.9
	2156	4.2			2114	4.4
12 TU	0341	1.1		27 W	0314	0.8
	1008	4.2			0933	4.5
	1559	0.9			1539	0.5
	2230	4.3			2201	4.7
13 W	0418	0.9		28 TH	0403	0.4
	1040	4.3			1019	4.7
	1635	0.7			1627	0.1
	2300	4.3			○ 2245	4.8
14 TH	0453	0.7		29 F	0449	0.2
	1110	4.3			1103	4.8
	1709	0.5			1711	-0.1
	● 2328	4.4			2328	4.9
15 F	0525	0.6		30 SA	0533	0.0
	1138	4.3			1146	4.9
	1740	0.5			1754	-0.1
	2356	4.4				
				31 SU	0010	4.9
					0614	0.0
					1229	4.8
					1833	0.0

APRIL

Day	Time	m		Day	Time	m
1 M	0052	4.8		16 TU	0025	4.3
	0653	0.2			0619	0.7
	1311	4.7			1243	4.3
	1912	0.3			1832	0.9
2 TU	0134	4.6		17 W	0057	4.3
	0731	0.5			0648	0.9
	1354	4.4			1317	4.2
	1950	0.7			1902	1.1
3 W	0217	4.3		18 TH	0132	4.2
	0811	0.9			0722	1.1
	1440	4.1			1355	4.1
	2033	1.2			1940	1.3
4 TH	0304	4.0		19 F	0212	4.0
	0857	1.3			0805	1.3
	1536	3.8			1443	3.9
	2127	1.7			2031	1.6
5 F	0403	3.7		20 SA	0304	3.9
	1001	1.7			0904	1.6
	1653	3.6			1550	3.8
	2251	2.0			2144	1.9
6 SA	0529	3.5		21 SU	0420	3.7
	1137	1.9			1029	1.7
	1836	3.6			1719	3.8
					2323	1.9
7 SU	0035	2.1		22 M	0553	3.7
	0708	3.5			1205	1.6
	1308	1.8			1847	3.9
	1956	3.8				
8 M	0148	1.8		23 TU	0050	1.6
	0817	3.8			0715	3.9
	1407	1.5			1322	1.3
	2049	4.0			1955	4.2
9 TU	0236	1.5		24 W	0156	1.2
	0904	4.0			0817	4.2
	1451	1.2			1421	0.9
	2128	4.2			2049	4.5
10 W	0314	1.2		25 TH	0250	0.8
	0940	4.1			0909	4.4
	1528	1.0			1513	0.5
	2200	4.3			2137	4.7
11 TH	0350	0.9		26 F	0340	0.5
	1012	4.2			0956	4.6
	1604	0.7			1601	0.2
	2229	4.3			2221	4.8
12 F	0424	0.7		27 SA	0426	0.2
	1041	4.3			1041	4.7
	1638	0.6			1647	0.1
	● 2257	4.4			○ 2304	4.9
13 SA	0456	0.6		28 SU	0511	0.1
	1109	4.3			1124	4.7
	1710	0.6			1730	0.1
	2325	4.4			2347	4.8
14 SU	0526	0.6		29 M	0552	0.2
	1139	4.3			1207	4.7
	1739	0.6			1811	0.3
	2354	4.4				
15 M	0553	0.6		30 TU	0029	4.7
	1210	4.3			0631	0.3
	1805	0.7			1251	4.5
					1849	0.6

Chart Datum: 2·74 metres below Ordnance Datum (Newlyn)

TIME ZONE (UTC)
For Summer Time add ONE hour in **non-shaded areas**

YEAR **2002**

ENGLAND–SOUTHAMPTON

LAT 50°54′N   LONG 1°24′W

TIMES AND HEIGHTS OF HIGH AND LOW WATERS

Note - Double HWs occur at Southampton. The predictions are for the first HW.

MAY

Day	Time m	Time m	Time m	Time m	Day	Time m	Time m	Time m	Time m
1 W	0111 4.5	0710 0.6	1335 4.3	1928 1.0	**16** TH	0038 4.3	0633 0.9	1303 4.3	1851 1.1
2 TH	0153 4.3	0749 1.0	1422 4.1	2011 1.4	**17** F	0118 4.2	0713 1.0	1347 4.2	1935 1.3
3 F	0240 4.0	0833 1.4	1516 3.9	2103 1.8	**18** SA	0203 4.1	0800 1.2	1440 4.1	2030 1.6
4 SA	0335 3.7	0930 1.7	1626 3.7	2219 2.1	**19** SU	0300 4.0	0900 1.4	1547 4.0	2142 1.7
5 SU	0449 3.5	1051 1.9	1753 3.6	2351 2.1	**20** M	0412 3.8	1017 1.5	1705 4.0	2305 1.7
6 M	0618 3.5	1216 1.9	1911 3.8		**21** TU	0533 3.9	1138 1.4	1822 4.1	
7 TU	0103 1.9	0730 3.7	1319 1.7	2005 4.0	**22** W	0022 1.5	0648 4.0	1250 1.2	1927 4.3
8 W	0154 1.6	0822 3.8	1407 1.4	2047 4.1	**23** TH	0127 1.2	0750 4.2	1351 1.0	2022 4.5
9 TH	0235 1.4	0902 4.0	1448 1.2	2121 4.2	**24** F	0223 0.9	0844 4.4	1445 0.7	2111 4.6
10 F	0313 1.1	0936 4.1	1526 1.0	2153 4.3	**25** SA	0314 0.6	0934 4.5	1535 0.5	2158 4.7
11 SA	0348 0.9	1008 4.2	1602 0.8	2223 4.3	**26** SU	0403 0.5	1020 4.5	1622 0.5	○2242 4.7
12 SU	0423 0.7	1040 4.2	1637 0.8	●2254 4.4	**27** M	0448 0.4	1106 4.5	1707 0.6	2326 4.6
13 M	0456 0.7	1112 4.3	1710 0.8	2327 4.4	**28** TU	0532 0.4	1150 4.5	1750 0.6	
14 TU	0528 0.7	1147 4.3	1742 0.9		**29** W	0009 4.5	0612 0.5	1235 4.4	1831 0.9
15 W	0001 4.4	0559 0.7	1224 4.3	1814 1.0	**30** TH	0051 4.4	0651 0.8	1319 4.3	1911 1.1
					31 F	0134 4.2	0730 1.0	1405 4.1	1953 1.4

JUNE

Day	Time m	Time m	Time m	Time m	Day	Time m	Time m	Time m	Time m
1 SA	0219 4.0	0812 1.3	1455 4.0	2041 1.7	**16** SU	0200 4.2	0800 1.1	1436 4.2	2029 1.4
2 SU	0308 3.8	0900 1.6	1551 3.8	2141 1.9	**17** M	0256 4.1	0856 1.2	1537 4.1	2132 1.5
3 M	0406 3.7	1000 1.8	1657 3.8	2252 2.0	**18** TU	0359 4.0	1000 1.3	1644 4.1	2241 1.5
4 TU	0514 3.6	1110 1.8	1805 3.8		**19** W	0509 4.0	1109 1.3	1753 4.2	2350 1.4
5 W	0001 2.0	0624 3.6	1217 1.8	1905 3.9	**20** TH	0618 4.0	1217 1.3	1857 4.2	
6 TH	0059 1.8	0725 3.7	1312 1.6	1955 4.0	**21** F	0055 1.3	0723 4.1	1320 1.2	1956 4.3
7 F	0147 1.6	0815 3.8	1400 1.4	2037 4.1	**22** SA	0156 1.1	0822 4.2	1418 1.0	2049 4.4
8 SA	0230 1.3	0857 4.0	1444 1.3	2115 4.2	**23** SU	0251 0.9	0916 4.3	1512 0.9	2139 4.5
9 SU	0311 1.1	0936 4.1	1526 1.1	2151 4.3	**24** M	0342 0.8	1006 4.3	1603 0.9	○2226 4.5
10 M	0350 0.9	1013 4.2	1606 1.0	●2228 4.4	**25** TU	0431 0.7	1053 4.4	1650 0.8	2311 4.5
11 TU	0429 0.8	1051 4.3	1645 0.9	2305 4.4	**26** W	0515 0.7	1138 4.4	1735 0.9	2353 4.4
12 W	0507 0.8	1130 4.3	1724 0.9	2345 4.4	**27** TH	0557 0.7	1221 4.3	1817 1.0	
13 TH	0546 0.8	1211 4.4	1804 1.0		**28** F	0034 4.3	0636 0.8	1303 4.3	1856 1.1
14 F	0026 4.4	0626 0.8	1255 4.3	1847 1.1	**29** SA	0115 4.2	0713 1.0	1345 4.2	1935 1.3
15 SA	0111 4.3	0710 0.9	1342 4.2	1935 1.2	**30** SU	0156 4.1	0756 0.9	1427 4.1	2014 1.5

JULY

Day	Time m	Time m	Time m	Time m	Day	Time m	Time m	Time m	Time m
1 M	0237 3.9	0827 1.4	1511 4.0	2058 1.7	**16** TU	0241 4.3	0842 0.9	1517 4.3	2111 1.2
2 TU	0322 3.8	0911 1.6	1600 3.9	2149 1.9	**17** W	0337 4.2	0936 1.1	1616 4.2	2210 1.3
3 W	0414 3.7	1003 1.7	1655 3.8	2249 1.9	**18** TH	0439 4.0	1037 1.3	1719 4.1	2316 1.5
4 TH	0513 3.6	1105 1.8	1756 3.8	2353 1.9	**19** F	0547 3.9	1144 1.4	1827 4.1	
5 F	0619 3.6	1211 1.8	1857 3.9		**20** SA	0026 1.5	0658 3.9	1255 1.5	1934 4.1
6 SA	0053 1.8	0723 3.7	1312 1.7	1952 4.0	**21** SU	0135 1.4	0807 4.0	1401 1.4	2036 4.2
7 SU	0148 1.6	0819 3.8	1406 1.5	2041 4.1	**22** M	0236 1.2	0907 4.1	1500 1.3	2130 4.3
8 M	0237 1.3	0907 4.0	1455 1.4	2125 4.2	**23** TU	0330 1.1	1000 4.2	1552 1.1	2218 4.3
9 TU	0323 1.1	0951 4.2	1542 1.2	2208 4.4	**24** W	0419 0.9	1046 4.3	1639 1.0	○2301 4.3
10 W	0408 0.9	1034 4.3	1627 1.0	●2250 4.5	**25** TH	0502 0.8	1128 4.3	1722 1.0	2340 4.3
11 TH	0453 0.8	1117 4.4	1712 0.9	2332 4.5	**26** F	0543 0.7	1206 4.3	1802 1.0	
12 F	0537 0.7	1200 4.5	1757 0.9		**27** SA	0017 4.3	0619 0.8	1243 4.3	1838 1.0
13 SA	0016 4.5	0621 0.6	1246 4.5	1842 0.9	**28** SU	0053 4.2	0652 0.9	1318 4.3	1911 1.1
14 SU	0102 4.5	0706 0.7	1333 4.5	1929 0.9	**29** M	0128 4.2	0723 1.0	1353 4.2	1943 1.3
15 M	0150 4.4	0753 0.8	1423 4.4	2018 1.0	**30** TU	0203 4.1	0753 1.2	1429 4.1	2015 1.5
					31 W	0240 3.9	0825 1.4	1508 4.0	2052 1.6

AUGUST

Day	Time m	Time m	Time m	Time m	Day	Time m	Time m	Time m	Time m
1 TH	0321 3.8	0904 1.6	1552 3.9	2139 1.8	**16** F	0407 4.0	1005 1.4	1645 4.0	2243 1.6
2 F	0410 3.7	0956 1.8	1646 3.8	2241 2.0	**17** SA	0517 3.8	1116 1.7	1800 3.9	
3 SA	0514 3.6	1105 2.0	1754 3.7	2357 2.0	**18** SU	0002 1.7	0641 3.8	1240 1.8	1921 3.9
4 SU	0631 3.6	1225 2.0	1907 3.8		**19** M	0124 1.7	0802 3.9	1356 1.7	2031 4.0
5 M	0110 1.8	0744 3.7	1335 1.8	2011 4.0	**20** TU	0231 1.5	0906 4.0	1457 1.5	2126 4.2
6 TU	0211 1.5	0844 4.0	1434 1.5	2104 4.2	**21** W	0323 1.2	0956 4.2	1545 1.3	2210 4.3
7 W	0304 1.2	0933 4.2	1525 1.2	2150 4.4	**22** TH	0407 1.0	1037 4.3	1627 1.1	○2248 4.4
8 TH	0353 0.9	1019 4.4	1614 1.0	●2234 4.5	**23** F	0446 0.7	1112 4.4	1706 0.9	2322 4.4
9 F	0440 0.6	1102 4.5	1701 0.8	2318 4.6	**24** SA	0523 0.7	1145 4.4	1742 0.8	2354 4.3
10 SA	0526 0.5	1146 4.6	1746 0.6		**25** SU	0557 0.7	1215 4.4	1814 0.8	
11 SU	0002 4.7	0610 0.4	1231 4.7	1830 0.6	**26** M	0025 4.3	0627 0.7	1246 4.3	1843 0.9
12 M	0047 4.7	0654 0.4	1316 4.7	1914 0.6	**27** TU	0056 4.2	0653 0.9	1316 4.3	1909 1.1
13 TU	0132 4.6	0737 0.5	1402 4.6	1959 0.8	**28** W	0128 4.1	0718 1.1	1348 4.2	1935 1.3
14 W	0219 4.5	0821 0.7	1450 4.4	2045 1.0	**29** TH	0200 4.0	0744 1.3	1421 4.1	2004 1.5
15 TH	0309 4.3	0908 1.1	1543 4.2	2138 1.3	**30** F	0235 3.9	0816 1.6	1458 3.9	2043 1.7
					31 SA	0317 3.8	0900 1.8	1546 3.8	2138 2.0

<table>
<tr><td>

TIME ZONE (UTC)
For Summer Time add ONE hour in **non-shaded areas**

YEAR **2002**

</td><td>

ENGLAND – SOUTHAMPTON

LAT 50°54′N   LONG 1°24′W

TIMES AND HEIGHTS OF HIGH AND LOW WATERS

</td><td>

Note - Double HWs occur at Southampton. The predictions are for the first HW.

</td></tr>
</table>

SEPTEMBER

Time	m		Time	m
1 0417	3.6	**16**	0632	3.7
1005	2.1		1232	2.0
SU 1655	3.7	M	1912	3.8
2301	2.1			
2 0543	3.6	**17**	0117	1.9
1142	2.2		0758	3.9
M 1824	3.7	TU	1354	1.9
			2024	4.0
3 0037	2.0	**18**	0222	1.6
0714	3.7		0857	4.1
TU 1312	2.0	W	1448	1.6
1943	3.9		2114	4.2
4 0150	1.6	**19**	0308	1.3
0822	4.0		0941	4.3
W 1416	1.6	TH	1529	1.3
2042	4.2		2154	4.3
5 0247	1.2	**20**	0346	1.0
0914	4.3		1017	4.4
TH 1510	1.2	F	1606	1.1
2131	4.4		2228	4.4
6 0337	0.8	**21**	0422	0.8
1000	4.5		1048	4.4
F 1559	0.9	SA	1641	0.9
2216	4.6	○	2257	4.4
7 0424	0.5	**22**	0456	0.7
1043	4.7		1116	4.4
SA 1645	0.6	SU	1714	0.8
● 2259	4.8		2326	4.4
8 0509	0.3	**23**	0528	0.7
1126	4.8		1143	4.4
SU 1730	0.4	M	1745	0.8
2342	4.9		2354	4.4
9 0552	0.1	**24**	0557	0.7
1209	4.9		1211	4.4
M 1813	0.3	TU	1812	0.8
10 0025	4.9	**25**	0023	4.3
0634	0.2		0621	0.9
TU 1253	4.8	W	1241	4.3
1854	0.4		1836	1.0
11 0109	4.8	**26**	0054	4.3
0715	0.4		0644	1.1
W 1336	4.7	TH	1311	4.3
1935	0.6		1900	1.2
12 0154	4.6	**27**	0125	4.2
0756	0.7		0710	1.3
TH 1422	4.6	F	1342	4.2
2018	1.0		1928	1.4
13 0242	4.3	**28**	0159	4.0
0840	1.1		0741	1.6
F 1512	4.2	SA	1417	4.0
2108	1.4		2005	1.6
14 0338	4.0	**29**	0240	3.9
0934	1.6		0823	1.8
SA 1614	3.9	SU	1503	3.9
2212	1.7		2056	1.9
15 0453	3.8	**30**	0339	3.7
1052	1.9		0927	2.1
SU 1737	3.7	M	1613	3.7
2344	1.9		2219	2.1

OCTOBER

Time	m		Time	m
1 0510	3.7	**16**	0053	2.0
1111	2.2		0737	3.5
TU 1749	3.7	W	1332	2.0
			1959	3.9
2 0007	2.0	**17**	0155	1.7
0646	3.8		0832	4.1
W 1249	2.0	TH	1422	1.7
1915	3.9		2048	4.1
3 0126	1.6	**18**	0238	1.4
0757	4.1		0912	4.3
TH 1356	1.6	F	1501	1.4
2018	4.2		2126	4.3
4 0224	1.2	**19**	0314	1.1
0850	4.4		0946	4.4
F 1449	1.2	SA	1535	1.1
2108	4.5		2158	4.4
5 0314	0.8	**20**	0349	0.9
0936	4.7		1016	4.5
SA 1538	0.8	SU	1609	0.9
2153	4.7		2227	4.4
6 0401	0.4	**21**	0423	0.8
1019	4.9		1043	4.5
SU 1624	0.5	M	1642	0.9
● 2236	4.9	○	2255	4.4
7 0446	0.2	**22**	0455	0.8
1102	5.0		1110	4.5
M 1708	0.3	TU	1713	0.9
2319	5.0		2324	4.4
8 0529	0.1	**23**	0525	0.8
1145	5.0		1139	4.4
TU 1751	0.3	W	1741	0.9
			2354	4.4
9 0002	4.9	**24**	0552	0.9
0610	0.2		1209	4.4
W 1228	4.9	TH	1807	1.0
1831	0.4			
10 0046	4.8	**25**	0026	4.3
0650	0.5		0617	1.1
TH 1311	4.7	F	1242	4.3
1912	0.6		1833	1.1
11 0131	4.6	**26**	0059	4.3
0731	0.8		0645	1.3
F 1356	4.5	SA	1315	4.2
1954	1.0		1904	1.3
12 0219	4.3	**27**	0136	4.2
0815	1.3		0720	1.6
SA 1445	4.2	SU	1353	4.1
2041	1.4		1944	1.6
13 0316	4.0	**28**	0221	4.0
0909	1.8		0805	1.8
SU 1547	3.9	M	1441	4.0
2145	1.8		2037	1.8
14 0434	3.7	**29**	0323	3.9
1031	2.1		0912	2.1
M 1712	3.7	TU	1551	3.8
2320	2.0		2157	2.0
15 0615	3.7	**30**	0449	3.8
1215	2.2		1049	2.1
TU 1850	3.7	W	1722	3.8
			2336	1.9
		31	0618	4.0
			1220	1.9
		TH	1846	4.0

NOVEMBER

Time	m		Time	m
1 0054	1.6	**16**	0154	1.6
0727	4.2		0832	4.2
F 1327	1.5	SA	1420	1.5
1950	4.3		2048	4.1
2 0154	1.2	**17**	0234	1.3
0822	4.5		0908	4.3
SA 1422	1.1	SU	1458	1.3
2042	4.5		2123	4.2
3 0246	0.8	**18**	0311	1.1
0909	4.7		0939	4.4
SU 1512	0.8	M	1533	1.1
2129	4.7		2155	4.3
4 0334	0.5	**19**	0347	1.0
0954	4.9		1010	4.5
M 1559	0.5	TU	1608	0.9
● 2214	4.8		2226	4.4
5 0419	0.3	**20**	0422	0.9
1038	5.0		1040	4.5
TU 1644	0.4	W	1641	0.9
2258	4.9	○	2258	4.4
6 0504	0.3	**21**	0455	0.9
1121	5.0		1112	4.5
W 1728	0.4	TH	1713	0.9
2342	4.8		2331	4.4
7 0546	0.4	**22**	0526	1.0
1205	4.9		1146	4.5
TH 1810	0.5	F	1744	1.0
8 0026	4.7	**23**	0006	4.4
0627	0.7		0557	1.1
F 1249	4.7	SA	1221	4.4
1851	0.7		1816	1.1
9 0112	4.5	**24**	0044	4.3
0709	1.0		0631	1.2
SA 1334	4.5	SU	1259	4.3
1933	1.1		1852	1.2
10 0201	4.3	**25**	0125	4.3
0754	1.4		0711	1.5
SU 1423	4.2	M	1341	4.2
2019	1.4		1935	1.4
11 0257	4.0	**26**	0213	4.1
0848	1.8		0800	1.7
M 1521	3.9	TU	1432	4.1
2118	1.8		2030	1.6
12 0408	3.8	**27**	0313	4.0
1001	2.1		0905	1.8
TU 1635	3.7	W	1537	3.9
2237	2.0		2140	1.7
13 0534	3.8	**28**	0427	4.0
1132	2.2		1025	1.9
W 1800	3.7	TH	1655	3.9
			2301	1.7
14 0002	2.0	**29**	0545	4.1
0651	3.9		1145	1.7
TH 1246	2.0	F	1812	4.0
1913	3.8			
15 0106	1.8	**30**	0016	1.5
0748	4.1		0653	4.3
F 1339	1.8	SA	1253	1.5
2006	4.0		1918	4.2

DECEMBER

Time	m		Time	m
1 0120	1.2	**16**	0148	1.6
0751	4.5		0824	4.1
SU 1351	1.2	M	1417	1.5
2014	4.4		2046	4.0
2 0215	0.9	**17**	0232	1.4
0843	4.7		0904	4.3
M 1444	0.9	TU	1458	1.3
2105	4.6		2126	4.2
3 0306	0.7	**18**	0313	1.2
0931	4.8		0941	4.4
TU 1535	0.7	W	1538	1.1
2154	4.7		2203	4.3
4 0355	0.6	**19**	0353	1.1
1017	4.8		1016	4.4
W 1623	0.6	TH	1616	1.0
● 2241	4.7	○	2239	4.3
5 0442	0.6	**20**	0431	1.0
1102	4.8		1052	4.5
TH 1708	0.5	F	1653	0.9
2327	4.7		2315	4.4
6 0527	0.7	**21**	0508	1.0
1147	4.7		1129	4.5
F 1752	0.6	SA	1730	0.9
			2353	4.4
7 0012	4.6	**22**	0546	1.0
0610	0.8		1208	4.5
SA 1231	4.6	SU	1808	1.0
1834	0.8			
8 0059	4.5	**23**	0033	4.4
0653	1.1		0624	1.1
SU 1316	4.4	M	1249	4.4
1916	1.0		1847	1.0
9 0145	4.3	**24**	0117	4.4
0737	1.4		0707	1.2
M 1402	4.2	TU	1333	4.3
1958	1.3		1931	1.1
10 0235	4.1	**25**	0204	4.3
0824	1.7		0755	1.3
TU 1451	4.0	W	1422	4.2
2046	1.6		2021	1.2
11 0330	4.0	**26**	0258	4.2
0921	1.9		0851	1.5
W 1547	3.8	TH	1518	4.1
2143	1.8		2119	1.4
12 0433	3.9	**27**	0400	4.1
1028	2.0		0955	1.6
TH 1652	3.7	F	1623	4.0
2250	1.9		2225	1.4
13 0541	3.8	**28**	0507	4.1
1139	2.0		1105	1.6
F 1802	3.7	SA	1733	4.0
2358	1.9		2336	1.4
14 0646	3.9	**29**	0616	4.2
1240	1.9		1215	1.5
SA 1908	3.8	SU	1844	4.0
15 0057	1.8	**30**	0044	1.3
0739	4.0		0720	4.3
SU 1332	1.7	M	1321	1.3
2001	3.9		1949	4.2
		31	0147	1.2
			0819	4.4
		TU	1421	1.1
			2048	4.3

Chart Datum: 2·74 metres below Ordnance Datum (Newlyn)
Register for your **FREE** weekly weather email service from Macmillan Reeds
》 at **www.nauticaldata.com – NOW!** 《
weekend weather reports sent to your email address, every Thursday

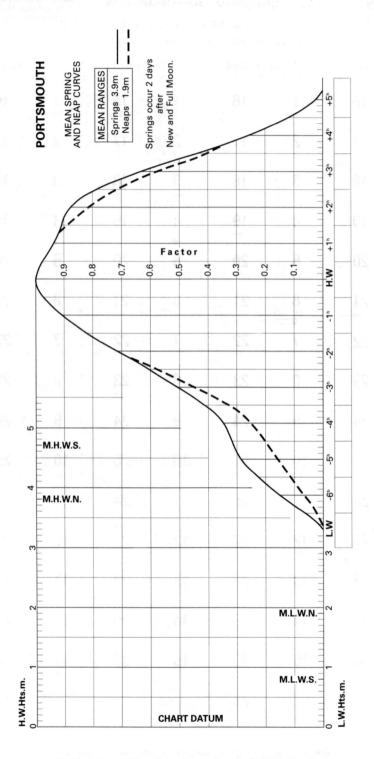

PORTSMOUTH

MEAN SPRING AND NEAP CURVES

MEAN RANGES

Springs 3.9m
Neaps 1.9m

Springs occur 2 days after New and Full Moon.

Factor

0.9 0.8 0.7 0.6 0.5 0.4 0.3 0.2 0.1

H.W.   -1ʰ -2ʰ -3ʰ -4ʰ -5ʰ -6ʰ   L.W

+5ʰ +4ʰ +3ʰ +2ʰ +1ʰ

M.H.W.S.

M.H.W.N.

M.L.W.N.

M.L.W.S.

H.W.Hts.m.

L.W.Hts.m.

CHART DATUM

TIME ZONE (UTC)
For Summer Time add ONE hour in **non-shaded areas**

ENGLAND – PORTSMOUTH

LAT 50°48′N   LONG 1°07′W

TIMES AND HEIGHTS OF HIGH AND LOW WATERS

YEAR **2002**

JANUARY

Time	m	Time	m
1 0010 / 0534 / TU 1224 / 1802	4.7 / 1.0 / 4.7 / 0.7	**16** 0050 / 0613 / W 1253 / 1834	4.5 / 1.2 / 4.4 / 1.0
2 0057 / 0622 / W 1310 / 1849	4.8 / 1.0 / 4.7 / 0.7	**17** 0124 / 0647 / TH 1328 / 1906	4.5 / 1.3 / 4.4 / 1.1
3 0145 / 0711 / TH 1358 / 1938	4.7 / 1.0 / 4.6 / 0.8	**18** 0159 / 0720 / F 1403 / 1937	4.4 / 1.4 / 4.3 / 1.2
4 0235 / 0802 / F 1448 / 2029	4.7 / 1.1 / 4.5 / 0.9	**19** 0235 / 0753 / SA 1440 / 2010	4.3 / 1.5 / 4.1 / 1.4
5 0329 / 0856 / SA 1542 / 2123	4.6 / 1.3 / 4.3 / 1.1	**20** 0313 / 0828 / SU 1518 / 2046	4.2 / 1.7 / 4.0 / 1.8
6 0425 / 0956 / SU 1640 / 2222	4.5 / 1.4 / 4.0 / 1.3	**21** 0355 / 0911 / M 1601 / 2131	4.1 / 1.8 / 3.9 / 1.7
7 0526 / 1101 / M 1745 / 2328	4.3 / 1.6 / 4.1 / 1.5	**22** 0443 / 1005 / TU 1654 / 2230	4.0 / 2.0 / 3.8 / 1.9
8 0632 / 1212 / TU 1857	4.3 / 1.6 / 4.0	**23** 0542 / 1115 / W 1803 / 2344	3.9 / 2.0 / 3.7 / 1.9
9 0038 / 0739 / W 1322 / 2008	1.5 / 4.3 / 1.6 / 4.1	**24** 0653 / 1236 / TH 1922	4.0 / 1.9 / 3.8
10 0146 / 0841 / TH 1423 / 2113	1.5 / 4.4 / 1.4 / 4.2	**25** 0102 / 0801 / F 1345 / 2032	1.8 / 4.1 / 1.7 / 4.0
11 0244 / 0936 / F 1516 / 2208	1.4 / 4.5 / 1.3 / 4.3	**26** 0206 / 0900 / SA 1440 / 2131	1.6 / 4.3 / 1.4 / 4.2
12 0334 / 1025 / SA 1602 / 2255	1.3 / 4.5 / 1.0 / 4.4	**27** 0300 / 0951 / SU 1530 / 2223	1.4 / 4.5 / 1.0 / 4.5
13 0418 / 1107 / SU 1645 / ● 2337	1.2 / 4.6 / 1.0 / 4.5	**28** 0350 / 1039 / M 1619 / ○ 2311	1.1 / 4.6 / 0.8 / 4.7
14 0459 / 1145 / M 1724	1.1 / 4.6 / 1.0	**29** 0439 / 1126 / TU 1707 / 2359	0.9 / 4.7 / 0.6 / 4.8
15 0015 / 0537 / TU 1220 / 1800	4.5 / 1.1 / 4.5 / 0.9	**30** 0527 / 1213 / W 1754	0.8 / 4.8 / 0.5
		31 0046 / 0614 / TH 1301 / 1840	4.9 / 0.7 / 4.8 / 0.5

FEBRUARY

Time	m	Time	m
1 0133 / 0700 / F 1348 / 1926	4.9 / 0.7 / 4.7 / 0.5	**16** 0132 / 0655 / SA 1341 / 1910	4.5 / 1.1 / 4.3 / 1.0
2 0221 / 0747 / SA 1436 / 2011	4.8 / 0.8 / 4.6 / 0.7	**17** 0204 / 0721 / SU 1413 / 1937	4.4 / 1.2 / 4.3 / 1.1
3 0308 / 0835 / SU 1524 / 2058	4.7 / 0.9 / 4.5 / 0.9	**18** 0235 / 0751 / M 1446 / 2008	4.3 / 1.3 / 4.2 / 1.3
4 0356 / 0925 / M 1614 / 2150	4.5 / 1.2 / 4.2 / 1.2	**19** 0309 / 0826 / TU 1522 / 2046	4.2 / 1.5 / 4.0 / 1.5
5 0449 / 1024 / TU 1711 / 2251	4.3 / 1.5 / 4.0 / 1.5	**20** 0348 / 0911 / W 1608 / 2137	4.0 / 1.7 / 3.9 / 1.8
6 0550 / 1135 / W 1822	4.1 / 1.7 / 3.8	**21** 0441 / 1013 / TH 1713 / 2251	3.9 / 1.9 / 3.7 / 2.0
7 0005 / 0704 / TH 1255 / 1947	1.7 / 4.0 / 1.7 / 3.8	**22** 0556 / 1144 / F 1840	3.8 / 2.0 / 3.7
8 0125 / 0821 / F 1406 / 2103	1.8 / 4.0 / 1.6 / 4.0	**23** 0029 / 0722 / SA 1319 / 2007	2.0 / 3.9 / 1.8 / 3.9
9 0231 / 0924 / SA 1503 / 2200	1.6 / 4.2 / 1.4 / 4.2	**24** 0150 / 0835 / SU 1424 / 2113	1.7 / 4.1 / 1.4 / 4.2
10 0324 / 1014 / SU 1549 / 2246	1.4 / 4.3 / 1.2 / 4.4	**25** 0249 / 0933 / M 1517 / 2207	1.4 / 4.4 / 1.0 / 4.5
11 0407 / 1055 / M 1629 / 2325	1.2 / 4.4 / 1.0 / 4.5	**26** 0340 / 1024 / TU 1606 / 2256	1.0 / 4.6 / 0.7 / 4.7
12 0446 / 1131 / TU 1707 / ● 2359	1.1 / 4.4 / 0.9 / 4.5	**27** 0428 / 1112 / W 1653 / ○ 2343	0.7 / 4.7 / 0.5 / 4.9
13 0522 / 1204 / W 1742	1.0 / 4.4 / 0.9	**28** 0515 / 1159 / TH 1739	0.5 / 4.8 / 0.3
14 0030 / 0555 / TH 1236 / 1814	4.5 / 1.0 / 4.4 / 0.9		
15 0101 / 0626 / F 1308 / 1843	4.5 / 1.0 / 4.4 / 0.9		

MARCH

Time	m	Time	m
1 0029 / 0600 / F 1246 / 1824	5.0 / 0.4 / 4.9 / 0.3	**16** 0035 / 0602 / SA 1246 / 1817	4.5 / 0.8 / 4.4 / 0.8
2 0115 / 0644 / SA 1332 / 1907	5.0 / 0.4 / 4.8 / 0.4	**17** 0104 / 0628 / SU 1317 / 1842	4.5 / 0.9 / 4.4 / 0.9
3 0159 / 0726 / SU 1418 / 1949	4.9 / 0.5 / 4.7 / 0.5	**18** 0133 / 0653 / M 1348 / 1908	4.4 / 1.0 / 4.3 / 1.0
4 0242 / 0809 / M 1502 / 2031	4.7 / 0.7 / 4.5 / 0.8	**19** 0202 / 0720 / TU 1419 / 1938	4.4 / 1.1 / 4.3 / 1.2
5 0325 / 0854 / TU 1549 / 2118	4.5 / 1.0 / 4.3 / 1.2	**20** 0233 / 0754 / W 1454 / 2014	4.2 / 1.2 / 4.1 / 1.4
6 0412 / 0947 / W 1642 / 2218	4.2 / 1.4 / 4.0 / 1.6	**21** 0309 / 0836 / TH 1540 / 2104	4.1 / 1.5 / 3.9 / 1.7
7 0508 / 1058 / TH 1752 / 2338	3.9 / 1.8 / 3.8 / 1.9	**22** 0400 / 0935 / F 1644 / 2219	3.9 / 1.8 / 3.8 / 2.0
8 0628 / 1228 / F 1931	3.7 / 1.9 / 3.7	**23** 0515 / 1110 / SA 1814	3.7 / 1.9 / 3.7
9 0107 / 0804 / SA 1348 / 2051	1.9 / 3.7 / 1.8 / 3.9	**24** 0009 / 0649 / SU 1258 / 1946	2.0 / 3.8 / 1.8 / 3.9
10 0220 / 0912 / SU 1446 / 2146	1.7 / 3.9 / 1.5 / 4.2	**25** 0136 / 0812 / M 1407 / 2054	1.7 / 4.0 / 1.4 / 4.2
11 0310 / 1000 / M 1530 / 2229	1.5 / 4.1 / 1.3 / 4.3	**26** 0235 / 0913 / TU 1501 / 2148	1.3 / 4.3 / 1.0 / 4.6
12 0351 / 1040 / TU 1608 / 2305	1.2 / 4.3 / 1.0 / 4.4	**27** 0325 / 1004 / W 1548 / 2236	0.9 / 4.6 / 0.6 / 4.8
13 0427 / 1114 / W 1644 / 2337	1.0 / 4.3 / 0.9 / 4.5	**28** 0412 / 1053 / TH 1634 / ○ 2322	0.6 / 4.7 / 0.4 / 4.9
14 0501 / 1145 / TH 1718 ●	0.9 / 4.4 / 0.8	**29** 0457 / 1140 / F 1719	0.4 / 4.9 / 0.3
15 0006 / 0533 / F 1215 / 1749	4.5 / 0.8 / 4.4 / 0.8	**30** 0008 / 0540 / SA 1227 / 1802	5.0 / 0.3 / 4.9 / 0.3
		31 0052 / 0623 / SU 1313 / 1843	5.0 / 0.3 / 4.9 / 0.4

APRIL

Time	m	Time	m
1 0134 / 0704 / M 1357 / 1924	4.9 / 0.4 / 4.8 / 0.6	**16** 0105 / 0627 / TU 1326 / 1843	4.5 / 0.9 / 4.4 / 1.0
2 0215 / 0744 / TU 1441 / 2004	4.7 / 0.7 / 4.6 / 0.9	**17** 0135 / 0657 / W 1359 / 1915	4.4 / 1.0 / 4.3 / 1.2
3 0256 / 0826 / W 1526 / 2050	4.5 / 1.0 / 4.3 / 1.3	**18** 0208 / 0733 / TH 1438 / 1955	4.3 / 1.1 / 4.2 / 1.4
4 0339 / 0915 / TH 1618 / 2148	4.1 / 1.4 / 4.0 / 1.7	**19** 0247 / 0817 / F 1526 / 2048	4.1 / 1.4 / 4.0 / 1.7
5 0432 / 1024 / F 1728 / 2310	3.8 / 1.8 / 3.8 / 2.0	**20** 0340 / 0919 / SA 1632 / 2206	3.9 / 1.7 / 3.9 / 1.9
6 0550 / 1157 / SA 1908	3.6 / 1.9 / 3.7	**21** 0454 / 1052 / SU 1757 / 2347	3.8 / 1.8 / 3.8 / 1.9
7 0042 / 0739 / SU 1321 / 2026	2.0 / 3.6 / 1.8 / 3.9	**22** 0623 / 1231 / M 1923	3.8 / 1.6 / 4.0
8 0155 / 0848 / M 1419 / 2119	1.8 / 3.8 / 1.6 / 4.2	**23** 0111 / 0745 / TU 1342 / 2030	1.7 / 4.0 / 1.3 / 4.3
9 0245 / 0935 / TU 1501 / 2200	1.5 / 4.0 / 1.3 / 4.3	**24** 0212 / 0848 / W 1436 / 2123	1.3 / 4.3 / 0.9 / 4.6
10 0324 / 1013 / W 1539 / 2235	1.2 / 4.2 / 1.1 / 4.4	**25** 0303 / 0941 / TH 1524 / 2212	0.9 / 4.5 / 0.7 / 4.8
11 0359 / 1046 / TH 1614 / 2306	1.0 / 4.2 / 0.9 / 4.5	**26** 0350 / 1031 / F 1610 / 2259	0.6 / 4.7 / 0.5 / 4.9
12 0433 / 1118 / F 1648 / ● 2335	0.9 / 4.3 / 0.8 / 4.5	**27** 0435 / 1119 / SA 1655 / ○ 2344	0.4 / 4.8 / 0.4 / 5.0
13 0506 / 1149 / SA 1720	0.8 / 4.4 / 0.8	**28** 0519 / 1206 / SU 1738	0.4 / 4.8 / 0.4
14 0005 / 0535 / SU 1221 / 1748	4.5 / 0.8 / 4.4 / 0.8	**29** 0028 / 0601 / M 1252 / 1819	4.9 / 0.4 / 4.8 / 0.5
15 0035 / 0601 / M 1253 / 1815	4.5 / 0.8 / 4.4 / 0.9	**30** 0110 / 0642 / TU 1336 / 1900	4.8 / 0.5 / 4.7 / 0.8

Chart Datum: 2·73 metres below Ordnance Datum (Newlyn)

ENGLAND – PORTSMOUTH

LAT 50°48'N   LONG 1°07'W

YEAR 2002

TIMES AND HEIGHTS OF HIGH AND LOW WATERS

TIME ZONE (UTC)
For Summer Time add ONE hour in **non-shaded areas**

MAY

Day	Time	m	Time	m	Time	m	Time	m
1 W	0150	4.7	0722	0.8	1420	4.5	1941	1.1
2 TH	0230	4.4	0803	1.1	1506	4.3	2026	1.4
3 F	0313	4.1	0851	1.4	1557	4.0	2122	1.8
4 SA	0403	3.8	0953	1.7	1701	3.8	2235	2.0
5 SU	0510	3.6	1114	1.9	1825	3.8	2359	2.1
6 M	0645	3.6	1235	1.9	1942	3.9		
7 TU	0112	1.9	0802	3.7	1336	1.7	2036	4.1
8 W	0205	1.6	0853	3.9	1421	1.5	2118	4.2
9 TH	0246	1.4	0933	4.0	1501	1.2	2154	4.3
10 F	0323	1.2	1009	4.1	1538	1.1	2228	4.4
11 SA	0359	1.0	1044	4.2	1613	1.0	2301	4.4
12 SU	0433	0.9	1119	4.3	1647	0.9	●2334	4.5
13 M	0505	0.9	1154	4.4	1719	0.9		
14 TU	0007	4.5	0536	0.9	1231	4.4	1750	1.0
15 W	0041	4.5	0607	0.9	1307	4.4	1824	1.1
16 TH	0116	4.4	0643	1.0	1346	4.4	1903	1.2
17 F	0153	4.3	0724	1.1	1429	4.3	1949	1.4
18 SA	0238	4.2	0814	1.3	1521	4.2	2046	1.6
19 SU	0333	4.0	0917	1.5	1625	4.1	2158	1.7
20 M	0441	3.9	1035	1.5	1740	4.0	2319	1.7
21 TU	0559	3.9	1156	1.5	1856	4.2		
22 W	0036	1.5	0715	4.1	1307	1.3	2000	4.4
23 TH	0140	1.3	0819	4.3	1405	1.0	2056	4.6
24 F	0235	1.0	0916	4.5	1457	0.8	2147	4.7
25 SA	0325	0.8	1009	4.6	1545	0.7	2235	4.8
26 SU	0413	0.6	1059	4.7	1631	0.6	○2322	4.9
27 M	0458	0.6	1147	4.7	1716	0.7		
28 TU	0006	4.8	0542	0.6	1234	4.7	1758	0.8
29 W	0048	4.7	0623	0.7	1318	4.6	1840	1.0
30 TH	0128	4.6	0704	0.9	1402	4.5	1921	1.2
31 F	0207	4.4	0744	1.1	1446	4.3	2005	1.4

JUNE

Day	Time	m	Time	m	Time	m	Time	m
1 SA	0249	4.1	0828	1.4	1533	4.1	2054	1.7
2 SU	0335	3.9	0919	1.6	1625	4.0	2152	1.9
3 M	0429	3.7	1021	1.8	1726	3.9	2301	2.0
4 TU	0534	3.6	1131	1.9	1832	3.9		
5 W	0012	2.0	0645	3.6	1237	1.8	1932	4.0
6 TH	0112	1.8	0749	3.7	1330	1.6	2022	4.1
7 F	0200	1.6	0841	3.9	1416	1.5	2106	4.2
8 SA	0242	1.4	0926	4.0	1457	1.3	2147	4.3
9 SU	0322	1.2	1009	4.2	1537	1.2	2226	4.4
10 M	0400	1.1	1050	4.3	1615	1.1	●2305	4.5
11 TU	0437	1.0	1131	4.4	1653	1.1	2343	4.5
12 W	0515	0.9	1211	4.5	1733	1.0		
13 TH	0022	4.5	0555	0.9	1253	4.5	1814	1.0
14 F	0102	4.5	0637	0.9	1337	4.5	1858	1.1
15 SA	0145	4.4	0723	1.0	1424	4.5	1947	1.2
16 SU	0233	4.3	0814	1.1	1516	4.4	2042	1.3
17 M	0326	4.2	0911	1.2	1614	4.4	2143	1.4
18 TU	0427	4.1	1013	1.3	1717	4.3	2249	1.5
19 W	0534	4.1	1120	1.3	1824	4.3	2359	1.5
20 TH	0644	4.1	1228	1.3	1929	4.4		
21 F	0107	1.3	0751	4.2	1333	1.2	2029	4.5
22 SA	0209	1.2	0854	4.3	1432	1.1	2124	4.6
23 SU	0304	1.0	0951	4.4	1524	1.0	2215	4.6
24 M	0354	0.9	1044	4.5	1613	1.0	○2303	4.7
25 TU	0442	0.8	1134	4.6	1659	1.0	2347	4.6
26 W	0526	0.8	1219	4.6	1742	1.0		
27 TH	0028	4.6	0608	0.9	1302	4.6	1823	1.1
28 F	0107	4.5	0647	1.0	1343	4.5	1902	1.2
29 SA	0145	4.3	0725	1.1	1423	4.4	1942	1.4
30 SU	0224	4.2	0802	1.3	1503	4.3	2023	1.5

JULY

Day	Time	m	Time	m	Time	m	Time	m
1 M	0305	4.0	0842	1.4	1546	4.1	2107	1.7
2 TU	0349	3.9	0927	1.6	1632	4.0	2158	1.9
3 W	0439	3.8	1019	1.8	1723	3.9	2258	1.9
4 TH	0536	3.7	1121	1.9	1821	3.9		
5 F	0005	1.9	0641	3.7	1228	1.8	1921	4.0
6 SA	0107	1.8	0747	3.8	1327	1.7	2018	4.1
7 SU	0200	1.6	0846	4.0	1418	1.6	2109	4.2
8 M	0247	1.4	0938	4.1	1505	1.4	2156	4.3
9 TU	0332	1.2	1026	4.3	1550	1.2	2240	4.5
10 W	0416	1.0	1111	4.5	1635	1.1	●2323	4.5
11 TH	0500	0.8	1156	4.6	1720	1.0		
12 F	0006	4.6	0545	0.8	1241	4.6	1805	0.9
13 SA	0051	4.6	0631	0.7	1327	4.7	1852	0.9
14 SU	0136	4.6	0717	0.7	1414	4.7	1940	0.9
15 M	0224	4.5	0805	0.8	1503	4.6	2029	1.0
16 TU	0315	4.4	0855	0.9	1554	4.5	2122	1.2
17 W	0408	4.3	0948	1.1	1649	4.4	2220	1.3
18 TH	0507	4.1	1048	1.3	1749	4.3	2326	1.5
19 F	0614	4.0	1155	1.5	1856	4.2		
20 SA	0038	1.5	0727	4.0	1308	1.5	2004	4.2
21 SU	0148	1.4	0839	4.1	1414	1.5	2107	4.3
22 M	0249	1.3	0942	4.2	1512	1.3	2202	4.4
23 TU	0342	1.1	1037	4.4	1602	1.2	2250	4.5
24 W	0429	1.0	1124	4.5	1646	1.1	○2332	4.5
25 TH	0512	0.9	1206	4.5	1728	1.1		
26 F	0011	4.5	0550	0.9	1245	4.5	1805	1.1
27 SA	0047	4.4	0627	0.9	1321	4.5	1841	1.1
28 SU	0121	4.3	0701	1.0	1355	4.4	1916	1.2
29 M	0156	4.3	0733	1.1	1429	4.4	1949	1.3
30 TU	0233	4.2	0804	1.3	1505	4.3	2023	1.5
31 W	0311	4.0	0838	1.4	1543	4.2	2101	1.7

AUGUST

Day	Time	m	Time	m	Time	m	Time	m
1 TH	0351	3.9	0917	1.7	1624	4.0	2148	1.8
2 F	0440	3.8	1009	1.9	1716	3.9	2250	2.0
3 SA	0542	3.7	1118	2.0	1821	3.9		
4 SU	0010	2.0	0659	3.7	1240	2.0	1934	4.0
5 M	0125	1.8	0814	3.9	1349	1.8	2038	4.1
6 TU	0223	1.5	0915	4.1	1445	1.6	2132	4.3
7 W	0313	1.2	1007	4.4	1534	1.3	2219	4.5
8 TH	0400	0.9	1054	4.6	1621	1.1	●2305	4.6
9 F	0446	0.7	1140	4.7	1707	0.9	2350	4.7
10 SA	0532	0.6	1225	4.8	1753	0.7		
11 SU	0036	4.7	0617	0.5	1311	4.8	1838	0.7
12 M	0122	4.7	0702	0.5	1357	4.8	1923	0.7
13 TU	0209	4.7	0747	0.6	1442	4.8	2009	0.8
14 W	0256	4.5	0832	0.8	1528	4.6	2057	1.0
15 TH	0345	4.4	0921	1.1	1617	4.4	2151	1.3
16 F	0440	4.1	1018	1.4	1714	4.2	2256	1.6
17 SA	0546	3.9	1129	1.7	1825	4.0		
18 SU	0016	1.7	0711	3.9	1251	1.8	1947	4.0
19 M	0136	1.7	0835	4.0	1406	1.7	2058	4.1
20 TU	0241	1.5	0939	4.2	1504	1.5	2154	4.3
21 W	0332	1.2	1029	4.4	1551	1.3	2239	4.4
22 TH	0414	1.0	1111	4.5	1632	1.2	○2318	4.5
23 F	0453	0.9	1149	4.6	1709	1.0	2352	4.5
24 SA	0529	0.8	1222	4.6	1744	1.0		
25 SU	0024	4.4	0602	0.8	1254	4.5	1817	1.0
26 M	0056	4.4	0633	0.9	1323	4.5	1847	1.1
27 TU	0128	4.4	0701	1.0	1354	4.5	1914	1.2
28 W	0200	4.3	0727	1.2	1425	4.4	1942	1.3
29 TH	0233	4.2	0755	1.3	1457	4.2	2015	1.5
30 F	0309	4.0	0830	1.6	1532	4.1	2055	1.7
31 SA	0351	3.9	0916	1.9	1618	3.9	2151	2.0

Chart Datum: 2·73 metres below Ordnance Datum (Newlyn)

TIME ZONE (UTC)
For Summer Time add ONE hour in **non-shaded areas**

ENGLAND – PORTSMOUTH

LAT 50°48′N   LONG 1°07′W

TIMES AND HEIGHTS OF HIGH AND LOW WATERS

YEAR 2002

SEPTEMBER

Day	Time m	Time m	Time m	Time m
1 SU	0452 3.7	1024 2.1	1725 3.8	2318 2.1
2 M	0618 3.7	1206 2.2	1853 3.8	
3 TU	0059 1.9	0748 3.9	1332 2.0	2012 4.0
4 W	0206 1.6	0856 4.2	1430 1.6	2111 4.3
5 TH	0258 1.2	0948 4.4	1519 1.3	2200 4.5
6 F	0344 0.9	1034 4.7	1605 0.9	2245 4.7
7 SA	0429 0.6	1119 4.8	1650 0.7	●2331 4.8
8 SU	0514 0.4	1204 4.9	1734 0.5	
9 M	0017 4.9	0557 0.4	1249 5.0	1818 0.5
10 TU	0103 4.9	0640 0.4	1333 5.0	1901 0.6
11 W	0148 4.8	0723 0.6	1416 4.8	1945 0.7
12 TH	0234 4.6	0806 0.8	1500 4.6	2030 1.0
13 F	0321 4.4	0853 1.2	1546 4.4	2122 1.4
14 SA	0415 4.1	0951 1.6	1641 4.1	2229 1.7
15 SU	0524 3.9	1109 1.9	1757 3.9	2357 1.9
16 M	0702 3.8	1239 2.0	1938 3.9	
17 TU	0125 1.8	0829 4.0	1357 1.9	2051 4.0
18 W	0229 1.6	0927 4.3	1452 1.6	2142 4.3
19 TH	0315 1.3	1012 4.5	1534 1.3	2223 4.4
20 F	0353 1.1	1050 4.6	1610 1.1	2258 4.5
21 SA	0429 0.9	1124 4.6	1645 1.0	○2329 4.5
22 SU	0502 0.8	1154 4.6	1718 0.9	2358 4.5
23 M	0535 0.8	1222 4.6	1749 0.9	
24 TU	0028 4.5	0604 0.9	1250 4.5	1816 1.0
25 W	0059 4.5	0629 1.0	1319 4.5	1841 1.1
26 TH	0130 4.4	0653 1.1	1348 4.4	1907 1.2
27 F	0201 4.3	0720 1.3	1417 4.3	1937 1.4
28 SA	0234 4.2	0753 1.6	1451 4.1	2016 1.7
29 SU	0316 4.0	0837 1.9	1536 4.0	2110 2.0
30 M	0418 3.8	0947 2.2	1644 3.8	2241 2.1

OCTOBER

Day	Time m	Time m	Time m	Time m
1 TU	0546 3.7	1141 2.3	1816 3.8	
2 W	0035 2.0	0722 3.9	1312 2.0	1944 4.0
3 TH	0145 1.6	0832 4.2	1411 1.6	2047 4.3
4 F	0237 1.2	0924 4.5	1459 1.2	2136 4.6
5 SA	0322 0.8	1010 4.8	1543 0.8	2223 4.8
6 SU	0406 0.6	1055 5.0	1627 0.6	●2309 4.9
7 M	0450 0.4	1139 5.0	1711 0.5	2355 5.0
8 TU	0533 0.4	1223 5.1	1755 0.5	
9 W	0040 5.0	0615 0.5	1307 5.0	1837 0.6
10 TH	0126 4.9	0657 0.7	1350 4.8	1919 0.8
11 F	0212 4.7	0740 1.0	1433 4.6	2004 1.1
12 SA	0259 4.4	0828 1.4	1519 4.3	2054 1.5
13 SU	0354 4.1	0927 1.8	1613 4.0	2202 1.8
14 M	0505 3.9	1047 2.1	1731 3.8	2332 2.0
15 TU	0646 3.9	1218 2.1	1919 3.8	
16 W	0100 1.9	0807 4.1	1335 1.9	2029 4.0
17 TH	0204 1.7	0901 4.3	1427 1.7	2118 4.2
18 F	0247 1.4	0944 4.5	1506 1.4	2157 4.3
19 SA	0324 1.2	1020 4.6	1541 1.2	2230 4.4
20 SU	0358 1.0	1051 4.6	1615 1.0	2300 4.5
21 M	0431 0.9	1120 4.6	1647 1.0	○2329 4.5
22 TU	0503 0.9	1149 4.6	1718 1.0	2355 5.0
23 W	0000 4.5	0532 1.0	1218 4.6	1746 1.0
24 TH	0032 4.5	0559 1.1	1248 4.5	1811 1.1
25 F	0104 4.5	0624 1.2	1317 4.5	1839 1.2
26 SA	0136 4.4	0653 1.4	1348 4.3	1911 1.4
27 SU	0212 4.3	0729 1.6	1423 4.2	1952 1.6
28 M	0257 4.1	0816 1.9	1511 4.0	2048 1.9
29 TU	0400 3.9	0928 2.2	1619 3.9	2215 2.0
30 W	0522 3.9	1112 2.2	1744 3.8	2357 1.9
31 TH	0651 4.0	1240 2.0	1911 4.0	

NOVEMBER

Day	Time m	Time m	Time m	Time m
1 F	0111 1.6	0801 4.3	1342 1.6	2016 4.3
2 SA	0207 1.2	0855 4.6	1432 1.2	2109 4.6
3 SU	0254 0.9	0942 4.9	1518 0.9	2158 4.8
4 M	0340 0.6	1029 5.0	1603 0.6	●2246 4.9
5 TU	0424 0.5	1114 5.1	1648 0.5	2334 5.0
6 W	0508 0.5	1159 5.1	1732 0.6	
7 TH	0021 5.0	0551 0.6	1243 5.0	1815 0.7
8 F	0107 4.9	0634 0.9	1326 4.8	1858 0.9
9 SA	0153 4.7	0718 1.1	1409 4.6	1943 1.2
10 SU	0241 4.5	0806 1.5	1454 4.3	2032 1.5
11 M	0335 4.2	0903 1.8	1546 4.0	2133 1.8
12 TU	0441 4.0	1015 2.1	1654 3.8	2250 2.0
13 W	0605 3.9	1138 2.2	1829 3.7	
14 TH	0012 2.0	0723 4.0	1253 2.0	1946 3.8
15 F	0118 1.8	0819 4.2	1348 1.8	2038 4.0
16 SA	0206 1.6	0903 4.3	1430 1.6	2119 4.1
17 SU	0245 1.4	0940 4.4	1507 1.4	2154 4.3
18 M	0321 1.2	1013 4.5	1542 1.2	2227 4.4
19 TU	0357 1.1	1044 4.6	1616 1.1	2300 4.4
20 W	0431 1.1	1116 4.6	1649 1.1	○2334 4.5
21 TH	0502 1.1	1149 4.6	1719 1.1	
22 F	0009 4.5	0532 1.2	1222 4.6	1749 1.1
23 SA	0044 4.5	0603 1.3	1255 4.5	1822 1.2
24 SU	0121 4.5	0638 1.4	1330 4.4	1859 1.3
25 M	0201 4.4	0719 1.6	1410 4.3	1944 1.4
26 TU	0249 4.2	0811 1.8	1459 4.1	2041 1.6
27 W	0348 4.1	0917 1.9	1601 4.0	2153 1.7
28 TH	0500 4.1	1038 2.0	1715 4.0	2313 1.7
29 F	0616 4.2	1157 1.8	1833 4.1	
30 SA	0026 1.5	0725 4.4	1305 1.6	1942 4.3

DECEMBER

Day	Time m	Time m	Time m	Time m
1 SU	0129 1.3	0823 4.6	1402 1.3	2042 4.5
2 M	0224 1.0	0916 4.8	1453 1.0	2136 4.6
3 TU	0313 0.9	1005 4.9	1542 0.8	2228 4.8
4 W	0401 0.8	1052 5.0	1629 0.7	●2318 4.8
5 TH	0448 0.8	1139 5.0	1716 0.7	
6 F	0006 4.8	0533 0.9	1223 4.9	1800 0.8
7 SA	0053 4.8	0617 1.0	1306 4.7	1843 0.9
8 SU	0139 4.7	0701 1.2	1349 4.5	1926 1.1
9 M	0225 4.5	0746 1.5	1432 4.3	2011 1.4
10 TU	0313 4.3	0836 1.7	1518 4.1	2100 1.6
11 W	0406 4.1	0933 2.0	1611 3.9	2158 1.8
12 TH	0506 4.0	1040 2.1	1712 3.7	2304 1.9
13 F	0610 4.0	1151 2.1	1822 3.7	
14 SA	0011 1.9	0712 4.0	1254 2.0	1930 3.8
15 SU	0110 1.8	0805 4.1	1345 1.8	2025 3.9
16 M	0159 1.7	0851 4.3	1428 1.6	2111 4.1
17 TU	0243 1.5	0932 4.4	1508 1.4	2154 4.2
18 W	0323 1.4	1011 4.5	1546 1.3	2234 4.3
19 TH	0401 1.3	1048 4.5	1623 1.1	○2312 4.5
20 F	0438 1.2	1125 4.6	1700 1.1	2351 4.5
21 SA	0514 1.2	1202 4.6	1736 1.0	
22 SU	0030 4.6	0551 1.2	1240 4.5	1815 1.0
23 M	0111 4.6	0632 1.3	1319 4.5	1856 1.0
24 TU	0154 4.5	0716 1.3	1402 4.4	1942 1.1
25 W	0241 4.4	0806 1.4	1451 4.3	2034 1.2
26 TH	0335 4.4	0903 1.5	1545 4.2	2131 1.3
27 F	0434 4.3	1006 1.6	1647 4.1	2234 1.4
28 SA	0539 4.3	1116 1.7	1755 4.1	2343 1.5
29 SU	0647 4.3	1227 1.6	1908 4.1	
30 M	0052 1.4	0752 4.4	1334 1.4	2017 4.2
31 TU	0157 1.3	0852 4.6	1434 1.2	2120 4.4

Chart Datum: 2·73 metres below Ordnance Datum (Newlyn)

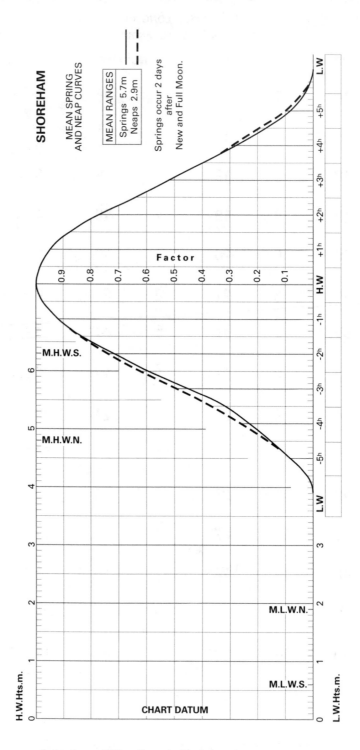

SHOREHAM

MEAN SPRING
AND NEAP CURVES

MEAN RANGES
Springs 5.7m
Neaps 2.9m

Springs occur 2 days
after
New and Full Moon.

Factor

0.9 0.8 0.7 0.6 0.5 0.4 0.3 0.2 0.1

H.W.Hts.m.

M.H.W.S.

M.H.W.N.

L.W.Hts.m.

M.L.W.N.

M.L.W.S.

CHART DATUM

L.W

H.W

L.W

Register for your **FREE** weekly weather email service from Macmillan Reeds
》 at **www.nauticaldata.com – NOW!** 《
weekend weather reports sent to your email address, every Thursday

34

ENGLAND – SHOREHAM

LAT 50°50'N   LONG 0°15'W

TIMES AND HEIGHTS OF HIGH AND LOW WATERS

YEAR **2002**

Section 1

JANUARY

Day	Time m	Time m	Time m	Time m
1 TU	0003 6.3	0612 0.9	1217 6.3	1839 0.7
16 W	0050 6.0	0651 1.1	1257 5.9	1910 1.0
2 W	0049 6.3	0658 0.8	1303 6.3	1926 0.7
17 TH	0123 5.9	0725 1.2	1328 5.8	1945 1.1
3 TH	0136 6.3	0747 0.9	1351 6.2	2015 0.8
18 F	0154 5.8	0800 1.3	1358 5.6	2020 1.2
4 F	0225 6.2	0838 1.0	1441 6.0	2107 0.9
19 SA	0222 5.7	0836 1.4	1429 5.5	2056 1.4
5 SA	0317 6.0	0933 1.2	1536 5.7	2204 1.1
20 SU	0253 5.5	0914 1.6	1506 5.3	2134 1.6
6 SU	0414 5.8	1035 1.4	1637 5.5	2306 1.3
21 M	0332 5.3	0958 1.8	1551 5.0	2219 1.8
7 M	0517 5.6	1143 1.5	1745 5.3	
22 TU	0421 5.1	1053 2.0	1648 4.8	2316 2.0
8 TU	0014 1.5	0627 5.5	1254 1.6	1900 5.2
23 W	0527 4.9	1159 2.0	1811 4.7	
9 W	0123 1.5	0739 5.5	1359 1.5	2014 5.3
24 TH	0027 2.0	0649 5.0	1310 1.9	1927 4.9
10 TH	0226 1.5	0843 5.6	1457 1.4	2116 5.5
25 F	0140 1.9	0756 5.2	1417 1.7	2030 5.2
11 F	0321 1.3	0938 5.8	1549 1.1	2209 5.7
26 SA	0245 1.7	0853 5.5	1515 1.4	2126 5.6
12 SA	0411 1.2	1026 5.9	1636 1.0	2255 5.9
27 SU	0339 1.4	0945 5.9	1606 1.0	2217 5.9
13 SU ●	0455 1.1	1109 6.0	1719 0.9	2337 6.0
28 M ○	0428 1.1	1034 6.2	1654 0.8	2306 6.2
14 M	0537 1.0	1148 6.0	1759 0.9	
29 TU	0515 0.8	1121 6.4	1741 0.5	2354 6.4
15 TU	0014 6.0	0615 1.1	1224 6.0	1835 0.9
30 W	0602 0.6	1208 6.5	1828 0.4	
31 TH	0041 6.6	0648 0.6	1255 6.5	1915 0.4

FEBRUARY

Day	Time m	Time m	Time m	Time m
1 F	0127 6.6	0735 0.6	1341 6.5	2002 0.4
16 SA	0124 5.9	0734 1.0	1330 5.8	1952 1.0
2 SA	0212 6.5	0823 0.6	1427 6.3	2049 0.6
17 SU	0148 5.9	0804 1.1	1358 5.7	2020 1.1
3 SU	0258 6.3	0912 0.8	1515 6.0	2138 0.9
18 M	0216 5.7	0833 1.3	1431 5.6	2049 1.3
4 M	0346 6.0	1005 1.1	1606 5.7	2231 1.2
19 TU	0250 5.6	0907 1.5	1508 5.3	2125 1.6
5 TU	0439 5.6	1104 1.5	1705 5.3	2334 1.6
20 W	0332 5.3	0951 1.7	1556 5.0	2216 1.8
6 W	0541 5.3	1217 1.7	1816 5.0	
21 TH	0425 5.0	1053 1.9	1701 4.8	2326 2.1
7 TH	0051 1.8	0657 5.1	1335 1.8	1946 4.9
22 F	0544 4.8	1218 2.0	1846 4.7	
8 F	0206 1.8	0822 5.1	1441 1.6	2103 5.1
23 SA	0059 2.1	0722 4.9	1345 1.8	2005 5.0
9 SA	0308 1.6	0926 5.3	1536 1.4	2159 5.4
24 SU	0221 1.8	0832 5.3	1455 1.4	2108 5.5
10 SU	0359 1.4	1016 5.6	1622 1.1	2245 5.7
25 M	0323 1.4	0929 5.7	1550 1.0	2203 5.9
11 M	0442 1.2	1058 5.8	1703 1.0	2324 5.9
26 TU	0414 1.0	1021 6.1	1639 0.6	2253 6.3
12 TU ●	0521 1.0	1136 5.9	1741 0.9	2359 6.0
27 W ○	0501 0.6	1110 6.4	1725 0.4	2341 6.6
13 W	0558 1.0	1209 6.0	1816 0.8	
28 TH	0547 0.4	1157 6.6	1811 0.2	
14 TH	0031 6.0	0631 1.0	1239 5.9	1849 0.8
15 F	0100 6.0	0707 1.0	1305 5.9	1921 0.9

MARCH

Day	Time m	Time m	Time m	Time m
1 F	0026 6.8	0632 0.3	1243 6.7	1856 0.1
16 SA	0031 6.0	0638 0.8	1239 5.9	1855 0.8
2 SA	0111 6.8	0717 0.3	1327 6.6	1941 0.2
17 SU	0053 6.0	0707 0.9	1304 5.9	1922 0.9
3 SU	0153 6.7	0802 0.4	1409 6.5	2024 0.4
18 M	0118 6.0	0733 0.9	1332 5.9	1947 1.0
4 M	0234 6.4	0846 0.6	1452 6.1	2108 0.8
19 TU	0146 5.9	0759 1.0	1402 5.7	2015 1.1
5 TU	0317 6.0	0932 1.0	1538 5.7	2155 1.2
20 W	0218 5.7	0832 1.2	1438 5.5	2052 1.4
6 W	0405 5.5	1024 1.5	1633 5.2	2252 1.7
21 TH	0257 5.4	0916 1.5	1522 5.2	2142 1.7
7 TH	0504 5.0	1135 1.9	1741 4.8	
22 F	0347 5.0	1016 1.8	1625 4.9	2253 2.0
8 F	0018 2.1	0618 4.7	1311 2.0	1916 4.6
23 SA	0502 4.7	1140 2.0	1815 4.7	
9 SA	0148 2.1	0801 4.7	1422 1.8	2050 4.9
24 SU	0030 2.1	0656 4.7	1320 1.8	1945 5.0
10 SU	0253 1.8	0913 5.0	1518 1.5	2145 5.3
25 M	0203 1.8	0813 5.1	1436 1.4	2052 5.5
11 M	0343 1.5	1002 5.4	1603 1.2	2228 5.7
26 TU	0306 1.3	0913 5.7	1531 0.9	2147 6.0
12 TU	0424 1.2	1042 5.7	1642 1.0	2304 5.9
27 W	0356 0.8	1006 6.1	1619 0.5	2236 6.4
13 W	0501 1.0	1118 5.8	1718 0.8	2338 6.0
28 TH ○	0442 0.4	1054 6.4	1704 0.2	2322 6.7
14 TH ●	0535 0.9	1149 5.9	1752 0.8	
29 F	0527 0.2	1140 6.6	1749 0.1	
15 F	0007 6.1	0607 0.8	1215 5.9	1824 0.7
30 SA	0006 6.9	0611 0.1	1226 6.7	1833 0.1
31 SU	0049 6.8	0655 0.2	1309 6.6	1916 0.2

APRIL

Day	Time m	Time m	Time m	Time m
1 M	0130 6.7	0738 0.3	1350 6.4	1958 0.5
16 TU	0051 6.0	0706 0.9	1310 5.9	1920 1.0
2 TU	0209 6.4	0820 0.6	1431 6.1	2040 0.8
17 W	0121 5.9	0735 0.9	1341 5.8	1953 1.1
3 W	0250 5.9	0903 1.0	1515 5.6	2125 1.3
18 TH	0155 5.7	0812 1.1	1419 5.6	2033 1.3
4 TH	0336 5.4	0951 1.5	1609 5.2	2218 1.8
19 F	0235 5.4	0858 1.4	1506 5.3	2127 1.7
5 F	0434 4.9	1053 1.9	1714 4.7	2338 2.2
20 SA	0327 5.1	1000 1.7	1612 4.9	2239 1.9
6 SA	0545 4.5	1238 2.1	1838 4.6	
21 SU	0446 4.8	1121 1.8	1755 4.8	
7 SU	0123 2.2	0728 4.5	1356 1.9	2022 4.8
22 M	0012 1.9	0633 4.8	1257 1.7	1922 5.1
8 M	0229 1.9	0849 4.8	1452 1.6	2117 5.2
23 TU	0141 1.6	0751 5.2	1412 1.3	2029 5.6
9 TU	0318 1.5	0937 5.2	1536 1.3	2159 5.6
24 W	0243 1.1	0853 5.6	1507 0.9	2124 6.1
10 W	0358 1.2	1016 5.5	1614 1.1	2235 5.8
25 TH	0333 0.7	0945 6.1	1555 0.5	2213 6.4
11 TH	0433 1.0	1050 5.7	1648 0.9	2306 5.9
26 F	0419 0.4	1034 6.4	1641 0.3	2259 6.7
12 F ●	0507 0.9	1122 5.9	1722 0.8	2334 6.0
27 SA ○	0504 0.2	1121 6.5	1726 0.2	2343 6.7
13 SA	0539 0.8	1145 5.9	1755 0.8	2358 6.0
28 SU	0549 0.2	1206 6.6	1810 0.3	
14 SU	0611 0.8	1211 5.9	1826 0.8	
29 M	0026 6.7	0632 0.3	1250 6.5	1853 0.4
15 M	0023 6.0	0639 0.8	1240 5.9	1854 0.9
30 TU	0107 6.5	0715 0.6	1331 6.3	1935 0.7

Chart Datum: 3·27 metres below Ordnance Datum (Newlyn)
Register for your **FREE** weekly weather email service from Macmillan Reeds
at **www.nauticaldata.com – NOW!**
weekend weather reports sent to your email address, every Thursday

35

TIME ZONE (UTC)
For Summer Time add ONE hour in **non-shaded areas**

ENGLAND – SHOREHAM

LAT 50°50′N   LONG 0°15′W

TIMES AND HEIGHTS OF HIGH AND LOW WATERS

YEAR **2002**

MAY

Day	Time m	Time m	Time m	Time m
1 W	0147 6.2	0757 0.7	1413 6.0	2016 1.0
2 TH	0227 5.8	0839 1.0	1457 5.6	2101 1.4
3 F	0312 5.3	0925 1.4	1548 5.2	2152 1.8
4 SA	0408 4.9	1021 1.8	1647 4.9	2259 2.1
5 SU	0513 4.6	1140 2.0	1756 4.7	
6 M	0040 2.2	0628 4.5	1313 2.0	1922 4.8
7 TU	0151 1.9	0800 4.7	1412 1.7	2032 5.1
8 W	0241 1.6	0855 5.0	1458 1.5	2117 5.4
9 TH	0322 1.4	0936 5.3	1538 1.2	2153 5.6
10 F	0359 1.1	1009 5.5	1614 1.1	2224 5.8
11 SA	0434 1.0	1040 5.7	1650 1.0	2254 5.9
12 SU	0508 0.9	1112 5.8	1725 0.9	●2325 6.0
13 M	0542 0.8	1145 5.9	1758 0.9	2356 6.0
14 TU	0614 0.8	1218 5.9	1830 0.9	
15 W	0029 6.0	0646 0.8	1253 5.9	1903 1.0
16 TH	0104 5.9	0721 0.9	1330 5.8	1940 1.1
17 F	0142 5.7	0803 1.1	1412 5.6	2026 1.3
18 SA	0227 5.5	0852 1.3	1504 5.4	2121 1.5
19 SU	0324 5.2	0953 1.5	1612 5.2	2231 1.7
20 M	0440 5.0	1108 1.6	1735 5.1	2353 1.7
21 TU	0607 5.0	1232 1.5	1854 5.3	
22 W	0112 1.5	0723 5.3	1343 1.2	2001 5.7
23 TH	0215 1.1	0827 5.6	1440 0.9	2058 6.0
24 F	0307 0.8	0922 5.9	1530 0.7	2148 6.3
25 SA	0356 0.6	1012 6.1	1618 0.5	2235 6.4
26 SU	0442 0.4	1101 6.3	1704 0.5	○2321 6.5
27 M	0528 0.4	1147 6.3	1749 0.6	
28 TU	0004 6.4	0612 0.5	1232 6.3	1833 0.7
29 W	0047 6.2	0655 0.6	1314 6.1	1915 0.9
30 TH	0127 6.0	0737 0.8	1356 5.9	1957 1.1
31 F	0208 5.7	0819 1.1	1439 5.7	2040 1.4

JUNE

Day	Time m	Time m	Time m	Time m
1 SA	0251 5.3	0902 1.4	1525 5.4	2127 1.7
2 SU	0340 5.0	0952 1.6	1617 5.1	2222 1.9
3 M	0437 4.7	1049 1.8	1714 4.9	2327 2.0
4 TU	0539 4.6	1156 1.9	1814 4.9	
5 W	0043 2.0	0642 4.6	1308 1.9	1915 5.0
6 TH	0148 1.8	0743 4.8	1407 1.7	2011 5.2
7 F	0237 1.6	0836 5.1	1454 1.5	2058 5.4
8 SA	0319 1.3	0921 5.3	1536 1.3	2139 5.6
9 SU	0358 1.2	1002 5.6	1616 1.2	2218 5.8
10 M	0437 1.0	1042 5.7	1655 1.1	●2256 5.9
11 TU	0515 0.9	1121 5.9	1733 1.0	2334 6.0
12 W	0553 0.9	1201 5.9	1812 1.0	
13 TH	0013 6.0	0632 0.8	1243 6.0	1851 1.0
14 F	0054 6.0	0714 0.9	1325 5.9	1934 1.0
15 SA	0138 5.9	0759 0.9	1411 5.8	2022 1.1
16 SU	0226 5.7	0850 1.1	1503 5.7	2117 1.3
17 M	0321 5.5	0947 1.2	1602 5.6	2219 1.4
18 TU	0425 5.3	1052 1.3	1708 5.5	2329 1.4
19 W	0536 5.3	1203 1.3	1818 5.5	
20 TH	0041 1.4	0648 5.3	1312 1.3	1927 5.6
21 F	0146 1.2	0758 5.4	1413 1.1	2029 5.8
22 SA	0243 1.0	0859 5.6	1508 1.0	2125 6.0
23 SU	0336 0.9	0954 5.8	1559 0.9	2216 6.1
24 M	0425 0.7	1045 6.0	1648 0.8	○2303 6.1
25 TU	0512 0.7	1132 6.1	1734 0.9	2348 6.1
26 W	0557 0.7	1217 6.1	1817 0.9	
27 TH	0030 6.0	0639 0.8	1259 6.0	1859 1.0
28 F	0110 5.9	0720 0.9	1339 5.9	1938 1.1
29 SA	0149 5.7	0759 1.1	1418 5.8	2018 1.3
30 SU	0227 5.5	0838 1.2	1458 5.6	2059 1.5

JULY

Day	Time m	Time m	Time m	Time m
1 M	0307 5.2	0920 1.4	1539 5.4	2144 1.7
2 TU	0352 5.0	1006 1.6	1625 5.2	2235 1.8
3 W	0445 4.8	1058 1.8	1719 5.0	2331 1.9
4 TH	0545 4.7	1156 1.9	1817 4.9	
5 F	0033 1.9	0647 4.7	1259 1.9	1916 5.0
6 SA	0136 1.8	0746 4.9	1401 1.8	2011 5.2
7 SU	0234 1.6	0841 5.2	1457 1.6	2102 5.4
8 M	0324 1.4	0931 5.4	1546 1.4	2148 5.7
9 TU	0409 1.1	1018 5.7	1631 1.2	2232 5.9
10 W	0453 0.9	1103 5.9	1714 1.0	●2316 6.0
11 TH	0536 0.9	1148 6.1	1757 0.9	
12 F	0000 6.1	0620 0.7	1233 6.2	1841 0.9
13 SA	0045 6.2	0705 0.7	1319 6.3	1927 0.8
14 SU	0131 6.1	0752 0.7	1404 6.2	2014 0.9
15 M	0218 6.0	0841 0.8	1452 6.1	2105 1.0
16 TU	0308 5.9	0932 0.9	1543 5.9	2200 1.1
17 W	0402 5.6	1028 1.1	1638 5.7	2301 1.3
18 TH	0503 5.4	1131 1.3	1740 5.5	
19 F	0009 1.4	0611 5.2	1241 1.5	1850 5.4
20 SA	0120 1.5	0728 5.2	1350 1.5	2003 5.4
21 SU	0225 1.4	0842 5.3	1452 1.4	2108 5.6
22 M	0322 1.2	0943 5.5	1547 1.2	2203 5.7
23 TU	0413 1.0	1036 5.8	1636 1.1	2252 5.9
24 W	0459 0.9	1122 5.9	1721 1.0	○2336 6.0
25 TH	0542 0.9	1204 6.0	1802 1.0	
26 F	0016 5.9	0622 0.9	1243 6.0	1841 1.0
27 SA	0053 5.9	0659 0.9	1319 6.0	1917 1.1
28 SU	0127 5.8	0734 1.0	1352 5.9	1952 1.2
29 M	0157 5.6	0809 1.1	1423 5.8	2027 1.3
30 TU	0227 5.5	0845 1.3	1451 5.6	2105 1.5
31 W	0258 5.3	0922 1.5	1523 5.4	2145 1.6

AUGUST

Day	Time m	Time m	Time m	Time m
1 TH	0337 5.1	1004 1.7	1604 5.2	2233 1.8
2 F	0428 4.8	1055 1.9	1701 4.9	2333 2.0
3 SA	0544 4.7	1200 2.1	1820 4.9	
4 SU	0041 2.0	0703 4.7	1313 2.0	1932 5.0
5 M	0153 1.8	0810 5.0	1424 1.8	2033 5.3
6 TU	0256 1.5	0907 5.3	1523 1.5	2126 5.6
7 W	0348 1.2	0959 5.7	1612 1.2	2215 5.9
8 TH	0435 0.9	1048 6.0	1657 1.0	●2302 6.2
9 F	0520 0.7	1134 6.2	1742 0.8	2348 6.3
10 SA	0605 0.5	1220 6.4	1827 0.6	
11 SU	0033 6.4	0650 0.4	1305 6.5	1912 0.6
12 M	0118 6.4	0736 0.4	1349 6.5	1958 0.6
13 TU	0203 6.3	0822 0.5	1433 6.4	2045 0.7
14 W	0248 6.1	0909 0.8	1518 6.2	2135 1.0
15 TH	0337 5.8	0959 1.1	1608 5.8	2230 1.3
16 F	0432 5.4	1057 1.5	1707 5.4	2337 1.6
17 SA	0540 5.1	1212 1.8	1817 5.1	
18 SU	0058 1.8	0705 4.9	1334 1.9	1945 5.1
19 M	0212 1.7	0835 5.1	1442 1.7	2101 5.3
20 TU	0312 1.5	0938 5.4	1537 1.5	2157 5.6
21 W	0402 1.2	1027 5.7	1624 1.2	2243 5.8
22 TH	0445 1.0	1109 6.0	1705 1.1	○2323 5.9
23 F	0524 0.9	1148 6.1	1743 1.0	2359 6.0
24 SA	0601 0.8	1222 6.1	1819 1.0	
25 SU	0032 6.0	0634 0.9	1254 6.1	1851 1.0
26 M	0100 5.9	0707 0.9	1320 6.0	1923 1.1
27 TU	0124 5.8	0738 1.0	1342 5.9	1954 1.2
28 W	0149 5.7	0808 1.2	1406 5.8	2024 1.3
29 TH	0217 5.5	0837 1.4	1436 5.6	2056 1.5
30 F	0252 5.3	0911 1.6	1513 5.3	2136 1.8
31 SA	0335 5.0	0957 1.9	1602 5.0	2233 2.0

Chart Datum: 3·27 metres below Ordnance Datum (Newlyn)

TIME ZONE (UTC)
For Summer Time add ONE hour in **non-shaded areas**

ENGLAND – SHOREHAM

LAT 50°50′N   LONG 0°15′W

TIMES AND HEIGHTS OF HIGH AND LOW WATERS

YEAR **2002**

SEPTEMBER

Day	Time	m	Time	m	Time	m	Time	m
1 SU	0435	4.7	1104	2.2	1714	4.7	2352	2.1
2 M	0624	4.6	1233	2.2	1859	4.8		
3 TU	0119	2.0	0745	4.9	1400	2.0	2010	5.1
4 W	0235	1.6	0849	5.3	1505	1.6	2108	5.6
5 TH	0330	1.2	0942	5.8	1554	1.2	2159	6.0
6 F	0416	0.8	1031	6.2	1639	0.8	2246	6.3
7 SA ●	0501	0.5	1116	6.5	1723	0.6	2331	6.5
8 SU	0545	0.4	1201	6.7	1807	0.4		
9 M	0016	6.6	0628	0.3	1245	6.8	1851	0.4
10 TU	0100	6.6	0713	0.6	1327	6.7	1935	0.5
11 W	0143	6.5	0757	0.5	1408	6.5	2020	0.7
12 TH	0225	6.2	0841	0.8	1451	6.2	2106	1.0
13 F	0312	5.8	0929	1.2	1539	5.7	2158	1.4
14 SA	0406	5.3	1025	1.7	1638	5.2	2305	1.8
15 SU	0515	4.9	1145	2.1	1751	4.8		
16 M	0039	2.1	0648	4.7	1320	2.1	1933	4.8
17 TU	0159	1.9	0827	5.0	1431	1.9	2053	5.1
18 W	0259	1.6	0926	5.4	1524	1.6	2145	5.5
19 TH	0346	1.3	1010	5.8	1607	1.3	2226	5.8
20 F	0425	1.0	1049	6.0	1644	1.1	2304	6.0
21 SA ○	0501	0.9	1124	6.2	1719	0.9	2337	6.0
22 SU	0534	0.8	1155	6.2	1752	0.9		
23 M	0005	6.0	0606	0.8	1223	6.1	1823	0.9
24 TU	0029	6.0	0637	0.9	1244	6.1	1853	1.0
25 W	0052	5.9	0706	1.0	1305	6.0	1920	1.1
26 TH	0117	5.8	0733	1.1	1331	5.9	1947	1.2
27 F	0145	5.7	0800	1.3	1400	5.7	2017	1.4
28 SA	0217	5.5	0834	1.6	1435	5.4	2056	1.7
29 SU	0258	5.2	0920	1.9	1522	5.0	2153	2.0
30 M	0355	4.8	1028	2.2	1630	4.7	2313	2.2

OCTOBER

Day	Time	m	Time	m	Time	m	Time	m
1 TU	0549	4.6	1202	2.3	1832	4.7		
2 W	0051	2.1	0722	4.9	1338	2.0	1949	5.1
3 TH	0213	1.7	0828	5.4	1444	1.5	2049	5.6
4 F	0308	1.2	0922	6.0	1532	1.1	2139	6.1
5 SA	0354	0.8	1009	6.4	1617	0.7	2226	6.4
6 SU ●	0437	0.5	1054	6.7	1700	0.4	2311	6.7
7 M	0521	0.3	1137	6.9	1743	0.3	2356	6.8
8 TU	0604	0.3	1220	6.9	1827	0.3		
9 W	0039	6.7	0648	0.4	1302	6.8	1911	0.4
10 TH	0122	6.5	0731	0.6	1344	6.5	1955	0.7
11 F	0205	6.2	0815	0.9	1426	6.1	2040	1.1
12 SA	0251	5.8	0902	1.4	1514	5.6	2131	1.5
13 SU	0346	5.3	0958	1.8	1613	5.1	2234	2.0
14 M	0454	4.9	1117	2.2	1727	4.7		
15 TU	0013	2.2	0623	4.7	1300	2.2	1911	4.7
16 W	0135	2.1	0802	5.0	1409	2.0	2030	5.0
17 TH	0234	1.7	0859	5.4	1501	1.6	2120	5.4
18 F	0320	1.4	0942	5.7	1541	1.3	2201	5.7
19 SA	0358	1.1	1019	6.0	1617	1.1	2236	5.9
20 SU	0432	1.0	1052	6.1	1650	1.0	2307	6.0
21 M ○	0505	0.9	1121	6.1	1723	0.9	2333	6.0
22 TU	0538	0.9	1145	6.1	1755	0.9	2357	6.0
23 W	0609	1.0	1209	6.1	1825	1.0		
24 TH	0023	6.0	0637	1.0	1235	6.0	1852	1.1
25 F	0052	5.9	0704	1.2	1303	5.9	1919	1.2
26 SA	0121	5.8	0734	1.3	1334	5.7	1952	1.4
27 SU	0155	5.6	0811	1.6	1411	5.4	2034	1.6
28 M	0237	5.3	0900	1.9	1458	5.1	2132	1.9
29 TU	0337	5.0	1008	2.1	1609	4.8	2248	2.1
30 W	0521	4.8	1137	2.2	1802	4.8		
31 TH	0022	2.0	0654	5.0	1309	1.9	1922	5.1

NOVEMBER

Day	Time	m	Time	m	Time	m	Time	m
1 F	0142	1.6	0801	5.5	1415	1.5	2024	5.6
2 SA	0240	1.2	0855	6.0	1506	1.0	2116	6.1
3 SU	0328	0.8	0943	6.4	1551	0.6	2204	6.4
4 M ●	0412	0.5	1029	6.7	1636	0.4	2250	6.6
5 TU	0457	0.4	1113	6.8	1720	0.3	2335	6.7
6 W	0541	0.4	1156	6.8	1805	0.4		
7 TH	0020	6.6	0625	0.5	1239	6.6	1850	0.5
8 F	0104	6.4	0709	0.7	1322	6.4	1934	0.8
9 SA	0148	6.2	0754	1.1	1405	6.0	2020	1.1
10 SU	0235	5.8	0841	1.5	1453	5.5	2109	1.5
11 M	0328	5.4	0935	1.9	1550	5.1	2206	1.9
12 TU	0429	5.1	1044	2.2	1657	4.8	2325	2.1
13 W	0541	4.9	1219	2.2	1818	4.7		
14 TH	0053	2.1	0710	5.0	1332	2.1	1946	4.8
15 F	0155	1.9	0816	5.2	1425	1.8	2042	5.1
16 SA	0243	1.6	0903	5.5	1508	1.1	2124	5.4
17 SU	0324	1.4	0941	5.8	1545	1.3	2159	5.7
18 M	0400	1.2	1013	5.9	1620	1.1	2229	5.8
19 TU	0435	1.1	1042	6.0	1654	1.0	2259	5.9
20 W ○	0509	1.1	1110	6.0	1727	1.0	2329	1.0
21 TH	0542	1.1	1140	6.0	1800	1.0		
22 F	0001	6.0	0613	1.1	1211	6.0	1831	1.1
23 SA	0034	5.9	0644	1.2	1244	5.9	1903	1.2
24 SU	0108	5.9	0719	1.3	1319	5.8	1941	1.3
25 M	0146	5.7	0800	1.5	1400	5.6	2025	1.5
26 TU	0232	5.5	0850	1.7	1451	5.3	2121	1.7
27 W	0332	5.2	0954	1.9	1558	5.1	2229	1.8
28 TH	0452	5.1	1111	1.9	1724	5.0	2349	1.8
29 F	0616	5.3	1232	1.8	1846	5.2		
30 SA	0105	1.6	0726	5.6	1341	1.4	1952	5.5

DECEMBER

Day	Time	m	Time	m	Time	m	Time	m
1 SU	0207	1.3	0825	5.9	1437	1.1	2049	5.9
2 M	0301	1.0	0916	6.3	1527	0.8	2141	6.2
3 TU	0349	0.8	1005	6.5	1615	0.6	2230	6.4
4 W ●	0437	0.7	1051	6.6	1702	0.5	2318	6.4
5 TH	0523	0.7	1137	6.6	1748	0.6		
6 F	0005	6.4	0608	0.7	1221	6.4	1834	0.7
7 SA	0050	6.3	0653	0.9	1305	6.2	1918	0.9
8 SU	0135	6.1	0738	1.1	1349	5.9	2003	1.1
9 M	0220	5.9	0823	1.4	1434	5.6	2048	1.4
10 TU	0307	5.6	0911	1.7	1524	5.2	2137	1.7
11 W	0358	5.3	1006	2.0	1619	4.9	2232	1.9
12 TH	0455	5.1	1109	2.1	1720	4.8	2336	1.9
13 F	0556	5.0	1224	2.1	1824	4.7		
14 SA	0048	2.0	0659	5.0	1332	2.0	1929	4.8
15 SU	0151	1.9	0758	5.2	1424	1.8	2025	5.1
16 M	0242	1.7	0847	5.4	1508	1.5	2110	5.3
17 TU	0325	1.5	0928	5.6	1548	1.3	2150	5.6
18 W	0405	1.4	1005	5.8	1626	1.2	2228	5.7
19 TH ○	0443	1.3	1041	5.9	1704	1.1	2306	5.9
20 F	0520	1.2	1117	6.0	1741	1.0	2344	6.0
21 SA	0556	1.1	1154	6.0	1817	1.0		
22 SU	0022	6.0	0632	1.1	1233	6.0	1855	1.1
23 M	0101	6.0	0711	1.2	1313	5.9	1935	1.1
24 TU	0143	5.9	0753	1.3	1356	5.8	2020	1.1
25 W	0229	5.8	0842	1.4	1445	5.7	2110	1.3
26 TH	0321	5.7	0938	1.5	1541	5.5	2208	1.4
27 F	0422	5.5	1043	1.6	1647	5.3	2315	1.5
28 SA	0531	5.5	1155	1.6	1800	5.3		
29 SU	0027	1.5	0643	5.5	1307	1.5	1914	5.4
30 M	0136	1.4	0752	5.7	1411	1.3	2022	5.5
31 TU	0237	1.3	0852	5.9	1508	1.1	2123	5.8

Chart Datum: 3·27 metres below Ordnance Datum (Newlyn)

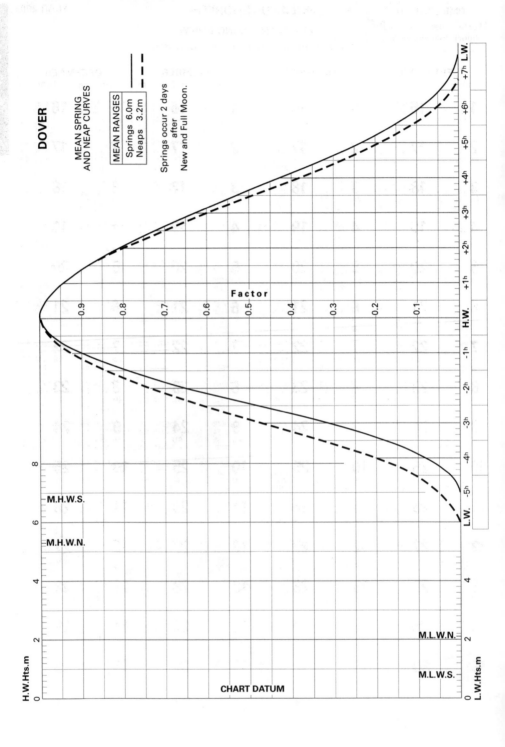

DOVER

MEAN SPRING
AND NEAP CURVES

MEAN RANGES
Springs 6.0m
Neaps 3.2m

Springs occur 2 days
after
New and Full Moon.

TIME ZONE (UTC)
For Summer Time add ONE hour in **non-shaded areas**

ENGLAND – DOVER

LAT 51°07′N   LONG 1°19′W

TIMES AND HEIGHTS OF HIGH AND LOW WATERS

YEAR 2002

JANUARY

Time	m	Time	m
1 0716	1.0	**16** 0038	6.5
1203	6.7	0753	1.2
TU 1939	1.0	W 1255	6.3
		2001	1.4
2 0029	6.8	**17** 0113	6.5
0802	0.9	0823	1.3
W 1250	6.6	TH 1328	6.1
2023	1.1	2029	1.4
3 0117	6.7	**18** 0144	6.3
0850	0.9	0853	1.4
TH 1340	6.5	F 1400	6.0
2109	1.2	2059	1.5
4 0207	6.6	**19** 0212	6.2
0939	1.0	0925	1.5
F 1434	6.3	SA 1430	5.8
2157	1.3	2134	1.6
5 0301	6.5	**20** 0242	6.0
1030	1.2	1001	1.6
SA 1534	6.1	SU 1503	5.6
2248	1.5	2212	1.8
6 0359	6.2	**21** 0320	5.8
1124	1.3	1042	1.8
SU 1640	5.8	M 1546	5.4
2344	1.7	2256	2.0
7 0504	6.0	**22** 0409	5.6
1223	1.5	1132	2.0
M 1753	5.7	TU 1649	5.2
		2351	2.2
8 0047	1.9	**23** 0518	5.4
0615	5.9	1238	2.1
TU 1326	1.6	W 1816	5.2
1905	5.6		
9 0155	1.9	**24** 0110	2.3
0728	5.8	0638	5.4
W 1432	1.6	TH 1357	2.1
2010	5.7	1927	5.3
10 0305	1.8	**25** 0231	2.1
0834	5.9	0746	5.6
TH 1542	1.6	F 1507	1.8
2108	5.9	2026	5.6
11 0415	1.6	**26** 0337	1.8
0931	6.1	0844	5.9
F 1649	1.4	SA 1608	1.5
2158	6.1	2117	6.0
12 0514	1.4	**27** 0435	1.5
1021	6.2	0935	6.2
SA 1741	1.3	SU 1704	1.3
2242	6.3	2205	6.3
13 0602	1.3	**28** 0528	1.2
1104	6.3	1024	6.5
SU 1823	1.3	M 1757	1.0
● 2322	6.4	○ 2251	6.6
14 0643	1.2	**29** 0620	0.9
1143	6.4	1111	6.7
M 1900	1.3	TU 1848	0.9
		2336	6.8
15 0000	6.5	**30** 0711	0.7
0720	1.2	1157	6.8
TU 1220	6.3	W 1937	0.8
1932	1.3		
		31 0021	6.9
		0800	0.6
		TH 1243	6.8
		2022	0.7

FEBRUARY

Time	m	Time	m
1 0106	7.0	**16** 0116	6.4
0847	0.5	0830	1.1
F 1328	6.7	SA 1328	6.1
2104	0.8	2037	1.2
2 0152	6.9	**17** 0137	6.3
0931	0.6	0859	1.2
SA 1415	6.5	SU 1350	6.1
2145	0.9	2108	1.3
3 0239	6.8	**18** 0203	6.3
1014	0.8	0930	1.3
SU 1506	6.3	M 1417	6.0
2227	1.1	2141	1.5
4 0330	6.5	**19** 0236	6.2
1058	1.1	1003	1.5
M 1601	6.0	TU 1454	5.8
2313	1.5	2217	1.7
5 0426	6.1	**20** 0318	5.9
1148	1.4	1043	1.8
TU 1705	5.6	W 1541	5.6
		2302	2.0
6 0008	1.8	**21** 0413	5.6
0532	5.7	1136	2.1
W 1248	1.8	TH 1649	5.3
1819	5.4		
7 0117	2.1	**22** 0007	2.3
0651	5.5	0540	5.3
TH 1357	2.0	F 1302	2.2
1939	5.3	1848	5.1
8 0233	2.1	**23** 0147	2.3
0816	5.5	0721	5.4
F 1512	1.9	SA 1435	2.0
2051	5.5	2004	5.4
9 0355	1.9	**24** 0308	1.9
0926	5.7	0829	5.7
SA 1631	1.7	SU 1545	1.7
2147	5.8	2103	5.8
10 0502	1.6	**25** 0413	1.5
1018	6.0	0926	6.1
SU 1729	1.5	M 1647	1.3
2231	6.1	2154	6.3
11 0552	1.3	**26** 0512	1.1
1058	6.2	1017	6.5
M 1812	1.3	TU 1745	1.0
2309	6.4	2240	6.6
12 0633	1.2	**27** 0609	0.7
1133	6.3	1103	6.7
TU 1848	1.3	W 1839	0.7
● 2345	6.5	○ 2324	6.9
13 0708	1.1	**28** 0702	0.4
1204	6.3	1146	6.9
W 1918	1.2	TH 1927	0.6
14 0019	6.5		
0737	1.1		
TH 1235	6.3		
1944	1.1		
15 0050	6.5		
0803	1.1		
F 1303	6.2		
2009	1.2		

MARCH

Time	m	Time	m
1 0007	7.1	**16** 0022	6.5
0750	0.3	0737	1.0
F 1229	6.9	SA 1235	6.3
2009	0.5	1945	1.1
2 0049	7.2	**17** 0045	6.4
0833	0.2	0804	1.0
SA 1310	6.9	SU 1257	6.3
2048	0.5	2013	1.1
3 0132	7.1	**18** 0106	6.4
0913	0.3	0832	1.1
SU 1353	6.7	M 1317	6.3
2124	0.7	2042	1.2
4 0215	6.9	**19** 0131	6.4
0950	0.6	0901	1.2
M 1438	6.4	TU 1345	6.3
2201	1.0	2113	1.3
5 0302	6.5	**20** 0203	6.3
1030	1.0	0932	1.4
TU 1529	6.1	W 1421	6.1
2243	1.4	2147	1.6
6 0355	6.1	**21** 0243	6.1
1115	1.5	1009	1.7
W 1628	5.6	TH 1506	5.8
2334	1.9	2230	1.9
7 0458	5.6	**22** 0335	5.7
1213	2.0	1059	2.1
TH 1740	5.3	F 1609	5.3
		2332	2.2
8 0044	2.2	**23** 0501	5.2
0617	5.2	1217	2.3
F 1327	2.3	SA 1820	5.1
1905	5.1		
9 0208	2.3	**24** 0113	2.3
0804	5.2	0705	5.3
SA 1448	2.2	SU 1408	2.2
2032	5.3	1944	5.4
10 0338	2.0	**25** 0243	1.9
0920	5.5	0817	5.7
SU 1613	1.9	M 1523	1.7
2131	5.7	2046	5.9
11 0449	1.6	**26** 0351	1.4
1008	5.8	0915	6.1
M 1712	1.6	TU 1627	1.3
2214	6.1	2138	6.3
12 0538	1.3	**27** 0453	1.0
1044	6.1	1004	6.5
TU 1754	1.4	W 1726	0.9
2251	6.3	2224	6.7
13 0616	1.1	**28** 0552	0.6
1115	6.2	1049	6.8
W 1829	1.2	TH 1820	0.7
2324	6.5	○ 2307	7.0
14 0648	1.0	**29** 0645	0.3
1142	6.3	1131	6.9
TH 1856	1.1	F 1907	0.5
● 2355	6.5	2348	7.2
15 0713	1.0	**30** 0732	0.2
1209	6.3	1210	7.0
F 1920	1.1	SA 1948	0.4
		31 0029	7.2
		0812	0.2
		SU 1250	6.9
		2025	0.5

APRIL

Time	m	Time	m
1 0110	7.1	**16** 0037	6.5
0849	0.4	0807	1.0
M 1331	6.8	TU 1251	6.4
2100	0.7	2019	1.1
2 0152	6.9	**17** 0105	6.5
0925	0.7	0836	1.2
TU 1414	6.5	W 1322	6.4
2136	1.0	2051	1.3
3 0237	6.5	**18** 0139	6.4
1002	1.1	0909	1.4
W 1503	6.1	TH 1400	6.2
2215	1.4	2127	1.5
4 0329	6.0	**19** 0221	6.1
1044	1.7	0948	1.7
TH 1600	5.7	F 1449	5.8
2304	1.9	2213	1.8
5 0432	5.5	**20** 0317	5.6
1141	2.2	1040	2.0
F 1708	5.3	SA 1558	5.4
		2316	2.1
6 0017	2.3	**21** 0459	5.3
0547	5.1	1157	2.2
SA 1300	2.4	SU 1756	5.3
1828	5.1		
7 0145	2.3	**22** 0053	2.1
0740	5.1	0647	5.4
SU 1422	2.3	M 1344	2.1
2001	5.3	1919	5.5
8 0310	2.1	**23** 0219	1.8
0858	5.4	0758	5.7
M 1538	2.0	TU 1458	1.7
2103	5.6	2023	5.9
9 0418	1.7	**24** 0326	1.3
0942	5.7	0856	6.1
TU 1636	1.7	W 1601	1.3
2146	6.0	2116	6.4
10 0506	1.4	**25** 0429	0.9
1017	6.0	0945	6.5
W 1721	1.4	TH 1700	1.0
2222	6.2	2202	6.7
11 0544	1.2	**26** 0529	0.6
1045	6.2	1029	6.7
TH 1756	1.2	F 1754	0.7
2254	6.4	2246	7.0
12 0614	1.1	**27** 0622	0.4
1112	6.3	1110	6.8
F 1824	1.2	SA 1841	0.6
● 2323	6.4	○ 2328	7.1
13 0641	1.0	**28** 0708	0.3
1139	6.3	1150	6.9
SA 1850	1.1	SU 1923	0.5
2350	6.4		
14 0708	1.0	**29** 0009	7.1
1204	6.3	0748	0.4
SU 1919	1.0	M 1230	6.8
		2001	0.6
15 0013	6.4	**30** 0050	6.9
0737	1.0	0826	0.6
M 1228	6.4	TU 1311	6.7
1949	1.1	2038	0.8

Chart Datum: 3·67 metres below Ordnance Datum (Newlyn)
Register for your **FREE** weekly weather email service from Macmillan Reeds
» at **www.nauticaldata.com – NOW!** «
weekend weather reports sent to your email address, every Thursday

TIME ZONE (UTC)
For Summer Time add ONE hour in **non-shaded areas**

ENGLAND–DOVER

YEAR **2002**

LAT 51°07'N   LONG 1°19'W

TIMES AND HEIGHTS OF HIGH AND LOW WATERS

MAY

Time	m		Time	m
1 W 0132	6.7		**16** TH 0048	6.4
0901	0.9		0820	1.2
1355	6.5		1310	6.4
2114	1.1		2038	1.3
2 TH 0217	6.3		**17** F 0127	6.3
0937	1.3		0856	1.4
1443	6.1		1354	6.2
2153	1.5		2119	1.4
3 F 0309	5.9		**18** SA 0215	6.0
1017	1.8		0939	1.6
1537	5.8		1449	5.9
2241	1.9		2208	1.7
4 SA 0408	5.5		**19** SU 0320	5.7
1110	2.2		1033	1.9
1638	5.4		1603	5.7
2350	2.2		2313	1.8
5 SU 0516	5.1		**20** M 0454	5.5
1227	2.4		1149	2.0
1748	5.2		1728	5.6
6 M 0111	2.3		**21** TU 0037	1.8
0642	5.1		0621	5.6
1344	2.4		1317	1.9
1909	5.3		1846	5.7
7 TU 0224	2.1		**22** W 0153	1.6
0810	5.3		0732	5.8
1450	2.1		1427	1.7
2018	5.6		1953	6.0
8 W 0325	1.8		**23** TH 0257	1.3
0859	5.6		0830	6.1
1546	1.8		1529	1.4
2106	5.8		2049	6.3
9 TH 0414	1.5		**24** F 0400	1.0
0934	5.8		0921	6.3
1633	1.6		1630	1.1
2143	6.1		2138	6.6
10 F 0455	1.3		**25** SA 0501	0.8
1005	6.0		1007	6.5
1712	1.4		1726	0.9
2216	6.2		2225	6.7
11 SA 0531	1.2		**26** SU 0557	0.7
1035	6.2		1050	6.6
1747	1.2		1816	0.8
2246	6.3		○ 2309	6.8
12 SU 0605	1.1		**27** M 0644	0.6
1105	6.2		1132	6.7
● 1820	1.1		1901	0.8
2315	6.4		2352	6.8
13 M 0640	1.1		**28** TU 0726	0.7
1134	6.3		1213	6.7
1854	1.1		1941	0.8
2344	6.4			
14 TU 0714	1.1		**29** W 0034	6.7
1203	6.4		0805	0.9
1928	1.1		1256	6.6
			2020	1.0
15 W 0014	6.4		**30** TH 0117	6.5
0746	1.1		0841	1.2
1234	6.4		1339	6.4
2002	1.1		2058	1.2
			31 F 0201	6.2
			0917	1.5
			1424	6.2
			2137	1.5

JUNE

Time	m		Time	m
1 SA 0249	5.9		**16** SU 0218	6.1
0954	1.8		0940	1.5
1513	5.9		1450	6.2
2220	1.8		2211	1.4
2 SU 0343	5.5		**17** M 0320	5.9
1037	2.0		1033	1.6
1606	5.6		1551	6.0
2314	2.0		2310	1.5
3 M 0442	5.3		**18** TU 0431	5.8
1138	2.3		1136	1.7
1705	5.4		1657	5.9
4 TU 0021	2.1		**19** W 0015	1.5
0547	5.2		0546	5.7
1249	2.3		1245	1.7
1811	5.4		1807	5.9
5 W 0126	2.1		**20** TH 0121	1.5
0657	5.2		0658	5.8
1353	2.2		1351	1.7
1917	5.4		1917	6.0
6 TH 0224	1.9		**21** F 0225	1.4
0756	5.4		0801	5.9
1450	2.0		1455	1.5
2011	5.6		2021	6.1
7 F 0315	1.7		**22** SA 0329	1.3
0842	5.6		0856	6.1
1541	1.8		1600	1.4
2055	5.8		2117	6.3
8 SA 0404	1.5		**23** SU 0435	1.1
0920	5.8		0947	6.2
1628	1.5		1702	1.2
2132	6.0		2209	6.4
9 SU 0449	1.3		**24** M 0535	1.0
0957	6.0		1035	6.4
1711	1.4		1756	1.1
2208	6.2		○ 2257	6.5
10 M 0533	1.2		**25** TU 0625	1.0
1033	6.2		1119	6.5
1753	1.2		1843	1.0
● 2245	6.3		2341	6.5
11 TU 0614	1.1		**26** W 0709	1.0
1109	6.3		1200	6.5
1833	1.1		1926	1.0
2322	6.4			
12 W 0654	1.1		**27** TH 0023	6.4
1145	6.4		0748	1.1
1912	1.1		1242	6.5
			2006	1.1
13 TH 0000	6.4		**28** F 0104	6.3
0733	1.1		0825	1.3
1225	6.4		1323	6.4
1952	1.1		2044	1.3
14 F 0041	6.4		**29** SA 0144	6.1
0812	1.2		0859	1.5
1308	6.4		1404	6.3
2034	1.1		2120	1.4
15 SA 0126	6.3		**30** SU 0226	5.9
0854	1.3		0930	1.6
1355	6.3		1445	6.1
2119	1.2		2155	1.6

JULY

Time	m		Time	m
1 M 0310	5.7		**16** TU 0303	6.2
1003	1.8		1023	1.3
1528	5.9		1529	6.4
2233	1.8		2255	1.1
2 TU 0359	5.5		**17** W 0401	6.0
1043	2.0		1113	1.5
1614	5.6		1626	6.2
2319	1.9		2348	1.3
3 W 0454	5.3		**18** TH 0506	5.8
1133	2.1		1210	1.7
1708	5.5		1730	6.0
4 TH 0016	2.0		**19** F 0047	1.5
0554	5.2		0618	5.7
1239	2.2		1315	1.8
1809	5.4		1841	5.8
5 F 0120	2.0		**20** SA 0152	1.6
0656	5.3		0731	5.6
1349	2.2		1424	1.8
1911	5.4		1957	5.8
6 SA 0223	1.9		**21** SU 0301	1.6
0752	5.4		0837	5.7
1452	2.0		1536	1.7
2005	5.6		2105	5.9
7 SU 0321	1.7		**22** M 0415	1.5
0841	5.6		0935	6.0
1549	1.8		1646	1.5
2054	5.8		2204	6.1
8 M 0415	1.5		**23** TU 0520	1.4
0926	5.9		1025	6.2
1641	1.5		1744	1.3
2139	6.1		2253	6.3
9 TU 0506	1.3		**24** W 0612	1.3
1008	6.1		1108	6.4
1729	1.3		1833	1.2
2223	6.3		○ 2335	6.3
10 W 0554	1.2		**25** TH 0656	1.2
1051	6.3		1148	6.5
1815	1.1		1915	1.1
● 2307	6.4			
11 TH 0640	1.1		**26** F 0013	6.3
1133	6.5		0733	1.2
1901	1.0		1227	6.5
2351	6.5		1953	1.1
12 F 0725	1.1		**27** SA 0049	6.3
1216	6.6		0807	1.3
1947	0.9		1304	6.5
			2026	1.2
13 SA 0035	6.5		**28** SU 0124	6.2
0809	1.1		0836	1.4
1301	6.6		1340	6.4
2033	0.9		2056	1.3
14 SU 0121	6.5		**29** M 0158	6.0
0854	1.1		0901	1.4
1347	6.6		1412	6.3
2119	0.9		2123	1.4
15 M 0210	6.4		**30** TU 0230	5.9
0938	1.1		0929	1.5
1436	6.5		1442	6.1
2206	1.0		2153	1.5
			31 W 0303	5.7
			1002	1.7
			1515	5.9
			2229	1.7

AUGUST

Time	m		Time	m
1 TH 0341	5.5		**16** F 0430	5.8
1041	1.9		1136	1.7
1558	5.6		1658	5.9
2312	1.9			
2 F 0435	5.3		**17** SA 0014	1.7
1130	2.1		0542	5.5
1657	5.4		1242	2.0
			1812	5.6
3 SA 0011	2.1		**18** SU 0123	2.0
0554	5.2		0703	5.4
1240	2.3		1359	2.1
1814	5.3		1941	5.5
4 SU 0131	2.2		**19** M 0241	2.0
0709	5.2		0823	5.5
1406	2.3		1524	2.0
1927	5.4		2105	5.7
5 M 0245	2.0		**20** TU 0407	1.8
0810	5.5		0927	5.8
1517	2.0		1642	1.7
2028	5.7		2205	6.0
6 TU 0348	1.7		**21** W 0514	1.6
0903	5.8		1016	6.1
1616	1.6		1738	1.4
2121	6.0		2249	6.2
7 W 0444	1.4		**22** TH 0602	1.4
0951	6.1		1055	6.4
1709	1.3		1824	1.2
2210	6.3		○ 2325	6.3
8 TH 0537	1.2		**23** F 0642	1.3
1036	6.4		1132	6.6
1759	1.0		1902	1.1
● 2256	6.5		2357	6.4
9 F 0627	1.0		**24** SA 0716	1.2
1119	6.7		1207	6.6
1850	0.8		1934	1.1
2340	6.6			
10 SA 0716	0.9		**25** SU 0027	6.4
1202	6.8		0743	1.3
1939	0.7		1241	6.6
			2000	1.1
11 SU 0023	6.7		**26** M 0057	6.3
0801	0.8		0806	1.3
1246	6.9		1311	6.5
2025	0.6		2024	1.2
12 M 0106	6.7		**27** TU 0124	6.2
0843	0.8		0828	1.3
1329	6.9		1339	6.4
2108	0.6		2048	1.3
13 TU 0150	6.6		**28** W 0146	6.1
0923	0.9		0855	1.4
1415	6.8		1357	6.3
2149	0.7		2116	1.4
14 W 0237	6.4		**29** TH 0208	6.0
1002	1.1		0926	1.5
1503	6.6		1424	6.1
2231	1.0		2148	1.6
15 TH 0330	6.2		**30** F 0239	5.8
1045	1.3		1001	1.8
1556	6.3		1501	5.9
2317	1.3		2225	1.9
			31 SA 0320	5.5
			1042	1.9
			1551	5.5
			2312	2.2

Chart Datum: 3·67 metres below Ordnance Datum (Newlyn)

TIME ZONE (UTC)
For Summer Time add ONE hour in **non-shaded areas**

ENGLAND–DOVER

LAT 51°07′N   LONG 1°19′W

TIMES AND HEIGHTS OF HIGH AND LOW WATERS

YEAR **2002**

SEPTEMBER

#	Time	m	Time	m	#	Time	m	Time	m
1 SU	0424 1139 1719	5.2 2.4 5.2			16 M	0059 0637 1343 1935	2.4 5.3 2.4 5.3		
2 M	0028 0633 1319 1901	2.4 5.1 2.5 5.3			17 TU	0229 0810 1522 2103	2.3 5.4 2.1 5.6		
3 TU	0214 0747 1448 2011	2.3 5.3 2.2 5.6			18 W	0401 0914 1634 2155	2.0 5.8 1.7 5.9		
4 W	0325 0845 1552 2107	1.9 5.8 1.7 6.0			19 TH	0459 0959 1724 2233	1.7 6.2 1.3 6.2		
5 TH	0424 0934 1648 2156	1.5 6.2 1.3 6.4			20 F	0543 1035 1805 2305	1.4 6.4 1.1 6.3		
6 F	0519 1019 1742 2241	1.2 6.6 0.9 6.7			21 SA	0619 1109 1839 O 2333	1.3 6.6 1.1 6.4		
7 SA	0610 1101 1834 ● 2323	1.0 6.9 0.7 6.8			22 SU	0649 1142 1906	1.2 6.6 1.1		
8 SU	0659 1143 1923	0.8 7.1 0.5			23 M	0000 0711 1212 1927	6.4 1.2 6.6 1.1		
9 M	0004 0742 1225 2006	6.9 0.7 7.2 0.4			24 TU	0027 0732 1238 1949	6.4 1.2 6.5 1.2		
10 TU	0044 0822 1307 2046	6.9 0.7 7.2 0.5			25 W	0049 0757 1258 2015	6.3 1.3 6.4 1.3		
11 W	0126 0859 1350 2124	6.8 0.8 7.0 0.7			26 TH	0107 0825 1318 2043	6.3 1.3 6.4 1.4		
12 TH	0211 0936 1437 2203	6.6 1.0 6.7 1.0			27 F	0129 0855 1345 2113	6.2 1.5 6.3 1.6		
13 F	0301 1017 1529 2247	6.2 1.4 6.3 1.5			28 SA	0200 0928 1421 2148	6.1 1.8 6.0 1.9		
14 SA	0401 1106 1632 2343	5.8 1.9 5.8 2.0			29 SU	0241 1009 1508 2234	5.8 2.1 5.6 2.2		
15 SU	0513 1214 1749	5.4 2.3 5.4			30 M	0337 1103 1628 2340	5.3 2.4 5.2 2.5		

OCTOBER

#	Time	m	Time	m	#	Time	m	Time	m
1 TU	0601 1236 1842	5.1 2.5 5.2			16 W	0209 0741 1501 2042	2.5 5.4 2.1 5.5		
2 W	0143 0722 1420 1953	2.5 5.4 2.2 5.6			17 TH	0330 0846 1606 2129	2.1 5.8 1.7 5.9		
3 TH	0301 0823 1527 2050	2.0 5.8 1.7 6.1			18 F	0425 0930 1654 2205	1.8 6.1 1.4 6.1		
4 F	0401 0913 1625 2138	1.6 6.3 1.2 6.5			19 SA	0508 1007 1732 2234	1.5 6.4 1.2 6.3		
5 SA	0456 0957 1719 2221	1.2 6.7 0.8 6.8			20 SU	0544 1040 1803 2301	1.3 6.5 1.2 6.4		
6 SU	0547 1039 1811 ● 2302	0.9 7.0 0.6 7.0			21 M	0613 1110 1828 O 2327	1.3 6.6 1.2 6.4		
7 M	0634 1120 1859 2341	0.7 7.2 0.4 7.0			22 TU	0636 1138 1852 2353	1.3 6.6 1.2 6.4		
8 TU	0717 1200 1942	0.7 7.3 0.4			23 W	0702 1202 1918	1.3 6.5 1.2		
9 W	0020 0756 1242 2021	7.0 0.7 7.2 0.5			24 TH	0016 0729 1224 1947	6.4 1.3 6.5 1.3		
10 TH	0102 0833 1325 2058	6.9 0.8 7.0 0.8			25 F	0036 0800 1247 2016	6.4 1.4 6.4 1.4		
11 F	0147 0911 1412 2136	6.6 1.1 6.6 1.2			26 SA	0102 0831 1317 2047	6.4 1.5 6.3 1.6		
12 SA	0237 0952 1506 2219	6.3 1.5 6.2 1.8			27 SU	0135 0906 1355 2124	6.2 1.7 6.1 1.9		
13 SU	0337 1042 1611 2316	5.8 2.0 5.7 2.3			28 M	0219 0948 1445 2210	5.9 2.0 5.7 2.2		
14 M	0446 1153 1726	5.4 2.4 5.3			29 TU	0320 1043 1613 2315	5.5 2.3 5.3 2.5		
15 TU	0037 0605 1326 1918	2.6 5.3 2.5 5.2			30 W	0525 1209 1818	5.3 2.4 5.3		
					31 TH	0107 0650 1349 1928	2.5 5.5 2.1 5.7		

NOVEMBER

#	Time	m	Time	m	#	Time	m	Time	m
1 F	0230 0753 1457 2025	2.1 5.9 1.6 6.1			16 SA	0335 0850 1604 2123	2.0 5.9 1.6 5.9		
2 SA	0331 0845 1556 2114	1.6 6.4 1.2 6.5			17 SU	0422 0929 1644 2155	1.7 6.2 1.4 6.1		
3 SU	0426 0931 1652 2157	1.2 6.8 0.9 6.8			18 M	0500 1003 1718 2224	1.5 6.3 1.3 6.3		
4 M	0518 1014 1745 ● 2238	1.0 7.0 0.6 6.9			19 TU	0533 1034 1749 2253	1.4 6.4 1.3 6.3		
5 TU	0607 1056 1834 2319	0.8 7.2 0.5 7.0			20 W	0604 1103 1820 O 2322	1.3 6.4 1.3 6.4		
6 W	0651 1138 1917	0.7 7.2 0.6			21 TH	0635 1131 1853 2349	1.3 6.4 1.3 6.4		
7 TH	0000 0732 1221 1957	7.0 0.8 7.1 0.7			22 F	0708 1159 1925	1.3 6.4 1.3		
8 F	0043 0812 1305 2035	6.9 0.9 6.8 1.0			23 SA	0016 0742 1229 1958	6.4 1.3 6.4 1.4		
9 SA	0129 0852 1353 2114	6.6 1.2 6.5 1.4			24 SU	0048 0816 1304 2032	6.4 1.5 6.3 1.6		
10 SU	0219 0934 1447 2157	6.3 1.6 6.1 1.9			25 M	0127 0854 1346 2111	6.3 1.6 6.1 1.8		
11 M	0315 1025 1549 2251	5.9 2.0 5.6 2.3			26 TU	0215 0939 1441 2159	6.0 1.8 5.8 2.0		
12 TU	0418 1132 1658	5.6 2.3 5.3			27 W	0319 1035 1603 2301	5.8 2.0 5.5 2.2		
13 W	0006 0527 1253 1825	2.5 5.4 2.4 5.2			28 TH	0445 1150 1742	5.6 2.0 5.5		
14 TH	0127 0649 1411 1954	2.5 5.4 2.2 5.4			29 F	0028 0608 1313 1855	2.2 5.7 1.9 5.7		
15 F	0237 0800 1514 2045	2.3 5.7 1.9 5.7			30 SA	0148 0716 1421 1955	2.0 6.0 1.6 6.0		

DECEMBER

#	Time	m	Time	m	#	Time	m	Time	m
1 SU	0253 0814 1522 2047	1.7 6.3 1.3 6.3			16 M	0326 0843 1548 2111	2.0 5.8 1.7 5.8		
2 M	0352 0904 1622 2134	1.4 6.6 1.0 6.5			17 TU	0414 0922 1633 2147	1.8 6.0 1.5 6.0		
3 TU	0450 0951 1720 2219	1.2 6.8 0.9 6.7			18 W	0456 0958 1715 2222	1.6 6.2 1.4 6.2		
4 W	0543 1037 1811 ● 2303	1.0 6.9 0.8 6.8			19 TH	0536 1033 1755 O 2257	1.4 6.3 1.3 6.3		
5 TH	0631 1122 1857 2346	0.9 6.9 0.8 6.8			20 F	0614 1108 1833 2331	1.3 6.4 1.3 6.4		
6 F	0716 1207 1940	0.9 6.8 1.0			21 SA	0652 1144 1911	1.2 6.4 1.3		
7 SA	0030 0758 1252 2019	6.7 1.1 6.6 1.2			22 SU	0007 0731 1222 1948	6.5 1.2 6.4 1.3		
8 SU	0115 0840 1339 2059	6.6 1.3 6.4 1.5			23 M	0045 0810 1301 2027	6.5 1.3 6.3 1.4		
9 M	0202 0923 1428 2140	6.4 1.5 6.0 1.8			24 TU	0127 0852 1346 2108	6.4 1.3 6.2 1.5		
10 TU	0251 1009 1522 2224	6.1 1.8 5.7 2.1			25 W	0214 0938 1437 2155	6.3 1.4 6.0 1.6		
11 W	0345 1101 1621 2318	5.8 2.0 5.4 2.3			26 TH	0308 1030 1538 2248	6.2 1.5 5.9 1.8		
12 TH	0444 1201 1727	5.6 2.2 5.2			27 F	0410 1129 1651 2352	6.0 1.6 5.7 1.9		
13 F	0023 0549 1305 1837	2.4 5.4 2.2 5.2			28 SA	0520 1235 1809	5.9 1.6 5.7		
14 SA	0130 0657 1404 1941	2.4 5.5 2.1 5.4			29 SU	0103 0633 1341 1919	1.9 5.9 1.6 5.8		
15 SU	0231 0756 1459 2030	2.2 5.6 1.9 5.6			30 M	0212 0741 1447 2020	1.8 6.0 1.5 5.9		
					31 TU	0319 0842 1553 2116	1.6 6.2 1.3 6.1		

Chart Datum: 3·67 metres below Ordnance Datum (Newlyn)

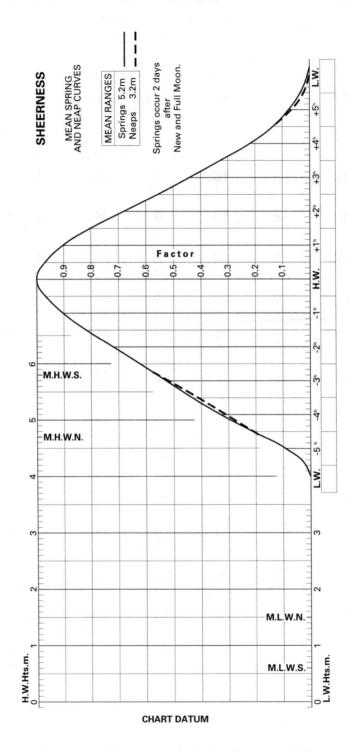

SHEERNESS

MEAN SPRING AND NEAP CURVES

MEAN RANGES	
Springs	5.2m
Neaps	3.2m

Springs occur 2 days after New and Full Moon.

Factor

0.9 0.8 0.7 0.6 0.5 0.4 0.3 0.2 0.1

H.W.   L.W.

−1ʰ H.W. +1ʰ +2ʰ +3ʰ +4ʰ +5ʰ
−5ʰ −4ʰ −3ʰ −2ʰ

M.H.W.S.

M.H.W.N.

M.L.W.N.

M.L.W.S.

H.W.Hts.m.   L.W.Hts.m.

CHART DATUM

TIME ZONE (UTC)
For Summer Time add ONE hour in **non-shaded areas**

ENGLAND – SHEERNESS

LAT 51°27′N LONG 0°45′W

TIMES AND HEIGHTS OF HIGH AND LOW WATERS

YEAR 2002

JANUARY

Day	Time m	Time m	Time m	Time m
1 TU	0126 5.7	0739 0.6	1351 5.8	2000 0.7
16 W	0202 5.5	0817 0.7	1429 5.5	2021 0.9
2 W	0210 5.7	0827 0.5	1437 5.8	2045 0.7
17 TH	0236 5.5	0848 0.8	1502 5.4	2051 1.0
3 TH	0254 5.7	0915 0.4	1525 5.7	2129 0.8
18 F	0309 5.4	0917 0.8	1535 5.2	2120 1.1
4 F	0341 5.6	1004 0.5	1614 5.6	2215 1.0
19 SA	0342 5.2	0947 0.8	1608 5.1	2150 1.2
5 SA	0430 5.5	1055 0.5	1707 5.4	2305 1.1
20 SU	0416 5.1	1022 0.9	1644 5.0	2224 1.4
6 SU	0524 5.3	1149 0.7	1805 5.2	
21 M	0454 4.9	1102 1.0	1726 4.8	2304 1.5
7 M	0001 1.3	0625 5.2	1250 0.8	1908 5.1
22 TU	0539 4.8	1150 1.2	1817 4.7	2356 1.7
8 TU	0105 1.4	0733 5.1	1356 0.9	2016 5.0
23 W	0637 4.6	1253 1.3	1921 4.6	
9 W	0215 1.4	0843 5.1	1505 1.0	2123 5.1
24 TH	0107 1.7	0751 4.6	1415 1.4	2033 4.7
10 TH	0327 1.3	0951 5.2	1610 1.0	2224 5.2
25 F	0237 1.7	0907 4.7	1532 1.2	2142 5.0
11 F	0434 1.2	1053 5.3	1705 0.9	2318 5.3
26 SA	0352 1.4	1014 5.0	1633 1.0	2244 5.2
12 SA	0531 1.0	1146 5.4	1752 0.9	
27 SU	0454 1.1	1113 5.3	1728 0.9	2338 5.5
13 SU	0005 5.4	0620 0.9	1233 5.5	●1833 0.9
28 M	0550 0.8	1206 5.6	1818 0.7	○
14 M	0047 5.5	0703 0.8	1315 5.5	1912 0.8
29 TU	0028 5.7	0643 0.6	1255 5.8	1906 0.6
15 TU	0126 5.5	0742 0.7	1353 5.5	1948 0.9
30 W	0114 5.8	0735 0.4	1342 5.9	1952 0.6
31 TH	0159 5.9	0824 0.2	1428 6.0	2037 0.6

FEBRUARY

Day	Time m	Time m	Time m	Time m
1 F	0243 5.9	0911 0.1	1513 5.9	2120 0.6
16 SA	0247 5.5	0858 0.6	1507 5.4	2058 0.9
2 SA	0327 5.8	0955 0.1	1558 5.8	2200 0.8
17 SU	0316 5.4	0926 0.6	1537 5.3	2124 1.0
3 SU	0411 5.5	1037 0.3	1644 5.6	2240 0.9
18 M	0346 5.3	0955 0.8	1609 5.2	2149 1.1
4 M	0459 5.5	1120 0.5	1734 5.3	2324 1.1
19 TU	0417 5.1	1025 0.9	1645 5.0	2218 1.3
5 TU	0553 5.3	1210 0.8	1831 5.0	
20 W	0455 5.0	1100 1.1	1729 4.8	2300 1.4
6 W	0019 1.3	0657 5.0	1313 1.1	1936 4.8
21 TH	0544 4.7	1151 1.3	1827 4.7	
7 TH	0132 1.4	0813 4.9	1428 1.2	2049 4.8
22 F	0003 1.6	0655 4.6	1314 1.5	1944 4.6
8 F	0259 1.4	0932 4.9	1544 1.2	2201 4.9
23 SA	0139 1.6	0824 4.6	1455 1.4	2106 4.8
9 SA	0422 1.2	1042 5.1	1649 1.2	2302 5.1
24 SU	0319 1.4	0947 4.9	1609 1.2	2219 5.1
10 SU	0526 1.0	1138 5.3	1740 1.1	2352 5.3
25 M	0433 1.0	1055 5.3	1710 0.9	2319 5.4
11 M	0614 0.9	1223 5.4	1822 1.0	
26 TU	0537 0.7	1151 5.6	1805 0.7	
12 TU	0034 5.4	0653 0.8	1302 5.5	●1858 0.9
27 W	0011 5.7	0634 0.4	1241 5.9	○1854 0.5
13 W	0111 5.5	0728 0.7	1337 5.5	1932 0.8
28 TH	0058 5.9	0725 0.2	1327 6.0	1939 0.5
14 TH	0145 5.6	0800 0.6	1408 5.5	2003 0.8
15 F	0216 5.6	0834 0.5	1438 5.5	2032 0.9

MARCH

Day	Time m	Time m	Time m	Time m
1 F	0142 6.0	0812 0.0	1411 6.1	2022 0.4
16 SA	0152 5.6	0804 0.5	1410 5.6	2008 0.8
2 SA	0224 6.1	0855 -0.1	1453 6.1	2102 0.5
17 SU	0221 5.6	0833 0.5	1438 5.6	2035 0.8
3 SU	0306 6.0	0935 0.0	1534 5.9	2138 0.6
18 M	0250 5.5	0902 0.6	1507 5.5	2100 0.9
4 M	0348 5.9	1012 0.3	1616 5.6	2213 0.8
19 TU	0319 5.4	0929 0.7	1538 5.4	2122 1.0
5 TU	0432 5.6	1048 0.6	1701 5.3	2250 1.0
20 W	0349 5.2	0954 0.9	1612 5.2	2148 1.1
6 W	0523 5.3	1130 0.9	1752 5.0	2338 1.2
21 TH	0426 5.1	1023 1.1	1654 5.0	2228 1.2
7 TH	0625 4.9	1229 1.3	1856 4.7	
22 F	0514 4.9	1111 1.3	1750 4.7	2330 1.4
8 F	0052 1.4	0745 4.7	1354 1.5	2015 4.6
23 SA	0622 4.6	1233 1.6	1907 4.6	
9 SA	0237 1.5	0914 4.7	1522 1.5	2137 4.7
24 SU	0105 1.5	0754 4.6	1425 1.5	2036 4.7
10 SU	0410 1.3	1027 5.0	1633 1.3	2243 5.0
25 M	0254 1.3	0925 4.9	1545 1.2	2155 5.0
11 M	0513 1.0	1122 5.3	1725 1.1	2333 5.2
26 TU	0414 0.9	1036 5.4	1650 0.9	2257 5.4
12 TU	0558 0.8	1205 5.5	1805 1.0	
27 W	0521 0.5	1133 5.7	1746 0.7	2350 5.7
13 W	0013 5.4	0633 0.7	1241 5.5	1839 0.9
28 TH	0618 0.3	1221 6.0	1835 0.5	○
14 TH	0049 5.5	0704 0.6	1313 5.6	●1910 0.8
29 F	0036 5.9	0706 0.1	1306 6.1	1919 0.4
15 F	0121 5.6	0734 0.5	1342 5.6	1940 0.8
30 SA	0119 6.1	0750 -0.1	1348 6.1	2000 0.4
31 SU	0201 6.1	0831 0.0	1428 6.1	2039 0.4

APRIL

Day	Time m	Time m	Time m	Time m
1 M	0242 6.1	0909 0.1	1508 5.9	2115 0.5
16 TU	0225 5.5	0837 0.6	1440 5.6	2039 0.8
2 TU	0324 5.9	0943 0.4	1548 5.6	2148 0.7
17 W	0255 5.4	0905 0.8	1513 5.4	2105 0.9
3 W	0408 5.6	1017 0.7	1629 5.3	2223 0.9
18 TH	0329 5.3	0933 1.0	1548 5.3	2136 1.0
4 TH	0457 5.3	1057 1.1	1717 5.0	2308 1.2
19 F	0409 5.1	1006 1.2	1632 5.0	2219 1.1
5 F	0558 4.9	1152 1.5	1819 4.6	
20 SA	0500 4.9	1057 1.4	1728 4.8	2323 1.2
6 SA	0019 1.4	0717 4.6	1319 1.7	1939 4.5
21 SU	0609 4.8	1219 1.6	1845 4.6	
7 SU	0212 1.5	0846 4.7	1453 1.7	2105 4.6
22 M	0056 1.3	0736 4.8	1400 1.5	2012 4.8
8 M	0341 1.2	1001 4.9	1605 1.4	2213 4.9
23 TU	0234 1.0	0902 5.0	1518 1.2	2129 5.1
9 TU	0442 1.0	1054 5.2	1657 1.2	2303 5.2
24 W	0352 0.7	1012 5.4	1623 1.0	2232 5.4
10 W	0526 0.8	1136 5.4	1737 1.0	2344 5.4
25 TH	0458 0.4	1109 5.7	1720 0.8	2324 5.7
11 TH	0601 0.7	1211 5.5	1811 0.9	
26 F	0554 0.2	1158 5.9	1809 0.6	
12 F	0020 5.5	0632 0.6	1242 5.6	1842 0.8
27 SA	0011 5.9	0641 0.1	1242 6.0	○1854 0.5
13 SA	0052 5.6	0703 0.6	1311 5.6	1912 0.8
28 SU	0056 6.0	0724 0.1	1323 6.0	1936 0.4
14 SU	0124 5.6	0734 0.6	1340 5.7	1942 0.7
29 M	0138 6.1	0804 0.1	1403 6.0	2016 0.4
15 M	0154 5.6	0806 0.5	1410 5.7	2012 0.8
30 TU	0221 6.0	0842 0.3	1443 5.8	2054 0.5

Chart Datum: 2·90 metres below Ordnance Datum (Newlyn)

ENGLAND – SHEERNESS

LAT 51°27'N   LONG 0°45'W

TIMES AND HEIGHTS OF HIGH AND LOW WATERS

YEAR **2002**

TIME ZONE (UTC)
For Summer Time add ONE hour in **non-shaded areas**

MAY

Day	Time m	Time m	Time m	Time m
1 W	0304 5.8	0917 0.6	1522 5.6	2130 0.7
16 TH	0239 5.5	0848 0.8	1455 5.5	2059 0.8
2 TH	0349 5.5	0952 0.9	1603 5.3	2204 0.9
17 F	0318 5.4	0922 1.0	1535 5.3	2137 0.8
3 F	0437 5.2	1030 1.3	1649 5.0	2246 1.1
18 SA	0403 5.2	1003 1.2	1621 5.1	2226 0.9
4 SA	0534 4.8	1121 1.6	1746 4.7	2350 1.3
19 SU	0457 5.1	1058 1.3	1719 4.9	2330 1.0
5 SU	0643 4.6	1238 1.8	1900 4.5	
20 M	0604 4.9	1211 1.4	1831 4.8	
6 M	0129 1.4	0802 4.6	1408 1.8	2020 4.5
21 TU	0052 1.0	0721 5.0	1334 1.4	1949 4.9
7 TU	0252 1.2	0916 4.8	1519 1.6	2130 4.8
22 W	0214 0.8	0837 5.2	1446 1.2	2101 5.2
8 W	0352 1.0	1013 5.0	1614 1.4	2223 5.1
23 TH	0325 0.6	0944 5.4	1550 1.0	2204 5.4
9 TH	0440 0.9	1056 5.2	1658 1.2	2307 5.3
24 F	0430 0.5	1042 5.6	1649 0.9	2258 5.6
10 F	0520 0.8	1133 5.4	1735 1.0	2345 5.4
25 SA	0526 0.4	1132 5.8	1741 0.7	2348 5.8
11 SA	0556 0.7	1206 5.5	1810 0.9	
26 SU ○	0614 0.3	1217 5.8	1830 0.6	
12 SU ●	0020 5.5	0630 0.6	1238 5.6	1843 0.8
27 M	0034 5.9	0657 0.3	1301 5.8	1914 0.5
13 M	0055 5.6	0705 0.6	1311 5.6	1917 0.8
28 TU	0120 5.9	0738 0.4	1342 5.8	1958 0.6
14 TU	0129 5.6	0740 0.6	1345 5.7	1951 0.8
29 W	0205 5.8	0818 0.6	1422 5.7	2039 0.6
15 W	0203 5.5	0814 0.7	1419 5.6	2025 0.8
30 TH	0249 5.7	0855 0.8	1502 5.5	2117 0.7
31 F	0333 5.4	0931 1.1	1543 5.3	2153 0.9

JUNE

Day	Time m	Time m	Time m	Time m
1 SA	0418 5.2	1007 1.3	1626 5.0	2231 1.0
16 SU	0400 5.4	1004 1.0	1617 5.3	2236 0.7
2 SU	0507 4.9	1050 1.5	1716 4.8	2321 1.2
17 M	0454 5.3	1055 1.2	1711 5.2	2334 0.7
3 M	0602 4.7	1148 1.7	1816 4.6	
18 TU	0553 5.2	1156 1.3	1814 5.1	
4 TU	0030 1.3	0704 4.6	1304 1.8	1924 4.6
19 W	0039 0.7	0659 5.1	1303 1.3	1922 5.1
5 W	0147 1.2	0811 4.6	1418 1.7	2032 4.7
20 TH	0148 0.7	0808 5.2	1411 1.2	2031 5.2
6 TH	0252 1.1	0913 4.8	1519 1.5	2132 4.9
21 F	0256 0.7	0914 5.3	1517 1.1	2136 5.3
7 F	0347 1.0	1004 5.0	1610 1.3	2223 5.1
22 SA	0400 0.6	1015 5.4	1620 1.0	2236 5.4
8 SA	0435 0.9	1048 5.2	1654 1.2	2307 5.3
23 SU	0459 0.6	1109 5.5	1719 0.9	2331 5.6
9 SU	0518 0.8	1129 5.4	1735 1.0	2349 5.4
24 M ○	0550 0.6	1158 5.6	1812 0.7	
10 M ●	0559 0.7	1208 5.6	1815 0.9	
25 TU	0022 5.6	0635 0.6	1244 5.6	1900 0.6
11 TU	0029 5.5	0639 0.7	1247 5.6	1854 0.8
26 W	0109 5.7	0718 0.7	1326 5.6	1946 0.6
12 W	0109 5.5	0718 0.7	1326 5.6	1935 0.7
27 TH	0154 5.6	0759 0.8	1407 5.6	2028 0.6
13 TH	0148 5.5	0757 0.7	1405 5.6	2016 0.7
28 F	0237 5.6	0837 0.9	1447 5.5	2107 0.7
14 F	0229 5.5	0837 0.8	1445 5.5	2059 0.6
29 SA	0317 5.4	0912 1.1	1525 5.3	2141 0.8
15 SA	0313 5.5	0919 0.9	1529 5.4	2145 0.6
30 SU	0357 5.2	0945 1.3	1603 5.1	2213 0.9

JULY

Day	Time m	Time m	Time m	Time m
1 M	0436 5.0	1019 1.4	1643 5.0	2250 1.0
16 TU	0441 5.5	1042 1.0	1656 5.4	2322 0.5
2 TU	0518 4.9	1100 1.5	1729 4.8	2336 1.1
17 W	0534 5.4	1131 1.1	1750 5.3	
3 W	0606 4.7	1151 1.7	1823 4.7	
18 TH	0015 0.6	0631 5.2	1227 1.2	1852 5.2
4 TH	0035 1.2	0700 4.6	1255 1.8	1925 4.6
19 F	0116 0.8	0735 5.1	1333 1.3	2002 5.1
5 F	0144 1.2	0802 4.7	1408 1.7	2032 4.7
20 SA	0224 0.9	0843 5.1	1446 1.3	2114 5.1
6 SA	0252 1.2	0904 4.8	1516 1.6	2134 4.8
21 SU	0334 1.0	0950 5.1	1600 1.2	2223 5.2
7 SU	0352 1.1	1002 5.1	1613 1.4	2230 5.1
22 M	0439 0.9	1052 5.3	1708 1.0	2324 5.4
8 M	0444 1.0	1054 5.3	1704 1.1	2321 5.3
23 TU	0534 0.9	1145 5.4	1805 0.9	
9 TU	0532 0.9	1142 5.5	1752 1.0	
24 W ○	0016 5.5	0621 0.9	1232 5.5	1854 0.7
10 W ●	0008 5.4	0617 0.8	1228 5.6	1838 0.8
25 TH	0102 5.6	0703 0.9	1314 5.6	1937 0.7
11 TH	0053 5.5	0701 0.8	1312 5.7	1925 0.6
26 F	0143 5.6	0743 0.9	1353 5.6	2016 0.6
12 F	0137 5.7	0745 0.7	1355 5.7	2013 0.5
27 SA	0221 5.5	0819 0.9	1429 5.5	2050 0.7
13 SA	0221 5.7	0830 0.7	1437 5.7	2100 0.4
28 SU	0256 5.5	0852 1.0	1503 5.4	2120 0.7
14 SU	0306 5.7	0914 0.8	1521 5.6	2148 0.3
29 M	0329 5.3	0920 1.1	1536 5.3	2148 0.8
15 M	0353 5.7	0958 0.9	1607 5.5	2234 0.4
30 TU	0402 5.2	0948 1.3	1610 5.2	2218 0.9
31 W	0436 5.1	1018 1.4	1645 5.0	2254 1.0

AUGUST

Day	Time m	Time m	Time m	Time m
1 TH	0514 4.9	1055 1.5	1727 4.8	2337 1.2
16 F	0559 5.2	1149 1.2	1823 5.2	
2 F	0600 4.8	1142 1.7	1819 4.7	
17 SA	0039 1.0	0701 5.0	1257 1.4	1936 5.0
3 SA	0034 1.3	0657 4.7	1246 1.8	1927 4.5
18 SU	0153 1.3	0813 4.9	1424 1.4	2058 4.9
4 SU	0152 1.4	0807 4.7	1415 1.7	2044 4.6
19 M	0314 1.3	0929 4.9	1554 1.3	2215 5.1
5 M	0311 1.4	0919 4.9	1534 1.5	2156 4.9
20 TU	0427 1.2	1038 5.1	1707 1.1	2318 5.3
6 TU	0415 1.2	1024 5.1	1637 1.2	2257 5.2
21 W	0525 1.1	1133 5.3	1802 0.9	
7 W	0510 1.0	1120 5.4	1733 0.9	2350 5.5
22 TH ○	0008 5.5	0616 1.0	1219 5.5	1844 0.7
8 TH ●	0600 0.9	1210 5.6	1826 0.7	
23 F	0050 5.6	0649 1.0	1258 5.6	1921 0.7
9 F	0038 5.7	0648 0.8	1257 5.8	1916 0.5
24 SA	0126 5.6	0724 0.9	1334 5.6	1953 0.6
10 SA	0124 5.9	0734 0.7	1340 5.9	2005 0.3
25 SU	0159 5.6	0756 0.9	1406 5.6	2024 0.6
11 SU	0208 6.0	0818 0.6	1423 5.9	2052 0.1
26 M	0229 5.6	0826 1.0	1437 5.6	2052 0.6
12 M	0252 6.0	0901 0.7	1505 5.9	2136 0.1
27 TU	0258 5.5	0852 1.0	1507 5.5	2119 0.7
13 TU	0335 5.9	0941 0.8	1548 5.8	2217 0.3
28 W	0327 5.4	0917 1.2	1536 5.4	2146 0.8
14 W	0420 5.7	1020 0.9	1632 5.7	2258 0.5
29 TH	0357 5.3	0941 1.3	1607 5.2	2216 1.0
15 TH	0506 5.5	1100 1.1	1722 5.4	2342 0.7
30 F	0431 5.1	1009 1.4	1642 5.0	2249 1.2
31 SA	0511 4.9	1047 1.5	1726 4.8	2335 1.5

Chart Datum: 2·90 metres below Ordnance Datum (Newlyn)

ENGLAND – SHEERNESS

YEAR 2002

LAT 51°27′N   LONG 0°45′W

TIMES AND HEIGHTS OF HIGH AND LOW WATERS

TIME ZONE (UTC)
For Summer Time add ONE hour in **non-shaded areas**

SEPTEMBER

Day	Time m	Time m	Day	Time m	Time m
1 SU	0604 4.7 / 1143 1.7	1830 4.6	16 M	0124 1.6 / 0744 4.7 / 1410 1.6	2043 4.8
2 M	0049 1.7 / 0715 4.6 / 1313 1.8	1957 4.5	17 TU	0257 1.7 / 0909 4.8 / 1548 1.3	2203 5.1
3 TU	0232 1.6 / 0839 4.7 / 1458 1.6	2124 4.8	18 W	0413 1.5 / 1020 5.1 / 1657 1.0	2303 5.4
4 W	0348 1.4 / 0955 5.1 / 1613 1.2	2234 5.2	19 TH	0510 1.3 / 1114 5.3 / 1745 0.9	2349 5.6
5 TH	0448 1.1 / 1057 5.4 / 1715 0.8	2331 5.6	20 F	0552 1.1 / 1158 5.5	1822 0.8
6 F	0542 0.9 / 1149 5.7	1811 0.5	21 SA	0027 5.6 / 0626 1.0 / 1235 5.6	○ 1853 0.7
7 SA	0020 5.9 / 0631 0.7 / 1236 5.9	● 1902 0.3	22 SU	0100 5.7 / 0657 1.0 / 1308 5.7	1922 0.7
8 SU	0105 6.0 / 0716 0.6 / 1320 6.0	1949 0.1	23 M	0129 5.7 / 0727 0.9 / 1338 5.7	1951 0.6
9 M	0148 6.1 / 0759 0.6 / 1401 6.1	2032 0.1	24 TU	0157 5.7 / 0756 0.9 / 1408 5.7	2020 0.6
10 TU	0230 6.1 / 0840 0.6 / 1442 6.1	2113 0.1	25 W	0224 5.6 / 0822 1.0 / 1436 5.6	2048 0.9
11 W	0311 6.0 / 0917 0.7 / 1523 6.0	2151 0.3	26 TH	0253 5.6 / 0847 1.1 / 1505 5.5	2115 0.9
12 TH	0352 5.8 / 0953 0.9 / 1607 5.8	2228 0.6	27 F	0323 5.4 / 0910 1.2 / 1535 5.3	2142 1.1
13 F	0436 5.5 / 1030 1.0 / 1656 5.5	2308 1.0	28 SA	0355 5.3 / 0935 1.3 / 1609 5.1	2210 1.3
14 SA	0526 5.1 / 1116 1.3	1756 5.1	29 SU	0434 5.1 / 1011 1.4 / 1653 4.9	2252 1.5
15 SU	0003 1.3 / 0627 4.8 / 1225 1.5	1913 4.8	30 M	0525 4.8 / 1107 1.6	1755 4.7

OCTOBER

Day	Time m	Time m	Day	Time m	Time m
1 TU	0004 1.8 / 0635 4.6 / 1235 1.7	1921 4.6	16 W	0230 1.8 / 0839 4.7 / 1523 1.3	2137 5.0
2 W	0154 1.8 / 0805 4.7 / 1427 1.5	2055 4.8	17 TH	0345 1.6 / 0951 5.0 / 1626 1.1	2235 5.3
3 TH	0319 1.5 / 0927 5.0 / 1547 1.1	2209 5.3	18 F	0440 1.4 / 1045 5.3 / 1712 0.9	2320 5.5
4 F	0422 1.2 / 1031 5.4 / 1652 0.7	2307 5.7	19 SA	0521 1.2 / 1128 5.5 / 1747 0.8	2356 5.6
5 SA	0518 0.9 / 1124 5.8 / 1749 0.4	2356 6.0	20 SU	0555 1.1 / 1204 5.6	1818 0.8
6 SU	0607 0.8 / 1210 6.0	● 1839 0.3	21 M	0027 5.6 / 0626 1.0 / 1237 5.6	1847 0.7
7 M	0041 6.1 / 0652 0.7 / 1254 6.1	1924 0.1	22 TU	0056 5.7 / 0655 0.9 / 1308 5.7	○ 1847 0.7
8 TU	0123 6.2 / 0734 0.6 / 1336 6.2	2006 0.1	23 W	0124 5.7 / 0725 0.9 / 1338 5.7	1948 0.7
9 W	0204 6.1 / 0814 0.6 / 1417 6.2	2046 0.3	24 TH	0153 5.7 / 0754 0.9 / 1409 5.6	2018 0.8
10 TH	0244 6.0 / 0852 0.7 / 1500 6.0	2122 0.5	25 F	0223 5.6 / 0822 1.0 / 1439 5.5	2048 0.9
11 F	0325 5.7 / 0928 0.9 / 1544 5.8	2158 0.9	26 SA	0255 5.5 / 0849 1.1 / 1512 5.3	2116 1.1
12 SA	0407 5.4 / 1005 1.1 / 1634 5.4	2238 1.2	27 SU	0329 5.3 / 0918 1.2 / 1549 5.2	2146 1.3
13 SU	0456 5.1 / 1050 1.3 / 1734 5.0	2331 1.6	28 M	0409 5.1 / 0957 1.3 / 1636 5.0	2231 1.5
14 M	0556 4.8 / 1159 1.5	1851 4.8	29 TU	0500 4.9 / 1055 1.4 / 1737 4.8	2341 1.7
15 TU	0053 1.9 / 0714 4.6 / 1351 1.6	2018 4.8	30 W	0609 4.7 / 1218 1.5	1859 4.7
			31 TH	0119 1.8 / 0735 4.8 / 1359 1.3	2025 5.0

NOVEMBER

Day	Time m	Time m	Day	Time m	Time m
1 F	0243 1.5 / 0855 5.1 / 1518 1.0	2139 5.3	16 SA	0354 1.5 / 1005 5.1 / 1624 1.0	2240 5.2
2 SA	0349 1.2 / 1000 5.4 / 1624 0.7	2238 5.7	17 SU	0439 1.3 / 1050 5.3 / 1703 0.9	2317 5.4
3 SU	0445 1.0 / 1054 5.7 / 1721 0.4	2328 5.9	18 M	0517 1.2 / 1129 5.5 / 1738 0.8	2350 5.5
4 M	0537 0.8 / 1142 6.0 / 1811 0.3	●	19 TU	0552 1.1 / 1204 5.6	1812 0.8
5 TU	0014 6.0 / 0623 0.7 / 1228 6.1	1856 0.3	20 W	0022 5.6 / 0624 1.0 / 1239 5.6	○ 1845 0.7
6 W	0057 6.0 / 0708 0.6 / 1312 6.1	1938 0.3	21 TH	0054 5.7 / 0657 0.9 / 1312 5.6	1919 0.8
7 TH	0139 6.0 / 0750 0.6 / 1356 6.1	2018 0.5	22 F	0127 5.7 / 0730 0.9 / 1346 5.6	1953 0.8
8 F	0220 5.9 / 0831 0.7 / 1441 5.9	2056 0.7	23 SA	0201 5.6 / 0804 0.9 / 1421 5.5	2027 0.9
9 SA	0301 5.6 / 0910 0.8 / 1527 5.7	2133 1.0	24 SU	0235 5.5 / 0838 1.0 / 1458 5.4	2100 1.1
10 SU	0344 5.4 / 0949 1.0 / 1617 5.3	2212 1.4	25 M	0313 5.4 / 0914 1.0 / 1539 5.3	2137 1.3
11 M	0431 5.1 / 1033 1.2 / 1714 5.0	2301 1.7	26 TU	0355 5.2 / 0958 1.1 / 1628 5.1	2223 1.4
12 TU	0528 4.8 / 1135 1.4	1821 4.7	27 W	0447 5.0 / 1055 1.2 / 1727 5.0	2327 1.6
13 W	0013 1.9 / 0638 4.6 / 1311 1.5	1937 4.7	28 TH	0551 4.9 / 1208 1.2	1838 4.9
14 TH	0142 1.9 / 0756 4.6 / 1434 1.4	2052 4.8	29 F	0045 1.6 / 0705 4.9 / 1330 1.1	1954 5.0
15 F	0256 1.8 / 0908 4.8 / 1535 1.2	2153 5.0	30 SA	0202 1.5 / 0820 5.1 / 1444 0.9	2105 5.3

DECEMBER

Day	Time m	Time m	Day	Time m	Time m
1 SU	0309 1.3 / 0926 5.3 / 1550 0.7	2206 5.5	16 M	0349 1.6 / 1005 5.0 / 1617 1.1	2231 5.1
2 M	0409 1.1 / 1024 5.6 / 1650 0.6	2300 5.7	17 TU	0436 1.4 / 1052 5.2 / 1701 0.9	2312 5.3
3 TU	0506 0.9 / 1117 5.8 / 1743 0.5	2349 5.8	18 W	0518 1.2 / 1134 5.4 / 1741 0.9	2352 5.5
4 W	0558 0.8 / 1206 5.9 / 1830 0.5	●	19 TH	0557 1.1 / 1214 5.4 / 1820 0.8	○
5 TH	0034 5.8 / 0646 0.7 / 1255 5.9	1914 0.5	20 F	0030 5.6 / 0635 0.9 / 1253 5.5	1857 0.8
6 F	0118 5.8 / 0733 0.6 / 1341 5.9	1956 0.6	21 SA	0108 5.6 / 0713 0.8 / 1331 5.5	1935 0.8
7 SA	0201 5.7 / 0818 0.7 / 1428 5.8	2036 0.8	22 SU	0146 5.6 / 0753 0.8 / 1410 5.4	2013 0.9
8 SU	0244 5.6 / 0901 0.8 / 1514 5.6	2114 1.1	23 M	0225 5.5 / 0835 0.7 / 1450 5.5	2052 0.9
9 M	0326 5.4 / 0940 0.9 / 1601 5.3	2151 1.4	24 TU	0305 5.4 / 0918 0.7 / 1534 5.4	2132 1.1
10 TU	0410 5.1 / 1020 1.1 / 1650 5.0	2232 1.6	25 W	0348 5.3 / 1004 0.8 / 1621 5.3	2217 1.2
11 W	0459 4.9 / 1107 1.2 / 1742 4.8	2323 1.8	26 TH	0436 5.2 / 1054 0.8 / 1714 5.2	2308 1.3
12 TH	0555 4.7 / 1209 1.3	1841 4.6	27 F	0531 5.1 / 1151 0.9	1814 5.1
13 F	0031 1.9 / 0659 4.6 / 1322 1.4	1946 4.6	28 SA	0008 1.4 / 0633 5.0 / 1257 0.9	1921 5.0
14 SA	0147 1.9 / 0808 4.7 / 1430 1.3	2050 4.7	29 SU	0117 1.4 / 0743 5.1 / 1407 0.9	2030 5.1
15 SU	0253 1.7 / 0911 4.8 / 1527 1.2	2145 4.9	30 M	0227 1.4 / 0853 5.2 / 1517 0.8	2135 5.2
			31 TU	0336 1.2 / 0959 5.3 / 1622 0.8	2236 5.3

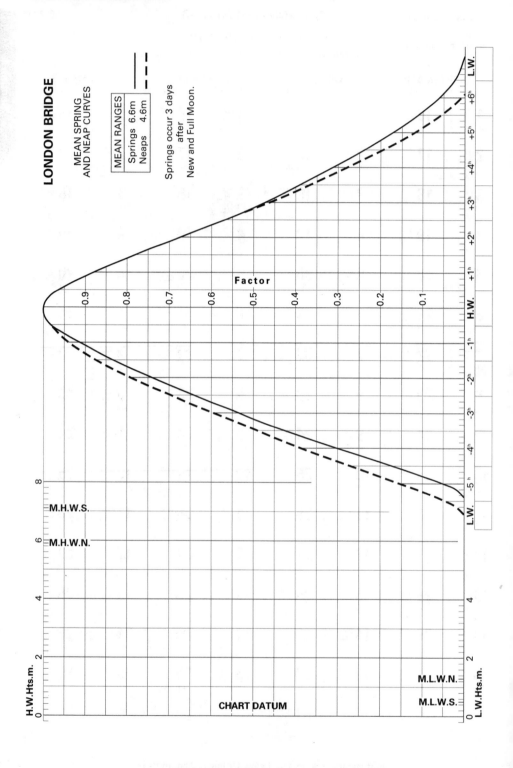

LONDON BRIDGE

MEAN SPRING
AND NEAP CURVES

MEAN RANGES
Springs 6.6m
Neaps 4.6m

Springs occur 3 days
after
New and Full Moon.

Factor

0.9
0.8
0.7
0.6
0.5
0.4
0.3
0.2
0.1

H.W.

+1ʰ +2ʰ +3ʰ +4ʰ +5ʰ +6ʰ L.W.

-1ʰ -2ʰ -3ʰ -4ʰ -5ʰ L.W.

M.H.W.S.

M.H.W.N.

H.W.Hts.m.

M.L.W.N.

M.L.W.S.

L.W.Hts.m.

CHART DATUM

TIME ZONE (UTC)
For Summer Time add ONE hour in **non-shaded areas**

ENGLAND – LONDON BRIDGE

LAT 50°30′N   LONG 0°05′W

TIMES AND HEIGHTS OF HIGH AND LOW WATERS

YEAR 2002

JANUARY

Day	Time	m	Day	Time	m
1 TU	0248 / 0931 / 1514 / 2141	6.9 / 0.5 / 7.1 / 0.8	**16** W	0317 / 1011 / 1548 / 2209	6.6 / 0.8 / 6.6 / 1.1
2 W	0332 / 1020 / 1601 / 2222	6.9 / 0.5 / 7.2 / 0.8	**17** TH	0348 / 1042 / 1621 / 2231	6.5 / 1.0 / 6.5 / 1.2
3 TH	0415 / 1105 / 1648 / 2302	6.9 / 0.4 / 7.1 / 0.9	**18** F	0419 / 1102 / 1654 / 2250	6.5 / 1.1 / 6.5 / 1.2
4 F	0459 / 1150 / 1737 / 2343	6.8 / 0.5 / 7.0 / 0.8	**19** SA	0453 / 1120 / 1730 / 2320	6.4 / 1.1 / 6.4 / 1.1
5 SA	0546 / 1235 / 1828	6.6 / 0.6 / 6.7	**20** SU	0531 / 1150 / 1809 / 2357	6.3 / 1.0 / 6.3 / 1.1
6 SU	0028 / 0637 / 1324 / 1925	1.1 / 6.4 / 0.8 / 6.4	**21** M	0614 / 1228 / 1854	6.2 / 1.1 / 6.1
7 M	0121 / 0738 / 1421 / 2029	1.3 / 6.2 / 1.0 / 6.2	**22** TU	0041 / 0702 / 1315 / 1944	1.3 / 6.0 / 1.2 / 6.0
8 TU	0223 / 0849 / 1527 / 2136	1.5 / 6.1 / 1.1 / 6.1	**23** W	0135 / 0759 / 1414 / 2042	1.4 / 5.9 / 1.3 / 5.9
9 W	0337 / 0959 / 1638 / 2240	1.6 / 6.1 / 1.1 / 6.2	**24** TH	0244 / 0903 / 1528 / 2148	1.6 / 5.8 / 1.4 / 5.9
10 TH	0459 / 1104 / 1743 / 2338	1.4 / 6.3 / 1.0 / 6.4	**25** F	0402 / 1013 / 1644 / 2258	1.5 / 5.9 / 1.4 / 6.0
11 F	0610 / 1202 / 1838	1.2 / 6.5 / 0.9	**26** SA	0514 / 1123 / 1754	1.3 / 6.1 / 1.2
12 SA	0031 / 0708 / 1256 / 1928	6.6 / 0.9 / 6.7 / 0.8	**27** SU	0001 / 0623 / 1226 / 1857	6.3 / 1.1 / 6.5 / 1.0
13 SU	0120 / 0801 / 1346 / ● 2015	6.7 / 0.7 / 6.8 / 0.8	**28** M	0057 / 0730 / 1322 / ○ 1956	6.6 / 0.8 / 6.8 / 0.8
14 M	0204 / 0849 / 1431 / 2058	6.7 / 0.7 / 6.9 / 0.8	**29** TU	0147 / 0832 / 1413 / 2049	6.8 / 0.5 / 7.1 / 0.7
15 TU	0243 / 0933 / 1512 / 2137	6.7 / 0.7 / 6.8 / 1.0	**30** W	0235 / 0927 / 1502 / 2138	7.0 / 0.3 / 7.3 / 0.6
			31 TH	0320 / 1016 / 1549 / 2222	7.1 / 0.1 / 7.4 / 0.6

FEBRUARY

Day	Time	m	Day	Time	m
1 F	0403 / 1100 / 1635 / 2301	7.1 / 0.0 / 7.4 / 0.6	**16** SA	0400 / 1047 / 1628 / 2234	6.5 / 1.0 / 6.6 / 1.1
2 SA	0446 / 1140 / 1720 / 2337	7.1 / 0.1 / 7.3 / 0.7	**17** SU	0430 / 1057 / 1700 / 2258	6.5 / 1.0 / 6.6 / 1.0
3 SU	0529 / 1217 / 1806	7.0 / 0.3 / 7.0	**18** M	0504 / 1119 / 1736 / 2330	6.5 / 0.9 / 6.5 / 0.9
4 M	0013 / 0613 / 1254 / 1855	0.8 / 6.7 / 0.6 / 6.6	**19** TU	0542 / 1151 / 1817	6.4 / 0.8 / 6.4
5 TU	0053 / 0703 / 1336 / 1951	1.0 / 6.4 / 0.9 / 6.1	**20** W	0007 / 0626 / 1229 / 1903	0.9 / 6.3 / 1.0 / 6.1
6 W	0141 / 0808 / 1429 / 2058	1.3 / 6.1 / 1.2 / 5.8	**21** TH	0051 / 0718 / 1316 / 1957	1.2 / 6.0 / 1.2 / 5.9
7 TH	0242 / 0928 / 1539 / 2209	1.6 / 5.9 / 1.5 / 5.8	**22** F	0148 / 0820 / 1423 / 2101	1.4 / 5.8 / 1.4 / 5.7
8 F	0400 / 1043 / 1705 / 2314	1.7 / 5.9 / 1.5 / 5.9	**23** SA	0318 / 0931 / 1605 / 2218	1.6 / 5.8 / 1.6 / 5.7
9 SA	0551 / 1147 / 1813	1.5 / 6.2 / 1.3	**24** SU	0447 / 1053 / 1731 / 2334	1.5 / 6.0 / 1.4 / 6.1
10 SU	0011 / 0655 / 1243 / 1907	6.2 / 1.1 / 6.5 / 1.0	**25** M	0609 / 1206 / 1843	1.1 / 6.4 / 1.1
11 M	0103 / 0746 / 1333 / 1956	6.5 / 0.8 / 6.7 / 0.9	**26** TU	0036 / 0722 / 1306 / 1944	6.5 / 0.7 / 6.8 / 0.8
12 TU	0148 / 0834 / 1414 / ● 2041	6.6 / 0.6 / 6.8 / 0.8	**27** W	0129 / 0822 / 1358 / ○ 2038	6.8 / 0.3 / 7.2 / 0.6
13 W	0228 / 0917 / 1457 / 2122	6.6 / 0.6 / 6.8 / 0.9	**28** TH	0217 / 0915 / 1446 / 2126	7.1 / 0.0 / 7.5 / 0.4
14 TH	0302 / 0956 / 1530 / 2157	6.6 / 0.7 / 6.6 / 1.0			
15 F	0332 / 1027 / 1559 / 2220	6.5 / 0.9 / 6.6 / 1.1			

MARCH

Day	Time	m	Day	Time	m
1 F	0302 / 1002 / 1532 / 2210	7.3 / -0.2 / 7.6 / 0.4	**16** SA	0311 / 1003 / 1533 / 2203	6.5 / 0.8 / 6.6 / 1.0
2 SA	0344 / 1044 / 1615 / 2248	7.4 / -0.2 / 7.5 / 0.4	**17** SU	0338 / 1023 / 1600 / 2216	6.5 / 0.9 / 6.6 / 1.0
3 SU	0425 / 1120 / 1658 / 2321	7.4 / -0.1 / 7.4 / 0.4	**18** M	0406 / 1031 / 1631 / 2237	6.6 / 0.9 / 6.6 / 0.9
4 M	0506 / 1151 / 1739 / 2352	7.2 / 0.2 / 7.0 / 0.6	**19** TU	0438 / 1051 / 1705 / 2305	6.6 / 0.8 / 6.6 / 0.8
5 TU	0547 / 1220 / 1821	7.0 / 0.5 / 6.6	**20** W	0515 / 1120 / 1744 / 2339	6.6 / 0.8 / 6.5 / 0.8
6 W	0024 / 0632 / 1257 / 1907	0.8 / 6.5 / 0.9 / 6.1	**21** TH	0559 / 1155 / 1829	6.4 / 0.9 / 6.2
7 TH	0106 / 0729 / 1345 / 2008	1.2 / 6.0 / 1.4 / 5.6	**22** F	0019 / 0650 / 1240 / 1922	1.0 / 6.1 / 1.2 / 5.9
8 F	0202 / 0858 / 1450 / 2137	1.5 / 5.6 / 1.7 / 5.4	**23** SA	0112 / 0752 / 1342 / 2025	1.4 / 5.8 / 1.6 / 5.6
9 SA	0315 / 1023 / 1617 / 2249	1.8 / 5.7 / 1.8 / 5.6	**24** SU	0241 / 0905 / 1529 / 2146	1.6 / 5.7 / 1.8 / 5.6
10 SU	0535 / 1128 / 1747 / 2348	1.6 / 6.0 / 1.5 / 6.0	**25** M	0431 / 1032 / 1713 / 2310	1.5 / 5.9 / 1.5 / 6.0
11 M	0637 / 1224 / 1845	1.1 / 6.4 / 1.1	**26** TU	0559 / 1148 / 1826	1.0 / 6.4 / 1.1
12 TU	0041 / 0726 / 1313 / 1934	6.4 / 0.7 / 6.7 / 0.9	**27** W	0013 / 0706 / 1247 / 1925	6.4 / 0.5 / 6.9 / 0.8
13 W	0127 / 0811 / 1357 / 2020	6.6 / 0.5 / 6.8 / 0.8	**28** TH	0106 / 0803 / 1338 / ○ 2018	6.9 / 0.1 / 7.3 / 0.5
14 TH	0207 / 0853 / 1434 / ● 2102	6.7 / 0.5 / 6.8 / 0.8	**29** F	0154 / 0853 / 1425 / 2106	7.2 / -0.2 / 7.5 / 0.3
15 F	0242 / 0931 / 1505 / 2138	6.6 / 0.6 / 6.7 / 0.9	**30** SA	0238 / 0938 / 1509 / 2149	7.4 / -0.3 / 7.6 / 0.2
			31 SU	0321 / 1018 / 1552 / 2228	7.5 / -0.2 / 7.5 / 0.2

APRIL

Day	Time	m	Day	Time	m
1 M	0403 / 1053 / 1632 / 2301	7.4 / 0.0 / 7.3 / 0.3	**16** TU	0343 / 1006 / 1604 / 2219	6.6 / 0.9 / 6.6 / 0.8
2 TU	0443 / 1122 / 1710 / 2331	7.3 / 0.2 / 7.0 / 0.5	**17** W	0417 / 1028 / 1639 / 2247	6.6 / 0.8 / 6.6 / 0.7
3 W	0525 / 1151 / 1748	7.0 / 0.6 / 6.6	**18** TH	0456 / 1058 / 1718 / 2321	6.6 / 0.8 / 6.4 / 0.8
4 TH	0000 / 0608 / 1225 / 1827	0.7 / 6.5 / 1.0 / 6.1	**19** F	0541 / 1135 / 1803	6.4 / 0.9 / 6.2
5 F	0039 / 0702 / 1310 / 1917	1.1 / 6.0 / 1.4 / 5.6	**20** SA	0002 / 0633 / 1222 / 1856	1.0 / 6.2 / 1.3 / 5.8
6 SA	0134 / 0832 / 1415 / 2059	1.5 / 5.6 / 1.8 / 5.3	**21** SU	0058 / 0736 / 1325 / 2001	1.3 / 5.9 / 1.6 / 5.6
7 SU	0247 / 0959 / 1537 / 2219	1.7 / 5.6 / 1.9 / 5.5	**22** M	0233 / 0851 / 1509 / 2124	1.5 / 5.8 / 1.8 / 5.7
8 M	0455 / 1102 / 1712 / 2319	1.6 / 6.0 / 1.7 / 5.9	**23** TU	0418 / 1017 / 1650 / 2244	1.3 / 6.1 / 1.5 / 6.0
9 TU	0606 / 1157 / 1816	1.1 / 6.4 / 1.2	**24** W	0539 / 1127 / 1800 / 2346	0.8 / 6.6 / 1.1 / 6.5
10 W	0011 / 0654 / 1245 / 1906	6.3 / 0.7 / 6.7 / 0.9	**25** TH	0641 / 1223 / 1859	0.3 / 7.0 / 0.7
11 TH	0058 / 0739 / 1328 / 1952	6.5 / 0.5 / 6.8 / 0.8	**26** F	0039 / 0735 / 1314 / 1951	6.9 / 0.0 / 7.3 / 0.5
12 F	0139 / 0821 / 1404 / ● 2033	6.6 / 0.5 / 6.8 / 0.7	**27** SA	0128 / 0824 / 1401 / ○ 2040	7.2 / -0.1 / 7.5 / 0.3
13 SA	0214 / 0859 / 1435 / 2109	6.6 / 0.6 / 6.7 / 0.8	**28** SU	0214 / 0910 / 1445 / 2126	7.4 / -0.2 / 7.5 / 0.2
14 SU	0245 / 0931 / 1504 / 2136	6.5 / 0.8 / 6.6 / 0.9	**29** M	0259 / 0950 / 1527 / 2206	7.4 / -0.1 / 7.4 / 0.2
15 M	0313 / 0952 / 1532 / 2156	6.5 / 0.9 / 6.6 / 0.9	**30** TU	0342 / 1025 / 1606 / 2242	7.4 / 0.1 / 7.2 / 0.3

Chart Datum: 2·90 metres below Ordnance Datum (Newlyn)

ENGLAND – LONDON BRIDGE

TIME ZONE (UTC)
For Summer Time add ONE hour in **non-shaded areas**

LAT 50°30′N   LONG 0°05′W

TIMES AND HEIGHTS OF HIGH AND LOW WATERS

YEAR **2002**

MAY

Day	Time	m	Time	m	Day	Time	m	Time	m
1 W	0424 1057 1644 2313	7.2 0.4 6.9 0.5			16 TH	0403 1014 1620 2240	6.7 0.9 6.6 0.7		
2 TH	0507 1126 1720 2343	6.9 0.7 6.5 0.8			17 F	0444 1048 1701 2318	6.6 0.9 6.4 0.8		
3 F	0552 1159 1758	6.5 1.1 6.1			18 SA	0532 1128 1747	6.5 1.1 6.2		
4 SA	0020 0644 1243 1844	1.0 6.0 1.5 5.7			19 SU	0003 0625 1218 1840	1.0 6.3 1.3 6.0		
5 SU	0113 0802 1343 2005	1.3 5.6 1.8 5.4			20 M	0105 0728 1322 1946	1.2 6.1 1.6 5.8		
6 M	0221 0924 1457 2138	1.5 5.6 1.9 5.5			21 TU	0232 0842 1452 2105	1.2 6.1 1.6 5.9		
7 TU	0338 1027 1616 2241	1.5 5.9 1.8 5.8			22 W	0357 0957 1619 2216	1.0 6.3 1.4 6.2		
8 W	0510 1121 1730 2334	1.2 6.2 1.4 6.1			23 TH	0510 1102 1729 2318	0.7 6.7 1.1 6.6		
9 TH	0609 1208 1826	0.9 6.5 1.1			24 F	0611 1158 1830	0.4 7.0 0.8		
10 F	0021 0656 1251 1912	6.4 0.7 6.7 0.9			25 SA	0013 0705 1250 1925	6.9 0.2 7.2 0.5		
11 SA	0103 0739 1328 1954	6.5 0.7 6.7 0.8			26 SU	0104 0755 1337 ○2016	7.1 0.1 7.3 0.4		
12 SU	0141 0818 1403 ●2032	6.6 0.7 6.7 0.8			27 M	0153 0841 1422 2103	7.2 0.1 7.3 0.3		
13 M	0216 0852 1435 2105	6.6 0.8 6.7 0.8			28 TU	0240 0923 1505 2147	7.2 0.2 7.1 0.3		
14 TU	0250 0920 1509 2136	6.6 0.9 6.7 0.8			29 W	0325 1001 1545 2226	7.2 0.4 7.0 0.4		
15 W	0325 0946 1543 2207	6.6 0.9 6.6 0.7			30 TH	0409 1035 1622 2300	7.0 0.6 6.7 0.6		
					31 F	0452 1107 1658 2332	6.8 0.9 6.5 0.8		

JUNE

Day	Time	m	Time	m	Day	Time	m	Time	m
1 SA	0536 1139 1736	6.4 1.2 6.2			16 SU	0527 1130 1738	6.7 1.0 6.4		
2 SU	0007 0624 1218 1820	1.0 6.1 1.4 5.9			17 M	0014 0619 1219 1829	0.7 6.5 1.2 6.3		
3 M	0052 0721 1308 1918	1.2 5.8 1.7 5.7			18 TU	0111 0718 1317 1931	0.8 6.4 1.4 6.1		
4 TU	0149 0824 1410 2035	1.3 5.6 1.8 5.6			19 W	0215 0824 1426 2040	0.9 6.3 1.4 6.1		
5 W	0251 0935 1516 2146	1.4 5.8 1.8 5.7			20 TH	0326 0931 1541 2147	0.9 6.3 1.4 6.3		
6 TH	0354 1031 1619 2244	1.3 6.0 1.6 5.9			21 F	0436 1035 1655 2251	0.7 6.5 1.2 6.4		
7 F	0457 1122 1720 2336	1.1 6.2 1.4 6.1			22 SA	0540 1133 1802 2350	0.6 6.7 1.0 6.7		
8 SA	0556 1208 1817	1.0 6.4 1.1			23 SU	0636 1227 1902	0.5 6.9 0.7		
9 SU	0023 0648 1251 1907	6.3 0.8 6.6 0.9			24 M	0045 0728 1317 ○1956	6.9 0.4 7.0 0.6		
10 M	0107 0734 1331 ●1954	6.5 0.8 6.7 0.8			25 TU	0137 0816 1404 2046	7.0 0.4 7.0 0.5		
11 TU	0149 0816 1411 2039	6.6 0.8 6.7 0.7			26 W	0226 0901 1447 2133	7.0 0.5 6.9 0.5		
12 W	0230 0855 1450 2121	6.7 0.8 6.7 0.6			27 TH	0313 0942 1528 2214	7.0 0.6 6.8 0.5		
13 TH	0311 0932 1529 2203	6.6 0.8 6.7 0.6			28 F	0356 1019 1604 2251	6.9 0.8 6.7 0.7		
14 F	0354 1009 1610 2244	6.8 0.9 6.6 0.6			29 SA	0437 1052 1639 2322	6.7 1.0 6.5 0.8		
15 SA	0439 1047 1652 2327	6.8 0.9 6.5 0.6			30 SU	0517 1121 1715 2351	6.5 1.2 6.4 0.9		

JULY

Day	Time	m	Time	m	Day	Time	m	Time	m
1 M	0556 1152 1755	6.3 1.3 6.2			16 TU	0013 0606 1213 1813	0.4 6.8 1.0 6.6		
2 TU	0024 0639 1231 1841	1.0 6.1 1.4 6.0			17 W	0057 0658 1300 1906	0.5 6.6 1.1 6.4		
3 W	0107 0728 1319 1935	1.1 5.9 1.6 5.8			18 TH	0146 0757 1354 2008	0.7 6.3 1.3 6.2		
4 TH	0159 0823 1418 2037	1.2 5.8 1.6 5.7			19 F	0244 0902 1458 2117	0.9 6.2 1.5 6.1		
5 F	0258 0924 1522 2141	1.3 5.8 1.6 5.8			20 SA	0354 1008 1614 2227	1.1 6.2 1.5 6.2		
6 SA	0400 1025 1625 2244	1.2 6.0 1.5 5.9			21 SU	0508 1110 1738 2333	1.0 6.3 1.3 6.4		
7 SU	0502 1122 1727 2342	1.1 6.2 1.3 6.1			22 M	0611 1207 1845	0.9 6.5 1.0		
8 M	0603 1215 1827	1.0 6.4 1.0			23 TU	0032 0705 1300 1942	6.6 0.7 6.7 0.7		
9 TU	0035 0658 1304 1925	6.4 0.8 6.6 0.8			24 W	0126 0756 1349 ○2033	6.8 0.7 6.8 0.5		
10 W	0125 0750 1350 ●2020	6.6 0.8 6.7 0.6			25 TH	0215 0843 1433 2120	6.9 0.7 6.8 0.5		
11 TH	0213 0839 1435 2113	6.8 0.7 6.8 0.5			26 F	0301 0927 1513 2203	6.9 0.7 6.8 0.5		
12 F	0259 0925 1518 2202	7.0 0.7 6.8 0.4			27 SA	0342 1006 1547 2239	6.8 0.9 6.7 0.7		
13 SA	0345 1009 1601 2248	7.1 0.8 6.8 0.3			28 SU	0418 1039 1619 2309	6.7 1.0 6.6 0.8		
14 SU	0431 1050 1643 2331	7.1 0.8 6.8 0.3			29 M	0451 1104 1650 2330	6.5 1.2 6.5 0.9		
15 M	0517 1131 1727	7.0 0.9 6.8			30 TU	0524 1125 1726 2350	6.4 1.2 6.4 1.0		
					31 W	0600 1155 1805	6.3 1.2 6.3		

AUGUST

Day	Time	m	Time	m	Day	Time	m	Time	m
1 TH	0020 0641 1234 1850	1.0 6.2 1.3 6.1			16 F	0109 0722 1320 1932	0.8 6.2 1.2 6.2		
2 F	0101 0728 1323 1942	1.1 6.0 1.4 5.9			17 SA	0158 0827 1417 2047	1.2 5.9 1.5 5.9		
3 SA	0155 0823 1428 2042	1.3 5.8 1.6 5.7			18 SU	0305 0941 1531 2210	1.5 5.7 1.7 5.9		
4 SU	0306 0928 1541 2151	1.4 5.8 1.6 5.7			19 M	0433 1049 1722 2320	1.5 5.9 1.5 6.1		
5 M	0420 1038 1651 2303	1.4 5.9 1.4 5.9			20 TU	0549 1150 1834	1.3 6.2 1.1		
6 TU	0530 1143 1759	1.2 6.2 1.1			21 W	0020 0647 1244 1928	6.5 1.0 6.5 0.7		
7 W	0008 0633 1241 1907	6.3 1.0 6.5 0.8			22 TH	0114 0737 1332 ○2017	6.8 0.8 6.8 0.5		
8 TH	0105 0732 1332 ●2010	6.7 0.8 6.7 0.5			23 F	0202 0825 1416 2103	7.0 0.7 6.8 0.4		
9 F	0156 0827 1419 2106	7.0 0.7 6.9 0.3			24 SA	0244 0909 1454 2144	7.0 0.7 6.8 0.5		
10 SA	0244 0918 1503 2155	7.2 0.6 7.0 0.1			25 SU	0321 0949 1527 2219	6.8 0.8 6.7 0.6		
11 SU	0330 1003 1545 2240	7.3 0.6 7.1 0.0			26 M	0352 1022 1554 2247	6.7 1.0 6.6 0.8		
12 M	0415 1045 1626 2320	7.3 0.6 7.1 0.1			27 TU	0420 1044 1623 2302	6.6 1.1 6.5 1.0		
13 TU	0459 1122 1707 2356	7.2 0.6 7.1 0.2			28 W	0448 1058 1654 2312	6.5 1.1 6.5 1.0		
14 W	0544 1158 1750	7.0 0.8 6.9			29 TH	0521 1122 1729 2335	6.3 1.1 6.4 0.9		
15 TH	0031 0630 1236 1836	0.5 6.6 1.0 6.6			30 F	0559 1155 1810	6.3 1.1 6.3		
					31 SA	0009 0641 1236 1858	1.0 6.1 1.3 6.0		

Chart Datum: 2·90 metres below Ordnance Datum (Newlyn)

TIME ZONE (UTC)
For Summer Time add ONE hour in **non-shaded areas**

ENGLAND – LONDON BRIDGE

LAT 50°30′N   LONG 0°05′W

TIMES AND HEIGHTS OF HIGH AND LOW WATERS

YEAR **2002**

SEPTEMBER

#	Time	m	#	Time	m
1 SU	0052 0733 1331 1956	1.3 5.8 1.6 5.8	**16** M	0223 0913 1459 2155	1.8 5.4 1.8 5.7
2 M	0156 0835 1500 2105	1.6 5.6 1.7 5.7	**17** TU	0356 1028 1712 2305	1.9 5.6 1.6 6.0
3 TU	0340 0953 1624 2227	1.7 5.6 1.6 5.8	**18** W	0527 1129 1817	1.6 6.0 1.1
4 W	0504 1114 1741 2345	1.5 5.9 1.2 6.2	**19** TH	0003 0625 1223 1907	6.5 1.1 6.5 0.6
5 TH	0615 1217 1855	1.2 6.4 0.8	**20** F	0055 0715 1310 1953	6.8 0.8 6.8 0.4
6 F	0045 0716 1310 1956	6.7 0.9 6.7 0.4	**21** SA	0140 0802 1353 O 2036	7.0 0.6 6.9 0.3
7 SA	0137 0812 1357 ● 2050	7.1 0.7 7.0 0.1	**22** SU	0220 0846 1430 2116	7.0 0.6 6.8 0.5
8 SU	0224 0902 1440 2138	7.4 0.5 7.2 -0.1	**23** M	0254 0925 1501 2151	6.8 0.7 6.8 0.7
9 M	0309 0948 1522 2221	7.5 0.4 7.3 -0.1	**24** TU	0321 0958 1527 2217	6.7 0.9 6.6 0.9
10 TU	0352 1028 1603 2258	7.5 0.4 7.3 0.0	**25** W	0346 1018 1553 2226	6.6 1.1 6.5 1.1
11 W	0434 1105 1643 2330	7.3 0.5 7.3 0.2	**26** TH	0413 1029 1623 2234	6.6 1.1 6.6 1.0
12 TH	0516 1137 1724 2359	7.0 0.7 7.1 0.6	**27** F	0444 1052 1657 2259	6.6 1.0 6.5 0.9
13 F	0557 1209 1808	6.6 0.9 6.7	**28** SA	0520 1122 1738 2331	6.4 1.0 6.4 1.0
14 SA	0032 0642 1249 1900	0.9 6.1 1.2 6.2	**29** SU	0602 1159 1826	6.2 1.2 6.1
15 SU	0118 0742 1344 2021	1.4 5.8 1.6 5.7	**30** M	0012 0652 1249 1924	1.3 5.8 1.5 5.8

OCTOBER

#	Time	m	#	Time	m
1 TU	0108 0754 1418 2033	1.7 5.6 1.8 5.7	**16** W	0319 1000 1642 2240	2.1 5.5 1.6 6.0
2 W	0250 0912 1603 2158	2.0 5.5 1.6 5.8	**17** TH	0454 1100 1746 2337	1.8 5.9 1.1 6.4
3 TH	0440 1043 1726 2321	1.7 5.8 1.1 6.3	**18** F	0556 1153 1836	1.3 6.4 0.7
4 F	0553 1149 1835	1.3 6.3 0.7	**19** SA	0026 0646 1241 1920	6.6 0.9 6.7 0.5
5 SA	0021 0654 1241 1933	6.8 0.9 6.8 0.3	**20** SU	0111 0733 1323 2002	7.0 0.7 6.8 0.5
6 SU	0113 0748 1328 ● 2025	7.2 0.7 7.1 0.0	**21** M	0149 0816 1400 O 2042	6.9 0.7 6.6 0.6
7 M	0159 0838 1413 2112	7.5 0.5 7.3 -0.1	**22** TU	0221 0854 1431 2116	6.8 0.8 6.6 0.8
8 TU	0244 0924 1456 2154	7.5 0.4 7.4 0.0	**23** W	0248 0926 1459 2140	6.7 0.9 6.6 1.0
9 W	0326 1006 1538 2230	7.5 0.4 7.5 0.1	**24** TH	0314 0947 1527 2150	6.6 1.0 6.6 1.1
10 TH	0407 1043 1620 2302	7.3 0.5 7.4 0.4	**25** F	0342 1004 1558 2206	6.6 1.0 6.6 1.0
11 F	0447 1116 1702 2330	7.0 0.6 7.1 0.7	**26** SA	0414 1029 1634 2233	6.6 1.0 6.6 1.0
12 SA	0526 1148 1747	6.6 0.9 6.7	**27** SU	0450 1100 1716 2308	6.5 1.0 6.4 1.0
13 SU	0002 0605 1226 1839	1.1 6.1 1.2 6.1	**28** M	0533 1139 1805 2350	6.2 1.2 6.2 1.3
14 M	0046 0652 1321 2003	1.5 5.8 1.5 5.6	**29** TU	0623 1230 1904	5.9 1.4 5.9
15 TU	0150 0842 1437 2134	2.0 5.3 1.8 5.6	**30** W	0046 0724 1357 2013	1.7 5.6 1.7 5.8
			31 TH	0212 0841 1543 2136	2.0 5.6 1.5 5.9

NOVEMBER

#	Time	m	#	Time	m
1 F	0409 1008 1702 2253	1.8 5.9 1.0 6.4	**16** SA	0511 1116 1752 2350	1.6 6.2 1.0 6.5
2 SA	0523 1115 1807 2353	1.3 6.4 0.6 6.9	**17** SU	0607 1204 1839	1.2 6.4 0.8
3 SU	0625 1209 1904	1.0 6.8 0.3	**18** M	0034 0654 1247 1921	6.7 1.0 6.6 0.7
4 M	0045 0720 1259 ● 1955	7.2 0.7 7.1 0.1	**19** TU	0112 0737 1326 2000	6.7 0.9 6.6 0.8
5 TU	0133 0811 1346 2042	7.4 0.5 7.3 0.1	**20** W	0146 0815 1400 O 2034	6.7 0.9 6.6 0.9
6 W	0218 0859 1432 2125	7.5 0.4 7.4 0.1	**21** TH	0217 0849 1433 2101	6.7 0.9 6.6 1.0
7 TH	0301 0943 1517 2203	7.4 0.4 7.4 0.3	**22** F	0248 0918 1506 2123	6.7 0.9 6.6 1.0
8 F	0342 1023 1601 2236	7.2 0.5 7.3 0.5	**23** SA	0319 0947 1541 2149	6.6 0.9 6.6 1.0
9 SA	0422 1059 1646 2307	6.9 0.6 7.0 0.8	**24** SU	0353 1018 1620 2221	6.6 0.9 6.6 1.0
10 SU	0500 1133 1732 2340	6.6 0.9 6.6 1.2	**25** M	0431 1054 1704 2258	6.5 1.0 6.5 1.1
11 M	0538 1211 1825	6.2 1.2 6.1	**26** TU	0514 1136 1754 2343	6.3 1.1 6.3 1.3
12 TU	0021 0622 1304 1937	1.6 5.8 1.4 5.7	**27** W	0603 1230 1851	6.1 1.3 6.1
13 W	0120 0751 1411 2100	1.9 5.4 1.6 5.9	**28** TH	0038 0702 1348 1957	1.6 5.9 1.4 6.0
14 TH	0236 0921 1535 2205	2.1 5.5 1.6 5.9	**29** F	0152 0815 1514 2111	1.8 5.8 1.2 6.1
15 F	0359 1023 1657 2300	1.9 5.8 1.3 6.2	**30** SA	0328 0934 1629 2222	1.7 6.0 1.0 6.4

DECEMBER

#	Time	m	#	Time	m
1 SU	0447 1041 1735 2324	1.4 6.4 0.7 6.7	**16** M	0457 1119 1737 2349	1.6 6.0 1.2 6.3
2 M	0553 1140 1833	1.1 6.7 0.5	**17** TU	0555 1207 1828	1.3 6.3 1.1
3 TU	0018 0652 1234 1925	7.0 0.8 7.0 0.3	**18** W	0032 0645 1251 1913	6.4 1.1 6.4 1.0
4 W	0108 0746 1325 ● 2014	7.2 0.6 7.2 0.3	**19** TH	0112 0731 1332 O 1954	6.6 0.9 6.5 1.0
5 TH	0155 0838 1414 2059	7.2 0.5 7.3 0.4	**20** F	0151 0815 1411 2032	6.6 0.9 6.6 1.0
6 F	0240 0925 1501 2140	7.1 0.5 7.3 0.5	**21** SA	0228 0858 1451 2107	6.7 0.8 6.7 1.0
7 SA	0322 1009 1548 2218	7.0 0.5 7.1 0.7	**22** SU	0305 0939 1531 2142	6.6 0.8 6.8 1.0
8 SU	0402 1049 1633 2251	6.8 0.7 6.9 1.0	**23** M	0342 1019 1613 2219	6.6 0.8 6.8 1.0
9 M	0440 1125 1718 2324	6.6 0.9 6.6 1.2	**24** TU	0421 1100 1658 2258	6.6 0.8 6.7 1.1
10 TU	0518 1201 1805	6.3 1.1 6.3	**25** W	0503 1143 1745 2341	6.5 0.9 6.6 1.0
11 W	0000 0559 1243 1858	1.5 6.0 1.3 5.9	**26** TH	0550 1232 1838	6.4 1.0 6.5
12 TH	0046 0653 1335 2002	1.7 5.7 1.4 5.7	**27** F	0031 0643 1329 1936	1.3 6.2 1.0 6.3
13 F	0144 0811 1433 2109	1.9 5.6 1.5 5.7	**28** SA	0130 0746 1434 2042	1.5 6.1 1.1 6.2
14 SA	0250 0926 1534 2208	1.9 5.6 1.5 5.8	**29** SU	0241 0858 1547 2151	1.6 6.1 1.1 6.2
15 SU	0355 1026 1637 2301	1.8 5.8 1.4 6.0	**30** M	0402 1009 1701 2256	1.5 6.2 1.0 6.4
			31 TU	0521 1115 1805 2354	1.3 0.8 0.8 6.6

Chart Datum: 2·90 metres below Ordnance Datum (Newlyn)
Register for your **FREE** weekly weather email service from Macmillan Reeds
》 at **www.nauticaldata.com – NOW!**
weekend weather reports sent to your email address, every Thursday 《

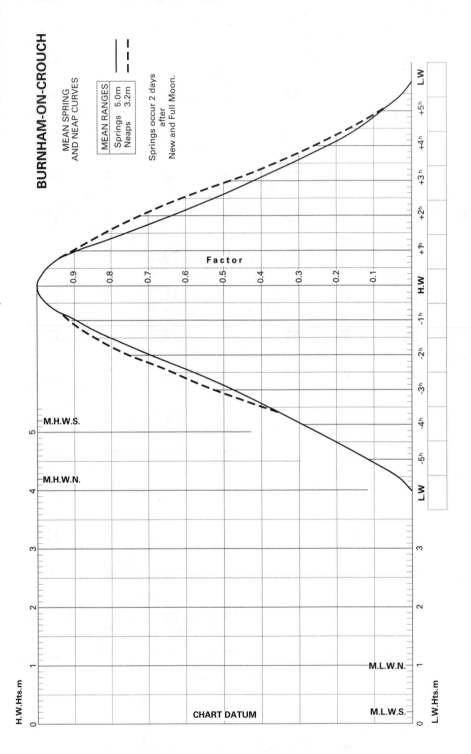

BURNHAM-ON-CROUCH

MEAN SPRING
AND NEAP CURVES

MEAN RANGES	
Springs	5.0m
Neaps	3.2m

Springs occur 2 days
after
New and Full Moon.

Factor

0.9 0.8 0.7 0.6 0.5 0.4 0.3 0.2 0.1

H.W.Hts.m

L.W.Hts.m

M.H.W.S.
M.H.W.N.
M.L.W.N.
M.L.W.S.
CHART DATUM

L.W +5ʰ +4ʰ +3ʰ +2ʰ +1ʰ H.W -1ʰ -2ʰ -3ʰ -4ʰ -5ʰ L.W

TIME ZONE (UTC)
For Summer Time add ONE hour in **non-shaded areas**

ENGLAND – BURNHAM-ON-CROUCH

LAT 51°37′N   LONG 0°48′W

TIMES AND HEIGHTS OF HIGH AND LOW WATERS

YEAR 2002

JANUARY

Day	Time	m	Time	m	Time	m	Time	m
1 TU	0120	5.1	0750	0.3	1342	5.2	2003	0.5
16 W	0155	4.8	0833	0.4	1419	4.8	2026	0.8
2 W	0201	5.1	0835	0.4	1427	5.2	2042	0.7
17 TH	0224	4.8	0904	0.4	1451	4.7	2055	0.8
3 TH	0243	5.0	0919	0.2	1513	5.2	2123	0.7
18 F	0254	4.7	0932	0.4	1523	4.7	2124	0.8
4 F	0328	5.0	1006	0.2	1601	5.1	2207	0.8
19 SA	0327	4.7	1002	0.5	1557	4.6	2158	0.8
5 SA	0415	4.8	1056	0.2	1653	4.8	2256	0.9
20 SU	0404	4.6	1037	0.5	1635	4.5	2237	0.9
6 SU	0507	4.7	1152	0.3	1749	4.6	2351	1.0
21 M	0446	4.5	1120	0.7	1720	4.3	2324	1.0
7 M	0606	4.6	1303	0.4	1852	4.5		
22 TU	0535	4.3	1215	0.8	1812	4.1		
8 TU	0107	1.1	0715	4.5	1418	0.5	2002	4.5
23 W	0025	1.1	0633	4.2	1323	0.9	1917	4.1
9 W	0229	1.0	0826	4.6	1528	0.5	2110	4.3
24 TH	0139	1.2	0744	4.2	1435	0.9	2028	4.2
10 TH	0345	0.9	0935	4.6	1628	0.5	2213	4.6
25 F	0254	1.1	0856	4.3	1545	0.9	2137	4.3
11 F	0450	0.8	1037	4.7	1723	0.5	2308	4.7
26 SA	0406	0.9	1002	4.5	1648	0.8	2237	4.6
12 SA	0548	0.5	1132	4.8	1810	0.5	2358	4.8
27 SU	0511	0.7	1101	4.8	1743	0.7	2332	4.8
13 SU ●	0638	0.4	1223	5.0	1849	0.7		
28 M ○	0610	0.4	1156	5.1	1832	0.5		
14 M	0043	4.8	0720	0.4	1306	5.0	1924	0.7
29 TU	0022	5.0	0658	0.2	1247	5.2	1913	0.4
15 TU	0121	4.8	0759	0.3	1345	4.8	1956	0.7
30 W	0107	5.1	0743	0.1	1333	5.3	1952	0.4
31 TH	0151	5.2	0826	0.0	1416	5.5	2030	0.4

FEBRUARY

Day	Time	m	Time	m	Time	m	Time	m
1 F	0233	5.2	0908	-0.1	1500	5.3	2110	0.4
16 SA	0233	4.8	0903	0.4	1456	4.7	2100	0.5
2 SA	0314	5.2	0951	0.0	1545	5.2	2150	0.5
17 SU	0301	4.8	0930	0.4	1526	4.7	2131	0.5
3 SU	0357	5.2	1034	0.1	1630	5.0	2233	0.7
18 M	0334	4.8	1001	0.4	1601	4.7	2205	0.7
4 M	0443	5.0	1121	0.2	1720	4.7	2321	0.8
19 TU	0411	4.7	1036	0.5	1641	4.6	2246	0.8
5 TU	0535	4.7	1219	0.5	1814	4.5		
20 W	0453	4.5	1119	0.8	1728	4.3	2335	1.0
6 W	0023	1.0	0638	4.5	1331	0.8	1922	4.2
21 TH	0545	4.3	1221	0.9	1825	4.1		
7 TH	0146	1.0	0757	4.3	1450	0.9	2038	4.1
22 F	0045	1.1	0653	4.1	1346	1.0	1939	4.0
8 F	0319	1.0	0916	4.3	1603	0.9	2150	4.2
23 SA	0211	1.1	0815	4.1	1510	1.0	2100	4.1
9 SA	0437	0.8	1024	4.6	1704	0.9	2250	4.5
24 SU	0337	0.9	0937	4.3	1623	0.9	2213	4.3
10 SU	0540	0.5	1122	4.7	1754	0.8	2343	4.7
25 M	0453	0.7	1045	4.7	1725	0.7	2313	4.7
11 M	0630	0.4	1212	4.8	1834	0.8		
26 TU	0557	0.5	1143	5.1	1817	0.5		
12 TU ●	0028	4.8	0709	0.3	1255	5.0	1908	0.7
27 W ○	0006	5.0	0647	0.1	1233	5.3	1857	0.4
13 W	0106	4.8	0744	0.3	1331	4.8	1938	0.7
28 TH	0053	5.2	0729	-0.1	1319	5.5	1936	0.3
14 TH	0139	4.8	0814	0.3	1401	4.8	2006	0.7
15 F	0207	4.8	0840	0.3	1429	4.7	2032	0.7

MARCH

Day	Time	m	Time	m	Time	m	Time	m
1 F	0135	5.3	0810	-0.3	1401	5.6	2014	0.2
16 SA	0144	4.8	0810	0.3	1403	4.8	2009	0.5
2 SA	0216	5.5	0850	-0.3	1442	5.5	2053	0.2
17 SU	0210	4.8	0834	0.3	1428	4.8	2037	0.4
3 SU	0256	5.5	0929	-0.1	1524	5.3	2131	0.3
18 M	0236	4.8	0900	0.3	1457	4.8	2108	0.4
4 M	0336	5.3	1008	0.0	1606	5.1	2211	0.4
19 TU	0308	4.8	0929	0.4	1531	4.8	2141	0.4
5 TU	0419	5.1	1050	0.3	1649	4.7	2255	0.7
20 W	0343	4.8	1000	0.5	1610	4.6	2218	0.7
6 W	0507	4.8	1139	0.7	1738	4.3	2348	0.9
21 TH	0423	4.6	1039	0.8	1654	4.3	2303	0.8
7 TH	0608	4.5	1247	0.9	1840	4.0		
22 F	0513	4.3	1132	1.0	1749	4.1		
8 F	0111	1.0	0732	4.2	1410	1.1	2006	3.8
23 SA	0009	1.0	0618	4.1	1305	1.1	1900	3.8
9 SA	0257	1.0	0859	4.2	1535	1.1	2126	4.1
24 SU	0142	1.0	0746	4.1	1441	1.1	2029	4.0
10 SU	0421	0.8	1009	4.5	1641	1.0	2230	4.3
25 M	0317	0.9	0918	4.3	1601	1.0	2149	4.3
11 M	0523	0.6	1106	4.7	1733	0.9	2323	4.6
26 TU	0437	0.5	1030	4.7	1702	0.7	2250	4.7
12 TU	0613	0.4	1154	4.8	1816	0.8		
27 W	0539	0.2	1126	5.1	1755	0.5	2343	5.0
13 W	0008	4.8	0650	0.3	1236	5.0	1849	0.7
28 TH ○	0629	-0.1	1216	5.3	1838	0.3		
14 TH ●	0046	4.8	0720	0.3	1310	5.0	1918	0.5
29 F	0030	5.2	0711	-0.3	1301	5.5	1918	0.2
15 F	0117	4.8	0746	0.3	1339	4.8	1944	0.5
30 SA	0114	5.5	0749	-0.4	1342	5.5	1955	0.1
31 SU	0156	5.5	0828	-0.3	1422	5.5	2034	0.1

APRIL

Day	Time	m	Time	m	Time	m	Time	m
1 M	0235	5.5	0905	-0.1	1501	5.2	2113	0.2
16 TU	0215	4.8	0834	0.4	1433	4.8	2048	0.4
2 TU	0316	5.3	0942	0.1	1541	5.0	2152	0.3
17 W	0247	4.8	0904	0.4	1506	4.7	2122	0.4
3 W	0358	5.1	1022	0.4	1621	4.7	2235	0.5
18 TH	0324	4.8	0935	0.5	1546	4.6	2200	0.5
4 TH	0445	4.7	1108	0.8	1706	4.3	2328	0.8
19 F	0406	4.6	1015	0.8	1630	4.3	2248	0.7
5 F	0545	4.3	1208	1.1	1804	4.0		
20 SA	0457	4.3	1109	1.0	1725	4.1	2353	0.8
6 SA	0047	0.9	0707	4.1	1331	1.3	1930	3.8
21 SU	0604	4.2	1237	1.2	1836	4.0		
7 SU	0231	1.0	0832	4.1	1501	1.3	2052	4.0
22 M	0126	0.8	0730	4.1	1414	1.2	2003	4.0
8 M	0353	0.8	0943	4.3	1611	1.1	2159	4.2
23 TU	0259	0.7	0858	4.5	1534	1.0	2119	4.3
9 TU	0454	0.5	1039	4.7	1705	0.9	2251	4.5
24 W	0414	0.3	1006	4.7	1636	0.8	2221	4.7
10 W	0541	0.4	1126	4.8	1748	0.8	2338	4.7
25 TH	0514	0.1	1102	5.1	1728	0.5	2315	5.0
11 TH	0621	0.3	1207	5.0	1824	0.7		
26 F	0606	-0.1	1152	5.3	1817	0.3		
12 F ●	0016	4.8	0650	0.3	1242	5.0	1853	0.5
27 SA ○	0005	5.2	0649	-0.3	1239	5.3	1857	0.2
13 SA	0049	4.8	0716	0.3	1310	4.8	1919	0.5
28 SU	0051	5.3	0727	-0.3	1321	5.2	1937	0.1
14 SU	0117	4.8	0740	0.3	1335	4.8	1946	0.4
29 M	0134	5.5	0805	-0.1	1401	5.2	2017	0.1
15 M	0145	4.8	0807	0.4	1402	4.8	2016	0.4
30 TU	0216	5.3	0842	0.1	1439	5.1	2057	0.2

ENGLAND – BURNHAM-ON-CROUCH
LAT 51°37'N   LONG 0°48'W
TIMES AND HEIGHTS OF HIGH AND LOW WATERS

YEAR **2002**

TIME ZONE (UTC)
For Summer Time add ONE hour in **non-shaded areas**

MAY

Time	m		Time	m
1 W	0257 5.2 / 0919 0.3 / 1518 4.8 / 2139 0.3	**16** TH	0232 4.8 / 0847 0.5 / 1450 4.7 / 2112 0.4	
2 TH	0341 5.0 / 0958 0.5 / 1557 4.6 / 2222 0.4	**17** F	0312 4.8 / 0923 0.7 / 1530 4.6 / 2154 0.4	
3 F	0428 4.7 / 1042 0.9 / 1640 4.3 / 2315 0.7	**18** SA	0357 4.7 / 1005 0.9 / 1616 4.3 / 2246 0.5	
4 SA	0523 4.3 / 1136 1.2 / 1734 4.1	**19** SU	0452 4.5 / 1101 1.0 / 1713 4.2 / 2348 0.7	
5 SU	0024 0.8 / 0633 4.1 / 1251 1.3 / 1846 4.0	**20** M	0557 4.3 / 1215 1.1 / 1821 4.1	
6 M	0153 0.9 / 0751 4.1 / 1416 1.3 / 2004 4.0	**21** TU	0111 0.5 / 0713 4.3 / 1343 1.1 / 1937 4.2	
7 TU	0312 0.8 / 0901 4.3 / 1531 1.2 / 2112 4.2	**22** W	0236 0.4 / 0830 4.5 / 1501 1.0 / 2046 4.5	
8 W	0412 0.7 / 0959 4.5 / 1627 1.0 / 2208 4.5	**23** TH	0348 0.2 / 0937 4.7 / 1606 0.8 / 2149 4.7	
9 TH	0500 0.5 / 1046 4.7 / 1713 0.8 / 2254 4.6	**24** F	0448 0.1 / 1034 5.0 / 1701 0.5 / 2245 5.0	
10 F	0540 0.4 / 1128 4.8 / 1752 0.7 / 2335 4.7	**25** SA	0540 0.0 / 1126 5.1 / 1754 0.4 / 2339 5.1	
11 SA	0615 0.4 / 1205 4.8 / 1824 0.5	**26** SU	0626 0.0 / 1215 5.2 / 1840 0.3 ○	
12 SU	0013 4.7 / 0644 0.4 / 1238 4.8 / 1854 0.5 ●	**27** M	0029 5.2 / 0706 0.0 / 1300 5.1 / 1923 0.2	
13 M	0048 4.8 / 0714 0.4 / 1308 4.8 / 1926 0.4	**28** TU	0115 5.2 / 0745 0.1 / 1341 5.1 / 2005 0.2	
14 TU	0121 4.8 / 0744 0.4 / 1340 4.8 / 1959 0.4	**29** W	0159 5.2 / 0822 0.3 / 1420 5.0 / 2047 0.2	
15 W	0156 4.8 / 0814 0.5 / 1414 4.8 / 2034 0.4	**30** TH	0241 5.1 / 0859 0.5 / 1459 4.8 / 2129 0.3	
		31 F	0325 4.8 / 0937 0.7 / 1537 4.6 / 2212 0.4	

JUNE

Time	m		Time	m
1 SA	0410 4.6 / 1018 0.9 / 1618 4.5 / 2259 0.5	**16** SU	0352 4.8 / 1000 0.9 / 1609 4.6 / 2242 0.3	
2 SU	0458 4.5 / 1103 1.1 / 1705 4.2 / 2351 0.8	**17** M	0445 4.7 / 1050 1.0 / 1702 4.5 / 2338 0.4	
3 M	0554 4.2 / 1202 1.3 / 1802 4.1	**18** TU	0544 4.6 / 1149 1.1 / 1802 4.5	
4 TU	0059 0.8 / 0657 4.1 / 1316 1.3 / 1907 4.1	**19** W	0049 0.4 / 0649 4.6 / 1306 1.1 / 1907 4.5	
5 W	0211 0.8 / 0804 4.2 / 1432 1.2 / 2013 4.2	**20** TH	0205 0.4 / 0758 4.6 / 1424 1.0 / 2013 4.6	
6 TH	0314 0.8 / 0905 4.3 / 1535 1.1 / 2113 4.3	**21** F	0317 0.3 / 0904 4.7 / 1535 0.9 / 2119 4.7	
7 F	0407 0.7 / 0957 4.6 / 1626 1.0 / 2206 4.5	**22** SA	0420 0.2 / 1006 4.8 / 1638 0.7 / 2220 4.8	
8 SA	0453 0.5 / 1044 4.7 / 1711 0.8 / 2252 4.6	**23** SU	0515 0.2 / 1102 4.8 / 1736 0.5 / 2319 5.0	
9 SU	0534 0.5 / 1126 4.8 / 1752 0.7 / 2338 4.7	**24** M	0606 0.2 / 1154 5.0 / 1828 0.4 ○	
10 M	0616 0.5 / 1207 4.8 / 1831 0.5 ●	**25** TU	0013 5.0 / 0649 0.3 / 1243 5.0 / 1914 0.3	
11 TU	0020 4.8 / 0651 0.5 / 1245 4.8 / 1908 0.4	**26** W	0103 5.1 / 0727 0.4 / 1326 5.0 / 1957 0.3	
12 W	0101 4.8 / 0726 0.5 / 1323 4.8 / 1946 0.4	**27** TH	0147 5.0 / 0804 0.5 / 1405 4.8 / 2039 0.3	
13 TH	0140 5.0 / 0801 0.5 / 1400 4.8 / 2027 0.3	**28** F	0229 5.0 / 0841 0.7 / 1442 4.8 / 2119 0.3	
14 F	0221 5.0 / 0838 0.7 / 1439 4.7 / 2108 0.3	**29** SA	0309 4.8 / 0916 0.8 / 1518 4.7 / 2155 0.4	
15 SA	0304 5.0 / 0917 0.8 / 1522 4.7 / 2152 0.3	**30** SU	0349 4.7 / 0953 0.9 / 1553 4.6 / 2232 0.5	

JULY

Time	m		Time	m
1 M	0428 4.5 / 1028 1.0 / 1633 4.5 / 2311 0.7	**16** TU	0430 5.0 / 1033 0.8 / 1643 4.8 / 2317 0.2	
2 TU	0511 4.3 / 1111 1.1 / 1719 4.3 / 2356 0.8	**17** W	0523 4.8 / 1124 0.9 / 1736 4.7	
3 W	0559 4.2 / 1205 1.2 / 1811 4.2	**18** TH	0016 0.3 / 0619 4.6 / 1227 1.0 / 1834 4.6	
4 TH	0056 0.8 / 0655 4.2 / 1314 1.3 / 1912 4.2	**19** F	0128 0.5 / 0724 4.5 / 1346 1.0 / 1944 4.6	
5 F	0201 0.9 / 0800 4.2 / 1424 1.2 / 2016 4.2	**20** SA	0244 0.5 / 0834 4.5 / 1507 1.0 / 2055 4.6	
6 SA	0305 0.8 / 0902 4.3 / 1530 1.1 / 2118 4.3	**21** SU	0353 0.7 / 0942 4.6 / 1621 0.9 / 2205 4.7	
7 SU	0404 0.8 / 1000 4.6 / 1627 1.0 / 2215 4.5	**22** M	0455 0.5 / 1044 4.7 / 1726 0.7 / 2308 4.8	
8 M	0458 0.7 / 1051 4.7 / 1721 0.8 / 2307 4.7	**23** TU	0548 0.5 / 1140 4.8 / 1823 0.4	
9 TU	0547 0.7 / 1140 4.8 / 1812 0.7 / 2357 4.8	**24** W	0005 5.0 / 0634 0.7 / 1229 5.0 / 1908 0.4 ○	
10 W	0632 0.5 / 1225 5.0 / 1855 0.4 ●	**25** TH	0054 5.0 / 0711 0.7 / 1313 5.0 / 1949 0.3	
11 TH	0045 5.0 / 0711 0.5 / 1308 5.0 / 1937 0.3	**26** F	0136 5.0 / 0747 0.7 / 1351 5.0 / 2027 0.3	
12 F	0129 5.1 / 0749 0.7 / 1350 5.0 / 2019 0.2	**27** SA	0215 5.0 / 0821 0.8 / 1424 4.8 / 2100 0.3	
13 SA	0213 5.1 / 0828 0.7 / 1431 5.0 / 2101 0.2	**28** SU	0249 4.8 / 0852 0.8 / 1455 4.8 / 2130 0.4	
14 SU	0257 5.1 / 0908 0.7 / 1512 5.0 / 2144 0.1	**29** M	0321 4.7 / 0922 0.9 / 1526 4.8 / 2156 0.4	
15 M	0342 5.1 / 0949 0.8 / 1556 5.0 / 2229 0.2	**30** TU	0353 4.7 / 0953 0.9 / 1558 4.7 / 2227 0.5	
		31 W	0428 4.6 / 1030 1.0 / 1636 4.6 / 2304 0.7	

AUGUST

Time	m		Time	m
1 TH	0508 4.5 / 1114 1.1 / 1722 4.5 / 2351 0.8	**16** F	0547 4.6 / 1153 1.0 / 1806 4.7	
2 F	0556 4.3 / 1209 1.2 / 1815 4.2	**17** SA	0047 0.8 / 0650 4.3 / 1312 1.1 / 1919 4.5	
3 SA	0056 0.9 / 0655 4.2 / 1322 1.2 / 1920 4.2	**18** SU	0207 0.9 / 0807 4.2 / 1446 1.1 / 2041 4.3	
4 SU	0209 1.0 / 0806 4.2 / 1437 1.2 / 2032 4.2	**19** M	0329 1.0 / 0923 4.3 / 1611 0.9 / 2157 4.6	
5 M	0321 1.0 / 0918 4.3 / 1549 1.1 / 2142 4.3	**20** TU	0437 1.0 / 1030 4.6 / 1721 0.7 / 2302 4.7	
6 TU	0426 0.9 / 1021 4.6 / 1655 0.9 / 2244 4.6	**21** W	0532 0.9 / 1126 4.8 / 1816 0.4 / 2355 5.0	
7 W	0524 0.8 / 1118 4.8 / 1755 0.7 / 2341 5.0	**22** TH	0619 0.8 / 1214 5.0 / 1857 0.3 ○	
8 TH	0615 0.7 / 1208 5.0 / 1843 0.4 ●	**23** F	0042 5.1 / 0655 0.8 / 1257 5.1 / 1933 0.3	
9 F	0030 5.1 / 0656 0.7 / 1253 5.1 / 1926 0.2	**24** SA	0121 5.1 / 0728 0.8 / 1333 5.0 / 2005 0.3	
10 SA	0116 5.3 / 0734 0.5 / 1335 5.2 / 2007 0.1	**25** SU	0156 5.0 / 0759 0.8 / 1402 5.0 / 2033 0.4	
11 SU	0159 5.3 / 0813 0.5 / 1416 5.3 / 2047 0.0	**26** M	0224 4.8 / 0827 0.8 / 1428 5.0 / 2056 0.4	
12 M	0241 5.5 / 0851 0.5 / 1456 5.3 / 2127 0.0	**27** TU	0249 4.8 / 0854 0.8 / 1454 4.8 / 2119 0.4	
13 TU	0325 5.3 / 0930 0.5 / 1536 5.2 / 2207 0.1	**28** W	0316 4.8 / 0923 0.8 / 1524 4.8 / 2147 0.5	
14 W	0409 5.2 / 1012 0.7 / 1620 5.1 / 2250 0.2	**29** TH	0348 4.7 / 0956 0.8 / 1558 4.7 / 2219 0.7	
15 TH	0455 5.0 / 1059 0.8 / 1708 5.0 / 2340 0.4	**30** F	0425 4.6 / 1035 0.9 / 1637 4.6 / 2259 0.8	
		31 SA	0508 4.5 / 1124 1.1 / 1725 4.3 / 2353 1.0	

TIME ZONE (UTC)
For Summer Time add ONE hour in **non-shaded areas**

ENGLAND – BURNHAM-ON-CROUCH

LAT 51°37′N   LONG 0°48′W

TIMES AND HEIGHTS OF HIGH AND LOW WATERS

YEAR **2002**

SEPTEMBER

Time	m		Time	m
1 SU 0603	4.2		**16** M 0132	1.2
1232	1.2		0740	4.1
1827	4.1		1431	1.1
			2030	4.3
2 M 0117	1.2		**17** TU 0304	1.3
0714	4.1		0903	4.2
1356	1.2		1558	0.9
1949	4.1		2147	4.5
3 TU 0244	1.2		**18** W 0417	1.2
0838	4.2		1010	4.5
1519	1.1		1704	0.7
2115	4.3		2247	4.8
4 W 0358	1.1		**19** TH 0512	1.1
0954	4.5		1105	4.8
1634	0.9		1756	0.4
2225	4.6		2338	5.0
5 TH 0501	0.9		**20** F 0557	0.9
1054	4.8		1152	5.0
1737	0.5		1836	0.3
2323	5.0			
6 F 0554	0.8		**21** SA 0021	5.1
1146	5.1		0635	0.8
1827	0.2		1233	5.1
			O 1908	0.3
7 SA 0013	5.3		**22** SU 0059	5.1
0636	0.5		0705	0.8
1231	5.3		1307	5.1
● 1908	0.1		1936	0.4
8 SU 0059	5.5		**23** M 0130	5.0
0715	0.5		0732	0.3
1314	5.5		1334	5.0
1947	-0.1		2000	0.4
9 M 0141	5.6		**24** TU 0154	5.0
0753	0.4		0800	0.7
1355	5.5		1358	5.0
2027	-0.1		2022	0.5
10 TU 0221	5.6		**25** W 0216	4.8
0831	0.4		0827	0.7
1434	5.6		1424	5.0
2104	0.0		2046	0.5
11 W 0301	5.5		**26** TH 0242	4.8
0911	0.4		0856	0.7
1514	5.5		1453	4.8
2141	0.1		2113	0.5
12 TH 0343	5.2		**27** F 0313	4.8
0952	0.5		0929	0.8
1556	5.2		1527	4.8
2222	0.3		2142	0.7
13 F 0427	5.0		**28** SA 0349	4.7
1036	0.7		1005	0.9
1643	5.0		1604	4.7
2308	0.7		2217	0.9
14 SA 0515	4.6		**29** SU 0430	4.6
1130	0.9		1051	1.0
1741	4.6		1650	4.5
			2304	1.1
15 SU 0008	1.0		**30** M 0523	4.2
0616	4.2		1155	1.2
1249	1.1		1751	4.2
1859	4.3			

OCTOBER

Time	m		Time	m
1 TU 0027	1.3		**16** W 0232	1.6
0630	4.1		0832	4.1
1325	1.2		1532	0.9
1915	4.1		2121	4.5
2 W 0209	1.3		**17** TH 0347	1.3
0802	4.1		0940	4.5
1454	1.0		1634	0.7
2051	4.2		2219	4.7
3 TH 0330	1.2		**18** F 0442	1.1
0924	4.3		1034	4.7
1611	0.8		1724	0.5
2204	4.7		2308	5.0
4 F 0434	1.0		**19** SA 0528	0.9
1025	4.7		1120	5.0
1712	0.4		1804	0.4
2300	5.1		2350	5.1
5 SA 0527	0.8		**20** SU 0608	0.8
1117	5.1		1200	5.0
1804	0.1		1836	0.4
2350	5.3			
6 SU 0614	0.5		**21** M 0026	5.1
1205	5.3		0640	0.8
● 1847	0.0		1235	5.0
			O 1904	0.5
7 M 0036	5.6		**22** TU 0057	5.0
0653	0.4		0707	0.7
1249	5.5		1304	5.0
1925	-0.1		1927	0.5
8 TU 0117	5.6		**23** W 0122	5.0
0732	0.3		0734	0.7
1331	5.6		1330	4.8
2002	-0.1		1952	0.5
9 W 0158	5.6		**24** TH 0146	5.0
0812	0.3		0803	0.7
1411	5.6		1358	4.8
2040	0.0		2017	0.7
10 TH 0237	5.3		**25** F 0214	5.0
0852	0.3		0834	0.7
1452	5.5		1429	4.8
2118	0.2		2045	0.7
11 F 0318	5.2		**26** SA 0245	4.8
0933	0.4		0908	0.7
1535	5.2		1503	4.8
2156	0.5		2115	0.8
12 SA 0359	4.8		**27** SU 0321	4.7
1019	0.7		0946	0.8
1623	5.0		1543	4.7
2241	0.9		2150	0.9
13 SU 0445	4.5		**28** M 0402	4.5
1115	0.9		1033	0.9
1722	4.5		1630	4.5
2338	1.2		2237	1.1
14 M 0545	4.2		**29** TU 0453	4.2
1233	1.0		1135	1.0
1839	4.2		1731	4.2
			2348	1.3
15 TU 0059	1.5		**30** W 0601	4.1
0709	4.0		1300	1.0
1410	1.0		1850	4.2
2007	4.2			
			31 TH 0130	1.5
			0729	4.1
			1427	0.9
			2021	4.3

NOVEMBER

Time	m		Time	m
1 F 0255	1.2		**16** SA 0403	1.2
0847	4.3		0949	4.6
1541	0.5		1642	0.7
2134	4.7		2226	4.7
2 SA 0401	1.0		**17** SU 0452	1.0
0950	4.7		1037	4.7
1643	0.3		1724	0.5
2231	5.1		2309	4.8
3 SU 0456	0.8		**18** M 0533	0.8
1044	5.1		1119	4.8
1736	0.1		1800	0.5
2321	5.3		2347	5.0
4 M 0546	0.5		**19** TU 0611	0.7
1134	5.3		1156	4.9
1822	0.0		1831	0.5
●				
5 TU 0009	5.5		**20** W 0020	5.0
0632	0.4		0641	0.7
1221	5.5		1231	4.8
1903	0.0		O 1859	0.7
6 W 0053	5.5		**21** TH 0051	5.0
0713	0.3		0711	0.5
1307	5.6		1304	4.8
1940	0.1		1927	0.7
7 TH 0134	5.3		**22** F 0121	5.0
0755	0.3		0744	0.5
1350	5.5		1337	4.8
2018	0.2		1957	0.7
8 F 0215	5.2		**23** SA 0152	4.8
0837	0.3		0818	0.5
1433	5.3		1412	4.8
2056	0.4		2027	0.8
9 SA 0255	5.1		**24** SU 0225	4.8
0921	0.4		0856	0.5
1518	5.2		1449	4.8
2136	0.7		2100	0.9
10 SU 0335	4.8		**25** M 0302	4.7
1008	0.5		0936	0.7
1607	4.8		1531	4.7
2219	1.0		2138	1.0
11 M 0419	4.5		**26** TU 0344	4.6
1103	0.8		1023	0.8
1702	4.5		1620	4.6
2311	1.3		2225	1.1
12 TU 0514	4.2		**27** W 0434	4.3
1212	0.9		1121	0.8
1810	4.2		1718	4.5
			2326	1.2
13 W 0020	1.6		**28** TH 0538	4.2
0626	4.1		1234	0.8
1336	0.9		1827	4.3
1928	4.2			
14 TH 0146	1.6		**29** F 0047	1.3
0745	4.1		0653	4.2
1451	0.9		1354	0.7
2038	4.3		1946	4.5
15 F 0303	1.5		**30** SA 0210	1.2
0902	4.3		0808	4.5
1552	0.8		1508	0.5
2138	4.6		2056	4.6

DECEMBER

Time	m		Time	m
1 SU 0323	1.0		**16** M 0405	1.1
0913	4.7		0948	4.5
1611	0.3		1636	0.8
2157	4.8		2223	4.6
2 M 0424	0.8		**17** TU 0453	0.9
1011	5.0		1037	4.6
1707	0.2		1718	0.7
2251	5.1		2307	4.7
3 TU 0521	0.5		**18** W 0536	0.8
1106	5.2		1122	4.7
1758	0.1		1759	0.7
2343	5.2		2348	4.8
4 W 0613	0.4		**19** TH 0617	0.7
1158	5.3		1204	4.8
1842	0.0		1836	0.7
●			O	
5 TH 0030	5.2		**20** F 0025	4.8
0659	0.3		0653	0.5
1248	5.3		1244	4.8
1922	0.2		1909	0.7
6 F 0114	5.1		**21** SA 0103	4.8
0743	0.3		0730	0.5
1334	5.3		1322	5.0
2000	0.4		1943	0.7
7 SA 0156	5.1		**22** SU 0138	4.8
0828	0.3		0808	0.4
1419	5.2		1359	5.0
2039	0.5		2016	0.8
8 SU 0235	5.0		**23** M 0214	4.8
0913	0.3		0848	0.4
1504	5.1		1439	5.0
2118	0.8		2052	0.8
9 M 0316	4.7		**24** TU 0252	4.7
0959	0.4		0930	0.4
1550	4.8		1523	4.8
2157	1.0		2130	0.9
10 TU 0357	4.6		**25** W 0333	4.7
1047	0.5		1015	0.4
1638	4.6		1610	4.7
2240	1.1		2215	0.9
11 W 0443	4.5		**26** TH 0420	4.6
1140	0.5		1104	0.4
1731	4.3		1702	4.6
2332	1.3		2305	1.0
12 TH 0538	4.2		**27** F 0515	4.5
1243	0.9		1202	0.5
1830	4.2		1802	4.5
13 F 0040	1.5		**28** SA 0005	1.1
0642	4.1		0618	4.5
1351	0.9		1313	0.5
1938	4.1		1909	4.5
14 SA 0157	1.5		**29** SU 0122	1.1
0751	4.2		0729	4.5
1453	0.9		1429	0.5
2040	4.2		2018	4.5
15 SU 0308	1.2		**30** M 0242	1.0
0854	4.3		0838	4.6
1548	0.8		1539	0.4
2136	4.5		2125	4.6
			31 TU 0355	0.9
			0945	4.7
			1642	0.4
			2226	4.7

Chart Datum: 2·35 metres below Ordnance Datum (Newlyn)
Register for your **FREE** weekly weather email service from Macmillan Reeds
》》 at **www.nauticaldata.com – NOW!** 《《
weekend weather reports sent to your email address, every Thursday

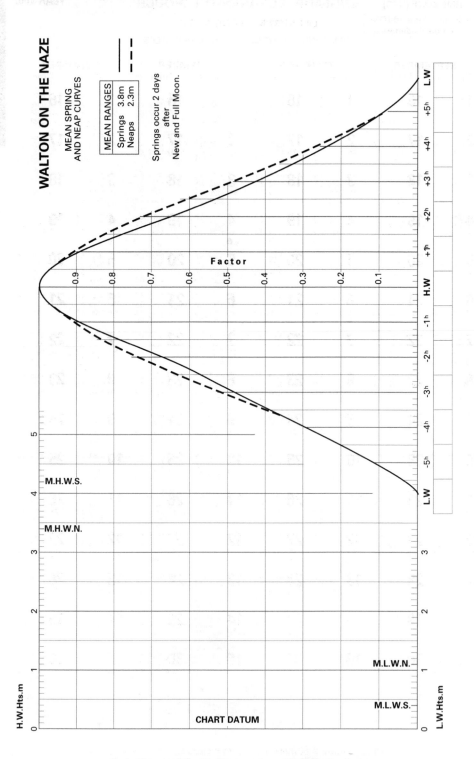

WALTON ON THE NAZE

MEAN SPRING AND NEAP CURVES

MEAN RANGES	
Springs	3.8m
Neaps	2.3m

Springs occur 2 days after New and Full Moon.

Factor

H.W.Hts.m

L.W.Hts.m

M.H.W.S.

M.H.W.N.

M.L.W.N.

M.L.W.S.

CHART DATUM

TIME ZONE (UTC)
For Summer Time add ONE hour in **non-shaded areas**

ENGLAND – WALTON-ON-THE-NAZE

LAT 51°51′N   LONG 1°17′W

YEAR 2002

TIMES AND HEIGHTS OF HIGH AND LOW WATERS

JANUARY

Day	Time m	Time m	Time m	Time m	Day	Time m	Time m	Time m	Time m
1 TU	0031 4.1	0642 0.5	1254 4.2	1856 0.7	**16** W	0107 3.9	0728 0.6	1333 3.9	1920 0.9
2 W	0114 4.1	0730 0.4	1341 4.2	1938 0.8	**17** TH	0138 3.9	0801 0.6	1406 3.8	1951 0.9
3 TH	0158 4.0	0818 0.4	1429 4.2	2022 0.8	**18** F	0209 3.8	0832 0.6	1439 3.8	2023 0.9
4 F	0244 4.0	0909 0.4	1519 4.1	2110 0.8	**19** SA	0243 3.8	0904 0.7	1515 3.7	2100 0.9
5 SA	0334 3.9	1002 0.4	1613 3.9	2202 1.0	**20** SU	0322 3.7	0942 0.7	1555 3.6	2142 1.0
6 SU	0428 3.8	1102 0.5	1712 3.7	2301 1.1	**21** M	0406 3.6	1028 0.8	1641 3.5	2232 1.1
7 M	0530 3.7	1208 0.6	1816 3.6		**22** TU	0457 3.5	1123 0.9	1736 3.4	2333 1.2
8 TU	0012 1.2	0638 3.6	1318 0.7	1923 3.6	**23** W	0558 3.4	1227 1.0	1840 3.3	
9 W	0129 1.1	0746 3.6	1423 0.7	2029 3.6	**24** TH	0042 1.3	0706 3.4	1334 1.0	1948 3.4
10 TH	0239 1.0	0852 3.7	1520 0.7	2129 3.7	**25** F	0152 1.2	0815 3.6	1439 1.0	2054 3.5
11 F	0340 0.9	0952 3.8	1611 0.7	2222 3.8	**26** SA	0259 1.0	0918 3.6	1538 0.9	2152 3.7
12 SA	0435 0.7	1045 3.9	1655 0.7	2310 3.9	**27** SU	0400 0.8	1015 3.9	1630 0.8	2245 3.9
13 SU	0525 0.6	1134 4.0	1736 0.8	● 2353 3.9	**28** M	0455 0.6	1108 4.1	1718 0.7	○ 2333 4.0
14 M	0610 0.6	1217 4.0	1814 0.8		**29** TU	0546 0.4	1157 4.2	1802 0.6	
15 TU	0032 3.9	0651 0.5	1257 3.9	1848 0.8	**30** W	0018 4.1	0634 0.3	1244 4.3	1844 0.6
					31 TH	0103 4.2	0720 0.2	1330 4.4	1925 0.6

FEBRUARY

Day	Time m	Time m	Time m	Time m	Day	Time m	Time m	Time m	Time m
1 F	0147 4.2	0806 0.1	1416 4.3	2008 0.6	**16** SA	0147 3.9	0800 0.6	1411 3.8	1957 0.7
2 SA	0230 4.2	0852 0.2	1502 4.2	2051 0.7	**17** SU	0217 3.9	0829 0.6	1442 3.8	2031 0.7
3 SU	0315 4.2	0939 0.3	1550 4.0	2138 0.8	**18** M	0251 3.9	0903 0.6	1519 3.8	2108 0.8
4 M	0403 4.0	1029 0.4	1641 3.8	2229 0.9	**19** TU	0329 3.8	0941 0.7	1601 3.7	2151 0.9
5 TU	0457 3.8	1127 0.7	1738 3.6	2331 1.1	**20** W	0413 3.6	1027 0.9	1650 3.5	2244 1.1
6 W	0603 3.6	1235 0.9	1845 3.4		**21** TH	0507 3.5	1129 1.0	1750 3.3	2352 1.2
7 TH	0049 1.1	0717 3.5	1348 1.0	1958 3.3	**22** F	0617 3.3	1249 1.1	1901 3.3	
8 F	0215 1.1	0834 3.5	1456 1.0	2107 3.4	**23** SA	0112 1.2	0736 3.3	1407 1.1	2019 3.3
9 SA	0328 0.9	0940 3.7	1553 1.0	2205 3.6	**24** SU	0232 1.0	0854 3.5	1515 1.0	2129 3.5
10 SU	0427 0.7	1035 3.8	1640 0.9	2255 3.8	**25** M	0343 0.8	1000 3.8	1613 0.8	2227 3.8
11 M	0516 0.6	1123 3.9	1720 0.9	2339 3.9	**26** TU	0443 0.5	1055 4.1	1702 0.7	2317 4.0
12 TU	0558 0.5	1205 4.0	1757 0.8	●	**27** W	0534 0.3	1144 4.3	1745 0.6	○
13 W	0017 3.9	0635 0.5	1242 3.9	1829 0.8	**28** TH	0003 4.2	0619 0.1	1230 4.4	1827 0.5
14 TH	0051 3.9	0707 0.5	1314 3.9	1859 0.6					
15 F	0120 3.9	0735 0.5	1343 3.8	1927 0.8					

MARCH

Day	Time m	Time m	Time m	Time m	Day	Time m	Time m	Time m	Time m
1 F	0047 4.3	0703 0.0	1314 4.5	1908 0.4	**16** SA	0056 3.9	0703 0.5	1316 3.9	1902 0.7
2 SA	0129 4.4	0746 0.0	1357 4.4	1949 0.4	**17** SU	0123 3.9	0729 0.5	1342 3.9	1932 0.6
3 SU	0211 4.4	0828 0.1	1440 4.3	2031 0.5	**18** M	0151 3.9	0757 0.5	1412 3.9	2005 0.6
4 M	0253 4.3	0911 0.2	1524 4.1	2114 0.6	**19** TU	0224 3.9	0828 0.6	1448 3.9	2041 0.6
5 TU	0338 4.1	0956 0.5	1609 3.8	2201 0.8	**20** W	0300 3.9	0902 0.7	1528 3.7	2121 0.8
6 W	0428 3.9	1048 0.8	1700 3.5	2258 1.0	**21** TH	0342 3.7	0944 0.9	1614 3.5	2210 0.9
7 TH	0532 3.6	1153 1.0	1805 3.4		**22** F	0434 3.5	1041 1.1	1712 3.3	2318 1.1
8 F	0016 1.1	0654 3.4	1311 1.2	1927 3.1	**23** SA	0542 3.3	1210 1.2	1824 3.1	
9 SA	0154 1.1	0818 3.4	1430 1.2	2044 3.3	**24** SU	0045 1.1	0708 3.3	1340 1.2	1949 3.2
10 SU	0313 0.9	0925 3.6	1532 1.1	2145 3.5	**25** M	0213 1.0	0836 3.5	1454 1.1	2106 3.5
11 M	0411 0.7	1020 3.8	1621 1.0	2236 3.7	**26** TU	0328 0.7	0945 3.8	1552 0.8	2205 3.8
12 TU	0458 0.6	1106 3.9	1701 0.9	2319 3.9	**27** W	0426 0.4	1039 4.1	1641 0.7	2255 4.0
13 W	0537 0.5	1146 4.0	1736 0.8	2356 3.9	**28** TH	0515 0.1	1127 4.3	1725 0.5	○ 2341 4.2
14 TH	0610 0.5	1221 4.0	1808 0.7	●	**29** F	0600 0.0	1211 4.4	1807 0.4	
15 F	0028 3.9	0638 0.5	1251 3.9	1835 0.7	**30** SA	0025 4.4	0641 -0.1	1254 4.4	1847 0.3
					31 SU	0108 4.4	0722 0.0	1336 4.4	1929 0.3

APRIL

Day	Time m	Time m	Time m	Time m	Day	Time m	Time m	Time m	Time m
1 M	0149 4.4	0802 0.1	1417 4.2	2011 0.4	**16** TU	0128 3.9	0729 0.6	1347 3.9	1944 0.6
2 TU	0232 4.3	0843 0.3	1458 4.0	2054 0.5	**17** W	0202 3.9	0801 0.6	1422 3.8	2021 0.6
3 W	0316 4.1	0926 0.6	1540 3.8	2140 0.7	**18** TH	0240 3.9	0835 0.7	1503 3.7	2102 0.7
4 TH	0405 3.8	1015 0.9	1627 3.5	2236 0.9	**19** F	0324 3.7	0918 0.9	1550 3.5	2154 0.8
5 F	0507 3.5	1117 1.2	1727 3.2	2353 1.0	**20** SA	0418 3.5	1016 1.1	1647 3.3	2303 0.9
6 SA	0630 3.3	1235 1.4	1852 3.1		**21** SU	0527 3.4	1144 1.3	1801 3.2	
7 SU	0130 1.1	0752 3.3	1358 1.4	2011 3.2	**22** M	0030 0.9	0652 3.3	1315 1.3	1924 3.2
8 M	0247 0.9	0900 3.5	1504 1.2	2115 3.4	**23** TU	0156 0.8	0817 3.6	1429 1.1	2037 3.5
9 TU	0344 0.7	0954 3.8	1554 1.0	2206 3.6	**24** W	0307 0.5	0922 3.8	1527 0.9	2137 3.8
10 W	0428 0.6	1039 3.9	1635 0.9	2250 3.8	**25** TH	0403 0.3	1016 4.1	1616 0.7	2229 4.0
11 TH	0506 0.5	1118 4.0	1710 0.8	2327 3.9	**26** F	0452 0.1	1104 4.3	1702 0.5	2316 4.2
12 F	0538 0.5	1152 4.0	1741 0.7	● 2359 3.9	**27** SA	0536 0.0	1149 4.3	1745 0.4	○
13 SA	0605 0.5	1221 3.9	1809 0.7		**28** SU	0001 4.3	0617 0.0	1232 4.3	1828 0.3
14 SU	0028 3.9	0631 0.5	1247 3.9	1838 0.6	**29** M	0046 4.4	0658 0.1	1314 4.2	1911 0.3
15 M	0057 3.9	0700 0.6	1310 3.9	1910 0.6	**30** TU	0129 4.3	0738 0.3	1354 4.1	1954 0.4

Chart Datum: 2·16 metres below Ordnance Datum (Newlyn)

ENGLAND – WALTON-ON-THE-NAZE

TIME ZONE (UTC)
For Summer Time add ONE hour in **non-shaded areas**

LAT 51°51'N   LONG 1°17'W

YEAR 2002

TIMES AND HEIGHTS OF HIGH AND LOW WATERS

MAY

	Time	m		Time	m
1	0212	4.2	**16**	0146	3.9
	0818	0.5		0743	0.7
W	1434	3.9	TH	1405	3.8
	2039	0.5		2010	0.6
2	0258	4.0	**17**	0228	3.9
	0900	0.7		0822	0.8
TH	1515	3.7	F	1447	3.7
	2126	0.6		2056	0.6
3	0347	3.8	**18**	0315	3.8
	0947	1.0		0908	1.0
F	1600	3.5	SA	1535	3.5
	2222	0.8		2151	0.7
4	0445	3.5	**19**	0412	3.6
	1045	1.3		1007	1.1
SA	1656	3.3	SU	1634	3.4
	2332	0.9		2258	0.8
5	0558	3.3	**20**	0520	3.5
	1157	1.4		1123	1.2
SU	1810	3.2	M	1745	3.3
6	0055	1.0	**21**	0016	0.7
	0713	3.3		0636	3.5
M	1317	1.4	TU	1246	1.2
	1925	3.2		1859	3.4
7	0208	0.9	**22**	0135	0.6
	0820	3.5		0750	3.6
TU	1426	1.3	W	1358	1.1
	2030	3.4		2006	3.6
8	0305	0.8	**23**	0242	0.4
	0915	3.6		0854	3.8
W	1519	1.1	TH	1459	0.9
	2124	3.6		2106	3.8
9	0350	0.7	**24**	0338	0.3
	1001	3.8		0949	4.0
TH	1602	0.9	F	1551	0.7
	2209	3.7		2200	4.0
10	0427	0.6	**25**	0427	0.2
	1041	3.9		1039	4.1
F	1638	0.8	SA	1640	0.6
	2248	3.8		2251	4.1
11	0500	0.6	**26**	0512	0.2
	1116	3.9		1126	4.2
SA	1710	0.7	SU	1727	0.5
	2324	3.8		○ 2340	4.2
12	0531	0.6	**27**	0555	0.2
	1148	3.9		1210	4.1
SU	1742	0.7	M	1813	0.4
	● 2358	3.9			
13	0603	0.6	**28**	0026	4.2
	1219	3.9		0636	0.3
M	1816	0.6	TU	1253	4.1
				1858	0.4
14	0032	3.9	**29**	0112	4.2
	0635	0.6		0716	0.5
TU	1252	3.9	W	1334	4.0
	1851	0.6		1943	0.4
15	0108	3.9	**30**	0156	4.1
	0708	0.7		0756	0.7
W	1327	3.9	TH	1414	3.9
	1929	0.6		2028	0.5
			31	0241	3.9
				0837	0.8
			F	1454	3.7
				2115	0.6

JUNE

	Time	m		Time	m
1	0328	3.7	**16**	0310	3.9
	0921	1.0		0902	1.0
SA	1537	3.6	SU	1527	3.7
	2205	0.7		2147	0.5
2	0419	3.6	**17**	0405	3.8
	1011	1.2		0956	1.1
SU	1626	3.4	M	1623	3.6
	2301	0.9		2247	0.6
3	0517	3.4	**18**	0506	3.7
	1111	1.4		1059	1.2
M	1725	3.3	TU	1725	3.6
				2355	0.6
4	0005	0.9	**19**	0613	3.7
	0621	3.3		1211	1.2
TU	1221	1.4	W	1830	3.6
	1830	3.3			
5	0112	0.9	**20**	0106	0.6
	0725	3.4		0719	3.7
W	1331	1.3	TH	1324	1.1
	1934	3.4		1934	3.7
6	0210	0.9	**21**	0213	0.5
	0824	3.5		0823	3.8
TH	1430	1.2	F	1430	1.0
	2031	3.5		2037	3.8
7	0300	0.8	**22**	0312	0.4
	0916	3.7		0922	3.9
F	1518	1.1	SA	1529	0.8
	2122	3.6		2136	3.9
8	0343	0.7	**23**	0404	0.4
	0959	3.8		1016	3.9
SA	1600	0.9	SU	1623	0.7
	2207	3.7		2232	4.0
9	0422	0.7	**24**	0452	0.4
	1039	3.9		1106	4.0
SU	1638	0.8	M	1714	0.6
	2250	3.8		○ 2324	4.0
10	0501	0.7	**25**	0536	0.5
	1118	3.9		1153	4.0
M	1717	0.7	TU	1803	0.5
	● 2331	3.9			
11	0539	0.7	**26**	0013	4.1
	1155	3.9		0617	0.6
TU	1757	0.6	W	1237	4.0
				1849	0.5
12	0011	3.9	**27**	0059	4.0
	0616	0.7		0657	0.7
W	1234	3.9	TH	1318	3.9
	1838	0.6		1934	0.5
13	0052	4.0	**28**	0143	4.0
	0654	0.7		0736	0.8
TH	1313	3.9	F	1357	3.9
	1921	0.5		2017	0.5
14	0135	4.0	**29**	0225	3.9
	0733	0.8		0814	0.9
F	1354	3.8	SA	1434	3.8
	2006	0.5		2057	0.6
15	0220	4.0	**30**	0306	3.8
	0815	0.9		0852	1.0
SA	1438	3.8	SU	1511	3.7
	2054	0.5		2136	0.7

JULY

	Time	m		Time	m
1	0347	3.6	**16**	0350	4.0
	0932	1.1		0938	0.9
M	1553	3.6	TU	1603	3.9
	2218	0.8		2225	0.4
2	0432	3.5	**17**	0444	3.9
	1018	1.2		1032	1.0
TU	1640	3.5	W	1658	3.8
	2306	0.9		2324	0.6
3	0522	3.4	**18**	0543	3.7
	1114	1.3		1135	1.1
W	1735	3.4	TH	1759	3.7
4	0002	0.9	**19**	0032	0.7
	0619	3.4		0647	3.6
TH	1219	1.4	F	1249	1.1
	1835	3.4		1906	3.7
5	0103	1.0	**20**	0142	0.7
	0721	3.4		0754	3.6
F	1324	1.3	SA	1404	1.1
	1937	3.4		2014	3.7
6	0202	0.9	**21**	0247	0.6
	0821	3.5		0859	3.7
SA	1425	1.2	SU	1513	1.0
	2036	3.5		2121	3.8
7	0257	0.9	**22**	0345	0.7
	0916	3.7		0959	3.8
SU	1519	1.1	M	1614	0.8
	2131	3.6		2222	3.9
8	0348	0.8	**23**	0435	0.7
	1006	3.8		1052	3.9
M	1609	0.9	TU	1709	0.6
	2221	3.8		2316	4.0
9	0434	0.8	**24**	0520	0.8
	1052	3.9		1140	4.0
TU	1657	0.8	W	1757	0.6
	2309	3.9		○	
10	0518	0.7	**25**	0004	4.0
	1136	4.0		0600	0.8
W	1743	0.6	TH	1224	4.0
	● 2355	4.0		1841	0.5
11	0600	0.7	**26**	0048	4.0
	1219	4.0		0639	0.8
TH	1828	0.5	F	1303	4.0
				1921	0.5
12	0040	4.1	**27**	0128	4.0
	0641	0.8		0715	0.9
F	1302	4.0	SA	1338	3.9
	1913	0.4		1957	0.5
13	0126	4.1	**28**	0204	3.9
	0722	0.8		0748	0.9
SA	1345	4.0	SU	1410	3.9
	1958	0.4		2029	0.6
14	0212	4.1	**29**	0237	3.8
	0805	0.8		0821	1.0
SU	1428	4.0	M	1442	3.9
	2045	0.3		2058	0.6
15	0259	4.1	**30**	0311	3.8
	0850	0.9		0855	1.0
M	1514	4.0	TU	1516	3.8
	2133	0.4		2131	0.7
			31	0347	3.7
				0934	1.1
			W	1556	3.7
				2211	0.8

AUGUST

	Time	m		Time	m
1	0429	3.6	**16**	0510	3.7
	1021	1.2		1103	1.1
TH	1643	3.6	F	1729	3.8
	2301	0.9		2353	0.9
2	0519	3.5	**17**	0614	3.5
	1118	1.3		1217	1.2
F	1739	3.4	SA	1842	3.6
3	0002	1.0	**18**	0108	1.0
	0619	3.4		0728	3.4
SA	1226	1.3	SU	1344	1.2
	1843	3.4		2001	3.5
4	0110	1.1	**19**	0224	1.1
	0727	3.4		0841	3.5
SU	1336	1.3	M	1504	1.0
	1952	3.4		2114	3.7
5	0217	1.1	**20**	0328	1.1
	0836	3.5		0945	3.7
M	1443	1.2	TU	1609	0.8
	2059	3.5		2216	3.8
6	0318	1.0	**21**	0420	1.0
	0937	3.7		1039	3.9
TU	1545	1.0	W	1701	0.6
	2159	3.7		2307	4.0
7	0412	0.9	**22**	0504	0.9
	1031	3.9		1125	4.0
W	1641	0.8	TH	1745	0.5
	2253	4.0		○ 2352	4.1
8	0500	0.8	**23**	0543	0.9
	1119	4.0		1207	4.1
TH	1730	0.6	F	1824	0.5
	● 2341	4.1			
9	0544	0.8	**24**	0032	4.1
	1203	4.1		0618	0.9
F	1816	0.4	SA	1244	4.0
				1858	0.5
10	0027	4.3	**25**	0108	4.0
	0625	0.7		0651	0.9
SA	1247	4.2	SU	1315	4.0
	1900	0.3		1928	0.6
11	0112	4.3	**26**	0138	3.9
	0706	0.7		0721	0.9
SU	1329	4.3	M	1342	4.0
	1943	0.2		1953	0.6
12	0156	4.4	**27**	0204	3.9
	0747	0.7		0750	0.9
M	1411	4.3	TU	1409	3.9
	2026	0.2		2018	0.6
13	0241	4.3	**28**	0232	3.9
	0830	0.7		0822	0.9
TU	1453	4.2	W	1440	3.9
	2110	0.3		2048	0.7
14	0327	4.2	**29**	0305	3.8
	0915	0.8		0858	0.9
W	1539	4.1	TH	1516	3.8
	2156	0.4		2123	0.8
15	0416	4.0	**30**	0344	3.7
	1005	0.9		0940	1.0
TH	1629	4.0	F	1557	3.7
	2249	0.6		2205	0.9
			31	0429	3.6
				1032	1.2
			SA	1647	3.5
				2303	1.1

Chart Datum: 2·16 metres below Ordnance Datum (Newlyn)
Register for your **FREE** weekly weather email service from Macmillan Reeds
》》 at **www.nauticaldata.com – NOW!** 《《
weekend weather reports sent to your email address, every Thursday

TIME ZONE (UTC)
For Summer Time add ONE hour in **non-shaded areas**

ENGLAND – WALTON-ON-THE-NAZE

YEAR **2002**

LAT 51°51′N   LONG 1°17′W

TIMES AND HEIGHTS OF HIGH AND LOW WATERS

SEPTEMBER
Time m   Time m

1 0526 3.4 / 1139 1.3 / SU 1752 3.3
16 0036 1.3 / 0702 3.3 / M 1330 1.2 / 1950 3.5

2 0022 1.3 / 0637 3.3 / M 1258 1.3 / 1911 3.3
17 0201 1.4 / 0822 3.4 / TU 1452 1.0 / 2104 3.6

3 0142 1.3 / 0758 3.4 / TU 1415 1.2 / 2033 3.5
18 0309 1.3 / 0926 3.6 / W 1553 0.8 / 2202 3.9

4 0252 1.2 / 0911 3.6 / W 1525 1.0 / 2141 3.7
19 0401 1.2 / 1019 3.8 / TH 1642 0.6 / 2250 4.0

5 0351 1.0 / 1009 3.9 / TH 1624 0.7 / 2236 4.0
20 0443 1.0 / 1104 4.0 / F 1722 0.5 / 2332 4.1

6 0440 0.9 / 1058 4.1 / F 1713 0.4 / 2324 4.3
21 0521 0.9 / 1144 4.1 / SA 1757 0.5 ○

7 0523 0.7 / 1142 4.3 / SA 1757 0.3 ●
22 0009 4.1 / 0554 0.9 / SU 1218 4.1 / 1827 0.6

8 0009 4.4 / 0604 0.7 / SU 1225 4.4 / 1839 0.1
23 0041 4.0 / 0624 0.9 / M 1246 4.0 / 1853 0.6

9 0053 4.5 / 0645 0.6 / M 1307 4.4 / 1921 0.1
24 0106 4.0 / 0652 0.8 / TU 1311 4.0 / 1916 0.7

10 0135 4.5 / 0726 0.6 / TU 1348 4.5 / 2001 0.2
25 0130 3.9 / 0721 0.8 / W 1338 4.0 / 1942 0.7

11 0217 4.4 / 0809 0.6 / W 1430 4.4 / 2042 0.3
26 0157 3.9 / 0753 0.8 / TH 1408 3.9 / 2011 0.7

12 0300 4.2 / 0853 0.7 / TH 1514 4.3 / 2126 0.5
27 0229 3.9 / 0828 0.9 / F 1443 3.9 / 2043 0.8

13 0346 4.0 / 0941 0.8 / F 1603 4.0 / 2215 0.8
28 0306 3.8 / 0908 1.0 / SA 1522 3.8 / 2120 1.0

14 0436 3.7 / 1039 1.0 / SA 1703 3.7 / 2317 1.1
29 0350 3.7 / 0957 1.1 / SU 1610 3.6 / 2211 1.0

15 0540 3.4 / 1155 1.2 / SU 1823 3.5
30 0444 3.4 / 1105 1.3 / M 1714 3.4 / 2335 1.4

OCTOBER
Time m   Time m

1 0555 3.3 / 1229 1.3 / TU 1838 3.3
16 0131 1.6 / 0752 3.3 / W 1427 1.0 / 2039 3.6

2 0110 1.4 / 0723 3.3 / W 1352 1.1 / 2010 3.4
17 0241 1.4 / 0857 3.6 / TH 1525 0.8 / 2135 3.8

3 0225 1.3 / 0842 3.5 / TH 1504 0.9 / 2120 3.8
18 0333 1.2 / 0949 3.8 / F 1612 0.7 / 2222 4.0

4 0325 1.1 / 0941 3.8 / F 1601 0.6 / 2214 4.1
19 0416 1.0 / 1033 4.0 / SA 1650 0.6 / 2302 4.1

5 0415 0.9 / 1030 4.1 / SA 1650 0.3 / 2302 4.3
20 0453 0.9 / 1112 4.0 / SU 1723 0.6 / 2337 4.1

6 0459 0.7 / 1116 4.3 / SU 1734 0.2 / 2346 4.5 ●
21 0527 0.9 / 1145 4.0 / M 1752 0.7 ○

7 0541 0.6 / 1159 4.4 / M 1815 0.1
22 0007 4.0 / 0556 0.8 / TU 1214 4.0 / 1817 0.7

8 0028 4.5 / 0622 0.5 / TU 1242 4.5 / 1855 0.1
23 0033 4.0 / 0625 0.8 / W 1241 3.9 / 1844 0.7

9 0111 4.5 / 0705 0.5 / W 1324 4.5 / 1935 0.2
24 0058 4.0 / 0656 0.8 / TH 1311 3.9 / 1911 0.8

10 0152 4.3 / 0748 0.5 / TH 1407 4.4 / 2016 0.4
25 0127 4.0 / 0729 0.8 / F 1343 3.9 / 1941 0.8

11 0234 4.2 / 0833 0.6 / F 1452 4.2 / 2058 0.7
26 0200 3.9 / 0806 0.8 / SA 1419 3.9 / 2013 0.9

12 0317 3.9 / 0923 0.8 / SA 1542 4.0 / 2146 1.0
27 0237 3.8 / 0847 0.9 / SU 1500 3.8 / 2051 1.0

13 0405 3.6 / 1022 1.0 / SU 1643 3.6 / 2247 1.3
28 0320 3.6 / 0937 1.0 / M 1550 3.6 / 2142 1.2

14 0507 3.4 / 1140 1.1 / M 1804 3.4
29 0413 3.4 / 1044 1.1 / TU 1653 3.4 / 2258 1.4

15 0005 1.5 / 0632 3.2 / TU 1311 1.1 / 1928 3.4
30 0524 3.3 / 1206 1.1 / W 1814 3.4

31 0034 1.5 / 0651 3.3 / TH 1327 1.0 / 1942 3.5

NOVEMBER
Time m   Time m

1 0153 1.3 / 0807 3.5 / F 1436 0.7 / 2051 3.8
16 0256 1.3 / 0906 3.7 / SA 1533 0.8 / 2142 3.8

2 0254 1.1 / 0907 3.8 / SA 1534 0.5 / 2146 4.1
17 0342 1.1 / 0952 3.8 / SU 1612 0.7 / 2223 3.9

3 0346 0.9 / 0959 4.1 / SU 1623 0.3 / 2234 4.3
18 0421 0.9 / 1032 3.9 / M 1646 0.7 / 2259 4.0

4 0433 0.7 / 1047 4.3 / M 1708 0.2 / 2320 4.4 ●
19 0456 0.8 / 1108 3.9 / TU 1717 0.7 / 2331 4.0

5 0518 0.6 / 1132 4.4 / TU 1751 0.2
20 0528 0.8 / 1142 3.9 / W 1747 0.8 ○

6 0003 4.4 / 0602 0.5 / W 1218 4.5 / 1831 0.3
21 0001 4.0 / 0600 0.7 / TH 1215 3.9 / 1817 0.8

7 0046 4.3 / 0647 0.5 / TH 1302 4.4 / 1912 0.4
22 0032 4.0 / 0635 0.7 / F 1249 3.9 / 1849 0.8

8 0128 4.2 / 0732 0.5 / F 1347 4.3 / 1953 0.6
23 0104 3.9 / 0712 0.7 / SA 1325 3.9 / 1921 0.9

9 0210 4.1 / 0820 0.6 / SA 1434 4.2 / 2036 0.8
24 0139 3.9 / 0752 0.7 / SU 1404 3.9 / 1957 1.0

10 0252 3.9 / 0911 0.7 / SU 1525 3.9 / 2122 1.1
25 0218 3.8 / 0836 0.8 / M 1448 3.8 / 2038 1.1

11 0338 3.6 / 1010 0.9 / M 1623 3.6 / 2218 1.4
26 0301 3.7 / 0927 0.9 / TU 1539 3.7 / 2129 1.2

12 0435 3.4 / 1121 1.0 / TU 1734 3.4 / 2328 1.6
27 0354 3.5 / 1029 0.9 / W 1639 3.6 / 2234 1.3

13 0551 3.3 / 1239 1.0 / W 1850 3.4
28 0500 3.4 / 1141 0.9 / TH 1752 3.5 / 2353 1.4

14 0049 1.6 / 0707 3.3 / TH 1349 1.0 / 1958 3.5
29 0617 3.4 / 1256 0.8 / F 1908 3.6

15 0200 1.5 / 0812 3.5 / F 1446 0.9 / 2055 3.7
30 0111 1.3 / 0729 3.6 / SA 1405 0.7 / 2015 3.7

DECEMBER
Time m   Time m

1 0219 1.1 / 0831 3.8 / SU 1504 0.5 / 2114 3.9
16 0258 1.2 / 0905 3.6 / M 1527 0.9 / 2139 3.7

2 0316 0.9 / 0927 4.0 / M 1556 0.4 / 2206 4.1
17 0343 1.0 / 0952 3.7 / TU 1607 0.8 / 2221 3.8

3 0409 0.7 / 1020 4.2 / TU 1644 0.3 / 2255 4.2
18 0423 0.9 / 1035 3.8 / W 1645 0.8 / 2300 3.9

4 0458 0.6 / 1110 4.3 / W 1729 0.4 / 2341 4.2 ●
19 0502 0.8 / 1115 3.9 / TH 1722 0.8 / 2336 3.9 ○

5 0547 0.5 / 1158 4.3 / TH 1812 0.4
20 0541 0.7 / 1154 3.9 / F 1758 0.8

6 0025 4.1 / 0634 0.5 / F 1246 4.3 / 1853 0.6
21 0013 3.9 / 0620 0.7 / SA 1233 4.0 / 1834 0.9

7 0108 4.1 / 0722 0.5 / SA 1333 4.2 / 1934 0.7
22 0050 3.9 / 0701 0.6 / SU 1312 4.0 / 1910 0.9

8 0150 4.0 / 0811 0.5 / SU 1420 4.1 / 2016 0.9
23 0127 3.9 / 0744 0.6 / M 1354 4.0 / 1948 0.9

9 0232 3.8 / 0901 0.6 / M 1507 3.9 / 2059 1.1
24 0207 3.8 / 0829 0.6 / TU 1439 3.9 / 2030 1.0

10 0315 3.7 / 0953 0.7 / TU 1558 3.7 / 2145 1.3
25 0250 3.8 / 0918 0.6 / W 1528 3.8 / 2118 1.0

11 0403 3.6 / 1049 0.9 / W 1653 3.5 / 2241 1.4
26 0339 3.7 / 1011 0.6 / TH 1623 3.7 / 2212 1.1

12 0500 3.4 / 1150 1.0 / TH 1755 3.4 / 2347 1.5
27 0436 3.6 / 1111 0.7 / F 1725 3.6 / 2314 1.2

13 0607 3.3 / 1253 1.0 / F 1900 3.3
28 0542 3.6 / 1218 0.7 / SA 1832 3.6

14 0059 1.5 / 0713 3.4 / SA 1351 1.0 / 2000 3.4
29 0026 1.2 / 0651 3.6 / SU 1329 0.7 / 1939 3.6

15 0205 1.3 / 0813 3.5 / SU 1442 0.9 / 2053 3.6
30 0141 1.1 / 0758 3.7 / M 1434 0.6 / 2043 3.7

31 0249 1.0 / 0902 3.8 / TU 1533 0.6 / 2142 3.8

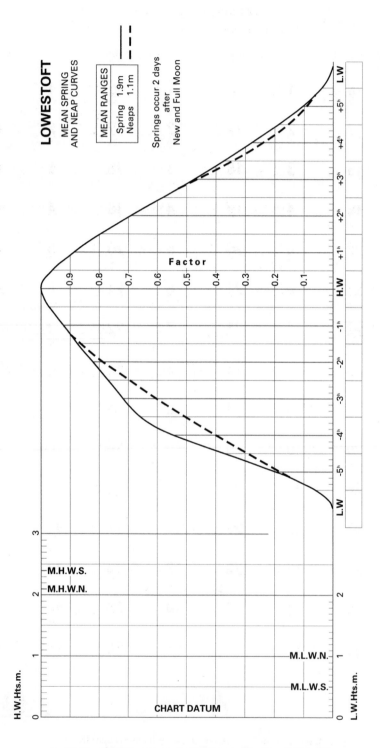

LOWESTOFT

MEAN SPRING
AND NEAP CURVES

MEAN RANGES	
Spring	1.9m
Neaps	1.1m

Springs occur 2 days
after
New and Full Moon

Factor

0.9 0.8 0.7 0.6 0.5 0.4 0.3 0.2 0.1

H.W.Hts.m.

M.H.W.S.
M.H.W.N.

M.L.W.N.
M.L.W.S.

CHART DATUM

L.W.Hts.m.

TIME ZONE (UTC)
For Summer Time add ONE hour in **non-shaded areas**

ENGLAND – LOWESTOFT

LAT 52°28′N   LONG 1°45′W

TIMES AND HEIGHTS OF HIGH AND LOW WATERS

YEAR **2002**

JANUARY

Day	Time m	Time m	Time m	Time m		Day	Time m	Time m	Time m	Time m
1 TU	0428 0.6	1045 2.5	1639 0.8	2249 2.6		**16** W	0520 0.5	1135 2.2	1658 1.0	2312 2.5
2 W	0515 0.5	1132 2.5	1721 0.8	2329 2.6		**17** TH	0552 0.6	1208 2.2	1725 1.0	2345 2.5
3 TH	0602 0.4	1221 2.4	1803 0.9			**18** F	0625 0.6	1242 2.1	1754 1.0	
4 F	0012 2.6	0650 0.5	1315 2.4	1846 1.0		**19** SA	0020 2.5	0701 0.7	1323 2.1	1827 1.1
5 SA	0058 2.5	0744 0.5	1418 2.2	1934 1.1		**20** SU	0059 2.4	0744 0.8	1411 2.0	1908 1.1
6 SU	0149 2.5	0845 0.6	1529 2.2	2029 1.2		**21** M	0143 2.3	0839 0.9	1509 2.0	1958 1.2
7 M	0246 2.4	0954 0.6	1636 2.1	2134 1.2		**22** TU	0233 2.3	0940 0.9	1612 2.0	2104 1.3
8 TU	0405 2.3	1107 0.7	1736 2.2	2320 1.2		**23** W	0329 2.2	1039 0.9	1713 2.0	2244 1.3
9 W	0531 2.3	1215 0.7	1830 2.2			**24** TH	0438 2.2	1135 0.9	1809 2.1	2354 1.2
10 TH	0042 1.0	0639 2.3	1314 0.7	1917 2.3		**25** F	0556 2.2	1229 0.9	1859 2.2	
11 F	0142 0.9	0739 2.3	1406 0.8	2002 2.3		**26** SA	0053 1.0	0700 2.2	1322 0.8	1944 2.3
12 SA	0233 0.7	0836 2.3	1452 0.8	2044 2.4		**27** SU	0150 0.9	0759 2.3	1412 0.8	2027 2.4
13 SU	0321 0.6	0929 2.3	1532 0.9	●2124 2.4		**28** M	0244 0.7	0855 2.4	1501 0.8	○2109 2.5
14 M	0404 0.5	1016 2.3	1607 0.9	2203 2.5		**29** TU	0336 0.5	0948 2.4	1547 0.7	2152 2.6
15 TU	0444 0.5	1058 2.3	1634 1.0	2239 2.5		**30** W	0424 0.4	1037 2.5	1630 0.7	2234 2.7
						31 TH	0509 0.2	1123 2.5	1710 0.7	2316 2.7

FEBRUARY

Day	Time m	Time m	Time m	Time m		Day	Time m	Time m	Time m	Time m
1 F	0553 0.2	1208 2.4	1749 0.7	2358 2.7		**16** SA	0553 0.6	1204 2.2	1729 0.9	2357 2.5
2 SA	0637 0.2	1254 2.3	1829 0.8			**17** SU	0620 0.6	1237 2.1	1801 0.9	
3 SU	0042 2.6	0723 0.3	1346 2.2	1911 0.9		**18** M	0034 2.4	0650 0.7	1315 2.1	1837 0.9
4 M	0130 2.5	0813 0.6	1448 2.1	2000 1.0		**19** TU	0116 2.3	0726 0.8	1358 2.0	1920 1.0
5 TU	0225 2.4	0911 0.7	1557 2.0	2100 1.1		**20** W	0203 2.2	0817 0.9	1449 2.0	2012 1.1
6 W	0344 2.2	1021 0.8	1701 2.0	2222 1.1		**21** TH	0256 2.1	0949 1.0	1559 1.9	2127 1.2
7 TH	0518 2.2	1149 0.9	1759 2.1			**22** F	0359 2.1	1101 1.0	1722 2.0	2322 1.1
8 F	0030 1.0	0632 2.2	1302 0.9	1851 2.1		**23** SA	0520 2.1	1203 1.0	1823 2.1	
9 SA	0134 0.8	0737 2.2	1357 1.0	1939 2.2		**24** SU	0033 1.0	0642 2.2	1303 0.9	1914 2.2
10 SU	0225 0.7	0835 2.2	1443 1.0	2024 2.3		**25** M	0137 0.8	0750 2.3	1359 0.9	2001 2.3
11 M	0311 0.6	0925 2.3	1523 1.0	2106 2.4		**26** TU	0234 0.5	0847 2.4	1450 0.8	2046 2.5
12 TU	0353 0.5	1008 2.3	1556 1.0	2144 2.4		**27** W	0324 0.3	0937 2.4	1535 0.7	○2132 2.6
13 W	0430 0.5	1042 2.2	1619 1.0	2220 2.5		**28** TH	0411 0.1	1022 2.5	1617 0.6	2216 2.7
14 TH	0500 0.5	1110 2.2	1638 0.9	2252 2.5						
15 F	0527 0.5	1136 2.2	1701 0.9	2324 2.5						

MARCH

Day	Time m	Time m	Time m	Time m		Day	Time m	Time m	Time m	Time m
1 F	0454 0.0	1104 2.5	1657 0.6	2259 2.7		**16** SA	0455 0.5	1101 2.3	1639 0.8	2301 2.4
2 SA	0536 0.0	1145 2.4	1734 0.6	2342 2.7		**17** SU	0520 0.5	1130 2.2	1707 0.7	2335 2.4
3 SU	0616 0.1	1225 2.3	1811 0.6			**18** M	0545 0.6	1201 2.2	1739 0.7	
4 M	0026 2.6	0657 0.3	1308 2.2	1851 0.7		**19** TU	0012 2.4	0613 0.7	1236 2.1	1814 0.8
5 TU	0113 2.5	0743 0.5	1358 2.1	1938 0.8		**20** W	0053 2.3	0648 0.8	1315 2.1	1854 0.8
6 W	0209 2.3	0836 0.8	1508 2.0	2038 0.9		**21** TH	0140 2.2	0733 0.9	1401 2.0	1944 1.0
7 TH	0337 2.1	0938 1.0	1623 2.0	2156 1.0		**22** F	0233 2.1	0835 1.1	1456 1.9	2053 1.0
8 F	0512 2.1	1114 1.1	1727 2.0	2255 1.0		**23** SA	0338 2.1	1025 1.1	1603 1.9	2255 1.0
9 SA	0017 0.9	0627 2.1	1251 1.1	1824 2.1		**24** SU	0206 1.1	1141 1.1	1734 2.0	
10 SU	0119 0.8	0732 2.2	1343 1.1	1915 2.2		**25** M	0016 0.8	0638 2.2	1247 1.0	1839 2.1
11 M	0208 0.6	0826 2.2	1427 1.0	2002 2.3		**26** TU	0121 0.6	0743 2.3	1344 0.9	1932 2.3
12 TU	0252 0.5	0911 2.3	1505 1.0	2044 2.3		**27** W	0216 0.4	0834 2.4	1433 0.8	2021 2.5
13 W	0331 0.5	0947 2.3	1536 0.9	2122 2.4		**28** TH	0305 0.2	0919 2.4	1518 0.6	○2109 2.6
14 TH	0405 0.5	1013 2.3	1559 0.9	●2157 2.4		**29** F	0350 0.0	1000 2.5	1600 0.5	2155 2.7
15 F	0432 0.5	1036 2.2	1617 0.8	2229 2.4		**30** SA	0433 0.0	1039 2.4	1639 0.5	2241 2.7
						31 SU	0513 0.0	1117 2.4	1717 0.4	2325 2.7

APRIL

Day	Time m	Time m	Time m	Time m		Day	Time m	Time m	Time m	Time m
1 M	0553 0.2	1155 2.3	1755 0.5			**16** TU	0517 0.6	1131 2.3	1721 0.6	2352 2.4
2 TU	0010 2.6	0632 0.4	1235 2.2	1835 0.6		**17** W	0549 0.7	1205 2.2	1758 0.7	
3 W	0059 2.4	0714 0.6	1319 2.1	1923 0.7		**18** TH	0033 2.3	0625 0.8	1245 2.1	1840 0.8
4 TH	0201 2.2	0805 0.9	1418 2.1	2025 0.8		**19** F	0121 2.2	0710 1.0	1331 2.1	1933 0.8
5 F	0336 2.1	0905 1.1	1542 2.0	2144 0.9		**20** SA	0217 2.1	0810 1.1	1424 2.0	2044 0.9
6 SA	0503 2.1	1018 1.3	1652 2.0	2349 0.9		**21** SU	0328 2.1	0934 1.2	1525 2.0	2233 0.9
7 SU	0613 2.1	1224 1.2	1753 2.1			**22** M	0510 2.1	1113 1.2	1641 2.1	2355 0.7
8 M	0052 0.7	0713 2.2	1317 1.2	1846 2.2		**23** TU	0629 2.2	1225 1.1	1803 2.2	
9 TU	0141 0.6	0804 2.3	1359 1.1	1934 2.3		**24** W	0058 0.5	0725 2.3	1322 0.9	1903 2.3
10 W	0223 0.6	0845 2.3	1436 1.0	2016 2.3		**25** TH	0152 0.3	0812 2.4	1411 0.8	1956 2.4
11 TH	0300 0.6	0913 2.3	1507 0.9	2054 2.3		**26** F	0241 0.1	0853 2.4	1456 0.6	2046 2.5
12 F	0331 0.6	0935 2.3	1529 0.8	●2129 2.4		**27** SA	0326 0.1	0933 2.4	1540 0.5	○2135 2.6
13 SA	0356 0.6	1001 2.3	1551 0.8	2204 2.4		**28** SU	0409 0.1	1012 2.4	1621 0.4	2223 2.6
14 SU	0421 0.6	1030 2.3	1617 0.7	2239 2.4		**29** M	0450 0.2	1050 2.4	1702 0.4	2309 2.6
15 M	0448 0.6	1101 2.3	1647 0.6	2314 2.4		**30** TU	0529 0.3	1129 2.3	1742 0.4	2357 2.4

Chart Datum: 1·50 metres below Ordnance Datum (Newlyn)
Register for your **FREE** weekly weather email service from Macmillan Reeds
》 at **www.nauticaldata.com – NOW!** 《
weekend weather reports sent to your email address, every Thursday

ENGLAND – LOWESTOFT

LAT 52°28′N LONG 1°45′W

TIMES AND HEIGHTS OF HIGH AND LOW WATERS

YEAR **2002**

TIME ZONE (UTC)
For Summer Time add ONE hour in **non-shaded areas**

MAY

Day	Time	m	Day	Time	m
1 W	0607 / 1208 / 1825	0.5 / 2.3 / 0.5	16 TH	0530 / 1143 / 1750	0.8 / 2.3 / 0.6
2 TH	0049 / 0647 / 1251 / 1914	2.3 / 0.8 / 2.2 / 0.6	17 F	0019 / 0610 / 1223 / 1836	2.3 / 0.9 / 2.3 / 0.7
3 F	0158 / 0735 / 1344 / 2017	2.1 / 1.0 / 2.1 / 0.7	18 SA	0109 / 0657 / 1309 / 1932	2.2 / 1.0 / 2.2 / 0.7
4 SA	0327 / 0833 / 1459 / 2130	2.1 / 1.2 / 2.1 / 0.8	19 SU	0208 / 0753 / 1401 / 2041	2.2 / 1.2 / 2.2 / 0.7
5 SU	0441 / 0937 / 1610 / 2257	2.1 / 1.3 / 2.1 / 0.8	20 M	0332 / 0900 / 1500 / 2210	2.1 / 1.2 / 2.1 / 0.7
6 M	0545 / 1056 / 1713	2.1 / 1.3 / 2.1	21 TU	0458 / 1026 / 1608 / 2327	2.2 / 1.2 / 2.2 / 0.6
7 TU	0011 / 0642 / 1233 / 1808	0.8 / 2.2 / 1.3 / 2.2	22 W	0604 / 1151 / 1731	2.2 / 1.1 / 2.2
8 W	0103 / 0730 / 1320 / 1857	0.7 / 2.2 / 1.2 / 2.2	23 TH	0031 / 0658 / 1254 / 1837	0.4 / 2.3 / 1.0 / 2.3
9 TH	0144 / 0805 / 1357 / 1941	0.7 / 2.3 / 1.0 / 2.3	24 F	0126 / 0744 / 1346 / 1934	0.3 / 2.4 / 0.8 / 2.4
10 F	0218 / 0830 / 1426 / 2020	0.6 / 2.3 / 0.9 / 2.3	25 SA	0216 / 0826 / 1435 / 2028	0.2 / 2.4 / 0.7 / 2.5
11 SA	0248 / 0857 / 1453 / 2059	0.6 / 2.3 / 0.8 / 2.4	26 SU	0302 / 0907 / 1521 / ○ 2119	0.2 / 2.4 / 0.5 / 2.5
12 SU	0317 / 0930 / 1523 / ● 2138	0.6 / 2.3 / 0.8 / 0.8	27 M	0346 / 0947 / 1606 / 2210	0.3 / 2.4 / 0.4 / 2.5
13 M	0347 / 1004 / 1556 / 2217	0.6 / 2.4 / 0.7 / 2.4	28 TU	0428 / 1027 / 1650 / 2259	0.4 / 2.4 / 0.4 / 2.4
14 TU	0420 / 1036 / 1631 / 2255	0.6 / 2.4 / 0.6 / 2.4	29 W	0506 / 1107 / 1733 / 2349	0.5 / 2.4 / 0.4 / 2.3
15 W	0454 / 1109 / 1709 / 2335	0.7 / 2.3 / 0.6 / 2.3	30 TH	0543 / 1147 / 1818	0.7 / 2.4 / 0.5
			31 F	0043 / 0621 / 1228 / 1906	2.2 / 0.9 / 2.3 / 0.6

JUNE

Day	Time	m	Day	Time	m
1 SA	0149 / 0703 / 1315 / 2002	2.1 / 1.1 / 2.3 / 0.7	16 SU	0102 / 0644 / 1253 / 1929	2.3 / 1.0 / 2.4 / 0.6
2 SU	0300 / 0754 / 1414 / 2102	2.1 / 1.2 / 2.2 / 0.7	17 M	0204 / 0735 / 1343 / 2031	2.2 / 1.1 / 2.3 / 0.6
3 M	0404 / 0853 / 1521 / 2201	2.1 / 1.3 / 2.2 / 0.8	18 TU	0321 / 0832 / 1438 / 2142	2.2 / 1.2 / 2.3 / 0.6
4 TU	0502 / 0955 / 1622 / 2300	2.1 / 1.4 / 2.2 / 0.8	19 W	0431 / 0937 / 1543 / 2255	2.2 / 1.2 / 2.3 / 0.5
5 W	0556 / 1059 / 1720 / 2354	2.1 / 1.3 / 2.2 / 0.8	20 TH	0533 / 1105 / 1705	2.2 / 1.2 / 2.3
6 TH	0640 / 1202 / 1812	2.2 / 1.2 / 2.2	21 F	0001 / 0628 / 1224 / 1816	0.5 / 2.3 / 1.0 / 2.3
7 F	0041 / 0714 / 1255 / 1900	0.8 / 2.2 / 1.1 / 2.2	22 SA	0100 / 0716 / 1325 / 1918	0.5 / 2.3 / 1.0 / 2.3
8 SA	0123 / 0748 / 1339 / 1946	0.7 / 2.3 / 1.0 / 2.3	23 SU	0154 / 0801 / 1418 / 2015	0.5 / 2.3 / 0.7 / 2.4
9 SU	0201 / 0825 / 1419 / 2030	0.7 / 2.3 / 0.9 / 2.3	24 M	0243 / 0844 / 1509 / ○ 2111	0.5 / 2.4 / 0.6 / 2.4
10 M	0240 / 0903 / 1459 / ● 2114	0.7 / 2.4 / 0.8 / 2.3	25 TU	0328 / 0927 / 1556 / 2204	0.6 / 2.4 / 0.5 / 2.4
11 TU	0318 / 0941 / 1539 / 2158	0.7 / 2.4 / 0.7 / 2.3	26 W	0410 / 1008 / 1642 / 2255	0.6 / 2.5 / 0.4 / 2.3
12 W	0357 / 1016 / 1620 / 2241	0.7 / 2.4 / 0.6 / 2.4	27 TH	0448 / 1048 / 1726 / 2344	0.7 / 2.5 / 0.4 / 2.3
13 TH	0436 / 1051 / 1703 / 2325	0.7 / 2.4 / 0.6 / 2.4	28 F	0522 / 1127 / 1808	0.9 / 2.5 / 0.5
14 F	0516 / 1127 / 1748	0.8 / 2.4 / 0.6	29 SA	0032 / 0604 / 1206 / 1850	2.2 / 1.0 / 2.5 / 0.5
15 SA	0011 / 0558 / 1208 / 1835	2.3 / 0.9 / 2.4 / 0.6	30 SU	0122 / 0629 / 1245 / 1935	2.1 / 1.1 / 2.4 / 0.6

JULY

Day	Time	m	Day	Time	m
1 M	0213 / 0710 / 1327 / 2023	2.1 / 1.2 / 2.4 / 0.7	16 TU	0146 / 0713 / 1325 / 2011	2.3 / 1.0 / 2.5 / 0.5
2 TU	0306 / 0800 / 1418 / 2114	2.0 / 1.3 / 2.3 / 0.8	17 W	0251 / 0804 / 1418 / 2111	2.2 / 1.1 / 2.4 / 0.5
3 W	0358 / 0901 / 1518 / 2205	2.0 / 1.3 / 2.2 / 0.8	18 TH	0359 / 0903 / 1521 / 2219	2.2 / 1.1 / 2.3 / 0.6
4 TH	0450 / 1006 / 1622 / 2257	2.1 / 1.3 / 2.2 / 0.8	19 F	0501 / 1019 / 1648 / 2331	2.2 / 1.1 / 2.3 / 0.7
5 F	0541 / 1109 / 1723 / 2348	2.1 / 1.3 / 2.2 / 0.8	20 SA	0559 / 1156 / 1805	2.2 / 1.1 / 2.3
6 SA	0629 / 1207 / 1820	2.2 / 1.2 / 2.2	21 SU	0039 / 0650 / 1311 / 1911	0.7 / 2.2 / 0.9 / 2.3
7 SU	0037 / 0714 / 1301 / 1913	0.8 / 2.3 / 1.1 / 2.2	22 M	0139 / 0738 / 1410 / 2012	0.7 / 2.3 / 0.7 / 2.3
8 M	0125 / 0757 / 1351 / 2004	0.8 / 2.3 / 1.0 / 2.3	23 TU	0231 / 0824 / 1502 / 2109	0.8 / 2.4 / 0.6 / 2.3
9 TU	0210 / 0839 / 1440 / 2054	0.8 / 2.4 / 0.8 / 2.3	24 W	0318 / 0908 / 1549 / ○ 2201	0.8 / 2.5 / 0.5 / 2.3
10 W	0255 / 0919 / 1527 / ● 2144	0.8 / 2.5 / 0.7 / 2.4	25 TH	0358 / 0950 / 1633 / 2248	0.9 / 2.6 / 0.4 / 2.3
11 TH	0339 / 0958 / 1614 / 2232	0.8 / 2.5 / 0.6 / 2.4	26 F	0433 / 1029 / 1713 / 2330	0.9 / 2.6 / 0.4 / 2.3
12 F	0422 / 1035 / 1659 / 2318	0.8 / 2.6 / 0.5 / 2.4	27 SA	0501 / 1106 / 1749	0.9 / 2.6 / 0.5
13 SA	0504 / 1114 / 1744	0.8 / 2.6 / 0.4	28 SU	0006 / 0526 / 1140 / 1822	2.2 / 1.0 / 2.6 / 0.5
14 SU	0003 / 0545 / 1155 / 1829	2.4 / 0.8 / 2.6 / 0.4	29 M	0039 / 0555 / 1214 / 1857	2.2 / 1.0 / 2.5 / 0.6
15 M	0052 / 0628 / 1238 / 1918	2.4 / 0.9 / 2.6 / 0.4	30 TU	0114 / 0627 / 1250 / 1936	2.1 / 1.1 / 2.5 / 0.7
			31 W	0157 / 0704 / 1331 / 2024	2.1 / 1.1 / 2.4 / 0.8

AUGUST

Day	Time	m	Day	Time	m
1 TH	0252 / 0750 / 1418 / 2119	2.0 / 1.2 / 2.3 / 0.9	16 F	0318 / 0837 / 1505 / 2143	2.1 / 1.0 / 2.3 / 0.8
2 F	0353 / 0905 / 1514 / 2216	2.0 / 1.3 / 2.2 / 0.9	17 SA	0429 / 0952 / 1641 / 2301	2.1 / 1.1 / 2.2 / 0.9
3 SA	0454 / 1028 / 1627 / 2311	2.1 / 1.3 / 2.1 / 0.9	18 SU	0531 / 1144 / 1801	2.1 / 1.1 / 2.2
4 SU	0551 / 1133 / 1741	2.1 / 1.2 / 2.1	19 M	0028 / 0626 / 1305 / 1910	1.0 / 2.2 / 0.9 / 2.3
5 M	0005 / 0642 / 1234 / 1845	0.9 / 2.2 / 1.1 / 2.2	20 TU	0132 / 0716 / 1402 / 2011	1.0 / 2.3 / 0.7 / 2.3
6 TU	0058 / 0729 / 1331 / 1945	0.9 / 2.3 / 1.0 / 2.3	21 W	0223 / 0803 / 1451 / 2105	1.0 / 2.4 / 0.6 / 2.4
7 W	0149 / 0813 / 1426 / 2041	0.9 / 2.4 / 0.8 / 2.3	22 TH	0306 / 0848 / 1535 / ○ 2151	1.0 / 2.5 / 0.5 / 2.4
8 TH	0239 / 0855 / 1518 / ● 2133	0.9 / 2.5 / 0.6 / 2.4	23 F	0344 / 0929 / 1615 / 2231	1.0 / 2.5 / 0.4 / 2.4
9 F	0326 / 0936 / 1605 / 2220	0.8 / 2.6 / 0.5 / 2.5	24 SA	0415 / 1006 / 1650 / 2303	1.0 / 2.6 / 0.5 / 2.3
10 SA	0409 / 1016 / 1649 / 2304	0.8 / 2.7 / 0.3 / 2.5	25 SU	0437 / 1040 / 1720 / 2328	1.0 / 2.6 / 0.5 / 2.3
11 SU	0450 / 1057 / 1732 / 2346	0.7 / 2.7 / 0.2 / 2.5	26 M	0458 / 1112 / 1747 / 2351	0.9 / 2.6 / 0.6 / 2.3
12 M	0530 / 1138 / 1814	0.7 / 2.8 / 0.2	27 TU	0524 / 1145 / 1814	0.9 / 2.5 / 0.7
13 TU	0028 / 0609 / 1221 / 1857	2.4 / 0.8 / 2.7 / 0.3	28 W	0020 / 0552 / 1220 / 1841	2.2 / 0.9 / 2.5 / 0.7
14 W	0113 / 0651 / 1306 / 1944	2.3 / 0.8 / 2.6 / 0.5	29 TH	0056 / 0625 / 1259 / 1912	2.2 / 1.0 / 2.4 / 0.9
15 TH	0207 / 0739 / 1358 / 2039	2.2 / 0.9 / 2.5 / 0.6	30 F	0137 / 0704 / 1343 / 1959	2.1 / 1.1 / 2.3 / 1.0
			31 SA	0229 / 0755 / 1435 / 2131	2.1 / 1.2 / 2.2 / 1.1

Chart Datum: 1·50 metres below Ordnance Datum (Newlyn)

TIME ZONE (UTC)
For Summer Time add ONE hour in **non-shaded areas**

ENGLAND – LOWESTOFT

LAT 52°28′N   LONG 1°45′W

TIMES AND HEIGHTS OF HIGH AND LOW WATERS

YEAR 2002

SEPTEMBER

Day	Time	m	Day	Time	m
1 SU	0351 / 0944 / 1540 / 2239	2.1 / 1.3 / 2.1 / 1.1	**16** M	0502 / 1141 / 1759	2.1 / 1.0 / 2.2
2 M	0510 / 1107 / 1709 / 2339	2.1 / 1.2 / 2.1 / 1.1	**17** TU	0018 / 0600 / 1252 / 1906	1.2 / 2.2 / 0.8 / 2.3
3 TU	0610 / 1213 / 1829	2.2 / 1.1 / 2.2	**18** W	0117 / 0653 / 1344 / 2002	1.2 / 2.3 / 0.7 / 2.4
4 W	0037 / 0659 / 1315 / 1935	1.1 / 2.3 / 0.9 / 2.3	**19** TH	0204 / 0741 / 1430 / 2050	1.1 / 2.4 / 0.6 / 2.4
5 TH	0133 / 0744 / 1411 / 2030	1.0 / 2.4 / 0.7 / 2.4	**20** F	0245 / 0824 / 1512 / 2130	1.1 / 2.5 / 0.5 / 2.4
6 F	0224 / 0827 / 1502 / 2118	0.9 / 2.5 / 0.5 / 2.5	**21** SA	0320 / 0900 / 1549 / 2202 ○	1.0 / 2.5 / 0.5 / 2.4
7 SA	0310 / 0910 / 1548 / 2201 ●	0.8 / 2.7 / 0.3 / 2.6	**22** SU	0348 / 0939 / 1620 / 2225	1.0 / 2.6 / 0.6 / 2.4
8 SU	0353 / 0953 / 1631 / 2241	0.7 / 2.8 / 0.2 / 2.6	**23** M	0408 / 1012 / 1645 / 2245	0.9 / 2.6 / 0.6 / 2.4
9 M	0433 / 1036 / 1712 / 2320	0.7 / 2.8 / 0.1 / 2.6	**24** TU	0429 / 1044 / 1707 / 2311	0.9 / 2.6 / 0.6 / 2.4
10 TU	0512 / 1119 / 1752 / 2358	0.6 / 2.8 / 0.2 / 2.5	**25** W	0455 / 1118 / 1730 / 2341	0.8 / 2.5 / 0.7 / 2.4
11 W	0550 / 1202 / 1832	0.7 / 2.8 / 0.3	**26** TH	0525 / 1154 / 1755	0.8 / 2.5 / 0.8
12 TH	0038 / 0631 / 1248 / 1915	2.4 / 0.7 / 2.6 / 0.6	**27** F	0014 / 0557 / 1233 / 1824	2.3 / 0.9 / 2.4 / 0.9
13 F	0123 / 0718 / 1341 / 2007	2.3 / 0.8 / 2.4 / 0.8	**28** SA	0052 / 0636 / 1317 / 1903	2.2 / 1.0 / 2.3 / 1.0
14 SA	0224 / 0818 / 1501 / 2110	2.1 / 1.0 / 2.3 / 1.0	**29** SU	0137 / 0724 / 1409 / 2000	2.2 / 1.1 / 2.2 / 1.2
15 SU	0353 / 0939 / 1640 / 2232	2.1 / 1.0 / 2.2 / 1.2	**30** M	0230 / 0842 / 1512 / 2159	2.1 / 1.0 / 2.1 / 1.3

OCTOBER

Day	Time	m	Day	Time	m
1 TU	0338 / 1043 / 1652 / 2313	2.1 / 1.2 / 2.1 / 1.3	**16** W	0531 / 1226 / 1849	2.3 / 0.8 / 2.3
2 W	0522 / 1154 / 1822	2.2 / 1.0 / 2.2	**17** TH	0049 / 0625 / 1318 / 1941	1.3 / 2.4 / 0.7 / 2.4
3 TH	0017 / 0621 / 1256 / 1923	1.2 / 2.3 / 0.8 / 2.4	**18** F	0136 / 0713 / 1402 / 2025	1.2 / 2.4 / 0.6 / 2.4
4 F	0114 / 0709 / 1350 / 2013	1.1 / 2.5 / 0.6 / 2.5	**19** SA	0215 / 0756 / 1441 / 2059	1.1 / 2.5 / 0.6 / 2.4
5 SA	0204 / 0756 / 1439 / 2056	0.9 / 2.6 / 0.4 / 2.5	**20** SU	0249 / 0834 / 1515 / 2123	1.0 / 2.5 / 0.6 / 2.4
6 SU	0249 / 0842 / 1524 / 2135 ●	0.8 / 2.7 / 0.2 / 2.6	**21** M	0314 / 0909 / 1542 / 2144 ○	1.0 / 2.5 / 0.7 / 2.4
7 M	0332 / 0929 / 1607 / 2213	0.7 / 2.8 / 0.1 / 2.6	**22** TU	0335 / 0944 / 1605 / 2211	0.9 / 2.5 / 0.7 / 2.4
8 TU	0413 / 1014 / 1648 / 2251	0.6 / 2.8 / 0.1 / 2.6	**23** W	0401 / 1019 / 1629 / 2240	0.8 / 2.5 / 0.7 / 2.4
9 W	0453 / 1100 / 1727 / 2329	0.6 / 2.8 / 0.3 / 2.5	**24** TH	0431 / 1055 / 1655 / 2311	0.8 / 2.5 / 0.8 / 2.4
10 TH	0533 / 1145 / 1806	0.6 / 2.7 / 0.5	**25** F	0503 / 1131 / 1724 / 2344	0.8 / 2.4 / 0.8 / 2.4
11 F	0008 / 0614 / 1233 / 1847	2.4 / 0.7 / 2.5 / 0.7	**26** SA	0539 / 1211 / 1757	0.9 / 2.4 / 0.9
12 SA	0050 / 0704 / 1332 / 1936	2.3 / 0.8 / 2.4 / 1.0	**27** SU	0021 / 0619 / 1256 / 1837	2.3 / 0.9 / 2.3 / 1.1
13 SU	0142 / 0808 / 1504 / 2037	2.2 / 0.9 / 2.2 / 1.2	**28** M	0106 / 0710 / 1349 / 1931	2.3 / 1.0 / 2.2 / 1.3
14 M	0310 / 0935 / 1635 / 2155	2.0 / 1.0 / 2.2 / 1.4	**29** TU	0157 / 0825 / 1455 / 2047	2.2 / 1.1 / 2.1 / 1.4
15 TU	0429 / 1120 / 1746 / 2351	2.2 / 0.9 / 2.2 / 1.4	**30** W	0255 / 1016 / 1647 / 2233	2.2 / 1.0 / 2.2 / 1.4
			31 TH	0403 / 1129 / 1805 / 2348	2.2 / 0.9 / 2.3 / 1.3

NOVEMBER

Day	Time	m	Day	Time	m
1 F	0529 / 1230 / 1901	2.3 / 0.7 / 2.4	**16** SA	0058 / 0638 / 1326 / 1949	1.3 / 2.4 / 0.7 / 2.3
2 SA	0047 / 0632 / 1324 / 1947	1.1 / 2.5 / 0.5 / 2.4	**17** SU	0138 / 0722 / 1403 / 2017	1.2 / 2.4 / 0.7 / 2.4
3 SU	0138 / 0726 / 1412 / 2028	1.0 / 2.6 / 0.3 / 2.5	**18** M	0209 / 0802 / 1433 / 2041	1.1 / 2.4 / 0.8 / 2.4
4 M	0225 / 0817 / 1458 / 2107 ●	0.8 / 2.7 / 0.2 / 2.5	**19** TU	0235 / 0840 / 1459 / 2111	1.0 / 2.4 / 0.8 / 2.4
5 TU	0310 / 0907 / 1542 / 2146	0.7 / 2.7 / 0.2 / 2.6	**20** W	0304 / 0918 / 1527 / 2144 ○	0.9 / 2.4 / 0.8 / 2.5
6 W	0354 / 0955 / 1624 / 2225	0.6 / 2.8 / 0.3 / 2.5	**21** TH	0337 / 0957 / 1558 / 2216	0.9 / 2.4 / 0.8 / 2.5
7 TH	0437 / 1044 / 1703 / 2304	0.5 / 2.7 / 0.4 / 2.5	**22** F	0413 / 1036 / 1630 / 2248	0.8 / 2.4 / 0.8 / 2.5
8 F	0519 / 1132 / 1742 / 2344	0.5 / 2.6 / 0.6 / 2.5	**23** SA	0450 / 1115 / 1704 / 2321	0.8 / 2.4 / 0.9 / 2.5
9 SA	0604 / 1224 / 1822	0.6 / 2.4 / 0.9	**24** SU	0529 / 1156 / 1741 / 2359	0.8 / 2.3 / 1.0 / 2.4
10 SU	0025 / 0655 / 1328 / 1906	2.4 / 0.7 / 2.3 / 1.1	**25** M	0613 / 1242 / 1823	0.9 / 2.3 / 1.1
11 M	0112 / 0800 / 1457 / 2001	2.3 / 0.8 / 2.2 / 1.3	**26** TU	0043 / 0705 / 1335 / 1913	2.4 / 0.9 / 2.2 / 1.2
12 TU	0223 / 0918 / 1615 / 2108	2.3 / 0.9 / 2.2 / 1.4	**27** W	0133 / 0811 / 1442 / 2015	2.3 / 0.9 / 2.2 / 1.3
13 W	0345 / 1041 / 1720 / 2232	2.3 / 0.9 / 2.2 / 1.5	**28** TH	0228 / 0937 / 1623 / 2126	2.3 / 0.9 / 2.2 / 1.4
14 TH	0450 / 1149 / 1819	2.3 / 0.8 / 2.2	**29** F	0327 / 1056 / 1733 / 2300	2.3 / 0.8 / 2.2 / 1.3
15 F	0006 / 0548 / 1242 / 1909	1.4 / 2.4 / 0.8 / 2.3	**30** SA	0438 / 1159 / 1829	2.4 / 0.6 / 2.3

DECEMBER

Day	Time	m	Day	Time	m
1 SU	0014 / 0558 / 1255 / 1916	1.2 / 2.4 / 0.5 / 2.4	**16** M	0034 / 0642 / 1307 / 1933	1.2 / 2.3 / 0.9 / 2.3
2 M	0112 / 0701 / 1346 / 1959	1.0 / 2.5 / 0.4 / 2.4	**17** TU	0119 / 0728 / 1344 / 2007	1.1 / 2.3 / 0.9 / 2.3
3 TU	0203 / 0757 / 1434 / 2040	0.8 / 2.6 / 0.4 / 2.5	**18** W	0200 / 0812 / 1420 / 2044	1.0 / 2.3 / 0.8 / 2.4
4 W	0252 / 0850 / 1520 / 2121 ●	0.7 / 2.6 / 0.4 / 2.5	**19** TH	0240 / 0856 / 1457 / 2121 ○	0.9 / 2.4 / 0.8 / 2.5
5 TH	0339 / 0943 / 1603 / 2203	0.6 / 2.6 / 0.5 / 2.5	**20** F	0320 / 0940 / 1534 / 2156	0.8 / 2.4 / 0.8 / 2.5
6 F	0426 / 1034 / 1643 / 2243	0.5 / 2.5 / 0.6 / 2.5	**21** SA	0401 / 1024 / 1612 / 2230	0.8 / 2.4 / 0.9 / 2.5
7 SA	0512 / 1125 / 1721 / 2324	0.5 / 2.4 / 0.8 / 2.5	**22** SU	0442 / 1106 / 1650 / 2304	0.7 / 2.4 / 0.9 / 2.5
8 SU	0558 / 1219 / 1758	0.5 / 2.3 / 1.0	**23** M	0525 / 1148 / 1729 / 2343	0.7 / 2.4 / 1.0 / 2.5
9 M	0004 / 0647 / 1321 / 1836	2.5 / 0.6 / 2.2 / 1.1	**24** TU	0609 / 1233 / 1811	0.7 / 2.3 / 1.0
10 TU	0047 / 0743 / 1432 / 1922	2.4 / 0.7 / 2.1 / 1.3	**25** W	0025 / 0658 / 1323 / 1857	2.5 / 0.7 / 2.2 / 1.1
11 W	0138 / 0843 / 1538 / 2017	2.4 / 0.8 / 2.1 / 1.4	**26** TH	0113 / 0753 / 1422 / 1948	2.4 / 0.7 / 2.2 / 1.2
12 TH	0244 / 0945 / 1639 / 2120	2.3 / 0.8 / 2.1 / 1.5	**27** F	0204 / 0857 / 1542 / 2046	2.4 / 0.7 / 2.1 / 1.2
13 F	0353 / 1045 / 1735 / 2227	2.3 / 0.9 / 2.1 / 1.4	**28** SA	0300 / 1012 / 1654 / 2154	2.4 / 0.7 / 2.1 / 1.2
14 SA	0455 / 1142 / 1823 / 2335	2.2 / 0.9 / 2.2 / 1.4	**29** SU	0404 / 1123 / 1754 / 2333	2.3 / 0.7 / 2.2 / 1.2
15 SU	0552 / 1228 / 1901	2.3 / 0.9 / 2.2	**30** M	0532 / 1226 / 1846	2.3 / 0.6 / 2.2
			31 TU	0047 / 0644 / 1323 / 1932	1.0 / 2.4 / 0.6 / 2.3

Chart Datum: 1·50 metres below Ordnance Datum (Newlyn)

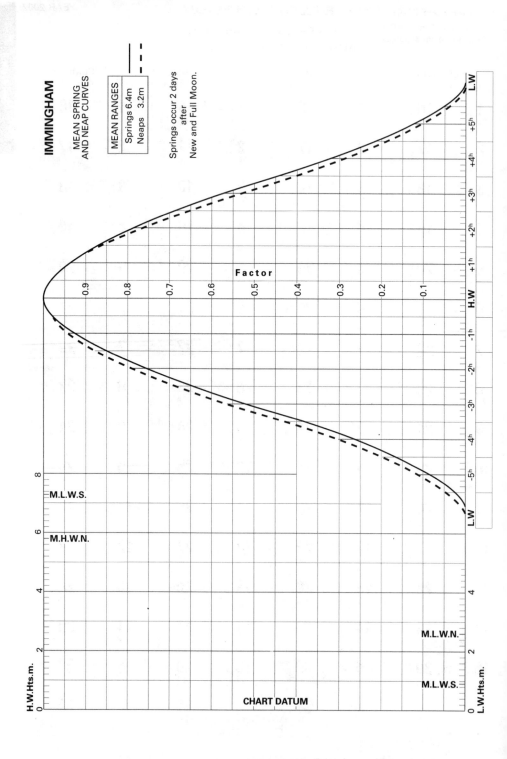

IMMINGHAM

MEAN SPRING
AND NEAP CURVES

MEAN RANGES

Springs 6.4m
Neaps   3.2m

Springs occur 2 days
after
New and Full Moon.

Factor

0.9 0.8 0.7 0.6 0.5 0.4 0.3 0.2 0.1

L.W   +5ʰ +4ʰ +3ʰ +2ʰ +1ʰ H.W -1ʰ -2ʰ -3ʰ -4ʰ -5ʰ L.W

M.L.W.S.

M.H.W.N.

M.L.W.N.

M.L.W.S.

CHART DATUM

H.W.Hts.m.

L.W.Hts.m.

TIME ZONE (UTC)
For Summer Time add ONE hour in **non-shaded areas**

ENGLAND – IMMINGHAM

YEAR **2002**

LAT 53°38'N   LONG 0°11'W

TIMES AND HEIGHTS OF HIGH AND LOW WATERS

JANUARY

Time	m	Time	m
1 0104	1.1	**16** 0145	1.4
TU 0701	7.2	W 0745	6.7
1316	1.4	1347	1.7
1913	7.3	1943	7.0
2 0151	1.0	**17** 0218	1.5
W 0749	7.2	TH 0817	6.5
1400	1.4	1419	1.8
1956	7.3	2016	6.9
3 0239	1.0	**18** 0249	1.6
TH 0838	7.0	F 0849	6.4
1445	1.6	1449	1.9
2041	7.2	2049	6.8
4 0328	1.1	**19** 0320	1.7
F 0929	6.8	SA 0922	6.2
1531	1.8	1519	2.1
2129	7.1	2122	6.6
5 0419	1.3	**20** 0353	1.9
SA 1025	6.6	SU 0959	6.1
1621	2.1	1554	2.3
2224	6.8	2200	6.3
6 0514	1.5	**21** 0431	2.1
SU 1128	6.3	M 1041	5.8
1717	2.3	1637	2.6
2327	6.6	2245	6.1
7 0615	1.7	**22** 0521	2.4
M 1235	6.2	TU 1136	5.7
1823	2.5	1734	2.8
		2343	5.9
8 0039	6.4	**23** 0624	2.5
TU 0721	1.9	W 1249	5.6
1340	6.1	1846	2.9
1939	2.5		
9 0152	6.3	**24** 0100	5.8
W 0828	1.9	TH 0734	2.5
1442	6.2	1405	5.7
2054	2.4	2001	2.8
10 0300	6.4	**25** 0220	5.9
TH 0929	1.8	F 0843	2.4
1539	6.3	1509	6.0
2158	2.1	2112	2.4
11 0402	6.5	**26** 0326	6.2
F 1022	1.8	SA 0945	2.1
1630	6.6	1604	6.3
2253	1.8	2215	2.0
12 0457	6.6	**27** 0424	6.6
SA 1111	1.7	SU 1040	1.8
1714	6.8	1652	6.7
2343	1.6	2312	1.6
13 0545	6.7	**28** 0517	6.9
SU 1155	1.6	M 1131	1.5
1755	6.9	1736	7.0
●		○	
14 0028	1.4	**29** 0005	1.1
M 0629	6.8	TU 0606	7.1
1236	1.6	1220	1.3
1833	7.0	1819	7.3
15 0109	1.4	**30** 0056	0.8
TU 0709	6.7	W 0655	7.3
1313	1.6	1307	1.2
1909	7.1	1902	7.5
		31 0144	0.6
		TH 0741	7.3
		1352	1.1
		1945	7.6

FEBRUARY

Time	m	Time	m
1 0230	0.5	**16** 0228	1.4
F 0827	7.3	SA 0820	6.6
1435	1.2	1426	1.7
2029	7.6	2024	6.9
2 0315	0.6	**17** 0253	1.5
SA 0912	7.1	SU 0848	6.5
1518	1.3	1452	1.8
2114	7.4	2052	6.7
3 0359	0.9	**18** 0318	1.7
SU 0959	6.8	M 0918	6.3
1600	1.6	1521	1.9
2202	7.1	2123	6.5
4 0445	1.3	**19** 0346	1.9
M 1049	6.4	TU 0952	6.1
1640	2.0	1556	2.2
2256	6.7	2200	6.3
5 0536	1.8	**20** 0424	2.2
TU 1149	6.1	W 1034	5.8
1739	2.4	1643	2.5
		2249	6.0
6 0003	6.3	**21** 0519	2.5
W 0637	2.2	TH 1130	5.6
1257	5.8	1751	2.7
1852	2.6	2357	5.7
7 0124	6.0	**22** 0639	2.7
TH 0753	2.4	F 1301	5.5
1407	5.8	1918	2.8
2031	2.6		
8 0243	5.9	**23** 0139	5.7
F 0905	2.4	SA 0804	2.6
1512	5.9	1436	5.7
2146	2.3	2042	2.5
9 0354	6.1	**24** 0309	6.0
SA 1005	2.3	SU 0919	2.3
1610	6.2	1541	6.1
2243	2.0	2156	2.0
10 0453	6.3	**25** 0414	6.4
SU 1055	2.0	M 1022	1.9
1657	6.5	1633	6.6
2332	1.6	2259	1.4
11 0540	6.5	**26** 0509	6.9
M 1140	1.8	TU 1117	1.5
1739	6.8	1720	7.1
		2353	0.9
12 0015	1.4	**27** 0558	7.2
TU 0619	6.6	W 1206	1.2
1221	1.6	1804	7.4
● 1816	7.0	○	
13 0055	1.3	**28** 0043	0.5
W 0653	6.7	TH 0643	7.4
1258	1.6	1253	1.0
1851	7.1	1846	7.7
14 0129	1.3		
TH 0724	6.7		
1331	1.5		
1924	7.1		
15 0200	1.3		
F 0753	6.7		
1400	1.6		
1954	7.0		

MARCH

Time	m	Time	m
1 0129	0.2	**16** 0134	1.2
F 0726	7.5	SA 0724	6.8
1337	0.8	1338	1.4
1928	7.8	1929	7.0
2 0213	0.2	**17** 0201	1.3
SA 0807	7.4	SU 0750	6.7
1419	0.8	1403	1.5
2011	7.8	1956	6.9
3 0254	0.4	**18** 0225	1.4
SU 0847	7.2	M 0816	6.7
1458	1.0	1428	1.6
2054	7.6	2024	6.8
4 0333	0.8	**19** 0247	1.6
M 0927	6.9	TU 0843	6.5
1537	1.3	1455	1.7
2138	7.2	2054	6.7
5 0412	1.3	**20** 0312	1.9
TU 1010	6.5	W 0915	6.3
1616	1.8	1528	2.0
2229	6.6	2131	6.4
6 0455	1.9	**21** 0346	2.1
W 1101	6.0	TH 0955	6.0
1702	2.3	1612	2.3
2334	6.0	2219	6.1
7 0551	2.5	**22** 0437	2.4
TH 1211	5.7	F 1047	5.7
1809	2.7	1718	2.6
		2327	5.7
8 0103	5.7	**23** 0556	2.8
F 0714	2.9	SA 1207	5.5
1332	5.5	1850	2.7
2015	2.8		
9 0231	5.6	**24** 0117	5.6
SA 0845	2.8	SU 0735	2.8
1446	5.7	1402	5.6
2134	2.4	2022	2.4
10 0348	5.9	**25** 0258	6.0
SU 0948	2.5	M 0858	2.5
1548	6.1	1516	6.1
2228	2.0	2141	1.8
11 0444	6.2	**26** 0403	6.5
M 1038	2.2	TU 1004	2.0
1637	6.4	1611	6.7
2314	1.6	2242	1.2
12 0526	6.5	**27** 0455	6.9
TU 1121	1.8	W 1059	1.5
1718	6.7	1658	7.2
2354	1.3	2334	0.6
13 0600	6.6	**28** 0542	7.3
W 1201	1.6	TH 1148	1.1
1754	6.9	1742	7.5
		○	
14 0031	1.2	**29** 0022	0.3
TH 0629	6.7	F 0624	7.5
1237	1.5	1234	0.8
● 1827	7.0	1825	7.8
15 0104	1.2	**30** 0107	0.1
F 0657	6.8	SA 0703	7.6
1309	1.4	1318	0.6
1859	7.0	1908	7.9
		31 0149	0.2
		SU 0742	7.5
		1359	0.7
		1951	7.8

APRIL

Time	m	Time	m
1 0228	0.4	**16** 0157	1.4
M 0819	7.3	TU 0747	6.6
1438	0.9	1407	1.5
2033	7.5	2001	6.8
2 0305	0.9	**17** 0222	1.6
TU 0857	6.9	W 0817	6.7
1514	1.2	1438	1.6
2118	7.0	2035	6.7
3 0342	1.5	**18** 0251	1.8
W 0936	6.5	TH 0850	6.5
1552	1.7	1513	1.8
2207	6.4	2116	6.4
4 0421	2.1	**19** 0328	2.1
TH 1022	6.0	F 0931	6.2
1637	2.2	1600	2.1
2314	5.8	2208	6.0
5 0513	2.7	**20** 0420	2.4
F 1129	5.6	SA 1026	5.9
1742	2.6	1709	2.3
		2321	5.7
6 0048	5.5	**21** 0537	2.8
SA 0631	3.1	SU 1145	5.7
1259	5.5	1838	2.4
1954	2.7		
7 0213	5.5	**22** 0112	5.7
SU 0815	3.0	M 0713	2.8
1417	5.6	1329	5.8
2110	2.4	2005	2.1
8 0325	5.8	**23** 0240	6.1
M 0922	2.7	TU 0835	2.4
1520	6.0	1446	6.2
2201	2.0	2119	1.5
9 0418	6.1	**24** 0342	6.5
TU 1012	2.3	W 0940	1.9
1609	6.3	1543	6.7
2244	1.6	2218	1.0
10 0458	6.4	**25** 0433	7.0
W 1054	1.9	TH 1035	1.5
1650	6.6	1633	7.2
2323	1.4	2310	0.6
11 0530	6.6	**26** 0518	7.3
TH 1133	1.6	F 1125	1.1
1726	6.8	1719	7.5
2358	1.2	2357	0.3
12 0559	6.7	**27** 0559	7.4
F 1209	1.5	SA 1212	0.8
1758	6.9	1804	7.7
●		○	
13 0032	1.2	**28** 0041	0.3
SA 0625	6.8	SU 0638	7.5
1242	1.4	1256	0.7
1829	6.9	1848	7.7
14 0103	1.2	**29** 0123	0.4
SU 0652	6.8	M 0716	7.4
1311	1.4	1339	0.7
1900	6.9	1933	7.5
15 0131	1.3	**30** 0203	0.7
M 0720	6.8	TU 0754	7.2
1339	1.4	1419	0.9
1930	6.9	2017	7.2

Chart Datum: 3·90 metres below Ordnance Datum (Newlyn)
Register for your **FREE** weekly weather email service from Macmillan Reeds
》 at www.nauticaldata.com – NOW! 《
weekend weather reports sent to your email address, every Thursday

TIME ZONE (UTC)
For Summer Time add ONE hour in **non-shaded areas**

ENGLAND – IMMINGHAM

YEAR **2002**

LAT 53°38'N   LONG 0°11'W

TIMES AND HEIGHTS OF HIGH AND LOW WATERS

MAY

Time m	Time m
1 0240 1.2 / 0831 6.9 / W 1457 1.3 / 2102 6.8	**16** 0205 1.6 / 0800 6.8 / TH 1429 1.5 / 2027 6.7
2 0316 1.7 / 0909 6.5 / TH 1536 1.7 / 2152 6.2	**17** 0240 1.8 / 0837 6.6 / F 1511 1.7 / 2113 6.4
3 0356 2.2 / 0953 6.1 / F 1621 2.1 / 2258 5.7	**18** 0323 2.0 / 0922 6.4 / SA 1604 1.8 / 2210 6.1
4 0445 2.7 / 1054 5.7 / SA 1723 2.5	**19** 0417 2.4 / 1019 6.1 / SU 1711 2.0 / 2324 5.9
5 0023 5.5 / 0552 3.1 / SU 1220 5.5 / 1855 2.8	**20** 0528 2.6 / 1134 6.0 / M 1828 2.0
6 0139 5.5 / 0719 3.1 / M 1338 5.6 / 2025 2.4	**21** 0056 5.9 / 0650 2.6 / TU 1259 6.1 / 1943 1.7
7 0245 5.7 / 0838 2.8 / TU 1441 5.9 / 2119 2.1	**22** 0212 6.2 / 0806 2.3 / W 1413 6.4 / 2051 1.4
8 0338 6.0 / 0933 2.4 / W 1533 6.2 / 2203 1.8	**23** 0313 6.5 / 0912 1.9 / TH 1514 6.7 / 2150 1.1
9 0420 6.3 / 1018 2.1 / TH 1615 6.4 / 2242 1.6	**24** 0406 6.8 / 1010 1.5 / F 1608 7.1 / 2243 0.8
10 0454 6.5 / 1058 1.8 / F 1651 6.6 / 2319 1.4	**25** 0452 7.1 / 1102 1.2 / SA 1658 7.3 / 2331 0.7
11 0523 6.7 / 1135 1.6 / SA 1725 6.7 / 2355 1.3	**26** 0534 7.2 / 1150 1.0 / SU 1747 7.4 ○
12 0552 6.8 / 1210 1.5 / SU 1800 6.8 ●	**27** 0016 0.7 / 0614 7.2 / M 1237 0.9 / 1834 7.3
13 0030 1.3 / 0622 6.8 / M 1254 1.4 / 1834 6.9	**28** 0100 0.8 / 0654 7.2 / TU 1322 0.9 / 1920 7.2
14 0103 1.4 / 0654 6.9 / TU 1318 1.4 / 1910 6.9	**29** 0140 1.1 / 0733 7.1 / W 1404 1.1 / 2006 6.9
15 0133 1.4 / 0726 6.8 / W 1352 1.4 / 1947 6.8	**30** 0219 1.4 / 0811 6.9 / TH 1444 1.3 / 2051 6.6
	31 0256 1.8 / 0850 6.6 / F 1525 1.6 / 2139 6.2

JUNE

Time m	Time m
1 0335 2.2 / 0932 6.3 / SA 1608 2.0 / 2233 5.8	**16** 0322 1.9 / 0920 6.7 / SU 1607 1.4 / 2211 6.4
2 0420 2.6 / 1023 6.0 / SU 1700 2.2 / 2338 5.6	**17** 0414 2.1 / 1014 6.5 / M 1705 1.5 / 2317 6.2
3 0515 2.8 / 1128 5.8 / M 1801 2.4	**18** 0514 2.3 / 1119 6.4 / TU 1810 1.6
4 0047 5.5 / 0619 2.9 / TU 1240 5.7 / 1906 2.4	**19** 0030 6.2 / 0622 2.3 / W 1231 6.4 / 1916 1.6
5 0150 5.6 / 0729 2.9 / W 1345 5.8 / 2011 2.3	**20** 0138 6.2 / 0734 2.3 / TH 1342 6.4 / 2022 1.5
6 0246 5.8 / 0834 2.6 / TH 1442 6.0 / 2106 2.1	**21** 0240 6.4 / 0843 2.1 / F 1448 6.6 / 2123 1.4
7 0332 6.0 / 0929 2.3 / F 1530 6.2 / 2155 1.8	**22** 0337 6.6 / 0946 1.8 / SA 1548 6.8 / 2218 1.3
8 0411 6.3 / 1016 2.0 / SA 1612 6.4 / 2239 1.7	**23** 0427 6.7 / 1042 1.5 / SU 1644 6.9 / 2309 1.2
9 0446 6.5 / 1059 1.8 / SU 1653 6.6 / 2320 1.5	**24** 0513 6.9 / 1135 1.3 / M 1736 7.0 / ○ 2356 1.2
10 0521 6.7 / 1141 1.6 / M 1734 6.7 ●	**25** 0556 7.0 / 1224 1.1 / TU 1826 7.0
11 0000 1.5 / 0557 6.8 / TU 1221 1.4 / 1814 6.8	**26** 0041 1.3 / 0637 7.0 / W 1311 1.1 / 1913 6.9
12 0038 1.4 / 0634 6.9 / W 1302 1.3 / 1857 6.9	**27** 0123 1.4 / 0717 7.0 / TH 1354 1.2 / 1957 6.7
13 0116 1.5 / 0712 6.9 / TH 1343 1.3 / 1940 6.9	**28** 0202 1.6 / 0755 6.9 / F 1434 1.3 / 2038 6.5
14 0155 1.5 / 0751 6.9 / F 1427 1.3 / 2025 6.8	**29** 0239 1.8 / 0833 6.7 / SA 1512 1.5 / 2118 6.3
15 0236 1.7 / 0833 6.8 / SA 1515 1.3 / 2115 6.6	**30** 0315 2.0 / 0911 6.5 / SU 1549 1.8 / 2157 6.0

JULY

Time m	Time m
1 0352 2.3 / 0952 6.3 / M 1629 2.0 / 2240 5.8	**16** 0402 1.7 / 1001 7.0 / TU 1649 1.2 / 2255 6.5
2 0434 2.5 / 1040 6.1 / TU 1715 2.2 / 2330 5.7	**17** 0452 2.0 / 1057 6.7 / W 1743 1.5 / 2356 6.3
3 0524 2.7 / 1136 5.9 / W 1808 2.3	**18** 0551 2.2 / 1202 6.5 / TH 1845 1.7
4 0030 5.6 / 0623 2.8 / TH 1239 5.8 / 1906 2.4	**19** 0102 6.1 / 0659 2.3 / F 1314 6.3 / 1952 1.9
5 0133 5.6 / 0728 2.8 / F 1343 5.8 / 2008 2.3	**20** 0207 6.1 / 0817 2.3 / SA 1427 6.3 / 2059 1.9
6 0233 5.8 / 0833 2.6 / SA 1443 6.0 / 2108 2.2	**21** 0309 6.2 / 0929 2.1 / SU 1535 6.4 / 2159 1.8
7 0326 6.1 / 0933 2.3 / SU 1537 6.2 / 2201 2.0	**22** 0406 6.4 / 1031 1.8 / M 1638 6.5 / 2253 1.7
8 0412 6.3 / 1026 2.0 / M 1627 6.4 / 2250 1.8	**23** 0456 6.6 / 1126 1.5 / TU 1733 6.7 / 2341 1.6
9 0456 6.6 / 1116 1.7 / TU 1715 6.7 / 2335 1.6	**24** 0540 6.8 / 1215 1.3 / W 1821 6.7 ○
10 0538 6.8 / 1203 1.4 / W 1802 6.9 ●	**25** 0026 1.5 / 0621 7.0 / TH 1301 1.2 / 1904 6.8
11 0020 1.5 / 0619 7.0 / TH 1251 1.2 / 1848 7.0	**26** 0108 1.5 / 0700 7.0 / F 1342 1.2 / 1943 6.7
12 0104 1.4 / 0700 7.1 / F 1338 1.0 / 1935 7.0	**27** 0145 1.6 / 0737 7.0 / SA 1419 1.3 / 2017 6.6
13 0147 1.4 / 0742 7.2 / SA 1425 0.9 / 2022 7.0	**28** 0220 1.7 / 0812 6.9 / SU 1451 1.4 / 2048 6.5
14 0231 1.4 / 0826 7.2 / SU 1511 0.9 / 2110 6.9	**29** 0251 1.8 / 0846 6.8 / M 1522 1.6 / 2118 6.3
15 0315 1.5 / 0911 7.1 / M 1559 1.0 / 2200 6.7	**30** 0321 2.0 / 0920 6.6 / TU 1552 1.8 / 2152 6.1
	31 0352 2.2 / 0957 6.3 / W 1625 2.0 / 2230 5.9

AUGUST

Time m	Time m
1 0429 2.4 / 1039 6.1 / TH 1707 2.3 / 2320 5.7	**16** 0517 2.2 / 1134 6.4 / F 1809 2.1
2 0519 2.7 / 1134 5.8 / F 1804 2.5	**17** 0023 6.0 / 0624 2.5 / SA 1252 6.1 / 1923 2.4
3 0026 5.6 / 0624 2.8 / SA 1247 5.7 / 1912 2.6	**18** 0136 5.8 / 0759 2.6 / SU 1414 5.9 / 2041 2.5
4 0143 5.6 / 0739 2.8 / SU 1403 5.8 / 2024 2.5	**19** 0246 5.9 / 0923 2.4 / M 1532 6.1 / 2146 2.3
5 0250 5.9 / 0853 2.6 / M 1511 6.0 / 2129 2.3	**20** 0348 6.2 / 1025 2.0 / TU 1639 6.3 / 2240 2.1
6 0347 6.2 / 1000 2.1 / TU 1610 6.3 / 2226 2.0	**21** 0440 6.5 / 1116 1.6 / W 1729 6.6 / 2327 1.8
7 0436 6.6 / 1058 1.7 / W 1703 6.7 / 2317 1.7	**22** 0523 6.8 / 1202 1.3 / TH 1810 6.7 ○
8 0521 6.9 / 1151 1.3 / TH 1752 7.0 ●	**23** 0009 1.6 / 0602 7.0 / F 1244 1.2 / 1846 6.8
9 0005 1.5 / 0603 7.2 / F 1241 0.9 / 1839 7.2	**24** 0049 1.5 / 0639 7.1 / SA 1321 1.1 / 1918 6.8
10 0052 1.3 / 0646 7.4 / SA 1328 0.7 / 1924 7.3	**25** 0124 1.5 / 0713 7.1 / SU 1354 1.2 / 1947 6.7
11 0136 1.2 / 0728 7.6 / SU 1413 0.5 / 2009 7.3	**26** 0156 1.5 / 0747 7.1 / M 1423 1.3 / 2014 6.7
12 0218 1.1 / 0811 7.6 / M 1456 0.6 / 2052 7.2	**27** 0223 1.6 / 0817 6.9 / TU 1449 1.5 / 2040 6.6
13 0300 1.2 / 0854 7.5 / TU 1539 0.8 / 2136 7.0	**28** 0248 1.8 / 0846 6.8 / W 1512 1.7 / 2108 6.4
14 0342 1.4 / 0941 7.3 / W 1623 1.1 / 2223 6.6	**29** 0314 2.0 / 0916 6.5 / TH 1537 2.0 / 2139 6.2
15 0426 1.8 / 1032 6.9 / TH 1711 1.6 / 2318 6.3	**30** 0346 2.2 / 0950 6.3 / F 1609 2.2 / 2217 5.9
	31 0428 2.5 / 1035 5.9 / SA 1658 2.6 / 2311 5.6

Chart Datum: 3·90 metres below Ordnance Datum (Newlyn)
Register for your **FREE** weekly weather email service from Macmillan Reeds
》 at **www.nauticaldata.com – NOW!** 《
weekend weather reports sent to your email address, every Thursday

TIME ZONE (UTC)
For Summer Time add ONE hour in **non-shaded areas**

ENGLAND – IMMINGHAM

YEAR 2002

LAT 53°38′N   LONG 0°11′W

TIMES AND HEIGHTS OF HIGH AND LOW WATERS

SEPTEMBER

#	Time	m	Time	m	#	Time	m	Time	m
1 SU	0531 1143 1815	2.8 5.7 2.8			16 M	0106 0753 1406 2025	5.7 2.8 5.7 2.9		
2 M	0049 0656 1331 1944	5.5 2.9 5.6 2.8			17 TU	0223 0914 1527 2131	5.8 2.4 6.0 2.6		
3 TU	0220 0823 1454 2103	5.7 2.7 5.9 2.6			18 W	0328 1010 1630 2222	6.1 1.9 6.3 2.2		
4 W	0323 0941 1557 2207	6.1 2.2 6.3 2.2			19 TH	0419 1057 1712 2306	6.5 1.6 6.6 1.9		
5 TH	0415 1042 1651 2300	6.6 1.6 6.8 1.7			20 F	0501 1139 1747 2346	6.9 1.3 6.8 1.6		
6 F	0500 1135 1739 2348	7.0 1.1 7.1 1.4			21 SA	0538 1217 1818	7.1 1.2 6.9 ○		
7 SA ●	0543 1223 1823	7.4 0.7 7.4			22 SU	0024 0612 1252 1846	1.5 7.2 1.2 6.9		
8 SU	0033 0624 1309 1905	1.1 7.7 1.0 7.5			23 M	0058 0645 1323 1913	1.4 7.2 1.2 6.9		
9 M	0117 0706 1352 1945	0.9 7.9 1.0 7.5			24 TU	0127 0716 1350 1938	1.5 7.1 1.4 6.8		
10 TU	0158 0749 1433 2025	0.9 7.9 0.4 7.4			25 W	0153 0746 1413 2003	1.6 7.0 1.5 6.8		
11 W	0239 0832 1512 2105	1.0 7.4 0.8 7.1			26 TH	0218 0813 1435 2029	1.7 6.8 1.7 6.6		
12 TH	0318 0917 1552 2147	1.3 7.3 1.3 6.2			27 F	0243 0842 1458 2058	1.9 6.6 1.9 6.4		
13 F	0358 1007 1634 2237	1.7 6.8 1.9 6.2			28 SA	0313 0916 1528 2134	2.1 6.4 2.2 6.1		
14 SA	0444 1111 1728 2344	2.2 6.2 2.5 5.8			29 SU	0354 1000 1613 2223	2.4 6.0 2.6 5.8		
15 SU	0552 1236 1853	2.7 5.8 2.9			30 M	0455 1107 1725 2342	2.7 5.7 3.0 5.5		

OCTOBER

#	Time	m	Time	m	#	Time	m	Time	m
1 TU	0625 1307 1909	2.9 5.6 3.1			16 W	0154 0851 1503 2104	5.8 2.4 5.9 2.8		
2 W	0145 0759 1437 2036	5.7 2.6 5.9 2.7			17 TH	0259 0944 1600 2155	6.1 2.0 6.3 2.4		
3 TH	0255 0920 1540 2143	6.1 2.0 6.4 2.2			18 F	0350 1028 1641 2238	6.5 1.6 6.6 2.0		
4 F	0349 1020 1632 2236	6.7 1.4 6.9 1.7			19 SA	0432 1107 1715 2317	6.8 1.4 6.8 1.7		
5 SA	0434 1111 1718 2324	7.2 0.9 7.3 1.3			20 SU	0509 1143 1745 2353	7.0 1.3 6.9 1.5		
6 SU ●	0517 1158 1759	7.6 0.5 7.5			21 M	0543 1216 1813	7.1 1.3 7.0 ○		
7 M	0009 0559 1243 1838	1.0 7.9 0.3 7.6			22 TU	0026 0615 1247 1839	1.5 7.1 1.3 7.0		
8 TU	0054 0642 1323 1917	0.8 8.0 0.3 7.6			23 W	0057 0646 1315 1905	1.5 7.1 1.4 7.0		
9 W	0136 0726 1405 1955	0.8 7.9 0.5 7.4			24 TH	0125 0717 1340 1932	1.5 7.0 1.6 6.9		
10 TH	0216 0810 1443 2034	1.0 7.7 1.0 7.1			25 F	0152 0747 1404 1959	1.7 6.9 1.7 6.8		
11 F	0255 0856 1521 2114	1.3 7.2 1.5 6.7			26 SA	0220 0819 1431 2030	1.8 6.7 1.9 6.6		
12 SA	0334 0947 1600 2200	1.7 6.6 2.1 6.3			27 SU	0253 0856 1504 2107	2.0 6.4 2.2 6.3		
13 SU	0420 1053 1651 2306	2.2 6.0 2.8 5.8			28 M	0336 0944 1551 2156	2.3 6.1 2.6 6.0		
14 M	0529 1223 1813	2.7 5.7 3.2			29 TU	0439 1054 1659 2309	2.6 5.7 3.0 5.7		
15 TU	0035 0736 1348 1957	5.6 2.7 5.6 3.2			30 W	0605 1244 1834	2.6 5.7 3.1		
					31 TH	0057 0734 1411 2003	5.8 2.4 6.0 2.8		

NOVEMBER

#	Time	m	Time	m	#	Time	m	Time	m
1 F	0217 0850 1514 2111	6.2 1.9 6.5 2.3			16 SA	0313 0947 1601 2201	6.3 1.9 6.4 2.2		
2 SA	0315 0950 1605 2207	6.7 1.3 6.9 1.8			17 SU	0358 1026 1638 2242	6.6 1.7 6.6 1.9		
3 SU	0404 1042 1651 2257	7.2 0.9 7.3 1.4			18 M	0436 1102 1710 2319	6.8 1.6 6.8 1.7		
4 M ●	0451 1129 1732 2344	7.6 0.6 7.5 1.0			19 TU	0511 1137 1739 2354	6.9 1.5 6.9 1.6		
5 TU	0536 1214 1812	7.8 0.5 7.6			20 W	0545 1210 1808	6.9 1.5 7.0 ○		
6 W	0030 0621 1257 1850	0.9 7.8 0.6 7.5			21 TH	0028 0619 1243 1838	1.5 7.0 1.5 7.0		
7 TH	0114 0706 1338 1929	0.9 7.7 0.8 7.4			22 F	0100 0654 1312 1909	1.6 6.9 1.6 7.0		
8 F	0156 0753 1417 2008	1.0 7.4 1.2 7.1			23 SA	0132 0730 1342 1940	1.6 6.8 1.7 6.9		
9 SA	0237 0840 1455 2048	1.3 7.0 1.7 6.8			24 SU	0207 0808 1415 2014	1.7 6.7 1.9 6.7		
10 SU	0318 0933 1535 2133	1.7 6.5 2.3 6.4			25 M	0246 0850 1454 2054	1.8 6.5 2.2 6.5		
11 M	0405 1038 1623 2231	2.1 6.0 2.8 6.0			26 TU	0333 0941 1541 2144	2.0 6.2 2.5 6.3		
12 TU	0509 1159 1729 2353	2.5 5.7 3.2 5.8			27 W	0433 1047 1643 2250	2.2 6.0 2.7 6.1		
13 W	0646 1314 1858	2.6 5.6 3.2			28 TH	0546 1214 1801	2.2 5.9 2.8		
14 TH	0113 0807 1420 2019	5.8 2.5 5.8 3.0			29 F	0012 0703 1334 1922	6.1 2.1 6.1 2.7		
15 F	0219 0903 1517 2115	6.0 2.2 6.1 2.6			30 SA	0133 0814 1438 2034	6.3 1.8 6.4 2.4		

DECEMBER

#	Time	m	Time	m	#	Time	m	Time	m
1 SU	0238 0916 1533 2136	6.7 1.4 6.7 1.9			16 M	0314 0935 1556 2159	6.2 2.1 6.3 2.3		
2 M	0335 1011 1622 2231	7.0 1.1 7.0 1.5			17 TU	0359 1019 1633 2243	6.4 1.9 6.5 2.0		
3 TU	0428 1101 1706 2322	7.3 1.0 7.2 1.2			18 W	0440 1100 1708 2324	6.6 1.7 6.7 1.8		
4 W ●	0517 1148 1749	7.5 0.9 7.3			19 TH	0520 1139 1743	6.7 1.7 6.9 ○		
5 TH	0010 0606 1233 1829	1.1 7.5 1.0 7.4			20 F	0003 0559 1216 1818	1.6 6.8 1.6 7.0		
6 F	0057 0654 1316 1910	1.0 7.4 1.2 7.3			21 SA	0042 0639 1252 1854	1.5 6.9 1.6 7.0		
7 SA	0142 0743 1356 1950	1.1 7.1 1.5 7.1			22 SU	0121 0721 1329 1929	1.5 6.9 1.7 7.0		
8 SU	0226 0831 1436 2030	1.3 6.8 1.8 6.9			23 M	0202 0803 1407 2007	1.5 6.8 1.8 7.0		
9 M	0308 0920 1515 2112	1.6 6.4 2.2 6.6			24 TU	0245 0847 1449 2048	1.5 6.6 1.9 6.9		
10 TU	0352 1014 1558 2200	1.9 6.1 2.5 6.3			25 W	0331 0936 1535 2135	1.6 6.5 2.1 6.7		
11 W	0441 1116 1648 2300	2.2 5.8 2.9 6.0			26 TH	0423 1032 1627 2231	1.7 6.3 2.3 6.6		
12 TH	0538 1221 1749	2.4 5.6 3.0			27 F	0522 1139 1728 2336	1.8 6.1 2.5 6.4		
13 F	0011 0643 1324 1858	5.9 2.5 5.6 3.1			28 SA	0627 1251 1839	1.8 6.1 2.5		
14 SA	0120 0748 1422 2009	5.9 2.4 5.8 2.9			29 SU	0050 0735 1359 1955	6.4 1.8 6.2 2.4		
15 SU	0221 0846 1514 2110	6.0 2.3 6.0 2.6			30 M	0204 0842 1500 2107	6.5 1.7 6.4 2.2		
					31 TU	0311 0943 1556 2210	6.7 1.6 6.6 1.9		

Chart Datum: 3·90 metres below Ordnance Datum (Newlyn)

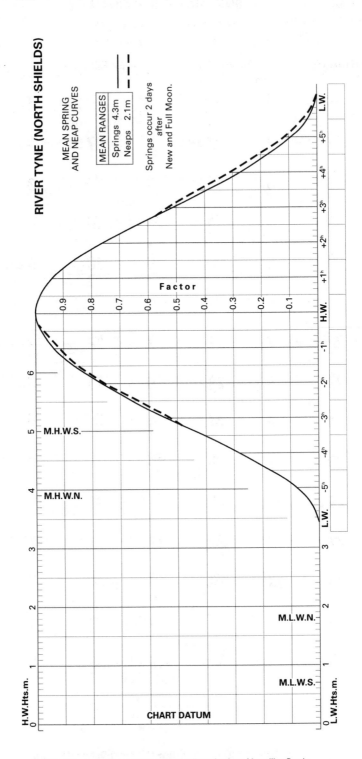

RIVER TYNE (NORTH SHIELDS)

MEAN SPRING
AND NEAP CURVES

MEAN RANGES
Springs 4.3m   Neaps 2.1m

Springs occur 2 days
after
New and Full Moon.

ENGLAND – NORTH SHIELDS

LAT 55°01′N   LONG 1°26′W

TIMES AND HEIGHTS OF HIGH AND LOW WATERS

YEAR 2002

TIME ZONE (UTC)
For Summer Time add ONE hour in **non-shaded areas**

JANUARY

Day	Time m	Time m	Time m	Time m
1 TU	0425 5.1	1041 1.0	1639 5.2	2312 0.7
2 W	0513 5.1	1125 1.1	1724 5.2	
3 TH	0000 0.6	0602 5.0	1211 1.2	1811 5.1
4 F	0051 0.7	0655 4.8	1300 1.4	1903 5.0
5 SA	0144 0.8	0752 4.6	1353 1.6	2000 4.8
6 SU	0241 1.0	0853 4.4	1453 1.7	2104 4.7
7 M	0346 1.2	0959 4.3	1604 1.8	2215 4.6
8 TU	0455 1.4	1107 4.3	1719 1.8	2327 4.5
9 W	0605 1.4	1212 4.4	1831 1.7	
10 TH	0035 4.6	0706 1.4	1310 4.5	1932 1.5
11 F	0136 4.7	0759 1.4	1401 4.7	2026 1.3
12 SA	0228 4.8	0844 1.3	1445 4.8	2112 1.2
13 SU ●	0313 4.8	0925 1.3	1524 4.9	2154 1.1
14 M	0355 4.8	1002 1.3	1601 5.0	2232 1.0
15 TU	0433 4.8	1036 1.3	1636 5.0	2307 1.0
16 W	0510 4.8	1109 1.3	1709 4.9	2341 1.0
17 TH	0545 4.7	1141 1.4	1743 4.8	
18 F	0013 1.1	0621 4.5	1213 1.5	1819 4.7
19 SA	0048 1.2	0658 4.4	1248 1.7	1857 4.6
20 SU	0126 1.4	0740 4.2	1327 1.8	1940 4.4
21 M	0209 1.6	0826 4.0	1414 2.0	2030 4.3
22 TU	0300 1.8	0921 3.9	1515 2.2	2128 4.1
23 W	0403 1.9	1025 3.9	1631 2.2	2236 4.1
24 TH	0515 1.9	1133 4.0	1749 2.1	2348 4.1
25 F	0624 1.8	1236 4.2	1856 1.8	
26 SA	0054 4.3	0723 1.6	1330 4.5	1952 1.5
27 SU	0151 4.6	0814 1.4	1417 4.7	2042 1.2
28 M ○	0242 4.8	0902 1.1	1501 5.0	2130 0.8
29 TU	0329 5.1	0947 1.0	1543 5.2	2217 0.5
30 W	0416 5.2	1031 0.9	1626 5.3	2303 0.3
31 TH	0502 5.2	1114 0.8	1710 5.4	2349 0.3

FEBRUARY

Day	Time m	Time m	Time m	Time m
1 F	0549 5.2	1157 0.9	1756 5.4	
2 SA	0035 0.4	0636 5.0	1241 1.0	1843 5.2
3 SU	0123 0.6	0726 4.7	1326 1.3	1935 5.0
4 M	0213 0.9	0820 4.5	1418 1.5	2034 4.7
5 TU	0310 1.3	0920 4.2	1523 1.8	2143 4.5
6 W	0418 1.6	1030 4.1	1646 1.9	2303 4.3
7 TH	0537 1.8	1144 4.1	1815 1.8	
8 F	0023 4.3	0650 1.8	1254 4.3	1927 1.6
9 SA	0132 4.4	0749 1.7	1350 4.5	2022 1.4
10 SU	0225 4.5	0835 1.5	1436 4.7	2107 1.2
11 M	0307 4.7	0914 1.4	1514 4.8	2144 1.1
12 TU ●	0344 4.7	0948 1.3	1547 4.9	2217 0.9
13 W	0417 4.8	1019 1.2	1618 5.0	2248 0.9
14 TH	0449 4.8	1049 1.2	1648 5.0	2317 0.9
15 F	0519 4.7	1118 1.2	1719 4.9	2346 0.9
16 SA	0550 4.6	1146 1.2	1750 4.9	
17 SU	0016 1.0	0621 4.5	1217 1.4	1823 4.7
18 M	0048 1.2	0656 4.4	1250 1.5	1900 4.6
19 TU	0123 1.4	0734 4.2	1328 1.7	1943 4.4
20 W	0205 1.6	0821 4.0	1418 1.9	2036 4.2
21 TH	0300 1.9	0922 3.9	1528 2.1	2145 4.0
22 F	0417 2.0	1038 3.9	1700 2.1	2309 4.0
23 SA	0547 1.9	1158 4.0	1828 1.8	
24 SU	0031 4.2	0701 1.7	1305 4.3	1933 1.4
25 M	0136 4.5	0759 1.4	1357 4.7	2027 1.0
26 TU	0229 4.8	0848 1.1	1443 5.0	2116 0.6
27 W ○	0316 5.1	0933 0.8	1526 5.3	2202 0.2
28 TH	0401 5.3	1015 0.7	1608 5.5	2247 0.0

MARCH

Day	Time m	Time m	Time m	Time m
1 F	0444 5.3	1057 0.0	1651 5.6	2331 0.0
2 SA	0528 5.2	1137 0.6	1735 5.5	
3 SU	0013 0.2	0611 5.0	1218 0.8	1821 5.3
4 M	0056 0.5	0656 4.8	1300 1.0	1911 5.0
5 TU	0141 1.0	0745 4.5	1349 1.3	2008 4.6
6 W	0233 1.4	0842 4.2	1451 1.7	2117 4.3
7 TH	0341 1.8	0951 4.0	1619 1.9	2242 4.0
8 F	0510 2.1	1115 3.9	1802 1.8	
9 SA	0012 4.0	0635 2.0	1235 4.1	1918 1.6
10 SU	0123 4.2	0736 1.8	1335 4.3	2010 1.4
11 M	0213 4.4	0820 1.6	1420 4.5	2050 1.2
12 TU	0251 4.6	0856 1.4	1456 4.7	2123 1.0
13 W	0324 4.7	0927 1.2	1527 4.8	2153 0.9
14 TH ●	0354 4.8	0956 1.1	1555 4.9	2221 0.8
15 F	0423 4.8	1025 1.0	1624 5.0	2249 0.7
16 SA	0451 4.8	1053 1.0	1653 4.9	2317 0.8
17 SU	0519 4.7	1121 1.0	1723 4.9	2345 0.9
18 M	0548 4.6	1150 1.1	1754 4.8	
19 TU	0014 1.1	0619 4.5	1222 1.3	1829 4.6
20 W	0046 1.3	0654 4.3	1258 1.5	1911 4.4
21 TH	0124 1.5	0739 4.1	1345 1.7	2005 4.2
22 F	0217 1.8	0838 3.9	1454 1.9	2116 4.0
23 SA	0337 2.0	0957 3.8	1630 1.9	2247 3.9
24 SU	0520 2.0	1126 4.0	1804 1.6	
25 M	0014 4.2	0641 1.7	1239 4.3	1913 1.2
26 TU	0120 4.5	0740 1.2	1334 4.6	2008 0.7
27 W	0212 4.9	0828 1.0	1421 5.0	2056 0.3
28 TH ○	0257 5.1	0912 0.7	1504 5.3	2142 0.1
29 F	0340 5.3	0954 0.5	1546 5.5	2225 -0.1
30 SA	0421 5.3	1035 0.4	1630 5.6	2307 0.0
31 SU	0502 5.2	1115 0.5	1714 5.5	2348 0.3

APRIL

Day	Time m	Time m	Time m	Time m
1 M	0544 5.0	1155 0.6	1801 5.2	
2 TU	0028 0.7	0626 4.8	1239 0.9	1851 4.9
3 W	0111 1.1	0713 4.5	1327 1.2	1947 4.5
4 TH	0200 1.5	0807 4.2	1428 1.6	2055 4.1
5 F	0305 2.0	0914 3.9	1554 1.8	2219 3.9
6 SA	0437 2.2	1039 3.8	1737 1.8	2349 3.9
7 SU	0609 2.1	1203 3.9	1852 1.6	
8 M	0058 4.1	0710 1.9	1306 4.2	1942 1.3
9 TU	0146 4.3	0753 1.6	1351 4.4	2020 1.2
10 W	0223 4.5	0827 1.4	1426 4.6	2052 1.0
11 TH	0255 4.6	0859 1.2	1458 4.7	2121 0.8
12 F ●	0324 4.7	0929 1.0	1527 4.8	2150 0.7
13 SA	0353 4.8	0958 0.9	1556 4.9	2218 0.7
14 SU	0421 4.8	1028 0.9	1627 4.9	2247 0.8
15 M	0449 4.8	1058 0.9	1658 4.8	2316 0.9
16 TU	0519 4.7	1129 1.0	1731 4.7	2346 1.0
17 W	0551 4.6	1202 1.1	1809 4.6	
18 TH	0019 1.3	0628 4.4	1242 1.3	1854 4.4
19 F	0100 1.5	0714 4.2	1333 1.5	1952 4.1
20 SA	0156 1.8	0815 4.0	1444 1.6	2106 4.0
21 SU	0319 2.0	0933 3.9	1614 1.6	2233 4.0
22 M	0458 1.9	1058 4.0	1740 1.3	2354 4.2
23 TU	0616 1.7	1210 4.3	1848 1.0	
24 W	0057 4.5	0714 1.3	1308 4.7	1943 0.6
25 TH	0149 4.8	0803 1.0	1356 5.0	2032 0.3
26 F	0233 5.1	0847 0.7	1441 5.3	2117 0.1
27 SA ○	0315 5.2	0930 0.5	1525 5.4	2200 0.1
28 SU	0356 5.2	1013 0.5	1609 5.4	2242 0.2
29 M	0437 5.1	1055 0.5	1656 5.3	2322 0.5
30 TU	0518 5.0	1138 0.6	1744 5.0	

TIME ZONE (UTC)
For Summer Time add ONE hour in **non-shaded areas**

ENGLAND – NORTH SHIELDS

LAT 55°01'N   LONG 1°26'W

TIMES AND HEIGHTS OF HIGH AND LOW WATERS

YEAR **2002**

MAY

Day	Time	m	Day	Time	m
1 W	0002	0.9	**16** TH	0532	4.6
	0600	4.8		1153	1.0
	1222	0.9		1759	4.6
	1834	4.7			
2 TH	0044	1.3	**17** F	0005	1.2
	0645	4.5		0613	4.5
	1311	1.1		1238	1.1
	1929	4.3		1848	4.4
3 F	0131	1.7	**18** SA	0051	1.5
	0736	4.2		0703	4.4
	1408	1.4		1333	1.2
	2032	4.0		1948	4.2
4 SA	0230	2.0	**19** SU	0150	1.7
	0838	4.0		0803	4.2
	1522	1.6		1440	1.3
	2146	3.8		2058	4.1
5 SU	0350	2.2	**20** M	0306	1.8
	0953	3.9		0914	4.1
	1649	1.7		1557	1.3
	2305	3.8		2215	4.1
6 M	0519	2.2	**21** TU	0430	1.8
	1113	3.9		1030	4.2
	1804	1.6		1713	1.1
				2328	4.3
7 TU	0014	3.9	**22** W	0543	1.6
	0624	2.0		1140	4.4
	1220	4.0		1819	0.9
	1856	1.4			
8 W	0105	4.1	**23** TH	0030	4.5
	0712	1.7		0643	1.4
	1309	4.2		1240	4.7
	1937	1.2		1916	0.6
9 TH	0145	4.3	**24** F	0122	4.7
	0750	1.5		0737	1.2
	1348	4.4		1332	4.9
	2012	1.1		2006	0.5
10 F	0219	4.5	**25** SA	0209	4.9
	0825	1.3		0824	0.9
	1423	4.6		1420	5.1
	2045	0.9		2053	0.4
11 SA	0251	4.6	**26** SU	0252	5.0
	0859	1.1		0910	0.7
	1456	4.7		1507	5.2
	2117	0.8		○2137	0.5
12 SU	0321	4.7	**27** M	0333	5.1
	0931	1.0		0955	0.6
	1529	4.8		1554	5.1
	●2148	0.8		2219	0.6
13 M	0352	4.8	**28** TU	0415	5.0
	1004	0.9		1040	0.6
	1602	4.8		1642	5.0
	2220	0.8		2300	0.8
14 TU	0423	4.8	**29** W	0456	4.9
	1038	0.9		1125	0.7
	1638	4.8		1730	4.8
	2252	0.9		2341	1.1
15 W	0456	4.7	**30** TH	0539	4.8
	1113	0.9		1209	0.9
	1716	4.7		1819	4.6
	2326	1.1			
			31 F	0021	1.4
				0622	4.6
				1255	1.1
				1909	4.3

JUNE

Day	Time	m	Day	Time	m
1 SA	0104	1.7	**16** SU	0047	1.3
	0709	4.4		0653	4.6
	1345	1.3		1330	0.9
	2003	4.1		1940	4.4
2 SU	0154	1.9	**17** M	0143	1.5
	0749	4.5		0749	4.5
	1441	1.5		1429	1.0
	2102	3.9		2043	4.3
3 M	0256	2.1	**18** TU	0246	1.6
	0902	4.0		0853	4.4
	1546	1.6		1534	1.0
	2207	3.8		2150	4.3
4 TU	0409	2.1	**19** W	0355	1.7
	1010	3.9		1001	4.4
	1654	1.6		1642	1.0
	2313	3.9		2257	4.3
5 W	0520	2.0	**20** TH	0506	1.6
	1117	4.0		1110	4.5
	1755	1.5		1749	1.0
6 TH	0010	4.1	**21** F	0000	4.4
	0618	1.9		0612	1.5
	1215	4.1		1214	4.6
	1845	1.4		1850	0.9
7 F	0058	4.2	**22** SA	0057	4.6
	0706	1.7		0712	1.3
	1304	4.3		1313	4.8
	1929	1.3		1944	0.9
8 SA	0139	4.4	**23** SU	0147	4.7
	0749	1.5		0806	1.1
	1346	4.4		1407	4.9
	2008	1.1		2034	0.9
9 SU	0216	4.5	**24** M	0233	4.8
	0828	1.3		0857	0.9
	1426	4.6		1458	4.9
	2045	1.0		○2119	0.9
10 M	0251	4.7	**25** TU	0317	4.9
	0906	1.1		0945	0.8
	1504	4.7		1546	4.9
	●2121	1.0		2202	1.0
11 TU	0326	4.8	**26** W	0358	4.9
	0944	1.0		1030	0.7
	1543	4.7		1632	4.8
	2158	1.0		2243	1.1
12 W	0401	4.8	**27** TH	0439	4.9
	1023	0.9		1113	0.8
	1623	4.8		1717	4.7
	2236	1.0		2321	1.2
13 TH	0438	4.8	**28** F	0519	4.8
	1104	0.8		1154	0.9
	1706	4.7		1800	4.6
	2316	1.1		2358	1.4
14 F	0519	4.8	**29** SA	0559	4.7
	1148	0.8		1234	1.0
	1753	4.7		1843	4.4
	2359	1.2			
15 SA	0603	4.7	**30** SU	0036	1.5
	1236	0.8		0640	4.6
	1844	4.6		1314	1.1
				1927	4.2

JULY

Day	Time	m	Day	Time	m
1 M	0116	1.7	**16** TU	0125	1.3
	0724	4.4		0730	4.9
	1357	1.3		1409	0.7
	2014	4.1		2018	4.5
2 TU	0203	1.9	**17** W	0218	1.4
	0813	4.2		0827	4.7
	1446	1.5		1506	1.0
	2107	3.9		2119	4.3
3 W	0259	2.0	**18** TH	0320	1.6
	0909	4.1		0932	4.6
	1543	1.6		1610	1.2
	2205	3.9		2224	4.3
4 TH	0405	2.1	**19** F	0431	1.7
	1010	4.0		1043	4.5
	1646	1.7		1720	1.3
	2306	3.9		2331	4.3
5 F	0515	2.0	**20** SA	0548	1.6
	1114	4.0		1156	4.5
	1748	1.6		1829	1.4
6 SA	0004	4.0	**21** SU	0035	4.4
	0618	1.9		0658	1.5
	1216	4.1		1304	4.5
	1844	1.6		1930	1.3
7 SU	0057	4.2	**22** M	0133	4.5
	0712	1.7		0800	1.3
	1310	4.3		1404	4.6
	1933	1.4		2022	1.3
8 M	0143	4.4	**23** TU	0222	4.7
	0800	1.4		0853	1.1
	1359	4.4		1455	4.7
	2018	1.3		2108	1.2
9 TU	0224	4.6	**24** W	0306	4.8
	0844	1.2		0939	0.9
	1444	4.6		1540	4.8
	2100	1.2		○2148	1.2
10 W	0304	4.8	**25** TH	0345	4.9
	0927	1.0		1020	0.8
	1527	4.8		1621	4.8
	●2142	1.0		2226	1.2
11 TH	0343	4.9	**26** F	0423	5.0
	1011	0.7		1058	0.8
	1611	4.9		1659	4.8
	2224	1.0		2300	1.2
12 F	0423	5.0	**27** SA	0458	4.9
	1056	0.6		1133	0.8
	1656	4.9		1736	4.7
	2307	1.0		2333	1.3
13 SA	0506	5.0	**28** SU	0533	4.9
	1141	0.5		1206	0.9
	1743	4.9		1812	4.5
	2351	1.0			
14 SU	0550	5.0	**29** M	0005	1.4
	1228	0.5		0608	4.8
	1832	4.8		1240	1.1
				1848	4.4
15 M	0036	1.1	**30** TU	0039	1.5
	0638	5.0		0646	4.6
	1317	0.6		1314	1.2
	1923	4.7		1927	4.3
			31 W	0116	1.7
				0728	4.4
				1354	1.4
				2011	4.1

AUGUST

Day	Time	m	Day	Time	m
1 TH	0200	1.8	**16** F	0247	1.6
	0815	4.3		0906	4.6
	1441	1.6		1538	1.5
	2101	4.0		2151	4.2
2 F	0256	2.0	**17** SA	0404	1.8
	0911	4.1		1023	4.3
	1539	1.8		1655	1.7
	2201	3.9		2305	4.1
3 SA	0407	2.1	**18** SU	0535	1.8
	1016	4.0		1147	4.3
	1648	1.9		1816	1.8
	2308	3.9			
4 SU	0527	2.1	**19** M	0019	4.3
	1129	4.0		0656	1.6
	1801	1.9		1304	4.4
				1922	1.7
5 M	0015	4.1	**20** TU	0123	4.5
	0638	1.9		0758	1.3
	1239	4.2		1403	4.5
	1904	1.7		2014	1.6
6 TU	0112	4.3	**21** W	0213	4.7
	0736	1.6		0847	1.1
	1337	4.4		1450	4.7
	1956	1.5		2056	1.4
7 W	0200	4.6	**22** TH	0255	4.8
	0826	1.2		0928	0.9
	1427	4.7		1528	4.8
	2043	1.3		○2133	1.3
8 TH	0244	4.8	**23** F	0330	5.0
	0912	0.9		1003	0.8
	1513	4.9		1603	4.8
	●2128	1.0		2205	1.2
9 F	0325	5.1	**24** SA	0402	5.0
	0957	0.5		1035	0.8
	1557	5.1		1635	4.8
	2210	0.9		2236	1.1
10 SA	0406	5.3	**25** SU	0433	5.0
	1042	0.3		1105	0.8
	1641	5.2		1707	4.8
	2253	0.8		2306	1.2
11 SU	0447	5.4	**26** M	0504	5.0
	1126	0.2		1134	0.8
	1726	5.2		1737	4.7
	2334	0.8		2335	1.2
12 M	0531	5.4	**27** TU	0536	4.9
	1210	0.2		1203	1.0
	1811	5.0		1809	4.6
13 TU	0016	0.9	**28** W	0005	1.3
	0616	5.3		0610	4.8
	1255	0.4		1234	1.1
	1858	4.9		1843	4.4
14 W	0100	1.1	**29** TH	0038	1.5
	0706	5.1		0647	4.6
	1342	0.7		1307	1.4
	1948	4.6		1920	4.3
15 TH	0148	1.3	**30** F	0115	1.7
	0801	4.8		0729	4.4
	1435	1.1		1347	1.6
	2045	4.4		2005	4.1
			31 SA	0204	1.9
				0821	4.1
				1439	1.9
				2102	4.0

Chart Datum: 2·60 metres below Ordnance Datum (Newlyn)

TIME ZONE (UTC)
For Summer Time add ONE hour in **non-shaded areas**

ENGLAND – NORTH SHIELDS

LAT 55°01′N   LONG 1°26′W

TIMES AND HEIGHTS OF HIGH AND LOW WATERS

YEAR **2002**

SEPTEMBER

Time	m		Time	m
1 0311	2.1	**16** 0528	1.8	
0928	4.0	1141	4.1	
SU 1552	2.1	M 1805	2.1	
2215	3.9			
2 0440	2.1	**17** 0004	4.2	
1050	3.9	0651	1.6	
M 1722	2.1	TU 1259	4.3	
2335	4.0	1912	1.9	
3 0609	1.9	**18** 0110	4.4	
1213	4.1	0748	1.3	
TU 1840	1.9	W 1353	4.5	
		2000	1.7	
4 0043	4.3	**19** 0158	4.6	
0714	1.5	0832	1.1	
W 1319	4.4	TH 1434	4.7	
1937	1.6	2038	1.5	
5 0137	4.6	**20** 0236	4.8	
0806	1.1	0907	1.0	
TH 1410	4.8	F 1508	4.8	
2025	1.3	2110	1.3	
6 0221	5.0	**21** 0308	5.0	
0853	0.7	0937	0.9	
F 1455	5.1	SA 1538	4.9	
2109	1.0	O 2140	1.2	
7 0302	5.3	**22** 0338	5.0	
0938	0.3	1005	0.8	
SA 1537	5.3	SU 1607	4.9	
● 2150	0.8	2209	1.1	
8 0343	5.5	**23** 0406	5.1	
1021	0.1	1033	0.8	
SU 1619	5.4	M 1635	4.9	
2231	0.7	2238	1.1	
9 0424	5.6	**24** 0436	5.0	
1104	0.0	1100	0.8	
M 1701	5.3	TU 1704	4.8	
2311	0.7	2306	1.1	
10 0507	5.6	**25** 0506	5.0	
1146	0.2	1128	1.0	
TU 1744	5.2	W 1733	4.7	
2352	0.8	2335	1.2	
11 0553	5.5	**26** 0539	4.8	
1228	0.5	1157	1.2	
W 1828	5.0	TH 1804	4.6	
12 0034	1.0	**27** 0006	1.4	
0642	5.2	0613	4.6	
TH 1313	0.9	F 1228	1.4	
1916	4.7	1838	4.4	
13 0122	1.3	**28** 0043	1.6	
0738	4.8	0654	4.4	
F 1403	1.4	SA 1304	1.7	
2011	4.4	1920	4.2	
14 0222	1.6	**29** 0129	1.8	
0845	4.4	0746	4.2	
SA 1508	1.8	SU 1352	2.0	
2118	4.2	2016	4.0	
15 0345	1.8	**30** 0234	2.0	
1009	4.2	0855	4.0	
SU 1634	2.1	M 1508	2.2	
2241	4.1	2132	3.9	

OCTOBER

Time	m		Time	m
1 0407	2.1	**16** 0630	1.6	
1023	3.9	1236	4.2	
TU 1651	2.2	W 1848	2.0	
2259	4.0			
2 0541	1.8	**17** 0043	4.4	
1151	4.1	0723	1.4	
W 1816	2.0	TH 1328	4.4	
		1934	1.8	
3 0013	4.3	**18** 0131	4.6	
0649	1.4	0803	1.2	
TH 1257	4.5	F 1406	4.6	
1914	1.6	2010	1.6	
4 0109	4.7	**19** 0209	4.7	
0742	0.9	0836	1.1	
F 1348	4.9	SA 1439	4.8	
2002	1.3	2042	1.4	
5 0155	5.1	**20** 0240	4.9	
0829	0.5	0905	1.0	
SA 1432	5.2	SU 1508	4.9	
2045	0.9	2112	1.2	
6 0237	5.4	**21** 0310	5.0	
0913	0.2	0933	0.9	
SU 1513	5.4	M 1537	4.9	
● 2126	0.7	O 2142	1.1	
7 0318	5.6	**22** 0340	5.0	
0956	0.1	1001	0.9	
M 1554	5.4	TU 1605	5.0	
2207	0.6	2211	1.1	
8 0400	5.7	**23** 0410	5.0	
1038	0.1	1029	0.9	
TU 1634	5.4	W 1633	4.9	
2247	0.6	2241	1.1	
9 0445	5.7	**24** 0441	4.9	
1120	0.3	1057	1.1	
W 1716	5.2	TH 1702	4.8	
2329	0.7	2312	1.2	
10 0532	5.4	**25** 0514	4.8	
1201	0.7	1126	1.2	
TH 1759	5.0	F 1732	4.7	
		2345	1.3	
11 0013	0.9	**26** 0550	4.6	
0622	5.1	1158	1.5	
F 1245	1.1	SA 1807	4.5	
1846	4.7			
12 0103	1.2	**27** 0022	1.5	
0720	4.7	0633	4.4	
SA 1335	1.6	SU 1235	1.7	
1940	4.4	1850	4.4	
13 0205	1.6	**28** 0111	1.7	
0829	4.3	0727	4.2	
SU 1439	2.1	M 1325	2.0	
2048	4.2	1947	4.2	
14 0329	1.8	**29** 0217	1.8	
0953	4.0	0837	4.0	
M 1606	2.3	TU 1441	2.2	
2212	4.1	2100	4.0	
15 0511	1.8	**30** 0342	1.8	
1123	4.0	1001	4.0	
TU 1743	2.2	W 1620	2.2	
2337	4.2	2224	4.1	
		31 0510	1.6	
		1124	4.2	
		TH 1744	2.0	
		2339	4.4	

NOVEMBER

Time	m		Time	m
1 0619	1.3	**16** 0053	4.4	
1228	4.5	0723	1.4	
F 1844	1.6	SA 1330	4.5	
		1935	1.7	
2 0037	4.7	**17** 0134	4.6	
0713	0.9	0758	1.3	
SA 1321	4.4	SU 1405	4.6	
1933	1.3	2010	1.5	
3 0127	5.1	**18** 0209	4.7	
0802	0.5	0830	1.2	
SU 1405	5.1	M 1437	4.8	
2018	1.0	2044	1.3	
4 0211	5.4	**19** 0243	4.8	
0847	0.3	0901	1.1	
M 1447	5.3	TU 1507	4.9	
● 2101	0.8	2116	1.2	
5 0255	5.6	**20** 0315	4.9	
0931	0.3	0932	1.1	
TU 1528	5.4	W 1537	4.9	
2144	0.6	O 2149	1.2	
6 0340	5.6	**21** 0348	4.9	
1014	0.4	1003	1.1	
W 1609	5.4	TH 1607	4.9	
2228	0.6	2221	1.1	
7 0427	5.5	**22** 0422	4.9	
1056	0.6	1033	1.2	
TH 1651	5.4	F 1638	4.9	
2312	0.7	2256	1.2	
8 0516	5.3	**23** 0458	4.8	
1138	1.0	1106	1.3	
F 1735	5.0	SA 1711	4.8	
2359	0.9	2332	1.2	
9 0609	4.9	**24** 0537	4.7	
1222	1.4	1141	1.5	
SA 1821	4.8	SU 1749	4.7	
10 0050	1.2	**25** 0014	1.3	
0706	4.6	0623	4.5	
SU 1310	1.6	M 1222	1.7	
1913	4.5	1834	4.5	
11 0150	1.5	**26** 0105	1.4	
0810	4.3	0717	4.3	
M 1410	2.1	TU 1314	1.9	
2016	4.3	1929	4.4	
12 0303	1.7	**27** 0206	1.5	
0924	4.0	0822	4.2	
TU 1528	2.3	W 1422	2.0	
2131	4.1	2035	4.3	
13 0428	1.8	**28** 0318	1.5	
1043	4.0	0936	4.2	
W 1656	2.3	TH 1544	2.1	
2252	4.1	2149	4.3	
14 0545	1.7	**29** 0434	1.4	
1154	4.1	1050	4.3	
TH 1805	2.1	F 1702	1.9	
		2301	4.5	
15 0000	4.2	**30** 0543	1.2	
0641	1.5	1155	4.5	
F 1248	4.3	SA 1807	1.7	
1855	1.9			

DECEMBER

Time	m		Time	m
1 0004	4.7	**16** 0051	4.3	
0642	1.0	0716	1.6	
SU 1251	4.8	M 1327	4.4	
1902	1.4	1936	1.7	
2 0100	5.0	**17** 0136	4.5	
0735	0.8	0756	1.5	
M 1339	5.0	TU 1405	4.6	
1953	1.2	2016	1.5	
3 0150	5.2	**18** 0216	4.6	
0824	0.7	0833	1.4	
TU 1424	5.1	W 1440	4.7	
2041	0.9	2054	1.4	
4 0239	5.4	**19** 0254	4.7	
0910	0.6	0908	1.3	
W 1507	5.2	TH 1514	4.8	
● 2129	0.8	O 2131	1.2	
5 0328	5.4	**20** 0331	4.8	
0954	0.7	0942	1.3	
TH 1550	5.2	F 1547	4.9	
2216	0.7	2208	1.1	
6 0417	5.3	**21** 0408	4.8	
1038	0.9	1018	1.3	
F 1632	5.2	SA 1621	4.9	
2303	0.8	2246	1.1	
7 0507	5.1	**22** 0447	4.8	
1120	1.2	1054	1.3	
SA 1716	5.0	SU 1657	4.9	
2350	0.9	2327	1.0	
8 0557	4.8	**23** 0529	4.8	
1203	1.5	1133	1.4	
SU 1801	4.9	M 1737	4.9	
9 0038	1.1	**24** 0010	1.0	
0649	4.6	0615	4.7	
M 1247	1.7	TU 1217	1.5	
1849	4.6	1822	4.8	
10 0129	1.3	**25** 0059	1.1	
0743	4.3	0705	4.6	
TU 1336	2.0	W 1304	1.6	
1941	4.4	1912	4.7	
11 0224	1.6	**26** 0152	1.2	
0842	4.1	0802	4.4	
W 1434	2.2	TH 1400	1.8	
2041	4.2	2010	4.6	
12 0326	1.7	**27** 0251	1.2	
0946	4.0	0905	4.3	
TH 1544	2.3	F 1504	1.9	
2149	4.1	2114	4.5	
13 0434	1.8	**28** 0357	1.3	
1052	4.0	1013	4.3	
F 1657	2.3	SA 1616	1.9	
2258	4.1	2224	4.6	
14 0538	1.8	**29** 0506	1.3	
1153	4.1	1120	4.4	
SA 1801	2.1	SU 1729	1.8	
2359	4.2	2333	4.6	
15 0632	1.7	**30** 0613	1.2	
1244	4.2	1222	4.5	
SU 1853	1.9	M 1836	1.6	
		31 0038	4.8	
		0713	1.2	
		TU 1318	4.7	
		1937	1.4	

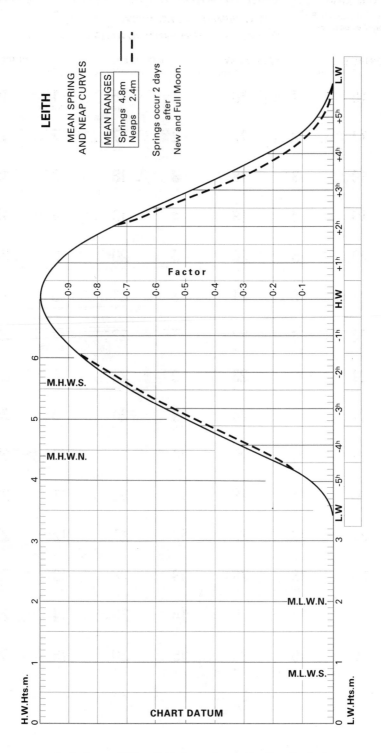

LEITH

MEAN SPRING AND NEAP CURVES

MEAN RANGES	
Springs	4.8m
Neaps	2.4m

Springs occur 2 days after New and Full Moon.

Register for your **FREE** weekly weather email service from Macmillan Reeds
》 at **www.nauticaldata.com – NOW!** 《
weekend weather reports sent to your email address, every Thursday

70

TIME ZONE (UTC)
For Summer Time add ONE hour in **non-shaded areas**

SCOTLAND – LEITH

YEAR **2002**

LAT 55°59′N   LONG 3°11′W

TIMES AND HEIGHTS OF HIGH AND LOW WATERS

JANUARY

Time	m	Time	m
1 0335	5.6	**16** 0421	5.1
0932	1.1	0951	1.3
TU 1554	5.6	W 1625	5.3
2208	0.7	2222	1.1
2 0420	5.7	**17** 0457	5.0
1020	1.1	1020	1.4
W 1637	5.6	TH 1659	5.2
2256	0.7	2249	1.2
3 0508	5.6	**18** 0533	4.8
1106	1.3	1050	1.5
TH 1724	5.5	F 1735	5.1
2345	0.8	2320	1.3
4 0558	5.4	**19** 0611	4.8
1152	1.5	1123	1.6
F 1815	5.4	SA 1815	4.9
		2355	1.5
5 0035	0.9	**20** 0653	4.6
0651	5.2	1200	1.8
SA 1241	1.7	SU 1858	4.7
1911	5.2		
6 0130	1.2	**21** 0035	1.7
0752	4.9	0739	4.5
SU 1337	1.9	M 1245	2.1
2018	5.1	1946	4.6
7 0233	1.4	**22** 0125	1.9
0859	4.8	0831	4.4
M 1447	2.0	TU 1350	2.3
2128	5.0	2042	4.4
8 0346	1.5	**23** 0229	2.0
1006	4.7	0931	4.3
TU 1603	2.0	W 1520	2.3
2235	4.9	2148	4.4
9 0457	1.6	**24** 0352	2.1
1112	4.8	1035	4.4
W 1714	1.9	TH 1645	2.2
2340	5.0	2257	4.5
10 0600	1.5	**25** 0510	1.9
1213	4.9	1139	4.6
TH 1819	1.7	F 1748	1.9
11 0040	5.1	**26** 0003	4.7
0651	1.5	0609	1.7
F 1307	5.0	SA 1239	4.8
1915	1.4	1842	1.6
12 0134	5.2	**27** 0102	5.0
0735	1.4	0701	1.5
SA 1354	5.2	SU 1330	5.1
2004	1.2	1933	1.2
13 0222	5.2	**28** 0153	5.3
0814	1.4	0750	1.2
SU 1435	5.3	M 1415	5.4
● 2046	1.1	○ 2023	0.8
14 0304	5.2	**29** 0238	5.6
0849	1.3	0839	1.0
M 1514	5.3	TU 1457	5.6
2124	1.0	2113	0.5
15 0344	5.2	**30** 0322	5.8
0921	1.2	0926	0.9
TU 1550	5.3	W 1539	5.7
2155	1.0	2201	0.3
		31 0406	5.8
		1012	0.8
		TH 1622	5.8
		2247	0.2

FEBRUARY

Time	m	Time	m
1 0452	5.8	**16** 0503	5.0
1054	0.9	1029	1.2
F 1708	5.8	SA 1707	5.2
2331	0.4	2254	1.1
2 0539	5.6	**17** 0537	4.9
1134	1.1	1054	1.3
SA 1755	5.6	SU 1742	5.0
		2320	1.2
3 0014	0.6	**18** 0614	4.8
0628	5.3	1118	1.5
SU 1212	1.3	M 1819	4.9
1847	5.4	2347	1.4
4 0058	1.0	**19** 0655	4.6
0722	5.0	1147	1.7
M 1254	1.6	TU 1901	4.7
1948	5.1		
5 0148	1.4	**20** 0022	1.7
0824	4.7	0741	4.4
TU 1354	1.9	W 1232	2.0
2058	4.8	1950	4.5
6 0259	1.8	**21** 0114	2.0
0932	4.5	0838	4.3
W 1526	2.1	TH 1347	2.2
2210	4.7	2056	4.3
7 0426	1.9	**22** 0239	2.2
1043	4.5	0948	4.2
TH 1659	2.0	F 1555	2.2
2324	4.6	2216	4.3
8 0542	1.9	**23** 0437	2.1
1155	4.6	1103	4.4
F 1819	1.8	SA 1724	1.9
		2336	4.5
9 0034	4.7	**24** 0552	1.9
0640	1.8	1212	4.7
SA 1258	4.8	SU 1826	1.5
1918	1.5		
10 0131	4.9	**25** 0042	4.9
0724	1.7	0648	1.6
SU 1347	5.0	M 1309	5.0
2003	1.3	1921	1.0
11 0216	5.0	**26** 0136	5.3
0801	1.5	0739	1.2
M 1427	5.1	TU 1355	5.4
2039	1.1	2012	0.6
12 0254	5.1	**27** 0221	5.6
0833	1.3	0827	0.9
TU 1502	5.3	W 1438	5.7
● 2110	1.0	○ 2100	0.2
13 0328	5.2	**28** 0304	5.9
0904	1.2	0912	0.6
W 1534	5.3	TH 1519	5.9
2137	0.9	2146	0.0
14 0359	5.1		
0933	1.1		
TH 1604	5.3		
2202	0.9		
15 0430	5.1		
1002	1.1		
F 1635	5.3		
2228	0.9		

MARCH

Time	m	Time	m
1 0347	5.9	**16** 0402	5.2
0955	0.5	0941	0.9
F 1602	6.0	SA 1609	5.3
2229	-0.1	2202	0.8
2 0431	5.8	**17** 0433	5.1
1035	0.6	1006	1.0
SA 1647	6.0	SU 1640	5.2
2310	0.1	2226	0.9
3 0516	5.6	**18** 0506	5.0
1111	0.8	1027	1.1
SU 1734	5.8	M 1714	5.1
2348	0.5	2245	1.1
4 0603	5.3	**19** 0541	4.9
1144	1.1	1046	1.3
M 1825	5.4	TU 1750	4.9
		2305	1.3
5 0024	1.0	**20** 0619	4.7
0652	4.9	1113	1.5
TU 1220	1.4	W 1831	4.7
1923	5.0	2335	1.6
6 0105	1.5	**21** 0702	4.5
0750	4.6	1154	1.7
W 1315	1.8	TH 1921	4.5
2032	4.7		
7 0211	2.0	**22** 0022	1.9
0859	4.4	0756	4.3
TH 1459	2.1	F 1302	2.0
2147	4.4	2025	4.3
8 0358	2.2	**23** 0151	2.2
1014	4.3	0908	4.2
F 1656	2.0	SA 1519	2.1
2308	4.4	2148	4.3
9 0525	2.0	**24** 0416	2.2
1135	4.4	1032	4.3
SA 1819	1.7	SU 1702	1.8
		2312	4.6
10 0025	4.6	**25** 0534	1.9
0627	2.0	1146	4.6
SU 1243	4.6	M 1808	1.3
1912	1.5		
11 0120	4.8	**26** 0021	5.0
0709	1.7	0630	1.5
M 1332	4.9	TU 1244	5.1
1951	1.2	1903	0.8
12 0202	5.0	**27** 0114	5.4
0743	1.5	0720	1.1
TU 1411	5.1	W 1331	5.5
2021	1.1	1954	0.4
13 0236	5.1	**28** 0159	5.7
0813	1.2	0806	0.7
W 1443	5.2	TH 1414	5.8
2047	0.9	○ 2040	0.1
14 0306	5.1	**29** 0242	5.9
0842	1.1	0850	0.5
TH 1512	5.3	F 1457	6.0
● 2112	0.8	2124	-0.1
15 0334	5.2	**30** 0324	5.9
0912	0.9	0933	0.4
F 1540	5.3	SA 1541	6.1
2137	0.8	2206	-0.1
		31 0407	5.8
		1013	0.4
		SU 1626	6.0
		2245	0.2

APRIL

Time	m	Time	m
1 0451	5.6	**16** 0438	5.1
1050	0.6	1007	1.0
M 1714	5.7	TU 1651	5.1
2322	0.7	2216	1.1
2 0537	5.3	**17** 0513	5.0
1123	0.9	1027	1.2
TU 1806	5.3	W 1729	5.0
2353	1.2	2237	1.3
3 0625	4.9	**18** 0551	4.8
1158	1.3	1057	1.4
W 1904	4.9	TH 1813	4.8
		2309	1.6
4 0028	1.7	**19** 0635	4.6
0721	4.6	1143	1.6
TH 1251	1.7	F 1905	4.6
2010	4.5		
5 0132	2.2	**20** 0001	2.0
0828	4.3	0729	4.4
F 1439	2.0	SA 1303	1.8
2122	4.3	2008	4.5
6 0328	2.4	**21** 0154	2.2
0943	4.2	0842	4.3
SA 1641	2.0	SU 1506	1.8
2242	4.3	2129	4.5
7 0456	2.3	**22** 0355	2.2
1104	4.3	1006	4.4
SU 1757	1.7	M 1638	1.5
		2249	4.7
8 0000	4.5	**23** 0507	1.8
0555	2.0	1118	4.7
M 1214	4.5	TU 1743	1.1
1846	1.5	2355	5.0
9 0055	4.7	**24** 0603	1.5
0638	1.8	1216	5.1
TU 1304	4.8	W 1839	0.7
1921	1.3		
10 0135	4.9	**25** 0048	5.4
0712	1.5	0652	1.1
W 1343	5.0	TH 1305	5.5
1949	1.1	1929	0.4
11 0208	5.0	**26** 0134	5.6
0744	1.2	0740	0.8
TH 1415	5.1	F 1350	5.8
2014	0.9	2016	0.2
12 0237	5.1	**27** 0217	5.8
0815	1.0	0826	0.5
F 1444	5.2	SA 1434	6.0
● 2039	0.8	○ 2100	0.1
13 0304	5.2	**28** 0300	5.8
0846	0.9	0910	0.4
SA 1512	5.3	SU 1520	6.0
2106	0.8	2142	0.2
14 0333	5.2	**29** 0344	5.7
0917	0.9	0953	0.5
SU 1543	5.3	M 1608	5.8
2133	0.8	2221	0.5
15 0404	5.2	**30** 0428	5.5
0945	0.9	1033	0.6
M 1615	5.2	TU 1657	5.6
2157	0.9	2256	1.0

Chart Datum: 2·90 metres below Ordnance Datum (Newlyn)
Register for your **FREE** weekly weather email service from Macmillan Reeds
》》 at **www.nauticaldata.com – NOW!** 《《
weekend weather reports sent to your email address, every Thursday

TIME ZONE (UTC)
For Summer Time add ONE hour in **non-shaded areas**

SCOTLAND – LEITH

LAT 55°59'N   LONG 3°11'W

TIMES AND HEIGHTS OF HIGH AND LOW WATERS

YEAR **2002**

MAY

Day	Time	m	Time	m	Time	m	Time	m		Day	Time	m	Time	m	Time	m	Time	m
1 W	0513	5.3	1110	0.9	1749	5.2	2327	1.4		16 TH	0450	5.1	1031	1.1	1714	5.1	2230	1.4
2 TH	0601	5.0	1146	1.3	1845	4.8				17 F	0531	4.9	1110	1.2	1800	4.9	2311	1.7
3 F	0000	1.8	0655	4.7	1235	1.6	1945	4.5		18 SA	0618	4.8	1207	1.4	1853	4.8		
4 SA	0058	2.2	0758	4.4	1400	1.9	2050	4.3		19 SU	0020	1.9	0713	4.6	1322	1.5	1956	4.7
5 SU	0239	2.4	0907	4.3	1557	1.9	2200	4.2		20 M	0156	2.1	0823	4.6	1449	1.5	2109	4.7
6 M	0407	2.3	1018	4.3	1707	1.6	2313	4.3		21 TU	0324	2.0	0940	4.7	1609	1.3	2222	4.8
7 TU	0506	2.1	1127	4.4	1757	1.6				22 W	0434	1.8	1049	4.9	1713	1.1	2327	5.0
8 W	0012	4.6	0552	1.8	1222	4.7	1834	1.4		23 TH	0531	1.5	1147	5.2	1810	0.8		
9 TH	0056	4.8	0632	1.6	1303	4.9	1904	1.2		24 F	0021	5.3	0623	1.2	1239	5.4	1902	0.6
10 F	0130	4.9	0709	1.3	1339	5.0	1932	1.1		25 SA	0110	5.4	0714	0.9	1328	5.6	1950	0.5
11 SA	0202	5.1	0744	1.0	1411	5.1	2002	1.0		26 SU	0155	5.6	0804	0.7	1416	5.7	O 2035	0.5
12 SU	0233	5.2	0819	1.0	1444	5.2	● 2033	0.9		27 M	0239	5.6	0852	0.6	1504	5.7	2118	0.6
13 M	0305	5.2	0853	0.9	1518	5.2	2104	0.9		28 TU	0323	5.6	0937	0.6	1553	5.6	2157	0.9
14 TU	0338	5.2	0926	0.9	1554	5.2	2134	1.0		29 W	0408	5.4	1020	0.7	1642	5.4	2233	1.2
15 W	0413	5.2	0958	1.0	1632	5.2	2201	1.2		30 TH	0453	5.2	1059	1.0	1732	5.1	2304	1.5
										31 F	0539	5.0	1134	1.2	1822	4.8	2337	1.8

JUNE

Day	Time	m	Time	m	Time	m	Time	m		Day	Time	m	Time	m	Time	m	Time	m
1 SA	0628	4.8	1213	1.5	1915	4.6				16 SU	0604	5.1	1218	1.1	1841	5.0		
2 SU	0023	2.1	0723	4.6	1306	1.7	2009	4.4		17 M	0031	1.7	0658	4.9	1317	1.2	1939	4.9
3 M	0130	2.2	0822	4.4	1423	1.9	2106	4.3		18 TU	0135	1.8	0801	4.9	1423	1.2	2045	4.8
4 TU	0256	2.3	0923	4.4	1548	1.9	2206	4.3		19 W	0246	1.9	0912	4.9	1534	1.2	2153	4.8
5 W	0407	2.2	1024	4.4	1647	1.8	2305	4.4		20 TH	0355	1.8	1019	5.0	1641	1.2	2257	4.9
6 TH	0503	2.0	1121	4.5	1734	1.6	2359	4.6		21 F	0459	1.6	1121	5.1	1742	1.1	2356	5.0
7 F	0551	1.7	1213	4.7	1814	1.5				22 SA	0558	1.4	1219	5.2	1838	1.0		
8 SA	0044	4.8	0633	1.5	1258	4.8	1851	1.3		23 SU	0048	5.2	0655	1.1	1314	5.4	1928	0.9
9 SU	0124	5.0	0713	1.3	1339	5.0	1927	1.2		24 M	0137	5.3	0749	0.9	1405	5.4	O 2014	0.9
10 M	0202	5.1	0752	1.1	1418	5.1	● 2004	1.1		25 TU	0223	5.4	0839	0.8	1454	5.4	2057	1.0
11 TU	0239	5.2	0831	1.0	1457	5.2	2042	1.1		26 W	0308	5.4	0925	0.7	1541	5.4	2136	1.1
12 W	0316	5.2	0912	0.9	1536	5.3	2121	1.1		27 TH	0352	5.4	1007	0.8	1627	5.2	2211	1.3
13 TH	0354	5.3	0954	0.9	1617	5.3	2203	1.2		28 F	0434	5.2	1044	0.9	1711	5.1	2242	1.4
14 F	0434	5.2	1039	0.9	1701	5.3	2247	1.3		29 SA	0516	5.1	1115	1.1	1754	4.8	2312	1.6
15 SA	0517	5.2	1127	0.9	1749	5.2	2336	1.5		30 SU	0558	4.9	1127	1.3	1838	4.7	2349	1.8

JULY

Day	Time	m	Time	m	Time	m	Time	m		Day	Time	m	Time	m	Time	m	Time	m
1 M	0643	4.8	1223	1.5	1923	4.5				16 TU	0015	1.4	0639	5.3	1257	0.9	1917	5.1
2 TU	0036	1.9	0732	4.6	1311	1.7	2012	4.4		17 W	0104	1.6	0736	5.1	1351	1.1	2017	4.9
3 W	0136	2.1	0825	4.5	1410	1.9	2105	4.3		18 TH	0203	1.7	0843	5.0	1456	1.3	2123	4.7
4 TH	0251	2.2	0922	4.4	1522	1.9	2200	4.3		19 F	0317	1.8	0953	4.9	1610	1.5	2229	4.7
5 F	0407	2.1	1020	4.4	1633	1.8	2258	4.4		20 SA	0434	1.8	1101	4.9	1720	1.5	2334	4.8
6 SA	0509	2.0	1120	4.5	1729	1.7	2356	4.6		21 SU	0545	1.6	1208	5.0	1822	1.4		
7 SU	0600	1.7	1218	4.6	1817	1.6				22 M	0035	4.9	0650	1.3	1308	5.1	1914	1.4
8 M	0049	4.8	0646	1.5	1310	4.8	1900	1.4		23 TU	0129	5.1	0746	1.1	1401	5.2	1959	1.3
9 TU	0136	5.0	0730	1.2	1356	5.0	1943	1.3		24 W	0215	5.2	0834	0.9	1447	5.3	O 2040	1.2
10 W	0218	5.2	0815	1.0	1439	5.3	● 2028	1.1		25 TH	0257	5.3	0916	0.8	1529	5.3	2116	1.2
11 TH	0258	5.3	0901	0.8	1521	5.4	2114	1.0		26 F	0337	5.3	0952	0.8	1609	5.2	2148	1.2
12 F	0338	5.4	0948	0.6	1603	5.5	2200	1.0		27 SA	0414	5.3	1023	0.9	1646	5.1	2217	1.2
13 SA	0419	5.5	1035	0.5	1647	5.5	2246	1.1		28 SU	0450	5.2	1049	1.0	1722	5.0	2245	1.3
14 SU	0502	5.5	1122	0.5	1734	5.4	2330	1.2		29 M	0526	5.1	1114	1.1	1759	4.8	2316	1.5
15 M	0549	5.4	1208	0.7	1823	5.3				30 TU	0604	5.0	1145	1.3	1839	4.7	2350	1.7
										31 W	0645	4.8	1221	1.5	1923	4.5		

AUGUST

Day	Time	m	Time	m	Time	m	Time	m		Day	Time	m	Time	m	Time	m	Time	m
1 TH	0032	1.9	0731	4.6	1306	1.8	2012	4.4		16 F	0123	1.7	0818	5.0	1418	1.6	2054	4.6
2 F	0129	2.1	0825	4.4	1405	2.0	2108	4.3		17 SA	0245	1.9	0933	4.7	1545	1.8	2205	4.5
3 SA	0253	2.3	0927	4.3	1525	2.1	2209	4.3		18 SU	0424	1.9	1049	4.7	1708	1.9	2319	4.6
4 SU	0425	2.2	1034	4.3	1649	2.0	2314	4.4		19 M	0549	1.7	1204	4.8	1815	1.8		
5 M	0532	1.9	1143	4.5	1751	1.8				20 TU	0027	4.8	0655	1.4	1308	4.9	1906	1.6
6 TU	0017	4.7	0625	1.6	1245	4.8	1842	1.6		21 W	0123	5.0	0746	1.1	1357	5.1	1947	1.5
7 W	0112	4.9	0714	1.2	1337	5.1	1929	1.3		22 TH	0207	5.2	0826	0.9	1437	5.2	O 2022	1.3
8 TH	0158	5.2	0802	0.9	1421	5.4	● 2016	1.1		23 F	0244	5.3	0900	0.8	1513	5.3	2053	1.2
9 F	0239	5.5	0850	0.5	1504	5.6	2103	0.9		24 SA	0319	5.4	0929	0.8	1546	5.2	2123	1.1
10 SA	0319	5.7	0937	0.3	1545	5.8	2148	0.8		25 SU	0350	5.4	0955	0.8	1617	5.2	2151	1.1
11 SU	0400	5.8	1022	0.2	1629	5.8	2231	0.8		26 M	0421	5.3	1018	0.9	1649	5.1	2217	1.1
12 M	0443	5.8	1106	0.2	1713	5.7	2311	0.9		27 TU	0453	5.2	1041	1.0	1723	5.0	2243	1.3
13 TU	0528	5.7	1148	0.4	1800	5.4	2350	1.1		28 W	0528	5.1	1106	1.2	1759	4.8	2308	1.5
14 W	0617	5.5	1230	0.8	1851	5.2				29 TH	0606	4.9	1133	1.4	1839	4.7	2336	1.7
15 TH	0030	1.4	0712	5.3	1317	1.2	1948	4.9		30 F	0648	4.7	1205	1.7	1925	4.5		
										31 SA	0017	2.0	0737	4.4	1253	1.8	2019	4.3

SCOTLAND – LEITH

LAT 55°59′N   LONG 3°11′W

TIMES AND HEIGHTS OF HIGH AND LOW WATERS

YEAR **2002**

SEPTEMBER

Day	Time	m	Day	Time	m
1 SU	0130 / 0840 / 1417 / 2125	2.2 / 4.3 / 2.3 / 4.3	**16** M	0427 / 1038 / 1659 / 2303	2.0 / 4.5 / 2.2 / 4.5
2 M	0337 / 0955 / 1617 / 2238	2.3 / 4.3 / 2.3 / 4.4	**17** TU	0553 / 1158 / 1805	1.7 / 4.7 / 2.0
3 TU	0508 / 1113 / 1732 / 2349	2.0 / 4.5 / 2.0 / 4.6	**18** W	0015 / 0651 / 1258 / 1851	4.8 / 1.4 / 4.9 / 1.8
4 W	0607 / 1222 / 1827	1.6 / 4.8 / 1.7	**19** TH	0108 / 0733 / 1343 / 1927	5.0 / 1.2 / 5.1 / 1.5
5 TH	0047 / 0658 / 1316 / 1914	5.0 / 1.1 / 5.2 / 1.3	**20** F	0150 / 0807 / 1419 / 1957	5.2 / 1.0 / 5.2 / 1.3
6 F	0134 / 0747 / 1400 / 2000	5.3 / 0.7 / 5.6 / 0.9	**21** SA	0224 / 0834 / 1450 / 2026	5.4 / 0.9 / 5.3 / 1.1
7 SA	0216 / 0834 / 1442 / 2044	5.7 / 0.3 / 5.9 / 0.7	**22** SU	0254 / 0858 / 1518 / 2055	5.4 / 0.8 / 5.3 / 1.0
8 SU	0256 / 0919 / 1523 / 2128	5.9 / 0.0 / 6.0 / 0.6	**23** M	0323 / 0921 / 1547 / 2124	5.4 / 0.8 / 5.3 / 1.0
9 M	0337 / 1002 / 1605 / 2209	6.1 / -0.1 / 6.0 / 0.5	**24** TU	0352 / 0944 / 1617 / 2150	5.4 / 0.8 / 5.2 / 1.0
10 TU	0420 / 1044 / 1649 / 2248	6.1 / 0.1 / 5.8 / 0.7	**25** W	0423 / 1007 / 1649 / 2213	5.3 / 1.0 / 5.1 / 1.2
11 W	0506 / 1123 / 1735 / 2324	5.9 / 0.4 / 5.5 / 1.0	**26** TH	0457 / 1028 / 1724 / 2233	5.2 / 1.2 / 5.0 / 1.4
12 TH	0555 / 1201 / 1824	5.5 / 0.9 / 5.2	**27** F	0534 / 1049 / 1802 / 2259	5.0 / 1.4 / 4.8 / 1.6
13 F	0001 / 0651 / 1243 / 1920	1.3 / 5.2 / 1.4 / 4.8	**28** SA	0616 / 1115 / 1845 / 2336	4.7 / 1.7 / 4.6 / 1.8
14 SA	0055 / 0759 / 1344 / 2028	1.7 / 4.8 / 1.9 / 4.6	**29** SU	0705 / 1155 / 1937	4.5 / 2.1 / 4.4
15 SU	0229 / 0917 / 1526 / 2144	2.0 / 4.7 / 2.2 / 4.5	**30** M	0040 / 0806 / 1319 / 2046	2.2 / 4.3 / 2.4 / 4.3

OCTOBER

Day	Time	m	Day	Time	m
1 TU	0257 / 0925 / 1550 / 2206	2.3 / 4.3 / 2.4 / 4.4	**16** W	0535 / 1136 / 1737 / 2348	1.7 / 4.6 / 2.2 / 4.8
2 W	0443 / 1046 / 1711 / 2320	2.0 / 4.5 / 2.1 / 4.7	**17** TH	0628 / 1234 / 1821	1.5 / 4.9 / 1.9
3 TH	0546 / 1156 / 1805	1.5 / 4.9 / 1.7	**18** F	0041 / 0706 / 1317 / 1855	5.0 / 1.3 / 5.1 / 1.6
4 F	0019 / 0637 / 1250 / 1852	5.1 / 1.0 / 5.4 / 1.3	**19** SA	0122 / 0735 / 1351 / 1926	5.2 / 1.2 / 5.2 / 1.4
5 SA	0107 / 0725 / 1335 / 1936	5.5 / 0.6 / 5.7 / 1.0	**20** SU	0156 / 0759 / 1421 / 1957	5.3 / 1.0 / 5.3 / 1.2
6 SU	0149 / 0811 / 1417 / 2020	5.8 / 0.2 / 6.0 / 0.7	**21** M	0226 / 0821 / 1448 / 2028	5.4 / 0.9 / 5.3 / 1.1
7 M	0230 / 0855 / 1458 / 2103	6.1 / 0.0 / 6.1 / 0.5	**22** TU	0254 / 0846 / 1516 / 2058	5.4 / 0.9 / 5.3 / 1.0
8 TU	0313 / 0938 / 1540 / 2146	6.2 / 0.0 / 6.0 / 0.6	**23** W	0324 / 0912 / 1547 / 2126	5.4 / 1.0 / 5.3 / 1.1
9 W	0358 / 1019 / 1624 / 2226	6.2 / 0.2 / 5.8 / 0.7	**24** TH	0357 / 0936 / 1620 / 2151	5.3 / 1.1 / 5.2 / 1.2
10 TH	0446 / 1057 / 1710 / 2304	5.9 / 0.6 / 5.5 / 1.0	**25** F	0433 / 0957 / 1654 / 2213	5.2 / 1.3 / 5.1 / 1.4
11 F	0537 / 1134 / 1759 / 2344	5.6 / 1.2 / 5.2 / 1.3	**26** SA	0511 / 1018 / 1732 / 2240	5.0 / 1.5 / 4.9 / 1.6
12 SA	0635 / 1212 / 1855	5.1 / 1.7 / 4.9	**27** SU	0554 / 1046 / 1814 / 2321	4.8 / 1.8 / 4.7 / 1.8
13 SU	0039 / 0744 / 1314 / 2004	1.7 / 4.8 / 2.2 / 4.6	**28** M	0644 / 1129 / 1906	4.6 / 2.1 / 4.5
14 M	0221 / 0859 / 1502 / 2121	2.0 / 4.5 / 2.4 / 4.4	**29** TU	0035 / 0744 / 1302 / 2014	2.0 / 4.5 / 2.4 / 4.4
15 TU	0418 / 1018 / 1634 / 2238	2.0 / 4.5 / 2.4 / 4.5	**30** W	0232 / 0859 / 1519 / 2135	2.1 / 4.5 / 2.4 / 4.5
			31 TH	0410 / 1018 / 1639 / 2248	1.8 / 4.7 / 2.1 / 4.8

NOVEMBER

Day	Time	m	Day	Time	m
1 F	0516 / 1126 / 1735 / 2347	1.4 / 5.0 / 1.8 / 5.2	**16** SA	0001 / 0623 / 1239 / 1815	4.8 / 1.6 / 4.9 / 1.8
2 SA	0609 / 1221 / 1823	1.0 / 5.4 / 1.4	**17** SU	0046 / 0651 / 1316 / 1852	5.0 / 1.4 / 5.0 / 1.5
3 SU	0037 / 0658 / 1308 / 1908	5.6 / 0.6 / 5.7 / 1.0	**18** M	0123 / 0717 / 1348 / 1927	5.1 / 1.3 / 5.2 / 1.3
4 M ●	0122 / 0744 / 1351 / 1954	5.9 / 0.4 / 5.9 / 0.8	**19** TU	0156 / 0745 / 1418 / 2001	5.2 / 1.2 / 5.3 / 1.2
5 TU	0206 / 0829 / 1433 / 2040	6.1 / 0.3 / 6.0 / 0.6	**20** W ○	0228 / 0814 / 1449 / 2035	5.3 / 1.1 / 5.3 / 1.1
6 W	0252 / 0913 / 1517 / 2126	6.1 / 0.3 / 5.9 / 0.6	**21** TH	0302 / 0844 / 1522 / 2108	5.3 / 1.1 / 5.3 / 1.1
7 TH	0340 / 0955 / 1601 / 2210	6.0 / 0.6 / 5.8 / 0.7	**22** F	0337 / 0913 / 1556 / 2140	5.3 / 1.2 / 5.3 / 1.2
8 F	0430 / 1034 / 1648 / 2252	5.8 / 1.0 / 5.5 / 1.0	**23** SA	0414 / 0941 / 1631 / 2212	5.2 / 1.4 / 5.2 / 1.3
9 SA	0523 / 1110 / 1737 / 2336	5.5 / 1.5 / 5.2 / 1.3	**24** SU	0454 / 1009 / 1710 / 2249	5.1 / 1.6 / 5.0 / 1.5
10 SU	0620 / 1147 / 1832	5.1 / 1.9 / 4.9	**25** M	0538 / 1043 / 1753 / 2338	5.0 / 1.8 / 4.9 / 1.6
11 M	0028 / 0724 / 1242 / 1938	1.7 / 4.7 / 2.3 / 4.7	**26** TU	0628 / 1134 / 1844	4.8 / 2.1 / 4.8
12 TU	0153 / 0831 / 1416 / 2049	2.0 / 4.5 / 2.5 / 4.5	**27** W	0045 / 0725 / 1303 / 1946	1.7 / 4.7 / 2.3 / 4.7
13 W	0338 / 0941 / 1545 / 2200	2.0 / 4.4 / 2.5 / 4.6	**28** TH	0206 / 0833 / 1438 / 2101	2.0 / 4.7 / 2.3 / 4.7
14 TH	0451 / 1052 / 1647 / 2306	1.9 / 4.6 / 2.3 / 4.7	**29** F	0329 / 0945 / 1556 / 2213	1.6 / 4.8 / 2.1 / 4.9
15 F	0545 / 1153 / 1735	1.7 / 4.7 / 2.1	**30** SA	0439 / 1050 / 1658 / 2314	1.4 / 5.0 / 1.8 / 5.2

DECEMBER

Day	Time	m	Day	Time	m
1 SU	0537 / 1150 / 1751	1.1 / 5.2 / 1.5	**16** M	0602 / 1231 / 1819	1.7 / 4.8 / 1.8
2 M	0008 / 0630 / 1241 / 1842	5.5 / 0.9 / 5.5 / 1.2	**17** TU	0044 / 0638 / 1313 / 1900	4.9 / 1.6 / 5.0 / 1.6
3 TU	0059 / 0719 / 1328 / 1933	5.7 / 0.7 / 5.6 / 1.0	**18** W	0127 / 0714 / 1350 / 1938	5.0 / 1.4 / 5.1 / 1.4
4 W ●	0148 / 0807 / 1412 / 2024	5.8 / 0.7 / 5.7 / 0.8	**19** TH ○	0206 / 0749 / 1427 / 2016	5.1 / 1.4 / 5.2 / 1.3
5 TH	0237 / 0852 / 1457 / 2113	5.9 / 0.8 / 5.7 / 0.7	**20** F	0244 / 0825 / 1502 / 2055	5.2 / 1.3 / 5.3 / 1.3
6 F	0327 / 0935 / 1543 / 2200	5.8 / 0.9 / 5.6 / 0.8	**21** SA	0321 / 0902 / 1538 / 2135	5.3 / 1.3 / 5.3 / 1.1
7 SA	0417 / 1016 / 1630 / 2244	5.6 / 1.2 / 5.5 / 1.0	**22** SU	0400 / 0940 / 1615 / 2216	5.3 / 1.4 / 5.3 / 1.1
8 SU	0509 / 1052 / 1718 / 2326	5.3 / 1.5 / 5.3 / 1.2	**23** M	0441 / 1019 / 1654 / 2300	5.3 / 1.5 / 5.2 / 1.1
9 M	0601 / 1125 / 1809	5.1 / 1.9 / 5.0	**24** TU	0524 / 1101 / 1737 / 2347	5.2 / 1.6 / 5.2 / 1.2
10 TU	0007 / 0655 / 1205 / 1904	1.5 / 4.8 / 2.1 / 4.9	**25** W	0612 / 1146 / 1825	5.1 / 1.8 / 5.1
11 W	0055 / 0751 / 1303 / 2005	1.8 / 4.5 / 2.3 / 4.6	**26** TH	0037 / 0704 / 1242 / 1920	1.3 / 5.0 / 1.9 / 5.0
12 TH	0204 / 0849 / 1422 / 2106	2.0 / 4.4 / 2.4 / 4.5	**27** F	0136 / 0803 / 1349 / 2024	1.4 / 4.8 / 2.0 / 4.9
13 F	0328 / 0948 / 1540 / 2206	2.1 / 4.4 / 2.4 / 4.5	**28** SA	0244 / 0910 / 1505 / 2135	1.5 / 4.8 / 2.0 / 4.9
14 SA	0431 / 1047 / 1641 / 2304	2.0 / 4.4 / 2.2 / 4.6	**29** SU	0357 / 1017 / 1618 / 2243	1.5 / 4.8 / 1.9 / 5.0
15 SU	0521 / 1143 / 1733 / 2357	1.9 / 4.6 / 2.0 / 4.7	**30** M	0505 / 1120 / 1723 / 2346	1.4 / 5.0 / 1.7 / 5.2
			31 TU	0606 / 1218 / 1825	1.3 / 5.1 / 1.4

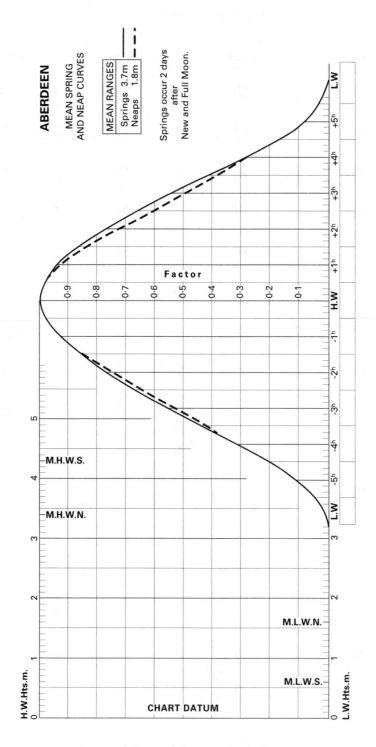

ABERDEEN

MEAN SPRING
AND NEAP CURVES

MEAN RANGES	
Springs	3.7m
Neaps	1.8m

Springs occur 2 days
after
New and Full Moon.

Factor

0·9 0·8 0·7 0·6 0·5 0·4 0·3 0·2 0·1

H.W -1ʰ -2ʰ -3ʰ -4ʰ -5ʰ L.W

+1ʰ +2ʰ +3ʰ +4ʰ +5ʰ L.W

H.W.Hts.m.

M.H.W.S.

M.H.W.N.

M.L.W.N.

M.L.W.S.

L.W.Hts.m.

CHART DATUM

SCOTLAND – ABERDEEN

LAT 57°09′N   LONG 2°05′W

TIMES AND HEIGHTS OF HIGH AND LOW WATERS

JANUARY

Day	Time	m	Time	m	Time	m	Time	m
1 TU	0220	4.3	0815	1.0	1433	4.4	2046	0.6
2 W	0308	4.3	0900	1.0	1517	4.4	2135	0.6
3 TH	0358	4.2	0947	1.1	1605	4.3	2226	0.7
4 F	0451	4.1	1036	1.3	1656	4.2	2320	0.8
5 SA	0547	3.9	1131	1.5	1753	4.1		
6 SU	0019	1.0	0648	3.8	1233	1.6	1857	4.0
7 M	0124	1.2	0754	3.7	1343	1.7	2008	3.9
8 TU	0233	1.3	0903	3.7	1458	1.7	2122	3.9
9 W	0344	1.3	1009	3.8	1610	1.6	2231	3.9
10 TH	0445	1.3	1106	3.9	1711	1.4	2330	4.0
11 F	0537	1.3	1155	4.0	1803	1.3		
12 SA	0022	4.1	0621	1.3	1238	4.1	1848	1.1
13 SU	0108	4.1	0701	1.2	1317	4.2	1929	1.0
14 M	0149	4.1	0738	1.2	1354	4.2	2008	0.9
15 TU	0228	4.1	0813	1.2	1429	4.3	2044	0.8
16 W	0305	4.0	0847	1.3	1503	4.2	2118	1.0
17 TH	0341	3.9	0920	1.3	1536	4.1	2151	1.1
18 F	0417	3.8	0953	1.4	1611	4.0	2226	1.2
19 SA	0455	3.7	1028	1.6	1650	3.9	2304	1.3
20 SU	0536	3.6	1108	1.7	1734	3.8	2348	1.5
21 M	0624	3.5	1156	1.8	1824	3.6		
22 TU	0040	1.6	0719	3.4	1258	2.0	1923	3.5
23 W	0142	1.7	0822	3.4	1412	2.0	2031	3.5
24 TH	0252	1.7	0929	3.5	1528	1.9	2144	3.6
25 F	0400	1.7	1032	3.6	1634	1.7	2251	3.7
26 SA	0459	1.5	1125	3.8	1728	1.4	2347	3.9
27 SU	0549	1.3	1212	4.0	1817	1.1		
28 M	0037	4.1	0636	1.1	1255	4.2	1904 ○	0.8
29 TU	0125	4.3	0721	1.0	1338	4.3	1950	0.5
30 W	0211	4.4	0805	0.9	1420	4.6	2037	0.4
31 TH	0257	4.5	0849	0.8	1504	4.6	2123	0.3

FEBRUARY

Day	Time	m	Time	m	Time	m	Time	m
1 F	0343	4.4	0932	0.9	1549	4.6	2210	0.4
2 SA	0431	4.2	1016	1.0	1637	4.5	2258	0.6
3 SU	0520	4.0	1104	1.2	1729	4.3	2349	0.9
4 M	0614	3.8	1157	1.4	1828	4.0		
5 TU	0047	1.2	0715	3.6	1304	1.6	1938	3.8
6 W	0156	1.5	0825	3.5	1426	1.7	2059	3.7
7 TH	0316	1.7	0940	3.5	1554	1.7	2219	3.7
8 F	0430	1.7	1048	3.7	1705	1.5	2326	3.8
9 SA	0527	1.6	1143	3.8	1758	1.3		
10 SU	0018	3.9	0611	1.4	1228	4.0	1841	1.1
11 M	0101	4.0	0649	1.3	1306	4.1	1918	1.0
12 TU	0138	4.0	0724	1.2	1340	4.2	1952 ●	0.9
13 W	0212	4.1	0756	1.1	1412	4.2	2024	0.8
14 TH	0243	4.1	0827	1.1	1442	4.2	2054	0.8
15 F	0314	4.0	0856	1.1	1512	4.2	2123	0.9
16 SA	0344	3.9	0925	1.2	1544	4.1	2153	1.0
17 SU	0417	3.8	0955	1.3	1618	4.0	2225	1.1
18 M	0452	3.7	1029	1.6	1656	3.9	2300	1.3
19 TU	0532	3.6	1108	1.6	1740	3.7	2343	1.5
20 W	0620	3.5	1158	1.7	1833	3.6		
21 TH	0039	1.7	0720	3.4	1311	1.9	1942	3.4
22 F	0156	1.8	0835	3.3	1441	1.9	2106	3.4
23 SA	0324	1.8	0954	3.5	1606	1.7	2227	3.6
24 SU	0438	1.6	1100	3.7	1710	1.3	2331	3.8
25 M	0534	1.3	1151	4.0	1802	0.9		
26 TU	0023	4.1	0622	1.1	1237	4.2	1849	0.6
27 W	0110	4.3	0706	0.8	1320	4.5	1935 ○	0.3
28 TH	0155	4.5	0749	0.7	1402	4.7	2020	0.1

MARCH

Day	Time	m	Time	m	Time	m	Time	m
1 F	0238	4.5	0830	0.6	1445	4.7	2103	0.1
2 SA	0321	4.4	0911	0.6	1529	4.7	2147	0.3
3 SU	0404	4.3	0952	0.8	1615	4.5	2230	0.6
4 M	0450	4.0	1036	1.0	1705	4.3	2317	0.9
5 TU	0539	3.8	1127	1.2	1803	3.9		
6 W	0010	1.3	0636	3.6	1232	1.5	1913	3.6
7 TH	0119	1.7	0747	3.4	1359	1.7	2040	3.5
8 F	0249	1.9	0910	3.4	1543	1.7	2209	3.5
9 SA	0416	1.8	1028	3.5	1656	1.5	2317	3.6
10 SU	0514	1.7	1126	3.7	1746	1.3		
11 M	0006	3.7	0556	1.5	1211	3.8	1824	1.1
12 TU	0045	3.9	0631	1.3	1247	4.0	1858	0.9
13 W	0117	4.0	0703	1.1	1318	4.1	1928	0.8
14 TH	0148	4.0	0734	1.0	1348	4.2	1957 ●	0.7
15 F	0216	4.0	0803	1.0	1417	4.2	2025	0.7
16 SA	0244	4.0	0830	0.9	1446	4.2	2052	0.8
17 SU	0312	4.0	0858	1.0	1517	4.1	2120	0.9
18 M	0342	3.9	0926	1.0	1550	4.0	2149	1.0
19 TU	0415	3.8	0958	1.2	1627	3.9	2221	1.2
20 W	0452	3.7	1035	1.3	1709	3.7	2301	1.4
21 TH	0536	3.5	1122	1.5	1803	3.5	2355	1.6
22 F	0635	3.3	1233	1.7	1914	3.4		
23 SA	0117	1.8	0753	3.3	1410	1.7	2043	3.4
24 SU	0258	1.8	0921	3.3	1542	1.5	2209	3.5
25 M	0419	1.6	1033	3.6	1650	1.1	2314	3.8
26 TU	0516	1.3	1128	3.9	1743	0.7		
27 W	0005	4.1	0603	1.0	1214	4.2	1830	0.4
28 TH	0050	4.3	0646	0.7	1258	4.5	1914 ○	0.1
29 F	0133	4.4	0727	0.5	1340	4.7	1957	0.0
30 SA	0214	4.5	0808	0.4	1423	4.7	2039	0.1
31 SU	0255	4.4	0848	0.5	1508	4.6	2120	0.3

APRIL

Day	Time	m	Time	m	Time	m	Time	m
1 M	0336	4.2	0930	0.6	1554	4.4	2202	0.6
2 TU	0420	4.0	1014	0.8	1645	4.1	2246	1.0
3 W	0506	3.8	1104	1.1	1743	3.8	2337	1.4
4 TH	0602	3.5	1208	1.4	1854	3.5		
5 F	0044	1.8	0710	3.3	1334	1.6	2018	3.3
6 SA	0216	2.0	0834	3.3	1521	1.6	2147	3.3
7 SU	0350	1.9	0957	3.4	1632	1.4	2254	3.5
8 M	0448	1.7	1057	3.5	1719	1.2	2340	3.6
9 TU	0530	1.5	1142	3.7	1756	1.0		
10 W	0017	3.8	0604	1.3	1218	3.8	1827	0.9
11 TH	0048	3.9	0636	1.1	1250	4.0	1857	0.8
12 F	0117	4.0	0706	1.0	1320	4.0	1926 ●	0.7
13 SA	0146	4.0	0735	0.9	1350	4.1	1954	0.7
14 SU	0214	4.0	0804	0.8	1421	4.1	2021	0.7
15 M	0242	4.0	0833	0.8	1453	4.0	2050	0.8
16 TU	0313	3.9	0903	0.9	1527	3.9	2120	1.0
17 W	0346	3.8	0936	1.0	1606	3.8	2154	1.1
18 TH	0424	3.7	1016	1.1	1651	3.7	2235	1.3
19 F	0509	3.5	1108	1.3	1748	3.5	2333	1.6
20 SA	0609	3.4	1221	1.4	1902	3.3		
21 SU	0059	1.8	0727	3.3	1353	1.4	2028	3.4
22 M	0236	1.7	0851	3.4	1519	1.2	2149	3.5
23 TU	0354	1.5	1004	3.6	1626	0.9	2251	3.8
24 W	0451	1.2	1100	3.9	1719	0.6	2342	4.0
25 TH	0539	0.9	1149	4.2	1807	0.3		
26 F	0026	4.2	0622	0.7	1234	4.4	1850	0.2
27 SA	0108	4.3	0704	0.5	1318	4.5	1933 ○	0.1
28 SU	0149	4.4	0746	0.4	1403	4.5	2014	0.3
29 M	0229	4.3	0828	0.4	1449	4.4	2055	0.5
30 TU	0311	4.2	0912	0.6	1538	4.2	2136	0.8

TIME ZONE (UTC)
For Summer Time add ONE hour in **non-shaded areas**

SCOTLAND – ABERDEEN

LAT 57°09'N   LONG 2°05'W

TIMES AND HEIGHTS OF HIGH AND LOW WATERS

YEAR **2002**

MAY

Day	Time m		Day	Time m	
1 W	0353 4.0 / 0957 0.8	1629 3.9 / 2220 1.2	**16** TH	0325 3.9 / 0926 0.9	1554 3.8 / 2139 1.1
2 TH	0439 3.8 / 1048 1.0	1727 3.6 / 2309 1.5	**17** F	0406 3.8 / 1011 1.0	1644 3.7 / 2227 1.3
3 F	0532 3.5 / 1148 1.3	1832 3.4	**18** SA	0455 3.6 / 1108 1.1	1743 3.5 / 2328 1.5
4 SA	0010 1.8 / 0635 3.4	1303 1.4 / 1945 3.2	**19** SU	0555 3.5 / 1218 1.2	1854 3.4
5 SU	0130 1.9 / 0750 3.3	1434 1.5 / 2104 3.2	**20** M	0046 1.6 / 0707 3.5	1336 1.1 / 2010 3.5
6 M	0301 1.9 / 0907 3.3	1548 1.4 / 2212 3.3	**21** TU	0208 1.6 / 0823 3.5	1456 1.2 / 2123 3.6
7 TU	0406 1.7 / 1012 3.4	1638 1.2 / 2301 3.5	**22**	0321 1.4 / 0932 3.7	1558 0.8 / 2224 3.8
8 W	0452 1.5 / 1101 3.5	1717 1.1 / 2339 3.6	**23** TH	0421 1.2 / 1032 3.9	1653 0.6 / 2316 3.9
9 TH	0530 1.3 / 1140 3.7	1751 1.0	**24** F	0513 1.0 / 1125 4.1	1743 0.5
10 F	0013 3.8 / 0604 1.2	1216 3.8 / 1822 0.9	**25** SA	0002 4.1 / 1214 4.3	1828 0.4
11 SA	0044 3.9 / 0636 1.0	1250 3.9 / 1852 0.8	**26** SU	0045 4.2 / 0645 0.6	1302 4.3 / O1911 0.4
12 SU	0114 4.0 / 0707 0.9	1323 4.0 / ●1923 0.8	**27** M	0127 4.2 / 0730 0.5	1349 4.3 / 1953 0.6
13 M	0145 4.0 / 0739 0.8	1357 4.0 / 1954 0.8	**28** TU	0208 4.2 / 0814 0.5	1437 4.2 / 2035 0.8
14 TU	0216 4.0 / 0812 0.8	1433 4.0 / 2026 0.9	**29** W	0250 4.1 / 0859 0.6	1525 4.0 / 2116 1.0
15 W	0249 4.0 / 0847 0.8	1511 3.9 / 2100 1.0	**30** TH	0332 4.0 / 0945 0.8	1615 3.8 / 2158 1.2
			31 F	0416 3.8 / 1032 1.0	1707 3.6 / 2243 1.5

JUNE

Day	Time m		Day	Time m	
1 SA	0504 3.7 / 1123 1.1	1802 3.4 / 2335 1.7	**16** SU	0445 3.9 / 1106 0.8	1735 3.7 / 2321 1.4
2 SU	0558 3.5 / 1221 1.3	1902 3.3	**17** M	0542 3.8 / 1207 0.9	1838 3.6
3 M	0038 1.8 / 0659 3.4	1329 1.4 / 2006 3.2	**18** TU	0025 1.5 / 0645 3.7	1313 1.0 / 1944 3.6
4 TU	0151 1.9 / 0805 3.3	1440 1.4 / 2110 3.3	**19** W	0136 1.5 / 0753 3.7	1421 0.9 / 2052 3.6
5 W	0304 1.8 / 0911 3.3	1541 1.4 / 2207 3.4	**20** TH	0246 1.5 / 0902 3.8	1528 0.9 / 2155 3.7
6 TH	0403 1.7 / 1009 3.4	1629 1.3 / 2253 3.5	**21** F	0352 1.3 / 1008 3.9	1629 0.9 / 2252 3.8
7 F	0449 1.5 / 1057 3.6	1710 1.2 / 2333 3.7	**22** SA	0451 1.2 / 1108 4.0	1723 0.8 / 2342 4.0
8 SA	0529 1.3 / 1140 3.7	1746 1.1	**23** SU	0545 1.0 / 1202 4.1	1811 0.8
9 SU	0010 3.8 / 0605 1.1	1220 3.8 / 1821 1.0	**24** M	0027 4.1 / 0634 0.8	1253 4.1 / O1855 0.8
10 M	0045 3.9 / 0641 1.0	1259 3.9 / ●1856 0.9	**25** TU	0111 4.1 / 0721 0.7	1341 4.1 / 1938 0.9
11 TU	0120 4.0 / 0718 0.9	1338 4.0 / 1932 0.9	**26** W	0153 4.2 / 0806 0.7	1428 4.1 / 2019 1.0
12 W	0155 4.0 / 0757 0.8	1418 4.0 / 2010 0.9	**27** TH	0233 4.1 / 0849 0.7	1513 4.0 / 2058 1.1
13 TH	0232 4.0 / 0838 0.7	1501 4.0 / 2050 1.0	**28** F	0314 4.1 / 0930 0.8	1557 3.8 / 2137 1.2
14 F	0312 4.0 / 0922 0.7	1548 3.9 / 2135 1.1	**29** SA	0354 4.0 / 1011 0.9	1641 3.7 / 2216 1.4
15 SA	0356 3.9 / 1011 0.8	1638 3.8 / 2224 1.2	**30** SU	0435 3.8 / 1053 1.1	1726 3.5 / 2258 1.5

JULY

Day	Time m		Day	Time m	
1 M	0519 3.7 / 1137 1.2	1813 3.4 / 2345 1.7	**16** TU	0523 4.1 / 1146 0.7	1813 3.8 / 2358 1.3
2 TU	0608 3.6 / 1227 1.3	1905 3.3	**17** W	0620 4.0 / 1244 0.9	1914 3.7
3 W	0042 1.8 / 0703 3.4	1325 1.5 / 2001 3.3	**18** TH	0101 1.5 / 0725 3.9	1349 1.1 / 2019 3.6
4 TH	0148 1.9 / 0804 3.4	1428 1.5 / 2101 3.3	**19** F	0212 1.5 / 0837 3.8	1459 1.2 / 2127 3.6
5 F	0258 1.8 / 0908 3.4	1531 1.5 / 2200 3.4	**20** SA	0329 1.5 / 0952 3.8	1609 1.3 / 2231 3.7
6 SA	0401 1.7 / 1011 3.5	1625 1.4 / 2252 3.6	**21** SU	0439 1.3 / 1100 3.8	1710 1.2 / 2327 3.8
7 SU	0453 1.5 / 1106 3.6	1712 1.3 / 2337 3.7	**22** M	0539 1.2 / 1159 3.9	1801 1.2
8 M	0538 1.3 / 1154 3.7	1754 1.2	**23** TU	0016 4.0 / 0629 1.0	1251 4.0 / 1845 1.2
9 TU	0018 3.9 / 0620 1.1	1240 3.9 / 1835 1.1	**24** W	0100 4.1 / 0715 0.8	1336 4.0 / O1925 1.1
10 W	0058 4.0 / 0702 0.9	1323 4.0 / ●1917 1.0	**25** TH	0140 4.2 / 0756 0.7	1417 4.0 / 2003 1.1
11 TH	0138 4.1 / 0745 0.7	1407 4.1 / 1959 0.9	**26** F	0217 4.2 / 0834 0.7	1456 4.0 / 2039 1.1
12 F	0218 4.2 / 0830 0.6	1452 4.1 / 2042 0.9	**27** SA	0253 4.2 / 0910 0.8	1533 3.9 / 2112 1.2
13 SA	0300 4.2 / 0916 0.5	1538 4.1 / 2127 1.0	**28** SU	0328 4.1 / 0943 0.8	1608 3.8 / 2146 1.3
14 SU	0344 4.2 / 1003 0.5	1627 4.0 / 2213 1.1	**29** M	0403 4.0 / 1017 1.0	1645 3.7 / 2220 1.4
15 M	0431 4.2 / 1053 0.6	1718 3.9 / 2302 1.2	**30** TU	0440 3.9 / 1053 1.1	1724 3.6 / 2257 1.5
			31 W	0521 3.8 / 1133 1.3	1808 3.5 / 2342 1.7

AUGUST

Day	Time m		Day	Time m	
1 TH	0609 3.6 / 1220 1.5	1859 3.4	**16** F	0029 1.4 / 0701 3.9	1317 1.3 / 1946 3.6
2 F	0038 1.8 / 0705 3.5	1318 1.6 / 1957 3.3	**17** SA	0146 1.6 / 0820 3.7	1435 1.6 / 2102 3.5
3 SA	0149 1.9 / 0811 3.4	1427 1.7 / 2104 3.4	**18** SU	0317 1.6 / 0945 3.6	1558 1.6 / 2216 3.6
4 SU	0308 1.9 / 0924 3.4	1540 1.7 / 2210 3.5	**19** M	0437 1.4 / 1100 3.7	1703 1.6 / 2317 3.8
5 M	0419 1.7 / 1035 3.5	1642 1.6 / 2307 3.7	**20** TU	0537 1.2 / 1158 3.9	1753 1.5
6 TU	0515 1.4 / 1133 3.7	1734 1.4 / 2355 3.9	**21** W	0007 4.0 / 0624 1.0	1245 4.0 / 1834 1.3
7 W	0603 1.1 / 1223 3.9	1819 1.2	**22** TH	0048 4.1 / 0704 0.9	1324 4.0 / O1910 1.2
8 TH	0038 4.1 / 0647 0.8	1309 4.1 / ●1903 1.0	**23** F	0124 4.2 / 0739 0.8	1359 4.1 / 1943 1.1
9 F	0120 4.3 / 0732 0.5	1353 4.3 / 1945 0.9	**24** SA	0157 4.2 / 0812 0.7	1431 4.1 / 2015 1.1
10 SA	0201 4.4 / 0816 0.3	1437 4.4 / 2028 0.8	**25** SU	0228 4.2 / 0842 0.7	1502 4.0 / 2045 1.1
11 SU	0242 4.5 / 0900 0.2	1521 4.4 / 2110 0.8	**26** M	0259 4.2 / 0911 0.8	1532 4.0 / 2114 1.2
12 M	0325 4.5 / 0945 0.3	1606 4.3 / 2152 0.9	**27** TU	0330 4.1 / 0940 1.0	1604 3.9 / 2144 1.3
13 TU	0411 4.5 / 1030 0.4	1652 4.1 / 2237 1.0	**28** W	0404 4.0 / 1010 1.1	1638 3.8 / 2216 1.4
14 W	0500 4.3 / 1119 0.7	1743 3.9 / 2328 1.2	**29** TH	0442 3.9 / 1044 1.3	1717 3.6 / 2254 1.6
15 TH	0555 4.1 / 1213 1.0	1840 3.7	**30** F	0525 3.7 / 1124 1.5	1803 3.5 / 2342 1.7
			31 SA	0618 3.5 / 1216 1.7	1900 3.4

Chart Datum: 2·25 metres below Ordnance Datum (Newlyn)

TIME ZONE (UTC)
For Summer Time add ONE hour in **non-shaded areas**

SCOTLAND – ABERDEEN

LAT 57°09'N   LONG 2°05'W

TIMES AND HEIGHTS OF HIGH AND LOW WATERS

YEAR **2002**

SEPTEMBER

Day	Time m	Day	Time m
1 SU	0051 1.9 / 0724 3.4 / 1330 1.9 / 2011 3.3	**16** M	0312 1.6 / 0941 3.5 / 1548 1.9 / 2159 3.6
2 M	0221 1.9 / 0847 3.4 / 1500 1.9 / 2131 3.4	**17** TU	0433 1.5 / 1055 3.7 / 1652 1.7 / 2303 3.8
3 TU	0349 1.7 / 1010 3.5 / 1619 1.7 / 2238 3.6	**18** W	0528 1.2 / 1148 3.8 / 1738 1.6 / 2350 3.9
4 W	0454 1.4 / 1114 3.7 / 1715 1.5 / 2331 3.9	**19** TH	0609 1.1 / 1228 4.0 / 1815 1.4
5 TH	0544 1.0 / 1205 4.0 / 1802 1.2	**20** F	0028 4.1 / 0642 0.9 / 1302 4.0 / 1847 1.2
6 F	0016 4.2 / 0628 0.7 / 1250 4.3 / 1844 1.0	**21** SA	0101 4.2 / 0713 0.8 / 1333 4.1 / 1918 1.1 ○
7 SA	0057 4.4 / 0712 0.3 / 1333 4.5 / 1925 0.8 ●	**22** SU	0131 4.3 / 0742 0.8 / 1401 4.1 / 1948 1.0
8 SU	0138 4.6 / 0755 0.1 / 1415 4.5 / 2006 0.7	**23** M	0200 4.3 / 0810 0.8 / 1429 4.1 / 2016 1.0
9 M	0220 4.8 / 0838 0.1 / 1456 4.5 / 2046 0.6	**24** TU	0230 4.3 / 0837 0.8 / 1457 4.1 / 2043 1.1
10 TU	0302 4.7 / 0920 0.2 / 1539 4.4 / 2127 0.7	**25** W	0300 4.2 / 0904 0.9 / 1527 4.0 / 2112 1.2
11 W	0348 4.6 / 1003 0.5 / 1623 4.2 / 2211 0.9	**26** TH	0334 4.1 / 0932 1.1 / 1559 3.9 / 2143 1.3
12 TH	0437 4.4 / 1049 0.8 / 1711 4.0 / 2301 1.2	**27** F	0410 3.9 / 1003 1.3 / 1635 3.8 / 2219 1.4
13 F	0534 4.1 / 1141 1.3 / 1807 3.7	**28** SA	0452 3.7 / 1040 1.5 / 1718 3.6 / 2305 1.6
14 SA	0003 1.4 / 0643 3.8 / 1247 1.6 / 1915 3.5	**29** SU	0544 3.5 / 1129 1.8 / 1813 3.5
15 SU	0127 1.6 / 0809 3.6 / 1414 1.9 / 2038 3.5	**30** M	0012 1.8 / 0653 3.4 / 1247 2.0 / 1928 3.4

OCTOBER

Day	Time m	Day	Time m
1 TU	0147 1.8 / 0820 3.4 / 1429 2.0 / 2055 3.4	**16** W	0413 1.5 / 1034 3.6 / 1628 1.8 / 2236 3.7
2 W	0321 1.6 / 0947 3.5 / 1555 1.8 / 2208 3.7	**17** TH	0503 1.3 / 1124 3.8 / 1712 1.6 / 2323 3.9
3 TH	0429 1.3 / 1052 3.8 / 1652 1.5 / 2303 4.0	**18** F	0541 1.1 / 1201 3.9 / 1748 1.4
4 F	0520 0.9 / 1142 4.1 / 1739 1.2 / 2349 4.3	**19** SA	0000 4.0 / 0612 1.0 / 1233 4.0 / 1819 1.3
5 SA	0605 0.5 / 1226 4.4 / 1821 0.9	**20** SU	0032 4.1 / 0642 1.0 / 1302 4.1 / 1850 1.1
6 SU	0031 4.6 / 0648 0.3 / 1308 4.5 / 1901 0.7 ●	**21** M	0103 4.2 / 0710 0.9 / 1330 4.2 / 1919 1.1
7 M	0113 4.6 / 0730 0.1 / 1348 4.6 / 1941 0.6	**22** TU	0133 4.2 / 0738 0.9 / 1357 4.2 / 1948 1.0
8 TU	0156 4.6 / 0812 0.1 / 1429 4.6 / 2022 0.6	**23** W	0203 4.2 / 0805 0.9 / 1426 4.2 / 2017 1.0
9 W	0240 4.8 / 0853 0.3 / 1511 4.4 / 2104 0.7	**24** TH	0235 4.2 / 0832 1.0 / 1455 4.1 / 2047 1.1
10 TH	0327 4.6 / 0936 0.7 / 1554 4.2 / 2149 0.9	**25** F	0310 4.1 / 0901 1.2 / 1527 4.0 / 2120 1.2
11 F	0418 4.3 / 1021 1.1 / 1641 4.0 / 2241 1.1	**26** SA	0347 3.9 / 0934 1.3 / 1603 3.9 / 2158 1.3
12 SA	0517 4.0 / 1112 1.5 / 1737 3.7 / 2345 1.4	**27** SU	0431 3.8 / 1012 1.6 / 1647 3.7 / 2246 1.5
13 SU	0629 3.7 / 1218 1.9 / 1846 3.6	**28** M	0525 3.6 / 1103 1.8 / 1742 3.5 / 2354 1.6
14 M	0110 1.6 / 0754 3.5 / 1347 2.1 / 2009 3.5	**29** TU	0635 3.4 / 1222 2.0 / 1856 3.5
15 TU	0256 1.6 / 0923 3.5 / 1525 2.0 / 2132 3.6	**30** W	0122 1.7 / 0758 3.4 / 1400 2.0 / 2019 3.5
		31 TH	0249 1.5 / 0919 3.6 / 1522 1.8 / 2133 3.7

NOVEMBER

Day	Time m	Day	Time m
1 F	0358 1.2 / 1024 3.9 / 1622 1.5 / 2231 4.0	**16** SA	0503 1.3 / 1124 3.8 / 1714 1.6 / 2325 3.9
2 SA	0452 0.8 / 1115 4.1 / 1711 1.2 / 2321 4.3	**17** SU	0537 1.2 / 1158 3.9 / 1749 1.4
3 SU	0539 0.5 / 1200 4.4 / 1755 1.0	**18** M	0001 4.0 / 0608 1.1 / 1229 4.1 / 1821 1.3
4 M	0006 4.6 / 0622 0.4 / 1242 4.5 / 1837 0.7 ●	**19** TU	0035 4.1 / 0638 1.0 / 1259 4.1 / 1853 1.2
5 TU	0051 4.7 / 0705 0.3 / 1323 4.6 / 1919 0.6	**20** W	0108 4.1 / 0708 1.0 / 1329 4.2 / 1925 1.1 ○
6 W	0136 4.8 / 0747 0.4 / 1404 4.5 / 2002 0.6	**21** TH	0141 4.2 / 0738 1.1 / 1400 4.2 / 1957 1.0
7 TH	0223 4.7 / 0830 0.6 / 1446 4.4 / 2047 0.7	**22** F	0216 4.1 / 0808 1.1 / 1431 4.1 / 2031 1.1
8 F	0312 4.5 / 0912 0.9 / 1529 4.3 / 2135 0.9	**23** SA	0253 4.1 / 0841 1.2 / 1505 4.1 / 2108 1.1
9 SA	0405 4.2 / 0957 1.3 / 1616 4.0 / 2227 1.1	**24** SU	0333 3.9 / 0917 1.4 / 1543 4.0 / 2150 1.2
10 SU	0504 3.9 / 1048 1.6 / 1710 3.8 / 2328 1.4	**25** M	0419 3.8 / 1000 1.5 / 1628 3.8 / 2241 1.3
11 M	0611 3.6 / 1148 1.9 / 1814 3.6	**26** TU	0514 3.7 / 1053 1.7 / 1722 3.7 / 2344 1.4
12 TU	0042 1.5 / 0725 3.5 / 1305 2.1 / 1928 3.5	**27** W	0619 3.6 / 1204 1.9 / 1829 3.6
13 W	0211 1.6 / 0843 3.4 / 1435 2.1 / 2046 3.5	**28** TH	0058 1.4 / 0732 3.6 / 1325 1.9 / 1943 3.7
14 TH	0330 1.5 / 0953 3.5 / 1545 2.0 / 2153 3.6	**29** F	0214 1.3 / 0846 3.7 / 1442 1.8 / 2054 3.8
15 F	0423 1.4 / 1045 3.7 / 1635 1.8 / 2244 3.8	**30** SA	0322 1.1 / 0951 3.9 / 1547 1.6 / 2158 4.0

DECEMBER

Day	Time m	Day	Time m
1 SU	0421 0.9 / 1046 4.1 / 1642 1.3 / 2254 4.3	**16** M	0457 1.5 / 1120 3.8 / 1716 1.6 / 2328 3.8
2 M	0513 0.8 / 1134 4.2 / 1731 1.1 / 2345 4.4	**17** TU	0535 1.4 / 1157 3.9 / 1755 1.4
3 TU	0600 0.7 / 1219 4.4 / 1818 0.9	**18** W	0009 3.9 / 0609 1.3 / 1233 4.0 / 1830 1.3
4 W	0034 4.5 / 0645 0.7 / 1302 4.4 / 1904 0.8 ●	**19** TH	0047 4.0 / 0643 1.2 / 1306 4.1 / 1906 1.2 ○
5 TH	0123 4.6 / 0729 0.7 / 1344 4.5 / 1951 0.7	**20** F	0125 4.1 / 0717 1.2 / 1340 4.2 / 1943 1.1
6 F	0212 4.5 / 0812 0.9 / 1427 4.4 / 2038 0.7	**21** SA	0203 4.1 / 0753 1.2 / 1414 4.2 / 2021 1.0
7 SA	0303 4.3 / 0855 1.1 / 1510 4.3 / 2126 0.9	**22** SU	0243 4.1 / 0830 1.2 / 1451 4.2 / 2102 1.0
8 SU	0354 4.1 / 0939 1.4 / 1556 4.1 / 2214 1.0	**23** M	0325 4.0 / 0910 1.3 / 1531 4.1 / 2146 1.0
9 M	0447 3.9 / 1024 1.6 / 1644 4.0 / 2306 1.2	**24** TU	0411 4.0 / 0954 1.4 / 1615 4.1 / 2235 1.0
10 TU	0542 3.7 / 1114 1.8 / 1737 3.8	**25** W	0502 3.9 / 1043 1.5 / 1705 4.0 / 2329 1.1
11 W	0002 1.4 / 0641 3.5 / 1213 2.0 / 1837 3.6	**26** TH	0559 3.8 / 1140 1.6 / 1803 3.9
12 TH	0106 1.6 / 0744 3.4 / 1323 2.1 / 1943 3.5	**27** F	0030 1.2 / 0701 3.7 / 1247 1.7 / 1907 3.9
13 F	0216 1.6 / 0850 3.4 / 1438 2.1 / 2050 3.5	**28** SA	0136 1.2 / 0808 3.7 / 1358 1.7 / 2017 3.9
14 SA	0322 1.6 / 0949 3.5 / 1543 1.9 / 2152 3.6	**29** SU	0245 1.2 / 0915 3.8 / 1509 1.6 / 2127 4.0
15 SU	0414 1.5 / 1039 3.7 / 1634 1.8 / 2244 3.7	**30** M	0351 1.2 / 1018 3.9 / 1616 1.5 / 2234 4.1
		31 TU	0452 1.1 / 1113 4.0 / 1716 1.3 / 2333 4.2

Chart Datum: 2·25 metres below Ordnance Datum (Newlyn)

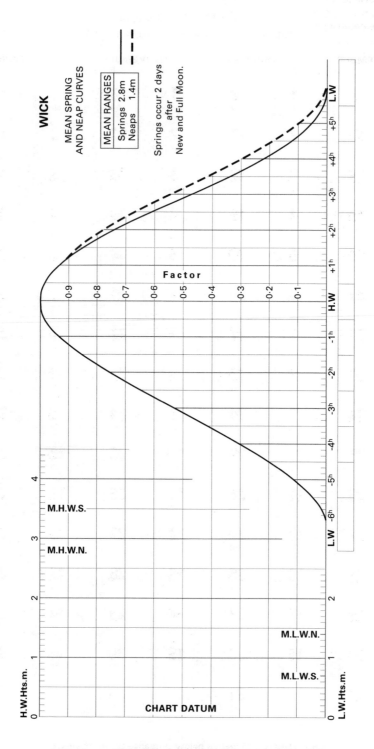

WICK

MEAN SPRING
AND NEAP CURVES

MEAN RANGES	
Springs	2.8m
Neaps	1.4m

Springs occur 2 days
after
New and Full Moon.

Factor

0·9 0·8 0·7 0·6 0·5 0·4 0·3 0·2 0·1

L.W +5ʰ +4ʰ +3ʰ +2ʰ +1ʰ H.W -1ʰ -2ʰ -3ʰ -4ʰ -5ʰ -6ʰ L.W

H.W.Hts.m.

M.H.W.S.

M.H.W.N.

M.L.W.N.

M.L.W.S.

CHART DATUM

L.W.Hts.m.

TIME ZONE (UTC)
For Summer Time add ONE hour in **non-shaded areas**

SCOTLAND – WICK

LAT 58°26′N LONG 3°05′W

TIMES AND HEIGHTS OF HIGH AND LOW WATERS

YEAR 2002

JANUARY

Day	Time m	Time m	Time m	Time m		Day	Time m	Time m	Time m	Time m
1 TU	0014 3.5	0602 0.9	1232 3.6	1834 0.6		**16** W	0059 3.2	0630 1.1	1304 3.5	1905 0.9
2 W	0101 3.5	0644 1.0	1315 3.6	1921 0.6		**17** TH	0135 3.1	0703 1.1	1339 3.4	1938 0.9
3 TH	0149 3.4	0729 1.1	1401 3.5	2011 0.6		**18** F	0210 3.0	0738 1.2	1413 3.3	2013 1.0
4 F	0241 3.3	0817 1.2	1452 3.4	2106 0.7		**19** SA	0246 2.9	0814 1.3	1449 3.2	2051 1.1
5 SA	0336 3.1	0914 1.3	1548 3.3	2209 0.8		**20** SU	0326 2.8	0856 1.4	1531 3.1	2135 1.3
6 SU	0437 3.0	1021 1.4	1651 3.2	2317 0.9		**21** M	0413 2.8	0945 1.6	1621 2.9	2228 1.4
7 M	0542 2.9	1135 1.4	1757 3.1			**22** TU	0507 2.7	1048 1.6	1717 2.9	2333 1.4
8 TU	0025 1.0	0648 2.9	1249 1.4	1906 3.0		**23** W	0606 2.7	1205 1.6	1820 2.8	
9 W	0130 1.0	0752 2.9	1358 1.3	2013 3.1		**24** TH	0044 1.4	0707 2.8	1323 1.6	1925 2.9
10 TH	0229 1.0	0851 3.0	1459 1.2	2115 3.1		**25** F	0152 1.3	0809 2.9	1430 1.4	2032 3.0
11 F	0319 1.0	0942 3.1	1551 1.0	2209 3.2		**26** SA	0250 1.2	0908 3.1	1525 1.2	2133 3.1
12 SA	0403 1.0	1028 3.3	1636 0.9	2256 3.2		**27** SU	0341 1.1	1000 3.3	1614 0.9	2228 3.3
13 SU	0443 1.0	1110 3.4	1717 0.8	● 2340 3.2		**28** M	0428 1.0	1049 3.4	1700 0.7	○ 2318 3.4
14 M	0520 1.0	1150 3.5	1755 0.8			**29** TU	0512 0.9	1134 3.6	1744 0.5	
15 TU	0020 3.2	0555 1.0	1228 3.5	1831 0.8		**30** W	0004 3.5	0554 0.8	1218 3.7	1827 0.6
						31 TH	0050 3.6	0635 0.8	1302 3.8	1911 0.3

FEBRUARY

Day	Time m	Time m	Time m	Time m		Day	Time m	Time m	Time m	Time m
1 F	0135 3.5	0717 0.8	1347 3.8	1955 0.4		**16** SA	0139 3.1	0712 0.9	1345 3.3	1939 0.8
2 SA	0221 3.4	0800 0.9	1433 3.6	2043 0.5		**17** SU	0209 3.0	0745 1.0	1417 3.2	2012 1.0
3 SU	0309 3.2	0847 1.0	1523 3.4	2136 0.8		**18** M	0243 2.9	0820 1.2	1453 3.1	2047 1.1
4 M	0401 3.0	0943 1.2	1621 3.2	2238 1.0		**19** TU	0325 2.8	0858 1.3	1537 2.9	2129 1.2
5 TU	0500 2.8	1054 1.4	1726 3.0	2349 1.2		**20** W	0415 2.7	0948 1.4	1632 2.8	2225 1.4
6 W	0606 2.7	1217 1.4	1841 2.9			**21** TH	0513 2.7	1059 1.5	1737 2.8	2341 1.5
7 TH	0105 1.3	0719 2.8	1343 1.4	2000 2.9		**22** F	0617 2.7	1230 1.5	1848 2.8	
8 F	0216 1.3	0830 2.8	1455 1.2	2108 2.9		**23** SA	0115 1.4	0726 2.8	1402 1.3	2005 2.9
9 SA	0311 1.2	0927 3.0	1549 1.0	2202 3.0		**24** SU	0233 1.3	0836 2.9	1508 1.1	2116 3.0
10 SU	0354 1.1	1014 3.1	1631 0.9	2248 3.1		**25** M	0329 1.1	0937 3.2	1600 0.8	2215 3.2
11 M	0431 1.1	1056 3.3	1708 0.8	2328 3.1		**26** TU	0416 0.9	1029 3.4	1646 0.5	2305 3.4
12 TU	0505 1.0	1135 3.4	1740 0.7	●		**27** W	0459 0.8	1117 3.6	1729 0.2	○ 2350 3.6
13 W	0004 3.1	0537 0.9	1212 3.4	1810 0.7		**28** TH	0540 0.6	1201 3.8	1811 0.1	
14 TH	0039 3.1	0609 0.9	1245 3.4	1839 0.7						
15 F	0110 3.1	0640 0.9	1316 3.4	1909 0.7						

MARCH

Day	Time m	Time m	Time m	Time m		Day	Time m	Time m	Time m	Time m
1 F	0033 3.6	0619 0.6	1245 3.9	1852 0.1		**16** SA	0041 3.1	0614 0.7	1248 3.3	1837 0.6
2 SA	0115 3.6	0659 0.6	1328 3.9	1933 0.2		**17** SU	0107 3.1	0645 0.8	1316 3.2	1907 0.7
3 SU	0156 3.5	0739 0.7	1412 3.7	2016 0.5		**18** M	0134 3.0	0717 0.9	1347 3.2	1938 0.8
4 M	0238 3.3	0822 0.9	1500 3.5	2103 0.8		**19** TU	0206 3.0	0749 1.0	1422 3.1	2010 1.0
5 TU	0325 3.1	0912 1.1	1554 3.2	2200 1.1		**20** W	0243 2.9	0825 1.1	1505 2.9	2047 1.2
6 W	0419 2.9	1022 1.3	1700 2.9	2315 1.4		**21** TH	0330 2.8	0911 1.2	1601 2.8	2139 1.3
7 TH	0524 2.7	1156 1.4	1822 2.7			**22** F	0430 2.7	1020 1.3	1708 2.7	2256 1.5
8 F	0043 1.5	0646 2.7	1331 1.3	1951 2.7		**23** SA	0540 2.6	1157 1.3	1825 2.7	
9 SA	0203 1.5	0807 2.7	1447 1.2	2100 2.8		**24** SU	0047 1.5	0653 2.7	1338 1.2	1947 2.8
10 SU	0259 1.3	0908 2.9	1537 1.0	2150 2.9		**25** M	0214 1.3	0807 2.9	1445 0.9	2100 3.0
11 M	0339 1.2	0955 3.1	1615 0.8	2232 3.0		**26** TU	0310 1.1	0912 3.1	1538 0.6	2158 3.2
12 TU	0413 1.0	1037 3.2	1647 0.7	2308 3.0		**27** W	0357 0.9	1007 3.4	1624 0.3	2246 3.4
13 W	0445 0.9	1114 3.3	1715 0.6	2342 3.1		**28** TH	0439 0.6	1055 3.6	1707 0.1	○ 2330 3.6
14 TH	0515 0.8	1148 3.3	1743 0.6	●		**29** F	0519 0.5	1140 3.8	1748 0.1	
15 F	0013 3.1	0544 0.7	1220 3.3	1809 0.6		**30** SA	0011 3.6	0558 0.4	1224 3.9	1828 0.1
						31 SU	0051 3.6	0638 0.5	1308 3.8	1908 0.3

APRIL

Day	Time m	Time m	Time m	Time m		Day	Time m	Time m	Time m	Time m
1 M	0130 3.5	0718 0.6	1352 3.7	1949 0.6		**16** TU	0104 3.1	0652 0.8	1322 3.2	1908 0.8
2 TU	0210 3.4	0801 0.8	1439 3.4	2032 1.0		**17** W	0136 3.0	0726 0.8	1400 3.1	1941 1.0
3 W	0253 3.1	0850 1.0	1533 3.1	2124 1.3		**18** TH	0214 2.9	0805 1.0	1446 2.9	2021 1.1
4 TH	0344 2.9	1002 1.2	1639 2.8	2241 1.6		**19** F	0301 2.8	0855 1.1	1544 2.8	2114 1.3
5 F	0447 2.7	1138 1.4	1802 2.7			**20** SA	0403 2.7	1007 1.2	1654 2.7	2234 1.5
6 SA	0012 1.7	0609 2.7	1306 1.3	1931 2.6		**21** SU	0515 2.7	1144 1.1	1811 2.7	
7 SU	0133 1.6	0734 2.7	1418 1.1	2038 2.7		**22** M	0024 1.4	0630 2.7	1312 0.9	1930 2.8
8 M	0231 1.4	0837 2.8	1507 1.0	2125 2.8		**23** TU	0146 1.3	0742 2.9	1418 0.7	2039 3.0
9 TU	0312 1.2	0926 3.0	1543 0.8	2204 2.9		**24** W	0243 1.0	0846 3.1	1511 0.4	2135 3.2
10 W	0346 1.1	1008 3.1	1614 0.7	2240 3.0		**25** TH	0330 0.8	0942 3.4	1558 0.3	2222 3.4
11 TH	0417 0.9	1045 3.1	1642 0.7	2313 3.1		**26** F	0414 0.6	1031 3.6	1641 0.2	2306 3.5
12 F	0447 0.8	1119 3.2	1709 0.6	● 2342 3.1		**27** SA	0456 0.5	1118 3.7	1723 0.2	○ 2347 3.6
13 SA	0517 0.7	1149 3.2	1738 0.6			**28** SU	0537 0.4	1203 3.7	1804 0.3	
14 SU	0009 3.1	0547 0.7	1218 3.2	1807 0.6		**29** M	0026 3.6	0617 0.5	1249 3.7	1843 0.5
15 M	0035 3.1	0619 0.7	1249 3.2	1837 0.7		**30** TU	0105 3.5	0659 0.6	1334 3.5	1923 0.8

Chart Datum: 1·71 metres below Ordnance Datum (Newlyn)
Register for your **FREE** weekly weather email service from Macmillan Reeds
at **www.nauticaldata.com – NOW!**
weekend weather reports sent to your email address, every Thursday

TIME ZONE (UTC)
For Summer Time add ONE hour in **non-shaded areas**

SCOTLAND – WICK

LAT 58°26′N   LONG 3°05′W

TIMES AND HEIGHTS OF HIGH AND LOW WATERS

YEAR 2002

MAY

Day	Time	m	Day	Time	m
1 W	0145 0744 1422 2005	3.4 0.8 3.3 1.1	16 TH	0117 0711 1348 1924	3.1 0.8 3.1 1.0
2 TH	0228 0836 1515 2053	3.2 1.0 3.0 1.4	17 F	0158 0756 1438 2008	3.0 0.8 2.9 1.1
3 F	0316 0946 1617 2201	3.0 1.2 2.8 1.6	18 SA	0247 0852 1537 2104	2.9 0.9 2.8 1.3
4 SA	0415 1110 1731 2328	2.8 1.3 2.6 1.7	19 SU	0348 1006 1645 2223	2.8 0.9 2.7 1.4
5 SU	0528 1226 1849	2.7 1.3 2.6	20 M	0459 1129 1757 2355	2.8 0.9 2.7 1.3
6 M	0044 0645 1331 1955	1.7 2.7 1.2 2.6	21 TU	0610 1243 1908	2.8 0.7 2.8
7 TU	0145 0752 1421 2046	1.5 2.8 1.0 2.8	22 W	0109 0717 1346 2012	1.2 2.9 0.6 2.9
8 W	0232 0845 1501 2127	1.3 2.9 0.9 2.9	23 TH	0210 0819 1441 2107	1.0 3.1 0.4 3.1
9 TH	0311 0929 1534 2204	1.1 3.0 0.8 3.0	24 F	0302 0916 1530 2156	0.8 3.3 0.4 3.2
10 F	0345 1008 1605 2238	1.0 3.0 0.7 3.0	25 SA	0349 1009 1616 2241	0.7 3.4 0.4 3.3
11 SA	0417 1044 1635 2309	0.8 3.1 0.7 3.1	26 SU	0434 1058 1659 ○2324	0.6 3.5 0.4 3.4
12 SU	0450 1117 1707 ●2338	0.7 3.2 0.7 3.2	27 M	0518 1146 1741	0.5 3.5 0.5
13 M	0523 1150 1739	0.7 3.2 0.7	28 TU	0004 0602 1233 1821	3.4 0.5 3.4 0.7
14 TU	0008 0557 1226 1812	3.2 0.7 3.2 0.7	29 W	0045 0646 1320 1902	3.4 0.6 3.3 0.9
15 W	0041 0633 1305 1847	3.2 0.7 3.1 0.8	30 TH	0125 0732 1407 1942	3.4 0.8 3.2 1.2
			31 F	0207 0822 1456 2025	3.3 0.9 3.0 1.4

JUNE

Day	Time	m	Day	Time	m
1 SA	0253 0920 1550 2115	3.1 1.1 2.8 1.5	16 SU	0238 0850 1528 2057	3.1 0.7 2.9 1.2
2 SU	0344 1027 1649 2224	3.0 1.2 2.7 1.6	17 M	0335 0956 1629 2205	3.0 0.7 2.8 1.2
3 M	0443 1134 1752 2342	2.8 1.2 2.6 1.6	18 TU	0439 1105 1734 2321	2.9 0.7 2.8 1.2
4 TU	0548 1235 1856	2.8 1.2 2.6	19 W	0546 1212 1839	2.9 0.7 2.8
5 W	0048 0653 1328 1953	1.5 2.8 1.1 2.7	20 TH	0032 0651 1315 1941	1.2 3.0 0.6 2.8
6 TH	0144 0752 1412 2041	1.4 2.8 1.0 2.8	21 F	0138 0755 1413 2039	1.0 3.1 0.6 3.0
7 F	0231 0843 1452 2123	1.2 2.9 1.0 2.9	22 SA	0237 0855 1507 2132	0.9 3.1 0.6 3.1
8 SA	0311 0927 1528 2201	1.1 3.0 0.9 3.0	23 SU	0331 0952 1555 2220	0.8 3.2 0.6 3.2
9 SU	0349 1008 1604 2236	1.0 3.0 0.8 3.1	24 M	0421 1045 1640 ○2305	0.7 3.3 0.7 3.3
10 M	0426 1048 1641 ●2311	0.8 3.1 0.8 3.2	25 TU	0508 1134 1723 2348	0.6 3.3 0.8 3.4
11 TU	0504 1129 1718 2347	0.7 3.2 0.8 3.2	26 W	0553 1221 1803	0.6 3.3 0.9
12 W	0542 1210 1756	0.7 3.2 0.8	27 TH	0028 0636 1306 1841	3.4 0.6 3.2 1.0
13 TH	0025 0622 1254 1834	3.3 0.6 3.2 0.8	28 F	0109 0718 1349 1919	3.4 0.7 3.1 1.1
14 F	0105 0706 1340 1916	3.2 0.6 3.1 0.9	29 SA	0148 0800 1432 1956	3.3 0.8 3.0 1.2
15 SA	0148 0754 1431 2002	3.2 0.6 3.0 1.0	30 SU	0229 0843 1516 2035	3.2 1.0 2.8 1.3

JULY

Day	Time	m	Day	Time	m
1 M	0311 0929 1603 2122	3.1 1.1 2.7 1.5	16 TU	0316 0934 1604 2139	3.2 0.6 2.9 1.1
2 TU	0359 1022 1653 2220	2.9 1.2 2.6 1.5	17 W	0414 1035 1703 2247	3.1 0.7 2.8 1.2
3 W	0452 1122 1748 2332	2.8 1.2 2.6 1.6	18 TH	0518 1140 1806	3.0 0.8 2.8
4 TH	0550 1222 1846	2.8 1.2 2.6	19 F	0000 0625 1247 1910	1.2 3.0 0.9 2.8
5 F	0044 0649 1318 1943	1.5 2.8 1.2 2.7	20 SA	0114 0735 1353 2015	1.2 2.9 0.9 2.9
6 SA	0146 0749 1409 2035	1.4 2.8 1.1 2.8	21 SU	0225 0844 1452 2114	1.0 3.0 0.9 3.0
7 SU	0238 0846 1455 2122	1.2 2.9 1.1 3.0	22 M	0326 0945 1543 2205	0.9 3.0 0.9 3.1
8 M	0325 0938 1539 2206	1.1 3.0 1.0 3.1	23 TU	0418 1039 1628 2251	0.8 3.1 0.9 3.2
9 TU	0409 1026 1622 2248	0.9 3.1 0.9 3.2	24 W	0503 1126 1708 ○2333	0.7 3.1 0.9 3.3
10 W	0451 1113 1704 ●2329	0.7 3.2 0.8 3.3	25 TH	0544 1209 1745	0.6 3.2 0.9
11 TH	0534 1159 1745	0.6 3.3 0.8	26 F	0013 0621 1249 1819	3.4 0.6 3.1 0.9
12 F	0011 0617 1244 1826	3.4 0.5 3.3 0.8	27 SA	0051 0656 1327 1853	3.4 0.7 3.1 1.0
13 SA	0053 0701 1331 1908	3.4 0.4 3.3 0.8	28 SU	0126 0729 1403 1926	3.4 0.7 3.0 1.1
14 SU	0137 0747 1418 1953	3.4 0.4 3.2 0.9	29 M	0200 0802 1439 2001	3.3 0.8 2.9 1.2
15 M	0224 0838 1509 2042	3.4 0.5 3.1 1.0	30 TU	0235 0838 1509 2040	3.2 1.0 2.8 1.3
			31 W	0315 0918 1558 2125	3.0 1.1 2.8 1.4

AUGUST

Day	Time	m	Day	Time	m
1 TH	0401 1006 1647 2222	2.9 1.3 2.7 1.5	16 F	0451 1110 1731 2335	3.0 1.1 2.8 1.3
2 F	0456 1105 1742 2335	2.8 1.4 2.7 1.6	17 SA	0605 1225 1843	2.9 1.2 2.7
3 SA	0556 1215 1841	2.7 1.4 2.7	18 SU	0103 0727 1343 1958	1.3 2.8 1.3 2.8
4 SU	0057 0701 1327 1943	1.5 2.7 1.4 2.8	19 M	0227 0843 1448 2101	1.2 2.9 1.2 3.0
5 M	0209 0809 1429 2044	1.4 2.8 1.3 2.9	20 TU	0329 0943 1536 2153	1.0 3.0 1.2 3.1
6 TU	0306 0914 1522 2138	1.1 3.0 1.1 3.1	21 W	0415 1031 1615 2237	0.8 3.0 1.1 3.3
7 W	0355 1010 1609 2226	0.9 3.1 1.0 3.3	22 TH	0453 1113 1650 ○2317	0.7 3.1 1.0 3.4
8 TH	0440 1059 1652 ●2311	0.7 3.3 0.9 3.5	23 F	0527 1151 1723 2353	0.6 3.1 0.9 3.4
9 F	0523 1146 1734 2354	0.5 3.4 0.8 3.6	24 SA	0558 1226 1754	0.6 3.2 0.9
10 SA	0606 1230 1814	0.3 3.5 0.7	25 SU	0027 0626 1259 1825	3.4 0.6 3.1 0.9
11 SU	0037 0647 1314 1854	3.7 0.2 3.5 0.7	26 M	0059 0654 1329 1856	3.4 0.7 3.1 0.9
12 M	0120 0731 1358 1936	3.7 0.2 3.4 0.8	27 TU	0128 0724 1359 1929	3.3 0.8 3.0 1.0
13 TU	0204 0816 1443 2020	3.6 0.4 3.3 0.9	28 W	0158 0756 1431 2004	3.2 0.9 3.0 1.2
14 W	0252 0905 1533 2111	3.5 0.6 3.1 1.1	29 TH	0233 0831 1509 2042	3.1 1.1 2.9 1.3
15 TH	0347 1003 1628 2215	3.3 0.8 2.9 1.2	30 F	0316 0912 1555 2131	3.0 1.3 2.8 1.5
			31 SA	0410 1005 1651 2239	2.8 1.4 2.7 1.6

Chart Datum: 1·71 metres below Ordnance Datum (Newlyn)

TIME ZONE (UTC)
For Summer Time add ONE hour in **non-shaded areas**

SCOTLAND – WICK

LAT 58°26'N   LONG 3°05'W

TIMES AND HEIGHTS OF HIGH AND LOW WATERS

SEPTEMBER

#	Day	Time m	Time m	Time m	Time m	#	Day	Time m	Time m	Time m	Time m
1	SU	0514 2.7	1119 1.6	1754 2.7		16	M	0100 1.4	0726 2.8	1335 1.6	1942 2.8
2	M	0012 1.6	0625 2.7	1252 1.5	1901 2.8	17	TU	0225 1.2	0841 2.9	1439 1.5	2046 3.0
3	TU	0144 1.4	0742 2.8	1411 1.4	2010 2.9	18	W	0320 1.0	0933 3.0	1522 1.3	2135 3.2
4	W	0247 1.1	0855 3.0	1507 1.3	2112 3.1	19	TH	0359 0.9	1015 3.1	1556 1.2	2216 3.3
5	TH	0337 0.8	0954 3.2	1553 1.1	2204 3.4	20	F	0431 0.8	1052 3.1	1627 1.0	2254 3.4
6	F	0422 0.6	1043 3.4	1636 0.9	2250 3.6	21	SA	0459 0.7	1126 3.2	1657 0.9	○ 2328 3.4
7	SA	0505 0.3	1128 3.6	1716 0.7	● 2334 3.8	22	SU	0526 0.7	1157 3.2	1726 0.9	
8	SU	0546 0.2	1210 3.7	1755 0.6		23	M	0000 3.4	0552 0.7	1227 3.2	1756 0.9
9	M	0016 3.9	0626 0.1	1251 3.7	1834 0.6	24	TU	0028 3.4	0620 0.7	1254 3.2	1827 0.9
10	TU	0059 3.9	0707 0.2	1332 3.6	1914 0.7	25	W	0056 3.4	0649 0.8	1321 3.2	1859 1.0
11	W	0142 3.8	0750 0.5	1414 3.4	1956 0.9	26	TH	0125 3.3	0720 1.0	1351 3.1	1932 1.1
12	TH	0229 3.6	0836 0.8	1459 3.2	2045 1.1	27	F	0159 3.2	0752 1.2	1426 3.0	2008 1.3
13	F	0323 3.3	0930 1.1	1552 3.0	2150 1.3	28	SA	0240 3.0	0829 1.3	1511 2.9	2052 1.4
14	SA	0429 3.0	1042 1.4	1657 2.8	2322 1.4	29	SU	0335 2.9	0918 1.5	1609 2.8	2200 1.6
15	SU	0553 2.8	1209 1.6	1819 2.8		30	M	0444 2.8	1035 1.7	1717 2.7	2341 1.5

OCTOBER

#	Day	Time m	Time m	Time m	Time m	#	Day	Time m	Time m	Time m	Time m
1	TU	0600 2.8	1227 1.7	1829 2.8		16	W	0200 1.3	0822 2.9	1411 1.6	2017 3.0
2	W	0118 1.3	0721 2.8	1350 1.5	1941 2.9	17	TH	0251 1.1	0909 3.0	1453 1.4	2106 3.2
3	TH	0222 1.1	0836 3.0	1445 1.3	2045 3.2	18	F	0327 1.0	0948 3.1	1527 1.3	2148 3.3
4	F	0312 0.8	0933 3.2	1531 1.1	2139 3.5	19	SA	0357 0.9	1022 3.2	1559 1.1	2225 3.4
5	SA	0358 0.5	1021 3.5	1613 0.9	2227 3.7	20	SU	0425 0.8	1055 3.2	1629 1.0	2259 3.4
6	SU	0440 0.3	1105 3.7	1653 0.7	● 2311 3.9	21	M	0451 0.8	1126 3.3	1659 0.9	○ 2329 3.4
7	M	0521 0.2	1146 3.8	1732 0.6	2354 4.0	22	TU	0519 0.8	1154 3.3	1730 0.9	2358 3.4
8	TU	0602 0.2	1226 3.8	1812 0.6		23	W	0548 0.8	1220 3.3	1802 0.9	
9	W	0037 4.0	0642 0.4	1305 3.7	1852 0.7	24	TH	0027 3.4	0618 0.9	1249 3.3	1834 1.0
10	TH	0122 3.8	0723 0.7	1346 3.6	1935 0.9	25	F	0059 3.3	0650 1.0	1320 3.2	1908 1.1
11	F	0210 3.6	0808 1.0	1430 3.3	2025 1.1	26	SA	0136 3.2	0722 1.2	1356 3.1	1945 1.2
12	SA	0304 3.3	0901 1.3	1520 3.1	2134 1.4	27	SU	0219 3.1	0759 1.4	1439 3.0	2031 1.3
13	SU	0412 3.0	1015 1.7	1626 2.9	2311 1.5	28	M	0315 2.9	0848 1.6	1537 2.9	2140 1.4
14	M	0539 2.8	1146 1.8	1750 2.8		29	TU	0425 2.8	1006 1.7	1648 2.8	2320 1.4
15	TU	0042 1.4	0712 2.8	1309 1.8	1913 2.9	30	W	0543 2.8	1157 1.7	1803 2.9	
						31	TH	0047 1.2	0701 2.9	1318 1.5	1914 3.0

NOVEMBER

#	Day	Time m	Time m	Time m	Time m	#	Day	Time m	Time m	Time m	Time m
1	F	0150 1.0	0811 3.1	1415 1.3	2017 3.2	16	SA	0245 1.1	0910 3.1	1454 1.4	2112 3.2
2	SA	0242 0.7	0907 3.3	1502 1.1	2112 3.5	17	SU	0319 1.0	0947 3.2	1529 1.2	2152 3.3
3	SU	0329 0.5	0955 3.5	1546 0.9	2202 3.7	18	M	0349 1.0	1022 3.3	1603 1.1	2227 3.3
4	M	0413 0.4	1039 3.6	1628 0.7	● 2249 3.9	19	TU	0419 0.9	1054 3.3	1635 1.0	2300 3.3
5	TU	0455 0.4	1121 3.7	1710 0.7	2334 3.9	20	W	0449 0.9	1124 3.4	1709 0.9	○ 2333 3.4
6	W	0537 0.5	1201 3.8	1752 0.7		21	TH	0521 0.9	1154 3.4	1743 1.0	
7	TH	0019 3.9	0618 0.7	1242 3.7	1835 0.8	22	F	0006 3.4	0554 1.0	1227 3.4	1817 1.0
8	F	0106 3.7	0700 0.9	1323 3.6	1921 0.9	23	SA	0043 3.3	0628 1.1	1301 3.3	1854 1.0
9	SA	0155 3.5	0744 1.2	1406 3.5	2013 1.1	24	SU	0123 3.2	0703 1.2	1339 3.2	1934 1.1
10	SU	0250 3.3	0834 1.5	1455 3.3	2121 1.3	25	M	0209 3.1	0743 1.4	1422 3.1	2024 1.2
11	M	0354 3.0	0941 1.8	1555 3.1	2246 1.4	26	TU	0304 3.0	0834 1.5	1517 3.0	2130 1.2
12	TU	0510 2.8	1105 1.9	1709 3.0		27	W	0410 2.9	0945 1.6	1624 2.9	2254 1.2
13	W	0004 1.4	0630 2.8	1221 1.9	1826 3.0	28	TH	0522 2.8	1117 1.6	1735 3.0	
14	TH	0112 1.3	0738 2.9	1324 1.7	1933 3.0	29	F	0010 1.1	0633 2.9	1235 1.5	1843 3.1
15	F	0204 1.2	0829 3.0	1413 1.5	2027 3.1	30	SA	0114 0.9	0739 3.0	1338 1.3	1947 3.2

DECEMBER

#	Day	Time m	Time m	Time m	Time m	#	Day	Time m	Time m	Time m	Time m
1	SU	0210 0.7	0836 3.2	1432 1.1	2045 3.4	16	M	0240 1.2	0909 3.1	1501 1.3	2116 3.1
2	M	0300 0.6	0927 3.4	1521 1.0	2139 3.6	17	TU	0317 1.1	0949 3.2	1541 1.2	2157 3.2
3	TU	0347 0.6	1014 3.5	1608 0.8	2230 3.7	18	W	0352 1.1	1025 3.3	1618 1.1	2236 3.2
4	W	0432 0.6	1059 3.6	1655 0.8	● 2319 3.7	19	TH	0427 1.0	1100 3.4	1655 1.0	○ 2314 3.3
5	TH	0516 0.7	1142 3.7	1740 0.7		20	F	0503 1.0	1135 3.4	1732 0.9	2353 3.3
6	F	0007 3.7	0559 0.9	1224 3.7	1826 0.8	21	SA	0539 1.0	1211 3.4	1809 0.9	
7	SA	0055 3.6	0641 1.1	1306 3.6	1913 0.9	22	SU	0033 3.3	0616 1.1	1249 3.4	1848 0.9
8	SU	0144 3.4	0724 1.3	1349 3.5	2003 1.0	23	M	0115 3.2	0654 1.1	1328 3.4	1931 0.9
9	M	0234 3.2	0808 1.5	1435 3.4	2059 1.2	24	TU	0201 3.2	0735 1.2	1411 3.3	2019 0.9
10	TU	0328 3.0	0858 1.7	1525 3.2	2204 1.3	25	W	0252 3.0	0823 1.3	1501 3.2	2116 0.9
11	W	0427 2.9	1003 1.8	1623 3.1	2311 1.4	26	TH	0350 2.9	0921 1.4	1559 3.1	2222 0.9
12	TH	0530 2.8	1119 1.8	1728 3.0		27	F	0453 2.9	1034 1.5	1704 3.1	2330 0.9
13	F	0015 1.4	0635 2.8	1228 1.8	1834 3.0	28	SA	0558 2.9	1149 1.4	1811 3.1	
14	SA	0111 1.4	0734 2.8	1327 1.6	1936 3.0	29	SU	0036 0.9	0702 2.9	1300 1.3	1917 3.1
15	SU	0159 1.3	0825 3.0	1418 1.5	2029 3.0	30	M	0139 0.9	0804 3.0	1405 1.2	2022 3.2
						31	TU	0237 0.9	0902 3.2	1504 1.1	2123 3.3

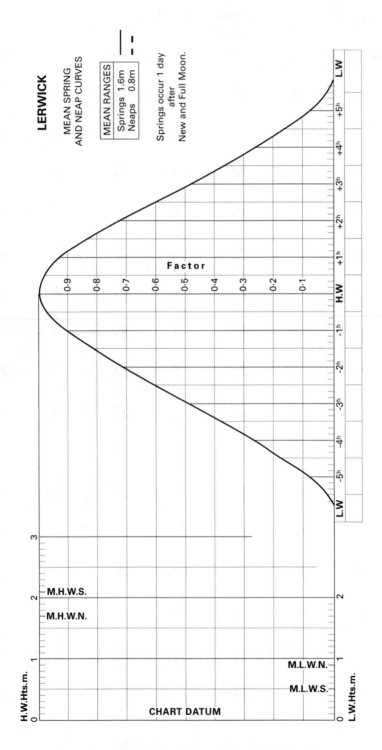

LERWICK

MEAN SPRING
AND NEAP CURVES

MEAN RANGES
Springs 1.6m
Neaps 0.8m

Springs occur 1 day
after
New and Full Moon.

Factor

0·9 0·8 0·7 0·6 0·5 0·4 0·3 0·2 0·1

L.W   +5ʰ +4ʰ +3ʰ +2ʰ +1ʰ H.W -1ʰ -2ʰ -3ʰ -4ʰ -5ʰ L.W

3

2 M.H.W.S.
   M.H.W.N.

H.W.Hts.m. 1

0

CHART DATUM

M.L.W.N. 1
M.L.W.S.

L.W.Hts.m.

2

0

TIME ZONE (UTC)
For Summer Time add ONE hour in **non-shaded areas**

SCOTLAND – LERWICK
LAT 60°09'N   LONG 1°08'W
TIMES AND HEIGHTS OF HIGH AND LOW WATERS

YEAR 2002

JANUARY

Day	Time m	Time m		Day	Time m	Time m
1 TU	0547 0.7 / 1203 2.3 / 1819 0.4			**16** W	0038 2.0 / 0621 0.8 / 1235 2.2 / 1853 0.6	
2 W	0042 2.2 / 0632 0.7 / 1249 2.3 / 1906 0.4			**17** TH	0112 2.0 / 0653 0.8 / 1308 2.1 / 1928 0.6	
3 TH	0132 2.1 / 0718 0.8 / 1336 2.2 / 1956 0.4			**18** F	0146 1.9 / 0725 0.9 / 1342 2.1 / 2003 0.7	
4 F	0225 2.0 / 0808 0.8 / 1428 2.2 / 2050 0.5			**19** SA	0222 1.8 / 0800 0.9 / 1418 2.0 / 2042 0.8	
5 SA	0319 1.9 / 0901 0.9 / 1525 2.1 / 2148 0.6			**20** SU	0301 1.7 / 0840 1.0 / 1500 1.9 / 2126 0.8	
6 SU	0417 1.8 / 1001 1.0 / 1628 2.0 / 2257 0.7			**21** M	0347 1.7 / 0930 1.0 / 1548 1.8 / 2218 0.9	
7 M	0520 1.8 / 1118 1.0 / 1737 1.9			**22** TU	0440 1.7 / 1035 1.1 / 1645 1.7 / 2325 1.0	
8 TU	0014 0.7 / 0626 1.8 / 1244 1.0 / 1849 1.9			**23** W	0544 1.7 / 1205 1.1 / 1755 1.7	
9 W	0120 0.8 / 0732 1.8 / 1351 0.9 / 2000 1.9			**24** TH	0041 1.0 / 0654 1.7 / 1319 1.0 / 1911 1.7	
10 TH	0217 0.8 / 0831 1.9 / 1447 0.8 / 2102 2.0			**25** F	0141 0.9 / 0756 1.8 / 1414 0.9 / 2018 1.8	
11 F	0306 0.8 / 0922 2.0 / 1537 0.7 / 2155 2.0			**26** SA	0233 0.9 / 0848 1.9 / 1503 0.8 / 2114 1.9	
12 SA	0351 0.8 / 1007 2.1 / 1621 0.7 / 2241 2.0			**27** SU	0321 0.8 / 0936 2.1 / 1550 0.6 / 2206 2.1	
13 SU	0432 0.8 / 1047 2.2 / 1703 0.6 / ●2323 2.1			**28** M	0407 0.7 / 1022 2.2 / 1636 0.5 / ○2256 2.2	
14 M	0510 0.8 / 1125 2.2 / 1742 0.6			**29** TU	0452 0.6 / 1108 2.3 / 1722 0.3 / 2344 2.2	
15 TU	0001 2.0 / 0546 0.8 / 1202 2.2 / 1818 0.6			**30** W	0536 0.6 / 1153 2.3 / 1807 0.2	
				31 TH	0031 2.2 / 0619 0.5 / 1238 2.3 / 1852 0.2	

FEBRUARY

Day	Time m		Day	Time m
1 F	0118 2.1 / 0703 0.6 / 1323 2.3 / 1938 0.2		**16** SA	0115 1.9 / 0656 0.7 / 1313 2.1 / 1927 0.6
2 SA	0205 2.1 / 0747 0.6 / 1411 2.2 / 2026 0.4		**17** SU	0145 1.8 / 0728 0.7 / 1346 2.0 / 2000 0.6
3 SU	0253 1.9 / 0835 0.7 / 1502 2.1 / 2118 0.5		**18** M	0219 1.8 / 0803 0.8 / 1423 1.9 / 2037 0.7
4 M	0343 1.8 / 0928 0.8 / 1559 2.0 / 2217 0.7		**19** TU	0258 1.7 / 0844 0.9 / 1505 1.8 / 2119 0.8
5 TU	0440 1.7 / 1036 0.9 / 1706 1.8 / 2336 0.8		**20** W	0345 1.7 / 0937 1.0 / 1558 1.7 / 2214 0.9
6 W	0545 1.7 / 1218 1.0 / 1825 1.6		**21** TH	0443 1.6 / 1052 1.0 / 1706 1.6 / 2335 1.0
7 TH	0057 0.9 / 0701 1.7 / 1338 0.9 / 1950 1.8		**22** F	0556 1.6 / 1238 1.0 / 1831 1.6
8 F	0203 0.9 / 0813 1.8 / 1443 0.8 / 2058 1.8		**23** SA	0110 1.0 / 0716 1.7 / 1349 0.9 / 1955 1.7
9 SA	0258 0.9 / 0910 1.9 / 1534 0.7 / 2149 1.9		**24** SU	0214 0.9 / 0823 1.8 / 1445 0.7 / 2100 1.9
10 SU	0342 0.9 / 0956 2.0 / 1615 0.6 / 2231 1.9		**25** M	0307 0.8 / 0917 2.0 / 1535 0.5 / 2153 2.0
11 M	0421 0.8 / 1035 2.1 / 1652 0.6 / 2308 2.0		**26** TU	0354 0.6 / 1006 2.1 / 1621 0.3 / 2242 2.1
12 TU	0456 0.7 / 1111 2.1 / 1725 0.5 / ●2343 2.0		**27** W	0438 0.5 / 1052 2.3 / 1705 0.1 / ○2329 2.2
13 W	0528 0.7 / 1144 2.2 / 1757 0.5		**28** TH	0519 0.4 / 1136 2.3 / 1748 0.0
14 TH	0015 2.0 / 0558 0.7 / 1215 2.1 / 1827 0.5			
15 F	0046 1.9 / 0627 0.7 / 1244 2.1 / 1856 0.5			

MARCH

Day	Time m		Day	Time m
1 F	0013 2.2 / 0600 0.4 / 1220 2.4 / 1831 0.0		**16** SA	0015 1.9 / 0600 0.5 / 1217 2.1 / 1823 0.4
2 SA	0056 2.1 / 0642 0.4 / 1304 2.3 / 1914 0.1		**17** SU	0042 1.9 / 0629 0.5 / 1246 2.0 / 1853 0.5
3 SU	0138 2.1 / 0724 0.4 / 1350 2.2 / 1959 0.3		**18** M	0110 1.9 / 0701 0.6 / 1317 2.0 / 1925 0.6
4 M	0221 1.9 / 0810 0.6 / 1439 2.1 / 2047 0.5		**19** TU	0141 1.8 / 0736 0.7 / 1353 1.9 / 1959 0.7
5 TU	0307 1.8 / 0901 0.7 / 1533 1.9 / 2141 0.8		**20** W	0217 1.8 / 0816 0.7 / 1434 1.8 / 2039 0.8
6 W	0359 1.7 / 1007 0.8 / 1638 1.7 / 2256 0.9		**21** TH	0300 1.7 / 0906 0.8 / 1527 1.7 / 2131 0.9
7 TH	0503 1.6 / 1158 0.9 / 1804 1.6		**22** F	0356 1.6 / 1016 0.9 / 1637 1.6 / 2249 1.0
8 F	0035 1.0 / 0627 1.6 / 1326 0.9 / 1944 1.6		**23** SA	0512 1.6 / 1201 0.9 / 1807 1.6
9 SA	0148 1.0 / 0754 1.7 / 1433 0.8 / 2049 1.7		**24** SU	0047 1.0 / 0641 1.6 / 1326 0.8 / 1939 1.7
10 SU	0245 0.9 / 0852 1.8 / 1521 0.7 / 2134 1.8		**25** M	0157 0.9 / 0759 1.7 / 1425 0.6 / 2044 1.8
11 M	0327 0.8 / 0936 1.9 / 1558 0.6 / 2211 1.8		**26** TU	0250 0.7 / 0856 1.9 / 1515 0.3 / 2136 2.0
12 TU	0403 0.7 / 1015 2.0 / 1631 0.5 / 2245 1.9		**27** W	0335 0.6 / 0946 2.1 / 1600 0.2 / 2223 2.1
13 W	0435 0.6 / 1049 2.0 / 1701 0.4 / 2317 1.9		**28** TH	0417 0.4 / 1031 2.2 / 1643 0.0 / ○2306 2.1
14 TH	0505 0.6 / 1121 2.1 / 1729 0.4 / ●2347 1.9		**29** F	0458 0.3 / 1115 2.3 / 1725 0.0 / 2348 2.2
15 F	0532 0.5 / 1150 2.1 / 1756 0.4		**30** SA	0539 0.3 / 1159 2.3 / 1807 0.0
			31 SU	0028 2.1 / 0619 0.3 / 1243 2.3 / 1849 0.2

APRIL

Day	Time m		Day	Time m
1 M	0108 2.0 / 0702 0.3 / 1329 2.1 / 1932 0.4		**16** TU	0040 1.9 / 0639 0.5 / 1254 1.9 / 1856 0.6
2 TU	0149 1.9 / 0749 0.5 / 1418 2.0 / 2018 0.6		**17** W	0111 1.9 / 0716 0.6 / 1332 1.9 / 1931 0.7
3 W	0232 1.8 / 0841 0.6 / 1512 1.8 / 2110 0.8		**18** TH	0147 1.8 / 0759 0.6 / 1416 1.8 / 2013 0.8
4 TH	0322 1.7 / 0948 0.7 / 1616 1.6 / 2219 1.0		**19** F	0230 1.7 / 0851 0.7 / 1512 1.6 / 2108 0.9
5 F	0423 1.6 / 1134 0.8 / 1742 1.5		**20** SA	0327 1.6 / 1001 0.8 / 1626 1.6 / 2229 1.0
6 SA	0004 1.1 / 0547 1.6 / 1301 0.8 / 1925 1.5		**21** SU	0444 1.6 / 1136 0.7 / 1754 1.5
7 SU	0122 1.0 / 0720 1.6 / 1406 0.7 / 2024 1.6		**22** M	0023 0.9 / 0613 1.6 / 1300 0.6 / 1919 1.6
8 M	0219 0.9 / 0821 1.7 / 1453 0.6 / 2105 1.7		**23** TU	0134 0.8 / 0731 1.7 / 1400 0.4 / 2022 1.8
9 TU	0301 0.8 / 0907 1.8 / 1529 0.5 / 2141 1.8		**24** W	0226 0.7 / 0831 1.9 / 1451 0.3 / 2112 1.9
10 W	0336 0.7 / 0945 1.9 / 1600 0.5 / 2215 1.8		**25** TH	0312 0.5 / 0922 2.0 / 1536 0.1 / 2158 2.0
11 TH	0408 0.6 / 1020 1.9 / 1629 0.4 / 2246 1.9		**26** F	0354 0.4 / 1008 2.1 / 1619 0.1 / 2240 2.1
12 F	0436 0.5 / 1052 2.0 / 1656 0.4 / 2316 1.9		**27** SA	0435 0.3 / 1054 2.2 / 1701 0.1 / ○2320 2.1
13 SA	0504 0.5 / 1121 2.0 / 1723 0.4 / 2343 1.9		**28** SU	0517 0.2 / 1138 2.2 / 1743 0.2
14 SU	0534 0.5 / 1150 2.0 / 1752 0.4		**29** M	0000 2.1 / 0600 0.2 / 1224 2.2 / 1824 0.3
15 M	0010 1.9 / 0605 0.5 / 1221 2.0 / 1823 0.5		**30** TU	0040 2.0 / 0644 0.3 / 1311 2.0 / 1908 0.5

TIME ZONE (UTC)
For Summer Time add ONE hour in **non-shaded areas**

SCOTLAND – LERWICK
LAT 60°09'N   LONG 1°08'W
TIMES AND HEIGHTS OF HIGH AND LOW WATERS

YEAR **2002**

MAY

Day	Time m	Time m	Time m	Time m
1 W	0121 2.0	0733 0.4	1401 1.9	1953 0.7
2 TH	0204 1.9	0826 0.6	1453 1.7	2044 0.9
3 F	0252 1.7	0930 0.7	1552 1.6	2146 1.0
4 SA	0348 1.6	1053 0.7	1705 1.5	2310 1.1
5 SU	0459 1.6	1217 0.7	1835 1.5	
6 M	0035 1.0	0628 1.6	1322 0.7	1939 1.5
7 TU	0137 0.9	0737 1.6	1411 0.6	2024 1.6
8 W	0223 0.8	0827 1.7	1450 0.6	2103 1.7
9 TH	0301 0.7	0909 1.8	1523 0.5	2139 1.8
10 F	0335 0.6	0946 1.8	1553 0.5	2212 1.9
11 SA	0406 0.6	1020 1.9	1622 0.5	2242 1.9
12 SU	0437 0.5	1052 1.9	1652 0.5	●2312 2.0
13 M	0510 0.5	1125 2.0	1724 0.5	2342 2.0
14 TU	0545 0.5	1200 1.9	1759 0.5	
15 W	0015 2.0	0622 0.5	1239 1.9	1835 0.6
16 TH	0050 1.9	0703 0.5	1321 1.8	1915 0.7
17 F	0129 1.9	0750 0.5	1410 1.7	2001 0.8
18 SA	0216 1.8	0845 0.6	1509 1.7	2100 0.9
19 SU	0314 1.7	0952 0.6	1619 1.6	2214 0.9
20 M	0428 1.6	1111 0.6	1736 1.6	2347 0.9
21 TU	0548 1.7	1230 0.5	1851 1.6	
22 W	0102 0.8	0701 1.7	1332 0.4	1953 1.7
23 TH	0159 0.7	0803 1.9	1425 0.3	2045 1.9
24 F	0247 0.5	0857 2.0	1512 0.3	2131 2.0
25 SA	0332 0.4	0948 2.1	1556 0.2	2215 2.0
26 SU	0416 0.3	1036 2.1	1639 0.3	○2256 2.1
27 M	0500 0.3	1124 2.1	1722 0.4	2337 2.1
28 TU	0545 0.3	1211 2.0	1805 0.5	
29 W	0017 2.0	0631 0.3	1258 1.9	1848 0.6
30 TH	0100 2.0	0720 0.4	1345 1.8	1932 0.8
31 F	0143 1.9	0810 0.5	1433 1.7	2019 0.9

JUNE

Day	Time m	Time m	Time m	Time m
1 SA	0227 1.8	0904 0.6	1524 1.6	2110 1.0
2 SU	0316 1.7	1003 0.7	1620 1.5	2210 1.0
3 M	0412 1.6	1109 0.7	1727 1.5	2322 1.0
4 TU	0521 1.6	1217 0.7	1837 1.5	
5 W	0036 0.9	0638 1.6	1315 0.7	1934 1.6
6 TH	0134 0.9	0740 1.6	1401 0.7	2020 1.7
7 F	0220 0.8	0828 1.7	1440 0.6	2100 1.8
8 SA	0259 0.7	0910 1.8	1515 0.6	2136 1.8
9 SU	0335 0.6	0948 1.8	1549 0.6	2210 1.9
10 M	0412 0.6	1026 1.9	1625 0.6	●2244 2.0
11 TU	0449 0.5	1105 1.9	1702 0.6	2320 2.0
12 W	0529 0.5	1146 1.9	1741 0.6	2358 2.0
13 TH	0611 0.4	1230 1.9	1822 0.6	
14 F	0038 2.0	0655 0.4	1317 1.9	1906 0.7
15 SA	0122 2.0	0744 0.4	1408 1.8	1955 0.7
16 SU	0210 1.9	0837 0.4	1504 1.7	2049 0.8
17 M	0307 1.8	0936 0.5	1605 1.7	2151 0.8
18 TU	0412 1.8	1043 0.5	1711 1.6	2304 0.8
19 W	0522 1.8	1157 0.5	1817 1.7	
20 TH	0026 0.8	0632 1.8	1304 0.5	1920 1.7
21 F	0131 0.7	0738 1.8	1401 0.5	2017 1.8
22 SA	0226 0.6	0839 1.9	1452 0.5	2108 1.9
23 SU	0317 0.5	0935 2.0	1538 0.5	2155 2.0
24 M	0404 0.5	1027 2.0	1623 0.5	○2239 2.0
25 TU	0451 0.4	1116 2.0	1707 0.6	2321 2.1
26 W	0536 0.4	1201 2.0	1749 0.6	
27 TH	0003 2.1	0620 0.4	1245 1.9	1830 0.7
28 F	0043 2.0	0704 0.4	1327 1.8	1910 0.7
29 SA	0123 2.0	0747 0.5	1408 1.7	1950 0.8
30 SU	0202 1.9	0830 0.6	1449 1.7	2030 0.9

JULY

Day	Time m	Time m	Time m	Time m
1 M	0243 1.8	0915 0.7	1533 1.6	2116 0.9
2 TU	0329 1.7	1004 0.7	1623 1.5	2212 1.0
3 W	0420 1.7	1103 0.8	1722 1.5	2324 1.0
4 TH	0522 1.6	1209 0.8	1830 1.6	
5 F	0038 1.0	0635 1.6	1309 0.8	1930 1.6
6 SA	0137 0.9	0741 1.7	1358 0.8	2018 1.7
7 SU	0225 0.8	0833 1.7	1441 0.8	2101 1.8
8 M	0309 0.7	0920 1.8	1523 0.7	2141 1.9
9 TU	0351 0.6	1005 1.9	1604 0.7	2222 2.0
10 W	0433 0.5	1050 2.0	1647 0.6	●2303 2.1
11 TH	0516 0.4	1136 2.0	1729 0.6	2346 2.1
12 F	0601 0.3	1223 2.0	1813 0.6	
13 SA	0029 2.1	0645 0.3	1310 2.0	1856 0.6
14 SU	0114 2.1	0732 0.3	1358 1.9	1942 0.6
15 M	0201 2.1	0821 0.3	1449 1.8	2031 0.7
16 TU	0253 2.0	0914 0.4	1542 1.8	2124 0.8
17 W	0351 1.9	1012 0.5	1640 1.7	2227 0.8
18 TH	0455 1.8	1123 0.6	1742 1.7	2351 0.8
19 F	0606 1.8	1238 0.7	1849 1.7	
20 SA	0111 0.8	0720 1.8	1343 0.7	1954 1.8
21 SU	0215 0.7	0831 1.8	1439 0.7	2053 1.9
22 M	0311 0.6	0932 1.9	1529 0.7	2144 2.0
23 TU	0401 0.6	1023 1.9	1614 0.7	2229 2.1
24 W	0445 0.5	1108 2.0	1655 0.7	○2310 2.1
25 TH	0526 0.4	1149 2.0	1734 0.7	2349 2.1
26 F	0605 0.4	1227 1.9	1811 0.7	
27 SA	0025 2.1	0642 0.4	1303 1.9	1844 0.7
28 SU	0100 2.1	0717 0.5	1337 1.8	1917 0.7
29 M	0133 2.0	0752 0.6	1411 1.8	1950 0.8
30 TU	0208 1.9	0828 0.6	1447 1.7	2028 0.8
31 W	0247 1.8	0908 0.7	1529 1.7	2113 0.9

AUGUST

Day	Time m	Time m	Time m	Time m
1 TH	0332 1.8	0956 0.8	1617 1.6	2213 1.0
2 F	0425 1.7	1057 0.9	1715 1.6	2337 1.0
3 SA	0529 1.6	1214 1.0	1825 1.6	
4 SU	0057 1.0	0647 1.6	1321 0.9	1934 1.7
5 M	0156 0.9	0801 1.7	1415 0.9	2029 1.8
6 TU	0247 0.8	0858 1.8	1503 0.8	2117 1.9
7 W	0333 0.6	0948 1.9	1549 0.7	2203 2.1
8 TH	0418 0.5	1036 2.0	1633 0.6	●2247 2.2
9 F	0502 0.3	1123 2.1	1716 0.6	2331 2.2
10 SA	0545 0.2	1209 2.1	1758 0.5	
11 SU	0014 2.3	0628 0.2	1254 2.1	1839 0.5
12 M	0059 2.3	0712 0.2	1338 2.1	1922 0.5
13 TU	0144 2.2	0758 0.3	1424 2.0	2007 0.6
14 W	0233 2.1	0847 0.4	1512 1.9	2057 0.7
15 TH	0327 2.0	0941 0.6	1606 1.8	2158 0.8
16 F	0430 1.9	1049 0.8	1707 1.7	2328 0.9
17 SA	0546 1.8	1219 0.9	1820 1.7	
18 SU	0103 0.9	0714 1.7	1332 0.9	1938 1.8
19 M	0213 0.8	0832 1.8	1432 0.9	2043 1.9
20 TU	0310 0.7	0929 1.9	1522 0.9	2134 2.0
21 W	0356 0.6	1014 1.9	1603 0.8	2217 2.1
22 TH	0434 0.5	1053 2.0	1640 0.7	○2255 2.1
23 F	0509 0.5	1129 2.0	1714 0.7	2330 2.2
24 SA	0542 0.4	1202 2.0	1745 0.7	
25 SU	0002 2.2	0613 0.5	1233 2.0	1815 0.7
26 M	0032 2.1	0643 0.5	1302 1.9	1844 0.7
27 TU	0101 2.1	0712 0.6	1332 1.9	1915 0.7
28 W	0133 2.0	0744 0.7	1404 1.8	1949 0.8
29 TH	0208 1.9	0820 0.8	1441 1.8	2030 0.9
30 F	0250 1.8	0900 0.9	1525 1.7	2121 1.0
31 SA	0341 1.7	0951 1.0	1619 1.7	2234 1.1

Chart Datum: 1·22 metres below Ordnance Datum (Local)

TIME ZONE (UTC)
For Summer Time add ONE hour in **non-shaded areas**

SCOTLAND – LERWICK

LAT 60°09'N   LONG 1°08'W

TIMES AND HEIGHTS OF HIGH AND LOW WATERS

YEAR **2002**

SEPTEMBER

Day	Time m	Day	Time m
1 SU	0444 1.7 / 1109 1.1 / 1727 1.7	**16** M	0056 0.9 / 0716 1.7 / 1321 1.1 / 1922 1.8
2 M	0021 1.1 / 0605 1.6 / 1250 1.1 / 1848 1.7	**17** TU	0207 0.8 / 0828 1.8 / 1421 1.0 / 2028 1.9
3 TU	0132 1.0 / 0735 1.7 / 1355 1.0 / 2001 1.8	**18** W	0300 0.7 / 0916 1.9 / 1507 0.9 / 2116 2.0
4 W	0226 0.8 / 0841 1.8 / 1447 0.9 / 2055 2.0	**19** TH	0339 0.6 / 0954 2.0 / 1544 0.8 / 2156 2.1
5 TH	0314 0.6 / 0932 2.0 / 1533 0.8 / 2143 2.1	**20** F	0413 0.6 / 1029 2.1 / 1618 0.7 / 2232 2.2
6 F	0359 0.4 / 1019 2.1 / 1615 0.6 / 2228 2.3	**21** SA	0444 0.5 / 1101 2.1 / 1648 0.7 / O 2304 2.2
7 SA	0442 0.2 / 1104 2.2 / 1656 0.5 / ● 2311 2.4	**22** SU	0513 0.5 / 1132 2.1 / 1717 0.7 / 2334 2.2
8 SU	0524 0.1 / 1147 2.2 / 1736 0.4 / 2354 2.4	**23** M	0540 0.5 / 1200 2.1 / 1745 0.6
9 M	0606 0.1 / 1229 2.2 / 1817 0.4	**24** TU	0002 2.2 / 0607 0.5 / 1227 2.0 / 1814 0.7
10 TU	0037 2.4 / 0648 0.2 / 1311 2.2 / 1859 0.5	**25** W	0030 2.1 / 0636 0.6 / 1254 2.0 / 1845 0.7
11 W	0122 2.3 / 0732 0.3 / 1353 2.1 / 1944 0.6	**26** TH	0101 2.1 / 0707 0.7 / 1324 2.0 / 1920 0.8
12 TH	0211 2.2 / 0819 0.5 / 1439 2.0 / 2034 0.7	**27** F	0136 2.0 / 0740 0.8 / 1359 1.9 / 1959 0.9
13 F	0306 2.0 / 0911 0.8 / 1531 1.9 / 2137 0.8	**28** SA	0217 1.9 / 0817 1.0 / 1440 1.8 / 2048 1.0
14 SA	0411 1.8 / 1020 1.0 / 1633 1.8 / 2320 0.9	**29** SU	0308 1.8 / 0905 1.1 / 1533 1.8 / 2157 1.1
15 SU	0532 1.7 / 1203 1.1 / 1752 1.7	**30** M	0415 1.7 / 1021 1.2 / 1644 1.7 / 2344 1.1

OCTOBER

Day	Time m	Day	Time m
1 TU	0540 1.7 / 1224 1.2 / 1810 1.7	**16** W	0145 0.8 / 0805 1.8 / 1357 1.1 / 1959 1.9
2 W	0106 0.9 / 0714 1.7 / 1335 1.1 / 1932 1.8	**17** TH	0234 0.8 / 0848 1.9 / 1442 1.0 / 2047 2.0
3 TH	0203 0.8 / 0821 1.9 / 1427 0.9 / 2030 2.0	**18** F	0312 0.7 / 0924 1.9 / 1518 0.9 / 2127 2.1
4 F	0251 0.6 / 0911 2.0 / 1511 0.8 / 2119 2.2	**19** SA	0344 0.6 / 0957 2.0 / 1550 0.8 / 2202 2.1
5 SA	0336 0.4 / 0956 2.2 / 1553 0.6 / 2204 2.3	**20** SU	0413 0.6 / 1029 2.1 / 1620 0.7 / 2235 2.2
6 SU	0418 0.2 / 1039 2.3 / 1633 0.5 / ● 2248 2.4	**21** M	0440 0.6 / 1059 2.1 / 1649 0.7 / O 2305 2.2
7 M	0500 0.2 / 1120 2.3 / 1713 0.4 / 2331 2.5	**22** TU	0507 0.6 / 1127 2.1 / 1718 0.7 / 2334 2.2
8 TU	0541 0.4 / 1200 2.3 / 1754 0.4	**23** W	0535 0.6 / 1154 2.1 / 1749 0.7
9 W	0015 2.5 / 0623 0.3 / 1241 2.3 / 1837 0.5	**24** TH	0004 2.2 / 0604 0.7 / 1222 2.1 / 1822 0.7
10 TH	0102 2.3 / 0706 0.5 / 1323 2.2 / 1924 0.6	**25** F	0037 2.1 / 0636 0.8 / 1253 2.1 / 1858 0.8
11 F	0152 2.2 / 0753 0.7 / 1408 2.1 / 2017 0.7	**26** SA	0114 2.0 / 0710 0.9 / 1328 2.0 / 1939 0.9
12 SA	0249 2.0 / 0845 1.0 / 1459 1.9 / 2124 0.9	**27** SU	0156 1.9 / 0748 1.0 / 1409 1.9 / 2030 0.9
13 SU	0354 1.8 / 0954 1.1 / 1601 1.8 / 2306 0.9	**28** M	0249 1.8 / 0839 1.1 / 1502 1.8 / 2136 1.0
14 M	0516 1.7 / 1137 1.2 / 1721 1.8	**29** TU	0358 1.7 / 0954 1.2 / 1613 1.8 / 2307 1.0
15 TU	0037 0.9 / 0701 1.7 / 1257 1.2 / 1853 1.8	**30** W	0521 1.7 / 1147 1.2 / 1739 1.8
		31 TH	0034 0.9 / 0647 1.8 / 1307 1.1 / 1859 1.9

NOVEMBER

Day	Time m	Day	Time m
1 F	0134 0.7 / 0753 1.9 / 1400 0.9 / 2001 2.0	**16** SA	0235 0.8 / 0846 1.9 / 1446 0.9 / 2052 2.0
2 SA	0224 0.5 / 0844 2.1 / 1446 0.8 / 2052 2.2	**17** SU	0309 0.7 / 0922 2.0 / 1520 0.9 / 2130 2.1
3 SU	0310 0.4 / 0929 2.2 / 1528 0.6 / 2139 2.3	**18** M	0339 0.7 / 0956 2.1 / 1552 0.8 / 2206 2.1
4 M	0353 0.3 / 1012 2.3 / 1610 0.5 / ● 2225 2.4	**19** TU	0408 0.7 / 1027 2.1 / 1623 0.7 / 2238 2.1
5 TU	0435 0.3 / 1053 2.3 / 1652 0.5 / 2311 2.4	**20** W	0437 0.7 / 1057 2.2 / 1655 0.7 / O 2310 2.1
6 W	0518 0.4 / 1133 2.3 / 1735 0.4 / 2357 2.4	**21** TH	0507 0.7 / 1126 2.2 / 1729 0.7 / 2344 2.1
7 TH	0600 0.4 / 1214 2.3 / 1821 0.5	**22** F	0540 0.8 / 1158 2.2 / 1805 0.7
8 F	0046 2.3 / 0644 0.7 / 1257 2.2 / 1910 0.6	**23** SA	0021 2.1 / 0614 0.9 / 1232 2.2 / 1845 0.7
9 SA	0139 2.1 / 0731 0.9 / 1343 2.1 / 2005 0.7	**24** SU	0101 2.1 / 0652 0.9 / 1309 2.1 / 1929 0.8
10 SU	0234 2.0 / 0823 1.1 / 1434 1.9 / 2109 0.8	**25** M	0147 2.0 / 0735 1.0 / 1352 2.0 / 2020 0.8
11 M	0335 1.8 / 0925 1.2 / 1532 1.9 / 2230 0.9	**26** TU	0241 1.9 / 0827 1.1 / 1445 1.9 / 2121 0.8
12 TU	0445 1.7 / 1045 1.3 / 1641 1.8 / 2356 0.9	**27** W	0346 1.8 / 0934 1.1 / 1551 1.9 / 2233 0.8
13 W	0610 1.7 / 1212 1.2 / 1804 1.9	**28** TH	0459 1.8 / 1057 1.1 / 1708 1.9 / 2354 0.8
14 TH	0104 0.9 / 0718 1.7 / 1317 1.1 / 1915 1.9	**29** F	0614 1.8 / 1226 1.1 / 1824 1.9
15 F	0155 0.8 / 0806 1.8 / 1406 1.0 / 2008 1.9	**30** SA	0101 0.7 / 0719 1.9 / 1328 1.0 / 1930 1.9

DECEMBER

Day	Time m	Day	Time m
1 SU	0156 0.6 / 0814 2.0 / 1419 0.8 / 2026 2.1	**16** M	0229 0.9 / 0846 1.9 / 1449 0.9 / 2058 1.9
2 M	0245 0.5 / 0902 2.1 / 1506 0.7 / 2119 2.2	**17** TU	0305 0.8 / 0924 2.0 / 1526 0.9 / 2138 2.0
3 TU	0331 0.5 / 0947 2.2 / 1551 0.6 / 2209 2.3	**18** W	0338 0.8 / 0958 2.1 / 1601 0.8 / 2215 2.1
4 W	0415 0.5 / 1031 2.3 / 1637 0.5 / ● 2258 2.3	**19** TH	0412 0.8 / 1032 2.2 / 1637 0.7 / O 2252 2.1
5 TH	0459 0.6 / 1113 2.3 / 1723 0.5 / 2348 2.3	**20** F	0447 0.8 / 1106 2.2 / 1715 0.7 / 2331 2.1
6 F	0543 0.7 / 1156 2.3 / 1811 0.5	**21** SA	0524 0.8 / 1142 2.2 / 1754 0.6
7 SA	0038 2.2 / 0628 0.8 / 1240 2.3 / 1900 0.6	**22** SU	0012 2.1 / 0602 0.8 / 1220 2.2 / 1836 0.6
8 SU	0128 2.1 / 0714 0.9 / 1325 2.2 / 1951 0.6	**23** M	0056 2.1 / 0643 0.9 / 1300 2.2 / 1921 0.6
9 M	0217 2.0 / 0801 1.0 / 1412 2.1 / 2045 0.7	**24** TU	0142 2.0 / 0727 0.9 / 1343 2.1 / 2009 0.6
10 TU	0308 1.8 / 0851 1.1 / 1501 2.0 / 2143 0.8	**25** W	0232 1.9 / 0816 0.9 / 1433 2.0 / 2102 0.6
11 W	0402 1.7 / 0947 1.2 / 1556 1.9 / 2247 0.9	**26** TH	0329 1.9 / 0911 1.0 / 1531 2.0 / 2201 0.7
12 TH	0504 1.7 / 1054 1.2 / 1700 1.8 / 2359 0.9	**27** F	0430 1.8 / 1015 1.0 / 1638 1.9 / 2310 0.7
13 F	0612 1.7 / 1213 1.2 / 1815 1.8	**28** SA	0536 1.8 / 1133 1.0 / 1749 1.9
14 SA	0100 0.9 / 0713 1.7 / 1318 1.1 / 1920 1.8	**29** SU	0025 0.7 / 0642 1.8 / 1255 1.0 / 1900 2.0
15 SU	0149 0.9 / 0803 1.8 / 1407 1.0 / 2013 1.9	**30** M	0130 0.7 / 0744 1.9 / 1357 0.9 / 2006 2.0
		31 TU	0225 0.7 / 0840 2.0 / 1451 0.8 / 2107 2.1

Chart Datum: 1·22 metres below Ordnance Datum (Local)

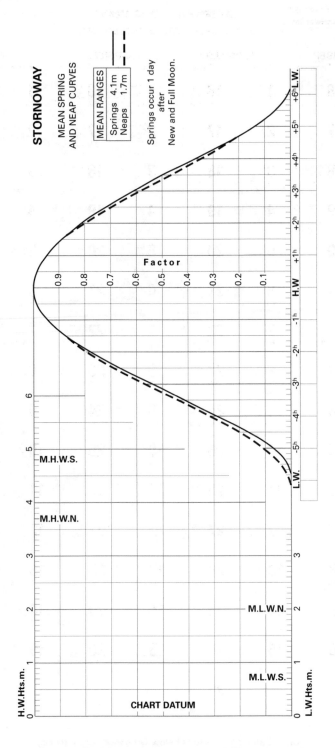

STORNOWAY

MEAN SPRING
AND NEAP CURVES

MEAN RANGES	
Springs	4.1m
Neaps	1.7m

Springs occur 1 day
after
New and Full Moon.

Factor

0.9
0.8
0.7
0.6
0.5
0.4
0.3
0.2
0.1

M.H.W.S.

M.H.W.N.

M.L.W.N.

M.L.W.S.

CHART DATUM

H.W.Hts.m.

L.W.Hts.m.

TIME ZONE (UTC)
For Summer Time add ONE hour in **non-shaded areas**

SCOTLAND – STORNOWAY

LAT 58°12′N   LONG 6°23′W

TIMES AND HEIGHTS OF HIGH AND LOW WATERS

YEAR 2002

JANUARY

Time	m	Time	m
1 0152	0.8	**16** 0232	1.0
0752	4.9	0824	4.6
TU 1429	0.7	W 1459	1.0
2024	4.6	2045	4.1
2 0235	0.8	**17** 0306	1.1
0837	4.9	0900	4.5
W 1515	0.7	TH 1533	1.1
2112	4.5	2120	4.0
3 0319	1.0	**18** 0341	1.3
0925	4.8	0937	4.4
TH 1603	0.8	F 1609	1.2
2205	4.3	2158	3.8
4 0405	1.1	**19** 0418	1.5
1021	4.6	1019	4.2
F 1655	0.9	SA 1648	1.4
2306	4.1	2242	3.7
5 0457	1.4	**20** 0459	1.7
1125	4.4	1106	3.9
SA 1752	1.1	SU 1731	1.6
		2336	3.5
6 0013	3.9	**21** 0546	1.9
0557	1.6	1201	3.8
SU 1235	4.2	M 1819	1.7
1855	1.3		
7 0123	3.8	**22** 0039	3.4
0707	1.8	0641	2.1
M 1347	4.1	TU 1301	3.7
2005	1.4	1915	1.9
8 0234	3.8	**23** 0148	3.5
0824	1.8	0747	2.1
TU 1458	4.0	W 1406	3.7
2117	1.5	2021	1.9
9 0338	3.9	**24** 0257	3.6
0940	1.7	0902	2.1
W 1602	4.0	TH 1514	3.7
2221	1.4	2131	1.8
10 0433	4.0	**25** 0357	3.8
1044	1.6	1012	1.9
TH 1658	4.1	F 1618	3.9
2313	1.3	2234	1.6
11 0520	4.2	**26** 0448	4.1
1139	1.4	1111	1.6
F 1745	4.1	SA 1713	4.1
2359	1.2	2327	1.4
12 0601	4.4	**27** 0534	4.4
1226	1.2	1202	1.2
SA 1826	4.2	SU 1801	4.4
13 0040	1.1	**28** 0015	1.1
0638	4.5	0617	4.7
SU 1309	1.1	M 1250	0.9
● 1903	4.2	○ 1846	4.6
14 0120	1.0	**29** 0100	0.8
0715	4.6	0700	4.9
M 1347	1.0	TU 1335	0.6
1938	4.2	1929	4.8
15 0156	1.0	**30** 0143	0.6
0750	4.9	0741	5.1
TU 1424	1.0	W 1419	0.4
2012	4.2	2012	4.8
		31 0225	0.5
		0823	5.1
		TH 1502	0.3
		2054	4.7

FEBRUARY

Time	m	Time	m
1 0307	0.6	**16** 0316	1.0
0907	5.0	0901	4.4
F 1546	0.4	SA 1537	0.9
2140	4.5	2117	4.0
2 0349	0.7	**17** 0348	1.1
0954	4.8	0935	4.2
SA 1631	0.6	SU 1611	1.1
2230	4.3	2151	3.9
3 0435	1.0	**18** 0422	1.4
1049	4.5	1012	4.0
SU 1720	0.9	M 1648	1.3
2331	4.0	2230	3.7
4 0526	1.3	**19** 0500	1.6
1157	4.2	1059	3.8
M 1815	1.3	TU 1730	1.6
		2326	3.5
5 0043	3.7	**20** 0546	1.9
0625	1.6	1203	3.6
TU 1316	3.9	W 1821	1.8
1920	1.6		
6 0201	3.6	**21** 0042	3.4
0744	1.9	0646	2.0
W 1437	3.7	TH 1319	3.5
2042	1.7	1925	1.9
7 0315	3.6	**22** 0203	3.4
0921	1.9	0808	2.1
TH 1552	3.7	F 1441	3.6
2204	1.7	2048	2.0
8 0419	3.8	**23** 0321	3.6
1040	1.7	0945	1.9
F 1654	3.8	SA 1559	3.8
2304	1.6	2210	1.8
9 0510	4.0	**24** 0426	4.0
1136	1.5	1055	1.6
SA 1742	3.9	SU 1659	4.1
2350	1.4	2311	1.4
10 0551	4.2	**25** 0518	4.3
1221	1.2	1148	1.1
SU 1819	4.0	M 1748	4.4
11 0030	1.2	**26** 0001	1.1
0626	4.4	0602	4.7
M 1300	1.0	TU 1236	0.7
1851	4.1	1832	4.7
12 0107	1.0	**27** 0046	0.7
0659	4.6	0644	5.1
TU 1334	0.9	W 1319	0.3
1921	4.2	○ 1912	4.9
13 0142	0.9	**28** 0128	0.5
0730	4.7	0724	5.3
W 1406	0.8	TH 1401	0.1
1950	4.2	1952	5.0
14 0214	0.8		
0800	4.7		
TH 1436	0.8		
2018	4.2		
15 0245	0.8		
0830	4.6		
F 1506	0.8		
2046	4.2		

MARCH

Time	m	Time	m
1 0208	0.3	**16** 0220	0.7
0804	5.4	0800	4.6
F 1441	0.0	SA 1435	0.7
2031	5.0	2014	4.3
2 0248	0.3	**17** 0248	0.8
0844	5.2	0829	4.5
SA 1522	0.2	SU 1504	0.8
2112	4.7	2042	4.2
3 0329	0.5	**18** 0318	1.0
0927	5.0	0858	4.3
SU 1603	0.5	M 1535	1.0
2156	4.4	2110	4.1
4 0411	0.8	**19** 0350	1.2
1017	4.6	0930	4.1
M 1648	0.9	TU 1610	1.2
2250	4.1	2142	3.9
5 0457	1.2	**20** 0425	1.4
1122	4.1	1011	3.8
TU 1737	1.4	W 1648	1.5
		2225	3.7
6 0005	3.8	**21** 0507	1.7
0552	1.6	1118	3.6
W 1253	3.7	TH 1735	1.8
1839	1.8	2349	3.5
7 0131	3.6	**22** 0605	1.9
0710	2.0	1252	3.5
TH 1422	3.5	F 1840	2.0
2010	2.1		
8 0252	3.6	**23** 0127	3.5
0909	2.0	0736	2.0
F 1545	3.5	SA 1424	3.5
2149	2.0	2015	2.1
9 0402	3.7	**24** 0254	3.6
1036	1.8	0926	1.8
SA 1650	3.6	SU 1544	3.8
2251	1.8	2150	1.9
10 0454	4.0	**25** 0404	4.0
1128	1.5	1038	1.4
SU 1734	3.8	M 1643	4.1
2335	1.5	2252	1.5
11 0534	4.2	**26** 0458	4.4
1207	1.3	1130	1.0
M 1806	4.0	TU 1730	4.5
		2341	1.1
12 0013	1.2	**27** 0543	4.8
0608	4.4	1215	0.5
TU 1241	1.0	W 1812	4.8
1833	4.1		
13 0048	1.0	**28** 0025	0.7
0638	4.6	0624	5.2
W 1312	0.8	TH 1258	0.2
1859	4.3	○ 1851	5.0
14 0121	0.8	**29** 0107	0.4
0707	4.7	0703	5.4
TH 1340	0.7	F 1338	0.0
● 1924	4.3	1929	5.1
15 0151	0.7	**30** 0148	0.3
0733	4.7	0742	5.4
F 1407	0.7	SA 1417	0.0
1948	4.4	2006	5.1
		31 0227	0.3
		0823	5.2
		SU 1456	0.2
		2045	4.9

APRIL

Time	m	Time	m
1 0307	0.5	**16** 0252	0.9
0904	4.9	0832	4.3
M 1536	0.6	TU 1505	0.9
2128	4.6	2043	4.2
2 0349	0.8	**17** 0325	1.1
0952	4.5	0908	4.1
TU 1618	1.1	W 1539	1.2
2219	4.2	2117	4.0
3 0435	1.3	**18** 0401	1.3
1057	4.0	0954	3.8
W 1704	1.6	TH 1618	1.5
2333	3.9	2204	3.8
4 0529	1.7	**19** 0447	1.6
1233	3.6	1108	3.6
TH 1803	2.0	F 1705	1.8
		2330	3.6
5 0102	3.7	**20** 0550	1.8
0647	2.0	1242	3.5
F 1402	3.4	SA 1813	2.0
1936	2.3		
6 0222	3.6	**21** 0107	3.6
0847	2.1	0727	1.9
SA 1527	3.5	SU 1409	3.6
2120	2.2	1953	2.1
7 0332	3.8	**22** 0229	3.6
1014	1.8	0905	1.6
SU 1633	3.6	M 1523	3.8
2224	2.0	2124	1.8
8 0427	3.9	**23** 0338	4.1
1103	1.6	1013	1.2
M 1713	3.8	TU 1621	4.1
2309	1.7	2226	1.5
9 0508	4.1	**24** 0433	4.5
1139	1.3	1105	0.9
TU 1742	4.0	W 1708	4.5
2347	1.4	2316	1.1
10 0542	4.3	**25** 0520	4.8
1212	1.1	1150	0.5
W 1808	4.1	TH 1749	4.8
11 0021	1.1	**26** 0001	0.8
0612	4.5	0602	5.1
TH 1242	0.9	F 1233	0.3
1832	4.3	1827	5.0
12 0054	0.9	**27** 0044	0.6
0639	4.6	0642	5.2
F 1309	0.8	SA 1313	0.2
● 1856	4.4	○ 1905	5.1
13 0124	0.8	**28** 0126	0.5
0705	4.6	0722	5.2
SA 1336	0.7	SU 1352	0.3
1920	4.5	1943	5.0
14 0152	0.8	**29** 0207	0.5
0732	4.6	0802	5.0
SU 1404	0.7	M 1432	0.5
1946	4.5	2023	4.8
15 0221	0.8	**30** 0249	0.7
0801	4.5	0846	4.7
M 1433	0.8	TU 1511	0.8
2014	4.4	2106	4.6

Chart Datum: 2·71 metres below Ordnance Datum (Newlyn)
Register for your **FREE** weekly weather email service from Macmillan Reeds
》 at **www.nauticaldata.com** – NOW! 《
weekend weather reports sent to your email address, every Thursday

TIME ZONE (UTC)
For Summer Time add ONE hour in **non-shaded areas**

SCOTLAND – STORNOWAY

LAT 58°12′N   LONG 6°23′W

TIMES AND HEIGHTS OF HIGH AND LOW WATERS

YEAR **2002**

MAY

Day	Time	m	Day	Time	m
1 W	0332 / 0936 / 1553 / 2157	1.0 / 4.3 / 1.2 / 4.3	16 TH	0309 / 0902 / 1519 / 2111	1.1 / 4.1 / 1.2 / 4.2
2 TH	0418 / 1040 / 1638 / 2305	1.3 / 3.9 / 1.7 / 4.0	17 F	0352 / 0956 / 1600 / 2207	1.2 / 3.9 / 1.4 / 4.0
3 F	0513 / 1205 / 1734	1.7 / 3.6 / 2.1	18 SA	0443 / 1109 / 1651 / 2326	1.4 / 3.7 / 1.7 / 3.8
4 SA	0025 / 0625 / 1328 / 1855	3.8 / 2.0 / 3.4 / 2.3	19 SU	0552 / 1229 / 1801	1.6 / 3.6 / 1.9
5 SU	0140 / 0801 / 1448 / 2032	3.8 / 2.0 / 3.4 / 2.3	20 M	0047 / 0714 / 1345 / 1929	3.8 / 1.6 / 3.6 / 1.9
6 M	0248 / 0924 / 1554 / 2141	3.8 / 1.9 / 3.5 / 2.1	21 TU	0202 / 0834 / 1455 / 2050	3.9 / 1.4 / 3.8 / 1.8
7 TU	0346 / 1019 / 1638 / 2231	3.9 / 1.7 / 3.7 / 1.8	22 W	0309 / 0941 / 1553 / 2154	4.1 / 1.1 / 4.1 / 1.5
8 W	0432 / 1100 / 1711 / 2312	4.0 / 1.5 / 3.9 / 1.6	23 TH	0406 / 1036 / 1642 / 2248	4.4 / 0.9 / 4.4 / 1.2
9 TH	0509 / 1135 / 1738 / 2349	4.2 / 1.3 / 4.1 / 1.4	24 F	0456 / 1124 / 1726 / 2336	4.6 / 0.7 / 4.6 / 1.0
10 F	0541 / 1206 / 1804	4.3 / 1.1 / 4.3	25 SA	0541 / 1208 / 1806	4.8 / 0.6 / 4.8
11 SA	0022 / 0610 / 1236 / 1828	1.2 / 4.4 / 0.9 / 4.4	26 SU ○	0022 / 0623 / 1251 / 1845	0.8 / 4.8 / 0.5 / 4.8
12 SU ●	0054 / 0639 / 1305 / 1854	1.0 / 4.5 / 0.8 / 4.5	27 M	0108 / 0706 / 1332 / 1925	0.7 / 4.8 / 0.6 / 4.8
13 M	0125 / 0709 / 1336 / 1923	1.0 / 4.5 / 0.8 / 4.5	28 TU	0152 / 0749 / 1412 / 2006	0.8 / 4.6 / 0.8 / 4.7
14 TU	0158 / 0743 / 1408 / 1955	0.9 / 4.4 / 0.9 / 4.5	29 W	0235 / 0835 / 1452 / 2050	0.9 / 4.4 / 1.0 / 4.6
15 W	0232 / 0819 / 1442 / 2030	1.0 / 4.3 / 1.0 / 4.4	30 TH	0320 / 0923 / 1533 / 2139	1.1 / 4.1 / 1.3 / 4.4
			31 F	0406 / 1018 / 1617 / 2235	1.3 / 3.9 / 1.6 / 4.2

JUNE

Day	Time	m	Day	Time	m
1 SA	0456 / 1122 / 1708 / 2338	1.5 / 3.6 / 1.9 / 4.0	16 SU	0443 / 1058 / 1644 / 2311	1.1 / 3.9 / 1.5 / 4.1
2 SU	0554 / 1232 / 1810	1.8 / 3.4 / 2.1	17 M	0543 / 1205 / 1746	1.2 / 3.7 / 1.6
3 M	0045 / 0701 / 1347 / 1928	3.8 / 1.9 / 3.4 / 2.2	18 TU	0022 / 0649 / 1313 / 1858	4.0 / 1.3 / 3.7 / 1.7
4 TU	0151 / 0815 / 1457 / 2044	3.8 / 1.9 / 3.4 / 2.2	19 W	0132 / 0758 / 1421 / 2013	4.0 / 1.2 / 3.8 / 1.7
5 W	0253 / 0920 / 1552 / 2143	3.8 / 1.8 / 3.6 / 2.0	20 TH	0239 / 0905 / 1524 / 2122	4.1 / 1.2 / 3.9 / 1.5
6 TH	0346 / 1010 / 1632 / 2231	3.8 / 1.7 / 3.8 / 1.8	21 F	0341 / 1007 / 1618 / 2223	4.2 / 1.1 / 4.1 / 1.4
7 F	0430 / 1052 / 1704 / 2312	4.0 / 1.5 / 4.0 / 1.6	22 SA	0436 / 1100 / 1706 / 2318	4.3 / 1.0 / 4.3 / 1.2
8 SA	0507 / 1128 / 1733 / 2349	4.1 / 1.3 / 4.2 / 1.4	23 SU	0526 / 1149 / 1749	4.4 / 0.9 / 4.5
9 SU	0542 / 1202 / 1802	4.2 / 1.2 / 4.3	24 M ○	0009 / 0613 / 1235 / 1831	1.1 / 4.4 / 0.9 / 4.6
10 M ●	0025 / 0617 / 1238 / 1832	1.2 / 4.3 / 1.0 / 4.5	25 TU	0058 / 0658 / 1318 / 1911	1.0 / 4.4 / 0.9 / 4.7
11 TU	0103 / 0654 / 1313 / 1907	1.1 / 4.4 / 0.9 / 4.5	26 W	0143 / 0741 / 1358 / 1952	0.9 / 4.3 / 1.0 / 4.7
12 W	0141 / 0733 / 1350 / 1943	1.0 / 4.4 / 0.9 / 4.5	27 TH	0226 / 0823 / 1438 / 2033	0.9 / 4.2 / 1.1 / 4.6
13 TH	0221 / 0815 / 1428 / 2024	0.9 / 4.3 / 1.0 / 4.5	28 F	0308 / 0905 / 1517 / 2115	1.0 / 4.1 / 1.2 / 4.5
14 F	0303 / 0902 / 1509 / 2109	0.9 / 4.2 / 1.1 / 4.4	29 SA	0349 / 0948 / 1557 / 2200	1.2 / 3.9 / 1.4 / 4.3
15 SA	0350 / 0956 / 1553 / 2204	1.0 / 4.0 / 1.3 / 4.2	30 SU	0431 / 1035 / 1639 / 2249	1.3 / 3.7 / 1.6 / 4.1

JULY

Day	Time	m	Day	Time	m
1 M	0515 / 1126 / 1726 / 2343	1.5 / 3.5 / 1.9 / 3.9	16 TU	0520 / 1133 / 1723 / 2351	0.9 / 3.9 / 1.4 / 4.2
2 TU	0603 / 1226 / 1821	1.7 / 3.4 / 2.0	17 W	0617 / 1239 / 1825	1.1 / 3.8 / 1.6
3 W	0041 / 0656 / 1335 / 1925	3.8 / 1.8 / 3.4 / 2.1	18 TH	0101 / 0719 / 1348 / 1936	4.0 / 1.3 / 3.7 / 1.7
4 TH	0143 / 0756 / 1446 / 2036	3.7 / 1.8 / 3.5 / 2.1	19 F	0213 / 0830 / 1457 / 2055	4.0 / 1.4 / 3.8 / 1.7
5 F	0245 / 0901 / 1542 / 2140	3.7 / 1.8 / 3.6 / 2.0	20 SA	0324 / 0943 / 1559 / 2211	3.9 / 1.4 / 3.9 / 1.6
6 SA	0343 / 1000 / 1624 / 2232	3.7 / 1.7 / 3.8 / 1.8	21 SU	0428 / 1047 / 1653 / 2313	4.0 / 1.3 / 4.1 / 1.4
7 SU	0432 / 1049 / 1702 / 2318	3.9 / 1.6 / 4.0 / 1.6	22 M	0523 / 1139 / 1739	4.0 / 1.2 / 4.3
8 M	0518 / 1133 / 1738	4.0 / 1.4 / 4.2	23 TU	0006 / 0610 / 1226 / 1820	1.2 / 4.1 / 1.1 / 4.5
9 TU	0002 / 0601 / 1216 / 1815	1.4 / 4.2 / 1.2 / 4.4	24 W ○	0054 / 0652 / 1307 / 1859	1.1 / 4.2 / 1.1 / 4.6
10 W ●	0046 / 0644 / 1257 / 1854	1.1 / 4.3 / 1.0 / 4.6	25 TH	0135 / 0729 / 1346 / 1936	0.9 / 4.2 / 1.1 / 4.7
11 TH	0129 / 0726 / 1338 / 1934	0.9 / 4.4 / 0.9 / 4.7	26 F	0213 / 0805 / 1422 / 2011	0.9 / 4.2 / 1.0 / 4.7
12 F	0212 / 0809 / 1419 / 2015	0.7 / 4.5 / 0.9 / 4.7	27 SA	0249 / 0839 / 1457 / 2046	0.9 / 4.1 / 1.1 / 4.6
13 SA	0256 / 0854 / 1500 / 2059	0.6 / 4.4 / 0.9 / 4.7	28 SU	0323 / 0914 / 1532 / 2123	1.0 / 4.0 / 1.2 / 4.4
14 SU	0341 / 0941 / 1543 / 2148	0.6 / 4.3 / 1.0 / 4.6	29 M	0358 / 0950 / 1607 / 2202	1.1 / 3.9 / 1.4 / 4.2
15 M	0428 / 1034 / 1630 / 2245	0.7 / 4.1 / 1.2 / 4.4	30 TU	0434 / 1030 / 1645 / 2247	1.3 / 3.7 / 1.6 / 4.0
			31 W	0513 / 1118 / 1729 / 2339	1.5 / 3.6 / 1.9 / 3.8

AUGUST

Day	Time	m	Day	Time	m
1 TH	0558 / 1215 / 1819	1.7 / 3.5 / 2.1	16 F	0037 / 0642 / 1321 / 1903	4.0 / 1.5 / 3.7 / 1.8
2 F	0038 / 0649 / 1320 / 1920	3.6 / 1.9 / 3.4 / 2.2	17 SA	0159 / 0759 / 1437 / 2042	3.8 / 1.7 / 3.7 / 1.9
3 SA	0144 / 0749 / 1432 / 2036	3.6 / 2.0 / 3.5 / 2.2	18 SU	0319 / 0931 / 1548 / 2214	3.7 / 1.8 / 3.8 / 1.8
4 SU	0255 / 0903 / 1539 / 2154	3.6 / 2.0 / 3.7 / 2.0	19 M	0429 / 1041 / 1646 / 2316	3.8 / 1.7 / 4.1 / 1.5
5 M	0403 / 1014 / 1632 / 2255	3.7 / 1.8 / 3.9 / 1.8	20 TU	0524 / 1132 / 1731	3.9 / 1.5 / 4.3
6 TU	0500 / 1111 / 1718 / 2345	3.9 / 1.6 / 4.2 / 1.4	21 W	0004 / 0605 / 1216 / 1809	1.3 / 4.0 / 1.3 / 4.5
7 W	0548 / 1159 / 1800	4.2 / 1.3 / 4.5	22 TH ○	0044 / 0640 / 1253 / 1843	1.1 / 4.1 / 1.1 / 4.7
8 TH ●	0031 / 0631 / 1243 / 1840	1.1 / 4.4 / 1.1 / 4.8	23 F	0119 / 0711 / 1328 / 1915	0.9 / 4.2 / 1.0 / 4.8
9 F	0115 / 0713 / 1325 / 1919	0.7 / 4.6 / 0.8 / 5.0	24 SA	0152 / 0740 / 1401 / 1945	0.8 / 4.3 / 0.9 / 4.8
10 SA	0157 / 0754 / 1405 / 1959	0.5 / 4.7 / 0.7 / 5.1	25 SU	0222 / 0808 / 1432 / 2015	0.8 / 4.3 / 0.9 / 4.7
11 SU	0239 / 0834 / 1445 / 2040	0.3 / 4.8 / 0.6 / 5.1	26 M	0251 / 0837 / 1503 / 2045	0.9 / 4.2 / 1.1 / 4.5
12 M	0321 / 0917 / 1526 / 2124	0.3 / 4.6 / 0.7 / 4.9	27 TU	0321 / 0906 / 1534 / 2117	1.0 / 4.1 / 1.2 / 4.3
13 TU	0404 / 1004 / 1609 / 2215	0.5 / 4.4 / 0.9 / 4.6	28 W	0353 / 0940 / 1607 / 2153	1.2 / 4.0 / 1.5 / 4.1
14 W	0451 / 1059 / 1657 / 2319	0.8 / 4.1 / 1.2 / 4.3	29 TH	0429 / 1019 / 1644 / 2239	1.4 / 3.8 / 1.7 / 3.8
15 TH	0542 / 1206 / 1752	1.1 / 3.9 / 1.5	30 F	0509 / 1112 / 1728 / 2344	1.7 / 3.6 / 2.0 / 3.6
			31 SA	0557 / 1223 / 1825	1.9 / 3.5 / 2.2

Chart Datum: 2·71 metres below Ordnance Datum (Newlyn)
Register for your **FREE** weekly weather email service from Macmillan Reeds
》 at **www.nauticaldata.com – NOW!** 《
weekend weather reports sent to your email address, every Thursday

SCOTLAND – STORNOWAY

LAT 58°12'N   LONG 6°23'W

TIMES AND HEIGHTS OF HIGH AND LOW WATERS

YEAR **2002**

Section 1

SEPTEMBER

Day	Time	m	Day	Time	m
1 SU	0101	3.5	16 M	0317	3.7
	0656	2.1		0924	2.1
	1340	3.5		1536	3.9
	1944	2.3		2216	1.9
2 M	0224	3.5	17 TU	0430	3.8
	0817	2.2		1031	1.9
	1500	3.6		1634	4.1
	2127	2.1		2309	1.6
3 TU	0343	3.7	18 W	0520	3.9
	0948	2.0		1118	1.7
	1606	3.9		1717	4.4
	2237	1.8		2349	1.3
4 W	0443	4.0	19 TH	0553	4.1
	1052	1.7		1156	1.4
	1658	4.1		1751	4.6
	2328	1.4			
5 TH	0531	4.3	20 F	0023	1.1
	1140	1.4		0620	4.2
	1741	4.7		1232	1.2
				1821	4.7
6 F	0013	0.9	21 SA	0054	1.0
	0613	4.7		0646	4.4
	1224	1.0		1304	1.0
	1821	5.1	O	1850	4.8
7 SA	0055	0.5	22 SU	0123	0.9
	0653	4.9		0712	4.5
	1305	0.7		1335	0.9
●	1900	5.3		1917	4.8
8 SU	0136	0.3	23 M	0150	0.8
	0731	5.1		0744	4.5
	1345	0.5		1404	0.9
	1938	5.4		1943	4.8
9 M	0216	0.1	24 TU	0217	0.9
	0810	5.1		0801	4.5
	1424	0.5		1433	1.0
	2017	5.4		2010	4.6
10 TU	0255	0.2	25 W	0245	1.0
	0850	4.9		0828	4.4
	1504	0.6		1502	1.2
	2059	5.1		2039	4.4
11 W	0337	0.5	26 TH	0316	1.1
	0934	4.7		0856	4.2
	1546	1.0		1533	1.4
	2147	4.8		2110	4.2
12 TH	0420	0.9	27 F	0350	1.4
	1027	4.3		0928	4.0
	1631	1.4		1608	1.7
	2251	4.3		2148	3.9
13 F	0508	1.3	28 SA	0427	1.7
	1138	4.0		1010	3.8
	1725	1.7		1648	2.0
				2255	3.7
14 SA	0022	3.9	29 SU	0512	2.0
	0607	1.8		1136	3.6
	1300	3.8		1744	2.2
	1839	2.0			
15 SU	0152	3.7	30 M	0036	3.5
	0734	2.1		0614	2.2
	1421	3.8		1307	3.6
	2043	2.1		1912	2.3

OCTOBER

Day	Time	m	Day	Time	m
1 TU	0206	3.6	16 W	0416	3.8
	0745	2.3		1006	2.1
	1430	3.7		1609	4.2
	2105	2.1		2245	1.7
2 W	0324	3.8	17 TH	0500	4.0
	0925	2.2		1051	1.8
	1540	4.1		1651	4.4
	2216	1.7		2322	1.5
3 TH	0422	4.2	18 F	0529	4.1
	1028	1.8		1129	1.6
	1634	4.5		1726	4.5
	2305	1.2		2353	1.3
4 F	0509	4.5	19 SA	0555	4.3
	1117	1.4		1203	1.4
	1719	4.9		1756	4.7
	2349	0.8			
5 SA	0550	4.9	20 SU	0023	1.1
	1200	1.0		0619	4.5
	1759	5.2		1236	1.2
				1823	4.7
6 SU	0030	0.5	21 M	0051	1.0
	0629	5.1		0643	4.6
	1242	0.7		1307	1.1
●	1838	5.5	O	1849	4.8
7 M	0110	0.2	22 TU	0117	0.9
	0707	5.3		0706	4.6
	1322	0.6		1336	1.0
	1916	5.6		1915	4.7
8 TU	0150	0.2	23 W	0144	0.9
	0744	5.3		0731	4.6
	1402	0.5		1405	1.1
	1956	5.4		1943	4.6
9 W	0229	0.4	24 TH	0214	1.0
	0824	5.1		0758	4.5
	1442	0.7		1435	1.2
	2038	5.2		2013	4.5
10 TH	0309	0.7	25 F	0245	1.2
	0907	4.8		0827	4.4
	1521	1.0		1508	1.4
	2127	4.7		2047	4.2
11 F	0352	1.1	26 SA	0319	1.4
	1000	4.5		0900	4.2
	1611	1.4		1543	1.6
	2233	4.3		2129	4.0
12 SA	0439	1.6	27 SU	0356	1.7
	1115	4.2		0944	4.0
	1705	1.8		1626	1.9
				2242	3.7
13 SU	0009	3.9	28 M	0441	2.0
	0536	2.1		1109	3.8
	1238	4.0		1725	2.1
	1824	2.1			
14 M	0136	3.7	29 TU	0020	3.6
	0708	2.4		0545	2.2
	1356	3.9		1243	3.7
	2027	2.2		1857	2.1
15 TU	0303	3.7	30 W	0144	3.7
	0859	2.4		0719	2.3
	1509	4.0		1416	3.9
	2157	2.0		2035	1.9
			31 TH	0257	3.9
				0853	2.1
				1509	4.2
				2145	1.6

NOVEMBER

Day	Time	m	Day	Time	m
1 F	0355	4.2	16 SA	0457	4.1
	0958	1.8		1054	1.8
	1606	4.5		1654	4.3
	2236	1.2		2316	1.5
2 SA	0443	4.6	17 SU	0526	4.2
	1048	1.4		1132	1.6
	1653	4.9		1727	4.5
	2321	0.8		2348	1.3
3 SU	0525	4.9	18 M	0552	4.4
	1133	1.1		1206	1.4
	1736	5.2		1757	4.5
4 M	0003	0.6	19 TU	0018	1.2
	0604	5.1		0616	4.5
	1217	0.8		1239	1.3
●	1816	5.3		1825	4.6
5 TU	0045	0.4	20 W	0047	1.1
	0643	5.2		0641	4.6
	1259	0.7		1311	1.2
	1857	5.4	O	1854	4.6
6 W	0125	0.5	21 TH	0117	1.1
	0722	5.2		0709	4.7
	1342	0.7		1343	1.2
	1938	5.2		1926	4.5
7 TH	0205	0.6	22 F	0149	1.1
	0803	5.1		0740	4.6
	1425	0.8		1417	1.2
	2023	4.9		2001	4.4
8 F	0246	0.9	23 SA	0223	1.2
	0848	4.8		0813	4.5
	1509	1.1		1453	1.3
	2114	4.6		2041	4.2
9 SA	0329	1.3	24 SU	0259	1.4
	0941	4.6		0852	4.3
	1557	1.4		1533	1.5
	2220	4.2		2130	4.0
10 SU	0416	1.7	25 M	0339	1.6
	1049	4.3		0942	4.1
	1653	1.6		1620	1.6
	2343	3.8		2238	3.8
11 M	0512	2.1	26 TU	0426	1.8
	1204	4.1		1054	4.0
	1805	2.1		1721	1.8
				2358	3.7
12 TU	0102	3.7	27 W	0528	2.0
	0630	2.4		1214	3.9
	1316	4.0		1838	1.8
	1938	2.1			
13 W	0222	3.6	28 TH	0112	3.7
	0806	2.4		0649	2.1
	1425	4.0		1326	4.0
	2104	2.0		1956	1.7
14 TH	0334	3.7	29 F	0221	3.9
	0920	2.3		0811	2.0
	1526	4.1		1433	4.2
	2200	1.8		2106	1.4
15 F	0423	3.9	30 SA	0322	4.1
	1012	2.0		0920	1.8
	1615	4.2		1534	4.4
	2241	1.7		2203	1.2

DECEMBER

Day	Time	m	Day	Time	m
1 SU	0414	4.4	16 M	0455	4.0
	1017	1.5		1058	1.8
	1626	4.7		1657	4.1
	2253	0.9		2313	1.5
2 M	0500	4.7	17 TU	0526	4.2
	1107	1.2		1137	1.6
	1714	4.8		1733	4.2
	2339	0.8		2348	1.4
3 TU	0542	4.9	18 W	0554	4.4
	1156	1.0		1215	1.4
	1759	5.0		1807	4.3
4 W	0023	0.7	19 TH	0022	1.2
	0624	5.0		0623	4.5
	1243	0.9		1252	1.3
●	1843	5.0	O	1842	4.4
5 TH	0106	0.7	20 F	0058	1.1
	0705	5.0		0655	4.6
	1329	0.9		1329	1.2
	1928	4.9		1918	4.4
6 F	0148	0.9	21 SA	0134	1.1
	0748	5.0		0730	4.6
	1415	0.9		1407	1.1
	2015	4.7		1957	4.4
7 SA	0230	1.1	22 SU	0211	1.1
	0834	4.9		0807	4.6
	1501	1.1		1447	1.1
	2104	4.4		2039	4.3
8 SU	0313	1.3	23 M	0249	1.2
	0923	4.7		0848	4.5
	1548	1.3		1529	1.1
	2158	4.1		2126	4.1
9 M	0358	1.6	24 TU	0330	1.3
	1017	4.5		0934	4.4
	1637	1.5		1616	1.2
	2259	3.9		2220	4.0
10 TU	0447	1.9	25 W	0416	1.5
	1117	4.2		1031	4.2
	1733	1.8		1709	1.3
				2324	3.8
11 W	0007	3.6	26 TH	0510	1.6
	0545	2.2		1138	4.1
	1221	4.1		1809	1.4
	1836	1.9			
12 TH	0120	3.5	27 F	0032	3.8
	0658	2.3		0614	1.8
	1326	4.0		1248	4.1
	1947	2.0		1914	1.4
13 F	0232	3.6	28 SA	0141	3.8
	0815	2.3		0726	1.8
	1431	3.9		1356	4.1
	2055	2.0		2023	1.4
14 SA	0332	3.7	29 SU	0246	3.9
	0921	2.1		0839	1.7
	1528	4.0		1503	4.2
	2150	1.8		2129	1.3
15 SU	0418	3.8	30 M	0346	4.1
	1013	2.0		0948	1.6
	1616	4.0		1604	4.3
	2235	1.7		2229	1.2
			31 TU	0439	4.3
				1049	1.4
				1700	4.4
				2322	1.1

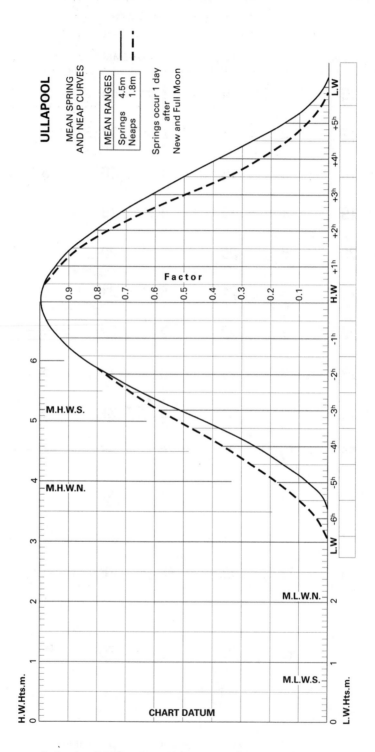

ULLAPOOL

MEAN SPRING
AND NEAP CURVES

MEAN RANGES	
Springs	4.5m
Neaps	1.8m

Springs occur 1 day
after
New and Full Moon

Factor

0.9 0.8 0.7 0.6 0.5 0.4 0.3 0.2 0.1

M.H.W.S.

M.H.W.N.

M.L.W.N.

M.L.W.S.

H.W.Hts.m.

L.W.Hts.m.

CHART DATUM

TIME ZONE (UTC)
For Summer Time add ONE hour in **non-shaded areas**

SCOTLAND – ULLAPOOL

LAT 57°54′N   LONG 5°10′W

TIMES AND HEIGHTS OF HIGH AND LOW WATERS

YEAR 2002

JANUARY

Time m	Time m
1 TU 0201 1.0 / 0757 5.3 / 1434 0.9 / 2033 5.1	**16** W 0241 1.3 / 0830 5.1 / 1508 1.2 / 2058 4.6
2 W 0245 1.0 / 0841 5.3 / 1520 0.9 / 2123 5.0	**17** TH 0316 1.4 / 0905 4.9 / 1543 1.3 / 2133 4.5
3 TH 0330 1.1 / 0929 5.2 / 1609 1.0 / 2218 4.8	**18** F 0351 1.5 / 0941 4.8 / 1619 1.4 / 2208 4.3
4 F 0418 1.3 / 1022 5.0 / 1701 1.1 / 2317 4.6	**19** SA 0427 1.7 / 1020 4.6 / 1656 1.6 / 2249 4.1
5 SA 0511 1.5 / 1124 4.8 / 1758 1.4	**20** SU 0506 1.9 / 1105 4.4 / 1736 1.8 / 2339 4.0
6 SU 0022 4.4 / 0609 1.8 / 1234 4.6 / 1902 1.6	**21** M 0549 2.1 / 1159 4.2 / 1822 2.0
7 M 0132 4.3 / 0716 2.0 / 1350 4.4 / 2014 1.7	**22** TU 0040 3.8 / 0642 2.3 / 1305 4.0 / 1919 2.1
8 TU 0242 4.3 / 0832 2.0 / 1506 4.4 / 2128 1.7	**23** W 0154 3.8 / 0750 2.4 / 1417 4.0 / 2030 2.1
9 W 0347 4.4 / 0949 1.9 / 1614 4.5 / 2232 1.6	**24** TH 0308 3.9 / 0914 2.3 / 1528 4.1 / 2147 2.0
10 TH 0444 4.6 / 1054 1.8 / 1711 4.6 / 2325 1.5	**25** F 0410 4.2 / 1028 2.1 / 1629 4.3 / 2249 1.8
11 F 0531 4.8 / 1148 1.6 / 1757 4.7	**26** SA 0459 4.5 / 1123 1.7 / 1721 4.6 / 2339 1.5
12 SA 0011 1.4 / 0611 4.9 / 1235 1.4 / 1837 4.7	**27** SU 0543 4.8 / 1211 1.4 / 1807 4.9
13 SU 0053 1.4 / 0646 5.0 / 1317 1.3 / ●1913 4.8	**28** M 0024 1.2 / 0624 5.1 / 1256 1.0 / ○1851 5.1
14 M 0131 1.3 / 0721 5.1 / 1356 1.2 / 1949 4.8	**29** TU 0107 1.0 / 0704 5.4 / 1339 0.7 / 1935 5.3
15 TU 0207 1.3 / 0756 5.1 / 1432 1.2 / 2024 4.7	**30** W 0150 0.8 / 0745 5.5 / 1423 0.6 / 2019 5.3
	31 TH 0233 0.7 / 0826 5.5 / 1507 0.4 / 2104 5.2

FEBRUARY

Time m	Time m
1 F 0317 0.7 / 0910 5.4 / 1552 0.5 / 2153 5.0	**16** SA 0325 1.1 / 0906 4.9 / 1546 1.1 / 2125 4.5
2 SA 0401 0.9 / 0957 5.2 / 1639 0.7 / 2245 4.8	**17** SU 0357 1.3 / 0939 4.7 / 1619 1.2 / 2159 4.3
3 SU 0448 1.1 / 1051 4.9 / 1728 1.1 / 2344 4.5	**18** M 0430 1.5 / 1015 4.5 / 1653 1.4 / 2240 4.1
4 M 0539 1.5 / 1155 4.6 / 1823 1.5	**19** TU 0507 1.7 / 1058 4.2 / 1733 1.7 / 2330 3.9
5 TU 0050 4.3 / 0637 1.8 / 1313 4.3 / 1928 1.8	**20** W 0552 2.0 / 1156 4.0 / 1821 2.0
6 W 0204 4.1 / 0749 2.1 / 1442 4.1 / 2052 2.0	**21** TH 0041 3.8 / 0650 2.3 / 1318 3.9 / 1926 2.2
7 TH 0322 4.1 / 0926 2.1 / 1606 4.1 / 2214 2.0	**22** F 0212 3.7 / 0812 2.3 / 1451 3.9 / 2059 2.2
8 F 0430 4.3 / 1046 1.9 / 1708 4.2 / 2314 1.8	**23** SA 0336 4.0 / 1002 2.1 / 1608 4.1 / 2228 1.9
9 SA 0522 4.5 / 1143 1.7 / 1755 4.4	**24** SU 0438 4.3 / 1107 1.7 / 1706 4.5 / 2323 1.5
10 SU 0001 1.6 / 0602 4.7 / 1228 1.5 / 1830 4.5	**25** M 0525 4.7 / 1157 1.2 / 1753 4.8
11 M 0042 1.4 / 0634 4.8 / 1307 1.2 / 1901 4.6	**26** TU 0009 1.1 / 0607 5.1 / 1242 0.8 / 1835 5.2
12 TU 0117 1.3 / 0705 5.0 / 1341 1.1 / ●1930 4.7	**27** W 0053 0.8 / 0647 5.4 / 1324 0.4 / ○1917 5.4
13 W 0150 1.1 / 0736 5.1 / 1413 1.0 / 1959 4.7	**28** TH 0135 0.5 / 0726 5.6 / 1406 0.2 / 1958 5.5
14 TH 0222 1.0 / 0806 5.1 / 1444 0.9 / 2027 4.7	
15 F 0254 1.0 / 0835 5.0 / 1515 1.0 / 2054 4.6	

MARCH

Time m	Time m
1 F 0216 0.3 / 0806 5.7 / 1448 0.1 / 2040 5.4	**16** SA 0228 0.8 / 0805 5.0 / 1444 0.8 / 2020 4.7
2 SA 0258 0.4 / 0848 5.6 / 1530 0.2 / 2124 5.2	**17** SU 0258 0.9 / 0834 4.9 / 1514 0.8 / 2050 4.6
3 SU 0341 0.5 / 0932 5.3 / 1613 0.5 / 2212 4.9	**18** M 0328 1.0 / 0906 4.7 / 1545 1.0 / 2122 4.4
4 M 0425 0.8 / 1022 4.9 / 1657 1.0 / 2306 4.5	**19** TU 0400 1.2 / 0940 4.5 / 1618 1.3 / 2159 4.2
5 TU 0511 1.2 / 1122 4.4 / 1747 1.5	**20** W 0436 1.5 / 1021 4.2 / 1656 1.6 / 2244 4.0
6 W 0011 4.2 / 0604 1.7 / 1243 4.0 / 1847 1.9	**21** TH 0519 1.8 / 1118 3.9 / 1742 1.9 / 2353 3.8
7 TH 0129 4.0 / 0714 2.1 / 1426 3.8 / 2017 2.2	**22** F 0616 2.1 / 1246 3.7 / 1847 2.2
8 F 0258 3.9 / 0909 2.2 / 1600 3.9 / 2159 2.2	**23** SA 0134 3.7 / 0739 2.2 / 1430 3.8 / 2026 2.2
9 SA 0414 4.0 / 1041 2.0 / 1702 4.0 / 2303 2.0	**24** SU 0307 3.9 / 0942 2.0 / 1552 4.0 / 2206 1.9
10 SU 0508 4.3 / 1135 1.7 / 1746 4.2 / 2348 1.7	**25** M 0414 4.2 / 1049 1.5 / 1649 4.4 / 2303 1.5
11 M 0546 4.5 / 1215 1.4 / 1816 4.4	**26** TU 0504 4.7 / 1138 1.0 / 1735 4.8 / 2350 1.0
12 TU 0025 1.4 / 0616 4.7 / 1249 1.2 / 1841 4.5	**27** W 0547 5.1 / 1222 0.6 / 1817 5.2
13 W 0058 1.2 / 0644 4.9 / 1319 1.0 / 1906 4.6	**28** TH 0033 0.6 / 0626 5.4 / 1303 0.3 / ○1856 5.4
14 TH 0129 1.0 / 0712 5.0 / 1347 0.8 / ●1931 4.7	**29** F 0115 0.4 / 0706 5.6 / 1345 0.2 / 1936 5.5
15 F 0158 0.9 / 0739 5.0 / 1415 0.8 / 1954 4.8	**30** SA 0157 0.2 / 0745 5.6 / 1426 0.2 / 2016 5.4
	31 SU 0239 0.2 / 0826 5.5 / 1506 0.2 / 2057 5.2

APRIL

Time m	Time m
1 M 0320 0.4 / 0910 5.2 / 1547 0.6 / 2142 4.9	**16** TU 0303 1.0 / 0842 4.7 / 1516 1.0 / 2056 4.5
2 TU 0403 0.8 / 0959 4.8 / 1630 1.0 / 2233 4.5	**17** W 0338 1.2 / 0919 4.5 / 1551 1.2 / 2134 4.3
3 W 0448 1.2 / 1051 4.3 / 1716 1.6 / 2337 4.2	**18** TH 0416 1.4 / 1006 4.2 / 1630 1.5 / 2222 4.1
4 TH 0540 1.7 / 1222 3.9 / 1814 2.1	**19** F 0502 1.7 / 1110 3.9 / 1719 1.9 / 2335 3.9
5 F 0057 3.9 / 0650 2.1 / 1410 3.7 / 1945 2.4	**20** SA 0602 1.9 / 1241 3.7 / 1827 2.1
6 SA 0228 3.8 / 0844 2.2 / 1543 3.7 / 2135 2.3	**21** SU 0112 3.8 / 0728 2.0 / 1414 3.8 / 2006 2.2
7 SU 0347 3.9 / 1022 2.0 / 1644 3.9 / 2241 2.0	**22** M 0239 4.0 / 0916 1.8 / 1532 4.1 / 2138 1.9
8 M 0441 4.1 / 1113 1.7 / 1724 4.1 / 2324 1.8	**23** TU 0346 4.3 / 1023 1.3 / 1629 4.4 / 2237 1.4
9 TU 0518 4.3 / 1150 1.4 / 1751 4.3	**24** W 0439 4.7 / 1113 0.9 / 1715 4.8 / 2326 1.0
10 W 0000 1.5 / 0548 4.6 / 1221 1.2 / 1815 4.5	**25** TH 0525 5.0 / 1159 0.5 / 1756 5.1
11 TH 0032 1.2 / 0617 4.7 / 1249 1.0 / 1839 4.6	**26** F 0011 0.7 / 0606 5.3 / 1242 0.3 / 1835 5.4
12 F 0102 1.0 / 0644 4.9 / 1316 0.8 / ●1902 4.7	**27** SA 0055 0.4 / 0647 5.4 / 1323 0.2 / ○1914 5.4
13 SA 0131 0.9 / 0711 4.9 / 1345 0.8 / 1925 4.8	**28** SU 0138 0.3 / 0728 5.4 / 1404 0.2 / 1954 5.4
14 SU 0201 0.8 / 0738 4.9 / 1414 0.7 / 1952 4.8	**29** M 0220 0.4 / 0810 5.3 / 1444 0.5 / 2034 5.2
15 M 0232 0.9 / 0809 4.9 / 1444 0.8 / 2022 4.7	**30** TU 0303 0.6 / 0856 5.0 / 1525 0.8 / 2118 4.9

Chart Datum: 2·75 metres below Ordnance Datum (Newlyn)

TIME ZONE (UTC)
For Summer Time add ONE hour in **non-shaded areas**

SCOTLAND – ULLAPOOL

LAT 57°54′N   LONG 5°10′W

TIMES AND HEIGHTS OF HIGH AND LOW WATERS

YEAR **2002**

MAY

Day	Time	m		Day	Time	m
1 W	0346	0.9		16 TH	0323	1.1
	0946	4.6			0914	4.4
	1606	1.2			1533	1.3
	2208	4.5			2124	4.4
2 TH	0432	1.3		17 F	0406	1.3
	1047	4.2			1008	4.2
	1652	1.7			1617	1.5
	2311	4.2			2218	4.2
3 F	0524	1.6		18 SA	0456	1.5
	1203	3.8			1115	4.0
	1749	2.1			1709	1.8
					2329	4.1
4 SA	0026	4.0		19 SU	0558	1.7
	0631	2.0			1232	3.9
	1335	3.6			1818	2.0
	1909	2.4				
5 SU	0146	3.8		20 M	0050	4.0
	0759	2.1			0717	1.7
	1503	3.6			1351	3.9
	2043	2.3			1942	2.0
6 M	0259	3.9		21 TU	0207	4.1
	0928	2.0			0841	1.5
	1605	3.8			1504	4.1
	2156	2.1			2103	1.8
7 TU	0355	4.0		22 W	0315	4.3
	1027	1.8			0949	1.3
	1646	4.0			1603	4.4
	2244	1.9			2206	1.5
8 W	0437	4.2		23 TH	0413	4.6
	1107	1.5			1045	1.0
	1716	4.2			1653	4.7
	2323	1.6			2300	1.2
9 TH	0513	4.4		24 F	0503	4.8
	1141	1.3			1134	0.7
	1744	4.4			1736	5.0
	2357	1.4			2349	0.9
10 F	0546	4.6		25 SA	0549	5.0
	1212	1.1			1220	0.6
	1811	4.5			1817	5.2
11 SA	0030	1.2		26 SU	0036	0.7
	0616	4.7			0632	5.1
	1243	1.0			1304	0.5
	1835	4.7			○ 1857	5.2
12 SU	0103	1.1		27 M	0121	0.6
	0645	4.8			0716	5.1
	1314	0.9			1345	0.6
	● 1900	4.8			1936	5.2
13 M	0135	1.0		28 TU	0206	0.7
	0717	4.8			0800	5.0
	1346	0.9			1426	0.8
	1930	4.8			2017	5.1
14 TU	0209	1.0		29 W	0249	0.8
	0751	4.7			0846	4.7
	1419	0.9			1507	1.0
	2004	4.7			2101	4.8
15 W	0244	1.0		30 TH	0333	1.0
	0830	4.6			0923	4.5
	1455	1.1			1548	1.4
	2041	4.6			2149	4.6
				31 F	0419	1.3
					1030	4.2
					1633	1.7
					2244	4.3

JUNE

Day	Time	m		Day	Time	m
1 SA	0508	1.5		16 SU	0451	1.2
	1131	3.9			1106	4.2
	1724	2.0			1702	1.5
	2348	4.1			2314	4.4
2 SU	0604	1.8		17 M	0548	1.3
	1240	3.7			1211	4.1
	1826	2.2			1803	1.7
3 M	0055	4.0		18 TU	0023	4.3
	0706	1.9			0653	1.4
	1354	3.6			1321	4.1
	1938	2.3			1912	1.8
4 TU	0201	3.9		19 W	0134	4.2
	0812	1.9			0803	1.4
	1500	3.7			1430	4.2
	2048	2.2			2024	1.7
5 W	0259	3.9		20 TH	0244	4.3
	0915	1.9			0913	1.3
	1552	3.8			1535	4.3
	2148	2.0			2134	1.6
6 TH	0350	4.1		21 F	0349	4.4
	1008	1.7			1016	1.2
	1634	4.0			1630	4.5
	2237	1.8			2236	1.4
7 F	0434	4.2		22 SA	0446	4.5
	1053	1.6			1112	1.1
	1710	4.2			1719	4.7
	2319	1.6			2332	1.2
8 SA	0513	4.4		23 SU	0538	4.7
	1133	1.4			1202	1.0
	1742	4.4			1803	4.9
	2358	1.4				
9 SU	0549	4.5		24 M	0022	1.0
	1210	1.2			0624	4.8
	1811	4.6			1248	1.0
					○ 1844	5.0
10 M	0035	1.3		25 TU	0111	0.9
	0624	4.6			0709	4.8
	1247	1.1			1331	1.0
	● 1842	4.7			1923	5.0
11 TU	0113	1.1		26 W	0156	0.9
	0701	4.7			0751	4.8
	1323	1.0			1412	1.0
	1916	4.8			2003	5.0
12 W	0151	1.0		27 TH	0238	0.9
	0742	4.7			0834	4.6
	1401	1.0			1451	1.2
	1953	4.8			2043	4.9
13 TH	0231	1.0		28 F	0320	1.0
	0825	4.6			0917	4.4
	1440	1.1			1530	1.3
	2034	4.7			2125	4.7
14 F	0313	1.0		29 SA	0401	1.2
	0913	4.5			1002	4.3
	1523	1.2			1611	1.5
	2120	4.6			2211	4.5
15 SA	0400	1.1		30 SU	0442	1.3
	1007	4.4			1050	4.1
	1609	1.3			1653	1.7
	2213	4.5			2301	4.3

JULY

Day	Time	m		Day	Time	m
1 M	0526	1.5		16 TU	0527	1.0
	1141	3.9			1142	4.4
	1740	1.9			1739	1.4
	2357	4.1			2351	4.5
2 TU	0613	1.7		17 W	0622	1.2
	1239	3.7			1246	4.2
	1834	2.1			1839	1.6
3 W	0057	4.0		18 TH	0101	4.3
	0704	1.8			0724	1.4
	1344	3.7			1356	4.1
	1935	2.2			1947	1.7
4 TH	0158	3.9		19 F	0217	4.2
	0802	1.9			0836	1.5
	1449	3.7			1507	4.2
	2042	2.2			2104	1.8
5 F	0257	3.9		20 SA	0332	4.2
	0904	1.9			0952	1.6
	1546	3.8			1612	4.3
	2146	2.1			2221	1.6
6 SA	0351	4.0		21 SU	0440	4.3
	1004	1.8			1057	1.5
	1634	4.0			1707	4.5
	2241	1.9			2324	1.4
7 SU	0440	4.1		22 M	0536	4.4
	1057	1.7			1150	1.4
	1714	4.3			1754	4.7
	2329	1.7				
8 M	0525	4.3		23 TU	0016	1.3
	1143	1.5			0622	4.5
	1751	4.5			1237	1.3
					1833	4.8
9 TU	0013	1.4		24 W	0103	1.1
	0607	4.5			0702	4.6
	1226	1.3			1319	1.2
	1826	4.7			○ 1910	4.9
10 W	0055	1.2		25 TH	0145	1.0
	0649	4.7			0738	4.6
	1306	1.1			1357	1.1
	● 1904	4.9			1945	5.0
11 TH	0136	1.0		26 F	0223	0.9
	0731	4.8			0814	4.6
	1347	1.0			1433	1.1
	1942	5.0			2020	4.9
12 F	0219	0.8		27 SA	0259	0.9
	0815	4.8			0849	4.5
	1428	0.9			1508	1.2
	2023	5.0			2056	4.8
13 SA	0302	0.7		28 SU	0334	1.0
	0901	4.8			0924	4.4
	1512	0.9			1543	1.3
	2107	5.0			2131	4.7
14 SU	0348	0.7		29 M	0409	1.1
	0950	4.7			0959	4.2
	1557	1.0			1619	1.4
	2155	4.8			2208	4.5
15 M	0436	0.8		30 TU	0444	1.3
	1043	4.5			1035	4.1
	1646	1.2			1656	1.6
	2249	4.6			2250	4.2
				31 W	0522	1.5
					1118	3.9
					1737	1.9
					2341	4.0

AUGUST

Day	Time	m		Day	Time	m
1 TH	0604	1.7		16 F	0034	4.2
	1214	3.7			0648	1.6
	1825	2.1			1325	4.1
					1914	1.9
2 F	0043	3.9		17 SA	0200	4.0
	0652	1.9			0803	1.9
	1327	3.7			1445	4.1
	1926	2.3			2045	2.0
3 SA	0155	3.8		18 SU	0330	4.0
	0755	2.1			0937	1.9
	1449	3.7			1600	4.2
	2048	2.3			2220	1.8
4 SU	0307	3.8		19 M	0443	4.1
	0914	2.1			1049	1.8
	1557	3.9			1659	4.4
	2210	2.1			2322	1.6
5 M	0411	4.0		20 TU	0536	4.3
	1028	1.9			1142	1.6
	1649	4.2			1745	4.6
	2308	1.8				
6 TU	0505	4.2		21 W	0011	1.3
	1122	1.7			0617	4.4
	1731	4.5			1226	1.4
	2356	1.4			1821	4.8
7 W	0551	4.5		22 TH	0052	1.1
	1208	1.4			0649	4.5
	1809	4.8			1303	1.2
					○ 1852	4.9
8 TH	0039	1.1		23 F	0128	1.0
	0633	4.8			0718	4.6
	1250	1.1			1337	1.1
	● 1847	5.1			1923	5.0
9 F	0121	0.8		24 SA	0200	0.9
	0714	5.0			0746	4.7
	1331	0.8			1409	1.0
	1925	5.3			1953	5.0
10 SA	0202	0.5		25 SU	0230	0.8
	0756	5.1			0814	4.7
	1413	0.7			1441	1.0
	2004	5.4			2022	5.0
11 SU	0245	0.6		26 M	0301	0.9
	0839	5.1			0841	4.6
	1455	0.6			1512	1.1
	2045	5.3			2051	4.8
12 M	0328	0.4		27 TU	0332	1.0
	0925	5.0			0910	4.5
	1538	0.7			1544	1.2
	2129	5.1			2122	4.6
13 TU	0412	0.5		28 W	0403	1.1
	1014	4.8			0943	4.3
	1623	0.9			1616	1.5
	2220	4.9			2158	4.4
14 W	0459	0.8		29 TH	0437	1.4
	1109	4.6			1021	4.1
	1712	1.2			1652	1.7
	2320	4.5			2240	4.1
15 TH	0550	1.2		30 F	0514	1.7
	1212	4.3			1108	3.9
	1807	1.5			1733	2.0
					2337	3.9
				31 SA	0558	2.0
					1216	3.7
					1829	2.3

Chart Datum: 2·75 metres below Ordnance Datum (Newlyn)

TIME ZONE (UTC)
For Summer Time add ONE hour in **non-shaded areas**

SCOTLAND – ULLAPOOL

LAT 57°54'N   LONG 5°10'W

TIMES AND HEIGHTS OF HIGH AND LOW WATERS

YEAR **2002**

SEPTEMBER

Time m	Time m
1 SU 0100 3.7 / 0657 2.2 / 1355 3.7 / 1950 2.4	**16** M 0330 3.9 / 0930 2.2 / 1548 4.1 / 2221 1.9
2 M 0233 3.7 / 0825 2.3 / 1524 3.8 / 2150 2.2	**17** TU 0439 4.1 / 1042 2.0 / 1647 4.4 / 2317 1.6
3 TU 0350 3.9 / 1006 2.1 / 1624 4.2 / 2252 1.8	**18** W 0528 4.3 / 1130 1.8 / 1729 4.6 / 2358 1.4
4 W 0447 4.3 / 1104 1.7 / 1709 4.6 / 2338 1.3	**19** TH 0603 4.4 / 1208 1.5 / 1801 4.8
5 TH 0532 4.6 / 1149 1.3 / 1748 5.0	**20** F 0032 1.2 / 0628 4.6 / 1242 1.3 / 1829 5.0
6 F 0020 0.9 / 0613 5.0 / 1231 1.0 / 1825 5.3	**21** SA 0103 1.0 / 0652 4.7 / 1312 1.1 / ○ 1857 5.1
7 SA 0100 0.5 / 0653 5.3 / 1311 0.6 / ● 1903 5.6	**22** SU 0130 0.9 / 0716 4.8 / 1342 1.0 / 1924 5.1
8 SU 0141 0.2 / 0732 5.4 / 1352 0.4 / 1941 5.6	**23** M 0158 0.8 / 0739 4.8 / 1411 1.0 / 1950 5.1
9 M 0222 0.1 / 0813 5.4 / 1433 0.4 / 2021 5.6	**24** TU 0226 0.9 / 0803 4.8 / 1441 1.0 / 2017 4.9
10 TU 0303 0.2 / 0856 5.3 / 1516 0.5 / 2104 5.3	**25** W 0256 1.0 / 0831 4.7 / 1512 1.2 / 2047 4.8
11 W 0346 0.5 / 0943 5.0 / 1559 0.8 / 2153 5.0	**26** TH 0326 1.1 / 0904 4.5 / 1543 1.4 / 2120 4.5
12 TH 0430 0.9 / 1036 4.7 / 1646 1.2 / 2253 4.5	**27** F 0358 1.4 / 0939 4.3 / 1617 1.7 / 2200 4.2
13 F 0518 1.4 / 1141 4.4 / 1739 1.6	**28** SA 0434 1.7 / 1023 4.1 / 1658 2.0 / 2258 3.9
14 SA 0016 4.1 / 0615 1.9 / 1300 4.1 / 1848 2.0	**29** SU 0517 2.0 / 1131 3.8 / 1752 2.3
15 SU 0156 3.9 / 0738 2.2 / 1428 4.0 / 2043 2.2	**30** M 0032 3.7 / 0616 2.3 / 1319 3.7 / 1917 2.5

OCTOBER

Time m	Time m
1 TU 0212 3.7 / 0752 2.5 / 1451 3.9 / 2130 2.2	**16** W 0421 4.1 / 1021 2.2 / 1622 4.4 / 2255 1.7
2 W 0331 4.0 / 0943 2.2 / 1555 4.3 / 2230 1.7	**17** TH 0507 4.3 / 1105 1.9 / 1703 4.6 / 2332 1.5
3 TH 0427 4.4 / 1040 1.8 / 1643 4.7 / 2315 1.2	**18** F 0538 4.5 / 1141 1.7 / 1734 4.8
4 F 0511 4.8 / 1125 1.3 / 1724 5.1 / 2356 0.8	**19** SA 0003 1.3 / 0600 4.6 / 1213 1.4 / 1801 5.0
5 SA 0551 5.2 / 1207 0.9 / 1803 5.5	**20** SU 0031 1.1 / 0623 4.8 / 1243 1.2 / 1829 5.1
6 SU 0036 0.4 / 0630 5.5 / 1249 0.6 / ● 1840 5.7	**21** M 0057 1.0 / 0646 4.9 / 1313 1.1 / ○ 1856 5.1
7 M 0117 0.2 / 0709 5.6 / 1330 0.4 / 1919 5.8	**22** TU 0125 1.0 / 0708 5.0 / 1343 1.1 / 1922 5.1
8 TU 0157 0.2 / 0748 5.6 / 1412 0.4 / 2000 5.7	**23** W 0154 1.0 / 0733 5.0 / 1414 1.1 / 1951 5.0
9 W 0238 0.3 / 0830 5.5 / 1454 0.6 / 2043 5.4	**24** TH 0224 1.1 / 0803 4.9 / 1445 1.3 / 2022 4.8
10 TH 0320 0.6 / 0914 5.2 / 1538 0.9 / 2133 5.0	**25** F 0255 1.2 / 0836 4.7 / 1518 1.5 / 2058 4.5
11 F 0403 1.1 / 1006 4.8 / 1624 1.3 / 2237 4.5	**26** SA 0329 1.5 / 0913 4.5 / 1554 1.7 / 2143 4.3
12 SA 0450 1.6 / 1113 4.4 / 1718 1.8	**27** SU 0406 1.8 / 0959 4.2 / 1637 2.0 / 2248 4.0
13 SU 0005 4.1 / 0548 2.1 / 1237 4.2 / 1832 2.2	**28** M 0451 2.1 / 1110 4.0 / 1735 2.2
14 M 0148 3.9 / 0715 2.5 / 1406 4.1 / 2030 2.3	**29** TU 0021 3.8 / 0553 2.4 / 1250 4.0 / 1901 2.3
15 TU 0317 3.9 / 0910 2.5 / 1525 4.2 / 2206 2.0	**30** W 0150 3.9 / 0728 2.5 / 1415 4.1 / 2055 2.1
	31 TH 0304 4.1 / 0908 2.4 / 1521 4.4 / 2159 1.7

NOVEMBER

Time m	Time m
1 F 0401 4.5 / 1009 1.8 / 1614 4.8 / 2247 1.2	**16** SA 0502 4.4 / 1104 1.9 / 1659 4.7 / 2324 1.5
2 SA 0447 4.9 / 1058 1.4 / 1659 5.2 / 2330 0.8	**17** SU 0529 4.6 / 1139 1.7 / 1732 4.8 / 2354 1.4
3 SU 0529 5.2 / 1142 1.0 / 1740 5.5	**18** M 0555 4.7 / 1207 1.6 / 1804 4.9
4 M 0012 0.5 / 0608 5.5 / 1226 0.7 / ● 1821 5.7	**19** TU 0024 1.3 / 0620 4.9 / 1245 1.4 / 1833 5.0
5 TU 0054 0.4 / 0648 5.7 / 1309 0.6 / 1902 5.7	**20** W 0056 1.2 / 0645 5.0 / 1318 1.3 / ○ 1903 5.0
6 W 0135 0.4 / 0727 5.6 / 1353 0.6 / 1945 5.5	**21** TH 0127 1.2 / 0713 5.0 / 1351 1.3 / 1935 4.9
7 TH 0217 0.6 / 0809 5.5 / 1436 0.7 / 2031 5.3	**22** F 0200 1.2 / 0746 5.0 / 1426 1.4 / 2011 4.8
8 F 0258 0.9 / 0853 5.2 / 1521 1.0 / 2124 4.9	**23** SA 0234 1.3 / 0822 4.8 / 1502 1.5 / 2053 4.6
9 SA 0342 1.3 / 0944 4.9 / 1609 1.4 / 2228 4.5	**24** SU 0310 1.5 / 0902 4.7 / 1543 1.6 / 2144 4.4
10 SU 0429 1.8 / 1048 4.6 / 1704 1.8 / 2347 4.1	**25** M 0351 1.7 / 0951 4.5 / 1629 1.8 / 2248 4.2
11 M 0525 2.2 / 1205 4.3 / 1814 2.1	**26** TU 0439 2.0 / 1057 4.3 / 1727 2.0
12 TU 0117 3.9 / 0642 2.5 / 1327 4.2 / 1943 2.2	**27** W 0002 4.1 / 0539 2.2 / 1216 4.2 / 1841 2.0
13 W 0240 3.9 / 0816 2.6 / 1441 4.2 / 2115 2.1	**28** TH 0118 4.1 / 0659 2.3 / 1333 4.3 / 2008 1.9
14 TH 0344 4.0 / 0935 2.4 / 1539 4.3 / 2211 1.9	**29** F 0228 4.2 / 0823 2.2 / 1442 4.5 / 2119 1.6
15 F 0430 4.2 / 1025 2.1 / 1623 4.5 / 2251 1.7	**30** SA 0329 4.5 / 0932 1.9 / 1542 4.7 / 2215 1.3

DECEMBER

Time m	Time m
1 SU 0421 4.8 / 1028 1.5 / 1634 5.0 / 2304 1.1	**16** M 0455 4.4 / 1103 2.0 / 1702 4.5 / 2318 1.7
2 M 0507 5.1 / 1119 1.2 / 1722 5.2 / 2350 0.9	**17** TU 0529 4.6 / 1144 1.8 / 1740 4.7 / 2355 1.6
3 TU 0550 5.4 / 1207 1.0 / 1808 5.4	**18** W 0600 4.7 / 1222 1.6 / 1816 4.8
4 W 0035 0.8 / 0631 5.5 / 1254 0.9 / ● 1852 5.4	**19** TH 0031 1.4 / 0629 4.9 / 1259 1.5 / ○ 1850 4.9
5 TH 0118 0.8 / 0713 5.5 / 1340 0.9 / 1938 5.3	**20** F 0107 1.3 / 0701 5.0 / 1336 1.4 / 1927 4.9
6 F 0201 0.9 / 0755 5.4 / 1425 0.9 / 2025 5.1	**21** SA 0143 1.3 / 0737 5.0 / 1414 1.3 / 2007 4.8
7 SA 0243 1.2 / 0838 5.3 / 1511 1.1 / 2115 4.8	**22** SU 0220 1.3 / 0815 5.0 / 1453 1.3 / 2050 4.7
8 SU 0326 1.4 / 0926 5.0 / 1558 1.4 / 2211 4.5	**23** M 0300 1.4 / 0856 4.9 / 1535 1.3 / 2138 4.6
9 M 0411 1.8 / 1020 4.7 / 1648 1.6 / 2312 4.2	**24** TU 0342 1.5 / 0942 4.8 / 1622 1.4 / 2233 4.4
10 TU 0500 2.1 / 1122 4.5 / 1743 1.9	**25** W 0429 1.6 / 1035 4.7 / 1714 1.5 / 2333 4.3
11 W 0020 4.0 / 0558 2.3 / 1230 4.3 / 1845 2.1	**26** TH 0523 1.8 / 1138 4.5 / 1814 1.6
12 TH 0132 3.9 / 0706 2.5 / 1338 4.2 / 1952 2.2	**27** F 0039 4.3 / 0626 2.0 / 1247 4.4 / 1921 1.7
13 F 0238 3.9 / 0819 2.5 / 1440 4.2 / 2058 2.1	**28** SA 0147 4.3 / 0737 2.0 / 1400 4.5 / 2033 1.7
14 SA 0333 4.0 / 0925 2.3 / 1534 4.3 / 2153 2.0	**29** SU 0254 4.4 / 0851 1.9 / 1511 4.5 / 2142 1.5
15 SU 0417 4.2 / 1019 2.2 / 1620 4.4 / 2238 1.9	**30** M 0356 4.6 / 1000 1.8 / 1615 4.7 / 2242 1.4
	31 TU 0450 4.8 / 1101 1.5 / 1712 4.9 / 2334 1.3

Chart Datum: 2·75 metres below Ordnance Datum (Newlyn)

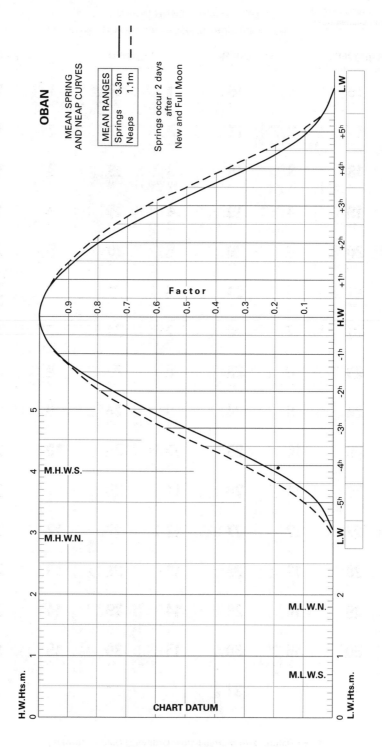

OBAN

MEAN SPRING
AND NEAP CURVES

MEAN RANGES	
Springs	3.3m
Neaps	1.1m

Springs occur 2 days
after
New and Full Moon

SCOTLAND – OBAN

LAT 56°25′N   LONG 5°29′W

TIMES AND HEIGHTS OF HIGH AND LOW WATERS

YEAR **2002**

Section 1

JANUARY

Time	m		Time	m
1 TU 0038 0.7 / 0638 4.0 / 1314 0.9 / 1908 3.9		**16** W 0124 1.1 / 0718 4.0 / 1350 1.3 / 1928 3.7		
2 W 0123 0.7 / 0721 4.0 / 1401 1.0 / 1951 3.8		**17** TH 0201 1.2 / 0754 3.9 / 1425 1.4 / 2001 3.6		
3 TH 0209 0.7 / 0806 3.9 / 1451 1.1 / 2037 3.6		**18** F 0236 1.3 / 0829 3.8 / 1501 1.6 / 2034 3.5		
4 F 0258 0.8 / 0855 3.8 / 1545 1.2 / 2127 3.4		**19** SA 0310 1.5 / 0905 3.6 / 1539 1.7 / 2107 3.4		
5 SA 0350 1.0 / 0949 3.6 / 1644 1.4 / 2226 3.2		**20** SU 0345 1.6 / 0942 3.5 / 1620 1.8 / 2144 3.2		
6 SU 0448 1.1 / 1052 3.4 / 1750 1.5 / 2342 3.0		**21** M 0424 1.8 / 1025 3.3 / 1709 1.9 / 2229 3.1		
7 M 0553 1.3 / 1216 3.3 / 1902 1.6		**22** TU 0513 1.9 / 1120 3.1 / 1808 2.0 / 2327 3.0		
8 TU 0113 3.0 / 0702 1.4 / 1347 3.3 / 2015 1.6		**23** W 0614 2.0 / 1253 3.1 / 1913 1.9		
9 W 0228 3.1 / 0814 1.4 / 1457 3.3 / 2118 1.5		**24** TH 0101 2.9 / 0725 1.9 / 1432 3.2 / 2017 1.8		
10 TH 0324 3.0 / 0922 1.4 / 1551 3.4 / 2209 1.4		**25** F 0239 3.1 / 0840 1.8 / 1533 3.3 / 2116 1.6		
11 F 0409 3.5 / 1020 1.3 / 1633 3.5 / 2252 1.3		**26** SA 0339 3.3 / 0951 1.6 / 1621 3.5 / 2208 1.3		
12 SA 0450 3.7 / 1110 1.3 / 1710 3.6 / 2331 1.2		**27** SU 0428 3.6 / 1049 1.3 / 1704 3.7 / 2256 1.0		
13 SU 0528 3.9 / 1154 1.2 / 1745 3.7 ●		**28** M 0511 3.8 / 1138 1.0 / 1744 3.9 / ○ 2341 0.7		
14 M 0009 1.1 / 0606 4.0 / 1235 1.2 / 1819 3.8		**29** TU 0553 4.0 / 1224 0.8 / 1823 4.0		
15 TU 0047 1.1 / 0642 4.0 / 1313 1.3 / 1854 3.8		**30** W 0026 0.5 / 0634 4.1 / 1309 0.7 / 1901 4.0		
		31 TH 0111 0.4 / 0715 4.2 / 1352 0.7 / 1940 3.9		

FEBRUARY

Time	m		Time	m
1 F 0156 0.4 / 0756 4.1 / 1436 0.7 / 2021 3.7		**16** SA 0209 1.1 / 0803 3.9 / 1430 1.3 / 2006 3.7		
2 SA 0242 0.5 / 0839 3.9 / 1522 0.9 / 2104 3.5		**17** SU 0234 1.2 / 0832 3.7 / 1457 1.4 / 2034 3.5		
3 SU 0329 0.7 / 0924 3.7 / 1611 1.2 / 2152 3.3		**18** M 0258 1.4 / 0901 3.5 / 1526 1.6 / 2104 3.4		
4 M 0421 0.9 / 1015 3.4 / 1706 1.4 / 2249 3.1		**19** TU 0327 1.6 / 0934 3.3 / 1605 1.7 / 2141 3.2		
5 TU 0519 1.2 / 1119 3.1 / 1811 1.6		**20** W 0406 1.8 / 1017 3.1 / 1703 1.9 / 2229 3.0		
6 W 0013 2.9 / 0625 1.5 / 1304 2.9 / 1928 1.7		**21** TH 0508 1.9 / 1121 2.9 / 1819 1.9 / 2338 2.9		
7 TH 0151 2.9 / 0743 1.6 / 1501 2.9 / 2055 1.7		**22** F 0642 2.0 / 1404 2.9 / 1936 1.8		
8 F 0310 3.1 / 0911 1.6 / 1623 3.1 / 2159 1.6		**23** SA 0207 2.9 / 0818 1.8 / 1525 3.1 / 2047 1.6		
9 SA 0403 3.3 / 1020 1.5 / 1650 3.2 / 2245 1.4		**24** SU 0328 3.2 / 0948 1.5 / 1615 3.4 / 2149 1.2		
10 SU 0442 3.5 / 1108 1.4 / 1711 3.4 / 2324 1.2		**25** M 0419 3.5 / 1046 1.2 / 1656 3.6 / 2241 0.9		
11 M 0519 3.7 / 1148 1.2 / 1740 3.6 / 2359 1.1		**26** TU 0502 3.9 / 1132 0.8 / 1734 3.8 / 2328 0.5		
12 TU 0554 3.9 / 1224 1.2 / 1811 3.7		**27** W 0543 4.1 / 1215 0.6 / 1810 4.0 ○		
13 W 0034 1.0 / 0629 4.0 / 1257 1.1 / 1841 3.8		**28** TH 0012 0.3 / 0621 4.3 / 1256 0.4 / 1845 4.1		
14 TH 0108 0.9 / 0702 4.0 / 1329 1.1 / 1911 3.8				
15 F 0139 1.0 / 0733 4.0 / 1400 1.2 / 1939 3.8				

MARCH

Time	m		Time	m
1 F 0056 0.1 / 0700 4.3 / 1335 0.4 / 1922 4.0		**16** SA 0113 0.9 / 0708 4.0 / 1330 1.0 / 1912 3.8		
2 SA 0139 0.1 / 0739 4.2 / 1415 0.5 / 1959 3.9		**17** SU 0139 1.0 / 0735 3.9 / 1356 1.1 / 1937 3.7		
3 SU 0223 0.2 / 0817 4.0 / 1455 0.7 / 2038 3.7		**18** M 0159 1.1 / 0800 3.7 / 1418 1.2 / 2002 3.6		
4 M 0308 0.5 / 0857 3.7 / 1539 1.0 / 2119 3.4		**19** TU 0220 1.3 / 0826 3.6 / 1445 1.3 / 2032 3.5		
5 TU 0356 0.8 / 0939 3.3 / 1628 1.3 / 2208 3.1		**20** W 0248 1.4 / 0858 3.3 / 1522 1.5 / 2107 3.3		
6 W 0450 1.2 / 1032 2.9 / 1728 1.6 / 2321 2.9		**21** TH 0326 1.6 / 0938 3.1 / 1616 1.7 / 2152 3.1		
7 TH 0555 1.5 / 1215 2.7 / 1844 1.8		**22** F 0425 1.8 / 1042 2.8 / 1737 1.8 / 2302 2.9		
8 F 0121 2.8 / 0719 1.7 / 1537 2.7 / 2030 1.8		**23** SA 0622 1.9 / 1352 2.8 / 1904 1.8		
9 SA 0304 2.9 / 0914 1.7 / 1632 2.9 / 2144 1.6		**24** SU 0145 2.9 / 0815 1.8 / 1510 3.0 / 2022 1.5		
10 SU 0358 3.2 / 1018 1.5 / 1658 3.1 / 2231 1.4		**25** M 0312 3.2 / 0939 1.4 / 1559 3.3 / 2128 1.2		
11 M 0428 3.4 / 1059 1.3 / 1659 3.3 / 2308 1.1		**26** TU 0402 3.6 / 1031 1.0 / 1640 3.6 / 2222 0.8		
12 TU 0501 3.6 / 1133 1.2 / 1722 3.5 / 2342 1.0		**27** W 0444 3.9 / 1115 0.7 / 1715 3.8 / 2309 0.4		
13 W 0535 3.8 / 1203 1.0 / 1750 3.7		**28** TH 0523 4.2 / 1155 0.4 / 1749 4.0 / ○ 2354 0.1		
14 TH 0014 0.8 / 0607 4.0 / 1233 1.0 / ● 1819 3.8		**29** F 0602 4.3 / 1234 0.3 / 1824 4.1		
15 F 0044 0.8 / 0639 4.0 / 1302 0.9 / 1847 3.9		**30** SA 0037 0.0 / 0639 4.3 / 1312 0.2 / 1859 4.1		
		31 SU 0120 0.1 / 0716 4.2 / 1350 0.4 / 1935 3.9		

APRIL

Time	m		Time	m
1 M 0203 0.3 / 0753 3.9 / 1429 0.7 / 2013 3.7		**16** TU 0130 1.1 / 0733 3.7 / 1349 1.1 / 1936 3.7		
2 TU 0247 0.6 / 0830 3.6 / 1510 1.0 / 2052 3.5		**17** W 0155 1.2 / 0802 3.5 / 1420 1.2 / 2008 3.5		
3 W 0334 0.9 / 0909 3.2 / 1558 1.3 / 2137 3.2		**18** TH 0227 1.4 / 0837 3.3 / 1500 1.4 / 2046 3.4		
4 TH 0427 1.3 / 0955 2.8 / 1655 1.6 / 2242 2.9		**19** F 0311 1.6 / 0923 3.0 / 1555 1.5 / 2136 3.1		
5 F 0531 1.6 / 1120 2.5 / 1808 1.8		**20** SA 0423 1.8 / 1035 2.8 / 1711 1.7 / 2253 3.0		
6 SA 0053 2.8 / 0659 1.8 / 1513 2.6 / 1951 1.8		**21** SU 0621 1.8 / 1326 2.7 / 1837 1.6		
7 SU 0237 2.9 / 0901 1.7 / 1606 2.8 / 2114 1.6		**22** M 0115 3.0 / 0803 1.6 / 1443 3.0 / 1955 1.4		
8 M 0329 3.1 / 0957 1.6 / 1624 3.0 / 2203 1.4		**23** TU 0243 3.3 / 0915 1.3 / 1533 3.3 / 2102 1.1		
9 TU 0402 3.3 / 1034 1.4 / 1627 3.2 / 2241 1.2		**24** W 0335 3.6 / 1007 1.0 / 1614 3.5 / 2158 0.7		
10 W 0434 3.6 / 1105 1.2 / 1652 3.4 / 2315 1.0		**25** TH 0419 3.9 / 1050 0.7 / 1650 3.8 / 2247 0.4		
11 TH 0507 3.8 / 1133 1.0 / 1721 3.6 / 2345 0.9		**26** F 0459 4.1 / 1130 0.5 / 1724 4.0 / 2333 0.2		
12 F 0540 3.9 / 1201 0.9 / 1751 3.8 ●		**27** SA 0538 4.2 / 1209 0.4 / 1800 4.1 ○		
13 SA 0014 0.8 / 0611 3.9 / 1229 0.8 / 1818 3.8		**28** SU 0017 0.2 / 0616 4.2 / 1247 0.4 / 1836 4.1		
14 SU 0042 0.9 / 0640 3.9 / 1258 0.7 / 1843 3.8		**29** M 0101 0.3 / 0653 4.0 / 1325 0.6 / 1913 4.0		
15 M 0108 0.9 / 0706 3.8 / 1323 0.9 / 1908 3.8		**30** TU 0144 0.5 / 0730 3.8 / 1404 0.8 / 1951 3.8		

Chart Datum: 2·10 metres below Ordnance Datum (Newlyn)

TIME ZONE (UTC)
For Summer Time add ONE hour in **non-shaded areas**

SCOTLAND – OBAN

LAT 56°25'N   LONG 5°29'W

TIMES AND HEIGHTS OF HIGH AND LOW WATERS

YEAR **2002**

MAY

Day	Time	m	Time	m		Day	Time	m	Time	m
1 W	0228 0807 1446 2032	0.8 3.5 1.0 3.5				**16** TH	0146 0749 1407 1956	1.2 3.5 1.1 3.6		
2 TH	0315 0846 1533 2117	1.1 3.1 1.3 3.3				**17** F	0227 0832 1452 2041	1.3 3.3 1.2 3.4		
3 F	0407 0932 1628 2216	1.4 2.8 1.5 3.0				**18** SA	0322 0925 1547 2137	1.5 3.1 1.3 3.3		
4 SA	0508 1042 1733	1.7 2.6 1.7				**19** SU	0439 1036 1655 2252	1.6 2.9 1.4 3.1		
5 SU	0000 0628 1350 1855	2.9 1.9 2.6 1.8				**20** M	0610 1235 1810	1.6 2.8 1.4		
6 M	0150 0813 1454 2025	2.9 1.8 2.7 1.7				**21** TU	0035 0735 1405 1924	3.2 1.5 3.0 1.5		
7 TU	0246 0914 1522 2122	3.1 1.6 2.9 1.5				**22** W	0206 0844 1500 2031	3.3 1.3 3.2 1.1		
8 W	0325 0954 1546 2204	3.3 1.5 3.1 1.3				**23** TH	0304 0938 1545 2131	3.6 1.0 3.5 0.8		
9 TH	0400 1025 1616 2238	3.5 1.3 3.3 1.2				**24** F	0352 1023 1623 2223	3.8 0.8 3.7 0.7		
10 F	0434 1055 1647 2309	3.6 1.1 3.5 1.1				**25** SA	0435 1105 1701 2312	3.9 0.7 3.9 0.5		
11 SA	0509 1124 1719 2339	3.8 1.0 3.7 1.0				**26** SU	0516 1145 1739 ○ 2358	4.0 0.7 4.0 0.5		
12 SU	0542 1155 1748 ●	3.8 0.9 3.8				**27** M	0556 1224 1817	3.9 0.7 4.0		
13 M	0010 0613 1226 1816	1.0 3.8 0.9 3.8				**28** TU	0043 0634 1304 1856	0.6 3.8 0.8 3.9		
14 TU	0041 0643 1257 1846	1.0 3.8 0.9 3.8				**29** W	0128 0713 1344 1936	0.8 3.6 0.9 3.8		
15 W	0112 0714 1330 1919	1.1 3.7 1.0 3.7				**30** TH	0212 0751 1426 2017	1.0 3.4 1.1 3.6		
						31 F	0258 0831 1511 2101	1.3 3.2 1.3 3.4		

JUNE

Day	Time	m	Time	m		Day	Time	m	Time	m
1 SA	0346 0915 1600 2152	1.5 3.0 1.5 3.2				**16** SU	0330 0922 1538 2135	1.3 3.2 1.1 3.4		
2 SU	0441 1010 1655 2256	1.7 2.8 1.6 3.1				**17** M	0433 1023 1636 2239	1.4 3.0 1.2 3.3		
3 M	0543 1131 1756	1.8 2.7 1.7				**18** TU	0545 1142 1742 2357	1.4 3.0 1.2 3.3		
4 TU	0025 0654 1322 1904	3.0 1.9 2.7 1.8				**19** W	0700 1851	1.4 1.2		
5 W	0146 0803 1417 2013	3.0 1.8 2.9 1.7				**20** TH	0124 0808 1423 2000	3.3 1.3 3.1 1.2		
6 TH	0238 0856 1458 2107	3.2 1.6 3.0 1.6				**21** F	0234 0908 1517 2104	3.4 1.2 3.3 1.1		
7 F	0321 0937 1536 2150	3.3 1.5 3.2 1.4				**22** SA	0331 0959 1603 2203	3.5 1.1 3.5 1.0		
8 SA	0400 1013 1612 2228	3.5 1.3 3.4 1.3				**23** SU	0419 1045 1644 2256	3.6 1.0 3.7 0.9		
9 SU	0439 1048 1648 2305	3.6 1.1 3.6 1.2				**24** M	0503 1127 1725 ○ 2344	3.7 0.9 3.8 0.9		
10 M	0517 1123 1723 ● 2343	3.7 1.0 3.7 1.1				**25** TU	0545 1208 1805	3.7 0.9 3.9		
11 TU	0553 1159 1758	3.7 0.9 3.7				**26** W	0031 0623 1249 1844	0.9 3.7 0.9 3.9		
12 W	0022 0628 1237 1833	1.0 3.7 0.9 3.8				**27** TH	0115 0701 1329 1923	1.0 3.6 1.0 3.9		
13 TH	0103 0705 1317 1911	1.0 3.6 0.8 3.7				**28** F	0158 0739 1409 2003	1.1 3.5 1.1 3.7		
14 F	0147 0745 1359 1954	1.1 3.5 0.9 3.7				**29** SA	0240 0816 1449 2043	1.3 3.3 1.2 3.6		
15 SA	0235 0830 1446 2041	1.2 3.4 1.0 3.6				**30** SU	0322 0854 1531 2124	1.5 3.2 1.4 3.4		

JULY

Day	Time	m	Time	m		Day	Time	m	Time	m
1 M	0406 0936 1615 2210	1.6 3.1 1.5 3.3				**16** TU	0412 0959 1615 2216	1.1 3.2 0.9 3.4		
2 TU	0454 1023 1702 2303	1.7 2.9 1.7 3.1				**17** W	0512 1101 1714 2321	1.3 3.1 1.1 3.3		
3 W	0548 1123 1754	1.8 2.9 1.8				**18** TH	0619 1223 1820	1.4 3.0 1.2		
4 TH	0011 0647 1243 1850	3.1 1.8 2.8 1.8				**19** F	0045 0731 1349 1930	3.1 1.5 3.0 1.3		
5 F	0130 0747 1358 1951	3.1 1.8 2.9 1.8				**20** SA	0213 0842 1459 2043	3.1 1.4 3.2 1.3		
6 SA	0237 0843 1455 2052	3.2 1.6 3.1 1.7				**21** SU	0325 0944 1555 2151	3.2 1.4 3.4 1.3		
7 SU	0330 0933 1543 2149	3.3 1.5 3.2 1.5				**22** M	0421 1034 1639 2249	3.3 1.2 3.6 1.2		
8 M	0417 1017 1627 2240	3.4 1.3 3.4 1.3				**23** TU	0505 1118 1718 2338	3.4 1.1 3.7 1.1		
9 TU	0501 1059 1708 2327	3.6 1.1 3.6 1.2				**24** W	0543 1158 1757 ○	3.5 1.0 3.9		
10 W	0542 1140 1748 ●	3.7 0.9 3.7				**25** TH	0021 0617 1237 1833	1.1 3.6 0.9 3.9		
11 TH	0013 0621 1222 1827	1.0 3.7 0.7 3.8				**26** F	0102 0651 1314 1909	1.1 3.6 0.9 4.0		
12 F	0058 0659 1304 1908	0.9 3.7 0.6 3.9				**27** SA	0140 0723 1350 1944	1.1 3.6 1.0 3.9		
13 SA	0144 0739 1348 1949	0.9 3.7 0.6 3.9				**28** SU	0216 0755 1425 2018	1.2 3.5 1.1 3.8		
14 SU	0230 0821 1434 2034	0.9 3.5 0.6 3.8				**29** M	0252 0827 1459 2053	1.3 3.5 1.3 3.6		
15 M	0319 0907 1522 2122	1.0 3.4 0.8 3.6				**30** TU	0328 0859 1533 2128	1.5 3.3 1.4 3.5		
						31 W	0407 0934 1611 2206	1.6 3.2 1.6 3.3		

AUGUST

Day	Time	m	Time	m		Day	Time	m	Time	m
1 TH	0452 1016 1655 2253	1.8 3.0 1.8 3.1				**16** F	0539 1140 1752	1.5 3.0 1.4		
2 F	0547 1109 1751	1.9 2.9 1.9				**17** SA	0009 0654 1327 1907	2.9 1.6 2.9 1.6		
3 SA	0004 0650 1237 1858	3.0 1.9 2.8 2.0				**18** SU	0211 0822 1457 2035	2.9 1.6 3.1 1.6		
4 SU	0158 0757 1424 2012	3.0 1.8 2.9 1.9				**19** M	0400 0936 1559 2157	3.0 1.5 3.3 1.5		
5 M	0314 0900 1528 2130	3.1 1.6 3.1 1.7				**20** TU	0447 1028 1636 2251	3.1 1.3 3.5 1.3		
6 TU	0408 0954 1617 2233	3.3 1.4 3.4 1.4				**21** W	0510 1109 1709 2332	3.3 1.1 3.7 1.2		
7 W	0452 1042 1700 2323	3.5 1.1 3.6 1.1				**22** TH	0534 1146 1742 ○	3.5 1.0 3.9		
8 TH	0533 1125 1740 ●	3.7 0.8 3.9				**23** F	0009 0602 1221 1815	1.1 3.6 0.9 4.0		
9 F	0007 0611 1208 1819	0.9 3.8 0.5 4.0				**24** SA	0043 0632 1255 1848	1.0 3.7 0.8 4.1		
10 SA	0050 0648 1250 1858	0.7 3.9 0.4 4.1				**25** SU	0115 0700 1327 1919	1.0 3.8 0.9 4.0		
11 SU	0132 0724 1333 1937	0.6 3.8 0.3 4.1				**26** M	0147 0728 1357 1949	1.1 3.8 0.9 3.9		
12 M	0214 0802 1417 2017	0.6 3.7 0.4 4.0				**27** TU	0218 0755 1425 2019	1.2 3.7 1.2 3.8		
13 TU	0258 0843 1503 2100	0.6 3.6 0.5 3.8				**28** W	0248 0822 1451 2047	1.3 3.5 1.4 3.6		
14 W	0344 0928 1553 2146	1.0 3.4 0.8 3.5				**29** TH	0319 0852 1519 2117	1.5 3.4 1.6 3.4		
15 TH	0437 1022 1648 2243	1.2 3.1 1.1 3.2				**30** F	0356 0928 1555 2154	1.7 3.2 1.8 3.2		
						31 SA	0450 1013 1652 2249	1.9 3.0 2.0 2.9		

Chart Datum: 2·10 metres below Ordnance Datum (Newlyn)

TIME ZONE (UTC)
For Summer Time add ONE hour in **non-shaded areas**

SCOTLAND – OBAN

LAT 56°25'N   LONG 5°29'W

TIMES AND HEIGHTS OF HIGH AND LOW WATERS

YEAR 2002

SEPTEMBER

Day	Time m	Time m	Time m	Time m
1 SU	0603 1.9	1120 2.8	1822 2.1	
16 M	0300 2.7	0804 1.7	1501 3.1	2048 1.8
2 M	0143 2.8	0720 1.9	1412 2.9	1957 2.0
17 TU	0410 2.9	0922 1.6	1556 3.3	2201 1.6
3 TU	0310 3.0	0833 1.7	1522 3.2	2132 1.7
18 W	0447 3.1	1012 1.3	1621 3.5	2242 1.4
4 W	0400 3.3	0935 1.4	1607 3.5	2229 1.3
19 TH	0454 3.3	1051 1.1	1648 3.7	2315 1.2
5 TH	0441 3.5	1024 1.0	1646 3.8	2313 1.0
20 F	0509 3.5	1125 1.0	1718 3.9	2345 1.1
6 F	0518 3.8	1108 0.7	1725 4.1	2353 0.7
21 SA ○	0536 3.7	1158 0.9	1750 4.1	
7 SA ●	0553 3.9	1150 0.4	1802 4.3	
22 SU	0015 1.0	0604 3.9	1229 0.8	1820 4.1
8 SU	0032 0.5	0627 4.0	1232 0.2	1838 4.3
23 M	0045 1.0	0632 3.9	1259 0.9	1850 4.1
9 M	0111 0.4	0701 4.0	1314 0.1	1915 4.3
24 TU	0114 1.0	0658 3.9	1326 1.0	1918 4.0
10 TU	0150 0.5	0737 3.9	1358 0.2	1953 4.1
25 W	0143 1.1	0723 3.8	1350 1.2	1944 3.9
11 W	0230 0.6	0816 3.8	1442 0.5	2032 3.8
26 TH	0209 1.2	0748 3.7	1411 1.4	2010 3.7
12 TH	0314 0.9	0857 3.5	1531 0.8	2114 3.4
27 F	0235 1.4	0817 3.5	1435 1.6	2038 3.4
13 F	0404 1.2	0947 3.2	1625 1.2	2205 3.1
28 SA	0308 1.6	0851 3.3	1508 1.9	2113 3.2
14 SA	0504 1.5	1102 3.0	1730 1.5	2334 2.7
29 SU	0358 1.8	0934 3.1	1603 2.1	2207 2.9
15 SU	0621 1.7	1317 2.9	1852 1.8	
30 M	0519 2.0	1041 2.9	1805 2.2	

OCTOBER

Day	Time m	Time m	Time m	Time m
1 TU	0140 2.8	0646 1.9	1401 3.0	1958 2.0
16 W	0346 2.9	0852 1.6	1526 3.3	2140 1.7
2 W	0253 3.0	0805 1.7	1503 3.3	2121 1.7
17 TH	0417 3.1	0943 1.4	1552 3.5	2216 1.5
3 TH	0341 3.3	0910 1.4	1546 3.6	2210 1.3
18 F	0417 3.3	1023 1.2	1619 3.7	2246 1.3
4 F	0420 3.6	1001 0.9	1624 4.0	2252 0.9
19 SA	0437 3.5	1058 1.1	1649 3.9	2314 1.1
5 SA	0455 3.8	1046 0.6	1701 4.3	2330 0.6
20 SU	0504 3.7	1130 1.0	1720 4.1	2342 1.0
6 SU ●	0528 4.0	1129 0.3	1737 4.4	
21 M ○	0533 3.9	1159 1.0	1751 4.1	
7 M	0008 0.4	0600 4.0	1212 0.2	1814 4.5
22 TU	0011 1.0	0601 4.0	1228 1.1	1820 4.1
8 TU	0046 0.4	0635 4.2	1254 0.2	1850 4.3
23 W	0041 1.0	0627 4.0	1255 1.1	1849 4.0
9 W	0123 0.5	0711 4.1	1337 0.3	1927 4.1
24 TH	0110 1.1	0654 3.9	1320 1.3	1915 3.9
10 TH	0203 0.7	0750 3.9	1422 0.6	2005 3.8
25 F	0137 1.2	0721 3.8	1343 1.5	1943 3.7
11 F	0246 1.0	0831 3.6	1511 1.0	2045 3.4
26 SA	0206 1.4	0751 3.6	1410 1.7	2014 3.4
12 SA	0335 1.3	0919 3.3	1606 1.4	2132 3.0
27 SU	0242 1.6	0827 3.5	1450 1.9	2054 3.2
13 SU	0434 1.6	1030 3.1	1712 1.7	2252 2.7
28 M	0331 1.7	0914 3.3	1555 2.1	2155 2.9
14 M	0548 1.8	1302 3.0	1839 1.9	
29 TU	0444 1.9	1025 3.1	1756 2.1	
15 TU	0244 2.7	0730 1.8	1437 3.1	2042 1.9
30 W	0105 2.8	0609 1.9	1311 3.1	1939 1.9
31 TH	0222 3.0	0729 1.7	1428 3.4	2051 1.6

NOVEMBER

Day	Time m	Time m	Time m	Time m
1 F	0312 3.3	0836 1.4	1515 3.7	2141 1.3
16 SA	0333 3.2	0949 1.4	1546 3.6	2208 1.5
2 SA	0352 3.6	0932 1.0	1555 4.0	2224 1.0
17 SU	0400 3.5	1026 1.3	1618 3.8	2237 1.3
3 SU	0427 3.8	1021 0.7	1634 4.3	2303 0.7
18 M	0431 3.7	1058 1.2	1650 3.9	2307 1.2
4 M ●	0500 4.0	1106 0.5	1712 4.4	2341 0.6
19 TU	0502 3.8	1128 1.2	1723 4.0	2338 1.1
5 TU	0535 4.2	1151 0.4	1750 4.4	
20 W ○	0533 3.9	1158 1.2	1755 4.0	
6 W	0020 0.6	0611 4.2	1235 0.4	1827 4.3
21 TH	0011 1.1	0602 3.9	1229 1.3	1826 4.0
7 TH	0059 0.6	0650 4.2	1320 0.6	1905 4.0
22 F	0043 1.1	0632 3.9	1300 1.4	1857 3.8
8 F	0140 0.8	0730 4.0	1405 0.9	1944 3.7
23 SA	0115 1.2	0703 3.8	1331 1.5	1929 3.7
9 SA	0223 1.0	0813 3.8	1454 1.2	2024 3.4
24 SU	0150 1.3	0738 3.7	1407 1.6	2007 3.5
10 SU	0309 1.3	0901 3.5	1548 1.6	2110 3.0
25 M	0230 1.4	0819 3.6	1454 1.8	2053 3.3
11 M	0407 1.6	1003 3.2	1650 1.8	2215 2.8
26 TU	0319 1.5	0909 3.4	1602 1.9	2153 3.1
12 TU	0513 1.8	1210 3.1	1810 2.0	
27 W	0420 1.6	1016 3.3	1732 1.9	2318 2.9
13 W	0131 2.7	0636 1.8	1346 3.2	1950 2.0
28 TH	0532 1.7	1150 3.3	1859 1.8	
14 TH	0245 2.9	0804 1.8	1440 3.3	2056 1.8
29 F	0130 3.0	0647 1.6	1336 3.4	2011 1.6
15 F	0314 3.0	0900 1.6	1515 3.5	2136 1.6
30 SA	0232 3.2	0758 1.4	1438 3.7	2107 1.4

DECEMBER

Day	Time m	Time m	Time m	Time m
1 SU	0318 3.5	0900 1.1	1526 3.9	2154 1.2
16 M	0321 3.3	0946 1.6	1547 3.6	2158 1.5
2 M	0358 3.7	0955 0.9	1609 4.1	2237 1.0
17 TU	0358 3.5	1024 1.5	1625 3.7	2234 1.4
3 TU	0436 3.9	1046 0.8	1651 4.2	2318 0.8
18 W	0435 3.6	1059 1.5	1702 3.8	2310 1.2
4 W ●	0515 4.1	1134 0.7	1731 4.2	2359 0.8
19 TH ○	0511 3.7	1135 1.4	1739 3.9	2346 1.1
5 TH	0555 4.2	1220 0.7	1811 4.1	
20 F	0546 3.8	1212 1.3	1814 3.9	
6 F	0040 0.8	0635 4.1	1306 0.9	1851 3.9
21 SA	0022 1.1	0620 3.9	1250 1.3	1848 3.8
7 SA	0122 0.9	0717 4.0	1352 1.1	1930 3.7
22 SU	0100 1.1	0656 3.9	1329 1.3	1924 3.7
8 SU	0206 1.1	0800 3.9	1439 1.3	2011 3.4
23 M	0138 1.1	0734 3.8	1410 1.4	2003 3.6
9 M	0252 1.3	0845 3.7	1528 1.6	2053 3.2
24 TU	0220 1.1	0816 3.7	1457 1.5	2047 3.4
10 TU	0341 1.5	0936 3.5	1621 1.8	2142 3.0
25 W	0306 1.2	0904 3.6	1551 1.6	2138 3.3
11 W	0435 1.7	1039 3.3	1721 2.0	2248 2.9
26 TH	0359 1.3	0959 3.5	1656 1.7	2239 3.1
12 TH	0535 1.8	1213 3.2	1829 2.0	
27 F	0459 1.4	1107 3.4	1809 1.7	2358 3.1
13 F	0041 2.8	0644 1.9	1338 3.2	1938 2.0
28 SA	0608 1.4	1232 3.4	1922 1.7	
14 SA	0156 2.9	0758 1.8	1430 3.3	2036 1.9
29 SU	0132 3.1	0720 1.4	1358 3.5	2029 1.5
15 SU	0242 3.1	0900 1.7	1510 3.4	2120 1.7
30 M	0243 3.3	0830 1.3	1503 3.6	2126 1.4
31 TU	0336 3.5	0934 1.2	1556 3.7	2217 1.2

Chart Datum: 2·10 metres below Ordnance Datum (Newlyn)
Register for your **FREE** weekly weather email service from Macmillan Reeds
》 at **www.nauticaldata.com – NOW!** 《
weekend weather reports sent to your email address, every Thursday

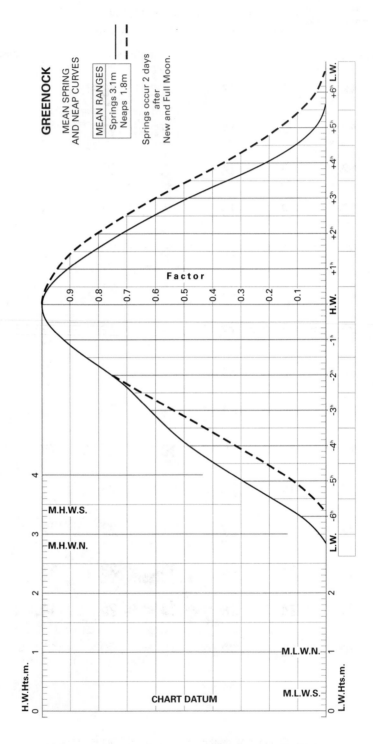

GREENOCK

MEAN SPRING
AND NEAP CURVES

MEAN RANGES	
Springs	3.1m
Neaps	1.8m

Springs occur 2 days after
New and Full Moon.

Factor

Register for your **FREE** weekly weather email service from Macmillan Reeds
at **www.nauticaldata.com – NOW!**
weekend weather reports sent to your email address, every Thursday

98

TIME ZONE (UTC)
For Summer Time add ONE hour in non-shaded areas

SCOTLAND – GREENOCK

LAT 55°57'N   LONG 4°46'W

TIMES AND HEIGHTS OF HIGH AND LOW WATERS

YEAR 2002

Section 1

JANUARY

Day	Time m		Day	Time m	
1 TU	0134 3.3 / 0654 0.5	1341 3.7 / 1914 0.3	**16** W	0211 3.2 / 0726 0.8	1423 3.6 / 1953 0.5
2 W	0222 3.3 / 0742 0.5	1423 3.8 / 2002 0.3	**17** TH	0247 3.2 / 0803 0.8	1457 3.6 / 2030 0.5
3 TH	0310 3.3 / 0832 0.6	1506 3.8 / 2052 0.3	**18** F	0323 3.2 / 0840 0.8	1532 3.5 / 2109 0.6
4 F	0359 3.2 / 0924 0.7	1552 3.7 / 2146 0.4	**19** SA	0400 3.1 / 0919 0.9	1607 3.4 / 2150 0.7
5 SA	0451 3.2 / 1019 0.8	1641 3.6 / 2244 0.5	**20** SU	0438 3.1 / 1000 0.9	1646 3.3 / 2236 0.8
6 SU	0547 3.1 / 1119 0.9	1735 3.5 / 2348 0.6	**21** M	0520 3.0 / 1046 1.0	1728 3.1 / 2329 0.9
7 M	0648 3.0 / 1225 1.0	1837 3.3	**22** TU	0606 2.9 / 1140 1.2	1818 3.0
8 TU	0055 0.7 / 0759 3.0	1335 1.0 / 1950 3.4	**23** W	0029 0.9 / 0658 2.9	1243 1.2 / 1916 2.9
9 W	0202 0.7 / 0914 3.0	1443 0.9 / 2115 3.2	**24** TH	0133 0.9 / 0800 2.8	1350 1.2 / 2030 2.8
10 TH	0304 0.7 / 1015 3.0	1543 0.7 / 2223 3.2	**25** F	0236 0.9 / 0915 2.9	1458 1.1 / 2149 2.9
11 F	0359 0.7 / 1106 3.3	1634 0.6 / 2319 3.2	**26** SA	0333 0.8 / 1022 3.1	1557 0.8 / 2254 3.0
12 SA	0447 0.7 / 1151 3.4	1719 0.5	**27** SU	0424 0.6 / 1114 3.3	1647 0.6 / 2347 3.1
13 SU	0008 3.2 / 0531 0.7	1233 3.5 / ● 1801 0.4	**28** M	0510 0.5 / 1200 3.4	○ 1732 0.6
14 M	0053 3.2 / 0611 0.7	1311 3.6 / 1839 0.4	**29** TU	0038 3.2 / 0555 0.4	1245 3.6 / 1816 0.2
15 TU	0134 3.2 / 0650 0.8	1348 3.6 / 1917 0.4	**30** W	0128 3.3 / 0641 0.4	1330 3.7 / 1902 0.1
			31 TH	0216 3.3 / 0728 0.3	1413 3.8 / 1948 0.0

FEBRUARY

Day	Time m		Day	Time m	
1 F	0301 3.3 / 0815 0.4	1457 3.9 / 2035 0.1	**16** SA	0256 3.1 / 0809 0.6	1507 3.4 / 2034 0.4
2 SA	0344 3.3 / 0903 0.4	1540 3.9 / 2124 0.2	**17** SU	0327 3.2 / 0844 0.6	1539 3.4 / 2110 0.5
3 SU	0427 3.3 / 0953 0.5	1624 3.7 / 2216 0.3	**18** M	0400 3.1 / 0921 0.6	1613 3.3 / 2150 0.6
4 M	0511 3.2 / 1048 0.7	1710 3.6 / 2314 0.6	**19** TU	0436 3.1 / 1002 0.7	1651 3.1 / 2237 0.7
5 TU	0558 3.0 / 1152 0.8	1800 3.3	**20** W	0517 3.0 / 1051 0.9	1734 2.9 / 2333 0.8
6 W	0022 0.8 / 0654 2.9	1307 0.9 / 1859 3.1	**21** TH	0604 2.8 / 1151 1.0	1829 2.8
7 TH	0138 0.9 / 0823 2.9	1424 0.9 / 2035 2.9	**22** F	0038 0.9 / 0703 2.7	1300 1.1 / 1943 2.7
8 F	0249 1.0 / 0952 3.0	1529 0.8 / 2216 2.9	**23** SA	0151 1.0 / 0825 2.7	1418 1.0 / 2121 2.7
9 SA	0349 0.9 / 1049 3.1	1622 0.6 / 2316 3.0	**24** SU	0306 0.8 / 0951 2.9	1534 0.8 / 2240 2.9
10 SU	0439 0.8 / 1136 3.3	1708 0.4	**25** M	0406 0.7 / 1052 3.1	1630 0.4 / 2337 3.1
11 M	0004 3.0 / 0522 0.7	1219 3.4 / 1747 0.3	**26** TU	0455 0.5 / 1142 3.4	1716 0.2
12 TU	0047 3.1 / 0559 0.7	1258 3.5 / ● 1824 0.3	**27** W	0027 3.2 / 0539 0.3	1229 3.6 / ○ 1759 0.0
13 W	0124 3.1 / 0633 0.6	1334 3.5 / 1857 0.3	**28** TH	0116 3.3 / 0623 0.2	1314 3.7 / 1843 -0.1
14 TH	0157 3.1 / 0704 0.6	1407 3.5 / 1929 0.4			
15 F	0227 3.1 / 0736 0.6	1437 3.4 / 2001 0.4			

MARCH

Day	Time m		Day	Time m	
1 F	0200 3.3 / 0707 0.1	1358 3.8 / 1926 -0.1	**16** SA	0159 3.1 / 0705 0.4	1411 3.3 / 1929 0.3
2 SA	0241 3.4 / 0751 0.1	1441 3.9 / 2011 -0.1	**17** SU	0225 3.1 / 0736 0.4	1439 3.3 / 2000 0.3
3 SU	0319 3.4 / 0837 0.2	1522 3.9 / 2057 0.1	**18** M	0253 3.2 / 0810 0.4	1511 3.3 / 2035 0.3
4 M	0355 3.4 / 0924 0.3	1603 3.8 / 2144 0.3	**19** TU	0325 3.2 / 0846 0.4	1545 3.2 / 2115 0.4
5 TU	0433 3.3 / 1016 0.5	1645 3.5 / 2238 0.6	**20** W	0358 3.1 / 0927 0.5	1621 3.1 / 2200 0.6
6 W	0515 3.1 / 1118 0.7	1730 3.2 / 2345 0.9	**21** TH	0434 3.0 / 1016 0.7	1702 2.9 / 2255 0.8
7 TH	0605 2.9 / 1241 0.9	1824 2.9	**22** F	0517 2.8 / 1116 0.8	1755 2.7
8 F	0114 1.1 / 0711 2.8	1405 0.9 / 1938 2.7	**23** SA	0001 0.9 / 0615 2.7	1227 0.9 / 1914 2.6
9 SA	0233 1.1 / 0928 2.8	1510 0.7 / 2212 2.7	**24** SU	0117 1.0 / 0742 2.7	1348 0.8 / 2104 2.6
10 SU	0335 1.0 / 1030 3.0	1604 0.5 / 2306 2.9	**25** M	0241 0.9 / 0922 2.8	1511 0.6 / 2227 2.8
11 M	0424 0.8 / 1118 3.2	1648 0.4 / 2350 3.0	**26** TU	0346 0.6 / 1029 3.1	1608 0.3 / 2322 3.0
12 TU	0505 0.7 / 1200 3.3	1726 0.3	**27** W	0435 0.4 / 1120 3.4	1655 0.0
13 W	0028 3.0 / 0539 0.6	1239 3.4 / 1800 0.2	**28** TH	0010 3.2 / 0519 0.2	1208 3.6 / ○ 1737 -0.1
14 TH	0103 3.0 / 0609 0.5	1314 3.3 / ● 1831 0.3	**29** F	0055 3.3 / 0601 0.1	1254 3.7 / 1819 -0.2
15 F	0133 3.0 / 0637 0.5	1344 3.3 / 1900 0.3	**30** SA	0137 3.4 / 0644 0.0	1339 3.8 / 1902 -0.1
			31 SU	0215 3.4 / 0726 0.0	1421 3.8 / 1945 0.0

APRIL

Day	Time m		Day	Time m	
1 M	0250 3.5 / 0810 0.1	1502 3.8 / 2030 0.2	**16** TU	0222 3.2 / 0741 0.3	1445 3.2 / 2008 0.3
2 TU	0325 3.4 / 0856 0.2	1541 3.7 / 2115 0.4	**17** W	0254 3.3 / 0819 0.3	1521 3.1 / 2050 0.4
3 W	0402 3.3 / 0946 0.4	1623 3.4 / 2205 0.7	**18** TH	0328 3.2 / 0903 0.4	1559 3.0 / 2137 0.6
4 TH	0443 3.2 / 1047 0.7	1708 3.1 / 2309 1.1	**19** F	0403 3.1 / 0954 0.5	1643 2.8 / 2233 0.7
5 F	0532 3.0 / 1216 0.8	1802 2.8	**20** SA	0446 2.9 / 1056 0.7	1742 2.6 / 2339 0.9
6 SA	0044 1.3 / 0635 2.8	1339 0.8 / 1915 2.6	**21** SU	0546 2.8 / 1209 0.7	1908 2.6
7 SU	0205 1.3 / 0848 2.7	1442 0.7 / 2150 2.6	**22** M	0055 1.0 / 0714 2.7	1329 0.7 / 2050 2.6
8 M	0308 1.1 / 1002 2.9	1535 0.5 / 2241 2.8	**23** TU	0215 0.9 / 0854 2.9	1445 0.4 / 2206 2.8
9 TU	0358 0.9 / 1050 3.1	1619 0.4 / 2322 2.9	**24** W	0321 0.6 / 1002 3.1	1542 0.2 / 2300 3.0
10 W	0438 0.7 / 1132 3.2	1657 0.3 / 2359 3.0	**25** TH	0412 0.4 / 1056 3.4	1630 0.0 / 2346 3.2
11 TH	0512 0.6 / 1210 3.2	1731 0.2	**26** F	0457 0.2 / 1144 3.5	1713 -0.1
12 F	0032 3.0 / 0541 0.5	1245 3.2 / ● 1801 0.2	**27** SA	0030 3.3 / 0539 0.0	1231 3.6 / ○ 1755 -0.1
13 SA	0102 3.0 / 0607 0.4	1314 3.2 / 1829 0.3	**28** SU	0111 3.4 / 0621 0.0	1317 3.7 / 1838 0.0
14 SU	0127 3.1 / 0635 0.4	1341 3.2 / 1858 0.3	**29** M	0148 3.4 / 0700 0.0	1400 3.7 / 1922 0.2
15 M	0153 3.2 / 0706 0.3	1412 3.2 / 1931 0.3	**30** TU	0224 3.5 / 0746 0.3	1442 3.6 / 2007 0.3

TIME ZONE (UTC)
For Summer Time add ONE hour in **non-shaded areas**

SCOTLAND – GREENOCK

YEAR **2002**

LAT 55°57'N   LONG 4°46'W

TIMES AND HEIGHTS OF HIGH AND LOW WATERS

MAY

Day	Time	m	Time	m	Time	m	Time	m
1 W	0300	3.5	0833	0.2	1523	3.5	2053	0.6
2 TH	0338	3.4	0923	0.4	1606	3.3	2142	0.8
3 F	0419	3.2	1023	0.6	1653	3.0	2241	1.1
4 SA	0508	3.0	1144	0.8	1749	2.8		
5 SU	0000	1.3	0608	2.8	1302	0.8	1857	2.6
6 M	0120	1.3	0734	2.7	1404	0.7	2049	2.6
7 TU	0226	1.2	0916	2.8	1457	0.6	2156	2.7
8 W	0320	1.0	1012	3.0	1543	0.4	2242	2.9
9 TH	0404	0.8	1056	3.1	1623	0.3	2321	2.9
10 F	0440	0.6	1134	3.1	1658	0.3	2356	3.0
11 SA	0511	0.5	1208	3.1	1729	0.3		
12 SU ●	0026	3.1	0539	0.4	1240	3.1	1759	0.3
13 M	0055	3.1	0609	0.3	1311	3.1	1831	0.3
14 TU	0124	3.2	0642	0.3	1347	3.1	1908	0.3
15 W	0157	3.3	0720	0.2	1425	3.1	1949	0.4
16 TH	0232	3.3	0801	0.2	1505	3.0	2035	0.4
17 F	0307	3.3	0849	0.3	1548	2.9	2125	0.6
18 SA	0346	3.2	0943	0.4	1639	2.8	2221	0.7
19 SU	0432	3.1	1046	0.5	1745	2.7	2325	0.8
20 M	0534	2.9	1156	0.5	1904	2.6		
21 TU	0035	0.9	0656	2.9	1310	0.5	2025	2.7
22 W	0146	0.8	0824	3.0	1417	0.3	2136	2.9
23 TH	0252	0.6	0934	3.2	1515	0.2	2232	3.0
24 F	0348	0.4	1030	3.3	1605	0.1	2320	3.1
25 SA	0436	0.2	1120	3.4	1651	0.1		
26 SU ○	0004	3.3	0520	0.1	1209	3.5	1735	0.1
27 M	0046	3.3	0604	0.1	1256	3.5	1819	0.2
28 TU	0125	3.4	0647	0.1	1341	3.4	1904	0.4
29 W	0203	3.5	0731	0.1	1425	3.4	1950	0.5
30 TH	0241	3.5	0817	0.2	1508	3.3	2036	0.7
31 F	0320	3.4	0906	0.4	1553	3.1	2124	0.8

JUNE

Day	Time	m	Time	m	Time	m	Time	m
1 SA	0401	3.3	1000	0.5	1640	3.0	2215	1.0
2 SU	0447	3.1	1104	0.7	1733	2.8	2313	1.1
3 M	0541	3.0	1215	0.7	1829	2.7		
4 TU	0019	1.2	0644	2.8	1318	0.7	1929	2.7
5 W	0127	1.2	0758	2.8	1413	0.6	2036	2.7
6 TH	0229	1.1	0913	2.8	1502	0.6	2142	2.8
7 F	0321	0.9	1009	2.9	1545	0.5	2234	2.9
8 SA	0403	0.8	1052	2.9	1624	0.4	2315	3.0
9 SU	0440	0.6	1130	3.0	1659	0.4	2352	3.1
10 M	0514	0.5	1207	3.0	1734	0.4		
11 TU	0026	3.2	0548	0.4	1246	3.0	1811	0.4
12 W	0101	3.3	0625	0.3	1328	3.0	1852	0.4
13 TH	0138	3.3	0706	0.2	1412	3.0	1937	0.4
14 F	0216	3.4	0751	0.2	1457	3.0	2026	0.4
15 SA	0256	3.4	0841	0.2	1546	2.9	2117	0.5
16 SU	0338	3.4	0935	0.3	1640	2.9	2211	0.6
17 M	0426	3.3	1035	0.3	1741	2.8	2309	0.7
18 TU	0524	3.1	1140	0.4	1845	2.8		
19 W	0011	0.7	0632	3.1	1246	0.4	1952	2.8
20 TH	0117	0.7	0749	3.1	1350	0.3	2101	2.9
21 F	0224	0.6	0904	3.1	1449	0.3	2203	3.0
22 SA	0326	0.5	1007	3.2	1544	0.3	2256	3.1
23 SU	0420	0.4	1102	3.2	1634	0.3	2344	3.2
24 M ○	0508	0.2	1153	3.3	1721	0.4		
25 TU ●	0027	3.3	0552	0.2	1242	3.2	1806	0.5
26 W	0109	3.4	0636	0.2	1329	3.2	1851	0.5
27 TH	0148	3.4	0719	0.2	1414	3.1	1936	0.6
28 F	0226	3.5	0802	0.3	1457	3.1	2019	0.7
29 SA	0304	3.4	0845	0.4	1539	3.0	2102	0.7
30 SU	0343	3.3	0931	0.5	1622	3.0	2145	0.8

JULY

Day	Time	m	Time	m	Time	m	Time	m
1 M	0424	3.2	1021	0.6	1706	2.9	2230	0.9
2 TU	0508	3.1	1118	0.7	1752	2.9	2319	1.0
3 W	0557	2.9	1220	0.8	1840	2.8		
4 TH	0016	1.1	0651	2.8	1320	0.8	1930	2.8
5 F	0119	1.1	0753	2.7	1415	0.7	2028	2.8
6 SA	0224	1.1	0903	2.8	1505	0.7	2135	2.8
7 SU	0323	0.9	1006	2.8	1551	0.6	2234	2.9
8 M	0411	0.7	1057	2.9	1633	0.5	2320	3.0
9 TU	0453	0.6	1143	3.0	1714	0.5		
10 W ●	0002	3.2	0533	0.4	1229	3.0	1756	0.4
11 TH	0043	3.3	0613	0.3	1316	3.0	1840	0.4
12 F	0123	3.4	0656	0.2	1405	3.0	1926	0.4
13 SA	0205	3.5	0742	0.1	1453	3.0	2013	0.4
14 SU	0247	3.5	0829	0.1	1541	3.0	2102	0.4
15 M	0330	3.5	0920	0.1	1630	3.0	2152	0.4
16 TU	0416	3.5	1015	0.2	1720	3.0	2246	0.5
17 W	0506	3.4	1114	0.3	1812	2.9	2345	0.6
18 TH	0603	3.2	1219	0.4	1909	2.9		
19 F	0049	0.7	0708	3.1	1325	0.5	2020	2.8
20 SA	0201	0.7	0831	3.0	1430	0.6	2137	2.9
21 SU	0311	0.6	0951	3.0	1531	0.6	2238	3.0
22 M	0410	0.5	1054	3.0	1625	0.6	2329	3.2
23 TU	0501	0.3	1148	3.1	1714	0.6		
24 W ○	0014	3.3	0544	0.2	1238	3.1	1758	0.6
25 TH	0056	3.4	0625	0.2	1323	3.1	1839	0.6
26 F	0135	3.4	0704	0.2	1404	3.0	1918	0.6
27 SA	0212	3.4	0741	0.3	1441	3.0	1955	0.6
28 SU	0247	3.4	0819	0.4	1517	3.0	2032	0.7
29 M	0321	3.4	0857	0.5	1553	3.0	2109	0.7
30 TU	0355	3.3	0937	0.6	1630	3.0	2148	0.7
31 W	0432	3.2	1021	0.6	1709	3.0	2230	0.8

AUGUST

Day	Time	m	Time	m	Time	m	Time	m
1 TH	0512	3.0	1112	0.8	1751	2.9	2318	1.0
2 F	0559	2.9	1212	0.9	1838	2.8		
3 SA	0014	1.1	0656	2.7	1317	0.9	1932	2.8
4 SU	0120	1.1	0807	2.7	1422	0.9	2040	2.8
5 M	0237	1.0	0927	2.7	1521	0.8	2154	2.9
6 TU	0344	0.8	1036	2.9	1611	0.7	2253	3.0
7 W	0435	0.6	1130	3.0	1657	0.5	2341	3.2
8 TH ●	0518	0.4	1219	3.1	1740	0.4		
9 F	0025	3.4	0559	0.2	1308	3.1	1823	0.4
10 SA	0108	3.5	0641	0.0	1356	3.2	1908	0.3
11 SU	0151	3.6	0725	0.0	1441	3.2	1953	0.3
12 M	0234	3.7	0810	0.0	1524	3.2	2039	0.3
13 TU	0316	3.7	0857	0.1	1605	3.2	2127	0.4
14 W	0358	3.7	0947	0.2	1646	3.2	2218	0.5
15 TH	0443	3.5	1043	0.5	1730	3.1	2316	0.6
16 F	0531	3.3	1148	0.7	1820	2.9		
17 SA	0024	0.8	0628	3.0	1304	0.9	1925	2.8
18 SU	0146	0.9	0752	2.8	1419	0.9	2115	2.8
19 M	0302	0.9	0952	2.8	1525	0.9	2224	3.0
20 TU	0401	0.6	1056	3.0	1619	0.8	2316	3.2
21 W	0450	0.4	1147	3.1	1705	0.7		
22 TH ○	0001	3.3	0531	0.3	1232	3.1	1745	0.7
23 F	0042	3.4	0609	0.2	1311	3.1	1820	0.7
24 SA	0120	3.4	0643	0.3	1347	3.1	1853	0.7
25 SU	0154	3.4	0715	0.3	1418	3.1	1924	0.6
26 M	0225	3.4	0746	0.4	1447	3.1	1956	0.6
27 TU	0254	3.4	0819	0.5	1517	3.2	2030	0.6
28 W	0325	3.3	0853	0.6	1549	3.2	2106	0.6
29 TH	0357	3.2	0931	0.7	1624	3.1	2146	0.7
30 F	0434	3.1	1016	0.8	1703	3.0	2231	0.8
31 SA	0516	2.9	1111	1.0	1748	2.9	2326	1.1

Chart Datum: 1·62 metres below Ordnance Datum (Newlyn)

TIME ZONE (UTC)
For Summer Time add ONE hour in **non-shaded areas**

SCOTLAND – GREENOCK

LAT 55°57'N   LONG 4°46'W

TIMES AND HEIGHTS OF HIGH AND LOW WATERS

YEAR **2002**

SEPTEMBER

Day	Time m	Day	Time m
1 SU	0612 2.7 / 1218 1.1 / 1844 2.8	**16** M	0135 1.0 / 0719 2.7 / 1408 1.3 / 2053 2.9
2 M	0032 1.2 / 0726 2.6 / 1337 1.1 / 1955 2.8	**17** TU	0247 0.8 / 0955 2.8 / 1512 1.2 / 2207 3.1
3 TU	0152 1.1 / 0901 2.7 / 1454 1.0 / 2120 2.9	**18** W	0344 0.6 / 1050 3.0 / 1604 1.0 / 2257 3.3
4 W	0319 0.6 / 1024 2.9 / 1551 0.8 / 2228 3.1	**19** TH	0430 0.5 / 1134 3.1 / 1647 0.9 / 2340 3.4
5 TH	0414 0.6 / 1119 3.1 / 1637 0.6 / 2319 3.3	**20** F	0510 0.3 / 1213 3.2 / 1724 0.8
6 F	0458 0.3 / 1207 3.2 / 1720 0.5	**21** SA	0020 3.5 / 0544 0.3 / 1248 3.2 / ○ 1755 0.7
7 SA	0005 3.5 / 0539 0.1 / 1253 3.3 / ● 1801 0.3	**22** SU	0057 3.5 / 0616 0.3 / 1319 3.2 / 1824 0.7
8 SU	0050 3.7 / 0619 0.0 / 1337 3.3 / 1844 0.3	**23** M	0129 3.4 / 0644 0.4 / 1347 3.2 / 1851 0.6
9 M	0133 3.8 / 0701 -0.1 / 1418 3.4 / 1927 0.2	**24** TU	0158 3.4 / 0712 0.5 / 1413 3.3 / 1921 0.6
10 TU	0216 3.9 / 0744 0.0 / 1456 3.4 / 2012 0.3	**25** W	0225 3.4 / 0742 0.5 / 1441 3.3 / 1954 0.6
11 W	0257 3.9 / 0829 0.2 / 1533 3.4 / 2058 0.4	**26** TH	0255 3.3 / 0815 0.6 / 1511 3.3 / 2029 0.6
12 TH	0337 3.8 / 0916 0.4 / 1610 3.4 / 2148 0.5	**27** F	0327 3.3 / 0852 0.7 / 1545 3.3 / 2108 0.7
13 F	0418 3.6 / 1008 0.7 / 1651 3.2 / 2246 0.7	**28** SA	0402 3.1 / 0935 0.9 / 1621 3.2 / 2154 0.9
14 SA	0504 3.3 / 1115 1.0 / 1739 3.1	**29** SU	0442 2.9 / 1029 1.1 / 1703 3.0 / 2251 1.0
15 SU	0003 0.9 / 0557 3.0 / 1247 1.2 / 1839 2.9	**30** M	0536 2.7 / 1137 1.2 / 1758 2.9 / 2359 1.1

OCTOBER

Day	Time m	Day	Time m
1 TU	0659 2.6 / 1258 1.3 / 1916 2.8	**16** W	0219 0.9 / 0937 2.9 / 1446 1.4 / 2137 3.1
2 W	0120 1.1 / 0844 2.7 / 1424 1.2 / 2048 2.9	**17** TH	0315 0.7 / 1027 3.0 / 1538 1.2 / 2229 3.3
3 TH	0249 0.9 / 1010 2.9 / 1525 0.9 / 2201 3.2	**18** F	0401 0.6 / 1107 3.2 / 1620 1.0 / 2313 3.4
4 F	0347 0.5 / 1102 3.2 / 1613 0.7 / 2254 3.4	**19** SA	0441 0.5 / 1143 3.3 / 1657 0.8 / 2352 3.5
5 SA	0432 0.3 / 1147 3.3 / 1656 0.5 / 2341 3.6	**20** SU	0515 0.4 / 1216 3.3 / 1727 0.8
6 SU	0514 0.1 / 1230 3.4 / ● 1737 0.3	**21** M	0028 3.4 / 0545 0.5 / 1247 3.3 / ○ 1754 0.7
7 M	0027 3.8 / 0554 0.0 / 1311 3.5 / 1818 0.3	**22** TU	0100 3.4 / 0613 0.5 / 1314 3.4 / 1821 0.7
8 TU	0112 3.9 / 0635 0.0 / 1350 3.6 / 1901 0.2	**23** W	0128 3.3 / 0641 0.6 / 1340 3.4 / 1850 0.6
9 W	0155 3.9 / 0718 0.1 / 1427 3.6 / 1945 0.3	**24** TH	0156 3.3 / 0711 0.6 / 1408 3.5 / 1923 0.6
10 TH	0236 3.9 / 0802 0.3 / 1502 3.6 / 2031 0.4	**25** F	0228 3.3 / 0745 0.6 / 1440 3.5 / 2000 0.6
11 F	0316 3.8 / 0848 0.6 / 1540 3.6 / 2121 0.6	**26** SA	0303 3.3 / 0825 0.8 / 1514 3.5 / 2042 0.7
12 SA	0357 3.6 / 0939 0.9 / 1621 3.4 / 2220 0.8	**27** SU	0340 3.1 / 0910 0.9 / 1549 3.4 / 2130 0.8
13 SU	0443 3.3 / 1044 1.1 / 1709 3.2 / 2344 1.0	**28** M	0421 3.0 / 1044 1.1 / 1630 3.2 / 2228 1.0
14 M	0539 2.9 / 1210 1.2 / 1810 3.0	**29** TU	0517 2.8 / 1112 1.3 / 1724 3.1 / 2338 1.0
15 TU	0112 1.0 / 0708 2.7 / 1342 1.5 / 2008 3.0	**30** W	0643 2.7 / 1230 1.3 / 1842 3.0
		31 TH	0057 1.0 / 0822 2.8 / 1349 1.2 / 2014 3.1

NOVEMBER

Day	Time m	Day	Time m
1 F	0214 0.8 / 0942 3.0 / 1454 1.0 / 2130 3.3	**16** SA	0325 0.7 / 1027 3.2 / 1547 1.1 / 2238 3.3
2 SA	0314 0.5 / 1035 3.2 / 1546 0.8 / 2227 3.5	**17** SU	0406 0.6 / 1105 3.3 / 1626 0.9 / 2319 3.4
3 SU	0403 0.3 / 1121 3.4 / 1631 0.5 / 2316 3.7	**18** M	0443 0.6 / 1141 3.3 / 1658 0.8 / 2356 3.3
4 M	0447 0.2 / 1203 3.5 / ● 1714 0.4	**19** TU	0516 0.6 / 1213 3.4 / 1728 0.8
5 TU	0003 3.8 / 0529 0.1 / 1244 3.6 / 1756 0.3	**20** W	0029 3.3 / 0545 0.6 / 1243 3.5 / ○ 1756 0.7
6 W	0050 3.9 / 0611 0.2 / 1323 3.7 / 1839 0.3	**21** TH	0100 3.3 / 0615 0.6 / 1311 3.5 / 1827 0.7
7 TH	0134 3.9 / 0655 0.4 / 1401 3.7 / 1924 0.3	**22** F	0132 3.3 / 0648 0.7 / 1343 3.6 / 1902 0.6
8 F	0217 3.8 / 0740 0.6 / 1439 3.8 / 2011 0.5	**23** SA	0208 3.3 / 0726 0.7 / 1417 3.6 / 1941 0.6
9 SA	0259 3.7 / 0828 0.8 / 1517 3.7 / 2101 0.4	**24** SU	0246 3.2 / 0809 0.8 / 1452 3.6 / 2026 0.6
10 SU	0343 3.5 / 0919 1.1 / 1600 3.6 / 2200 0.8	**25** M	0327 3.1 / 0857 0.9 / 1530 3.5 / 2116 0.7
11 M	0431 3.2 / 1021 1.4 / 1648 3.4 / 2315 1.0	**26** TU	0413 3.0 / 0951 1.1 / 1613 3.4 / 2214 0.8
12 TU	0529 3.0 / 1141 1.5 / 1747 3.2	**27** W	0512 2.9 / 1054 1.2 / 1706 3.2 / 2321 0.8
13 W	0035 1.0 / 0644 2.8 / 1300 1.6 / 1907 3.1	**28** TH	0627 2.8 / 1204 1.2 / 1816 3.2
14 TH	0141 1.0 / 0842 2.9 / 1405 1.5 / 2048 3.1	**29** F	0031 0.8 / 0748 2.9 / 1314 1.2 / 1936 3.2
15 F	0237 0.8 / 0943 3.0 / 1501 1.3 / 2150 3.3	**30** SA	0140 0.7 / 0904 3.0 / 1420 1.0 / 2054 3.3

DECEMBER

Day	Time m	Day	Time m
1 SU	0241 0.5 / 1003 3.2 / 1517 0.8 / 2158 3.5	**16** M	0330 0.8 / 1020 3.1 / 1552 1.1 / 2242 3.1
2 M	0335 0.4 / 1053 3.4 / 1608 0.6 / 2252 3.6	**17** TU	0411 0.7 / 1104 3.3 / 1630 0.9 / 2324 3.2
3 TU	0423 0.3 / 1138 3.5 / 1655 0.4 / 2342 3.7	**18** W	0448 0.7 / 1141 3.4 / 1705 0.8
4 W	0509 0.4 / 1221 3.6 / ● 1739 0.4	**19** TH	0001 3.3 / 0522 0.7 / 1215 3.4 / ○ 1737 0.7
5 TH	0031 3.7 / 0553 0.4 / 1302 3.7 / 1824 0.3	**20** F	0037 3.2 / 0557 0.7 / 1248 3.5 / 1812 0.6
6 F	0118 3.7 / 0639 0.6 / 1342 3.8 / 1909 0.4	**21** SA	0115 3.2 / 0634 0.7 / 1323 3.6 / 1849 0.6
7 SA	0204 3.6 / 0726 0.7 / 1422 3.8 / 1956 0.4	**22** SU	0155 3.2 / 0714 0.7 / 1400 3.6 / 1931 0.5
8 SU	0248 3.5 / 0814 0.9 / 1502 3.8 / 2046 0.6	**23** M	0237 3.2 / 0759 0.7 / 1439 3.6 / 2016 0.5
9 M	0333 3.4 / 0903 1.1 / 1545 3.7 / 2139 0.7	**24** TU	0321 3.1 / 0847 0.8 / 1519 3.6 / 2105 0.5
10 TU	0421 3.2 / 0955 1.2 / 1630 3.5 / 2238 0.9	**25** W	0408 3.1 / 0938 0.8 / 1603 3.5 / 2159 0.5
11 W	0513 3.1 / 1054 1.4 / 1722 3.3 / 2346 1.0	**26** TH	0500 3.0 / 1034 0.9 / 1652 3.4 / 2259 0.6
12 TH	0610 3.0 / 1201 1.5 / 1821 3.2	**27** F	0559 2.9 / 1135 1.0 / 1749 3.3
13 F	0052 1.0 / 0710 2.9 / 1310 1.5 / 1928 3.1	**28** SA	0002 0.7 / 0703 2.9 / 1240 1.0 / 1854 3.3
14 SA	0152 0.9 / 0818 2.9 / 1413 1.4 / 2046 3.1	**29** SU	0108 0.6 / 0816 3.0 / 1347 1.0 / 2011 3.2
15 SU	0244 0.9 / 0927 3.0 / 1507 1.2 / 2152 3.1	**30** M	0211 0.6 / 0928 3.1 / 1452 0.8 / 2128 3.3
		31 TU	0311 0.6 / 1028 3.2 / 1550 0.7 / 2233 3.4

Chart Datum: 1·62 metres below Ordnance Datum (Newlyn)
Register for your **FREE** weekly weather email service from Macmillan Reeds
>> at **www.nauticaldata.com – NOW!** <<
weekend weather reports sent to your email address, every Thursday

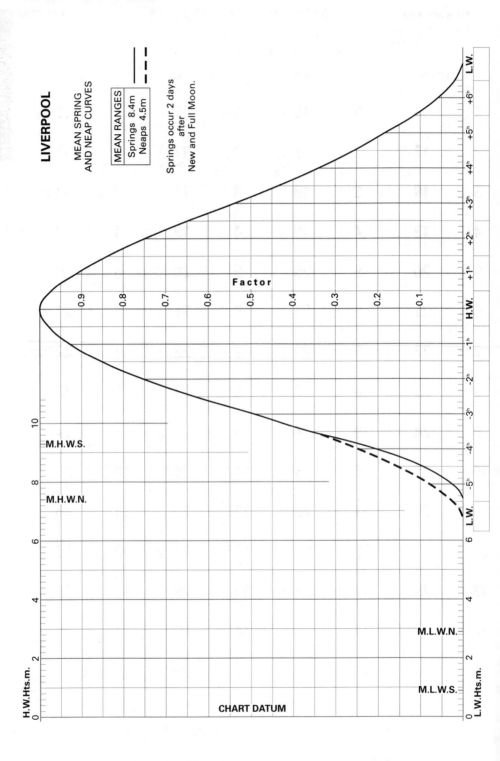

LIVERPOOL

MEAN SPRING
AND NEAP CURVES

MEAN RANGES
Springs 8.4m
Neaps 4.5m

Springs occur 2 days
after
New and Full Moon.

Factor

0.9 0.8 0.7 0.6 0.5 0.4 0.3 0.2 0.1

H.W.

+1ʰ +2ʰ +3ʰ +4ʰ +5ʰ +6ʰ L.W.

-1ʰ -2ʰ -3ʰ -4ʰ -5ʰ L.W.

M.H.W.S.
M.H.W.N.

H.W.Hts.m.

10   8   6   4   2   0

CHART DATUM

M.L.W.N.
M.L.W.S.

L.W.Hts.m.

6   4   2   0

TIME ZONE (UTC)
For Summer Time add ONE hour in **non-shaded areas**

ENGLAND – LIVERPOOL (ALFRED DK)

YEAR **2002**

LAT 53°24'N   LONG 3°01'W

TIMES AND HEIGHTS OF HIGH AND LOW WATERS

JANUARY

Day	Time / m	Day	Time / m
1 TU	0005 9.4 / 0642 1.2 / 1226 9.5 / 1917 1.1	**16** W	0041 8.8 / 0717 1.8 / 1256 9.1 / 1944 1.7
2 W	0053 9.4 / 0726 1.3 / 1313 9.6 / 2004 1.1	**17** TH	0115 8.7 / 0750 1.9 / 1331 9.0 / 2016 1.8
3 TH	0141 9.3 / 0812 1.4 / 1401 9.5 / 2052 1.2	**18** F	0150 8.5 / 0819 2.1 / 1408 8.8 / 2046 2.0
4 F	0230 9.1 / 0858 1.7 / 1451 9.3 / 2141 1.4	**19** SA	0226 8.3 / 0849 2.4 / 1445 8.6 / 2119 2.3
5 SA	0322 8.8 / 0948 1.9 / 1544 9.0 / 2234 1.7	**20** SU	0304 8.0 / 0927 2.6 / 1525 8.3 / 2158 2.5
6 SU	0418 8.4 / 1043 2.3 / 1642 8.6 / 2332 2.1	**21** M	0347 7.7 / 1013 2.9 / 1611 7.9 / 2247 2.8
7 M	0522 8.1 / 1145 2.6 / 1747 8.3	**22** TU	0439 7.4 / 1110 3.2 / 1707 7.6 / 2349 3.0
8 TU	0038 2.3 / 0631 7.9 / 1256 2.7 / 1858 8.2	**23** W	0542 7.2 / 1220 3.3 / 1812 7.5
9 W	0151 2.3 / 0741 8.0 / 1413 2.6 / 2008 8.2	**24** TH	0100 3.0 / 0654 7.3 / 1334 3.2 / 1921 7.7
10 TH	0300 2.2 / 0843 8.3 / 1524 2.3 / 2109 8.4	**25** F	0209 2.8 / 0802 7.7 / 1443 2.8 / 2027 8.0
11 F	0356 1.9 / 0936 8.6 / 1621 2.0 / 2202 8.7	**26** SA	0312 2.4 / 0901 8.2 / 1544 2.2 / 2125 8.5
12 SA	0444 1.7 / 1023 8.9 / 1709 1.7 / 2247 8.8	**27** SU	0408 1.9 / 0952 8.8 / 1640 1.7 / 2217 8.9
13 SU ●	0526 1.6 / 1104 9.1 / 1752 1.6 / 2328 8.9	**28** M ○	0459 1.5 / 1040 9.2 / 1732 1.2 / 2307 9.3
14 M	0605 1.6 / 1143 9.2 / 1832 1.5	**29** TU	0548 1.2 / 1127 9.6 / 1823 0.8 / 2354 9.6
15 TU	0005 8.9 / 0642 1.7 / 1220 9.2 / 1909 1.6	**30** W	0635 0.9 / 1214 9.9 / 1910 0.5
		31 TH	0042 9.7 / 0720 0.8 / 1301 10.0 / 1956 0.4

FEBRUARY

Day	Time / m	Day	Time / m
1 F	0129 9.7 / 0804 0.8 / 1348 10.0 / 2040 0.5	**16** SA	0126 8.7 / 0755 1.7 / 1343 9.0 / 2016 1.7
2 SA	0214 9.5 / 0846 1.0 / 1434 9.7 / 2123 0.9	**17** SU	0158 8.6 / 0822 1.9 / 1415 8.8 / 2043 1.9
3 SU	0300 9.2 / 0929 1.4 / 1521 9.3 / 2208 1.4	**18** M	0230 8.4 / 0854 2.1 / 1450 8.5 / 2116 2.2
4 M	0349 8.7 / 1016 1.9 / 1612 8.7 / 2258 2.0	**19** TU	0305 8.1 / 0932 2.5 / 1529 8.2 / 2156 2.6
5 TU	0444 8.1 / 1111 2.4 / 1711 8.1 / 2357 2.5	**20** W	0349 7.7 / 1020 2.9 / 1619 7.7 / 2249 3.0
6 W	0551 7.7 / 1218 2.8 / 1825 7.7	**21** TH	0447 7.3 / 1125 3.3 / 1724 7.4
7 TH	0110 2.8 / 0710 7.5 / 1341 3.0 / 1948 7.6	**22** F	0004 3.3 / 0601 7.2 / 1251 3.3 / 1841 7.3
8 F	0233 2.8 / 0824 7.8 / 1511 2.7 / 2058 7.9	**23** SA	0130 3.2 / 0723 7.4 / 1414 2.9 / 2000 7.7
9 SA	0342 2.5 / 0922 8.2 / 1614 2.3 / 2152 8.2	**24** SU	0246 2.7 / 0835 7.9 / 1526 2.3 / 2107 8.2
10 SU	0433 2.2 / 1010 8.6 / 1702 1.9 / 2237 8.5	**25** M	0351 2.1 / 0934 8.6 / 1626 1.5 / 2203 8.9
11 M	0515 1.9 / 1052 9.0 / 1743 1.6 / 2317 8.7	**26** TU	0446 1.5 / 1024 9.3 / 1720 0.9 / 2252 9.4
12 TU	0553 1.7 / 1129 9.1 / 1819 1.5 / 2351 8.8	**27** W ○	0536 0.9 / 1112 9.8 / 1809 0.3 / 2339 9.8
13 W	0629 1.6 / 1204 9.2 / 1853 1.4	**28** TH	0623 0.6 / 1158 10.1 / 1855 0.0
14 TH	0023 8.8 / 0702 1.6 / 1238 9.2 / 1924 1.4		
15 F	0055 8.8 / 0731 1.6 / 1310 9.1 / 1951 1.5		

MARCH

Day	Time / m	Day	Time / m
1 F	0024 10.0 / 0706 0.3 / 1243 10.3 / 1938 0.0	**16** SA	0030 8.9 / 0706 1.3 / 1245 9.1 / 1921 1.3
2 SA	0109 9.9 / 0748 0.3 / 1328 10.2 / 2019 0.1	**17** SU	0059 8.8 / 0730 1.4 / 1315 9.0 / 1944 1.4
3 SU	0152 9.7 / 0827 0.6 / 1411 9.9 / 2058 0.6	**18** M	0128 8.8 / 0756 1.5 / 1346 8.8 / 2012 1.6
4 M	0235 9.3 / 0907 1.0 / 1455 9.3 / 2139 1.3	**19** TU	0158 8.6 / 0827 1.8 / 1419 8.6 / 2043 1.9
5 TU	0318 8.8 / 0950 1.6 / 1542 8.6 / 2224 2.0	**20** W	0231 8.3 / 0902 2.2 / 1456 8.2 / 2118 2.4
6 W	0408 8.1 / 1041 2.3 / 1638 7.8 / 2320 2.7	**21** TH	0311 7.9 / 0944 2.6 / 1545 7.8 / 2205 2.9
7 TH	0512 7.5 / 1148 2.9 / 1755 7.2	**22** F	0407 7.5 / 1046 3.1 / 1650 7.3 / 2318 3.3
8 F	0033 3.2 / 0639 7.2 / 1314 3.1 / 1929 7.1	**23** SA	0524 7.1 / 1217 3.2 / 1813 7.2
9 SA	0206 3.2 / 0802 7.4 / 1459 2.9 / 2042 7.5	**24** SU	0054 3.3 / 0653 7.3 / 1351 2.8 / 1939 7.5
10 SU	0326 2.8 / 0903 7.9 / 1602 2.3 / 2135 8.0	**25** M	0222 2.8 / 0812 7.9 / 1507 2.1 / 2049 8.2
11 M	0418 2.4 / 0951 8.4 / 1647 1.9 / 2219 8.4	**26** TU	0332 2.1 / 0913 8.6 / 1609 1.3 / 2144 8.9
12 TU	0459 1.9 / 1032 8.8 / 1724 1.5 / 2256 8.7	**27** W	0428 1.4 / 1004 9.3 / 1701 0.6 / 2233 9.5
13 W	0535 1.6 / 1109 9.1 / 1758 1.3 / 2329 8.8	**28** TH ○	0517 0.7 / 1051 9.9 / 1748 0.1 / 2318 9.9
14 TH ●	0609 1.4 / 1142 9.1 / 1829 1.2	**29** F	0603 0.3 / 1137 10.2 / 1833 -0.2
15 F	0000 8.9 / 0640 1.3 / 1214 9.1 / 1856 1.2	**30** SA	0002 10.0 / 0646 0.1 / 1221 10.2 / 1914 -0.2
		31 SU	0045 10.0 / 0726 0.2 / 1305 10.1 / 1953 0.1

APRIL

Day	Time / m	Day	Time / m
1 M	0127 9.7 / 0806 0.4 / 1347 9.7 / 2031 0.7	**16** TU	0059 8.8 / 0733 1.4 / 1319 8.8 / 1944 1.5
2 TU	0208 9.3 / 0844 0.9 / 1430 9.1 / 2109 1.4	**17** W	0131 8.7 / 0805 1.6 / 1355 8.6 / 2017 1.8
3 W	0250 8.7 / 0926 1.6 / 1515 8.4 / 2152 2.2	**18** TH	0206 8.4 / 0841 2.0 / 1435 8.2 / 2054 2.3
4 TH	0336 8.1 / 1016 2.3 / 1610 7.6 / 2247 2.8	**19** F	0249 8.1 / 0926 2.4 / 1525 7.8 / 2143 2.8
5 F	0438 7.4 / 1122 2.9 / 1728 7.0	**20** SA	0346 7.6 / 1029 2.8 / 1631 7.4 / 2254 3.2
6 SA	0000 3.4 / 0607 7.1 / 1247 3.1 / 1901 6.9	**21** SU	0502 7.3 / 1157 2.9 / 1754 7.3
7 SU	0131 3.4 / 0730 7.3 / 1427 2.9 / 2013 7.2	**22** M	0026 3.2 / 0629 7.5 / 1327 2.6 / 1918 7.6
8 M	0253 3.0 / 0832 7.7 / 1532 2.4 / 2106 7.8	**23** TU	0154 2.7 / 0747 8.0 / 1443 1.9 / 2026 8.3
9 TU	0348 2.5 / 0922 8.2 / 1617 1.9 / 2149 8.2	**24** W	0305 2.0 / 0848 8.7 / 1544 1.1 / 2120 8.9
10 W	0430 2.0 / 1003 8.6 / 1653 1.6 / 2226 8.5	**25** TH	0403 1.3 / 0940 9.3 / 1636 0.5 / 2209 9.4
11 TH	0507 1.6 / 1041 8.9 / 1726 1.4 / 2259 8.7	**26** F	0453 0.8 / 1028 9.8 / 1723 0.1 / 2254 9.8
12 F ●	0540 1.4 / 1115 9.0 / 1755 1.2 / 2330 8.8	**27** SA ○	0539 0.4 / 1114 10.0 / 1807 0.0 / 2337 9.9
13 SA	0610 1.3 / 1146 9.0 / 1822 1.2	**28** SU	0623 0.2 / 1158 10.0 / 1848 0.1
14 SU	0000 8.9 / 0636 1.3 / 1217 9.0 / 1847 1.2	**29** M	0019 9.8 / 0704 0.3 / 1242 9.7 / 1926 0.5
15 M	0029 8.8 / 0703 1.3 / 1247 8.9 / 1915 1.3	**30** TU	0101 9.5 / 0744 0.6 / 1325 9.3 / 2004 1.0

Chart Datum: 4·93 metres below Ordnance Datum (Newlyn)
Register for your **FREE** weekly weather email service from Macmillan Reeds
》 at **www.nauticaldata.com – NOW!** 《
weekend weather reports sent to your email address, every Thursday

TIME ZONE (UTC)
For Summer Time add ONE hour in **non-shaded areas**

ENGLAND – LIVERPOOL (ALFRED DK)

LAT 53°24′N   LONG 3°01′W

TIMES AND HEIGHTS OF HIGH AND LOW WATERS

YEAR 2002

MAY

Day	Time m	Day	Time m
1 W	0142 9.1 / 0824 1.1 / 1407 8.8 / 2041 1.6	**16** TH	0112 8.7 / 0752 1.6 / 1339 8.6 / 2000 1.8
2 TH	0224 8.7 / 0907 1.7 / 1452 8.2 / 2124 2.3	**17** F	0153 8.6 / 0833 1.8 / 1424 8.4 / 2042 2.2
3 F	0310 8.1 / 0956 2.3 / 1544 7.5 / 2216 3.0	**18** SA	0240 8.3 / 0922 2.2 / 1516 8.0 / 2134 2.6
4 SA	0408 7.6 / 1057 2.8 / 1655 7.0 / 2324 3.4	**19** SU	0338 8.0 / 1025 2.4 / 1620 7.7 / 2242 2.8
5 SU	0529 7.2 / 1208 3.0 / 1819 6.9	**20** M	0448 7.8 / 1140 2.5 / 1736 7.6
6 M	0043 3.5 / 0647 7.3 / 1329 2.9 / 1929 7.1	**21** TU	0001 2.8 / 0605 7.9 / 1259 2.2 / 1851 7.8
7 TU	0201 3.2 / 0751 7.6 / 1440 2.6 / 2025 7.5	**22** W	0120 2.5 / 0717 8.2 / 1412 1.8 / 1957 8.3
8 W	0303 2.7 / 0843 8.0 / 1530 2.2 / 2110 8.0	**23** TH	0232 2.0 / 0820 8.7 / 1515 1.3 / 2054 8.8
9 TH	0349 2.3 / 0927 8.4 / 1610 1.8 / 2149 8.3	**24** F	0333 1.5 / 0915 9.1 / 1609 0.8 / 2144 9.2
10 F	0428 1.9 / 1006 8.6 / 1644 1.6 / 2225 8.6	**25** SA	0426 1.1 / 1005 9.4 / 1657 0.6 / 2230 9.5
11 SA	0502 1.6 / 1042 8.8 / 1715 1.4 / 2257 8.7	**26** SU	0515 0.8 / 1053 9.6 / 1741 0.5 / ○ 2314 9.6
12 SU	0534 1.4 / 1115 8.8 / 1745 1.3 / ● 2329 8.8	**27** M	0600 0.7 / 1138 9.5 / 1822 0.7 / 2357 9.5
13 M	0606 1.3 / 1148 8.8 / 1817 1.3	**28** TU	0644 0.8 / 1222 9.3 / 1902 1.0
14 TU	0001 8.8 / 0639 1.3 / 1222 8.8 / 1849 1.4	**29** W	0039 9.3 / 0726 1.0 / 1306 9.0 / 1940 1.4
15 W	0035 8.8 / 0714 1.4 / 1259 8.8 / 1924 1.5	**30** TH	0121 9.0 / 0808 1.3 / 1348 8.6 / 2018 1.9
		31 F	0203 8.7 / 0850 1.8 / 1431 8.2 / 2059 2.4

JUNE

Day	Time m	Day	Time m
1 SA	0247 8.3 / 0936 2.2 / 1518 7.7 / 2146 2.8	**16** SU	0235 8.7 / 0923 1.7 / 1509 8.4 / 2129 2.2
2 SU	0337 7.9 / 1027 2.6 / 1613 7.3 / 2243 3.2	**17** M	0330 8.5 / 1019 1.9 / 1607 8.2 / 2228 2.4
3 M	0439 7.5 / 1123 2.8 / 1722 7.0 / 2346 3.3	**18** TU	0431 8.4 / 1120 2.0 / 1712 8.0 / 2334 2.5
4 TU	0552 7.4 / 1223 2.9 / 1833 7.1	**19** W	0538 8.3 / 1226 2.0 / 1821 8.0
5 W	0052 3.3 / 0657 7.5 / 1324 2.8 / 1933 7.3	**20** TH	0044 2.4 / 0646 8.3 / 1336 1.9 / 1927 8.2
6 TH	0156 3.0 / 0755 7.7 / 1422 2.5 / 2025 7.7	**21** F	0156 2.2 / 0752 8.5 / 1444 1.7 / 2028 8.5
7 F	0252 2.6 / 0844 8.0 / 1512 2.2 / 2109 8.1	**22** SA	0304 1.9 / 0852 8.7 / 1543 1.5 / 2122 8.8
8 SA	0338 2.2 / 0927 8.3 / 1555 1.9 / 2148 8.4	**23** SU	0403 1.6 / 0947 8.9 / 1634 1.3 / 2211 9.1
9 SU	0420 1.9 / 1007 8.5 / 1635 1.6 / 2224 8.6	**24** M	0456 1.3 / 1037 9.0 / 1719 1.2 / ○ 2256 9.2
10 M	0500 1.6 / 1045 8.7 / 1714 1.5 / ● 2300 8.8	**25** TU	0544 1.2 / 1124 9.0 / 1802 1.3 / 2340 9.2
11 TU	0540 1.5 / 1123 8.8 / 1752 1.4 / 2337 8.9	**26** W	0629 1.2 / 1208 8.9 / 1843 1.4
12 W	0621 1.4 / 1203 8.8 / 1831 1.4	**27** TH	0022 9.2 / 0713 1.3 / 1254 8.8 / 1921 1.7
13 TH	0017 9.0 / 0703 1.4 / 1245 8.8 / 1911 1.5	**28** F	0103 9.0 / 0754 1.5 / 1330 8.5 / 1959 1.9
14 F	0100 8.9 / 0747 1.4 / 1330 8.8 / 1953 1.7	**29** SA	0143 8.8 / 0833 1.7 / 1409 8.3 / 2036 2.3
15 SA	0146 8.9 / 0833 1.5 / 1418 8.6 / 2038 1.9	**30** SU	0223 8.5 / 0912 2.1 / 1449 8.0 / 2114 2.6

JULY

Day	Time m	Day	Time m
1 M	0305 8.2 / 0951 2.3 / 1531 7.7 / 2156 2.9	**16** TU	0315 9.1 / 1003 1.4 / 1547 8.6 / 2209 2.0
2 TU	0351 7.9 / 1035 2.6 / 1620 7.4 / 2248 3.1	**17** W	0408 8.8 / 1054 1.7 / 1643 8.3 / 2306 2.3
3 W	0444 7.6 / 1125 2.8 / 1718 7.2 / 2348 3.2	**18** TH	0508 8.4 / 1153 2.1 / 1747 8.0
4 TH	0545 7.5 / 1222 2.9 / 1825 7.2	**19** F	0011 2.5 / 0615 8.1 / 1301 2.3 / 1857 7.9
5 F	0052 3.2 / 0650 7.5 / 1322 2.8 / 1928 7.4	**20** SA	0125 2.6 / 0728 8.1 / 1415 2.3 / 2006 8.1
6 SA	0155 2.9 / 0751 7.7 / 1421 2.6 / 2023 7.8	**21** SU	0243 2.4 / 0837 8.2 / 1523 2.1 / 2106 8.4
7 SU	0252 2.6 / 0845 7.9 / 1515 2.3 / 2111 8.2	**22** M	0351 2.1 / 0937 8.4 / 1619 1.9 / 2159 8.7
8 M	0345 2.2 / 0933 8.3 / 1604 2.0 / 2155 8.5	**23** TU	0447 1.7 / 1028 8.6 / 1706 1.7 / 2245 9.0
9 TU	0434 1.8 / 1019 8.5 / 1650 1.7 / 2237 8.8	**24** W	0536 1.5 / 1114 8.7 / 1749 1.6 / ○ 2327 9.1
10 W	0522 1.5 / 1103 8.8 / 1735 1.5 / ● 2320 9.1	**25** TH	0620 1.4 / 1156 8.8 / 1829 1.6
11 TH	0609 1.3 / 1149 8.9 / 1819 1.4	**26** F	0007 9.1 / 0700 1.4 / 1235 8.7 / 1906 1.7
12 F	0004 9.2 / 0656 1.1 / 1235 9.1 / 1903 1.4	**27** SA	0044 9.1 / 0737 1.5 / 1310 8.6 / 1940 1.8
13 SA	0050 9.3 / 0743 1.0 / 1321 9.1 / 1947 1.4	**28** SU	0120 9.0 / 0811 1.6 / 1344 8.5 / 2011 2.0
14 SU	0137 9.3 / 0829 1.0 / 1408 9.1 / 2032 1.5	**29** M	0156 8.8 / 0842 1.8 / 1418 8.3 / 2040 2.2
15 M	0225 9.3 / 0915 1.2 / 1456 8.9 / 2118 1.7	**30** TU	0232 8.5 / 0912 2.1 / 1453 8.1 / 2112 2.5
		31 W	0310 8.2 / 0945 2.3 / 1532 7.8 / 2152 2.8

AUGUST

Day	Time m	Day	Time m
1 TH	0353 7.9 / 1027 2.7 / 1617 7.5 / 2246 3.1	**16** F	0438 8.3 / 1121 2.3 / 1713 7.9 / 2343 2.7
2 F	0444 7.6 / 1122 2.9 / 1714 7.3 / 2354 3.3	**17** SA	0548 7.7 / 1230 2.7 / 1831 7.6
3 SA	0546 7.3 / 1229 3.1 / 1824 7.2	**18** SU	0103 2.9 / 0712 7.5 / 1353 2.9 / 1951 7.7
4 SU	0108 3.3 / 0656 7.3 / 1339 3.0 / 1936 7.5	**19** M	0238 2.7 / 0830 7.7 / 1513 2.6 / 2056 8.1
5 M	0218 2.9 / 0806 7.6 / 1443 2.7 / 2039 7.9	**20** TU	0350 2.3 / 0930 8.1 / 1611 2.3 / 2148 8.6
6 TU	0320 2.4 / 0906 8.0 / 1541 2.2 / 2131 8.4	**21** W	0443 1.9 / 1019 8.4 / 1657 2.0 / 2233 8.9
7 W	0416 1.9 / 0959 8.5 / 1633 1.8 / 2219 8.9	**22** TH	0527 1.5 / 1102 8.6 / 1737 1.7 / ○ 2313 9.1
8 TH	0508 1.4 / 1048 8.9 / 1722 1.5 / ● 2304 9.3	**23** F	0606 1.4 / 1139 8.7 / 1814 1.6 / 2349 9.2
9 F	0558 1.0 / 1135 9.2 / 1809 1.2 / 2350 9.6	**24** SA	0641 1.3 / 1213 8.8 / 1848 1.5
10 SA	0646 0.7 / 1221 9.4 / 1854 1.0	**25** SU	0022 9.1 / 0713 1.4 / 1244 8.7 / 1918 1.6
11 SU	0035 9.8 / 0731 0.5 / 1306 9.5 / 1937 0.9	**26** M	0055 9.0 / 0742 1.5 / 1315 8.6 / 1944 1.8
12 M	0121 9.8 / 0815 0.5 / 1351 9.4 / 2019 1.0	**27** TU	0126 8.9 / 0807 1.6 / 1345 8.5 / 2007 1.9
13 TU	0207 9.7 / 0857 0.7 / 1435 9.2 / 2101 1.2	**28** W	0158 8.7 / 0831 1.9 / 1416 8.3 / 2036 2.2
14 W	0253 9.4 / 0939 1.1 / 1521 8.9 / 2145 1.7	**29** TH	0232 8.4 / 0901 2.2 / 1450 8.1 / 2111 2.5
15 TH	0342 8.9 / 1026 1.7 / 1612 8.4 / 2238 2.2	**30** F	0310 8.1 / 0937 2.6 / 1530 7.7 / 2155 3.0
		31 SA	0357 7.6 / 1026 3.0 / 1622 7.3 / 2259 3.4

TIME ZONE (UTC)
For Summer Time add ONE hour in **non-shaded areas**

ENGLAND – LIVERPOOL (ALFRED DK)

YEAR **2002**

LAT 53°24′N LONG 3°01′W

TIMES AND HEIGHTS OF HIGH AND LOW WATERS

SEPTEMBER

Time	m		Time	m
1 SU	0458 7.2 / 1137 3.3 / 1731 7.1	**16** M	0050 3.1 / 0703 7.2 / 1339 3.3 / 1935 7.5	
2 M	0028 3.5 / 0613 7.1 / 1302 3.3 / 1854 7.2	**17** TU	0236 2.8 / 0819 7.5 / 1503 2.9 / 2040 8.0	
3 TU	0151 3.1 / 0736 7.4 / 1418 3.0 / 2012 7.7	**18** W	0342 2.3 / 0915 8.0 / 1558 2.4 / 2131 8.5	
4 W	0301 2.5 / 0846 7.9 / 1522 2.4 / 2111 8.4	**19** TH	0429 1.8 / 1001 8.4 / 1641 2.0 / 2213 8.9	
5 TH	0400 1.8 / 0942 8.5 / 1618 1.8 / 2200 9.1	**20** F	0507 1.5 / 1040 8.7 / 1718 1.7 / 2251 9.1	
6 F	0453 1.1 / 1030 9.1 / 1708 1.1 / 2246 9.6	**21** SA	0542 1.3 / 1115 8.8 / 1752 1.5 / ○ 2325 9.2	
7 SA	0542 0.6 / 1116 9.5 / 1754 0.8 / ● 2331 9.9	**22** SU	0613 1.2 / 1146 8.8 / 1823 1.4 / 2356 9.1	
8 SU	0628 0.2 / 1200 9.7 / 1838 0.6	**23** M	0642 1.3 / 1214 8.8 / 1851 1.5	
9 M	0015 10.1 / 0711 0.1 / 1244 9.8 / 1919 0.5	**24** TU	0026 9.0 / 0707 1.4 / 1243 8.8 / 1914 1.6	
10 TU	0059 10.1 / 0752 0.2 / 1327 9.7 / 1959 0.6	**25** W	0056 8.9 / 0730 1.5 / 1312 8.7 / 1938 1.7	
11 W	0143 9.8 / 0832 0.6 / 1410 9.4 / 2039 1.0	**26** TH	0126 8.7 / 0755 1.8 / 1342 8.5 / 2007 2.0	
12 TH	0228 9.4 / 0912 1.2 / 1453 8.9 / 2122 1.6	**27** F	0158 8.5 / 0825 2.1 / 1414 8.3 / 2040 2.3	
13 F	0315 8.7 / 0957 1.9 / 1541 8.3 / 2212 2.2	**28** SA	0235 8.1 / 0859 2.5 / 1452 7.9 / 2120 2.8	
14 SA	0410 8.0 / 1052 2.6 / 1642 7.7 / 2319 2.9	**29** SU	0321 7.7 / 0943 3.0 / 1543 7.5 / 2218 3.3	
15 SU	0526 7.3 / 1204 3.2 / 1808 7.3	**30** M	0423 7.2 / 1051 3.5 / 1653 7.1 / 2354 3.5	

OCTOBER

Time	m		Time	m
1 TU	0543 7.0 / 1228 3.5 / 1821 7.2	**16** W	0212 2.9 / 0754 7.4 / 1435 3.1 / 2012 7.9	
2 W	0126 3.1 / 0713 7.3 / 1353 3.1 / 1945 7.7	**17** TH	0315 2.4 / 0848 7.9 / 1530 2.6 / 2102 8.4	
3 TH	0240 2.4 / 0825 8.0 / 1501 2.4 / 2047 8.5	**18** F	0400 1.9 / 0932 8.3 / 1613 2.1 / 2145 8.8	
4 F	0341 1.6 / 0920 8.7 / 1558 1.7 / 2137 9.2	**19** SA	0437 1.6 / 1010 8.6 / 1649 1.7 / 2223 9.0	
5 SA	0432 0.8 / 1007 9.3 / 1648 1.1 / 2223 9.8	**20** SU	0509 1.4 / 1044 8.8 / 1723 1.5 / 2257 9.1	
6 SU	0519 0.3 / 1052 9.7 / 1733 0.6 / ● 2308 10.1	**21** M	0539 1.3 / 1115 8.9 / 1753 1.4 / ○ 2327 9.1	
7 M	0604 0.0 / 1135 9.9 / 1817 0.4 / 2351 10.2	**22** TU	0606 1.3 / 1143 8.9 / 1820 1.4 / 2356 9.0	
8 TU	0646 0.0 / 1218 9.9 / 1858 0.3	**23** W	0631 1.4 / 1212 8.9 / 1846 1.5	
9 W	0035 10.1 / 0726 0.2 / 1301 9.8 / 1938 0.6	**24** TH	0026 8.9 / 0657 1.5 / 1242 8.8 / 1914 1.7	
10 TH	0119 9.7 / 0805 0.7 / 1343 9.4 / 2018 1.0	**25** F	0058 8.7 / 0727 1.8 / 1313 8.6 / 1945 1.9	
11 F	0204 9.2 / 0845 1.4 / 1426 8.9 / 2101 1.6	**26** SA	0132 8.5 / 0758 2.1 / 1347 8.4 / 2019 2.2	
12 SA	0251 8.5 / 0929 2.2 / 1514 8.3 / 2152 2.3	**27** SU	0211 8.2 / 0834 2.5 / 1428 8.1 / 2101 2.7	
13 SU	0346 7.7 / 1025 2.9 / 1615 7.6 / 2301 2.9	**28** M	0259 7.8 / 0918 3.0 / 1520 7.7 / 2159 3.1	
14 M	0507 7.1 / 1139 3.4 / 1743 7.3	**29** TU	0401 7.3 / 1025 3.4 / 1629 7.4 / 2328 3.2	
15 TU	0033 3.2 / 0642 7.0 / 1313 3.5 / 1908 7.4	**30** W	0520 7.2 / 1156 3.5 / 1752 7.4	
		31 TH	0057 2.9 / 0646 7.4 / 1321 3.1 / 1913 7.9	

NOVEMBER

Time	m		Time	m
1 F	0212 2.2 / 0757 8.1 / 1432 2.4 / 2017 8.6	**16** SA	0317 2.3 / 0856 8.1 / 1534 2.4 / 2110 8.5	
2 SA	0314 1.5 / 0853 8.8 / 1531 1.7 / 2110 9.3	**17** SU	0356 1.9 / 0935 8.4 / 1613 2.1 / 2150 8.7	
3 SU	0406 0.8 / 0941 9.4 / 1622 1.1 / 2158 9.8	**18** M	0429 1.7 / 1011 8.7 / 1648 1.8 / 2225 8.9	
4 M	0454 0.4 / 1026 9.8 / 1709 0.7 / ● 2244 10.1	**19** TU	0500 1.5 / 1045 8.8 / 1720 1.6 / 2258 8.9	
5 TU	0538 0.2 / 1110 9.9 / 1754 0.5 / 2329 10.1	**20** W	0530 1.5 / 1114 8.9 / 1751 1.6 / ○ 2329 8.9	
6 W	0620 0.2 / 1153 9.9 / 1837 0.5	**21** TH	0601 1.5 / 1145 8.9 / 1823 1.6	
7 TH	0013 9.9 / 0701 0.5 / 1237 9.7 / 1919 0.7	**22** F	0002 8.9 / 0633 1.6 / 1218 8.9 / 1856 1.7	
8 F	0058 9.5 / 0741 1.0 / 1320 9.4 / 2001 1.1	**23** SA	0038 8.9 / 0706 1.8 / 1254 8.8 / 1932 1.9	
9 SA	0143 9.0 / 0822 1.6 / 1404 8.9 / 2046 1.7	**24** SU	0116 8.6 / 0742 2.0 / 1333 8.6 / 2011 2.1	
10 SU	0230 8.4 / 0907 2.3 / 1451 8.4 / 2137 2.3	**25** M	0159 8.4 / 0821 2.3 / 1417 8.4 / 2057 2.4	
11 M	0324 7.7 / 1000 3.0 / 1549 7.8 / 2240 2.8	**26** TU	0248 8.1 / 0909 2.7 / 1509 8.1 / 2154 2.7	
12 TU	0436 7.2 / 1107 3.4 / 1705 7.5 / 2355 3.1	**27** W	0346 7.7 / 1010 3.0 / 1612 7.9 / 2306 2.8	
13 W	0601 7.0 / 1225 3.5 / 1825 7.4	**28** TH	0456 7.6 / 1125 3.1 / 1724 7.9	
14 TH	0117 3.0 / 0713 7.2 / 1344 3.3 / 1931 7.7	**29** F	0023 2.6 / 0612 7.7 / 1241 2.9 / 1837 8.1	
15 F	0227 2.6 / 0809 7.6 / 1446 2.9 / 2025 8.1	**30** SA	0136 2.2 / 0723 8.0 / 1354 2.5 / 1943 8.6	

DECEMBER

Time	m		Time	m
1 SU	0241 1.7 / 0823 8.7 / 1459 1.9 / 2042 9.1	**16** M	0301 2.5 / 0856 8.0 / 1527 2.5 / 2113 8.3	
2 M	0338 1.2 / 0915 9.1 / 1556 1.4 / 2135 9.5	**17** TU	0344 2.1 / 0936 8.4 / 1609 2.2 / 2153 8.5	
3 TU	0428 0.8 / 1003 9.5 / 1647 1.1 / 2224 9.7	**18** W	0423 1.9 / 1013 8.7 / 1648 1.9 / 2230 8.7	
4 W	0515 0.7 / 1049 9.7 / 1735 0.9 / ● 2311 9.7	**19** TH	0501 1.7 / 1049 8.8 / 1727 1.8 / ○ 2307 8.8	
5 TH	0558 0.7 / 1134 9.7 / 1821 0.9 / 2357 9.6	**20** F	0538 1.6 / 1124 9.0 / 1806 1.7 / 2344 8.9	
6 F	0641 0.9 / 1218 9.6 / 1906 1.0	**21** SA	0616 1.6 / 1202 9.0 / 1847 1.6	
7 SA	0042 9.3 / 0722 1.3 / 1302 9.4 / 1950 1.3	**22** SU	0024 8.9 / 0655 1.7 / 1242 9.0 / 1928 1.7	
8 SU	0127 8.9 / 0804 1.8 / 1346 9.0 / 2035 1.7	**23** M	0107 8.8 / 0735 1.8 / 1325 9.0 / 2011 1.7	
9 M	0213 8.4 / 0848 2.3 / 1431 8.7 / 2122 2.1	**24** TU	0151 8.7 / 0817 2.0 / 1410 8.9 / 2057 1.9	
10 TU	0300 7.9 / 0935 2.8 / 1520 8.2 / 2212 2.5	**25** W	0238 8.5 / 0903 2.2 / 1459 8.7 / 2146 2.0	
11 W	0353 7.5 / 1028 3.1 / 1617 7.8 / 2307 2.8	**26** TH	0331 8.3 / 0955 2.4 / 1553 8.6 / 2242 2.2	
12 TH	0458 7.2 / 1128 3.4 / 1724 7.6	**27** F	0429 8.1 / 1054 2.6 / 1654 8.4 / 2345 2.3	
13 F	0006 3.0 / 0610 7.1 / 1232 3.4 / 1832 7.6	**28** SA	0536 7.9 / 1200 2.7 / 1801 8.3	
14 SA	0109 3.0 / 0715 7.3 / 1337 3.2 / 1934 7.7	**29** SU	0054 2.3 / 0645 8.0 / 1312 2.6 / 1910 8.4	
15 SU	0209 2.8 / 0810 7.7 / 1437 2.9 / 2027 8.0	**30** M	0206 2.1 / 0753 8.2 / 1426 2.3 / 2017 8.6	
		31 TU	0311 1.8 / 0853 8.7 / 1533 1.9 / 2117 8.9	

Chart Datum: 4·93 metres below Ordnance Datum (Newlyn)

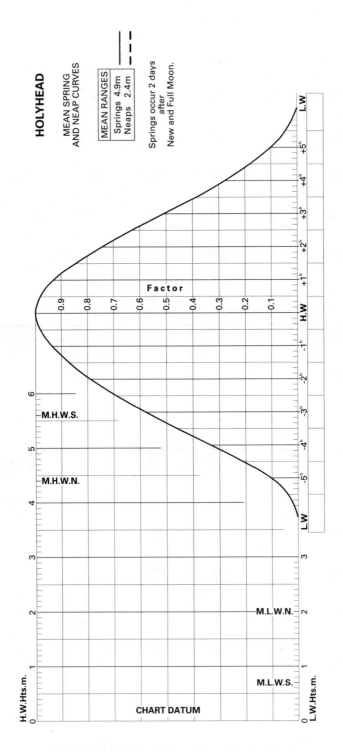

HOLYHEAD

MEAN SPRING
AND NEAP CURVES

MEAN RANGES	
Springs	4.9m
Neaps	2.4m

Springs occur 2 days
after
New and Full Moon.

Factor

0.9 0.8 0.7 0.6 0.5 0.4 0.3 0.2 0.1

H.W.Hts.m.

M.H.W.S.

M.H.W.N.

CHART DATUM

M.L.W.N.

M.L.W.S.

L.W.Hts.m.

TIME ZONE (UTC)
For Summer Time add ONE hour in **non-shaded areas**

WALES – HOLYHEAD
LAT 53°19'N   LONG 4°37'W

YEAR 2002

TIMES AND HEIGHTS OF HIGH AND LOW WATERS

JANUARY

Time m	Time m
1 0510 0.9 / 1126 5.8 / TU 1742 0.7 / 2354 5.6	**16** 0549 1.2 / 1201 5.5 / W 1814 1.1
2 0556 0.9 / 1212 5.8 / W 1830 0.7	**17** 0024 5.1 / 0623 1.3 / TH 1235 5.4 / 1849 1.2
3 0043 5.5 / 0643 1.0 / TH 1301 5.7 / 1920 0.8	**18** 0058 5.0 / 0658 1.5 / F 1311 5.3 / 1925 1.4
4 0135 5.3 / 0733 1.2 / F 1353 5.6 / 2015 0.9	**19** 0134 4.8 / 0734 1.6 / SA 1348 5.1 / 2003 1.3
5 0230 5.1 / 0828 1.4 / SA 1449 5.4 / 2115 1.1	**20** 0213 4.7 / 0815 1.9 / SU 1429 4.9 / 2046 1.7
6 0332 4.9 / 0930 1.6 / SU 1552 5.2 / 2220 1.3	**21** 0258 4.5 / 0902 2.1 / M 1517 4.7 / 2137 1.9
7 0440 4.8 / 1039 1.8 / M 1702 5.0 / 2329 1.4	**22** 0354 4.4 / 1000 2.2 / TU 1616 4.6 / 2239 2.0
8 0551 4.7 / 1151 1.8 / TU 1813 5.0	**23** 0505 4.3 / 1112 2.3 / W 1728 4.5 / 2349 2.0
9 0035 1.5 / 0657 4.8 / W 1301 1.7 / 1921 5.0	**24** 0620 4.4 / 1225 2.2 / TH 1842 4.6
10 0137 1.4 / 0756 5.0 / TH 1403 1.5 / 2021 5.1	**25** 0056 1.9 / 0724 4.6 / F 1330 1.9 / 1945 4.8
11 0232 1.4 / 0847 5.2 / F 1457 1.4 / 2113 5.2	**26** 0154 1.7 / 0818 4.9 / SA 1426 1.6 / 2039 5.0
12 0319 1.3 / 0931 5.4 / SA 1543 1.2 / 2157 5.2	**27** 0245 1.4 / 0904 5.2 / SU 1515 1.2 / 2127 5.3
13 0400 1.2 / 1012 5.5 / SU 1625 1.1 / ● 2238 5.2	**28** 0331 1.1 / 0947 5.5 / M 1601 0.8 / ○ 2212 5.5
14 0439 1.2 / 1050 5.6 / M 1703 1.1 / 2315 5.2	**29** 0415 0.8 / 1030 5.7 / TU 1645 0.5 / 2257 5.7
15 0515 1.2 / 1126 5.6 / TU 1740 1.1 / 2350 5.2	**30** 0459 0.6 / 1114 5.9 / W 1730 0.4 / 2342 5.7
	31 0543 0.6 / 1159 6.0 / TH 1816 0.3

FEBRUARY

Time m	Time m
1 0028 5.7 / 0627 0.6 / F 1245 6.0 / 1903 0.4	**16** 0028 5.1 / 0629 1.2 / SA 1242 5.4 / 1851 1.1
2 0115 5.5 / 0714 0.8 / SA 1333 5.8 / 1952 0.6	**17** 0100 5.0 / 0702 1.3 / SU 1315 5.3 / 1924 1.3
3 0204 5.3 / 0803 1.0 / SU 1423 5.5 / 2045 1.0	**18** 0133 4.9 / 0736 1.5 / M 1350 5.1 / 2000 1.5
4 0257 5.0 / 0858 1.4 / M 1520 5.2 / 2144 1.3	**19** 0209 4.7 / 0816 1.7 / TU 1430 4.8 / 2043 1.7
5 0358 4.7 / 1003 1.7 / TU 1627 4.9 / 2253 1.6	**20** 0254 4.5 / 0905 2.0 / W 1521 4.6 / 2138 2.0
6 0512 4.6 / 1120 1.9 / W 1748 4.7	**21** 0355 4.3 / 1013 2.2 / TH 1632 4.4 / 2253 2.1
7 0008 1.8 / 0631 4.6 / TH 1242 1.9 / 1911 4.6	**22** 0521 4.3 / 1140 2.2 / F 1804 4.4
8 0122 1.8 / 0742 4.7 / F 1355 1.7 / 2020 4.8	**23** 0018 2.1 / 0648 4.4 / SA 1302 1.9 / 1923 4.6
9 0223 1.7 / 0839 5.0 / SA 1453 1.5 / 2113 4.9	**24** 0130 1.8 / 0754 4.8 / SU 1406 1.5 / 2024 4.9
10 0311 1.5 / 0924 5.2 / SU 1538 1.3 / 2154 5.0	**25** 0228 1.4 / 0845 5.1 / M 1458 1.0 / 2113 5.3
11 0351 1.3 / 1001 5.4 / M 1615 1.1 / 2228 5.1	**26** 0316 1.0 / 0930 5.5 / TU 1545 0.6 / 2158 5.6
12 0426 1.2 / 1035 5.5 / TU 1649 1.0 / ● 2259 5.2	**27** 0400 0.7 / 1013 5.8 / W 1628 0.3 / ○ 2241 5.8
13 0458 1.1 / 1107 5.6 / W 1720 1.0 / 2329 5.2	**28** 0442 0.4 / 1056 6.1 / TH 1712 0.1 / 2323 5.9
14 0528 1.0 / 1138 5.6 / TH 1750 1.0 / 2358 5.2	
15 0559 1.1 / 1210 5.5 / F 1820 1.0	

MARCH

Time m	Time m
1 0524 0.3 / 1139 6.2 / F 1755 0.0	**16** 0532 0.9 / 1142 5.5 / SA 1750 0.9 / 2359 5.2
2 0006 5.8 / 0606 0.3 / SA 1224 6.1 / 1839 0.2	**17** 0601 1.0 / 1213 5.4 / SU 1819 1.0
3 0050 5.6 / 0651 0.5 / SU 1310 5.9 / 1925 0.5	**18** 0028 5.2 / 0632 1.1 / M 1245 5.3 / 1850 1.1
4 0135 5.4 / 0737 0.8 / M 1357 5.5 / 2013 0.9	**19** 0059 5.0 / 0705 1.3 / TU 1318 5.1 / 1924 1.3
5 0223 5.1 / 0829 1.2 / TU 1450 5.1 / 2109 1.4	**20** 0133 4.9 / 0743 1.5 / W 1356 4.9 / 2004 1.6
6 0319 4.7 / 0932 1.6 / W 1557 4.7 / 2217 1.9	**21** 0214 4.7 / 0831 1.8 / TH 1445 4.6 / 2057 1.9
7 0432 4.5 / 1053 1.9 / TH 1727 4.4 / 2341 2.1	**22** 0311 4.4 / 0936 2.0 / F 1556 4.4 / 2212 2.1
8 0603 4.4 / 1225 2.0 / F 1905 4.4	**23** 0436 4.3 / 1108 2.1 / SA 1736 4.3 / 2347 2.1
9 0105 2.1 / 0725 4.6 / SA 1345 1.8 / 2016 4.6	**24** 0616 4.4 / 1237 1.8 / SU 1904 4.5
10 0210 1.9 / 0825 4.8 / SU 1441 1.5 / 2104 4.8	**25** 0107 1.8 / 0728 4.7 / M 1345 1.4 / 2006 4.9
11 0257 1.6 / 0908 5.1 / M 1522 1.3 / 2139 5.0	**26** 0207 1.4 / 0822 5.2 / TU 1438 0.9 / 2055 5.3
12 0334 1.4 / 0942 5.3 / TU 1556 1.1 / 2209 5.1	**27** 0256 1.0 / 0908 5.6 / W 1523 0.4 / 2138 5.6
13 0406 1.2 / 1013 5.4 / W 1625 1.0 / 2236 5.2	**28** 0339 0.6 / 0951 5.9 / TH 1606 0.1 / ○ 2219 5.8
14 0435 1.0 / 1042 5.5 / TH 1653 0.9 / ● 2303 5.3	**29** 0420 0.3 / 1034 6.1 / F 1649 0.0 / 2300 5.9
15 0503 0.9 / 1112 5.5 / F 1721 0.9 / 2330 5.3	**30** 0502 0.2 / 1117 6.2 / SA 1731 0.0 / 2342 5.8
	31 0544 0.2 / 1201 6.1 / SU 1814 0.2

APRIL

Time m	Time m
1 0024 5.7 / 0628 0.4 / M 1247 5.8 / 1858 0.6	**16** 0000 5.3 / 0607 1.0 / TU 1219 5.2 / 1821 1.1
2 0108 5.4 / 0714 0.7 / TU 1334 5.4 / 1944 1.1	**17** 0033 5.2 / 0642 1.2 / W 1255 5.1 / 1858 1.3
3 0155 5.1 / 0806 1.2 / W 1427 4.9 / 2037 1.6	**18** 0109 5.0 / 0723 1.4 / TH 1336 4.9 / 1941 1.6
4 0248 4.8 / 0907 1.6 / TH 1532 4.5 / 2144 2.0	**19** 0153 4.8 / 0813 1.6 / F 1429 4.6 / 2036 1.8
5 0357 4.5 / 1028 1.9 / F 1704 4.2 / 2310 2.3	**20** 0252 4.6 / 0921 1.8 / SA 1542 4.4 / 2151 2.1
6 0527 4.4 / 1200 2.0 / SA 1844 4.2	**21** 0414 4.4 / 1049 1.8 / SU 1718 4.4 / 2322 2.1
7 0037 2.3 / 0653 4.5 / SU 1318 1.8 / 1953 4.5	**22** 0546 4.5 / 1212 1.6 / M 1841 4.6
8 0144 2.0 / 0755 4.7 / M 1413 1.6 / 2038 4.7	**23** 0040 1.8 / 0658 4.8 / TU 1318 1.2 / 1941 5.0
9 0231 1.7 / 0838 4.9 / TU 1453 1.3 / 2112 4.9	**24** 0141 1.4 / 0754 5.2 / W 1412 0.7 / 2030 5.3
10 0307 1.5 / 0912 5.1 / W 1526 1.1 / 2140 5.1	**25** 0230 1.0 / 0842 5.6 / TH 1459 0.4 / 2114 5.5
11 0338 1.2 / 0943 5.3 / TH 1555 1.0 / 2207 5.2	**26** 0314 0.6 / 0927 5.8 / F 1542 0.2 / 2155 5.7
12 0407 1.0 / 1013 5.4 / F 1623 0.9 / ● 2234 5.3	**27** 0357 0.4 / 1011 6.0 / SA 1625 0.1 / ○ 2236 5.8
13 0435 0.9 / 1043 5.4 / SA 1650 0.8 / 2301 5.3	**28** 0440 0.3 / 1056 6.0 / SU 1707 0.2 / 2319 5.8
14 0504 0.9 / 1114 5.4 / SU 1719 0.7 / 2330 5.3	**29** 0524 0.3 / 1141 5.8 / M 1751 0.5
15 0535 0.9 / 1145 5.4 / M 1750 1.0	**30** 0002 5.6 / 0609 0.5 / TU 1228 5.6 / 1834 0.8

Chart Datum: 3·05 metres below Ordnance Datum (Newlyn)

WALES – HOLYHEAD

YEAR 2002

LAT 53°19'N   LONG 4°37'W

TIMES AND HEIGHTS OF HIGH AND LOW WATERS

TIME ZONE (UTC)
For Summer Time add ONE hour in **non-shaded areas**

MAY

Day	Time m	Day	Time m
1 W	0046 5.4 / 0656 0.8 / 1315 5.2 / 1920 1.2	**16** TH	0015 5.2 / 0628 1.1 / 1241 5.1 / 1842 1.3
2 TH	0132 5.2 / 0747 1.2 / 1407 4.8 / 2011 1.7	**17** F	0056 5.1 / 0713 1.2 / 1327 4.9 / 1929 1.5
3 F	0223 4.9 / 0846 1.6 / 1509 4.4 / 2111 2.1	**18** SA	0145 5.0 / 0808 1.4 / 1424 4.7 / 2026 1.7
4 SA	0325 4.6 / 0958 1.9 / 1630 4.2 / 2229 2.3	**19** SU	0245 4.8 / 0914 1.5 / 1535 4.5 / 2137 1.9
5 SU	0442 4.4 / 1119 2.0 / 1758 4.2 / 2351 2.3	**20** M	0359 4.7 / 1031 1.5 / 1656 4.5 / 2256 1.9
6 M	0602 4.4 / 1232 1.9 / 1908 4.3	**21** TU	0517 4.8 / 1145 1.3 / 1811 4.7
7 TU	0059 2.1 / 0706 4.6 / 1329 1.7 / 1957 4.6	**22** W	0009 1.7 / 0626 5.0 / 1249 1.1 / 1912 4.9
8 W	0150 1.9 / 0754 4.8 / 1413 1.5 / 2034 4.8	**23** TH	0111 1.4 / 0725 5.2 / 1344 0.8 / 2003 5.2
9 TH	0230 1.6 / 0833 5.0 / 1448 1.3 / 2105 5.0	**24** F	0203 1.1 / 0816 5.5 / 1434 0.6 / 2049 5.4
10 F	0304 1.4 / 0908 5.1 / 1519 1.1 / 2134 5.1	**25** SA	0251 0.8 / 0905 5.6 / 1520 0.5 / 2133 5.6
11 SA	0335 1.2 / 0941 5.2 / 1550 1.0 / 2203 5.2	**26** SU	0337 0.6 / 0952 5.7 / 1604 0.5 / ○ 2216 5.6
12 SU	0406 1.1 / 1014 5.3 / 1620 0.9 / ● 2233 5.3	**27** M	0423 0.5 / 1038 5.7 / 1648 0.6 / 2259 5.7
13 M	0438 1.0 / 1047 5.3 / 1652 0.9 / 2304 5.3	**28** TU	0509 0.6 / 1125 5.5 / 1731 0.8 / 2343 5.6
14 TU	0512 1.0 / 1122 5.3 / 1725 1.0 / 2338 5.3	**29** W	0555 0.7 / 1212 5.3 / 1815 1.0
15 W	0548 1.0 / 1159 5.2 / 1802 1.1	**30** TH	0027 5.4 / 0641 0.9 / 1259 5.0 / 1859 1.3
		31 F	0113 5.2 / 0730 1.2 / 1347 4.7 / 1946 1.6

JUNE

Day	Time m	Day	Time m
1 SA	0159 5.0 / 0822 1.5 / 1440 4.5 / 2038 1.9	**16** SU	0139 5.2 / 0801 1.1 / 1417 4.9 / 2016 1.5
2 SU	0251 4.8 / 0920 1.7 / 1542 4.3 / 2139 2.2	**17** M	0236 5.1 / 0901 1.2 / 1520 4.8 / 2118 1.6
3 M	0351 4.6 / 1024 1.9 / 1653 4.2 / 2249 2.3	**18** TU	0339 5.0 / 1007 1.2 / 1628 4.7 / 2227 1.7
4 TU	0458 4.5 / 1130 1.9 / 1802 4.3 / 2357 2.2	**19** W	0447 5.0 / 1115 1.2 / 1738 4.7 / 2336 1.6
5 W	0603 4.5 / 1230 1.8 / 1900 4.4	**20** TH	0555 5.0 / 1219 1.1 / 1842 4.9
6 TH	0055 2.1 / 0700 4.6 / 1321 1.6 / 1946 4.6	**21** F	0041 1.5 / 0658 5.1 / 1319 1.0 / 1938 5.0
7 F	0144 1.8 / 0748 4.8 / 1404 1.5 / 2025 4.8	**22** SA	0140 1.3 / 0756 5.2 / 1413 1.0 / 2029 5.2
8 SA	0225 1.6 / 0831 4.9 / 1442 1.3 / 2100 5.0	**23** SU	0234 1.1 / 0850 5.3 / 1503 0.9 / 2116 5.4
9 SU	0303 1.4 / 0910 5.1 / 1517 1.2 / 2134 5.1	**24** M	0325 0.9 / 0940 5.4 / 1549 0.9 / ○ 2201 5.5
10 M	0339 1.2 / 0947 5.2 / 1553 1.1 / ● 2208 5.3	**25** TU	0413 0.8 / 1028 5.4 / 1633 0.9 / 2245 5.5
11 TU	0416 1.1 / 1025 5.2 / 1629 1.0 / 2243 5.3	**26** W	0458 0.8 / 1114 5.3 / 1716 1.0 / 2328 5.5
12 W	0455 1.0 / 1105 5.2 / 1707 1.0 / 2322 5.4	**27** TH	0543 0.9 / 1158 5.2 / 1757 1.1
13 TH	0536 0.9 / 1146 5.2 / 1748 1.1	**28** F	0010 5.5 / 0625 1.0 / 1240 5.0 / 1837 1.3
14 F	0003 5.4 / 0619 0.9 / 1232 5.1 / 1832 1.2	**29** SA	0051 5.3 / 0707 1.2 / 1322 4.8 / 1918 1.5
15 SA	0049 5.3 / 0708 1.0 / 1322 5.0 / 1921 1.3	**30** SU	0132 5.1 / 0750 1.4 / 1404 4.6 / 2001 1.7

JULY

Day	Time m	Day	Time m
1 M	0214 5.0 / 0835 1.6 / 1449 4.5 / 2048 1.9	**16** TU	0217 5.4 / 0840 0.9 / 1455 5.0 / 2053 1.3
2 TU	0301 4.8 / 0925 1.7 / 1542 4.3 / 2143 2.1	**17** W	0314 5.2 / 0939 1.1 / 1556 4.8 / 2156 1.5
3 W	0354 4.6 / 1021 1.9 / 1644 4.3 / 2245 2.2	**18** TH	0417 5.1 / 1044 1.3 / 1703 4.7 / 2306 1.6
4 TH	0456 4.5 / 1122 1.9 / 1751 4.3 / 2351 2.2	**19** F	0527 4.9 / 1152 1.4 / 1813 4.7
5 F	0601 4.5 / 1222 1.9 / 1852 4.4	**20** SA	0018 1.6 / 0639 4.9 / 1259 1.4 / 1919 4.9
6 SA	0052 2.1 / 0702 4.6 / 1317 1.7 / 1943 4.6	**21** SU	0127 1.5 / 0747 4.9 / 1400 1.4 / 2017 5.0
7 SU	0146 1.8 / 0756 4.7 / 1405 1.6 / 2028 4.8	**22** M	0228 1.4 / 0847 5.0 / 1454 1.3 / 2108 5.2
8 M	0233 1.6 / 0843 4.9 / 1449 1.4 / 2108 5.0	**23** TU	0321 1.2 / 0938 5.1 / 1541 1.2 / 2153 5.4
9 TU	0317 1.3 / 0927 5.1 / 1531 1.2 / 2147 5.2	**24** W	0408 1.0 / 1023 5.2 / 1622 1.1 / ○ 2234 5.5
10 W	0359 1.1 / 1009 5.2 / 1612 1.1 / ● 2227 5.4	**25** TH	0449 0.9 / 1103 5.2 / 1701 1.1 / 2312 5.5
11 TH	0441 0.9 / 1051 5.3 / 1653 1.0 / 2308 5.5	**26** F	0528 0.9 / 1140 5.2 / 1738 1.1 / 2349 5.5
12 F	0525 0.7 / 1135 5.4 / 1737 0.9 / 2352 5.6	**27** SA	0604 1.0 / 1215 5.1 / 1813 1.2
13 SA	0610 0.7 / 1221 5.4 / 1821 0.9	**28** SU	0025 5.4 / 0639 1.1 / 1250 5.0 / 1848 1.3
14 SU	0037 5.6 / 0656 0.7 / 1310 5.3 / 1908 1.0	**29** M	0100 5.3 / 0656 1.2 / 1324 4.8 / 1924 1.5
15 M	0126 5.5 / 0746 0.8 / 1400 5.1 / 1958 1.2	**30** TU	0136 5.1 / 0751 1.4 / 1401 4.7 / 2002 1.7
		31 W	0215 4.9 / 0831 1.6 / 1443 4.5 / 2046 1.9

AUGUST

Day	Time m	Day	Time m
1 TH	0259 4.7 / 0917 1.8 / 1533 4.4 / 2139 2.1	**16** F	0349 5.0 / 1013 1.6 / 1630 4.7 / 2240 1.8
2 F	0353 4.5 / 1014 2.0 / 1637 4.3 / 2247 2.3	**17** SA	0506 4.7 / 1128 1.8 / 1750 4.6
3 SA	0501 4.4 / 1122 2.1 / 1753 4.3	**18** SU	0003 1.8 / 0633 4.6 / 1246 1.8 / 1907 4.9
4 SU	0002 2.2 / 0617 4.4 / 1232 2.0 / 1902 4.5	**19** M	0123 1.7 / 0751 4.7 / 1354 1.7 / 2012 5.0
5 M	0111 2.0 / 0726 4.6 / 1334 1.8 / 1959 4.7	**20** TU	0228 1.5 / 0851 4.9 / 1449 1.6 / 2102 5.2
6 TU	0209 1.7 / 0823 4.8 / 1427 1.6 / 2046 5.0	**21** W	0318 1.3 / 0936 5.0 / 1532 1.4 / 2143 5.4
7 W	0259 1.4 / 0911 5.0 / 1513 1.3 / 2129 5.3	**22** TH	0358 1.1 / 1013 5.1 / 1609 1.2 / ○ 2218 5.5
8 TH	0343 1.0 / 0954 5.3 / 1556 1.0 / ● 2210 5.6	**23** F	0433 1.0 / 1045 5.2 / 1642 1.1 / 2251 5.6
9 F	0426 0.7 / 1037 5.5 / 1638 0.8 / 2252 5.8	**24** SA	0506 0.9 / 1116 5.2 / 1714 1.0 / 2323 5.6
10 SA	0509 0.5 / 1120 5.6 / 1720 0.6 / 2335 5.9	**25** SU	0536 0.9 / 1145 5.2 / 1745 1.1 / 2355 5.5
11 SU	0552 0.3 / 1203 5.6 / 1803 0.6	**26** M	0607 1.0 / 1215 5.1 / 1816 1.1
12 M	0019 5.9 / 0636 0.4 / 1250 5.5 / 1847 0.7	**27** TU	0027 5.4 / 0637 1.1 / 1247 5.0 / 1847 1.3
13 TU	0105 5.8 / 0723 0.6 / 1335 5.4 / 1934 0.9	**28** W	0100 5.2 / 0709 1.3 / 1319 4.9 / 1922 1.6
14 W	0153 5.6 / 0812 0.8 / 1425 5.1 / 2026 1.2	**29** TH	0134 5.1 / 0744 1.5 / 1354 4.7 / 2000 1.8
15 TH	0246 5.3 / 0908 1.1 / 1522 4.9 / 2126 1.5	**30** F	0212 4.9 / 0824 1.8 / 1437 4.6 / 2047 2.1
		31 SA	0301 4.6 / 0915 2.0 / 1533 4.4 / 2151 2.3

Chart Datum: 3·05 metres below Ordnance Datum (Newlyn)

TIME ZONE (UTC)
For Summer Time add ONE hour in **non-shaded areas**

WALES – HOLYHEAD

LAT 53°19′N   LONG 4°37′W

TIMES AND HEIGHTS OF HIGH AND LOW WATERS

YEAR **2002**

SEPTEMBER

Day	Time	m	Day	Time	m
1 SU	0408 / 1025 / 1655 / 2317	4.3 / 2.3 / 4.3 / 2.3	**16** M	0634 / 1234 / 1856	4.5 / 2.2 / 4.7
2 M	0540 / 1152 / 1825	4.3 / 2.3 / 4.4	**17** TU	0117 / 0752 / 1345 / 2001	1.8 / 4.6 / 2.0 / 5.0
3 TU	0042 / 0704 / 1308 / 1933	2.1 / 4.5 / 2.0 / 4.7	**18** W	0219 / 0844 / 1436 / 2047	1.5 / 4.9 / 1.7 / 5.2
4 W	0147 / 0806 / 1407 / 2025	1.7 / 4.8 / 1.7 / 5.1	**19** TH	0303 / 0922 / 1516 / 2124	1.3 / 5.0 / 1.5 / 5.4
5 TH	0239 / 0854 / 1454 / 2108	1.3 / 5.1 / 1.4 / 5.4	**20** F	0339 / 0953 / 1548 / 2155	1.1 / 5.2 / 1.3 / 5.5
6 F	0323 / 0936 / 1537 / 2149	0.8 / 5.4 / 0.9 / 5.8	**21** SA	0409 / 1020 / 1647 / ○ 2225	1.0 / 5.3 / 1.1 / 5.6
7 SA	0405 / 1017 / 1617 / ● 2230	0.4 / 5.7 / 0.6 / 6.0	**22** SU	0438 / 1047 / 1647 / 2254	1.0 / 5.3 / 1.1 / 5.6
8 SU	0447 / 1058 / 1658 / 2312	0.2 / 5.8 / 0.4 / 6.2	**23** M	0505 / 1115 / 1715 / 2324	0.9 / 5.1 / 1.1 / 5.6
9 M	0528 / 1140 / 1740 / 2356	0.1 / 5.8 / 0.4 / 6.1	**24** TU	0533 / 1142 / 1745 / 2355	1.0 / 5.3 / 1.1 / 5.5
10 TU	0612 / 1222 / 1823	0.2 / 5.7 / 0.5	**25** W	0602 / 1212 / 1815	1.1 / 5.2 / 1.3
11 W	0041 / 0656 / 1308 / 1909	6.0 / 0.5 / 5.5 / 0.8	**26** TH	0026 / 0632 / 1243 / 1848	5.3 / 1.3 / 5.1 / 1.5
12 TH	0128 / 0744 / 1355 / 2000	5.7 / 0.9 / 5.2 / 1.1	**27** F	0059 / 0705 / 1316 / 1925	5.1 / 1.5 / 4.9 / 1.7
13 F	0221 / 0838 / 1450 / 2101	5.3 / 1.4 / 4.9 / 1.6	**28** SA	0136 / 0744 / 1355 / 2011	4.9 / 1.8 / 4.7 / 2.0
14 SA	0326 / 0944 / 1601 / 2221	4.8 / 1.8 / 4.6 / 1.9	**29** SU	0223 / 0833 / 1449 / 2114	4.6 / 2.1 / 4.5 / 2.2
15 SU	0453 / 1108 / 1730 / 2354	4.5 / 2.1 / 4.6 / 2.0	**30** M	0331 / 0943 / 1610 / 2243	4.3 / 2.3 / 4.4 / 2.3

OCTOBER

Day	Time	m	Day	Time	m
1 TU	0511 / 1118 / 1750	4.3 / 2.4 / 4.4	**16** W	0055 / 0732 / 1321 / 1934	1.9 / 4.6 / 2.1 / 4.9
2 W	0014 / 0641 / 1242 / 1904	2.0 / 4.5 / 2.1 / 4.8	**17** TH	0154 / 0821 / 1411 / 2019	1.6 / 4.8 / 1.8 / 5.1
3 TH	0122 / 0744 / 1342 / 1958	1.6 / 4.9 / 1.7 / 5.2	**18** F	0236 / 0856 / 1449 / 2055	1.4 / 5.0 / 1.6 / 5.3
4 F	0214 / 0831 / 1430 / 2043	1.1 / 5.3 / 1.2 / 5.6	**19** SA	0310 / 0925 / 1521 / 2126	1.2 / 5.2 / 1.4 / 5.4
5 SA	0259 / 0913 / 1512 / 2124	0.7 / 5.6 / 0.8 / 5.9	**20** SU	0339 / 0951 / 1550 / 2155	1.1 / 5.3 / 1.2 / 5.5
6 SU	0340 / 0953 / 1553 / ● 2206	0.3 / 5.8 / 0.5 / 6.2	**21** M	0407 / 1017 / 1618 / ○ 2225	1.0 / 5.4 / 1.1 / 5.6
7 M	0421 / 1033 / 1634 / 2248	0.1 / 6.0 / 0.3 / 6.3	**22** TU	0434 / 1044 / 1647 / 2255	1.0 / 5.4 / 1.1 / 5.5
8 TU	0503 / 1114 / 1716 / 2332	0.1 / 6.0 / 0.3 / 6.2	**23** W	0502 / 1113 / 1717 / 2327	1.1 / 5.4 / 1.2 / 5.4
9 W	0546 / 1157 / 1801	0.3 / 5.8 / 0.5	**24** TH	0531 / 1142 / 1749 / 2359	1.2 / 5.3 / 1.3 / 5.3
10 TH	0018 / 0630 / 1242 / 1848	6.0 / 0.6 / 5.6 / 0.8	**25** F	0603 / 1214 / 1824	1.3 / 5.2 / 1.4
11 F	0107 / 0718 / 1330 / 1940	5.6 / 1.1 / 5.3 / 1.2	**26** SA	0034 / 0637 / 1249 / 1902	5.1 / 1.5 / 5.1 / 1.6
12 SA	0201 / 0811 / 1425 / 2043	5.1 / 1.6 / 5.0 / 1.6	**27** SU	0114 / 0718 / 1331 / 1951	4.9 / 1.8 / 4.9 / 1.8
13 SU	0308 / 0918 / 1535 / 2204	4.7 / 2.1 / 4.7 / 1.9	**28** M	0204 / 0809 / 1426 / 2054	4.7 / 2.1 / 4.7 / 2.0
14 M	0440 / 1043 / 1704 / 2336	4.4 / 2.4 / 4.6 / 2.0	**29** TU	0313 / 0919 / 1544 / 2219	4.4 / 2.3 / 4.5 / 2.1
15 TU	0620 / 1211 / 1830	4.4 / 2.3 / 4.7	**30** W	0446 / 1048 / 1716 / 2344	4.4 / 2.3 / 4.6 / 1.9
			31 TH	0613 / 1210 / 1831	4.6 / 2.0 / 4.9

NOVEMBER

Day	Time	m	Day	Time	m
1 F	0051 / 0715 / 1312 / 1927	1.5 / 5.0 / 1.7 / 5.3	**16** SA	0157 / 0819 / 1414 / 2018	1.6 / 4.9 / 1.8 / 5.1
2 SA	0145 / 0804 / 1402 / 2015	1.0 / 5.3 / 1.2 / 5.6	**17** SU	0234 / 0851 / 1449 / 2053	1.4 / 5.1 / 1.6 / 5.3
3 SU	0231 / 0847 / 1446 / 2059	0.6 / 5.6 / 0.9 / 5.9	**18** M	0306 / 0920 / 1521 / 2126	1.3 / 5.2 / 1.4 / 5.4
4 M	0315 / 0928 / 1529 / ● 2142	0.4 / 5.8 / 0.6 / 6.1	**19** TU	0335 / 0949 / 1552 / 2158	1.2 / 5.3 / 1.3 / 5.4
5 TU	0357 / 1009 / 1612 / 2227	0.3 / 5.9 / 0.4 / 6.2	**20** W	0405 / 1018 / 1624 / ○ 2231	1.2 / 5.4 / 1.2 / 5.4
6 W	0440 / 1052 / 1657 / 2313	0.3 / 5.9 / 0.4 / 6.0	**21** TH	0436 / 1048 / 1656 / 2305	1.2 / 5.4 / 1.2 / 5.4
7 TH	0524 / 1136 / 1743	0.5 / 5.8 / 0.6	**22** F	0508 / 1121 / 1731 / 2340	1.2 / 5.4 / 1.3 / 5.3
8 F	0001 / 0609 / 1222 / 1832	5.8 / 0.9 / 5.7 / 0.9	**23** SA	0543 / 1156 / 1809	1.3 / 5.3 / 1.3
9 SA	0051 / 0657 / 1310 / 1925	5.4 / 1.3 / 5.4 / 1.2	**24** SU	0019 / 0620 / 1235 / 1852	5.1 / 1.5 / 5.2 / 1.5
10 SU	0146 / 0749 / 1403 / 2026	5.0 / 1.7 / 5.1 / 1.6	**25** M	0104 / 0704 / 1320 / 1942	5.0 / 1.7 / 5.1 / 1.6
11 M	0250 / 0850 / 1507 / 2138	4.6 / 2.1 / 4.8 / 1.9	**26** TU	0156 / 0756 / 1415 / 2042	4.8 / 1.9 / 4.9 / 1.7
12 TU	0410 / 1007 / 1624 / 2259	4.4 / 2.4 / 4.7 / 2.0	**27** W	0300 / 0901 / 1523 / 2154	4.6 / 2.1 / 4.8 / 1.8
13 W	0538 / 1128 / 1742	4.3 / 2.4 / 4.7	**28** TH	0418 / 1017 / 1640 / 2309	4.6 / 2.1 / 4.8 / 1.6
14 TH	0012 / 0649 / 1238 / 1848	2.0 / 4.5 / 2.3 / 4.8	**29** F	0535 / 1132 / 1752	4.7 / 2.0 / 5.0
15 F	0112 / 0741 / 1332 / 1938	1.8 / 4.7 / 2.1 / 5.0	**30** SA	0016 / 0640 / 1237 / 1853	1.4 / 4.9 / 1.7 / 5.3

DECEMBER

Day	Time	m	Day	Time	m
1 SU	0114 / 0734 / 1333 / 1947	1.1 / 5.2 / 1.4 / 5.5	**16** M	0152 / 0814 / 1414 / 2019	1.7 / 4.9 / 1.8 / 5.0
2 M	0205 / 0822 / 1423 / 2037	0.8 / 5.5 / 1.0 / 5.7	**17** TU	0231 / 0850 / 1453 / 2059	1.6 / 5.0 / 1.6 / 5.1
3 TU	0252 / 0907 / 1510 / 2125	0.7 / 5.7 / 0.8 / 5.9	**18** W	0307 / 0924 / 1529 / 2136	1.4 / 5.2 / 1.5 / 5.2
4 W	0338 / 0951 / 1557 / ● 2213	0.6 / 5.8 / 0.7 / 5.9	**19** TH	0341 / 0957 / 1605 / ○ 2213	1.3 / 5.3 / 1.3 / 5.3
5 TH	0423 / 1035 / 1645 / 2301	0.6 / 5.8 / 0.7 / 5.8	**20** F	0416 / 1030 / 1642 / 2250	1.3 / 5.4 / 1.2 / 5.3
6 F	0508 / 1120 / 1732 / 2349	0.8 / 5.8 / 0.7 / 5.6	**21** SA	0452 / 1106 / 1720 / 2329	1.2 / 5.5 / 1.1 / 5.3
7 SA	0553 / 1206 / 1821	1.0 / 5.7 / 0.9	**22** SU	0530 / 1144 / 1801	1.2 / 5.5 / 1.1
8 SU	0038 / 0639 / 1253 / 1911	5.3 / 1.3 / 5.5 / 1.2	**23** M	0010 / 0610 / 1226 / 1844	5.2 / 1.3 / 5.4 / 1.2
9 M	0129 / 0727 / 1342 / 2003	5.0 / 1.6 / 5.3 / 1.5	**24** TU	0056 / 0655 / 1312 / 1932	5.1 / 1.4 / 5.4 / 1.3
10 TU	0222 / 0818 / 1434 / 2101	4.7 / 2.0 / 5.0 / 1.7	**25** W	0145 / 0744 / 1403 / 2026	5.0 / 1.5 / 5.2 / 1.3
11 W	0322 / 0917 / 1532 / 2204	4.5 / 2.2 / 4.8 / 1.9	**26** TH	0241 / 0839 / 1500 / 2126	4.9 / 1.8 / 5.1 / 1.4
12 TH	0431 / 1025 / 1637 / 2310	4.3 / 2.4 / 4.7 / 2.0	**27** F	0344 / 0943 / 1604 / 2233	4.8 / 1.8 / 5.1 / 1.4
13 F	0542 / 1135 / 1744	4.3 / 2.4 / 4.6	**28** SA	0454 / 1053 / 1713 / 2340	4.7 / 1.8 / 5.0 / 1.4
14 SA	0012 / 0643 / 1238 / 1843	2.0 / 4.5 / 2.3 / 4.7	**29** SU	0603 / 1202 / 1822	4.8 / 1.7 / 5.1
15 SU	0106 / 0733 / 1330 / 1935	1.9 / 4.7 / 2.1 / 4.8	**30** M	0044 / 0705 / 1307 / 1925	1.3 / 5.0 / 1.5 / 5.2
			31 TU	0143 / 0801 / 1406 / 2023	1.2 / 5.2 / 1.3 / 5.4

Chart Datum: 3·05 metres below Ordnance Datum (Newlyn)

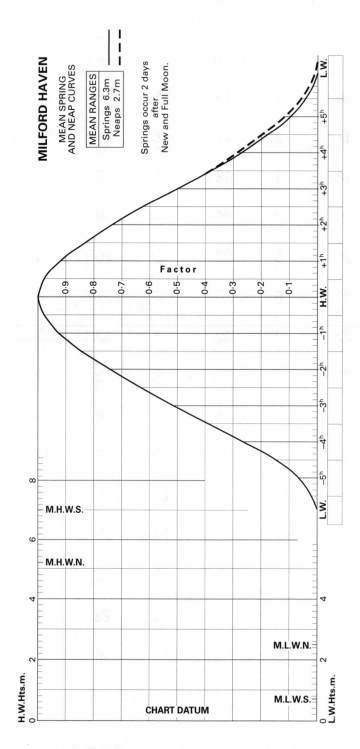

MILFORD HAVEN

MEAN SPRING
AND NEAP CURVES

MEAN RANGES
Springs 6.3m
Neaps 2.7m

Springs occur 2 days
after
New and Full Moon.

TIME ZONE (UTC)
For Summer Time add ONE hour in **non-shaded areas**

WALES – MILFORD HAVEN

LAT 51°42'N   LONG 5°03'W

YEAR **2002**

TIMES AND HEIGHTS OF HIGH AND LOW WATERS

JANUARY

Time	m		Time	m
1 0117	0.8	**16**	0151	1.2
0720	7.1		0756	6.6
TU 1345	0.7	W 1413	1.2
1946	6.9		2013	6.3
2 0202	0.8	**17**	0224	1.3
0804	7.1		0829	6.5
W 1430	0.7	TH 1446	1.3
2032	6.8		2045	6.1
3 0247	0.9	**18**	0255	1.5
0851	7.0		0902	6.3
TH 1517	0.9	F 1519	1.5
2119	6.6		2117	5.9
4 0334	1.1	**19**	0327	1.7
0940	6.8		0937	6.1
F 1607	1.1	SA 1553	1.7
2210	6.4		2152	5.7
5 0425	1.4	**20**	0402	1.9
1032	6.5		1014	5.9
SA 1700	1.4	SU 1631	2.0
2305	6.1		2230	5.5
6 0521	1.6	**21**	0444	2.2
1130	6.2		1057	5.6
SU 1800	1.7	M 1716	2.2
			2318	5.3
7 0006	5.8	**22**	0536	2.4
0625	1.9		1150	5.4
M 1235	6.0	TU 1814	2.4
1908	1.9		
8 0115	5.7	**23**	0020	5.1
0737	2.0		0644	2.6
TU 1345	5.8	W 1259	5.2
2020	1.9		1926	2.5
9 0226	5.7	**24**	0136	5.1
0849	1.9		0806	2.5
W 1456	5.8	TH 1413	5.3
2128	1.8		2043	2.3
10 0332	5.9	**25**	0251	5.4
0955	1.7		0920	2.2
TH 1600	6.0	F 1522	5.6
2227	1.7		2148	2.0
11 0430	6.1	**26**	0354	5.8
1052	1.5		1020	1.8
F 1655	6.1	SA 1621	6.0
2317	1.5		2243	1.6
12 0520	6.3	**27**	0447	6.3
1141	1.3		1113	1.3
SA 1743	6.3	SU 1714	6.4
			2333	1.1
13 0001	1.3	**28**	0537	6.7
0603	6.5		1202	0.9
SU 1224	1.2	M 1803	6.8
● 1825	6.4	○	
14 0041	1.2	**29**	0021	0.8
0643	6.6		0623	7.1
M 1303	1.1	TU 1250	0.6
1903	6.4		1849	7.1
15 0117	1.2	**30**	0107	0.5
0721	6.6		0709	7.3
TU 1339	1.1	W 1335	0.3
1939	6.4		1935	7.2
		31	0152	0.4
			0754	7.4
		TH 1420	0.3
			2020	7.2

FEBRUARY

Time	m		Time	m
1 0236	0.4	**16**	0231	1.1
0838	7.4		0836	6.6
F 1504	0.4	SA 1451	1.2
2104	7.0		2048	6.3
2 0320	0.6	**17**	0300	1.3
0924	7.1		0906	6.4
SA 1548	0.7	SU 1520	1.4
2149	6.7		2118	6.1
3 0404	0.9	**18**	0330	1.5
1010	6.8		0937	6.1
SU 1634	1.1	M 1552	1.6
2237	6.3		2150	5.8
4 0452	1.3	**19**	0403	1.8
1100	6.3		1012	5.9
M 1723	1.6	TU 1627	2.0
2330	5.9		2228	5.6
5 0547	1.8	**20**	0444	2.2
1157	5.8		1056	5.5
TU 1824	2.0	W 1713	2.3
			2318	5.4
6 0033	5.5	**21**	0540	2.5
0656	2.1		1156	5.2
W 1307	5.5	TH 1819	2.5
1941	2.3		
7 0151	5.3	**22**	0032	5.1
0821	2.3		0706	2.6
TH 1429	5.3	F 1321	5.1
2104	2.3		1953	2.5
8 0312	5.4	**23**	0206	5.1
0941	2.1		0844	2.4
F 1547	5.5	SA 1450	5.3
2214	2.0		2119	2.2
9 0418	5.8	**24**	0327	5.6
1044	1.8		0958	1.9
SA 1647	5.8	SU 1601	5.8
2308	1.7		2223	1.7
10 0510	6.1	**25**	0428	6.1
1133	1.5		1056	1.3
SU 1734	6.0	M 1658	6.4
2351	1.4		2316	1.1
11 0552	6.4	**26**	0520	6.7
1213	1.3		1146	0.7
M 1813	6.3	TU 1747	6.9
12 0028	1.2	**27**	0005	0.6
0629	6.5		0607	7.2
TU 1249	1.1	W 1234	0.3
● 1848	6.4	○ 1833	7.2
13 0101	1.1	**28**	0051	0.3
0704	6.6		0652	7.5
W 1321	1.0	TH 1319	0.0
1920	6.5		1917	7.4
14 0132	1.0		
0735	6.7		
TH 1352	1.0		
1950	6.4		
15 0202	1.0		
0806	6.6		
F 1421	1.1		
2019	6.4		

MARCH

Time	m		Time	m
1 0135	0.1	**16**	0136	0.9
0736	7.7		0738	6.8
F 1402	0.0	SA 1353	0.8
2000	7.4		1951	6.6
2 0217	0.1	**17**	0204	0.9
0819	7.6		0807	6.7
SA 1444	0.1	SU 1422	1.0
2042	7.3		2019	6.5
3 0259	0.3	**18**	0233	1.1
0901	7.3		0836	6.5
SU 1524	0.5	M 1450	1.2
2124	6.9		2047	6.3
4 0340	0.7	**19**	0302	1.3
0944	6.8		0906	6.3
M 1604	1.0	TU 1519	1.5
2207	6.4		2118	6.1
5 0422	1.2	**20**	0333	1.6
1028	6.3		0939	6.0
TU 1647	1.6	W 1552	1.8
2254	5.9		2153	5.8
6 0510	1.8	**21**	0410	2.0
1120	5.6		1020	5.6
W 1740	2.2	TH 1633	2.2
2353	5.4		2240	5.4
7 0617	2.3	**22**	0502	2.3
1229	5.1		1116	5.2
TH 1901	2.5	F 1735	2.5
			2349	5.1
8 0115	5.1	**23**	0626	2.6
0754	2.5		1244	5.0
F 1405	4.9	SA 1915	2.6
2043	2.6		
9 0253	5.2	**24**	0130	5.1
0927	2.3		0815	2.4
SA 1535	5.2	SU 1424	5.2
2200	2.2		2052	2.2
10 0403	5.6	**25**	0301	5.6
1031	1.9		0935	1.8
SU 1633	5.6	M 1541	5.8
2253	1.8		2200	1.6
11 0453	6.0	**26**	0406	6.2
1117	1.5		1034	1.2
M 1716	5.9	TU 1638	6.4
2333	1.5		2255	1.0
12 0533	6.3	**27**	0459	6.8
1154	1.2		1126	0.6
TU 1753	6.2	W 1727	6.9
			2344	0.5
13 0007	1.2	**28**	0546	7.3
0607	6.5		1212	0.2
W 1226	1.0	TH 1812	7.3
1825	6.4	○	
14 0039	1.0	**29**	0029	0.1
0639	6.7		0630	7.6
TH 1256	0.9	F 1257	-0.1
● 1855	6.5		1855	7.5
15 0108	0.9	**30**	0113	0.0
0709	6.8		0714	7.7
F 1325	0.8	SA 1339	-0.1
1923	6.6		1937	7.5
		31	0155	0.0
			0756	7.5
		SU 1419	0.1
			2017	7.3

APRIL

Time	m		Time	m
1 0235	0.3	**16**	0208	1.0
0837	7.2		0809	6.6
M 1457	0.5	TU 1424	1.1
2057	6.9		2021	6.4
2 0315	0.7	**17**	0239	1.2
0918	6.7		0841	6.3
TU 1535	1.1	W 1455	1.4
2138	6.4		2054	6.2
3 0355	1.2	**18**	0313	1.5
1000	6.1		0917	6.0
W 1615	1.7	TH 1529	1.7
2223	5.9		2132	5.9
4 0442	1.9	**19**	0353	1.9
1049	5.5		1001	5.7
TH 1704	2.3	F 1613	2.1
2319	5.3		2221	5.6
5 0545	2.4	**20**	0448	2.2
1156	4.9		1100	5.3
F 1822	2.7	SA 1718	2.4
			2332	5.3
6 0041	5.0	**21**	0611	2.3
0725	2.6		1226	5.1
SA 1335	4.7	SU 1852	2.4
2012	2.7		
7 0222	5.1	**22**	0107	5.3
0900	2.4		0750	2.2
SU 1509	5.0	M 1401	5.3
2132	2.4		2024	2.1
8 0334	5.4	**23**	0233	5.7
1002	2.0		0907	1.7
M 1606	5.4	TU 1515	5.8
2224	1.9		2133	1.6
9 0423	5.9	**24**	0339	6.3
1046	1.6		1008	1.1
TU 1647	5.9	W 1612	6.4
2303	1.6		2229	1.0
10 0503	6.2	**25**	0433	6.8
1122	1.3		1100	0.6
W 1723	6.2	TH 1702	6.9
2337	1.3		2319	0.6
11 0537	6.5	**26**	0521	7.2
1154	1.0		1147	0.3
TH 1755	6.4	F 1747	7.2
12 0008	1.0	**27**	0005	0.3
0609	6.6		0606	7.4
F 1225	0.9	SA 1232	0.1
● 1824	6.6	○ 1830	7.4
13 0038	0.9	**28**	0050	0.1
0639	6.7		0650	7.4
SA 1255	0.8	SU 1314	0.2
1853	6.7		1912	7.4
14 0108	0.8	**29**	0132	0.2
0709	6.8		0733	7.3
SU 1324	0.8	M 1354	0.4
1922	6.7		1953	7.1
15 0138	0.9	**30**	0213	0.5
0739	6.7		0814	6.9
M 1354	0.9	TU 1433	0.8
1951	6.6		2034	6.8

Chart Datum: 3·71 metres below Ordnance Datum (Newlyn)
Register for your **FREE** weekly weather email service from Macmillan Reeds
》 at **www.nauticaldata.com – NOW!** 《
weekend weather reports sent to your email address, every Thursday

WALES – MILFORD HAVEN

TIME ZONE (UTC)
For Summer Time add ONE hour in **non-shaded areas**

LAT 51°42′N   LONG 5°03′W

YEAR **2002**

TIMES AND HEIGHTS OF HIGH AND LOW WATERS

MAY

	Time	m		Time	m
1 W	0254	0.9	**16** TH	0225	1.2
	0855	6.4		0826	6.3
	1511	1.3		1440	1.3
	2115	6.3		2041	6.3
2 TH	0335	1.4	**17** F	0304	1.4
	0937	5.9		0907	6.1
	1550	1.8		1520	1.6
	2159	5.9		2124	6.1
3 F	0420	1.9	**18** SA	0349	1.7
	1025	5.4		0955	5.8
	1637	2.3		1609	1.9
	2252	5.4		2218	5.8
4 SA	0520	2.3	**19** SU	0447	1.9
	1126	5.0		1057	5.5
	1745	2.6		1714	2.1
				2326	5.6
5 SU	0004	5.1	**20** M	0601	2.0
	0644	2.5		1213	5.4
	1250	4.8		1834	2.1
	1921	2.7			
6 M	0132	5.1	**21** TU	0046	5.7
	0810	2.4		0723	1.9
	1420	4.9		1333	5.6
	2041	2.5		1953	1.9
7 TU	0247	5.3	**22** W	0203	5.9
	0914	2.1		0836	1.6
	1522	5.3		1444	5.9
	2138	2.1		2101	1.5
8 W	0341	5.7	**23** TH	0308	6.3
	1002	1.8		0938	1.2
	1607	5.7		1543	6.3
	2222	1.8		2200	1.2
9 TH	0423	6.0	**24** F	0405	6.6
	1041	1.5		1032	0.9
	1645	6.0		1635	6.7
	2259	1.5		2253	0.8
10 F	0500	6.3	**25** SA	0456	6.9
	1117	1.2		1121	0.6
	1719	6.3		1723	6.9
	2334	1.2		2341	0.6
11 SA	0535	6.5	**26** SU	0544	7.0
	1150	1.1		1207	0.5
	1751	6.5		1808	7.1 ○
12 SU	0007	1.1	**27** M	0027	0.5
	0607	6.6		0629	7.0
	1224	1.0		1251	0.6
	● 1823	6.6		1851	7.0
13 M	0041	1.0	**28** TU	0112	0.6
	0640	6.7		0713	6.9
	1257	0.9		1332	0.7
	1855	6.7		1933	6.9
14 TU	0114	1.0	**29** W	0155	0.8
	0714	6.6		0755	6.6
	1330	1.0		1412	1.0
	1928	6.6		2015	6.6
15 W	0149	1.0	**30** TH	0237	1.1
	0749	6.5		0837	6.2
	1404	1.1		1452	1.4
	2003	6.5		2056	6.3
			31 F	0318	1.4
				0919	5.8
				1531	1.8
				2139	5.9

JUNE

	Time	m		Time	m
1 SA	0402	1.8	**16** SU	0348	1.3
	1003	5.5		0953	6.1
	1614	2.1		1607	1.6
	2227	5.6		2215	6.2
2 SU	0451	2.1	**17** M	0443	1.5
	1054	5.1		1050	5.9
	1707	2.4		1705	1.7
	2324	5.3		2315	6.1
3 M	0553	2.4	**18** TU	0545	1.6
	1157	4.9		1153	5.8
	1817	2.6		1810	1.8
4 TU	0032	5.2	**19** W	0021	6.0
	0704	2.4		0653	1.7
	1311	4.9		1303	5.7
	1933	2.5		1921	1.8
5 W	0143	5.3	**20** TH	0131	6.0
	0811	2.3		0802	1.6
	1420	5.1		1411	5.9
	2038	2.3		2029	1.7
6 TH	0245	5.5	**21** F	0238	6.1
	0907	2.0		0907	1.5
	1515	5.4		1514	6.1
	2131	2.0		2133	1.5
7 F	0335	5.8	**22** SA	0339	6.3
	0954	1.8		1006	1.3
	1601	5.8		1611	6.3
	2217	1.8		2231	1.2
8 SA	0419	6.0	**23** SU	0436	6.4
	1037	1.5		1100	1.1
	1641	6.1		1703	6.5
	2258	1.5		2323	1.1
9 SU	0459	6.2	**24** M	0527	6.5
	1116	1.3		1148	1.0
	1719	6.3		1752	6.7
	2338	1.3		○	
10 M	0538	6.4	**25** TU	0012	1.0
	1154	1.2		0615	6.6
	1756	6.5		1234	1.0
	●			1836	6.7
11 TU	0016	1.1	**26** W	0058	0.9
	0616	6.5		0659	6.5
	1233	1.1		1316	1.0
	1833	6.6		1919	6.7
12 W	0056	1.1	**27** TH	0141	1.0
	0655	6.6		0741	6.4
	1312	1.0		1356	1.2
	1912	6.7		2000	6.5
13 TH	0135	1.0	**28** F	0221	1.2
	0735	6.5		0821	6.1
	1351	1.1		1434	1.4
	1952	6.6		2039	6.4
14 F	0217	1.1	**29** SA	0300	1.4
	0818	6.4		0859	6.0
	1432	1.2		1511	1.6
	2035	6.5		2118	6.1
15 SA	0300	1.2	**30** SU	0338	1.6
	0903	6.3		0937	5.7
	1517	1.4		1548	1.9
	2122	6.4		2158	5.9

JULY

	Time	m		Time	m
1 M	0418	1.9	**16** TU	0428	1.2
	1018	5.5		1032	6.3
	1628	2.1		1646	1.4
	2242	5.7		2255	6.4
2 TU	0502	2.1	**17** W	0521	1.4
	1104	5.2		1127	6.0
	1716	2.3		1743	1.6
	2333	5.5		2353	6.1
3 W	0555	2.3	**18** TH	0620	1.7
	1200	5.1		1230	5.8
	1817	2.5		1848	1.8
4 TH	0033	5.3	**19** F	0058	5.9
	0657	2.4		0728	1.9
	1306	5.1		1339	5.7
	1926	2.5		2000	1.9
5 F	0138	5.3	**20** SA	0210	5.8
	0803	2.3		0841	1.9
	1413	5.2		1450	5.8
	2035	2.4		2113	1.9
6 SA	0241	5.4	**21** SU	0321	5.8
	0904	2.1		0949	1.8
	1513	5.5		1556	6.0
	2134	2.1		2218	1.7
7 SU	0337	5.7	**22** M	0425	6.0
	0958	1.9		1047	1.6
	1604	5.8		1653	6.2
	2225	1.8		2315	1.4
8 M	0427	5.9	**23** TU	0519	6.1
	1046	1.6		1138	1.4
	1650	6.1		1742	6.4
	2312	1.5			
9 TU	0513	6.2	**24** W	0004	1.3
	1131	1.4		0606	6.3
	1734	6.4		1222	1.2
	2357	1.3		○ 1825	6.6
10 W	0557	6.4	**25** TH	0047	1.1
	1214	1.1		0648	6.4
	1817	6.6		1302	1.2
	●			1905	6.6
11 TH	0041	1.0	**26** F	0126	1.1
	0641	6.6		0726	6.4
	1258	1.0		1339	1.2
	1900	6.8		1943	6.6
12 F	0125	0.9	**27** SA	0202	1.1
	0725	6.7		0801	6.3
	1341	0.9		1413	1.3
	1943	6.9		2018	6.5
13 SA	0209	0.8	**28** SU	0236	1.2
	0809	6.7		0834	6.2
	1425	0.9		1445	1.4
	2028	6.9		2051	6.4
14 SU	0254	0.8	**29** M	0309	1.4
	0855	6.7		0907	6.0
	1509	1.0		1517	1.6
	2114	6.8		2125	6.2
15 M	0340	0.9	**30** TU	0341	1.6
	0942	6.5		0940	5.8
	1556	1.1		1550	1.8
	2202	6.7		2200	6.0
			31 W	0416	1.9
				1016	5.6
				1627	2.1
				2240	5.7

AUGUST

	Time	m		Time	m
1 TH	0457	2.1	**16** F	0546	1.9
	1058	5.3		1156	5.7
	1713	2.3		1816	2.1
	2328	5.4			
2 F	0548	2.4	**17** SA	0027	5.6
	1153	5.1		0656	2.2
	1815	2.6		1309	5.4
				1938	2.3
3 SA	0029	5.2	**18** SU	0148	5.4
	0654	2.5		0823	2.3
	1305	5.1		1434	5.4
	1934	2.6		2105	2.2
4 SU	0144	5.2	**19** M	0313	5.4
	0813	2.5		0942	2.2
	1424	5.2		1549	5.7
	2055	2.4		2216	1.9
5 M	0258	5.3	**20** TU	0421	5.7
	0924	2.2		1042	1.8
	1532	5.5		1646	6.1
	2159	2.1		2311	1.6
6 TU	0401	5.7	**21** W	0512	6.0
	1021	1.9		1130	1.5
	1627	6.0		1732	6.4
	2252	1.6		2355	1.3
7 W	0454	6.1	**22** TH	0555	6.3
	1111	1.4		1210	1.3
	1716	6.4		1812	6.6
	2340	1.2		○	
8 TH	0541	6.5	**23** F	0032	1.1
	1158	1.1		0631	6.4
	1801	6.8		1245	1.2
	●			1847	6.7
9 F	0026	0.8	**24** SA	0106	1.0
	0627	6.8		0705	6.5
	1243	0.8		1317	1.1
	1845	7.1		1920	6.7
10 SA	0111	0.6	**25** SU	0137	1.0
	0711	7.1		0736	6.5
	1327	0.6		1347	1.1
	1929	7.3		1951	6.7
11 SU	0155	0.4	**26** M	0207	1.1
	0755	7.1		0805	6.4
	1411	0.5		1416	1.2
	2013	7.4		2021	6.6
12 M	0239	0.4	**27** TU	0236	1.2
	0838	7.1		0834	6.3
	1454	0.6		1445	1.4
	2057	7.2		2051	6.4
13 TU	0321	0.6	**28** W	0305	1.4
	0922	6.9		0903	6.1
	1537	0.8		1514	1.6
	2142	7.0		2121	6.2
14 W	0405	1.0	**29** TH	0336	1.7
	1008	6.5		0934	5.9
	1622	1.2		1546	1.9
	2229	6.5		2155	5.9
15 TH	0451	1.4	**30** F	0409	2.0
	1058	6.1		1009	5.6
	1713	1.6		1624	2.3
	2323	6.1		2234	5.5
			31 SA	0451	2.4
				1054	5.3
				1717	2.6
				2329	5.2

Chart Datum: 3·71 metres below Ordnance Datum (Newlyn)

TIME ZONE (UTC)
For Summer Time add ONE hour in **non-shaded areas**

WALES – MILFORD HAVEN

LAT 51°42′N   LONG 5°03′W

YEAR **2002**

TIMES AND HEIGHTS OF HIGH AND LOW WATERS

SEPTEMBER

Time	m		Time	m
1 SU	0551 2.7 / 1201 5.0 / 1838 2.8	**16** M	0131 5.0 / 0812 2.7 / 1423 5.3 / 2102 2.4
2 M	0050 5.0 / 0724 2.8 / 1339 5.0 / 2022 2.7	**17** TU	0309 5.2 / 0936 2.4 / 1540 5.6 / 2211 2.0
3 TU	0226 5.1 / 0855 2.5 / 1505 5.4 / 2137 2.2	**18** W	0412 5.6 / 1033 1.9 / 1632 6.1 / 2259 1.6
4 W	0340 5.6 / 1000 2.0 / 1607 6.0 / 2233 1.6	**19** TH	0457 6.0 / 1115 1.6 / 1714 6.4 / 2337 1.3
5 TH	0435 6.2 / 1052 1.4 / 1657 6.6 / 2322 1.0	**20** F	0535 6.3 / 1150 1.3 / 1750 6.7
6 F	0523 6.7 / 1139 0.9 / 1742 7.1	**21** SA	0009 1.1 / 0607 6.5 / 1221 1.1 / ○ 1822 6.8
7 SA	0008 0.6 / 0608 7.1 / 1224 0.5 / ● 1826 7.5	**22** SU	0039 1.0 / 0638 6.6 / 1250 1.0 / 1852 6.9
8 SU	0052 0.2 / 0651 7.4 / 1308 0.3 / 1909 7.7	**23** M	0108 1.0 / 0707 6.7 / 1318 1.0 / 1921 6.8
9 M	0135 0.1 / 0734 7.5 / 1350 0.2 / 1952 7.7	**24** TU	0136 1.0 / 0734 6.6 / 1346 1.1 / 1950 6.8
10 TU	0217 0.2 / 0816 7.4 / 1432 0.4 / 2034 7.4	**25** W	0204 1.1 / 0802 6.5 / 1415 1.2 / 2018 6.6
11 W	0258 0.5 / 0858 7.1 / 1514 0.7 / 2117 7.0	**26** TH	0232 1.3 / 0830 6.3 / 1444 1.5 / 2048 6.3
12 TH	0338 1.0 / 0941 6.6 / 1557 1.2 / 2202 6.5	**27** F	0301 1.6 / 0859 6.1 / 1514 1.8 / 2119 6.0
13 F	0421 1.5 / 1028 6.1 / 1645 1.8 / 2253 5.9	**28** SA	0332 2.0 / 0933 5.8 / 1549 2.2 / 2157 5.6
14 SA	0512 2.1 / 1125 5.6 / 1749 2.3 / 2359 5.3	**29** SU	0409 2.4 / 1015 5.4 / 1638 2.6 / 2248 5.2
15 SU	0628 2.6 / 1244 5.2 / 1925 2.6	**30** M	0507 2.7 / 1119 5.1 / 1759 2.8

OCTOBER

Time	m		Time	m
1 TU	0012 4.9 / 0645 2.9 / 1302 5.1 / 1954 2.7	**16** W	0249 5.1 / 0914 2.5 / 1515 5.6 / 2147 2.1
2 W	0159 5.1 / 0828 2.5 / 1438 5.5 / 2113 2.2	**17** TH	0348 5.5 / 1007 2.1 / 1605 6.0 / 2231 1.7
3 TH	0317 5.6 / 0936 2.0 / 1542 6.1 / 2210 1.5	**18** F	0431 6.0 / 1047 1.7 / 1645 6.4 / 2307 1.4
4 F	0413 6.3 / 1029 1.5 / 1633 6.8 / 2259 0.9	**19** SA	0506 6.3 / 1121 1.4 / 1720 6.6 / 2338 1.2
5 SA	0501 6.9 / 1116 0.8 / 1719 7.3 / 2345 0.4	**20** SU	0538 6.5 / 1151 1.2 / 1753 6.8
6 SU	0545 7.3 / 1201 0.4 / ● 1804 7.6	**21** M	0008 1.0 / 0608 6.7 / 1221 1.1 / ○ 1823 6.8
7 M	0029 0.1 / 0628 7.6 / 1245 0.2 / 1846 7.8	**22** TU	0038 1.0 / 0637 6.7 / 1250 1.0 / 1852 6.8
8 TU	0112 0.1 / 0710 7.6 / 1328 0.2 / 1929 7.7	**23** W	0106 1.0 / 0705 6.7 / 1316 1.1 / 1922 6.6
9 W	0153 0.2 / 0752 7.5 / 1410 0.4 / 2011 7.4	**24** TH	0136 1.1 / 0734 6.6 / 1350 1.2 / 1951 6.6
10 TH	0233 0.6 / 0833 7.1 / 1451 0.8 / 2054 6.9	**25** F	0205 1.3 / 0803 6.5 / 1421 1.5 / 2022 6.3
11 F	0313 1.1 / 0915 6.6 / 1534 1.3 / 2138 6.3	**26** SA	0235 1.6 / 0835 6.2 / 1453 1.8 / 2056 6.0
12 SA	0355 1.7 / 1002 6.1 / 1622 1.9 / 2228 5.7	**27** SU	0308 1.9 / 0911 5.9 / 1531 2.1 / 2136 5.7
13 SU	0445 2.3 / 1059 5.5 / 1728 2.5 / 2334 5.1	**28** M	0349 2.3 / 0956 5.6 / 1623 2.5 / 2231 5.3
14 M	0602 2.8 / 1218 5.2 / 1908 2.7	**29** TU	0448 2.6 / 1101 5.3 / 1741 2.6 / 2352 5.1
15 TU	0111 4.9 / 0752 2.8 / 1400 5.2 / 2044 2.5	**30** W	0620 2.7 / 1234 5.3 / 1923 2.5
		31 TH	0129 5.2 / 0756 2.4 / 1404 5.6 / 2041 2.0

NOVEMBER

Time	m		Time	m
1 F	0247 5.7 / 1511 6.2 / 2141 1.4	**16** SA	0352 5.7 / 1008 1.9 / 1608 6.1 / 2228 1.6
2 SA	0345 6.3 / 1001 1.5 / 1605 6.8 / 2232 0.9	**17** SU	0431 6.1 / 1046 1.6 / 1646 6.4 / 2303 1.4
3 SU	0435 6.9 / 1051 0.8 / 1654 7.2 / 2319 0.5	**18** M	0506 6.3 / 1120 1.4 / 1721 6.6 / 2336 1.2
4 M	0520 7.3 / 1137 0.5 / 1740 7.5 / ●	**19** TU	0538 6.5 / 1153 1.2 / 1754 6.7
5 TU	0004 0.3 / 0604 7.5 / 1223 0.3 / 1824 7.6	**20** W	0009 1.1 / 0609 6.6 / 1226 1.2 / ○ 1826 6.7
6 W	0048 0.3 / 0647 7.5 / 1307 0.3 / 1908 7.5	**21** TH	0041 1.1 / 0641 6.7 / 1259 1.1 / 1859 6.6
7 TH	0130 0.4 / 0730 7.4 / 1350 0.5 / 1951 7.2	**22** F	0114 1.2 / 0713 6.6 / 1332 1.3 / 1932 6.5
8 F	0211 0.8 / 0812 7.0 / 1433 0.9 / 2035 6.7	**23** SA	0147 1.3 / 0746 6.5 / 1407 1.4 / 2007 6.3
9 SA	0252 1.3 / 0856 6.6 / 1518 1.4 / 2119 6.1	**24** SU	0221 1.5 / 0822 6.4 / 1444 1.6 / 2046 6.1
10 SU	0335 1.8 / 0942 6.1 / 1606 1.9 / 2209 5.6	**25** M	0259 1.8 / 0902 6.1 / 1527 1.9 / 2130 5.8
11 M	0424 2.3 / 1036 5.6 / 1707 2.4 / 2309 5.1	**26** TU	0344 2.0 / 0951 5.8 / 1619 2.1 / 2226 5.6
12 TU	0531 2.7 / 1146 5.3 / 1830 2.6	**27** W	0442 2.3 / 1053 5.7 / 1728 2.2 / 2337 5.4
13 W	0030 4.9 / 0705 2.8 / 1312 5.2 / 1956 2.5	**28** TH	0557 2.4 / 1209 5.7 / 1848 2.2
14 TH	0200 5.0 / 0826 2.6 / 1429 5.5 / 2101 2.3	**29** F	0056 5.5 / 0718 2.2 / 1328 5.9 / 2003 1.9
15 F	0305 5.4 / 0924 2.3 / 1524 5.8 / 2149 1.9	**30** SA	0211 5.8 / 0830 1.9 / 1436 6.2 / 2108 1.5

DECEMBER

Time	m		Time	m
1 SU	0313 6.2 / 0931 1.4 / 1536 6.6 / 2204 1.1	**16** M	0349 5.7 / 1006 2.0 / 1608 6.0 / 2226 1.7
2 M	0407 6.6 / 1025 1.1 / 1629 6.9 / 2255 0.8	**17** TU	0432 6.0 / 1049 1.7 / 1650 6.2 / 2306 1.5
3 TU	0457 7.0 / 1116 0.8 / 1719 7.1 / 2343 0.7	**18** W	0510 6.2 / 1128 1.5 / 1729 6.3 / 2344 1.4
4 W	0544 7.2 / 1203 0.8 / 1807 7.2 / ●	**19** TH	0547 6.4 / 1206 1.3 / 1806 6.5 / ○
5 TH	0028 0.6 / 0630 7.2 / 1251 0.6 / 1852 7.1	**20** F	0021 1.3 / 0622 6.6 / 1244 1.2 / 1843 6.5
6 F	0113 0.7 / 0714 7.1 / 1337 0.7 / 1937 6.8	**21** SA	0058 1.2 / 0659 6.6 / 1321 1.2 / 1921 6.5
7 SA	0155 1.0 / 0758 6.9 / 1421 1.0 / 2021 6.5	**22** SU	0135 1.2 / 0736 6.6 / 1400 1.2 / 2000 6.5
8 SU	0237 1.3 / 0841 6.6 / 1505 1.4 / 2104 6.1	**23** M	0214 1.3 / 0816 6.6 / 1440 1.3 / 2041 6.4
9 M	0319 1.7 / 0925 6.2 / 1550 1.8 / 2149 5.7	**24** TU	0255 1.4 / 0859 6.5 / 1524 1.4 / 2127 6.3
10 TU	0403 2.1 / 1013 5.8 / 1639 2.1 / 2239 5.3	**25** W	0340 1.6 / 0946 6.3 / 1612 1.6 / 2217 6.0
11 W	0453 2.4 / 1106 5.5 / 1736 2.4 / 2337 5.0	**26** TH	0431 1.7 / 1040 6.2 / 1708 1.7 / 2315 5.8
12 TH	0558 2.6 / 1210 5.3 / 1844 2.5	**27** F	0531 1.9 / 1142 6.0 / 1812 1.9
13 F	0047 5.0 / 0712 2.7 / 1321 5.3 / 1953 2.4	**28** SA	0021 5.7 / 0639 2.0 / 1251 6.0 / 1922 1.8
14 SA	0159 5.1 / 0822 2.5 / 1426 5.5 / 2052 2.2	**29** SU	0132 5.8 / 0751 1.9 / 1401 6.0 / 2033 1.7
15 SU	0300 5.4 / 0919 2.3 / 1522 5.7 / 2143 2.0	**30** M	0240 6.0 / 0901 1.7 / 1508 6.2 / 2138 1.5
		31 TU	0343 6.2 / 1015 1.6 / 1610 6.4 / 2236 1.3

Chart Datum: 3·71 metres below Ordnance Datum (Newlyn)
Register for your **FREE** weekly weather email service from Macmillan Reeds
》 at **www.nauticaldata.com – NOW!** 《
weekend weather reports sent to your email address, every Thursday

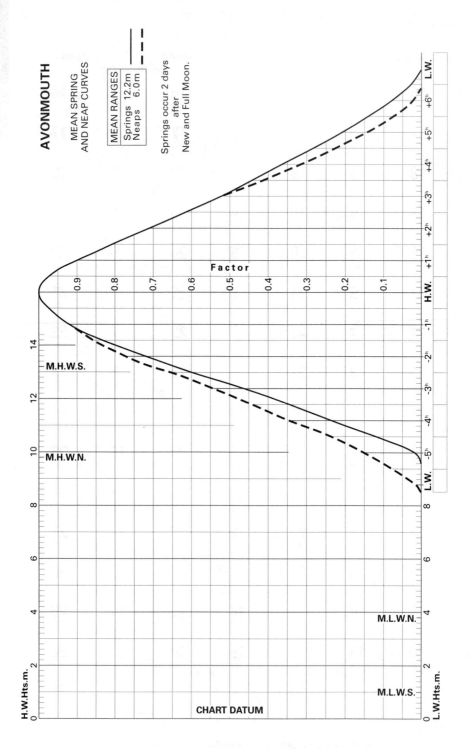

AVONMOUTH

MEAN SPRING
AND NEAP CURVES

MEAN RANGES	
Springs	12.2m
Neaps	6.0m

Springs occur 2 days
after
New and Full Moon.

Factor

0.9 0.8 0.7 0.6 0.5 0.4 0.3 0.2 0.1

H.W. −1ʰ −2ʰ −3ʰ −4ʰ −5ʰ L.W.
+6ʰ +5ʰ +4ʰ +3ʰ +2ʰ +1ʰ H.W.
L.W.

M.H.W.S.

M.H.W.N.

M.L.W.N.

M.L.W.S.

H.W.Hts.m.

L.W.Hts.m.

CHART DATUM

TIME ZONE (UTC)
For Summer Time add ONE hour in **non-shaded areas**

ENGLAND – AVONMOUTH

LAT 51°30'N   LONG 2°44'W

TIMES AND HEIGHTS OF HIGH AND LOW WATERS

Section 1

JANUARY

Time m	Time m
1 TU 0246 1.3 / 0820 13.4 / 1513 1.4 / 2049 13.1	**16** W 0320 1.8 / 0855 12.5 / 1538 2.0 / 2114 12.1
2 W 0330 1.3 / 0906 13.4 / 1556 1.4 / 2134 13.0	**17** TH 0348 2.1 / 0928 12.2 / 1605 2.2 / 2144 11.8
3 TH 0411 1.4 / 0951 13.2 / 1637 1.6 / 2219 12.7	**18** F 0409 2.3 / 0958 11.8 / 1628 2.4 / 2213 11.5
4 F 0451 1.7 / 1037 12.8 / 1718 1.8 / 2305 12.1	**19** SA 0431 2.4 / 1027 11.5 / 1653 2.5 / 2242 11.2
5 SA 0532 2.0 / 1125 12.3 / 1801 2.2 / 2354 11.7	**20** SU 0459 2.6 / 1058 11.1 / 1726 2.6 / 2316 10.9
6 SU 0618 2.4 / 1220 11.7 / 1850 2.6	**21** M 0535 2.8 / 1136 10.7 / 1806 3.0 / 2358 10.5
7 M 0052 11.1 / 0712 2.9 / 1327 11.2 / 1949 3.0	**22** TU 0620 3.2 / 1226 10.3 / 1856 3.4
8 TU 0205 10.7 / 0822 3.2 / 1441 11.0 / 2109 3.3	**23** W 0054 10.1 / 0718 3.7 / 1333 10.0 / 2004 3.7
9 W 0318 10.8 / 0945 3.2 / 1549 11.1 / 2226 3.1	**24** TH 0207 10.0 / 0838 3.9 / 1453 10.1 / 2129 3.6
10 TH 0422 11.1 / 1055 2.9 / 1650 11.5 / 2329 2.6	**25** F 0331 10.3 / 1005 3.5 / 1611 10.6 / 2247 3.1
11 F 0519 11.6 / 1154 2.4 / 1745 11.9	**26** SA 0443 11.1 / 1119 2.9 / 1716 11.4 / 2352 2.4
12 SA 0023 2.2 / 0609 12.2 / 1247 1.9 / 1834 12.3	**27** SU 0542 12.0 / 1222 2.2 / 1812 12.2
13 SU 0114 1.8 / 0655 12.7 / 1336 1.7 / ● 1919 12.5	**28** M 0051 1.8 / 0633 12.8 / 1322 1.7 / ○ 1903 12.9
14 M 0201 1.6 / 0738 12.7 / 1422 1.6 / 2001 12.5	**29** TU 0147 1.4 / 0723 13.4 / 1417 1.3 / 1952 13.4
15 TU 0243 1.6 / 0818 12.7 / 1504 1.7 / 2040 12.4	**30** W 0239 1.0 / 0810 13.8 / 1509 0.9 / 2039 13.7
	31 TH 0327 0.8 / 0857 14.0 / 1554 0.8 / 2124 13.7

FEBRUARY

Time m	Time m
1 F 0409 0.8 / 0941 14.0 / 1634 0.8 / 2207 13.5	**16** SA 0359 2.0 / 0936 12.2 / 1612 2.1 / 2149 12.0
2 SA 0445 0.9 / 1024 13.6 / 1709 1.1 / 2248 13.1	**17** SU 0413 2.1 / 1001 11.9 / 1629 2.1 / 2214 11.8
3 SU 0519 1.3 / 1106 13.0 / 1741 1.6 / 2329 12.4	**18** M 0434 2.1 / 1028 11.6 / 1654 2.2 / 2243 11.5
4 M 0553 1.8 / 1150 12.2 / 1815 2.2	**19** TU 0504 2.3 / 1101 11.2 / 1727 2.5 / 2320 11.1
5 TU 0014 11.5 / 0632 2.6 / 1243 11.3 / 1856 3.0	**20** W 0541 2.7 / 1143 10.7 / 1807 3.0
6 W 0112 10.6 / 0723 3.3 / 1354 10.5 / 1954 3.6	**21** TH 0008 10.5 / 0627 3.3 / 1241 10.1 / 1903 3.6
7 TH 0235 10.1 / 0840 3.9 / 1517 10.2 / 2138 4.0	**22** F 0113 10.0 / 0735 3.9 / 1358 9.8 / 2031 3.9
8 F 0353 10.2 / 1024 3.7 / 1627 10.5 / 2302 3.5	**23** SA 0240 9.9 / 0920 3.9 / 1536 10.1 / 2215 3.5
9 SA 0458 10.8 / 1132 3.0 / 1728 11.1	**24** SU 0414 10.6 / 1055 3.2 / 1656 11.0 / 2331 2.7
10 SU 0002 2.8 / 0553 11.6 / 1228 2.3 / 1819 11.7	**25** M 0523 11.7 / 1208 2.3 / 1758 12.1
11 M 0054 2.1 / 0641 12.2 / 1318 1.8 / 1905 12.2	**26** TU 0036 1.9 / 0619 12.8 / 1311 1.5 / 1849 13.1
12 TU 0142 1.7 / 0723 12.6 / 1405 1.5 / ● 1946 12.8	**27** W 0135 1.2 / 0709 13.7 / 1407 0.9 / ○ 1938 13.8
13 W 0227 1.5 / 0802 12.8 / 1448 1.5 / 2022 12.5	**28** TH 0228 0.7 / 0756 14.2 / 1458 0.4 / 2023 14.2
14 TH 0306 1.5 / 0837 12.7 / 1525 1.6 / 2054 12.4	
15 F 0338 1.8 / 0908 12.5 / 1553 1.9 / 2122 12.2	

MARCH

Time m	Time m
1 F 0315 0.3 / 0841 14.5 / 1542 0.2 / 2106 14.3	**16** SA 0318 1.5 / 0842 12.6 / 1533 1.7 / 2056 12.4
2 SA 0356 0.2 / 0923 14.5 / 1619 0.4 / 2147 14.1	**17** SU 0341 1.8 / 0909 12.3 / 1551 1.9 / 2121 12.2
3 SU 0430 0.5 / 1003 14.1 / 1649 0.8 / 2224 13.5	**18** M 0352 2.0 / 0934 12.1 / 1603 2.0 / 2145 12.1
4 M 0458 1.0 / 1041 13.3 / 1713 1.5 / 2300 12.6	**19** TU 0409 1.9 / 1000 11.9 / 1625 2.0 / 2215 11.8
5 TU 0525 1.7 / 1119 12.3 / 1739 2.2 / 2338 11.6	**20** W 0436 2.0 / 1033 11.5 / 1655 2.2 / 2251 11.4
6 W 0557 2.5 / 1202 11.1 / 1813 3.1	**21** TH 0510 2.3 / 1115 10.9 / 1732 2.7 / 2336 10.8
7 TH 0025 10.5 / 0640 3.4 / 1304 10.0 / 1903 4.0	**22** F 0552 3.0 / 1209 10.2 / 1822 3.5
8 F 0149 9.6 / 0747 4.2 / 1448 9.5 / 2029 4.6	**23** SA 0038 10.1 / 0654 3.7 / 1325 9.7 / 1942 4.1
9 SA 0327 9.6 / 0953 4.2 / 1606 9.8 / 2239 4.0	**24** SU 0205 9.8 / 0845 4.0 / 1511 9.9 / 2152 3.7
10 SU 0437 10.3 / 1112 3.3 / 1709 10.6 / 2340 3.0	**25** M 0351 10.4 / 1040 3.2 / 1639 10.9 / 2315 2.7
11 M 0534 11.3 / 1206 2.4 / 1800 11.5	**26** TU 0505 11.7 / 1154 2.1 / 1740 12.2
12 TU 0031 2.1 / 0620 12.1 / 1255 1.7 / 1843 12.2	**27** W 0019 1.7 / 0601 12.9 / 1254 1.2 / 1831 13.2
13 W 0119 1.6 / 0701 12.6 / 1341 1.3 / ● 1922 12.5	**28** TH 0116 0.9 / 0650 13.8 / 1348 0.6 / ○ 1917 14.0
14 TH 0204 1.3 / 0738 12.8 / 1425 1.2 / ● 1956 12.6	**29** F 0208 0.4 / 0736 14.4 / 1436 0.1 / 2001 14.4
15 F 0244 1.3 / 0812 12.8 / 1503 1.4 / 2027 12.6	**30** SA 0254 0.1 / 0820 14.6 / 1519 0.1 / 2043 14.4
	31 SU 0334 0.1 / 0901 14.5 / 1555 0.3 / 2122 14.1

APRIL

Time m	Time m
1 M 0407 0.4 / 0940 14.0 / 1623 0.9 / 2158 13.5	**16** TU 0330 1.9 / 0909 12.2 / 1540 1.9 / 2120 12.2
2 TU 0434 1.0 / 1016 13.1 / 1643 1.6 / 2232 12.5	**17** W 0348 1.9 / 0939 12.0 / 1602 1.9 / 2152 12.0
3 W 0457 1.7 / 1051 12.0 / 1706 2.3 / 2307 11.4	**18** TH 0416 1.9 / 1015 11.6 / 1633 2.1 / 2231 11.5
4 TH 0526 2.6 / 1129 10.8 / 1738 3.2 / 2349 10.3	**19** F 0451 2.2 / 1057 11.0 / 1711 2.6 / 2317 10.9
5 F 0608 3.5 / 1224 9.6 / 1826 4.1	**20** SA 0534 2.9 / 1152 10.3 / 1801 3.4
6 SA 0108 9.3 / 0714 4.3 / 1418 9.1 / 1950 4.7	**21** SU 0019 10.2 / 0636 3.6 / 1308 9.8 / 1921 4.0
7 SU 0300 9.3 / 0904 4.4 / 1539 9.5 / 2210 4.2	**22** M 0147 10.0 / 0831 3.8 / 1452 10.0 / 2131 3.6
8 M 0408 10.1 / 1042 3.5 / 1639 10.4 / 2312 3.2	**23** TU 0330 10.6 / 1020 3.0 / 1616 11.0 / 2251 2.6
9 TU 0503 11.0 / 1136 2.5 / 1730 11.3	**24** W 0441 11.7 / 1129 2.0 / 1716 12.2 / 2353 1.6
10 W 0001 2.2 / 0549 11.9 / 1225 1.7 / 1812 12.0	**25** TH 0537 12.8 / 1227 1.1 / 1807 13.2
11 TH 0048 1.6 / 0629 12.4 / 1310 1.4 / 1849 12.5	**26** F 0048 0.9 / 0626 13.7 / 1320 0.6 / 1852 13.9
12 F 0132 1.3 / 0706 12.6 / 1353 1.2 / ● 1924 12.6	**27** SA 0140 0.4 / 0712 14.2 / 1408 0.3 / ○ 1936 14.2
13 SA 0214 1.3 / 0741 12.6 / 1432 1.4 / 1956 12.6	**28** SU 0226 0.2 / 0756 14.3 / 1451 0.3 / 2017 14.1
14 SU 0249 1.5 / 0813 12.5 / 1504 1.6 / 2026 12.5	**29** M 0308 0.3 / 0837 14.1 / 1528 0.6 / 2057 13.8
15 M 0315 1.8 / 0842 12.3 / 1525 1.9 / 2053 12.4	**30** TU 0343 0.7 / 0917 13.5 / 1557 1.2 / 2134 13.1

Chart Datum: 6·50 metres below Ordnance Datum (Newlyn)

ENGLAND–AVONMOUTH

YEAR 2002

LAT 51°30′N LONG 2°44′W

TIMES AND HEIGHTS OF HIGH AND LOW WATERS

TIME ZONE (UTC)
For Summer Time add ONE hour in **non-shaded areas**

MAY

Time m	Time m
1 W 0411 1.3 / 0954 12.7 / 1619 1.9 / 2208 12.2	**16** TH 0337 1.8 / 0926 12.0 / 1552 1.9 / 2140 12.1
2 TH 0436 2.0 / 1029 11.7 / 1642 2.5 / 2243 11.3	**17** F 0408 2.0 / 1006 11.7 / 1625 2.1 / 2221 11.7
3 F 0505 2.7 / 1107 10.6 / 1714 3.2 / 2325 10.3	**18** SA 0446 2.3 / 1052 11.2 / 1706 2.6 / 2310 11.1
4 SA 0547 3.4 / 1157 9.7 / 1801 4.0	**19** SU 0534 2.7 / 1147 10.6 / 1800 3.1
5 SU 0035 9.4 / 0649 4.1 / 1331 9.1 / 1917 4.5	**20** M 0012 10.6 / 0640 3.2 / 1258 10.3 / 1920 3.5
6 M 0221 9.4 / 0812 4.1 / 1458 9.4 / 2056 4.3	**21** TU 0134 10.4 / 0816 3.2 / 1427 10.4 / 2102 3.2
7 TU 0328 9.9 / 0942 3.6 / 1557 10.1 / 2224 3.5	**22** W 0303 10.9 / 0947 2.7 / 1545 11.1 / 2218 2.5
8 W 0422 10.7 / 1050 2.8 / 1648 10.9 / 2320 2.6	**23** TH 0411 11.7 / 1056 2.0 / 1646 12.0 / 2322 1.7
9 TH 0509 11.4 / 1143 2.1 / 1732 11.7	**24** F 0509 12.5 / 1155 1.4 / 1739 12.8
10 F 0008 2.0 / 0551 12.0 / 1230 1.7 / 1811 12.2	**25** SA 0018 1.1 / 0600 13.2 / 1249 1.0 / 1826 13.3
11 SA 0054 1.7 / 0630 12.3 / 1315 1.5 / 1848 12.4	**26** SU 0110 0.8 / 0647 13.5 / 1338 0.7 / ○ 1911 13.6
12 SU 0136 1.6 / 0707 12.4 / 1356 1.5 / ● 1924 12.6	**27** M 0158 0.6 / 0732 13.6 / 1423 0.8 / 1954 13.5
13 M 0214 1.6 / 0743 12.4 / 1431 1.6 / 1957 12.5	**28** TU 0242 0.8 / 0816 13.3 / 1503 1.1 / 2035 13.2
14 TU 0246 1.7 / 0817 12.3 / 1500 1.7 / 2030 12.5	**29** W 0322 1.1 / 0858 12.9 / 1537 1.6 / 2114 12.7
15 W 0312 1.8 / 0851 12.2 / 1525 1.8 / 2103 12.3	**30** TH 0355 1.6 / 0937 12.2 / 1603 2.1 / 2151 12.0
	31 F 0423 2.1 / 1014 11.5 / 1628 2.6 / 2227 11.3

JUNE

Time m	Time m
1 SA 0453 2.6 / 1051 10.8 / 1700 3.0 / 2308 10.5	**16** SU 0456 2.0 / 1051 11.7 / 1713 2.2 / 2308 11.7
2 SU 0532 3.1 / 1134 10.1 / 1742 3.5	**17** M 0544 2.3 / 1142 11.3 / 1804 2.6
3 M 0000 9.9 / 0622 3.5 / 1232 9.6 / 1840 3.9	**18** TU 0004 11.3 / 0640 2.6 / 1243 11.0 / 1907 2.8
4 TU 0117 9.6 / 0725 3.7 / 1349 9.5 / 1952 4.0	**19** W 0114 11.1 / 0749 2.7 / 1355 10.8 / 2024 2.9
5 W 0231 9.8 / 0832 3.6 / 1458 9.9 / 2105 3.7	**20** TH 0230 11.1 / 0906 2.7 / 1509 11.1 / 2141 2.6
6 TH 0329 10.3 / 0939 3.1 / 1555 10.5 / 2215 3.2	**21** F 0339 11.5 / 1019 2.4 / 1614 11.5 / 2249 2.2
7 F 0421 10.9 / 1045 2.6 / 1645 11.1 / 2316 2.6	**22** SA 0440 11.9 / 1123 2.0 / 1711 12.1 / 2349 1.8
8 SA 0509 11.4 / 1142 2.2 / 1731 11.7	**23** SU 0536 12.3 / 1220 1.7 / 1803 12.5
9 SU 0008 2.1 / 0553 11.8 / 1233 1.8 / 1814 12.2	**24** M 0043 1.4 / 0626 12.6 / 1312 1.4 / ○ 1850 12.8
10 M 0056 1.8 / 0635 12.1 / 1319 1.6 / ● 1854 12.5	**25** TU 0134 1.2 / 0714 12.8 / 1401 1.3 / 1935 12.9
11 TU 0140 1.7 / 0717 12.3 / 1402 1.6 / 1934 12.6	**26** W 0222 1.3 / 0800 12.7 / 1445 1.5 / 2018 12.8
12 W 0222 1.7 / 0758 12.4 / 1441 1.6 / 2013 12.7	**27** TH 0306 1.4 / 0843 12.4 / 1524 1.7 / 2059 12.5
13 TH 0301 1.7 / 0839 12.4 / 1517 1.7 / 2053 12.6	**28** F 0344 1.8 / 0923 12.1 / 1556 2.1 / 2137 12.1
14 F 0337 1.7 / 0921 12.3 / 1553 1.8 / 2135 12.4	**29** SA 0415 2.1 / 0959 11.6 / 1621 2.4 / 2213 11.6
15 SA 0415 1.8 / 1005 12.0 / 1630 2.0 / 2219 12.1	**30** SU 0443 2.4 / 1032 11.2 / 1648 2.7 / 2247 11.1

JULY

Time m	Time m
1 M 0514 2.7 / 1107 10.7 / 1721 2.9 / 2326 10.6	**16** TU 0541 1.7 / 1128 12.1 / 1756 2.0 / 2348 12.0
2 TU 0552 2.9 / 1147 10.3 / 1803 3.2	**17** W 0624 2.1 / 1218 11.6 / 1843 2.4
3 W 0012 10.2 / 0639 3.1 / 1238 10.0 / 1855 3.5	**18** TH 0045 11.5 / 0713 2.5 / 1319 11.0 / 1941 2.9
4 TH 0113 9.9 / 0735 3.3 / 1341 9.9 / 2001 3.7	**19** F 0154 11.0 / 0817 3.0 / 1431 10.7 / 2057 3.1
5 F 0221 10.0 / 0839 3.3 / 1450 10.1 / 2111 3.6	**20** SA 0308 10.9 / 0941 3.2 / 1543 10.8 / 2219 3.0
6 SA 0325 10.3 / 0948 3.1 / 1555 10.5 / 2222 3.1	**21** SU 0416 11.1 / 1055 2.9 / 1648 11.2 / 2326 2.6
7 SU 0425 10.8 / 1055 2.7 / 1652 11.2 / 2326 2.6	**22** M 0517 11.4 / 1157 2.4 / 1745 11.8
8 M 0519 11.4 / 1154 2.2 / 1744 11.8	**23** TU 0023 2.1 / 0611 11.9 / 1252 2.0 / 1835 12.3
9 TU 0022 2.1 / 0609 11.9 / 1248 1.8 / 1831 12.4	**24** W 0117 1.7 / 0700 12.2 / 1343 1.7 / ○ 1922 12.6
10 W 0114 1.8 / 0656 12.3 / 1339 1.6 / ● 1916 12.8	**25** TH 0207 1.5 / 0746 12.4 / 1431 1.5 / 2005 12.7
11 TH 0205 1.6 / 0743 12.6 / 1428 1.5 / 2001 13.0	**26** F 0253 1.5 / 0829 12.4 / 1513 1.6 / 2045 12.6
12 F 0255 1.5 / 0830 12.7 / 1514 1.4 / 2046 13.1	**27** SA 0333 1.6 / 0906 12.2 / 1548 1.9 / 2120 12.4
13 SA 0341 1.4 / 0915 12.8 / 1601 1.4 / 2131 13.0	**28** SU 0405 1.9 / 0939 11.9 / 1613 2.1 / 2152 12.0
14 SU 0422 1.4 / 1000 12.7 / 1636 1.5 / 2215 12.9	**29** M 0430 2.2 / 1009 11.6 / 1633 2.4 / 2222 11.6
15 M 0502 1.5 / 1043 12.5 / 1714 1.6 / 2300 12.5	**30** TU 0452 2.3 / 1037 11.3 / 1656 2.5 / 2251 11.2
	31 W 0519 2.5 / 1108 11.0 / 1726 2.7 / 2323 10.7

AUGUST

Time m	Time m
1 TH 0553 2.8 / 1145 10.5 / 1805 3.1	**16** F 0012 11.5 / 0633 2.7 / 1241 10.9 / 1857 3.1
2 F 0006 10.2 / 0637 3.2 / 1234 10.1 / 1856 3.6	**17** SA 0116 10.6 / 0724 3.5 / 1356 10.2 / 2007 3.8
3 SA 0106 9.9 / 0738 3.6 / 1341 9.9 / 2010 3.9	**18** SU 0242 10.1 / 0858 4.0 / 1520 10.1 / 2156 3.8
4 SU 0225 9.8 / 0857 3.6 / 1504 10.0 / 2136 3.7	**19** M 0359 10.2 / 1036 3.7 / 1632 10.6 / 2311 3.2
5 M 0345 10.2 / 1016 3.3 / 1618 10.7 / 2253 3.1	**20** TU 0504 10.8 / 1141 2.9 / 1732 11.4
6 TU 0452 10.9 / 1125 2.6 / 1719 11.5 / 2358 2.4	**21** W 0008 2.4 / 0558 11.5 / 1236 2.2 / 1823 12.1
7 W 0550 11.7 / 1226 2.0 / 1813 12.4	**22** TH 0101 1.7 / 0647 12.1 / 1326 1.6 / ○ 1907 12.7
8 TH 0058 1.8 / 0641 12.4 / 1324 1.6 / ● 1901 13.0	**23** F 0149 1.3 / 0732 12.5 / 1413 1.3 / 1948 12.9
9 F 0155 1.4 / 0730 12.9 / 1418 1.3 / 1949 13.5	**24** SA 0235 1.2 / 0809 12.6 / 1455 1.3 / 2025 12.9
10 SA 0249 1.1 / 0818 13.3 / 1508 1.0 / 2035 13.7	**25** SU 0315 1.3 / 0843 12.5 / 1531 1.6 / 2057 12.6
11 SU 0336 0.9 / 0903 13.5 / 1552 0.9 / 2119 13.8	**26** M 0348 1.7 / 0913 12.2 / 1558 1.9 / 2126 12.3
12 M 0418 0.9 / 0945 13.4 / 1629 0.9 / 2201 13.6	**27** TU 0411 2.0 / 0939 12.0 / 1613 2.2 / 2152 11.9
13 TU 0453 1.0 / 1026 13.2 / 1703 1.2 / 2242 13.2	**28** W 0425 2.2 / 1004 11.7 / 1627 2.3 / 2216 11.5
14 W 0525 1.4 / 1107 12.6 / 1735 1.7 / 2325 12.4	**29** TH 0443 2.4 / 1030 11.3 / 1651 2.5 / 2243 11.1
15 TH 0556 2.0 / 1149 11.8 / 1811 2.3	**30** F 0511 2.6 / 1102 10.9 / 1722 2.8 / 2320 10.5
	31 SA 0547 3.0 / 1145 10.4 / 1803 3.4

Chart Datum: 6·50 metres below Ordnance Datum (Newlyn)

TIME ZONE (UTC)
For Summer Time add ONE hour in **non-shaded areas**

ENGLAND – AVONMOUTH

LAT 51°30′N   LONG 2°44′W

TIMES AND HEIGHTS OF HIGH AND LOW WATERS

YEAR 2002

SEPTEMBER

Time	m	Time	m
1 SU 0011 / 0636 / 1245 / 1905	9.9 / 3.7 / 9.8 / 4.1	**16** M 0224 / 0809 / 1505 / 2144	9.4 / 4.7 / 9.6 / 4.4
2 M 0128 / 0759 / 1413 / 2054	9.5 / 4.1 / 9.6 / 4.2	**17** TU 0344 / 1024 / 1616 / 2256	9.8 / 4.1 / 10.3 / 3.4
3 TU 0311 / 0946 / 1551 / 2232	9.7 / 3.8 / 10.3 / 3.5	**18** W 0448 / 1124 / 1714 / 2350	10.6 / 3.1 / 11.3 / 2.4
4 W 0433 / 1105 / 1700 / 2345	10.6 / 3.0 / 11.4 / 2.5	**19** TH 0541 / 1214 / 1803	11.5 / 2.1 / 12.2
5 TH 0534 / 1211 / 1756	11.7 / 2.2 / 12.5	**20** F 0038 / 0625 / 1302 / 1845	1.6 / 12.3 / 1.5 / 12.8
6 F 0046 / 0625 / 1310 / 1845	1.7 / 12.7 / 1.5 / 13.4	**21** SA 0125 / 0705 / 1347 / ○1923	1.1 / 12.7 / 1.1 / 13.1
7 SA 0143 / 0713 / 1404 / ●1932	1.1 / 13.4 / 1.0 / 14.0	**22** SU 0209 / 0741 / 1430 / 1957	1.0 / 12.8 / 1.2 / 13.0
8 SU 0235 / 0759 / 1453 / 2017	0.7 / 13.9 / 0.6 / 14.3	**23** M 0249 / 0813 / 1506 / 2028	1.2 / 12.7 / 1.4 / 12.7
9 M 0321 / 0842 / 1536 / 2059	0.4 / 14.0 / 0.5 / 14.3	**24** TU 0322 / 0842 / 1534 / 2056	1.6 / 12.4 / 1.9 / 12.4
10 TU 0400 / 0923 / 1612 / 2140	0.5 / 13.9 / 0.6 / 14.1	**25** W 0345 / 0908 / 1547 / 2120	2.0 / 12.1 / 2.2 / 12.0
11 W 0433 / 1002 / 1643 / 2219	0.9 / 13.5 / 1.1 / 13.4	**26** TH 0355 / 0931 / 1557 / 2143	2.3 / 11.9 / 2.3 / 11.7
12 TH 0459 / 1040 / 1710 / 2258	1.5 / 12.8 / 1.7 / 12.5	**27** F 0410 / 0957 / 1619 / 2211	2.3 / 11.6 / 2.4 / 11.3
13 F 0523 / 1119 / 1739 / 2340	2.2 / 11.8 / 2.5 / 11.3	**28** SA 0436 / 1029 / 1649 / 2248	2.5 / 11.2 / 2.7 / 10.7
14 SA 0554 / 1205 / 1819	3.1 / 10.6 / 3.5	**29** SU 0509 / 1111 / 1727 / 2338	2.9 / 10.5 / 3.3 / 10.0
15 SU 0038 / 0639 / 1326 / 1924	10.1 / 4.0 / 9.7 / 4.4	**30** M 0553 / 1208 / 1821	3.6 / 9.8 / 4.6

OCTOBER

Time	m	Time	m
1 TU 0050 / 0704 / 1335 / 2009	9.4 / 4.3 / 9.5 / 4.5	**16** W 0321 / 1001 / 1550 / 2231	9.6 / 4.3 / 10.3 / 3.5
2 W 0244 / 0921 / 1528 / 2217	9.5 / 4.2 / 10.1 / 3.7	**17** TH 0421 / 1058 / 1646 / 2322	10.4 / 3.2 / 11.2 / 2.5
3 TH 0414 / 1048 / 1640 / 2330	10.5 / 3.1 / 11.4 / 2.5	**18** F 0512 / 1146 / 1733	11.4 / 2.2 / 12.1
4 F 0514 / 1153 / 1736	11.8 / 2.1 / 12.6	**19** SA 0009 / 0555 / 1232 / 1814	1.7 / 12.2 / 1.6 / 12.7
5 SA 0028 / 0605 / 1249 / 1824	1.5 / 12.9 / 1.3 / 13.6	**20** SU 0053 / 0633 / 1315 / 1851	1.2 / 12.6 / 1.3 / 12.9
6 SU 0122 / 0651 / 1341 / ●1910	0.8 / 13.7 / 0.8 / 14.3	**21** M 0136 / 0708 / 1357 / ○1925	1.1 / 12.8 / 1.3 / 12.9
7 M 0211 / 0735 / 1429 / 1954	0.4 / 14.2 / 0.4 / 14.6	**22** TU 0216 / 0740 / 1434 / 1957	1.2 / 12.7 / 1.5 / 12.7
8 TU 0256 / 0817 / 1512 / 2036	0.3 / 14.3 / 0.4 / 14.5	**23** W 0250 / 0810 / 1503 / 2027	1.6 / 12.5 / 1.9 / 12.4
9 W 0335 / 0858 / 1548 / 2117	0.5 / 14.1 / 0.6 / 14.1	**24** TH 0314 / 0837 / 1520 / 2053	2.0 / 12.3 / 2.2 / 12.1
10 TH 0406 / 0937 / 1618 / 2155	1.0 / 13.5 / 1.2 / 13.3	**25** F 0328 / 0903 / 1534 / 2119	2.2 / 12.0 / 2.3 / 11.8
11 F 0430 / 1014 / 1644 / 2233	1.7 / 12.7 / 1.9 / 12.2	**26** SA 0345 / 0932 / 1557 / 2151	2.3 / 11.8 / 2.4 / 11.4
12 SA 0452 / 1051 / 1712 / 2313	2.5 / 11.6 / 2.8 / 11.0	**27** SU 0413 / 1007 / 1629 / 2230	2.4 / 11.4 / 2.6 / 10.9
13 SU 0522 / 1136 / 1751	3.3 / 10.4 / 3.7	**28** M 0447 / 1051 / 1708 / 2320	2.9 / 10.8 / 3.2 / 10.2
14 M 0008 / 0606 / 1303 / 1856	9.7 / 4.3 / 9.5 / 4.6	**29** TU 0532 / 1148 / 1802	3.5 / 10.1 / 3.9
15 TU 0205 / 0732 / 1444 / 2122	9.1 / 5.0 / 9.5 / 4.6	**30** W 0030 / 0639 / 1310 / 1939	9.6 / 4.2 / 9.8 / 4.3
		31 TH 0214 / 0850 / 1459 / 2148	9.6 / 4.1 / 10.3 / 3.6

NOVEMBER

Time	m	Time	m
1 F 0347 / 1020 / 1613 / 2302	10.6 / 3.2 / 11.4 / 2.5	**16** SA 0433 / 1107 / 1654 / 2329	10.9 / 2.8 / 11.6 / 2.3
2 SA 0448 / 1124 / 1709	11.8 / 2.1 / 12.6	**17** SU 0517 / 1153 / 1737	11.7 / 2.2 / 12.1
3 SU 0000 / 0539 / 1221 / 1759	1.6 / 12.9 / 1.3 / 13.5	**18** M 0014 / 0556 / 1237 / 1816	1.8 / 12.2 / 1.8 / 12.4
4 M 0053 / 0625 / 1312 / ●1845	0.9 / 13.7 / 0.8 / 14.1	**19** TU 0058 / 0633 / 1319 / 1852	1.5 / 12.5 / 1.7 / 12.6
5 TU 0141 / 0709 / 1400 / 1930	0.5 / 14.1 / 0.5 / 14.4	**20** W 0138 / 0708 / 1358 / ○1928	1.5 / 12.6 / 1.7 / 12.5
6 W 0227 / 0752 / 1444 / 2013	0.5 / 14.2 / 0.6 / 14.2	**21** TH 0215 / 0742 / 1431 / 2001	1.6 / 12.6 / 1.9 / 12.3
7 TH 0307 / 0823 / 1523 / 2055	0.7 / 13.9 / 0.9 / 13.7	**22** F 0246 / 0813 / 1458 / 2033	1.8 / 12.4 / 2.1 / 12.1
8 F 0341 / 0914 / 1557 / 2135	1.2 / 13.4 / 1.4 / 13.0	**23** SA 0310 / 0845 / 1521 / 2106	2.0 / 12.2 / 2.2 / 11.9
9 SA 0408 / 0953 / 1626 / 2214	1.9 / 12.5 / 2.1 / 12.0	**24** SU 0334 / 0919 / 1549 / 2142	2.2 / 12.0 / 2.4 / 11.6
10 SU 0432 / 1032 / 1656 / 2255	2.6 / 11.5 / 2.9 / 10.9	**25** M 0405 / 0958 / 1624 / 2224	2.4 / 11.7 / 2.6 / 11.2
11 M 0502 / 1117 / 1735 / 2346	3.4 / 10.5 / 3.7 / 9.8	**26** TU 0442 / 1043 / 1707 / 2314	2.7 / 11.2 / 3.0 / 10.7
12 TU 0546 / 1230 / 1834	4.1 / 9.7 / 4.3	**27** W 0529 / 1139 / 1803	3.2 / 10.7 / 3.4
13 W 0122 / 0657 / 1408 / 1959	9.2 / 4.7 / 9.4 / 4.5	**28** TH 0017 / 0633 / 1251 / 1922	10.2 / 3.6 / 10.4 / 3.7
14 TH 0243 / 0855 / 1513 / 2141	9.5 / 4.6 / 10.1 / 3.9	**29** F 0139 / 0807 / 1420 / 2103	10.2 / 3.7 / 10.7 / 3.4
15 F 0342 / 1015 / 1607 / 2240	10.1 / 3.7 / 10.9 / 3.0	**30** SA 0307 / 0939 / 1537 / 2223	10.7 / 3.2 / 11.4 / 2.7

DECEMBER

Time	m	Time	m
1 SU 0414 / 1049 / 1639 / 2326	11.6 / 2.4 / 12.2 / 2.0	**16** M 0431 / 1058 / 1655 / 2325	10.9 / 3.1 / 11.3 / 2.6
2 M 0510 / 1149 / 1733	12.4 / 1.7 / 13.0	**17** TU 0517 / 1151 / 1740	11.5 / 2.5 / 11.7
3 TU 0021 / 0600 / 1243 / 1822	1.4 / 13.1 / 1.2 / 13.5	**18** W 0015 / 0559 / 1239 / 1822	2.1 / 12.0 / 2.1 / 12.1
4 W 0112 / 0646 / 1333 / ●1909	1.0 / 13.6 / 1.0 / 13.7	**19** TH 0101 / 0640 / 1323 / ○1903	1.8 / 12.4 / 1.9 / 12.3
5 TH 0200 / 0731 / 1420 / 1954	0.9 / 13.7 / 0.9 / 13.6	**20** F 0144 / 0719 / 1404 / 1942	1.7 / 12.6 / 1.9 / 12.3
6 F 0244 / 0814 / 1504 / 2039	1.1 / 13.5 / 1.2 / 13.2	**21** SA 0223 / 0757 / 1443 / 2022	1.7 / 12.6 / 2.0 / 12.3
7 SA 0322 / 0857 / 1542 / 2121	1.5 / 13.1 / 1.6 / 12.7	**22** SU 0300 / 0835 / 1519 / 2101	1.8 / 12.5 / 2.0 / 12.2
8 SU 0355 / 0938 / 1616 / 2202	2.0 / 12.5 / 2.1 / 11.9	**23** M 0334 / 0914 / 1555 / 2141	2.0 / 12.4 / 2.1 / 12.1
9 M 0422 / 1018 / 1647 / 2241	2.6 / 11.8 / 2.7 / 11.2	**24** TU 0408 / 0955 / 1632 / 2223	2.1 / 12.2 / 2.2 / 11.8
10 TU 0452 / 1100 / 1722 / 2322	3.1 / 11.0 / 3.2 / 10.4	**25** W 0447 / 1040 / 1714 / 2309	2.3 / 12.0 / 2.4 / 11.5
11 W 0530 / 1150 / 1807	3.5 / 10.3 / 3.6	**26** TH 0531 / 1130 / 1801	2.5 / 11.6 / 2.7
12 TH 0015 / 0620 / 1300 / 1903	9.8 / 4.0 / 9.9 / 3.9	**27** F 0001 / 0622 / 1228 / 1858	11.1 / 2.9 / 11.2 / 3.0
13 F 0129 / 0725 / 1414 / 2007	9.6 / 4.2 / 9.9 / 3.9	**28** SA 0104 / 0727 / 1339 / 2009	10.8 / 3.1 / 11.0 / 3.2
14 SA 0241 / 0837 / 1513 / 2117	9.8 / 4.1 / 10.3 / 3.6	**29** SU 0220 / 0847 / 1457 / 2136	10.7 / 3.2 / 11.1 / 3.1
15 SU 0339 / 0951 / 1606 / 2226	10.3 / 3.7 / 10.7 / 3.1	**30** M 0336 / 1010 / 1607 / 2252	11.0 / 2.9 / 11.5 / 2.7
		31 TU 0441 / 1119 / 1709 / 2353	11.6 / 2.4 / 12.0 / 2.2

Chart Datum: 6·50 metres below Ordnance Datum (Newlyn)

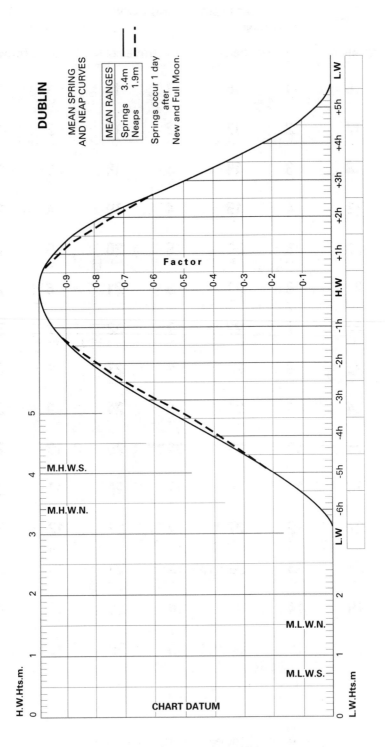

DUBLIN

MEAN SPRING
AND NEAP CURVES

MEAN RANGES	
Springs	3.4m
Neaps	1.9m

Springs occur 1 day
after
New and Full Moon.

Factor

0·9 0·8 0·7 0·6 0·5 0·4 0·3 0·2 0·1

L.W +5h +4h +3h +2h +1h H.W -1h -2h -3h -4h -5h -6h L.W

M.H.W.S.

M.H.W.N.

M.L.W.N.

M.L.W.S.

H.W.Hts.m.

L.W.Hts.m

CHART DATUM

TIME ZONE (UTC)
For Summer Time add ONE hour in **non-shaded areas**

IRELAND – DUBLIN (NORTH WALL)

YEAR 2002

LAT 53°21′N   LONG 6°13′W

TIMES AND HEIGHTS OF HIGH AND LOW WATERS

JANUARY

Day	Time m	Time m	Time m	Time m		Day	Time m	Time m	Time m	Time m
1 TU	0022 4.0	0554 0.8	1239 4.2	1827 0.5		**16** W	0108 3.7	0643 1.0	1314 4.0	1915 0.8
2 W	0109 4.0	0639 0.6	1327 4.2	1917 0.5		**17** TH	0143 3.7	0719 1.0	1351 4.0	1951 0.9
3 TH	0200 4.0	0729 0.9	1418 4.2	2012 0.6		**18** F	0221 3.6	0757 1.1	1430 3.9	2029 1.0
4 F	0255 3.9	0824 1.0	1513 4.1	2109 0.7		**19** SA	0302 3.5	0837 1.2	1511 3.8	2109 1.1
5 SA	0353 3.8	0924 1.2	1611 4.1	2210 0.8		**20** SU	0346 3.4	0922 1.4	1556 3.6	2152 1.2
6 SU	0456 3.7	1029 1.3	1714 3.9	2314 0.9		**21** M	0435 3.3	1014 1.5	1645 3.5	2241 1.3
7 M	0604 3.6	1137 1.4	1822 3.9			**22** TU	0534 3.3	1114 1.6	1742 3.4	2342 1.4
8 TU	0022 1.0	0711 3.6	1249 1.4	1932 3.8		**23** W	0641 3.2	1219 1.6	1849 3.3	
9 W	0130 1.1	0816 3.7	1358 1.4	2040 3.8		**24** TH	0047 1.5	0745 3.3	1323 1.6	1958 3.4
10 TH	0234 1.1	0916 3.8	1501 1.2	2143 3.8		**25** F	0150 1.4	0842 3.5	1421 1.4	2059 3.5
11 F	0330 1.0	1009 3.9	1555 1.1	2237 3.8		**26** SA	0246 1.2	0931 3.7	1513 1.1	2152 3.7
12 SA	0417 1.0	1055 4.0	1642 1.0	2323 3.8		**27** SU	0334 1.0	1015 3.9	1600 0.8	2239 3.9
13 SU ●	0458 1.0	1134 4.0	1723 0.9			**28** M ○	0417 0.8	1104 4.1	1644 0.6	2324 4.0
14 M	0001 3.8	0534 0.9	1207 4.0	1801 0.8		**29** TU	0459 0.7	1140 4.2	1729 0.4	
15 TU	0035 3.8	0609 0.9	1240 4.0	1838 0.8		**30** W	0008 4.1	0541 0.6	1224 4.3	1813 0.2
						31 TH	0054 4.1	0624 0.6	1310 4.4	1901 0.2

FEBRUARY

Day	Time m	Time m	Time m	Time m		Day	Time m	Time m	Time m	Time m
1 F	0141 4.1	0711 0.6	1358 4.3	1951 0.3		**16** SA	0144 3.6	0721 0.9	1357 3.9	1945 0.8
2 SA	0231 4.0	0801 0.7	1450 4.2	2044 0.5		**17** SU	0219 3.6	0755 0.9	1436 3.8	2019 0.9
3 SU	0323 3.8	0856 0.9	1545 4.1	2140 0.7		**18** M	0259 3.5	0834 1.1	1517 3.7	2057 1.0
4 M	0421 3.7	0956 1.1	1645 3.9	2239 0.9		**19** TU	0343 3.4	0917 1.2	1603 3.5	2142 1.2
5 TU	0526 3.6	1102 1.3	1755 3.7	2345 1.2		**20** W	0433 3.3	1008 1.4	1655 3.4	2235 1.4
6 W	0637 3.5	1216 1.4	1910 3.6			**21** TH	0534 3.2	1115 1.5	1800 3.2	2347 1.5
7 TH	0100 1.3	0747 3.5	1338 1.4	2023 3.5		**22** F	0650 3.2	1238 1.5	1921 3.2	
8 F	0216 1.3	0853 3.6	1451 1.3	2132 3.6		**23** SA	0112 1.5	0805 3.3	1352 1.3	2035 3.4
9 SA	0318 1.3	0953 3.7	1548 1.1	2230 3.6		**24** SU	0223 1.3	0905 3.5	1453 1.0	2134 3.6
10 SU	0406 1.2	1042 3.8	1633 1.0	2315 3.7		**25** M	0318 1.1	0955 3.8	1544 0.7	2224 3.8
11 M	0445 1.0	1121 3.9	1711 0.9	2350 3.7		**26** TU	0404 0.8	1040 4.1	1630 0.3	2308 4.0
12 TU ●	0519 0.9	1151 4.0	1745 0.8			**27** W ○	0445 0.5	1123 4.3	1713 0.1	2350 4.1
13 W	0017 3.7	0551 0.9	1220 4.0	1817 0.7		**28** TH	0526 0.4	1205 4.4	1756 0.0	
14 TH	0043 3.7	0621 0.8	1250 4.0	1847 0.8						
15 F	0112 3.7	0651 0.8	1322 3.9	1916 0.8						

MARCH

Day	Time m	Time m	Time m	Time m		Day	Time m	Time m	Time m	Time m
1 F	0032 4.1	0606 0.3	1250 4.4	1840 0.0		**16** SA	0041 3.7	0621 0.7	1253 3.9	1839 0.7
2 SA	0116 4.1	0650 0.4	1336 4.3	1926 0.2		**17** SU	0110 3.7	0649 0.7	1327 3.9	1907 0.7
3 SU	0201 4.0	0737 0.5	1425 4.2	2016 0.4		**18** M	0144 3.7	0722 0.8	1406 3.8	1941 0.8
4 M	0250 3.8	0829 0.7	1518 4.0	2108 0.7		**19** TU	0223 3.6	0759 0.9	1447 3.7	2021 0.9
5 TU	0343 3.7	0927 0.9	1617 3.8	2205 1.0		**20** W	0306 3.5	0843 1.0	1532 3.5	2105 1.1
6 W	0445 3.5	1032 1.2	1729 3.5	2308 1.3		**21** TH	0354 3.4	0934 1.2	1624 3.4	2159 1.3
7 TH	0600 3.4	1146 1.3	1848 3.4			**22** F	0452 3.2	1041 1.3	1729 3.2	2310 1.5
8 F	0025 1.5	0716 3.4	1318 1.4	2007 3.4		**23** SA	0607 3.2	1207 1.4	1855 3.2	
9 SA	0157 1.5	0829 3.4	1437 1.3	2121 3.4		**24** SU	0043 1.5	0732 3.3	1329 1.2	2014 3.4
10 SU	0302 1.4	0932 3.6	1533 1.1	2217 3.5		**25** M	0202 1.3	0839 3.5	1434 0.9	2116 3.6
11 M	0349 1.2	1022 3.7	1615 0.9	2259 3.6		**26** TU	0300 1.0	0933 3.8	1527 0.5	2206 3.8
12 TU	0426 1.0	1100 3.8	1650 0.8	2330 3.6		**27** W	0347 0.7	1020 4.1	1612 0.2	2249 4.0
13 W	0458 0.9	1130 3.9	1721 0.7	2353 3.6		**28** TH ○	0428 0.4	1104 4.3	1655 0.0	2330 4.1
14 TH ●	0528 0.8	1157 3.9	1750 0.7			**29** F	0507 0.3	1146 4.4	1736 -0.1	
15 F	0016 3.7	0555 0.7	1224 3.9	1815 0.7		**30** SA	0010 4.1	0547 0.2	1230 4.4	1818 0.0
						31 SU	0051 4.1	0630 0.2	1315 4.3	1902 0.2

APRIL

Day	Time m	Time m	Time m	Time m		Day	Time m	Time m	Time m	Time m
1 M	0134 4.0	0716 0.4	1404 4.1	1949 0.5		**16** TU	0115 3.8	0654 0.7	1341 3.8	1912 0.8
2 TU	0220 3.9	0808 0.6	1456 3.9	2039 0.8		**17** W	0155 3.7	0735 0.8	1424 3.7	1953 0.9
3 W	0311 3.7	0905 0.8	1555 3.6	2134 1.1		**18** TH	0240 3.6	0822 0.9	1512 3.6	2042 1.1
4 TH	0410 3.5	1008 1.1	1706 3.4	2235 1.4		**19** F	0329 3.5	0918 1.1	1606 3.4	2140 1.3
5 F	0524 3.4	1120 1.3	1824 3.2	2348 1.6		**20** SA	0428 3.4	1028 1.2	1713 3.3	2253 1.5
6 SA	0643 3.3	1249 1.3	1944 3.2			**21** SU	0541 3.3	1150 1.2	1835 3.3	
7 SU	0121 1.6	0757 3.4	1410 1.2	2057 3.3		**22** M	0019 1.5	0702 3.4	1307 1.0	1951 3.4
8 M	0233 1.5	0902 3.5	1505 1.0	2151 3.5		**23** TU	0136 1.3	0811 3.6	1412 0.7	2053 3.6
9 TU	0321 1.3	0952 3.7	1546 0.9	2230 3.6		**24** W	0235 1.0	0909 3.8	1505 0.4	2144 3.8
10 W	0358 1.1	1031 3.8	1621 0.8	2259 3.6		**25** TH	0324 0.7	0959 4.1	1552 0.2	2228 4.0
11 TH	0431 0.9	1102 3.8	1651 0.7	2324 3.7		**26** F	0408 0.5	1045 4.2	1635 0.1	2309 4.1
12 F ●	0501 0.8	1130 3.8	1718 0.7	2347 3.7		**27** SA ○	0449 0.4	1129 4.3	1717 0.1	2350 4.1
13 SA	0527 0.7	1156 3.8	1741 0.7			**28** SU	0531 0.3	1213 4.3	1758 0.2	
14 SU	0010 3.7	0552 0.7	1226 3.8	1805 0.7		**29** M	0029 4.1	0613 0.3	1259 4.2	1841 0.4
15 M	0039 3.8	0620 0.7	1301 3.8	1835 0.7		**30** TU	0111 4.0	0700 0.6	1347 4.0	1926 0.6

IRELAND – DUBLIN (NORTH WALL)

YEAR 2002

TIME ZONE (UTC)
For Summer Time add ONE hour in **non-shaded areas**

LAT 53°21'N   LONG 6°13'W

TIMES AND HEIGHTS OF HIGH AND LOW WATERS

MAY

Time	m		Time	m
1 0157	3.9	**16**	0135	3.8
0752	0.6		0719	0.8
W 1439	3.8	TH	1408	3.7
2015	0.9		1935	1.0
2 0246	3.8	**17**	0222	3.8
0848	0.8		0812	0.9
TH 1537	3.6	F	1459	3.6
2108	1.2		2028	1.1
3 0343	3.6	**18**	0315	3.7
0948	1.0		0912	0.9
F 1642	3.3	SA	1556	3.5
2207	1.4		2129	1.3
4 0452	3.4	**19**	0414	3.6
1054	1.2		1020	1.0
SA 1754	3.2	SU	1701	3.4
2312	1.6		2239	1.4
5 0607	3.4	**20**	0522	3.6
1208	1.2		1132	1.0
SU 1907	3.2	M	1813	3.4
			2353	1.4
6 0028	1.6	**21**	0635	3.6
0717	3.4		1242	0.9
M 1325	1.2	TU	1924	3.5
2014	3.3			
7 0144	1.5	**22**	0104	1.3
0819	3.5		0742	3.7
TU 1424	1.1	W	1345	0.7
2108	3.4		2025	3.7
8 0240	1.3	**23**	0205	1.1
0911	3.6		0843	3.9
W 1509	1.0	TH	1441	0.5
2148	3.5		2120	3.8
9 0322	1.2	**24**	0259	0.9
0953	3.7		0938	4.0
TH 1545	0.9	F	1531	0.4
2222	3.6		2208	3.9
10 0357	1.0	**25**	0348	0.7
1029	3.7		1028	4.1
F 1616	0.8	SA	1617	0.3
2251	3.7		2251	4.0
11 0428	0.9	**26**	0433	0.6
1100	3.8		1116	4.1
SA 1643	0.8	SU	1700	0.4
2316	3.7		○ 2332	4.0
12 0456	0.8	**27**	0518	0.5
1129	3.8		1201	4.1
SU 1708	0.8	M	1742	0.5
● 2342	3.8			
13 0524	0.8	**28**	0012	4.0
1201	3.8		0602	0.5
M 1736	0.8	TU	1247	4.0
			1823	0.6
14 0013	3.8	**29**	0054	4.0
0556	0.7		0649	0.6
TU 1239	3.8	W	1334	3.9
1810	0.8		1907	0.8
15 0052	3.8	**30**	0138	3.9
0634	0.8		0739	0.7
W 1321	3.8	TH	1422	3.7
1849	0.9		1953	1.0
		31	0225	3.8
			0831	0.8
		F	1515	3.5
			2043	1.2

JUNE

Time	m		Time	m
1 0317	3.7	**16**	0301	3.9
0927	1.0		0902	0.8
SA 1612	3.4	SU	1543	3.7
2138	1.4		2114	1.2
2 0416	3.6	**17**	0359	3.9
1024	1.1		1005	0.8
SU 1714	3.3	M	1643	3.6
2237	1.5		2217	1.2
3 0523	3.5	**18**	0501	3.8
1125	1.2		1110	0.8
M 1819	3.2	TU	1748	3.6
2339	1.6		2324	1.3
4 0630	3.4	**19**	0608	3.8
1228	1.2		1214	0.8
TU 1920	3.2	W	1854	3.6
5 0044	1.6	**20**	0031	1.2
0730	3.5		0715	3.8
W 1329	1.2	TH	1317	0.8
2014	3.3		1957	3.7
6 0145	1.5	**21**	0136	1.2
0824	3.5		0820	3.9
TH 1420	1.1	F	1417	0.8
2101	3.5		2056	3.7
7 0235	1.3	**22**	0237	1.1
0911	3.6		0921	3.9
F 1502	1.1	SA	1512	0.7
2141	3.6		2149	3.8
8 0317	1.2	**23**	0332	0.9
0952	3.6		1017	4.0
SA 1537	1.0	SU	1601	0.7
2216	3.7		2237	3.9
9 0353	1.1	**24**	0423	0.8
1029	3.7		1107	4.0
SU 1609	0.9	M	1647	0.7
2246	3.8		○ 2319	4.0
10 0426	1.0	**25**	0510	0.8
1104	3.8		1153	3.9
M 1640	0.9	TU	1729	0.8
● 2317	3.8		2359	4.0
11 0500	0.9	**26**	0555	0.7
1141	3.8		1236	3.9
TU 1714	0.8	W	1809	0.8
2353	3.9			
12 0538	0.9	**27**	0037	4.0
1221	3.8		0638	0.7
W 1752	0.8	TH	1318	3.8
			1848	0.9
13 0033	4.0	**28**	0118	4.0
0620	0.7		0723	0.8
TH 1306	3.8	F	1400	3.7
1834	0.9		1930	1.0
14 0118	4.0	**29**	0201	3.9
0708	0.7		0810	0.8
F 1355	3.8	SA	1445	3.5
1921	1.0		2015	1.1
15 0208	3.9	**30**	0246	3.8
0803	0.8		0858	0.9
SA 1447	3.7	SU	1533	3.4
2015	1.1		2103	1.3

JULY

Time	m		Time	m
1 0335	3.7	**16**	0337	4.1
0947	1.1		0941	0.7
M 1624	3.3	TU	1617	3.7
2156	1.4		2150	1.1
2 0428	3.6	**17**	0436	4.0
1039	1.2		1042	0.8
TU 1721	3.3	W	1718	3.6
2252	1.5		2253	1.2
3 0528	3.5	**18**	0541	3.9
1133	1.3		1144	0.9
W 1822	3.2	TH	1824	3.6
2350	1.5			
4 0632	3.4	**19**	0000	1.3
1228	1.3		0652	3.8
TH 1920	3.3	F	1250	1.0
			1931	3.6
5 0049	1.5	**20**	0112	1.3
0733	3.4		0803	3.7
F 1324	1.3	SA	1355	1.1
2013	3.4		2036	3.7
6 0145	1.5	**21**	0222	1.2
0828	3.4		0910	3.8
SA 1414	1.3	SU	1457	1.1
2100	3.5		2135	3.8
7 0235	1.4	**22**	0325	1.1
0917	3.5		1010	3.8
SU 1459	1.2	M	1550	1.0
2142	3.6		2226	3.9
8 0320	1.2	**23**	0418	1.0
1001	3.6		1103	3.8
M 1539	1.1	TU	1636	1.0
2220	3.8		2309	3.9
9 0401	1.0	**24**	0504	0.9
1043	3.7		1147	3.9
TU 1617	1.0	W	1716	0.9
2257	3.9		○ 2346	4.0
10 0441	0.9	**25**	0545	0.8
1124	3.8		1224	3.8
W 1656	0.9	TH	1752	0.9
● 2335	4.0			
11 0523	0.7	**26**	0019	4.0
1207	3.9		0623	0.8
TH 1736	0.8	F	1257	3.7
			1827	0.9
12 0017	4.1	**27**	0054	4.0
0607	0.6		0701	0.8
F 1251	3.9	SA	1332	3.6
1819	0.8		1903	1.0
13 0102	4.1	**28**	0131	4.0
0654	0.5		0740	0.8
SA 1339	3.9	SU	1408	3.6
1905	0.8		1941	1.0
14 0150	4.2	**29**	0210	3.9
0747	0.5		0819	0.9
SU 1429	3.7	M	1448	3.5
1956	0.9		2022	1.1
15 0242	4.1	**30**	0252	3.8
0843	0.6		0901	1.0
M 1521	3.8	TU	1530	3.4
2051	1.0		2106	1.2
		31	0336	3.7
			0944	1.1
		W	1616	3.3
			2155	1.4

AUGUST

Time	m		Time	m
1 0425	3.5	**16**	0515	3.8
1033	1.3		1113	1.1
TH 1709	3.3	F	1754	3.5
2251	1.5		2334	1.3
2 0523	3.4	**17**	0635	3.6
1128	1.4		1223	1.3
F 1814	3.2	SA	1908	3.5
2354	1.6			
3 0634	3.3	**18**	0054	1.4
1229	1.5		0752	3.6
SA 1922	3.3	SU	1338	1.4
			2018	3.6
4 0059	1.6	**19**	0216	1.3
0746	3.3		0904	3.6
SU 1331	1.5	M	1446	1.3
2021	3.4		2122	3.7
5 0200	1.5	**20**	0322	1.2
0847	3.4		1007	3.7
M 1428	1.4	TU	1540	1.2
2112	3.6		2215	3.8
6 0254	1.2	**21**	0412	1.0
0940	3.6		1057	3.7
TU 1517	1.2	W	1623	1.1
2157	3.8		2258	3.9
7 0342	1.0	**22**	0453	0.8
1026	3.7		1137	3.7
W 1600	1.0	TH	1700	1.0
2238	4.0		○ 2331	4.0
8 0425	0.7	**23**	0529	0.8
1108	3.9		1207	3.7
TH 1640	0.8	F	1733	0.9
● 2317	4.1		2358	4.0
9 0507	0.5	**24**	0602	0.7
1150	4.0		1232	3.7
F 1720	0.7	SA	1804	0.9
2358	4.3			
10 0550	0.3	**25**	0028	4.0
1232	4.1		0633	0.7
SA 1801	0.6	SU	1300	3.7
			1835	0.9
11 0040	4.3	**26**	0100	4.0
0635	0.3		0703	0.8
SU 1317	4.0	M	1332	3.7
1844	0.6		1906	0.9
12 0127	4.3	**27**	0136	3.9
0723	0.3		0734	0.9
M 1403	4.0	TU	1406	3.6
1931	0.7		1940	1.0
13 0216	4.3	**28**	0214	3.8
0815	0.4		0807	1.0
TU 1453	3.9	W	1444	3.6
2023	0.8		2018	1.1
14 0309	4.1	**29**	0256	3.7
0911	0.6		0845	1.1
W 1546	3.8	TH	1526	3.5
2120	1.0		2100	1.3
15 0407	4.0	**30**	0342	3.5
1010	0.8		0929	1.3
TH 1645	3.6	F	1614	3.4
2223	1.2		2150	1.4
		31	0435	3.4
			1022	1.5
		SA	1711	3.2
			2256	1.6

Chart Datum: 0·20 metres above Ordnance Datum (Dublin)
Register for your **FREE** weekly weather email service from Macmillan Reeds
》 at **www.nauticaldata.com – NOW!** 《
weekend weather reports sent to your email address, every Thursday

TIME ZONE (UTC)
For Summer Time add ONE hour in **non-shaded areas**

IRELAND – DUBLIN (NORTH WALL)

YEAR **2002**

LAT 53°21′N   LONG 6°13′W

TIMES AND HEIGHTS OF HIGH AND LOW WATERS

SEPTEMBER

Time m	Time m
1 0542 3.2 / 1135 1.6 / SU 1827 3.2	**16** 0041 1.4 / 0742 3.4 / M 1321 1.6 / 1959 3.6
2 0018 1.6 / 0710 3.2 / M 1256 1.6 / 1945 3.3	**17** 0210 1.3 / 0858 3.5 / TU 1432 1.5 / 2106 3.7
3 0133 1.5 / 0824 3.3 / TU 1404 1.5 / 2046 3.5	**18** 0311 1.1 / 0957 3.6 / W 1523 1.3 / 2159 3.9
4 0235 1.2 / 0921 3.6 / W 1459 1.2 / 2134 3.8	**19** 0356 0.9 / 1043 3.7 / TH 1604 1.1 / 2240 4.0
5 0325 0.8 / 1008 3.8 / TH 1543 1.0 / 2217 4.1	**20** 0433 0.8 / 1118 3.7 / F 1639 1.0 / 2311 4.0
6 0408 0.5 / 1050 4.0 / F 1623 0.7 / 2257 4.3	**21** 0505 0.7 / 1144 3.7 / SA 1710 0.9 / ○ 2337 4.0
7 0449 0.2 / 1130 4.1 / SA 1701 0.5 / ● 2337 4.4	**22** 0535 0.7 / 1206 3.7 / SU 1740 0.8
8 0530 0.1 / 1209 4.2 / SU 1741 0.4	**23** 0003 4.0 / 0601 0.7 / M 1231 3.8 / 1807 0.8
9 0018 4.5 / 0612 0.1 / M 1251 4.2 / 1822 0.4	**24** 0032 4.0 / 0626 0.8 / TU 1258 3.8 / 1835 0.8
10 0102 4.4 / 0657 0.2 / TU 1335 4.1 / 1907 0.5	**25** 0106 3.9 / 0652 0.9 / W 1331 3.8 / 1906 0.9
11 0150 4.3 / 0746 0.4 / W 1422 4.0 / 1957 0.7	**26** 0143 3.8 / 0724 0.9 / TH 1409 3.7 / 1942 1.0
12 0242 4.1 / 0840 0.7 / TH 1514 3.8 / 2054 0.9	**27** 0224 3.7 / 0802 1.1 / F 1450 3.6 / 2024 1.2
13 0341 3.9 / 0938 1.0 / F 1612 3.7 / 2158 1.2	**28** 0310 3.6 / 0846 1.3 / SA 1537 3.5 / 2114 1.4
14 0454 3.6 / 1042 1.3 / SA 1724 3.5 / 2312 1.4	**29** 0403 3.4 / 0940 1.5 / SU 1632 3.3 / 2219 1.5
15 0619 3.5 / 1156 1.5 / SU 1844 3.5	**30** 0509 3.2 / 1054 1.7 / M 1744 3.2 / 2347 1.6

OCTOBER

Time m	Time m
1 0640 3.2 / 1226 1.7 / TU 1909 3.3	**16** 0147 1.3 / 0839 3.5 / W 1406 1.6 / 2038 3.7
2 0108 1.4 / 0800 3.4 / W 1341 1.5 / 2016 3.6	**17** 0246 1.1 / 0935 3.6 / TH 1457 1.4 / 2132 3.8
3 0214 1.1 / 0900 3.6 / TH 1438 1.2 / 2109 3.8	**18** 0330 1.0 / 1017 3.7 / F 1538 1.2 / 2213 3.9
4 0305 0.7 / 0947 3.9 / F 1523 0.9 / 2154 4.1	**19** 0406 0.8 / 1050 3.8 / SA 1613 1.0 / 2245 4.0
5 0349 0.4 / 1028 4.1 / SA 1602 0.6 / 2235 4.3	**20** 0437 0.8 / 1116 3.8 / SU 1645 0.9 / 2313 4.0
6 0429 0.1 / 1107 4.2 / SU 1641 0.4 / ● 2316 4.5	**21** 0506 0.8 / 1139 3.8 / M 1715 0.9 / ○ 2339 4.0
7 0509 0.0 / 1146 4.3 / M 1720 0.3 / 2357 4.5	**22** 0531 0.8 / 1203 3.8 / TU 1742 0.9
8 0550 0.1 / 1226 4.2 / TU 1802 0.3	**23** 0007 3.9 / 0553 0.9 / W 1230 3.9 / 1809 0.9
9 0041 4.4 / 0633 0.2 / W 1309 4.2 / 1847 0.5	**24** 0041 3.9 / 0619 0.9 / TH 1303 3.8 / 1840 0.9
10 0129 4.3 / 0720 0.5 / TH 1356 4.0 / 1937 0.7	**25** 0118 3.8 / 0653 1.0 / F 1341 3.8 / 1918 1.0
11 0222 4.0 / 0812 0.8 / F 1447 3.9 / 2034 0.9	**26** 0201 3.7 / 0732 1.2 / SA 1424 3.7 / 2002 1.2
12 0323 3.8 / 0909 1.2 / SA 1545 3.7 / 2139 1.2	**27** 0248 3.6 / 0818 1.3 / SU 1512 3.6 / 2055 1.3
13 0438 3.5 / 1013 1.5 / SU 1657 3.6 / 2252 1.3	**28** 0343 3.4 / 0915 1.5 / M 1607 3.5 / 2201 1.4
14 0601 3.4 / 1126 1.7 / M 1816 3.5	**29** 0450 3.3 / 1029 1.7 / TU 1714 3.4 / 2322 1.4
15 0021 1.4 / 0724 3.4 / TU 1253 1.7 / 1931 3.6	**30** 0612 3.3 / 1156 1.7 / W 1831 3.5
	31 0040 1.2 / 0729 3.4 / TH 1311 1.5 / 1940 3.7

NOVEMBER

Time m	Time m
1 0146 1.0 / 0831 3.7 / F 1409 1.3 / 2038 3.9	**16** 0255 1.1 / 0938 3.7 / SA 1506 1.3 / 2136 3.8
2 0240 0.6 / 0920 3.9 / SA 1457 1.0 / 2128 4.1	**17** 0334 1.0 / 1013 3.8 / SU 1545 1.2 / 2214 3.9
3 0326 0.4 / 1004 4.1 / SU 1541 0.7 / 2213 4.3	**18** 0406 0.9 / 1043 3.8 / M 1619 1.0 / 2247 3.9
4 0409 0.2 / 1045 4.2 / M 1622 0.5 / ● 2257 4.4	**19** 0435 0.9 / 1112 3.9 / TU 1650 1.0 / 2317 3.9
5 0450 0.2 / 1125 4.3 / TU 1704 0.4 / 2341 4.4	**20** 0501 0.9 / 1138 3.9 / W 1719 1.0 / ○ 2347 3.9
6 0531 0.2 / 1206 4.3 / W 1747 0.4	**21** 0526 1.0 / 1206 3.9 / TH 1748 1.0
7 0027 4.3 / 0614 0.4 / TH 1250 4.2 / 1833 0.5	**22** 0021 3.9 / 0555 1.0 / F 1240 3.9 / 1821 1.0
8 0117 4.2 / 0659 0.7 / F 1336 4.1 / 1924 0.7	**23** 0100 3.8 / 0630 1.1 / SA 1320 3.9 / 1902 1.0
9 0210 4.0 / 0749 1.0 / SA 1427 4.0 / 2020 0.9	**24** 0144 3.7 / 0712 1.2 / SU 1405 3.8 / 1948 1.1
10 0310 3.7 / 0845 1.3 / SU 1523 3.8 / 2121 1.1	**25** 0234 3.7 / 0801 1.3 / M 1454 3.8 / 2043 1.1
11 0419 3.5 / 0946 1.5 / M 1629 3.7 / 2228 1.3	**26** 0329 3.6 / 0859 1.5 / TU 1548 3.7 / 2146 1.2
12 0533 3.4 / 1053 1.7 / TU 1742 3.6 / 2344 1.4	**27** 0432 3.5 / 1006 1.6 / W 1650 3.7 / 2256 1.2
13 0649 3.4 / 1208 1.7 / W 1852 3.6	**28** 0542 3.5 / 1121 1.6 / TH 1757 3.7
14 0104 1.3 / 0759 3.4 / TH 1323 1.7 / 1956 3.7	**29** 0007 1.1 / 0652 3.6 / F 1233 1.5 / 1903 3.8
15 0207 1.2 / 0855 3.6 / F 1421 1.5 / 2051 3.7	**30** 0113 0.9 / 0755 3.7 / SA 1335 1.3 / 2005 3.9

DECEMBER

Time m	Time m
1 0211 0.7 / 0850 3.9 / SU 1430 1.1 / 2102 4.1	**16** 0255 1.2 / 0931 3.7 / M 1512 1.4 / 2139 3.7
2 0303 0.6 / 0940 4.0 / M 1520 0.9 / 2155 4.2	**17** 0333 1.2 / 1009 3.8 / TU 1550 1.2 / 2219 3.7
3 0350 0.5 / 1026 4.1 / TU 1608 0.7 / 2245 4.2	**18** 0405 1.1 / 1044 3.9 / W 1625 1.1 / 2255 3.8
4 0435 0.5 / 1110 4.2 / W 1653 0.6 / 2333 4.2	**19** 0435 1.1 / 1115 3.9 / TH 1658 1.1 / ○ 2329 3.8
5 0517 0.5 / 1152 4.2 / TH 1739 0.6	**20** 0505 1.1 / 1146 4.0 / F 1731 1.0
6 0020 4.2 / 0600 0.7 / F 1236 4.2 / 1825 0.6	**21** 0006 3.8 / 0537 1.0 / SA 1222 4.0 / 1807 0.9
7 0108 4.0 / 0643 0.8 / SA 1321 4.2 / 1914 0.7	**22** 0046 3.8 / 0615 1.0 / SU 1303 4.0 / 1849 0.9
8 0159 3.9 / 0730 1.0 / SU 1409 4.1 / 2006 0.8	**23** 0130 3.8 / 0657 1.1 / M 1348 4.0 / 1936 0.9
9 0252 3.7 / 0820 1.2 / M 1500 3.9 / 2100 1.0	**24** 0219 3.8 / 0745 1.2 / TU 1436 4.0 / 2028 0.9
10 0351 3.5 / 0916 1.4 / TU 1557 3.8 / 2157 1.1	**25** 0311 3.7 / 0839 1.2 / W 1528 3.9 / 2125 0.9
11 0454 3.4 / 1015 1.6 / W 1659 3.7 / 2258 1.3	**26** 0408 3.7 / 0939 1.3 / TH 1624 3.9 / 2226 0.9
12 0559 3.3 / 1119 1.7 / TH 1804 3.6	**27** 0509 3.6 / 1044 1.4 / F 1724 3.9 / 2330 1.0
13 0004 1.4 / 0702 3.4 / F 1227 1.7 / 1906 3.6	**28** 0614 3.6 / 1152 1.4 / SA 1829 3.8
14 0111 1.4 / 0759 3.4 / SA 1331 1.6 / 2003 3.6	**29** 0037 1.0 / 0720 3.7 / SU 1301 1.3 / 1936 3.8
15 0209 1.3 / 0848 3.6 / SU 1426 1.5 / 2054 3.6	**30** 0142 0.9 / 0822 3.8 / M 1406 1.2 / 2042 3.9
	31 0242 0.9 / 0920 3.9 / TU 1506 1.1 / 2144 4.0

Chart Datum: 0·20 metres above Ordnance Datum (Dublin)
Register for your **FREE** weekly weather email service from Macmillan Reeds
》 at **www.nauticaldata.com – NOW!** 《
weekend weather reports sent to your email address, every Thursday

121

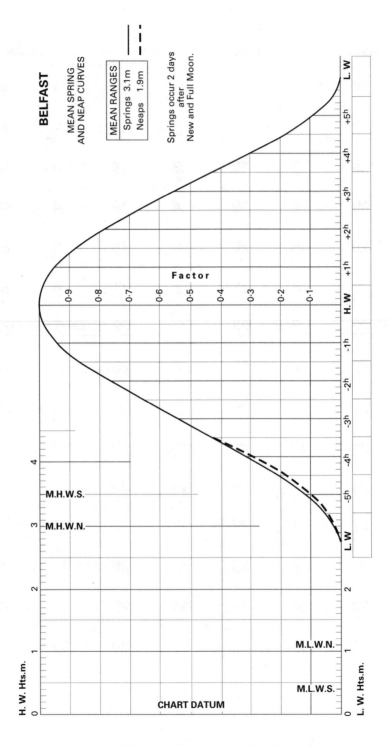

BELFAST

MEAN SPRING
AND NEAP CURVES

MEAN RANGES	
Springs	3.1m
Neaps	1.9m

Springs occur 2 days
after
New and Full Moon.

Factor

0·9 0·8 0·7 0·6 0·5 0·4 0·3 0·2 0·1

H. W. Hts.m.

4

3 —M.H.W.S.

—M.H.W.N.

2

1

0

CHART DATUM

L. W. Hts.m.

M.L.W.N.

M.L.W.S.

L. W   +5h   +4h   +3h   +2h   +1h   H. W   -1h   -2h   -3h   -4h   -5h   L. W

TIME ZONE (UTC)
For Summer Time add ONE hour in **non-shaded areas**

NORTHERN IRELAND – BELFAST

LAT 54°36′N   LONG 5°55′W

TIMES AND HEIGHTS OF HIGH AND LOW WATERS

YEAR **2002**

JANUARY

Time	m	Time	m
1 TU 0554 / 1213 / 1819	0.7 / 3.7 / 0.5	**16** W 0037 / 0626 / 1257 / 1904	3.2 / 0.9 / 3.5 / 0.7
2 W 0035 / 0641 / 1258 / 1905	3.4 / 0.7 / 3.7 / 0.5	**17** TH 0116 / 0702 / 1333 / 1937	3.1 / 0.9 / 3.5 / 0.7
3 TH 0125 / 0729 / 1345 / 1953	3.3 / 0.8 / 3.7 / 0.4	**18** F 0155 / 0739 / 1408 / 2012	3.1 / 0.9 / 3.4 / 0.7
4 F 0219 / 0819 / 1435 / 2045	3.2 / 0.8 / 3.6 / 0.5	**19** SA 0235 / 0818 / 1442 / 2050	3.0 / 0.9 / 3.4 / 0.8
5 SA 0316 / 0912 / 1529 / 2142	3.1 / 0.9 / 3.6 / 0.6	**20** SU 0317 / 0859 / 1519 / 2134	3.0 / 0.9 / 3.2 / 0.9
6 SU 0418 / 1010 / 1629 / 2246	3.0 / 1.0 / 3.5 / 0.7	**21** M 0404 / 0944 / 1603 / 2225	2.9 / 1.0 / 3.1 / 0.9
7 M 0522 / 1118 / 1735 / 2357	3.0 / 1.0 / 3.3 / 0.8	**22** TU 0455 / 1038 / 1658 / 2328	2.9 / 1.1 / 3.0 / 1.0
8 TU 0629 / 1233 / 1846	3.0 / 1.0 / 3.3	**23** W 0552 / 1144 / 1803	2.9 / 1.2 / 2.9
9 W 0108 / 0735 / 1344 / 1954	0.8 / 3.0 / 1.0 / 3.3	**24** TH 0041 / 0653 / 1303 / 1911	0.9 / 2.9 / 1.2 / 2.9
10 TH 0212 / 0836 / 1447 / 2055	0.8 / 3.1 / 0.9 / 3.3	**25** F 0147 / 0755 / 1410 / 2017	1.0 / 3.0 / 1.1 / 3.0
11 F 0304 / 0929 / 1541 / 2148	0.8 / 3.3 / 0.8 / 3.4	**26** SA 0241 / 0851 / 1504 / 2113	0.9 / 3.2 / 0.9 / 3.2
12 SA 0350 / 1016 / 1629 / 2235	0.8 / 3.4 / 0.7 / 3.4	**27** SU 0328 / 0940 / 1552 / 2202	0.8 / 3.3 / 0.7 / 3.3
13 SU 0432 / 1100 / 1713 / ●2318	0.8 / 3.5 / 0.7 / 3.3	**28** M 0413 / 1018 / 1638 / ○2249	0.7 / 3.5 / 0.5 / 3.3
14 M 0512 / 1141 / 1755 / 2358	0.9 / 3.5 / 0.7 / 3.2	**29** TU 0458 / 1112 / 1723 / 2337	0.6 / 3.6 / 0.4 / 3.3
15 TU 0550 / 1220 / 1831	0.9 / 3.6 / 0.7	**30** W 0543 / 1158 / 1809	0.6 / 3.7 / 0.3
		31 TH 0026 / 0629 / 1246 / 1854	3.3 / 0.6 / 3.7 / 0.2

FEBRUARY

Time	m	Time	m
1 F 0116 / 0715 / 1333 / 1939	3.3 / 0.6 / 3.8 / 0.2	**16** SA 0120 / 0709 / 1331 / 1937	3.1 / 0.7 / 3.4 / 0.6
2 SA 0205 / 0801 / 1420 / 2026	3.3 / 0.6 / 3.8 / 0.3	**17** SU 0151 / 0743 / 1359 / 2010	3.1 / 0.7 / 3.4 / 0.7
3 SU 0254 / 0849 / 1510 / 2117	3.2 / 0.6 / 3.7 / 0.4	**18** M 0226 / 0820 / 1433 / 2047	3.1 / 0.7 / 3.3 / 0.7
4 M 0347 / 0943 / 1604 / 2215	3.1 / 0.7 / 3.5 / 0.6	**19** TU 0307 / 0902 / 1515 / 2132	3.0 / 0.9 / 3.2 / 0.9
5 TU 0444 / 1048 / 1706 / 2325	3.0 / 0.9 / 3.3 / 0.8	**20** W 0357 / 0952 / 1610 / 2231	2.9 / 1.0 / 3.0 / 1.1
6 W 0552 / 1207 / 1818	2.9 / 1.0 / 3.1	**21** TH 0458 / 1056 / 1721 / 2354	2.9 / 1.2 / 2.9 / 1.1
7 TH 0043 / 0708 / 1325 / 1938	1.0 / 2.9 / 1.0 / 3.1	**22** F 0606 / 1228 / 1837	2.8 / 1.2 / 2.9
8 F 0154 / 0819 / 1435 / 2046	1.0 / 3.0 / 0.9 / 3.1	**23** SA 0123 / 0715 / 1350 / 1949	1.1 / 2.9 / 1.0 / 2.9
9 SA 0252 / 0916 / 1533 / 2140	0.9 / 3.2 / 0.8 / 3.2	**24** SU 0223 / 0819 / 1448 / 2052	0.9 / 3.1 / 0.9 / 3.1
10 SU 0340 / 1004 / 1621 / 2226	0.9 / 3.3 / 0.7 / 3.2	**25** M 0313 / 0914 / 1538 / 2145	0.9 / 3.3 / 0.6 / 3.2
11 M 0421 / 1047 / 1703 / 2306	0.9 / 3.4 / 0.6 / 3.2	**26** TU 0359 / 1003 / 1624 / 2233	0.7 / 3.5 / 0.4 / 3.3
12 TU 0458 / 1126 / 1738 / ●2344	0.8 / 3.5 / 0.6 / 3.1	**27** W 0444 / 1050 / 1709 / ○2322	0.6 / 3.6 / 0.2 / 3.3
13 W 0532 / 1203 / 1808	0.8 / 3.5 / 0.6	**28** TH 0529 / 1139 / 1753	0.5 / 3.7 / 0.1
14 TH 0017 / 0603 / 1236 / 1837	3.1 / 0.8 / 3.4 / 0.7		
15 F 0049 / 0636 / 1304 / 1906	3.1 / 0.8 / 3.4 / 0.6		

MARCH

Time	m	Time	m
1 F 0010 / 0613 / 1228 / 1836	3.3 / 0.4 / 3.8 / 0.1	**16** SA 0017 / 0610 / 1228 / 1836	3.1 / 0.6 / 3.3 / 0.6
2 SA 0058 / 0656 / 1315 / 1919	3.3 / 0.4 / 3.8 / 0.1	**17** SU 0043 / 0640 / 1253 / 1904	3.1 / 0.6 / 3.4 / 0.6
3 SU 0144 / 0740 / 1402 / 2002	3.3 / 0.4 / 3.8 / 0.2	**18** M 0113 / 0712 / 1324 / 1935	3.2 / 0.6 / 3.3 / 0.6
4 M 0228 / 0826 / 1449 / 2049	3.3 / 0.5 / 3.6 / 0.4	**19** TU 0147 / 0748 / 1359 / 2011	3.2 / 0.6 / 3.3 / 0.7
5 TU 0315 / 0917 / 1541 / 2142	3.2 / 0.6 / 3.4 / 0.7	**20** W 0225 / 0829 / 1442 / 2055	3.1 / 0.7 / 3.1 / 0.9
6 W 0407 / 1022 / 1639 / 2252	3.0 / 0.8 / 3.2 / 1.0	**21** TH 0313 / 0918 / 1538 / 2152	3.0 / 0.9 / 3.0 / 1.1
7 TH 0511 / 1144 / 1753	2.9 / 1.0 / 2.9	**22** F 0416 / 1021 / 1655 / 2309	2.9 / 1.1 / 2.8 / 1.2
8 F 0016 / 0637 / 1306 / 1925	1.1 / 2.8 / 1.0 / 2.9	**23** SA 0529 / 1157 / 1813	2.9 / 1.1 / 2.8
9 SA 0133 / 0759 / 1422 / 2035	1.1 / 3.0 / 0.8 / 2.9	**24** SU 0100 / 0642 / 1331 / 1927	1.2 / 2.9 / 0.9 / 2.9
10 SU 0237 / 0858 / 1522 / 2127	1.0 / 3.1 / 0.7 / 3.0	**25** M 0205 / 0750 / 1430 / 2034	1.0 / 3.1 / 0.7 / 3.0
11 M 0327 / 0946 / 1607 / 2210	0.9 / 3.2 / 0.6 / 3.1	**26** TU 0257 / 0848 / 1520 / 2127	0.8 / 3.3 / 0.4 / 3.2
12 TU 0406 / 1027 / 1643 / 2248	0.8 / 3.3 / 0.5 / 3.1	**27** W 0343 / 0939 / 1605 / 2214	0.6 / 3.5 / 0.2 / 3.3
13 W 0439 / 1105 / 1712 / 2322	0.8 / 3.4 / 0.6 / 3.1	**28** TH 0427 / 1028 / 1649 / ○2301	0.5 / 3.6 / 0.1 / 3.3
14 TH 0510 / 1138 / 1740 / ●2352	0.7 / 3.3 / 0.6 / 3.1	**29** F 0510 / 1117 / 1731 / 2349	0.4 / 3.7 / 0.1 / 3.4
15 F 0540 / 1205 / 1808	0.7 / 3.3 / 0.6	**30** SA 0554 / 1206 / 1813	0.4 / 3.7 / 0.1
		31 SU 0035 / 0636 / 1254 / 1854	3.4 / 0.3 / 3.7 / 0.2

APRIL

Time	m	Time	m
1 M 0119 / 0719 / 1341 / 1937	3.4 / 0.3 / 3.7 / 0.3	**16** TU 0045 / 0646 / 1256 / 1906	3.3 / 0.6 / 3.3 / 0.7
2 TU 0202 / 0804 / 1428 / 2022	3.4 / 0.4 / 3.5 / 0.6	**17** W 0119 / 0722 / 1335 / 1944	3.3 / 0.6 / 3.3 / 0.8
3 W 0247 / 0855 / 1519 / 2115	3.3 / 0.6 / 3.3 / 0.8	**18** TH 0159 / 0804 / 1421 / 2030	3.3 / 0.7 / 3.1 / 0.7
4 TH 0336 / 1002 / 1617 / 2222	3.1 / 0.8 / 3.0 / 1.1	**19** F 0247 / 0855 / 1521 / 2128	3.1 / 0.9 / 2.9 / 1.1
5 F 0435 / 1121 / 1729 / 2344	2.9 / 0.9 / 2.8 / 1.2	**20** SA 0348 / 1000 / 1640 / 2242	3.0 / 1.0 / 2.8 / 1.2
6 SA 0556 / 1237 / 1906	2.8 / 0.9 / 2.7	**21** SU 0501 / 1130 / 1755	3.0 / 1.0 / 2.8
7 SU 0059 / 0728 / 1353 / 2012	1.2 / 2.9 / 0.8 / 2.8	**22** M 0026 / 0614 / 1304 / 1907	1.2 / 3.0 / 0.8 / 2.9
8 M 0207 / 0830 / 1454 / 2102	1.1 / 3.0 / 0.7 / 2.9	**23** TU 0138 / 0723 / 1406 / 2012	1.0 / 3.1 / 0.6 / 3.0
9 TU 0301 / 0918 / 1537 / 2143	1.0 / 3.1 / 0.6 / 3.0	**24** W 0233 / 0824 / 1456 / 2105	0.8 / 3.3 / 0.4 / 3.2
10 W 0341 / 0958 / 1611 / 2219	0.9 / 3.2 / 0.5 / 3.0	**25** TH 0321 / 0917 / 1541 / 2152	0.7 / 3.5 / 0.2 / 3.3
11 TH 0414 / 1034 / 1640 / 2252	0.8 / 3.2 / 0.5 / 3.1	**26** F 0406 / 1007 / 1624 / 2239	0.5 / 3.6 / 0.2 / 3.4
12 F 0445 / 1105 / 1710 / ●2320	0.7 / 3.2 / 0.5 / 3.1	**27** SA 0450 / 1056 / 1706 / ○2325	0.4 / 3.7 / 0.2 / 3.4
13 SA 0515 / 1130 / 1739 / 2346	0.7 / 3.3 / 0.6 / 3.2	**28** SU 0533 / 1144 / 1748	0.4 / 3.7 / 0.3
14 SU 0545 / 1153 / 1807	0.6 / 3.3 / 0.6	**29** M 0011 / 0617 / 1233 / 1831	3.5 / 0.4 / 3.7 / 0.4
15 M 0013 / 0614 / 1222 / 1835	3.2 / 0.6 / 3.3 / 0.6	**30** TU 0056 / 0701 / 1320 / 1915	3.5 / 0.4 / 3.5 / 0.5

Chart Datum: 2·01 metres below Ordnance Datum (Belfast)

NORTHERN IRELAND – BELFAST

YEAR **2002**

LAT 54°36′N   LONG 5°55′W

TIMES AND HEIGHTS OF HIGH AND LOW WATERS

TIME ZONE (UTC)
For Summer Time add ONE hour in **non-shaded areas**

MAY

Day	Time	m	Time	m	Day	Time	m	Time	m
1 W	0139	3.4			16 TH	0102	3.4		
	0748	0.5				0705	0.6		
	1408	3.4				1320	3.2		
	2001	0.7				1929	0.8		
2 TH	0223	3.4			17 F	0144	3.4		
	0841	0.6				0750	0.7		
	1458	3.2				1410	3.1		
	2054	0.9				2018	1.0		
3 F	0312	3.2			18 SA	0233	3.3		
	0946	0.7				0842	0.8		
	1555	2.9				1513	3.0		
	2157	1.1				2115	1.1		
4 SA	0407	3.1			19 SU	0331	3.2		
	1055	0.8				0946	0.8		
	1701	2.8				1625	2.9		
	2308	1.2				2223	1.2		
5 SU	0512	2.9			20 M	0438	3.1		
	1201	0.9				1105	0.8		
	1824	2.7				1737	2.9		
						2341	1.1		
6 M	0015	1.2			21 TU	0549	3.1		
	0631	2.9				1227	0.7		
	1307	0.8				1845	2.9		
	1932	2.7							
7 TU	0119	1.2			22 W	0058	1.0		
	0744	2.9				0658	3.2		
	1406	0.7				1333	0.6		
	2023	2.8				1947	3.1		
8 W	0217	1.1			23 TH	0202	0.9		
	0837	3.0				0800	3.4		
	1454	0.7				1428	0.4		
	2104	2.9				2040	3.2		
9 TH	0303	1.0			24 F	0255	0.7		
	0919	3.1				0856	3.5		
	1531	0.6				1515	0.3		
	2141	3.0				2129	3.3		
10 F	0341	0.9			25 SA	0344	0.6		
	0956	3.1				0947	3.6		
	1605	0.6				1559	0.3		
	2214	3.1				2216	3.4		
11 SA	0415	0.8			26 SU	0430	0.5		
	1028	3.2				1036	3.6		
	1637	0.6				1642	0.4		
	2246	3.2				○ 2303	3.5		
12 SU	0448	0.7			27 M	0516	0.5		
	1058	3.2				1125	3.6		
	1726	0.6				1726	0.5		
	● 2318	3.3				2349	3.5		
13 M	0519	0.7			28 TU	0603	0.5		
	1127	3.3				1212	3.5		
	1739	0.6				1811	0.6		
	2350	3.3							
14 TU	0552	0.6			29 W	0034	3.5		
	1200	3.3				0650	0.5		
	1811	0.7				1300	3.4		
						1857	0.8		
15 W	0024	3.4			30 TH	0119	3.5		
	0626	0.6				0738	0.6		
	1238	3.3				1348	3.3		
	1847	0.7				1944	0.9		
					31 F	0204	3.4		
						0829	0.6		
						1438	3.1		
						2034	1.0		

JUNE

Day	Time	m	Day	Time	m
1 SA	0250	3.3	16 SU	0221	3.5
	0834	0.6		0834	0.6
	1531	2.9		1502	3.0
	2128	1.1		2104	0.9
2 SU	0340	3.2	17 M	0315	3.4
	0933	0.6		0933	0.6
	1627	2.8		1607	3.0
	2224	1.1		2203	1.0
3 M	0435	3.1	18 TU	0417	3.3
	1118	0.8		1039	0.7
	1725	2.8		1713	2.9
	2321	1.2		2308	1.0
4 TU	0532	3.0	19 W	0523	3.3
	1215	0.9		1150	0.7
	1824	2.8		1818	3.0
5 W	0021	1.2	20 TH	0020	1.0
	0633	2.9		0631	3.3
	1312	0.8		1259	0.6
	1920	2.8		1919	3.0
6 TH	0121	1.2	21 F	0130	0.9
	0734	2.9		0737	3.4
	1404	0.8		1400	0.6
	2010	2.9		2017	3.2
7 F	0215	1.1	22 SA	0231	0.8
	0828	3.0		0837	3.4
	1448	0.7		1453	0.5
	2055	3.0		2109	3.3
8 SA	0301	1.0	23 SU	0326	0.7
	0914	3.1		0931	3.5
	1527	0.7		1540	0.6
	2136	3.1		2158	3.4
9 SU	0342	0.9	24 M	0416	0.6
	0954	3.2		1021	3.5
	1603	0.7		1625	0.6
	2215	3.2		○ 2245	3.5
10 M	0419	0.8	25 TU	0505	0.6
	1031	3.2		1109	3.5
	1639	0.7		1710	0.7
	● 2253	3.3		2331	3.5
11 TU	0457	0.7	26 W	0554	0.6
	1107	3.3		1156	3.4
	1716	0.7		1755	0.8
	2329	3.4			
12 W	0535	0.7	27 TH	0016	3.5
	1144	3.3		0641	0.6
	1754	0.8		1242	3.3
				1840	0.9
13 TH	0007	3.5	28 F	0100	3.5
	0614	0.6		0726	0.6
	1226	3.3		1328	3.1
	1835	0.8		1924	0.9
14 F	0049	3.5	29 SA	0143	3.5
	0657	0.6		0809	0.7
	1312	3.2		1414	3.0
	1921	0.8		2006	1.0
15 SA	0133	3.5	30 SU	0226	3.4
	0743	0.6		0850	0.7
	1403	3.1		1501	3.0
	· 2010	0.9		2048	1.0

JULY

Day	Time	m	Day	Time	m
1 M	0310	3.3	16 TU	0257	3.6
	0932	0.8		0912	0.5
	1550	2.9		1543	3.1
	2132	1.0		2139	0.8
2 TU	0355	3.2	17 W	0353	3.5
	1019	0.8		1010	0.6
	1639	2.9		1643	3.0
	2219	1.1		2239	0.9
3 W	0444	3.1	18 TH	0455	3.4
	1112	0.9		1117	0.7
	1730	2.8		1746	3.0
	2313	1.1		2351	1.0
4 TH	0538	2.9	19 F	0604	3.3
	1210	0.9		1230	0.8
	1823	2.9		1853	3.0
5 F	0015	1.2	20 SA	0106	1.0
	0636	2.9		0716	3.2
	1310	0.9		1340	0.8
	1918	2.9		1957	3.1
6 SA	0122	1.2	21 SU	0216	0.9
	0738	2.9		0825	3.3
	1404	0.9		1438	0.8
	2012	3.0		2055	3.2
7 SU	0221	1.1	22 M	0316	0.8
	0836	3.0		0923	3.3
	1452	0.8		1528	0.8
	2101	3.2		2146	3.4
8 M	0311	1.0	23 TU	0409	0.7
	0925	3.1		1013	3.3
	1534	0.8		1614	0.8
	2146	3.3		2233	3.4
9 TU	0356	0.8	24 W	0458	0.6
	1009	3.2		1059	3.3
	1616	0.7		1658	0.9
	2227	3.4		○ 2317	3.5
10 W	0439	0.7	25 TH	0545	0.6
	1049	3.3		1143	3.2
	1657	0.7		1740	0.9
	● 2307	3.5		2359	3.5
11 TH	0521	0.6	26 F	0627	0.6
	1131	3.3		1224	3.1
	1740	0.8		1819	0.9
	2349	3.5			
12 F	0605	0.5	27 SA	0040	3.5
	1215	3.3		0704	0.7
	1825	0.8		1305	3.1
				1855	0.9
13 SA	0033	3.6	28 SU	0118	3.4
	0648	0.4		0735	0.7
	1302	3.2		1344	3.0
	1910	0.8		1931	0.9
14 SU	0119	3.6	29 M	0155	3.4
	0733	0.4		0805	0.7
	1352	3.2		1424	3.0
	1957	0.8		2007	0.9
15 M	0207	3.6	30 TU	0230	3.3
	0821	0.4		0839	0.7
	1445	3.1		1505	3.0
	2046	0.8		2046	0.9
			31 W	0306	3.2
				0918	0.8
				1550	2.9
				2129	1.0

AUGUST

Day	Time	m	Day	Time	m
1 TH	0346	3.1	16 F	0429	3.3
	1005	0.9		1044	0.8
	1639	2.9		1711	3.0
	2218	1.1		2328	1.0
2 F	0438	3.0	17 SA	0539	3.1
	1103	1.0		1206	1.0
	1732	2.9		1826	3.0
	2318	1.2			
3 SA	0542	2.9	18 SU	0051	1.0
	1217	1.1		0701	3.0
	1831	2.9		1324	1.0
				1942	3.0
4 SU	0036	1.2	19 M	0207	0.9
	0651	2.8		0819	3.1
	1328	1.1		1428	1.0
	1931	3.0		2045	3.2
5 M	0150	1.1	20 TU	0311	0.8
	0800	2.9		0918	3.2
	1425	1.0		1520	1.0
	2027	3.1		2136	3.3
6 TU	0248	1.0	21 W	0404	0.7
	0900	3.1		1006	3.2
	1513	0.9		1605	0.9
	2116	3.3		2221	3.4
7 W	0337	0.8	22 TH	0450	0.6
	0948	3.2		1049	3.2
	1557	0.8		1645	0.9
	2200	3.4		○ 2302	3.5
8 TH	0422	0.6	23 F	0530	0.6
	1032	3.3		1128	3.1
	1641	0.7		1721	0.9
	2243	3.5		2340	3.5
9 F	0507	0.5	24 SA	0604	0.7
	1116	3.3		1204	3.1
	1724	0.7		1753	0.9
	● 2328	3.6			
10 SA	0550	0.4	25 SU	0015	3.4
	1201	3.3		0631	0.7
	1809	0.7		1237	3.1
				1824	0.9
11 SU	0014	3.7	26 M	0047	3.4
	0633	0.3		0657	0.7
	1248	3.3		1308	3.1
	1853	0.6		1855	0.8
12 M	0101	3.7	27 TU	0115	3.4
	0716	0.3		0724	0.7
	1335	3.3		1340	3.1
	1937	0.6		1928	0.8
13 TU	0148	3.7	28 W	0144	3.3
	0800	0.3		0755	0.7
	1423	3.2		1414	3.1
	2023	0.6		2004	0.8
14 W	0237	3.7	29 TH	0216	3.3
	0846	0.4		0829	0.8
	1513	3.2		1453	3.1
	2112	0.7		2044	0.9
15 TH	0329	3.5	30 F	0254	3.2
	0939	0.6		0910	1.0
	1608	3.1		1541	3.0
	2211	0.9		2132	1.1
			31 SA	0345	3.0
				1004	1.1
				1640	2.9
				2231	1.2

Chart Datum: 2·01 metres below Ordnance Datum (Belfast)

NORTHERN IRELAND – BELFAST

LAT 54°36′N   LONG 5°55′W

TIMES AND HEIGHTS OF HIGH AND LOW WATERS

YEAR **2002**

Section 1

SEPTEMBER

	Time m		Time m
1 SU	0457 2.8 / 1121 1.3 / 1745 2.9 / 2355 1.3	**16** M	0035 1.0 / 0653 2.9 / 1305 1.3 / 1925 3.0
2 M	0615 2.8 / 1300 1.2 / 1852 3.0	**17** TU	0156 0.9 / 0811 3.0 / 1415 1.2 / 2030 3.2
3 TU	0126 1.1 / 0730 2.9 / 1404 1.1 / 1954 3.0	**18** W	0303 0.8 / 0906 3.1 / 1510 1.1 / 2120 3.3
4 W	0228 0.9 / 0837 3.0 / 1455 0.9 / 2047 3.1	**19** TH	0352 0.6 / 0951 3.1 / 1553 1.0 / 2203 3.4
5 TH	0319 0.7 / 0929 3.2 / 1540 0.8 / 2134 3.5	**20** F	0432 0.6 / 1030 3.2 / 1628 0.9 / 2241 3.4
6 F	0404 0.5 / 1013 3.3 / 1623 0.7 / 2219 3.6	**21** SA ○	0505 0.6 / 1106 3.1 / 1658 0.9 / 2316 3.4
7 SA ●	0447 0.4 / 1057 3.3 / 1706 0.6 / 2305 3.7	**22** SU	0532 0.7 / 1137 3.1 / 1726 0.9 / 2345 3.4
8 SU	0529 0.3 / 1142 3.4 / 1748 0.6 / 2353 3.7	**23** M	0556 0.7 / 1205 3.2 / 1754 0.8
9 M	0611 0.2 / 1228 3.4 / 1831 0.5	**24** TU	0010 3.4 / 0621 0.7 / 1232 3.2 / 1822 0.8
10 TU	0041 3.8 / 0652 0.2 / 1313 3.4 / 1913 0.5	**25** W	0035 3.4 / 0647 0.6 / 1301 3.3 / 1854 0.8
11 W	0129 3.8 / 0734 0.3 / 1357 3.4 / 1957 0.6	**26** TH	0105 3.4 / 0716 0.8 / 1333 3.3 / 1929 0.8
12 TH	0216 3.7 / 0818 0.5 / 1443 3.3 / 2046 0.7	**27** F	0138 3.3 / 0750 0.9 / 1409 3.2 / 2009 0.9
13 F	0307 3.5 / 0909 0.7 / 1535 3.2 / 2146 0.9	**28** SA	0218 3.2 / 0831 1.0 / 1454 3.1 / 2056 1.0
14 SA	0406 3.2 / 1012 1.0 / 1637 3.0 / 2309 1.0	**29** SU	0309 3.0 / 0924 1.2 / 1553 3.0 / 2156 1.2
15 SU	0518 3.0 / 1141 1.2 / 1757 2.9	**30** M	0426 2.8 / 1036 1.4 / 1706 2.9 / 2317 1.3

OCTOBER

	Time m		Time m
1 TU	0548 2.8 / 1231 1.4 / 1817 3.0	**16** W	0128 0.9 / 0749 2.9 / 1346 1.3 / 2002 3.1
2 W	0101 1.1 / 0703 2.9 / 1341 1.2 / 1922 3.1	**17** TH	0236 0.8 / 0842 3.0 / 1445 1.2 / 2054 3.2
3 TH	0205 0.9 / 0812 3.0 / 1434 1.0 / 2020 3.3	**18** F	0325 0.7 / 0925 3.1 / 1529 1.0 / 2136 3.3
4 F	0256 0.6 / 0905 3.2 / 1520 0.8 / 2110 3.5	**19** SA	0402 0.7 / 1003 3.2 / 1603 0.9 / 2214 3.3
5 SA ●	0340 0.4 / 0950 3.3 / 1602 0.7 / 2157 3.6	**20** SU	0431 0.7 / 1037 3.2 / 1631 0.9 / 2247 3.3
6 SU	0422 0.3 / 1035 3.4 / 1643 0.6 / 2244 3.7	**21** M ○	0457 0.7 / 1107 3.2 / 1658 0.9 / 2314 3.3
7 M	0502 0.3 / 1120 3.5 / 1724 0.5 / 2332 3.8	**22** TU	0523 0.8 / 1135 3.3 / 1726 0.8 / 2339 3.4
8 TU	0543 0.3 / 1205 3.5 / 1806 0.5	**23** W	0549 0.8 / 1202 3.4 / 1755 0.8
9 W	0021 3.8 / 0625 0.3 / 1250 3.5 / 1849 0.5	**24** TH	0005 3.4 / 0615 0.8 / 1233 3.4 / 1826 0.8
10 TH	0110 3.7 / 0707 0.5 / 1334 3.5 / 1934 0.6	**25** F	0037 3.4 / 0645 0.9 / 1305 3.4 / 1902 0.8
11 F	0158 3.6 / 0753 0.7 / 1418 3.4 / 2025 0.7	**26** SA	0113 3.3 / 0722 1.0 / 1342 3.4 / 1943 0.9
12 SA	0249 3.4 / 0844 0.9 / 1508 3.3 / 2127 0.9	**27** SU	0155 3.2 / 0805 1.1 / 1425 3.3 / 2031 1.0
13 SU	0348 3.1 / 0948 1.2 / 1607 3.1 / 2250 1.0	**28** M	0249 3.0 / 0900 1.3 / 1521 3.1 / 2131 1.1
14 M	0500 2.9 / 1112 1.4 / 1724 3.0	**29** TU	0406 2.9 / 1008 1.4 / 1632 3.1 / 2246 1.1
15 TU	0009 1.0 / 0635 2.8 / 1234 1.4 / 1855 3.0	**30** W	0525 2.8 / 1135 1.4 / 1745 3.1
		31 TH	0019 1.0 / 0636 2.9 / 1305 1.3 / 1852 3.2

NOVEMBER

	Time m		Time m
1 F	0130 0.8 / 0743 3.1 / 1403 1.1 / 1952 3.3	**16** SA	0239 0.8 / 0849 3.0 / 1449 1.1 / 2101 3.2
2 SA	0224 0.6 / 0838 3.2 / 1452 0.9 / 2046 3.5	**17** SU	0319 0.8 / 0928 3.1 / 1528 1.0 / 2141 3.2
3 SU	0310 0.5 / 0926 3.4 / 1536 0.7 / 2136 3.7	**18** M	0351 0.8 / 1003 3.2 / 1601 1.0 / 2216 3.3
4 M ●	0352 0.4 / 1011 3.5 / 1618 0.6 / 2224 3.7	**19** TU	0421 0.8 / 1037 3.3 / 1631 0.9 / 2247 3.3
5 TU	0433 0.4 / 1057 3.5 / 1701 0.5 / 2313 3.8	**20** W ○	0451 0.8 / 1109 3.4 / 1701 0.8 / 2316 3.3
6 W	0516 0.4 / 1143 3.6 / 1745 0.5	**21** TH	0521 0.8 / 1141 3.5 / 1733 0.8 / 2346 3.4
7 TH	0003 3.7 / 0559 0.5 / 1229 3.6 / 1830 0.5	**22** F	0552 0.9 / 1213 3.5 / 1808 0.8
8 F	0052 3.7 / 0645 0.7 / 1314 3.6 / 1918 0.6	**23** SA	0019 3.4 / 0626 0.9 / 1248 3.5 / 1845 0.8
9 SA	0142 3.5 / 0733 0.8 / 1400 3.5 / 2011 0.7	**24** SU	0059 3.3 / 0706 1.0 / 1326 3.5 / 1927 0.8
10 SU	0233 3.3 / 0826 1.0 / 1448 3.4 / 2114 0.8	**25** M	0144 3.2 / 0751 1.1 / 1410 3.4 / 2016 0.9
11 M	0331 3.1 / 0928 1.2 / 1544 3.3 / 2226 0.9	**26** TU	0238 3.1 / 0844 1.2 / 1502 3.3 / 2113 0.9
12 TU	0437 2.9 / 1039 1.3 / 1649 3.1 / 2334 0.9	**27** W	0346 3.0 / 0945 1.3 / 1604 3.2 / 2220 1.0
13 W	0557 2.8 / 1149 1.4 / 1805 3.0	**28** TH	0458 2.9 / 1054 1.3 / 1712 3.2 / 2334 0.9
14 TH	0040 0.9 / 0708 2.8 / 1256 1.3 / 1917 3.0	**29** F	0606 2.9 / 1209 1.2 / 1820 3.3
15 F	0146 0.9 / 0803 2.9 / 1358 1.2 / 2014 3.1	**30** SA	0045 0.8 / 0711 3.0 / 1321 1.1 / 1924 3.4

DECEMBER

	Time m		Time m
1 SU	0147 0.7 / 0809 3.2 / 1420 0.9 / 2023 3.5	**16** M	0231 0.9 / 0846 3.0 / 1446 1.1 / 2103 3.1
2 M	0239 0.6 / 0901 3.3 / 1510 0.8 / 2116 3.6	**17** TU	0311 0.9 / 0929 3.2 / 1528 1.0 / 2146 3.2
3 TU	0325 0.5 / 0950 3.5 / 1558 0.7 / 2207 3.7	**18** W	0348 0.9 / 1010 3.3 / 1605 0.9 / 2224 3.2
4 W ●	0410 0.5 / 1038 3.6 / 1644 0.6 / 2257 3.7	**19** TH ○	0423 0.8 / 1048 3.4 / 1641 0.9 / 2259 3.3
5 TH	0455 0.6 / 1125 3.6 / 1731 0.6 / 2347 3.6	**20** F	0459 0.9 / 1123 3.5 / 1718 0.8 / 2332 3.3
6 F	0541 0.7 / 1212 3.7 / 1820 0.6	**21** SA	0537 0.9 / 1158 3.5 / 1757 0.7
7 SA	0036 3.5 / 0629 0.8 / 1259 3.7 / 1909 0.6	**22** SU	0008 3.3 / 0615 0.9 / 1234 3.6 / 1836 0.7
8 SU	0126 3.4 / 0718 0.9 / 1345 3.6 / 2002 0.7	**23** M	0048 3.3 / 0657 0.9 / 1313 3.6 / 1919 0.7
9 M	0217 3.2 / 0809 1.0 / 1432 3.5 / 2057 0.7	**24** TU	0134 3.2 / 0742 0.9 / 1356 3.6 / 2005 0.6
10 TU	0310 3.1 / 0902 1.1 / 1521 3.4 / 2154 0.8	**25** W	0224 3.1 / 0830 1.0 / 1445 3.5 / 2056 0.7
11 W	0406 2.9 / 0957 1.2 / 1615 3.2 / 2251 0.9	**26** TH	0322 3.0 / 0923 1.0 / 1539 3.4 / 2154 0.7
12 TH	0504 2.9 / 1055 1.3 / 1712 3.1 / 2348 0.8	**27** F	0425 3.0 / 1021 1.1 / 1640 3.4 / 2259 0.8
13 F	0603 2.8 / 1155 1.3 / 1812 3.0	**28** SA	0529 3.0 / 1128 1.1 / 1746 3.3
14 SA	0046 1.0 / 0702 2.8 / 1258 1.3 / 1915 3.0	**29** SU	0008 0.8 / 0636 3.0 / 1244 1.1 / 1855 3.3
15 SU	0142 1.0 / 0757 2.9 / 1357 1.2 / 2014 3.0	**30** M	0117 0.7 / 0741 3.1 / 1354 1.0 / 2002 3.4
		31 TU	0217 0.7 / 0841 3.2 / 1453 0.8 / 2101 3.5

Chart Datum: 2·01 metres below Ordnance Datum (Belfast)
Register for your **FREE** weekly weather email service from Macmillan Reeds
》 at **www.nauticaldata.com – NOW!** 《
weekend weather reports sent to your email address, every Thursday

125

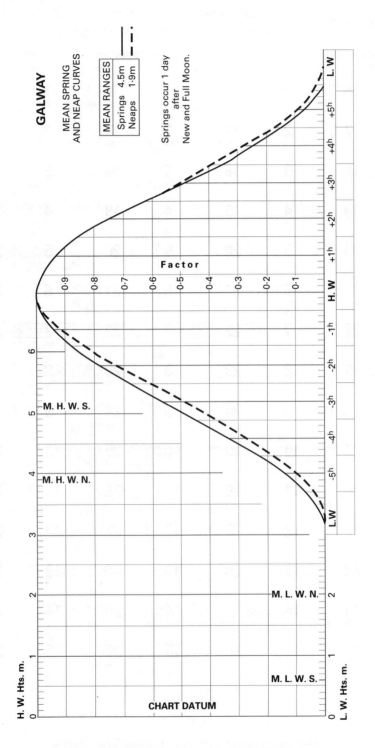

GALWAY

MEAN SPRING
AND NEAP CURVES

MEAN RANGES	
Springs	4.5m
Neaps	1·9m

Springs occur 1 day
after
New and Full Moon.

Factor

0·9 0·8 0·7 0·6 0·5 0·4 0·3 0·2 0·1

H. W.

+1ʰ +2ʰ +3ʰ +4ʰ +5ʰ L. W.

-1ʰ -2ʰ -3ʰ -4ʰ -5ʰ L.W

M. H. W. S.

M. H. W. N.

M. L. W. N.

M. L. W. S.

CHART DATUM

H. W. Hts. m.

L. W. Hts. m.

TIME ZONE (UTC)
For Summer Time add ONE hour in **non-shaded areas**

IRELAND – GALWAY

LAT 53°16'N   LONG 9°03'W

TIMES AND HEIGHTS OF HIGH AND LOW WATERS

YEAR **2002**

JANUARY

Day	Time	m	Time	m	Time	m	Time	m
1 TU	0612	5.1	1212	0.5	1842	5.0		
16 W	0022	1.1	0652	4.9	1244	0.9	1917	4.5
2 W	0026	0.8	0657	5.1	1256	0.5	1928	4.9
17 TH	0059	1.2	0730	4.8	1320	1.0	1955	4.4
3 TH	0112	0.9	0743	5.0	1341	0.6	2018	4.6
18 F	0136	1.3	0808	4.6	1357	1.1	2035	4.3
4 F	0200	1.1	0832	4.9	1430	0.9	2112	4.6
19 SA	0214	1.5	0846	4.5	1434	1.3	2116	4.1
5 SA	0252	1.4	0929	4.6	1524	1.1	2214	4.4
20 SU	0255	1.7	0925	4.3	1515	1.5	2200	4.0
6 SU	0354	1.6	1033	4.4	1629	1.4	2319	4.3
21 M	0342	1.9	1008	4.1	1601	1.7	2249	3.9
7 M	0507	1.8	1140	4.3	1752	1.6		
22 TU	0440	2.1	1057	3.9	1655	1.9	2341	3.8
8 TU	0025	4.3	0624	1.8	1251	4.3	1912	1.6
23 W	0555	2.2	1152	3.8	1807	1.9		
9 W	0132	4.4	0733	1.7	1400	4.3	2013	1.5
24 TH	0043	3.8	0713	2.0	1301	3.8	1929	1.9
10 TH	0231	4.5	0831	1.5	1459	4.4	2102	1.4
25 F	0154	4.0	0816	1.8	1419	4.0	2031	1.6
11 F	0322	4.7	0920	1.3	1550	4.5	2146	1.3
26 SA	0254	4.2	0908	1.4	1520	4.3	2120	1.3
12 SA	0407	4.8	1006	1.2	1635	4.6	2227	1.2
27 SU	0343	4.5	0954	1.1	1611	4.6	2205	1.0
13 SU	0451	4.8	1048	1.0	1718	4.6	● 2306	1.1
28 M	0430	4.8	1038	0.7	1658	4.8	○ 2249	0.7
14 M	0532	4.9	1129	0.9	1759	4.6	2345	1.1
29 TU	0516	5.1	1120	0.4	1744	5.0	2333	0.5
15 TU	0613	4.9	1208	0.9	1839	4.6		
30 W	0602	5.2	1202	0.2	1830	5.1		
31 TH	0016	0.4	0646	5.3	1244	0.1	1914	5.1

FEBRUARY

Day	Time	m	Time	m	Time	m	Time	m
1 F	0100	0.4	0731	5.2	1326	0.2	1959	5.0
16 SA	0109	1.0	0744	4.7	1326	0.8	2004	4.4
2 SA	0144	0.6	0816	5.0	1410	0.5	2047	4.7
17 SU	0142	1.1	0816	4.6	1359	1.0	2036	4.3
3 SU	0231	0.9	0906	4.7	1458	0.9	2142	4.4
18 M	0216	1.4	0848	4.4	1433	1.2	2111	4.1
4 M	0324	1.3	1003	4.4	1553	1.3	2244	4.2
19 TU	0254	1.6	0925	4.1	1512	1.5	2154	3.9
5 TU	0427	1.6	1108	4.1	1703	1.6	2351	4.0
20 W	0340	1.9	1014	3.9	1600	1.8	2249	3.8
6 W	0545	1.8	1221	3.9	1837	1.8		
21 TH	0438	2.0	1114	3.8	1700	2.0	2352	3.7
7 TH	0104	4.0	0706	1.8	1342	3.9	1957	1.8
22 F	0616	2.1	1222	3.7	1842	2.0		
8 F	0216	4.1	0818	1.7	1451	4.1	2053	1.6
23 SA	0106	3.8	0755	1.8	1351	3.8	2014	1.8
9 SA	0312	4.3	0912	1.4	1543	4.2	2136	1.4
24 SU	0231	4.0	0853	1.4	1506	4.1	2108	1.3
10 SU	0359	4.5	0956	1.2	1627	4.4	2215	1.2
25 M	0329	4.4	0941	0.9	1558	4.5	2154	0.9
11 M	0441	4.6	1036	1.0	1707	4.5	2252	1.1
26 TU	0417	4.8	1024	0.5	1644	4.9	2236	0.5
12 TU	0521	4.8	1113	0.8	1745	4.6	● 2328	0.9
27 W	0503	5.1	1105	0.1	1728	5.2	○ 2318	0.2
13 W	0559	4.8	1148	0.7	1821	4.6		
28 TH	0547	5.3	1145	-0.1	1812	5.3		
14 TH	0003	0.9	0635	4.9	1222	0.7	1856	4.6
15 F	0037	0.9	0710	4.8	1254	0.7	1931	4.6

MARCH

Day	Time	m	Time	m	Time	m	Time	m
1 F	0000	0.1	0630	5.4	1226	-0.2	1854	5.3
16 SA	0011	0.7	0646	4.8	1225	0.6	1902	4.7
2 SA	0042	0.1	0713	5.3	1306	0.0	1936	5.1
17 SU	0042	0.8	0717	4.7	1254	0.7	1932	4.6
3 SU	0124	0.3	0755	5.1	1346	0.3	2019	4.9
18 M	0112	0.9	0747	4.6	1325	0.9	1959	4.4
4 M	0208	0.6	0840	4.8	1430	0.8	2107	4.5
19 TU	0145	1.2	0816	4.4	1358	1.2	2027	4.2
5 TU	0256	1.1	0931	4.4	1519	1.3	2204	4.1
20 W	0222	1.4	0852	4.2	1437	1.5	2107	4.0
6 W	0355	1.5	1035	4.0	1625	1.8	2315	3.8
21 TH	0306	1.7	0942	3.9	1524	1.8	2208	3.8
7 TH	0512	1.8	1155	3.7	1802	1.9		
22 F	0402	1.9	1048	3.7	1624	2.1	2318	3.7
8 F	0039	3.7	0638	1.9	1327	3.7	1938	2.0
23 SA	0524	2.0	1200	3.7	1803	2.1		
9 SA	0200	3.9	0805	1.7	1441	3.9	2042	1.8
24 SU	0035	3.7	0734	1.8	1331	3.8	1957	1.8
10 SU	0258	4.1	0903	1.5	1530	4.1	2122	1.5
25 M	0210	4.0	0833	1.4	1450	4.2	2050	1.3
11 M	0344	4.3	0941	1.2	1611	4.3	2157	1.2
26 TU	0311	4.4	0920	0.9	1540	4.6	2135	0.9
12 TU	0424	4.5	1015	0.9	1648	4.5	2231	1.0
27 W	0359	4.8	1002	0.4	1624	5.0	2217	0.4
13 W	0502	4.7	1049	0.7	1724	4.7	2306	0.8
28 TH	0443	5.2	1043	0.1	1707	5.3	○ 2258	0.1
14 TH	0538	4.8	1122	0.6	1758	4.7	● 2339	0.7
29 F	0527	5.4	1123	-0.1	1749	5.4	2339	0.0
15 F	0613	4.9	1154	0.6	1831	4.7		
30 SA	0610	5.5	1202	-0.1	1830	5.4		
31 SU	0021	0.0	0652	5.4	1242	0.1	1910	5.2

APRIL

Day	Time	m	Time	m	Time	m	Time	m
1 M	0102	0.2	0733	5.1	1322	0.4	1952	5.0
16 TU	0045	0.9	0721	4.6	1255	1.0	1928	4.5
2 TU	0145	0.6	0816	4.8	1403	0.9	2036	4.6
17 W	0119	1.1	0754	4.4	1330	1.2	1958	4.4
3 W	0232	1.0	0905	4.3	1450	1.5	2128	4.2
18 TH	0158	1.3	0833	4.2	1411	1.5	2039	4.2
4 TH	0330	1.5	1006	3.9	1555	1.9	2239	3.8
19 F	0245	1.6	0926	4.0	1500	1.8	2143	3.9
5 F	0447	1.8	1130	3.6	1732	2.2		
20 SA	0342	1.8	1032	3.8	1604	2.1	2257	3.8
6 SA	0012	3.7	0609	1.9	1307	3.6	1902	2.1
21 SU	0506	1.9	1144	3.8	1748	2.1		
7 SU	0134	3.8	0730	1.8	1420	3.8	2015	1.9
22 M	0014	3.9	0705	1.7	1309	4.0	1930	1.8
8 M	0234	4.0	0834	1.5	1508	4.1	2055	1.6
23 TU	0141	4.2	0805	1.3	1423	4.4	2024	1.3
9 TU	0319	4.3	0912	1.3	1547	4.3	2130	1.3
24 W	0245	4.6	0854	0.8	1514	4.8	2110	0.9
10 W	0359	4.5	0946	1.0	1622	4.5	2205	1.0
25 TH	0334	4.9	0937	0.5	1559	5.1	2153	0.5
11 TH	0436	4.6	1020	0.8	1657	4.7	2239	0.8
26 F	0419	5.2	1019	0.2	1641	5.3	2235	0.3
12 F	0512	4.8	1052	0.7	1730	4.8	● 2312	0.7
27 SA	0504	5.4	1059	0.1	1723	5.4	○ 2317	0.2
13 SA	0546	4.8	1123	0.7	1801	4.8	2343	0.7
28 SU	0548	5.4	1139	0.2	1805	5.4		
14 SU	0619	4.8	1153	0.7	1832	4.8		
29 M	0000	0.2	0631	5.3	1219	0.4	1846	5.2
15 M	0013	0.8	0650	4.7	1223	0.8	1900	4.7
30 TU	0043	0.4	0713	5.0	1259	0.7	1928	5.0

Chart Datum: 0·20 metres above Ordnance Datum (Dublin)
Register for your **FREE** weekly weather email service from Macmillan Reeds
》 at **www.nauticaldata.com – NOW!** 《
weekend weather reports sent to your email address, every Thursday

TIME ZONE (UTC)
For Summer Time add ONE
hour in **non-shaded areas**

IRELAND – GALWAY

LAT 53°16′N   LONG 9°03′W

TIMES AND HEIGHTS OF HIGH AND LOW WATERS

YEAR **2002**

MAY

Time	m	Time	m
1 0126 0.7	W 1341 1.1	2012 4.6	
1 0126 0.7 W 1341 1.1 2012 4.6		**16** 0101 1.0 TH 1311 1.2 1943 4.5	
2 0214 1.1 TH 1428 1.6 2102 4.3	0844 4.3	**17** 0144 1.2 F 1355 1.5 2029 4.3	0822 4.3
3 0310 1.4 F 1531 2.0 2207 4.0	0942 3.9	**18** 0233 1.4 SA 1447 1.7 2131 4.2	0916 4.1
4 0421 1.7 SA 1659 2.2 2334 3.8	1059 3.7	**19** 0332 1.6 SU 1552 1.9 2242 4.1	1019 4.0
5 0535 1.8 SU 1818 2.2	1227 3.6	**20** 0451 1.6 M 1724 1.9 2354 4.1	1127 4.0
6 0054 3.8 M 1342 3.8 1924 2.0	0642 1.8	**21** 0629 1.5 TU 1856 1.7	1240 4.2
7 0156 4.0 TU 1434 4.0 2016 1.7	0743 1.6	**22** 0109 4.3 W 1351 4.5 1955 1.4	0753 1.2
8 0245 4.1 W 1514 4.3 2056 1.4	0831 1.4	**23** 0215 4.6 TH 1446 4.8 2044 1.0	0826 1.0
9 0326 4.3 TH 1550 4.5 2133 1.2	0910 1.2	**24** 0308 4.9 F 1532 5.0 2130 0.7	0912 0.7
10 0404 4.5 F 1624 4.6 2209 1.0	0946 1.0	**25** 0356 5.0 SA 1616 5.2 2213 0.5	0955 0.6
11 0440 4.6 SA 1656 4.7 2243 0.9	1020 0.9	**26** 0442 5.1 SU 1659 5.3 ○ 2257 0.4	1037 0.5
12 0515 4.7 SU 1727 4.8 ● 2316 0.8	1052 0.9	**27** 0528 5.1 M 1742 5.2 2341 0.5	1118 0.6
13 0549 4.7 M 1759 4.8 2348 0.9	1123 0.9	**28** 0613 5.0 TU 1825 5.1	1159 0.7
14 0624 4.7 TU 1832 4.7	1155 0.9	**29** 0025 0.6 W 1241 1.0 1908 4.9	0656 4.8
15 0022 0.9 W 1231 1.0 1905 4.6	0700 4.6	**30** 0110 0.8 TH 1323 1.3 1953 4.7	0740 4.6
		31 0157 1.1 F 1408 1.6 2041 4.4	0827 4.3

JUNE

Time	m	Time	m
1 0247 1.3 SA 1502 1.9 2137 4.1	0919 4.0	**16** 0224 1.0 SU 1437 1.5 2119 4.4	0903 4.4
2 0346 1.6 SU 1614 2.1 2243 3.9	1019 3.8	**17** 0320 1.2 M 1538 1.6 2225 4.3	1002 4.3
3 0451 1.7 M 1728 2.1 2352 3.8	1128 3.7	**18** 0426 1.3 TU 1653 1.7 2332 4.3	1105 4.2
4 0552 1.7 TU 1832 2.0	1237 3.7	**19** 0545 1.4 W 1817 1.6	1211 4.3
5 0058 3.8 W 1341 3.9 1929 1.8	0650 1.7	**20** 0040 4.3 TH 1318 4.4 1925 1.4	0658 1.3
6 0157 3.9 TH 1431 4.1 2018 1.6	0743 1.6	**21** 0147 4.5 F 1418 4.6 2021 1.2	0758 1.2
7 0245 4.1 F 1511 4.2 2100 1.4	0830 1.4	**22** 0245 4.6 SA 1509 4.8 2110 1.0	0849 1.1
8 0326 4.2 SA 1546 4.4 2139 1.2	0911 1.3	**23** 0337 4.7 SU 1556 4.9 2156 0.8	0935 1.0
9 0405 4.4 SU 1620 4.6 2216 1.0	0948 1.2	**24** 0425 4.8 M 1640 5.0 ○ 2242 0.7	1019 0.9
10 0443 4.5 M 1654 4.7 ● 2252 0.9	1023 1.1	**25** 0512 4.8 TU 1725 5.0 2327 0.7	1102 0.9
11 0522 4.6 TU 1731 4.8 2329 0.8	1059 1.0	**26** 0558 4.7 W 1809 4.9	1143 1.0
12 0602 4.7 W 1809 4.8	1136 1.0	**27** 0011 0.7 TH 1225 1.1 1852 4.8	0642 4.7
13 0008 0.8 TH 1217 1.0 1850 4.8	0643 4.7	**28** 0054 0.8 F 1305 1.2 1935 4.7	0724 4.5
14 0051 0.8 F 1300 1.1 1933 4.7	0726 4.6	**29** 0136 0.9 SA 1345 1.4 2019 4.5	0807 4.3
15 0135 0.9 SA 1346 1.2 2021 4.5	0812 4.5	**30** 0219 1.1 SU 1430 1.6 2106 4.3	0851 4.2

JULY

Time	m	Time	m
1 0305 1.3 M 1520 1.8 2156 4.1	0939 4.0	**16** 0259 0.9 TU 1516 1.3 2201 4.4	0938 4.4
2 0356 1.5 TU 1623 2.0 2249 3.9	1030 3.9	**17** 0356 1.1 W 1620 1.5 2306 4.3	1037 4.3
3 0452 1.7 W 1732 2.0 2343 3.8	1123 3.8	**18** 0503 1.4 TH 1736 1.6	1140 4.2
4 0550 1.8 TH 1838 2.0	1221 3.8	**19** 0013 4.2 F 1247 4.2 1856 1.6	0621 1.5
5 0044 3.8 F 1325 3.8 1936 1.8	0649 1.8	**20** 0124 4.2 SA 1355 4.3 2003 1.4	0733 1.5
6 0149 3.8 SA 1422 4.0 2028 1.6	0746 1.7	**21** 0230 4.3 SU 1454 4.5 2058 1.2	0832 1.4
7 0245 3.9 SU 1507 4.2 2113 1.4	0837 1.6	**22** 0326 4.4 M 1544 4.6 2145 1.0	0921 1.3
8 0332 4.1 M 1548 4.4 2155 1.1	0921 1.4	**23** 0416 4.5 TU 1629 4.7 2230 0.9	1006 1.2
9 0417 4.3 TU 1628 4.6 2236 0.9	1003 1.2	**24** 0502 4.5 W 1713 4.8 ○ 2313 0.8	1048 1.1
10 0501 4.5 W 1709 4.8 ● 2317 0.7	1044 1.0	**25** 0546 4.6 TH 1755 4.8 2354 0.7	1128 1.0
11 0545 4.7 TH 1753 4.9 2358 0.5	1125 0.8	**26** 0627 4.6 F 1836 4.8	1206 1.0
12 0629 4.8 F 1837 4.9	1207 0.8	**27** 0032 0.7 SA 1243 1.0 1915 4.7	0705 4.5
13 0040 0.5 SA 1250 0.8 1921 4.9	0712 4.8	**28** 0109 0.8 SU 1319 1.1 1954 4.6	0744 4.5
14 0124 0.5 SU 1335 0.9 2008 4.8	0757 4.7	**29** 0146 0.9 M 1356 1.3 2033 4.4	0822 4.3
15 0209 0.6 M 1422 1.1 2100 4.6	0844 4.6	**30** 0224 1.1 TU 1435 1.5 2114 4.2	0900 4.2
		31 0304 1.4 W 1518 1.8 2158 4.0	0940 4.0

AUGUST

Time	m	Time	m
1 0348 1.6 TH 1612 2.0 2246 3.8	1023 3.9	**16** 0427 1.5 F 1701 1.7 2348 4.0	1107 4.1
2 0439 1.8 F 1729 2.1 2340 3.7	1111 3.8	**17** 0550 1.8 SA 1833 1.8	1220 4.0
3 0543 1.9 SA 1856 2.0	1207 3.7	**18** 0107 3.9 SU 1340 4.0 1955 1.6	0714 1.8
4 0044 3.6 SU 1318 3.8 2002 1.8	0703 1.9	**19** 0222 4.0 M 1446 4.3 2054 1.4	0820 1.7
5 0204 3.7 M 1432 4.0 2054 1.5	0810 1.8	**20** 0320 4.2 TU 1536 4.5 2137 1.1	0909 1.5
6 0308 4.0 TU 1525 4.3 2139 1.1	0903 1.5	**21** 0406 4.4 W 1619 4.7 2216 0.9	0951 1.3
7 0358 4.3 W 1610 4.6 2221 0.8	0948 1.2	**22** 0449 4.5 TH 1700 4.8 ○ 2254 0.7	1030 1.1
8 0444 4.6 TH 1654 4.8 ● 2303 0.4	1031 0.9	**23** 0528 4.6 F 1739 4.9 2330 0.6	1108 1.0
9 0528 4.8 F 1738 5.0 2343 0.2	1113 0.6	**24** 0606 4.7 SA 1816 4.9	1143 0.9
10 0612 5.0 SA 1822 5.2	1154 0.4	**25** 0005 0.6 SU 1217 0.9 1851 4.8	0642 4.7
11 0024 0.1 SU 1236 0.4 1904 5.1	0654 5.1	**26** 0039 0.7 M 1250 0.9 1926 4.7	0717 4.6
12 0105 0.1 M 1317 0.5 1948 5.0	0736 5.0	**27** 0112 0.8 TU 1322 1.1 2000 4.5	0750 4.5
13 0148 0.4 TU 1401 0.7 2035 4.8	0820 4.8	**28** 0144 1.0 W 1355 1.3 2033 4.3	0822 4.4
14 0233 0.7 W 1449 1.1 2131 4.5	0908 4.6	**29** 0218 1.3 TH 1431 1.6 2112 4.1	0854 4.2
15 0324 1.1 TH 1547 1.4 2236 4.2	1003 4.3	**30** 0256 1.6 F 1513 1.9 2202 3.8	0932 4.0
		31 0340 1.9 SA 1608 2.1 2300 3.7	1021 3.8

Chart Datum: 0·20 metres above Ordnance Datum (Dublin)

IRELAND – GALWAY

LAT 53°16'N   LONG 9°03'W

TIMES AND HEIGHTS OF HIGH AND LOW WATERS

SEPTEMBER

Day	Time	m	Time	m	Time	m	Time	m
1 SU	0438	2.1	1120	3.7	1813	2.2		
2 M	0006	3.6	0622	2.2	1227	3.7	1943	1.9
3 TU	0131	3.7	0752	2.0	1400	3.9	2037	1.5
4 W	0250	4.0	0846	1.6	1508	4.3	2121	1.1
5 TH	0341	4.4	0931	1.2	1554	4.7	2202	0.6
6 F	0424	4.7	1013	0.8	1636	5.0	2242	0.4
7 SA	0507	5.0	1054	0.4	1719	5.3	● 2322	0.0
8 SU	0549	5.2	1134	0.2	1802	5.4		
9 M	0001	-0.1	0630	5.3	1215	0.2	1843	5.4
10 TU	0042	0.0	0711	5.2	1256	0.3	1925	5.2
11 W	0122	0.3	0752	5.0	1338	0.6	2009	4.9
12 TH	0205	0.8	0836	4.7	1423	1.0	2100	4.5
13 F	0254	1.3	0927	4.4	1518	1.5	2206	4.1
14 SA	0357	1.8	1032	4.0	1633	1.8	2327	3.8
15 SU	0528	2.1	1157	3.9	1813	1.9		
16 M	0057	3.8	0658	2.1	1327	3.9	1957	1.8
17 TU	0215	4.0	0806	1.9	1433	4.2	2051	1.5
18 W	0308	4.2	0853	1.6	1521	4.5	2124	1.2
19 TH	0349	4.4	0932	1.3	1602	4.7	2156	1.0
20 F	0428	4.6	1008	1.1	1640	4.9	2229	0.8
21 SA	0504	4.7	1043	0.9	1716	5.0	○ 2302	0.7
22 SU	0540	4.8	1117	0.8	1751	5.0	2335	0.7
23 M	0614	4.8	1149	0.8	1825	4.9		
24 TU	0006	0.7	0646	4.8	1220	0.9	1857	4.8
25 W	0037	0.9	0717	4.7	1250	1.1	1928	4.6
26 TH	0107	1.1	0746	4.5	1322	1.3	1958	4.4
27 F	0140	1.4	0814	4.3	1356	1.5	2035	4.2
28 SA	0217	1.7	0848	4.1	1437	1.8	2126	3.9
29 SU	0301	2.0	0940	3.9	1529	2.1	2231	3.7
30 M	0400	2.3	1046	3.8	1647	2.3	2341	3.7

OCTOBER

Day	Time	m	Time	m	Time	m	Time	m
1 TU	0543	2.4	1156	3.8	1918	2.0		
2 W	0105	3.8	0731	2.1	1325	4.0	2012	1.6
3 TH	0227	4.2	0824	1.6	1444	4.4	2057	1.1
4 F	0317	4.6	0909	1.2	1531	4.9	2138	0.6
5 SA	0359	5.0	0950	0.7	1614	5.2	2217	0.3
6 SU	0441	5.3	1031	0.4	1656	5.5	● 2256	0.1
7 M	0522	5.5	1111	0.2	1739	5.6	2336	0.0
8 TU	0604	5.5	1152	0.2	1821	5.5		
9 W	0016	0.2	0646	5.4	1234	0.3	1903	5.3
10 TH	0057	0.5	0725	5.2	1316	0.6	1947	5.0
11 F	0140	1.0	0808	4.8	1401	1.0	2037	4.5
12 SA	0228	1.5	0857	4.3	1455	1.5	2141	4.1
13 SU	0332	2.0	1001	4.1	1609	1.9	2308	3.8
14 M	0507	2.3	1133	3.9	1747	2.0		
15 TU	0040	3.8	0632	2.2	1303	4.0	1938	1.9
16 W	0156	4.0	0740	2.0	1409	4.2	2030	1.6
17 TH	0245	4.3	0828	1.7	1457	4.5	2058	1.3
18 F	0325	4.5	0906	1.5	1537	4.7	2128	1.1
19 SA	0401	4.7	0942	1.2	1614	4.8	2200	0.9
20 SU	0436	4.8	1017	1.0	1649	4.9	2232	0.9
21 M	0510	4.9	1050	0.9	1723	5.0	○ 2303	0.9
22 TU	0542	4.9	1121	0.9	1756	4.9	2333	0.9
23 W	0614	4.9	1151	1.0	1828	4.8		
24 TH	0003	1.1	0644	4.8	1222	1.1	1859	4.7
25 F	0035	1.3	0714	4.6	1255	1.3	1933	4.5
26 SA	0110	1.5	0744	4.5	1332	1.5	2012	4.3
27 SU	0149	1.8	0820	4.3	1415	1.8	2105	4.1
28 M	0236	2.1	0913	4.1	1508	2.0	2211	3.9
29 TU	0337	2.3	1021	4.0	1622	2.1	2321	3.9
30 W	0512	2.4	1131	4.0	1842	1.9		
31 TH	0037	4.1	0659	2.1	1250	4.2	1940	1.6

NOVEMBER

Day	Time	m	Time	m	Time	m	Time	m
1 F	0152	4.4	0755	1.7	1409	4.6	2028	1.1
2 SA	0246	4.8	0842	1.2	1503	5.0	2111	0.7
3 SU	0331	5.1	0925	0.8	1548	5.3	2151	0.5
4 M	0413	5.4	1007	0.5	1632	5.5	● 2231	0.3
5 TU	0455	5.6	1049	0.4	1716	5.6	2312	0.3
6 W	0538	5.6	1131	0.3	1801	5.5	2353	0.5
7 TH	0621	5.5	1214	0.5	1845	5.3		
8 F	0036	0.7	0704	5.2	1259	0.7	1930	4.9
9 SA	0120	1.2	0748	4.9	1345	1.1	2020	4.5
10 SU	0209	1.7	0837	4.6	1437	1.5	2120	4.2
11 M	0310	2.1	0937	4.2	1544	1.8	2240	3.9
12 TU	0435	2.3	1057	4.0	1708	2.0		
13 W	0004	3.9	0553	2.3	1221	4.0	1827	1.9
14 TH	0117	4.0	0657	2.1	1329	4.1	1934	1.8
15 F	0211	4.2	0751	1.9	1422	4.3	2019	1.6
16 SA	0253	4.4	0835	1.7	1506	4.5	2055	1.4
17 SU	0330	4.6	0913	1.4	1544	4.6	2129	1.2
18 M	0404	4.7	0949	1.3	1619	4.7	2201	1.1
19 TU	0437	4.8	1024	1.2	1653	4.8	2233	1.1
20 W	0510	4.9	1056	1.1	1727	4.8	○ 2304	1.1
21 TH	0543	4.9	1128	1.1	1802	4.8	2336	1.2
22 F	0616	4.8	1201	1.2	1838	4.7		
23 SA	0011	1.3	0650	4.8	1238	1.2	1916	4.6
24 SU	0050	1.5	0727	4.6	1318	1.4	1959	4.4
25 M	0134	1.7	0807	4.5	1404	1.5	2050	4.2
26 TU	0223	1.9	0858	4.4	1457	1.7	2152	4.1
27 W	0323	2.1	1001	4.3	1603	1.8	2259	4.1
28 TH	0441	2.2	1109	4.3	1740	1.8		
29 F	0007	4.2	0615	2.0	1219	4.4	1901	1.6
30 SA	0115	4.5	0721	1.7	1332	4.6	1957	1.2

DECEMBER

Day	Time	m	Time	m	Time	m	Time	m
1 SU	0214	4.8	0814	1.4	1434	4.9	2044	1.0
2 M	0303	5.1	0901	1.0	1524	5.1	2128	0.8
3 TU	0348	5.3	0946	0.8	1612	5.3	2210	0.7
4 W	0433	5.4	1031	0.6	1658	5.3	● 2253	0.7
5 TH	0518	5.4	1115	0.6	1745	5.2	2336	0.8
6 F	0603	5.4	1200	0.7	1831	5.1		
7 SA	0020	1.0	0648	5.2	1246	0.8	1917	4.8
8 SU	0105	1.3	0733	5.0	1331	1.0	2005	4.5
9 M	0152	1.6	0820	4.7	1419	1.3	2058	4.2
10 TU	0244	1.9	0912	4.4	1512	1.6	2201	4.0
11 W	0349	2.1	1013	4.2	1615	1.8	2309	3.9
12 TH	0501	2.2	1118	4.0	1724	1.9		
13 F	0015	3.9	0606	2.2	1226	4.0	1828	1.9
14 SA	0117	4.0	0705	2.1	1329	4.0	1927	1.8
15 SU	0210	4.2	0757	1.9	1424	4.1	2015	1.7
16 M	0253	4.3	0843	1.7	1508	4.3	2056	1.5
17 TU	0331	4.5	0923	1.5	1548	4.4	2133	1.4
18 W	0406	4.6	1001	1.3	1625	4.5	2209	1.3
19 TH	0441	4.7	1038	1.2	1703	4.6	○ 2244	1.2
20 F	0518	4.8	1115	1.1	1742	4.7	2321	1.2
21 SA	0556	4.8	1152	1.0	1823	4.7		
22 SU	0000	1.2	0635	4.9	1230	1.0	1904	4.7
23 M	0041	1.3	0715	4.8	1311	1.0	1947	4.6
24 TU	0125	1.4	0757	4.7	1355	1.1	2035	4.5
25 W	0213	1.5	0844	4.6	1444	1.2	2131	4.4
26 TH	0307	1.7	0940	4.5	1540	1.4	2232	4.3
27 F	0411	1.8	1043	4.4	1647	1.5	2335	4.3
28 SA	0525	1.8	1149	4.4	1808	1.5		
29 SU	0040	4.4	0641	1.7	1301	4.4	1924	1.4
30 M	0144	4.6	0747	1.5	1409	4.6	2022	1.3
31 TU	0241	4.8	0847	1.3	1507	4.7	2112	1.1

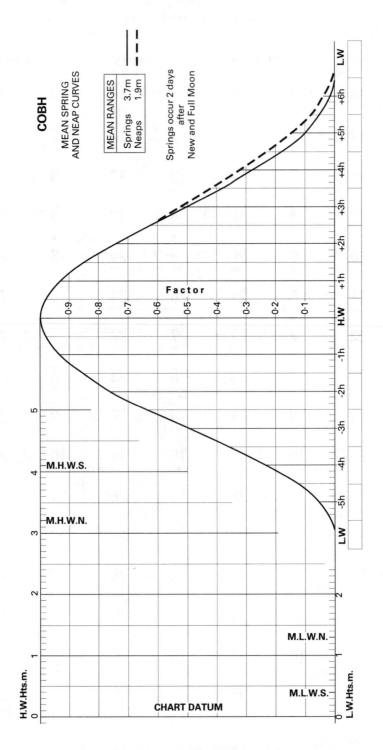

COBH

MEAN SPRING
AND NEAP CURVES

MEAN RANGES	
Springs	3.7m
Neaps	1.9m

Springs occur 2 days
after
New and Full Moon

Factor

0.9 0.8 0.7 0.6 0.5 0.4 0.3 0.2 0.1

H.W.Hts.m.

M.H.W.S.

M.H.W.N.

CHART DATUM

M.L.W.N.

M.L.W.S.

L.W.Hts.m.

LW +6h +5h +4h +3h +2h +1h H.W -1h -2h -3h -4h -5h LW

IRELAND – COBH

LAT 51°51′N   LONG 8°18′W

TIMES AND HEIGHTS OF HIGH AND LOW WATERS

YEAR **2002**

Section 1

JANUARY

Day	Time m	Time m	Day	Time m	Time m
1 TU	0037 0.5	0635 4.2	**16** W	0112 0.7	0707 4.0
	1305 0.6	1854 4.1		1329 0.8	1916 3.9
2 W	0121 0.5	0720 4.2	**17** TH	0145 0.8	0741 4.0
	1350 0.6	1940 4.1		1401 0.9	1949 3.8
3 TH	0208 0.6	0808 4.0	**18** F	0218 0.8	0816 3.9
	1438 0.7	2028 4.0		1436 1.0	2024 3.7
4 F	0257 0.6	0858 4.0	**19** SA	0254 1.0	0853 3.8
	1528 0.8	2119 3.8		1514 1.1	2102 3.7
5 SA	0349 0.8	0950 3.9	**20** SU	0333 1.1	0933 3.7
	1621 0.9	2212 3.7		1556 1.2	2145 3.6
6 SU	0446 0.9	1047 3.8	**21** M	0419 1.2	1016 3.6
	1720 1.0	2311 3.6		1645 1.3	2233 3.5
7 M	0548 1.0	1148 3.6	**22** TU	0514 1.4	1107 3.5
	1826 1.1			1743 1.4	2331 3.4
8 TU	0015 3.5	0657 1.0	**23** W	0619 1.4	1208 3.4
	1256 3.6	1935 1.1		1851 1.4	
9 W	0125 3.5	0808 1.0	**24** TH	0038 3.4	0728 1.4
	1404 3.6	2042 1.0		1316 3.4	1959 1.4
10 TH	0233 3.6	0914 1.0	**25** F	0149 3.4	0835 1.3
	1506 3.7	2142 0.9		1424 3.5	2103 1.2
11 F	0334 3.8	1013 0.9	**26** SA	0257 3.6	0937 1.0
	1602 3.8	2236 0.8		1528 3.7	2201 1.0
12 SA	0428 3.9	1104 0.8	**27** SU	0357 3.8	1034 0.8
	1651 3.9	2322 0.7		1624 3.9	2253 0.7
13 SU	0514 4.0	1147 0.7	**28** M	0450 4.0	1124 0.6
	1733 3.9 ●			1713 4.0	2341 0.5
14 M	0002 0.7	0555 4.1	**29** TU	0538 4.2	1210 0.4
	1224 0.7	1810 4.0		1759 4.1	
15 TU	0038 0.7	0632 4.1	**30** W	0025 0.3	0624 4.3
	1257 0.8	1844 3.9		1254 0.3	1843 4.2
			31 TH	0109 0.3	0709 4.3
				1338 0.3	1928 4.2

FEBRUARY

Day	Time m	Time m	Day	Time m	Time m
1 F	0154 0.3	0754 4.2	**16** SA	0148 0.7	0748 4.4
	1423 0.4	2013 4.1		1405 0.8	1957 3.8
2 SA	0240 0.4	0840 4.1	**17** SU	0220 0.8	0820 3.9
	1508 0.5	2058 4.0		1439 0.9	2030 3.8
3 SU	0327 0.5	0926 4.0	**18** M	0255 0.9	0854 3.8
	1555 0.7	2145 3.8		1515 1.1	2106 3.7
4 M	0417 0.7	1015 3.8	**19** TU	0334 1.1	0932 3.7
	1646 0.9	2236 3.6		1555 1.2	2148 3.6
5 TU	0512 0.9	1110 3.6	**20** W	0421 1.2	1018 3.5
	1744 1.1	2335 3.5		1644 1.3	2240 3.4
6 W	0616 1.1	1215 3.4	**21** TH	0522 1.4	1116 3.4
	1854 1.2			1754 1.5	2348 3.3
7 TH	0047 3.3	0732 1.2	**22** F	0640 1.4	1228 3.3
	1331 3.3	2011 1.2		1916 1.4	
8 F	0206 3.4	0853 1.1	**23** SA	0107 3.3	0800 1.3
	1445 3.4	2125 1.1		1349 3.3	2032 1.3
9 SA	0316 3.5	1001 1.0	**24** SU	0228 3.4	0912 1.1
	1547 3.5	2225 0.9		1505 3.5	2138 1.0
10 SU	0413 3.7	1054 0.8	**25** M	0337 3.7	1014 0.8
	1638 3.7	2312 0.7		1606 3.8	2235 0.6
11 M	0500 3.9	1136 0.7	**26** TU	0433 4.0	1107 0.4
	1720 3.8	2350 0.6		1657 4.0	2324 0.3
12 TU	0539 4.2	1210 0.7	**27** W	0521 4.2	1153 0.2
	1756 3.9 ●			1743 4.2 ○	
13 W	0022 0.6	0615 4.1	**28** TH	0008 0.1	0606 4.3
	1240 0.7	1827 3.9		1237 0.1	1826 4.3
14 TH	0052 0.6	0647 4.1			
	1306 0.7	1857 3.9			
15 F	0119 0.7	0718 4.0			
	1334 0.8	1926 3.9			

MARCH

Day	Time m	Time m	Day	Time m	Time m
1 F	0052 0.0	0649 4.4	**16** SA	0052 0.6	0651 4.1
	1319 0.1	1908 4.3		1306 0.6	1900 3.9
2 SA	0134 0.0	0732 4.3	**17** SU	0119 0.6	0718 3.9
	1401 0.1	1951 4.2		1335 0.7	1928 3.9
3 SU	0218 0.1	0815 4.2	**18** M	0149 0.7	0746 3.9
	1444 0.3	2033 4.1		1407 0.8	1959 3.8
4 M	0302 0.3	0858 4.0	**19** TU	0223 0.8	0819 3.8
	1527 0.5	2116 3.9		1441 0.9	2033 3.8
5 TU	0348 0.6	0943 3.7	**20** W	0301 1.0	0856 3.7
	1614 0.8	2202 3.6		1518 1.1	2113 3.6
6 W	0438 0.8	1033 3.4	**21** TH	0346 1.1	0941 3.5
	1708 1.0	2257 3.4		1605 1.2	2203 3.5
7 TH	0539 1.1	1136 3.2	**22** F	0445 1.3	1039 3.3
	1816 1.1			1712 1.4	2311 3.3
8 F	0012 3.2	0656 1.3	**23** SA	0604 1.4	1154 3.2
	1302 3.0	1940 1.3		1840 1.4	
9 SA	0143 3.2	0831 1.2	**24** SU	0035 3.2	0729 1.3
	1426 3.1	2107 1.2		1321 3.2	2002 1.2
10 SU	0258 3.4	0946 1.0	**25** M	0203 3.4	0846 1.0
	1530 3.4	2210 0.9		1442 3.4	2113 0.9
11 M	0354 3.6	1038 0.8	**26** TU	0314 3.7	0951 0.7
	1619 3.6	2256 0.7		1545 3.7	2212 0.5
12 TU	0439 3.8	1118 0.7	**27** W	0411 4.0	1044 0.3
	1700 3.8	2332 0.6		1636 4.0	2302 0.2
13 W	0518 4.0	1150 0.6	**28** TH	0459 4.2	1131 0.1
	1736 3.9			1722 4.2	○ 2347 0.0
14 TH	0002 0.5	0552 4.0	**29** F	0544 4.3	1214 0.0
	1217 0.6	1806 3.9 ●		1805 4.3	
15 F	0028 0.5	0623 4.0	**30** SA	0030 -0.1	0626 4.3
	1240 0.6	1834 3.9		1257 0.0	1846 4.3
			31 SU	0113 0.0	0708 4.3
				1338 0.0	1927 4.2

APRIL

Day	Time m	Time m	Day	Time m	Time m
1 M	0156 0.1	0749 4.1	**16** TU	0123 0.7	0718 3.9
	1420 0.2	2008 4.1		1341 0.7	1934 3.9
2 TU	0239 0.3	0831 3.9	**17** W	0159 0.8	0752 3.8
	1503 0.4	2049 3.9		1417 0.8	2010 3.8
3 W	0324 0.5	0914 3.6	**18** TH	0239 0.9	0832 3.7
	1549 0.7	2134 3.6		1458 1.0	2052 3.7
4 TH	0413 0.8	1001 3.3	**19** F	0327 1.0	0920 3.5
	1641 1.0	2228 3.3		1548 1.1	2145 3.5
5 F	0511 1.1	1102 3.1	**20** SA	0427 1.2	1020 3.3
	1747 1.2	2343 3.1		1654 1.3	2252 3.3
6 SA	0626 1.3	1231 2.9	**21** SU	0542 1.3	1134 3.2
	1911 1.3			1816 1.3	
7 SU	0118 3.1	0759 1.3	**22** M	0014 3.3	0704 1.2
	1400 3.0	2037 1.2		1258 3.2	1936 1.1
8 M	0231 3.3	0915 1.1	**23** TU	0139 3.4	0819 0.9
	1503 3.3	2140 0.9		1415 3.5	2046 0.8
9 TU	0326 3.5	1007 0.8	**24** W	0248 3.7	0923 0.6
	1552 3.5	2226 0.7		1518 3.8	2145 0.5
10 W	0410 3.7	1047 0.7	**25** TH	0345 4.0	1017 0.3
	1632 3.7	2303 0.6		1610 4.0	2238 0.2
11 TH	0449 3.9	1119 0.6	**26** F	0434 4.2	1106 0.1
	1708 3.8	2333 0.5		1658 4.2	2325 0.1
12 F	0524 3.9	1146 0.5	**27** SA	0520 4.3	1151 0.0
	1739 3.9	● 2358 0.5		1742 4.3 ○	
13 SA	0554 3.9	1210 0.6	**28** SU	0009 0.0	0604 4.3
	1807 3.9			1235 0.0	1824 4.3
14 SU	0022 0.6	0621 3.9	**29** M	0053 0.0	0646 4.2
	1246 0.6	1833 3.9		1318 0.1	1905 4.2
15 M	0051 0.6	0648 3.9	**30** TU	0136 0.2	0727 4.0
	1308 0.6	1902 3.9		1400 0.3	1946 4.0

IRELAND – COBH

YEAR **2002**

LAT 51°51′N   LONG 8°18′W

TIMES AND HEIGHTS OF HIGH AND LOW WATERS

TIME ZONE (UTC)
For Summer Time add ONE hour in **non-shaded areas**

MAY

Day	Time	m	Time	m	Time	m	Time	m
1 W	0219	0.4	0808	3.8	1444	0.5	2028	3.8
2 TH	0304	0.6	0850	3.6	1530	0.7	2113	3.6
3 F	0352	0.9	0937	3.3	1621	1.0	2205	3.3
4 SA	0448	1.1	1033	3.1	1723	1.2	2314	3.1
5 SU	0556	1.3	1151	3.0	1837	1.2		
6 M	0039	3.1	0713	1.3	1318	3.0	1951	1.2
7 TU	0151	3.2	0823	1.1	1422	3.2	2052	1.0
8 W	0246	3.4	0907	0.9	1512	3.4	2141	0.8
9 TH	0332	3.6	1001	0.8	1554	3.6	2221	0.7
10 F	0412	3.7	1037	0.7	1631	3.7	2254	0.6
11 SA	0449	3.8	1109	0.6	1705	3.8	2325	0.6
12 SU ●	0522	3.9	1139	0.6	1737	3.9	2355	0.6
13 M	0552	3.9	1212	0.6	1808	3.9		
14 TU	0028	0.6	0623	3.9	1247	0.7	1841	3.9
15 W	0105	0.7	0658	3.8	1324	0.7	1917	3.9
16 TH	0144	0.7	0737	3.8	1405	0.8	1957	3.8
17 F	0229	0.8	0821	3.7	1451	0.9	2044	3.7
18 SA	0320	0.9	0912	3.5	1544	1.0	2138	3.6
19 SU	0419	1.0	1012	3.4	1646	1.1	2243	3.5
20 M	0527	1.1	1120	3.3	1758	1.1	2357	3.5
21 TU	0641	1.0	1234	3.4	1911	0.9		
22 W	0113	3.6	0751	0.8	1346	3.6	2018	0.7
23 TH	0219	3.7	0854	0.6	1447	3.8	2119	0.5
24 F	0317	3.9	0951	0.4	1543	3.9	2214	0.3
25 SA	0410	4.0	1042	0.3	1634	4.1	2304	0.2
26 SU ○	0459	4.1	1130	0.2	1721	4.2	2351	0.2
27 M	0544	4.1	1216	0.2	1805	4.2		
28 TU	0035	0.3	0627	4.0	1300	0.3	1847	4.1
29 W	0119	0.4	0708	3.9	1343	0.4	1928	4.0
30 TH	0201	0.5	0749	3.8	1426	0.6	2010	3.8
31 F	0245	0.7	0830	3.6	1511	0.8	2054	3.6

JUNE

Day	Time	m	Time	m	Time	m	Time	m
1 SA	0331	0.9	0914	3.4	1559	1.0	2143	3.4
2 SU	0422	1.1	1003	3.2	1653	1.1	2239	3.3
3 M	0519	1.2	1102	3.1	1754	1.2	2345	3.2
4 TU	0622	1.2	1212	3.1	1857	1.2		
5 W	0054	3.2	0723	1.2	1321	3.2	1954	1.1
6 TH	0153	3.4	0817	1.1	1417	3.3	2045	1.0
7 F	0244	3.5	0906	1.0	1505	3.5	2131	0.9
8 SA	0329	3.6	0951	0.9	1549	3.6	2214	0.8
9 SU	0411	3.7	1033	0.8	1630	3.8	2254	0.7
10 M ●	0450	3.8	1113	0.7	1710	3.8	2333	0.7
11 TU	0528	3.9	1152	0.7	1748	3.9		
12 W	0012	0.6	0606	3.9	1232	0.6	1827	3.9
13 TH	0053	0.6	0646	3.9	1314	0.6	1907	3.9
14 F	0136	0.6	0729	3.8	1358	0.7	1952	3.9
15 SA	0223	0.7	0816	3.8	1446	0.7	2040	3.8
16 SU	0314	0.8	0907	3.7	1537	0.8	2133	3.7
17 M	0409	0.8	1003	3.6	1634	0.8	2232	3.7
18 TU	0509	0.9	1103	3.5	1736	0.9	2336	3.6
19 W	0615	0.9	1207	3.5	1843	0.9		
20 TH	0043	3.6	0722	0.9	1314	3.6	1949	0.8
21 F	0149	3.7	0826	0.8	1417	3.7	2053	0.7
22 SA	0250	3.8	0926	0.7	1517	3.8	2152	0.6
23 SU	0347	3.8	1022	0.6	1613	3.9	2247	0.5
24 M ○	0440	3.9	1113	0.5	1704	4.0	2336	0.5
25 TU	0528	3.9	1200	0.5	1750	4.0		
26 W	0020	0.5	0611	3.9	1244	0.5	1832	4.0
27 TH	0102	0.6	0652	3.8	1325	0.5	1912	3.9
28 F	0142	0.6	0730	3.7	1406	0.6	1952	3.8
29 SA	0222	0.7	0809	3.6	1447	0.8	2032	3.7
30 SU	0303	0.9	0848	3.5	1529	0.9	2114	3.6

JULY

Day	Time	m	Time	m	Time	m	Time	m
1 M	0346	1.0	0931	3.4	1613	1.0	2159	3.5
2 TU	0433	1.1	1017	3.3	1702	1.1	2249	3.4
3 W	0525	1.2	1109	3.3	1757	1.2	2344	3.3
4 TH	0622	1.2	1209	3.3	1855	1.2		
5 F	0046	3.3	0720	1.2	1312	3.3	1951	1.2
6 SA	0146	3.4	0816	1.1	1412	3.4	2046	1.1
7 SU	0242	3.5	0910	1.0	1507	3.5	2138	0.9
8 M	0334	3.6	1002	0.9	1559	3.7	2228	0.8
9 TU	0423	3.7	1051	0.8	1647	3.8	2315	0.7
10 W ●	0509	3.8	1136	0.6	1732	3.9	2359	0.6
11 TH	0553	3.9	1219	0.5	1815	4.0		
12 F	0042	0.5	0636	3.9	1303	0.5	1859	4.0
13 SA	0126	0.5	0721	3.9	1347	0.5	1944	4.0
14 SU	0212	0.5	0807	3.9	1434	0.5	2031	4.0
15 M	0300	0.6	0855	3.8	1522	0.6	2120	3.9
16 TU	0350	0.6	0945	3.8	1613	0.6	2212	3.8
17 W	0444	0.8	1038	3.7	1708	0.8	2308	3.7
18 TH	0543	0.9	1136	3.6	1810	0.9		
19 F	0010	3.6	0648	0.9	1241	3.5	1918	0.9
20 SA	0118	3.5	0757	1.0	1350	3.5	2029	0.9
21 SU	0226	3.5	0905	0.9	1457	3.6	2137	0.8
22 M	0330	3.6	1007	0.8	1558	3.7	2236	0.7
23 TU	0426	3.7	1101	0.7	1651	3.9	2325	0.6
24 W ○	0515	3.8	1148	0.6	1737	4.0		
25 TH	0008	0.6	0557	3.8	1229	0.5	1817	4.0
26 F	0045	0.6	0634	3.8	1306	0.6	1854	4.0
27 SA	0120	0.7	0710	3.8	1341	0.6	1930	3.9
28 SU	0153	0.8	0743	3.7	1415	0.7	2005	3.8
29 M	0227	0.9	0818	3.7	1449	0.8	2041	3.7
30 TU	0303	1.0	0855	3.6	1525	1.0	2118	3.6
31 W	0342	1.1	0934	3.5	1604	1.1	2158	3.5

AUGUST

Day	Time	m	Time	m	Time	m	Time	m
1 TH	0426	1.2	1018	3.4	1651	1.2	2245	3.4
2 F	0518	1.3	1110	3.3	1750	1.3	2340	3.3
3 SA	0622	1.3	1212	3.3	1858	1.3		
4 SU	0046	3.3	0730	1.3	1323	3.3	2005	1.3
5 M	0157	3.4	0836	1.2	1432	3.4	2109	1.1
6 TU	0303	3.5	0936	1.0	1534	3.6	2206	0.9
7 W	0401	3.7	1030	0.8	1628	3.8	2257	0.6
8 TH	0451	3.8	1118	0.6	1715	4.0	2343	0.4
9 F ●	0537	4.0	1202	0.4	1800	4.1		
10 SA	0027	0.3	0621	4.1	1246	0.3	1843	4.2
11 SU	0110	0.3	0704	4.1	1329	0.2	1926	4.2
12 M	0154	0.3	0749	4.0	1413	0.3	2011	4.1
13 TU	0239	0.4	0834	4.0	1459	0.4	2056	4.0
14 W	0325	0.5	0920	3.9	1546	0.5	2144	3.8
15 TH	0414	0.7	1009	3.7	1637	0.7	2235	3.6
16 F	0509	0.9	1104	3.5	1736	0.9	2336	3.4
17 SA	0615	1.1	1210	3.4	1847	1.1		
18 SU	0050	3.3	0731	1.1	1330	3.3	2010	1.1
19 M	0210	3.3	0851	1.1	1446	3.4	2129	1.0
20 TU	0318	3.4	0959	0.9	1548	3.6	2229	0.8
21 W	0414	3.6	1052	0.7	1639	3.8	2316	0.7
22 TH	0500	3.8	1135	0.6	1721	4.0	2353	0.4
23 F ○	0540	3.9	1211	0.5	1759	4.0		
24 SA	0025	0.6	0614	3.9	1242	0.5	1832	4.0
25 SU	0053	0.6	0645	3.9	1311	0.6	1903	4.0
26 M	0120	0.7	0715	3.8	1338	0.7	1933	3.9
27 TU	0149	0.8	0745	3.8	1407	0.8	2004	3.8
28 W	0221	0.9	0817	3.7	1440	0.9	2036	3.7
29 TH	0257	1.0	0853	3.6	1516	1.0	2113	3.6
30 F	0336	1.1	0933	3.5	1558	1.2	2155	3.5
31 SA	0423	1.3	1022	3.4	1653	1.4	2249	3.4

Chart Datum: 0·13 metres above Ordnance Datum (Dublin)

TIME ZONE (UTC)
For Summer Time add ONE hour in **non-shaded areas**

IRELAND – COBH

YEAR **2002**

LAT 51°51'N   LONG 8°18'W

TIMES AND HEIGHTS OF HIGH AND LOW WATERS

SEPTEMBER

Time	m		Time	m
1 SU	0526 1.4 / 1124 3.2 / 2357 3.2	**16** M	0028 3.1 / 0712 1.3 / 1808 1.5 / 1959 1.3	
2 M	0647 1.5 / 1241 3.2 / 1929 1.4	**17** TU	0158 3.2 / 0842 1.1 / 1435 3.4 / 2121 1.1	
3 TU	0118 3.2 / 0804 1.3 / 1403 3.3 / 2042 1.2	**18** W	0306 3.4 / 0948 0.9 / 1534 3.6 / 2216 0.9	
4 W	0238 3.4 / 0911 1.0 / 1513 3.6 / 2144 0.9	**19** TH	0358 3.6 / 1037 0.7 / 1620 3.8 / 2258 0.7	
5 TH	0340 3.7 / 1008 0.7 / 1608 3.9 / 2237 0.6	**20** F	0441 3.8 / 1116 0.6 / 1700 4.0 / 2332 0.6	
6 F	0431 3.9 / 1057 0.4 / 1655 4.1 / 2323 0.3	**21** SA	0518 3.9 / 1148 0.5 / 1735 4.1 / ○ 2359 0.6	
7 SA ●	0517 4.1 / 1141 0.2 / 1739 4.3	**22** SU	0550 3.9 / 1215 0.5 / 1806 4.1	
8 SU	0006 0.2 / 0559 4.2 / 1224 0.1 / 1821 4.3	**23** M	0022 0.6 / 0618 3.9 / 1239 0.6 / 1834 4.0	
9 M	0048 0.1 / 0642 4.2 / 1306 0.1 / 1903 4.3	**24** TU	0046 0.7 / 0645 3.9 / 1303 0.7 / 1900 3.9	
10 TU	0130 0.2 / 0725 4.2 / 1349 0.2 / 1946 4.2	**25** W	0114 0.8 / 0712 3.8 / 1331 0.8 / 1927 3.9	
11 W	0214 0.3 / 0808 4.1 / 1434 0.3 / 2029 4.0	**26** TH	0145 0.9 / 0742 3.8 / 1403 0.9 / 1958 3.8	
12 TH	0258 0.5 / 0852 3.9 / 1520 0.5 / 2114 3.8	**27** F	0219 1.0 / 0816 3.7 / 1439 1.1 / 2033 3.7	
13 F	0346 0.7 / 0940 3.7 / 1609 0.8 / 2204 3.5	**28** SA	0257 1.1 / 0855 3.6 / 1521 1.1 / 2116 3.6	
14 SA	0440 1.0 / 1034 3.4 / 1707 1.1 / 2304 3.3	**29** SU	0343 1.3 / 0944 3.4 / 1616 1.4 / 2210 3.4	
15 SU	0546 1.2 / 1146 3.2 / 1822 1.3	**30** M	0447 1.5 / 1048 3.3 / 1731 1.5 / 2322 3.2	

OCTOBER

Time	m		Time	m
1 TU	0612 1.5 / 1209 3.2 / 1858 1.5	**16** W	0138 3.1 / 0821 1.2 / 1414 3.4 / 2056 1.2	
2 W	0048 3.2 / 0735 1.3 / 1337 3.4 / 2015 1.2	**17** TH	0244 3.3 / 0922 1.0 / 1509 3.6 / 2148 1.0	
3 TH	0212 3.4 / 0844 1.0 / 1448 3.7 / 2119 0.9	**18** F	0333 3.6 / 1009 0.8 / 1553 3.8 / 2229 0.7	
4 F	0315 3.7 / 0942 0.7 / 1543 4.0 / 2212 0.5	**19** SA	0414 3.8 / 1047 0.6 / 1631 4.0 / 2302 0.7	
5 SA	0407 4.0 / 1033 0.4 / 1631 4.2 / 2259 0.3	**20** SU	0450 3.9 / 1118 0.6 / 1706 4.0 / 2328 0.7	
6 SU	0453 4.2 / 1118 0.2 / 1715 4.4 / ● 2343 0.1	**21** M	0521 4.0 / 1144 0.6 / 1737 4.1 / ○ 2351 0.7	
7 M	0536 4.3 / 1201 0.1 / 1758 4.4	**22** TU	0550 4.0 / 1207 0.7 / 1804 4.0	
8 TU	0025 0.1 / 0618 4.3 / 1245 0.1 / 1839 4.4	**23** W	0015 0.7 / 0616 4.0 / 1229 0.8 / 1829 4.0	
9 W	0107 0.2 / 0700 4.3 / 1328 0.2 / 1921 4.2	**24** TH	0045 0.8 / 0644 3.9 / 1303 0.8 / 1857 3.9	
10 TH	0151 0.3 / 0743 4.1 / 1412 0.4 / 2004 4.0	**25** F	0117 0.9 / 0715 3.9 / 1337 1.0 / 1929 3.9	
11 F	0236 0.5 / 0828 3.9 / 1458 0.6 / 2048 3.8	**26** SA	0153 1.0 / 0750 3.8 / 1415 1.1 / 2007 3.8	
12 SA	0324 0.8 / 0915 3.7 / 1548 0.9 / 2137 3.5	**27** SU	0233 1.1 / 0831 3.7 / 1501 1.2 / 2052 3.6	
13 SU	0418 1.0 / 1011 3.4 / 1646 1.2 / 2237 3.2	**28** M	0323 1.3 / 0923 3.5 / 1557 1.4 / 2148 3.4	
14 M	0526 1.3 / 1126 3.2 / 1802 1.4	**29** TU	0427 1.4 / 1027 3.4 / 1709 1.5 / 2259 3.3	
15 TU	0005 3.0 / 0652 1.3 / 1259 3.2 / 1940 1.4	**30** W	0546 1.4 / 1145 3.4 / 1831 1.4	
		31 TH	0022 3.3 / 0706 1.3 / 1309 3.5 / 1947 1.2	

NOVEMBER

Time	m		Time	m
1 F	0142 3.5 / 0816 1.0 / 1419 3.8 / 2051 0.9	**16** SA	0255 3.5 / 0927 1.0 / 1516 3.7 / 2146 1.0	
2 SA	0246 3.8 / 0915 0.7 / 1515 4.0 / 2146 0.6	**17** SU	0337 3.7 / 1007 0.9 / 1556 3.9 / 2222 0.9	
3 SU	0339 4.1 / 1008 0.4 / 1605 4.2 / 2235 0.4	**18** M	0415 3.9 / 1042 0.8 / 1633 4.0 / 2253 0.8	
4 M ●	0428 4.3 / 1056 0.3 / 1652 4.4 / 2321 0.2	**19** TU	0450 3.9 / 1113 0.8 / 1706 4.0 / 2322 0.8	
5 TU	0513 4.4 / 1142 0.2 / 1736 4.4 / ○ 2352 0.8	**20** W	0522 4.0 / 1142 0.8 / 1737 4.0	
6 W	0005 0.2 / 0557 4.4 / 1227 0.2 / 1819 4.3	**21** TH	0553 4.0 / 1213 0.8 / 1806 4.0	
7 TH	0049 0.3 / 0641 4.3 / 1311 0.3 / 1901 4.2	**22** F	0024 0.8 / 0624 4.0 / 1247 0.9 / 1837 4.0	
8 F	0133 0.4 / 0724 4.2 / 1356 0.5 / 1944 4.0	**23** SA	0100 0.8 / 0659 4.0 / 1324 1.0 / 1913 3.9	
9 SA	0218 0.6 / 0809 4.0 / 1442 0.8 / 2028 3.7	**24** SU	0140 1.0 / 0737 3.9 / 1405 1.1 / 1954 3.8	
10 SU	0307 0.9 / 0857 3.7 / 1532 1.0 / 2115 3.5	**25** M	0224 1.1 / 0822 3.8 / 1453 1.2 / 2041 3.7	
11 M	0401 1.1 / 0952 3.5 / 1628 1.3 / 2212 3.2	**26** TU	0315 1.2 / 0914 3.7 / 1548 1.3 / 2137 3.6	
12 TU	0504 1.3 / 1100 3.3 / 1737 1.4 / 2328 3.1	**27** W	0415 1.3 / 1014 3.6 / 1652 1.3 / 2243 3.5	
13 W	0621 1.4 / 1222 3.3 / 1858 1.4	**28** TH	0524 1.3 / 1124 3.6 / 1805 1.3 / 2355 3.5	
14 TH	0056 3.1 / 0737 1.3 / 1334 3.4 / 2009 1.3	**29** F	0636 1.2 / 1237 3.6 / 1917 1.2	
15 F	0204 3.3 / 0838 1.1 / 1430 3.5 / 2103 1.1	**30** SA	0108 3.6 / 0745 1.0 / 1346 3.8 / 2021 0.9	

DECEMBER

Time	m		Time	m
1 SU	0213 3.8 / 0847 0.8 / 1445 4.0 / 2119 0.7	**16** M	0250 3.6 / 0920 1.1 / 1515 3.7 / 2138 1.1	
2 M	0311 4.0 / 0944 0.6 / 1540 4.1 / 2212 0.6	**17** TU	0336 3.7 / 1004 1.0 / 1558 3.8 / 2220 1.0	
3 TU	0404 4.2 / 1037 0.5 / 1631 4.2 / 2302 0.4	**18** W	0418 3.9 / 1044 0.9 / 1638 3.9 / 2258 0.9	
4 W ●	0455 4.3 / 1127 0.4 / 1719 4.2 / 2349 0.4	**19** TH ○	0458 4.0 / 1123 0.9 / 1716 4.0 / 2335 0.8	
5 TH	0542 4.3 / 1213 0.4 / 1804 4.2	**20** F	0536 4.0 / 1200 0.8 / 1751 4.0	
6 F	0034 0.4 / 0627 4.3 / 1259 0.5 / 1846 4.1	**21** SA	0012 0.8 / 0613 4.1 / 1238 0.8 / 1827 4.0	
7 SA	0119 0.5 / 0711 4.2 / 1343 0.6 / 1928 4.0	**22** SU	0051 0.8 / 0651 4.0 / 1318 0.8 / 1906 4.0	
8 SU	0203 0.7 / 0755 4.0 / 1428 0.8 / 2010 3.8	**23** M	0132 0.8 / 0732 4.0 / 1400 0.9 / 1948 3.9	
9 M	0250 0.9 / 0841 3.8 / 1514 1.0 / 2055 3.6	**24** TU	0217 0.9 / 0817 4.0 / 1446 1.0 / 2035 3.8	
10 TU	0339 1.0 / 0930 3.6 / 1604 1.2 / 2143 3.4	**25** W	0306 0.9 / 0906 3.9 / 1536 1.0 / 2126 3.7	
11 W	0434 1.2 / 1024 3.5 / 1700 1.4 / 2239 3.3	**26** TH	0359 1.0 / 1000 3.8 / 1631 1.1 / 2223 3.6	
12 TH	0534 1.3 / 1127 3.4 / 1802 1.4 / 2346 3.2	**27** F	0457 1.1 / 1058 3.7 / 1733 1.2 / 2324 3.6	
13 F	0639 1.3 / 1234 3.4 / 1906 1.4	**28** SA	0602 1.1 / 1203 3.7 / 1841 1.2	
14 SA	0057 3.3 / 0739 1.3 / 1335 3.4 / 2003 1.3	**29** SU	0031 3.6 / 0710 1.1 / 1310 3.7 / 1949 1.1	
15 SU	0159 3.4 / 0832 1.2 / 1428 3.6 / 2053 1.2	**30** M	0139 3.7 / 0819 1.0 / 1415 3.8 / 2053 1.0	
		31 TU	0244 3.8 / 0924 0.9 / 1518 3.9 / 2154 0.8	

Chart Datum: 0·13 metres above Ordnance Datum (Dublin)
Register for your **FREE** weekly weather email service from Macmillan Reeds
》 at **www.nauticaldata.com – NOW!** 《
weekend weather reports sent to your email address, every Thursday

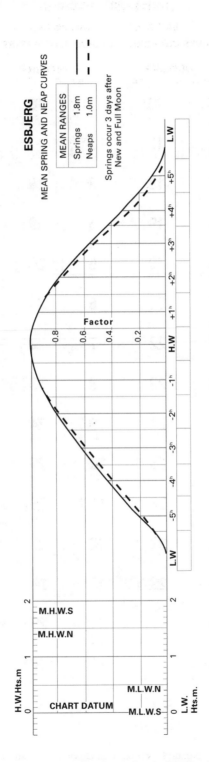

ESBJERG

MEAN SPRING AND NEAP CURVES

MEAN RANGES	
Springs	1.8m
Neaps	1.0m

Springs occur 3 days after
New and Full Moon

TIME ZONE (UTC)
For Summer Time add ONE hour in **non-shaded areas**

DENMARK – ESBJERG

LAT 55°28'N   LONG 8°27'E

TIMES AND HEIGHTS OF HIGH AND LOW WATERS

YEAR 2002

JANUARY

Day	Time m	Time m	Time m	Time m	Day	Time m	Time m	Time m	Time m
1 TU	0357 1.9	0957 0.2	1627 1.8	2210 0.3	**16** W	0430 1.9	1036 0.2	1654 1.6	2240 0.3
2 W	0438 1.9	1043 0.1	1711 1.8	2255 0.2	**17** TH	0458 1.9	1111 0.3	1720 1.6	2311 0.3
3 TH	0518 2.0	1128 0.1	1757 1.7	2341 0.3	**18** F	0524 1.8	1146 0.3	1746 1.6	2345 0.3
4 F	0602 2.0	1216 0.1	1845 1.7		**19** SA	0554 1.9	1218 0.3	1817 1.6	
5 SA	0028 0.3	0651 2.0	1308 0.1	1936 1.7	**20** SU	0020 0.3	0629 1.8	1255 0.3	1857 1.6
6 SU	0118 0.3	0745 2.0	1403 0.2	2033 1.6	**21** M	0100 0.3	0712 1.8	1336 0.3	1944 1.6
7 M	0214 0.3	0847 1.9	1503 0.3	2137 1.6	**22** TU	0146 0.3	0802 1.8	1423 0.3	2037 1.6
8 TU	0316 0.4	0955 1.9	1607 0.4	2244 1.7	**23** W	0239 0.4	0859 1.8	1519 0.4	2138 1.6
9 W	0424 0.4	1106 1.9	1712 0.4	2348 1.7	**24** TH	0341 0.4	1004 1.7	1623 0.4	2248 1.6
10 TH	0533 0.3	1214 1.9	1813 0.3		**25** F	0452 0.4	1118 1.7	1733 0.4	
11 F	0048 1.8	0637 0.3	1316 1.9	1909 0.3	**26** SA	0001 1.6	0604 0.4	1233 1.7	1839 0.4
12 SA	0143 1.8	0735 0.2	1412 1.8	2000 0.3	**27** SU	0107 1.7	0708 0.3	1340 1.7	1935 0.3
13 SU	0233 0.2	0826 0.2	1503 1.8	2046 0.3	**28** M	0205 1.7	0805 0.2	1438 1.7	2024 0.2 ○
14 M	0317 1.9	0914 0.2	1547 1.9	2126 0.3	**29** TU	0256 1.8	0856 0.1	1530 1.7	2111 0.2
15 TU	0356 1.9	0958 0.2	1623 1.7	2204 0.3	**30** W	0343 1.9	0944 0.0	1617 1.7	2156 0.1
					31 TH	0425 1.9	1027 0.0	1701 1.7	2241 0.1

FEBRUARY

Day	Time m	Time m	Time m	Time m	Day	Time m	Time m	Time m	Time m
1 F	0508 2.0	1113 -0.1	1744 1.7	2323 0.1	**16** SA	0503 1.8	1116 0.2	1719 1.6	2318 0.1
2 SA	0551 2.0	1159 0.0	1825 1.7		**17** SU	0528 1.8	1147 0.2	1747 1.6	2352 0.1
3 SU	0008 0.1	0637 1.9	1247 0.0	1911 1.6	**18** M	0559 1.8	1218 0.2	1820 1.6	
4 M	0057 0.1	0726 1.9	1337 0.1	2001 1.6	**19** TU	0029 0.1	0639 1.8	1256 0.2	1902 1.6
5 TU	0150 0.1	0823 1.8	1431 0.2	2059 1.6	**20** W	0110 0.1	0723 1.7	1341 0.2	1951 1.6
6 W	0249 0.2	0929 1.8	1533 0.3	2205 1.6	**21** TH	0159 0.2	0817 1.7	1432 0.3	2048 1.5
7 TH	0357 0.3	1043 1.7	1643 0.3	2315 1.6	**22** F	0257 0.3	0921 1.6	1535 0.3	2156 1.5
8 F	0511 0.3	1154 1.7	1751 0.3		**23** SA	0410 0.3	1039 1.5	1651 0.4	2315 1.5
9 SA	0022 1.6	0621 0.2	1259 1.7	1852 0.3	**24** SU	0534 0.3	1206 1.5	1807 0.3	
10 SU	0121 1.7	0722 0.1	1357 1.7	1944 0.2	**25** M	0035 1.6	0647 0.2	1320 1.6	1910 0.2
11 M	0214 1.8	0815 0.1	1448 1.7	2028 0.2	**26** TU	0140 1.7	0747 0.1	1421 1.6	2004 0.1
12 TU	0301 1.8	0902 0.1	1530 1.6	2109 0.2 ●	**27** W	0236 1.8	0838 -0.1	1513 1.7	2053 0.0 ○
13 W	0342 1.8	0942 0.1	1606 1.6	2147 0.2	**28** TH	0323 1.8	0923 -0.1	1600 1.7	2138 0.0
14 TH	0413 1.8	1015 0.1	1635 1.6	2217 0.2					
15 F	0440 1.8	1048 0.1	1658 1.5	2249 0.2					

MARCH

Day	Time m	Time m	Time m	Time m	Day	Time m	Time m	Time m	Time m
1 F	0408 1.9	1009 -0.2	1641 1.7	2219 -0.1	**16** SA	0417 1.7	1018 0.0	1634 1.5	2223 0.0
2 SA	0451 1.9	1053 -0.2	1720 1.7	2303 -0.1	**17** SU	0440 1.7	1047 0.0	1655 1.5	2253 0.0
3 SU	0533 1.9	1136 -0.1	1800 1.6	2348 -0.1	**18** M	0503 1.7	1114 0.0	1719 1.6	2325 0.0
4 M	0616 1.9	1219 -0.1	1840 1.6		**19** TU	0534 1.7	1148 0.0	1751 1.6	
5 TU	0033 -0.1	0703 1.8	1306 0.1	1925 1.6	**20** W	0001 0.0	0609 1.7	1224 0.1	1830 1.6
6 W	0122 0.0	0757 1.7	1358 0.2	2018 1.5	**21** TH	0043 0.0	0655 1.6	1306 0.1	1914 1.6
7 TH	0219 0.1	0901 1.6	1458 0.3	2125 1.5	**22** F	0131 0.1	0749 1.5	1357 0.2	2009 1.5
8 F	0330 0.2	1018 1.5	1610 0.4	2241 1.5	**23** SA	0229 0.2	0854 1.5	1459 0.3	2116 1.5
9 SA	0453 0.2	1134 1.5	1725 0.4	2353 1.6	**24** SU	0344 0.2	1015 1.4	1618 0.3	2238 1.5
10 SU	0606 0.2	1239 1.5	1829 0.3		**25** M	0510 0.2	1146 1.4	1741 0.3	
11 M	0056 1.6	0707 0.1	1336 1.5	1922 0.2	**26** TU	0004 1.5	0625 0.1	1300 1.5	1847 0.2
12 TU	0152 1.7	0758 0.0	1425 1.6	2008 0.1	**27** W	0113 1.6	0724 -0.1	1400 1.6	1942 0.0
13 W	0239 1.7	0841 0.0	1508 1.6	2049 0.1	**28** TH	0211 1.7	0815 -0.2	1452 1.6	2029 -0.1 ○
14 TH	0318 1.7	0917 0.0	1543 1.6	2122 0.1 ●	**29** F	0301 1.8	0902 -0.3	1536 1.6	2113 -0.2
15 F	0352 1.7	0951 0.0	1611 1.5	2155 0.0	**30** SA	0348 1.9	0947 -0.3	1616 1.6	2158 -0.2
					31 SU	0430 1.9	1027 -0.2	1654 1.6	2242 -0.2

APRIL

Day	Time m	Time m	Time m	Time m	Day	Time m	Time m	Time m	Time m
1 M	0511 1.8	1109 -0.2	1730 1.6	2323 -0.2	**16** TU	0443 1.6	1048 0.0	1657 1.6	2302 -0.1
2 TU	0554 1.7	1152 -0.1	1808 1.6		**17** W	0512 1.6	1120 0.0	1728 1.6	2341 -0.1
3 W	0009 -0.1	0638 1.6	1236 0.1	1851 1.5	**18** TH	0551 1.6	1158 0.0	1804 1.6	
4 TH	0059 0.0	0728 1.5	1323 0.2	1940 1.5	**19** F	0023 0.0	0636 1.5	1243 0.1	1850 1.5
5 F	0156 0.1	0831 1.4	1420 0.3	2043 1.5	**20** SA	0112 0.0	0730 1.4	1335 0.2	1945 1.5
6 SA	0306 0.2	0947 1.3	1534 0.4	2202 1.4	**21** SU	0212 0.1	0836 1.4	1437 0.3	2052 1.5
7 SU	0430 0.2	1103 1.3	1654 0.3	2320 1.5	**22** M	0327 0.1	1000 1.3	1554 0.3	2213 1.5
8 M	0544 0.1	1209 1.4	1800 0.3		**23** TU	0450 0.1	1128 1.4	1712 0.2	2338 1.5
9 TU	0025 1.6	0642 0.0	1305 1.4	1854 0.2	**24** W	0601 0.0	1238 1.4	1818 0.1	
10 W	0119 1.6	0729 0.0	1355 1.5	1941 0.1	**25** TH	0047 1.6	0700 -0.1	1336 1.5	1914 0.0
11 TH	0207 1.7	0811 -0.1	1438 1.5	2019 0.0	**26** F	0147 1.7	0751 -0.2	1425 1.6	2004 -0.1
12 F	0249 1.7	0849 -0.1	1513 1.6	2056 0.0 ●	**27** SA	0238 1.7	0837 -0.3	1510 1.6	2052 -0.2 ○
13 SA	0323 1.7	0919 -0.1	1544 1.6	2127 0.0	**28** SU	0325 1.8	0920 -0.3	1551 1.6	2137 -0.3
14 SU	0352 1.6	0950 0.0	1609 1.5	2158 0.0	**29** M	0409 1.8	1003 -0.2	1627 1.6	2219 -0.3
15 M	0416 1.6	1016 0.0	1632 1.5	2230 0.0	**30** TU	0451 1.7	1045 -0.1	1704 1.6	2304 -0.2

Chart Datum: 0·69 metres below Dansk Normal Null
Register for your **FREE** weekly weather email service from Macmillan Reeds
》 at www.nauticaldata.com – NOW! 《
weekend weather reports sent to your email address, every Thursday

135

TIME ZONE (UTC)
For Summer Time add ONE hour in **non-shaded areas**

DENMARK – ESBJERG

LAT 55°28′N   LONG 8°27′E

TIMES AND HEIGHTS OF HIGH AND LOW WATERS

YEAR **2002**

MAY

Day	Time	m	Day	Time	m
1 W	0532 / 1124 / 1741 / 2350	1.6 / 0.0 / 1.6 / -0.1	**16** TH	0501 / 1100 / 1712 / 2326	1.5 / 0.0 / 1.6 / -0.1
2 TH	0614 / 1207 / 1820	1.5 / 0.1 / 1.5	**17** F	0541 / 1142 / 1751	1.5 / 0.0 / 1.6
3 F	0038 / 0703 / 1253 / 1907	0.0 / 1.4 / 0.2 / 1.5	**18** SA	0011 / 0627 / 1227 / 1837	0.0 / 1.4 / 0.1 / 1.6
4 SA	0133 / 0759 / 1347 / 2005	0.1 / 1.3 / 0.3 / 1.5	**19** SU	0103 / 0721 / 1318 / 1931	0.0 / 1.4 / 0.2 / 1.6
5 SU	0239 / 0909 / 1452 / 2118	0.2 / 1.3 / 0.3 / 1.5	**20** M	0203 / 0827 / 1420 / 2036	0.0 / 1.3 / 0.2 / 1.6
6 M	0356 / 1023 / 1608 / 2235	0.2 / 1.3 / 0.3 / 1.5	**21** TU	0312 / 0945 / 1532 / 2153	0.0 / 1.3 / 0.2 / 1.6
7 TU	0506 / 1129 / 1717 / 2342	0.1 / 1.3 / 0.3 / 1.5	**22** W	0425 / 1102 / 1644 / 2311	0.0 / 1.4 / 0.2 / 1.6
8 W	0605 / 1225 / 1814	0.1 / 1.4 / 0.2	**23** TH	0533 / 1209 / 1750	0.0 / 1.4 / 0.1
9 TH	0039 / 0654 / 1315 / 1904	1.6 / 0.0 / 1.5 / 0.1	**24** F	0021 / 0632 / 1307 / 1849	1.7 / -0.1 / 1.5 / 0.0
10 F	0129 / 0736 / 1400 / 1947	1.6 / 0.0 / 1.6 / 0.1	**25** SA	0122 / 0723 / 1359 / 1942	1.7 / -0.2 / 1.6 / -0.1
11 SA	0212 / 0813 / 1441 / 2024	1.6 / 0.0 / 1.6 / 0.0	**26** SU	0216 / 0812 / 1446 / 2030 ○	1.7 / -0.2 / 1.6 / -0.2
12 SU	0251 / 0848 / 1514 / 2100 ●	1.6 / 0.0 / 1.6 / 0.0	**27** M	0306 / 0858 / 1527 / 2116	1.7 / -0.1 / 1.6 / -0.2
13 M	0324 / 0918 / 1545 / 2134	1.6 / 0.0 / 1.6 / 0.0	**28** TU	0352 / 0942 / 1606 / 2203	1.7 / -0.1 / 1.6 / -0.2
14 TU	0356 / 0952 / 1612 / 2208	1.6 / 0.0 / 1.6 / 0.0	**29** W	0435 / 1021 / 1644 / 2249	1.6 / 0.0 / 1.6 / -0.1
15 W	0426 / 1024 / 1641 / 2246	1.5 / 0.0 / 1.6 / -0.1	**30** TH	0514 / 1102 / 1719 / 2333	1.5 / 0.1 / 1.6 / -0.1
			31 F	0555 / 1144 / 1757	1.4 / 0.1 / 1.6

JUNE

Day	Time	m	Day	Time	m
1 SA	0019 / 0636 / 1226 / 1839	0.0 / 1.3 / 0.2 / 1.6	**16** SU	0004 / 0624 / 1215 / 1830	-0.1 / 1.5 / 0.1 / 1.7
2 SU	0109 / 0723 / 1312 / 1927	0.1 / 1.3 / 0.2 / 1.6	**17** M	0055 / 0716 / 1306 / 1922	0.0 / 1.4 / 0.1 / 1.7
3 M	0205 / 0819 / 1406 / 2026	0.2 / 1.3 / 0.3 / 1.5	**18** TU	0151 / 0815 / 1402 / 2023	0.0 / 1.4 / 0.2 / 1.7
4 TU	0307 / 0924 / 1510 / 2133	0.2 / 1.3 / 0.3 / 1.5	**19** W	0253 / 0922 / 1505 / 2133	0.0 / 1.4 / 0.2 / 1.7
5 W	0411 / 1031 / 1619 / 2242	0.2 / 1.3 / 0.3 / 1.5	**20** TH	0358 / 1032 / 1612 / 2246	0.0 / 1.4 / 0.2 / 1.7
6 TH	0512 / 1133 / 1723 / 2345	0.1 / 1.4 / 0.3 / 1.5	**21** F	0503 / 1139 / 1720 / 2357	0.0 / 1.5 / 0.1 / 1.7
7 F	0606 / 1229 / 1818	0.1 / 1.4 / 0.2	**22** SA	0605 / 1240 / 1822	0.0 / 1.5 / 0.1
8 SA	0042 / 0654 / 1318 / 1908	1.6 / 0.1 / 1.5 / 0.2	**23** SU	0101 / 0701 / 1335 / 1920	1.7 / 0.0 / 1.6 / 0.0
9 SU	0133 / 0736 / 1403 / 1953	1.6 / 0.1 / 1.6 / 0.1	**24** M	0200 / 0752 / 1424 / 2014 ○	1.7 / 0.0 / 1.6 / -0.1
10 M	0217 / 0814 / 1445 / 2033	1.6 / 0.0 / 1.6 / 0.1	**25** TU	0253 / 0839 / 1510 / 2104	1.7 / 0.0 / 1.7 / -0.1
11 TU	0300 / 0853 / 1521 / 2112 ●	1.6 / 0.0 / 1.6 / 0.0	**26** W	0341 / 0922 / 1552 / 2152	1.6 / 0.1 / 1.7 / -0.1
12 W	0339 / 0929 / 1556 / 2153	1.6 / 0.1 / 1.6 / 0.0	**27** TH	0423 / 1004 / 1630 / 2236	1.6 / 0.1 / 1.7 / 0.0
13 TH	0417 / 1007 / 1629 / 2234	1.5 / 0.1 / 1.6 / 0.0	**28** F	0501 / 1045 / 1704 / 2317	1.5 / 0.1 / 1.7 / 0.0
14 F	0457 / 1048 / 1704 / 2316	1.5 / 0.1 / 1.7 / 0.0	**29** SA	0536 / 1122 / 1738	1.4 / 0.2 / 1.7
15 SA	0539 / 1130 / 1745	1.5 / 0.1 / 1.7	**30** SU	0000 / 0609 / 1200 / 1813	0.1 / 1.4 / 0.2 / 1.7

JULY

Day	Time	m	Day	Time	m
1 M	0042 / 0646 / 1242 / 1854	0.2 / 1.4 / 0.2 / 1.7	**16** TU	0041 / 0703 / 1250 / 1911	0.0 / 1.5 / 0.1 / 1.8
2 TU	0124 / 0727 / 1325 / 1940	0.2 / 1.4 / 0.3 / 1.6	**17** W	0131 / 0755 / 1343 / 2007	0.0 / 1.5 / 0.1 / 1.8
3 W	0211 / 0818 / 1414 / 2032	0.3 / 1.4 / 0.3 / 1.6	**18** TH	0225 / 0852 / 1440 / 2111	0.1 / 1.5 / 0.2 / 1.8
4 TH	0303 / 0917 / 1511 / 2132	0.3 / 1.4 / 0.3 / 1.6	**19** F	0326 / 0957 / 1545 / 2223	0.2 / 1.5 / 0.2 / 1.7
5 F	0402 / 1022 / 1616 / 2239	0.3 / 1.4 / 0.4 / 1.6	**20** SA	0432 / 1105 / 1654 / 2337	0.2 / 1.5 / 0.2 / 1.7
6 SA	0503 / 1129 / 1723 / 2346	0.3 / 1.5 / 0.3 / 1.6	**21** SU	0539 / 1212 / 1804	0.2 / 1.6 / 0.2
7 SU	0602 / 1231 / 1825	0.3 / 1.5 / 0.3	**22** M	0046 / 0640 / 1313 / 1907	1.7 / 0.2 / 1.7 / 0.1
8 M	0049 / 0656 / 1325 / 1919	1.6 / 0.2 / 1.6 / 0.1	**23** TU	0148 / 0735 / 1408 / 2004	1.7 / 0.2 / 1.7 / 0.1
9 TU	0146 / 0745 / 1414 / 2009	1.6 / 0.2 / 1.6 / 0.2	**24** W	0243 / 0823 / 1457 / 2055 ○	1.7 / 0.2 / 1.8 / 0.0
10 W	0238 / 0828 / 1459 / 2056 ●	1.6 / 0.2 / 1.7 / 0.1	**25** TH	0330 / 0908 / 1541 / 2141	1.6 / 0.2 / 1.8 / 0.1
11 TH	0325 / 0910 / 1541 / 2140	1.6 / 0.1 / 1.7 / 0.0	**26** F	0411 / 0950 / 1618 / 2221	1.6 / 0.2 / 1.8 / 0.1
12 F	0409 / 0953 / 1619 / 2222	1.6 / 0.1 / 1.8 / 0.0	**27** SA	0447 / 1026 / 1651 / 2300	1.6 / 0.2 / 1.8 / 0.1
13 SA	0452 / 1035 / 1658 / 2307	1.6 / 0.1 / 1.8 / 0.0	**28** SU	0515 / 1101 / 1719 / 2335	1.5 / 0.2 / 1.8 / 0.2
14 SU	0533 / 1116 / 1739 / 2353	1.6 / 0.1 / 1.8 / -0.1	**29** M	0541 / 1136 / 1748	1.5 / 0.2 / 1.8
15 M	0616 / 1202 / 1822	1.6 / 0.1 / 1.8	**30** TU	0008 / 0609 / 1209 / 1819	0.2 / 1.5 / 0.2 / 1.8
			31 W	0044 / 0644 / 1247 / 1859	0.3 / 1.5 / 0.2 / 1.8

AUGUST

Day	Time	m	Day	Time	m
1 TH	0120 / 0725 / 1329 / 1945	0.3 / 1.6 / 0.3 / 1.7	**16** F	0157 / 0818 / 1412 / 2049	0.2 / 1.6 / 0.2 / 1.8
2 F	0203 / 0815 / 1417 / 2038	0.3 / 1.6 / 0.3 / 1.7	**17** SA	0255 / 0920 / 1516 / 2202	0.3 / 1.6 / 0.3 / 1.7
3 SA	0255 / 0913 / 1514 / 2139	0.4 / 1.5 / 0.4 / 1.6	**18** SU	0402 / 1034 / 1633 / 2321	0.4 / 1.6 / 0.3 / 1.7
4 SU	0356 / 1020 / 1624 / 2252	0.4 / 1.5 / 0.4 / 1.6	**19** M	0514 / 1148 / 1751	0.4 / 1.7 / 0.3
5 M	0506 / 1134 / 1742	0.4 / 1.6 / 0.4	**20** TU	0033 / 0621 / 1254 / 1858	1.7 / 0.4 / 1.7 / 0.2
6 TU	0009 / 0615 / 1244 / 1850	1.6 / 0.4 / 1.6 / 0.3	**21** W	0135 / 0718 / 1352 / 1954	1.7 / 0.4 / 1.8 / 0.2
7 W	0119 / 0714 / 1345 / 1948	1.6 / 0.3 / 1.7 / 0.2	**22** TH	0228 / 0808 / 1441 / 2043 ○	1.7 / 0.3 / 1.9 / 0.1
8 TH	0218 / 0806 / 1437 / 2038 ●	1.7 / 0.3 / 1.8 / 0.1	**23** F	0315 / 0853 / 1526 / 2123	1.7 / 0.3 / 1.9 / 0.1
9 F	0310 / 0853 / 1522 / 2122	1.7 / 0.2 / 1.9 / 0.0	**24** SA	0355 / 0930 / 1603 / 2203	1.7 / 0.2 / 1.9 / 0.2
10 SA	0357 / 0936 / 1605 / 2207	1.7 / 0.1 / 1.9 / 0.0	**25** SU	0426 / 1006 / 1633 / 2236	1.7 / 0.2 / 1.9 / 0.2
11 SU	0439 / 1017 / 1646 / 2251	1.7 / 0.1 / 2.0 / 0.0	**26** M	0452 / 1039 / 1657 / 2306	1.7 / 0.2 / 1.9 / 0.3
12 M	0518 / 1100 / 1726 / 2334	1.7 / 0.1 / 2.0 / 0.0	**27** TU	0512 / 1108 / 1720 / 2335	1.7 / 0.2 / 1.9 / 0.3
13 TU	0559 / 1145 / 1809	1.7 / 0.1 / 2.0	**28** W	0536 / 1140 / 1749	1.7 / 0.2 / 1.9
14 W	0018 / 0641 / 1230 / 1856	0.0 / 1.7 / 0.1 / 2.0	**29** TH	0004 / 0605 / 1212 / 1822	0.3 / 1.7 / 0.3 / 1.9
15 TH	0106 / 0725 / 1317 / 1948	0.1 / 1.7 / 0.1 / 1.9	**30** F	0039 / 0644 / 1252 / 1904	0.3 / 1.7 / 0.3 / 1.8
			31 SA	0117 / 0728 / 1338 / 1955	0.4 / 1.7 / 0.3 / 1.8

Chart Datum: 0·69 metres below Dansk Normal Null

TIME ZONE (UTC)
For Summer Time add ONE hour in **non-shaded areas**

DENMARK – ESBJERG

LAT 55°28′N LONG 8°27′E

TIMES AND HEIGHTS OF HIGH AND LOW WATERS

YEAR **2002**

SEPTEMBER

Time m	Time m	Time m	Time m
1 0205 0.4 / 0821 1.7 / SU 1431 1.7 / 2056 1.7	**16** 0331 0.6 / 1002 1.7 / M 1616 0.4 / 2303 1.7		
2 0303 0.5 / 0924 1.7 / M 1539 0.5 / 2209 1.7	**17** 0451 0.6 / 1123 1.8 / TU 1738 0.4		
3 0416 0.6 / 1041 1.7 / TU 1703 0.5 / 2336 1.7	**18** 0014 1.7 / 0602 0.6 / W 1232 1.8 / 1843 0.3		
4 0539 0.5 / 1203 1.7 / W 1822 0.4	**19** 0115 1.8 / 0700 0.5 / TH 1330 1.9 / 1936 0.3		
5 0053 1.7 / 0647 0.5 / TH 1313 1.8 / 1923 0.3	**20** 0208 1.8 / 0749 0.4 / F 1420 2.0 / 2021 0.2		
6 0157 1.8 / 0743 0.4 / F 1410 1.9 / 2015 0.2	**21** 0253 1.8 / 0830 0.3 / SA 1504 2.0 / ○ 2103 0.2		
7 0250 1.8 / 0830 0.3 / SA 1500 2.0 / ● 2102 0.1	**22** 0330 1.8 / 0908 0.3 / SU 1541 2.0 / 2137 0.2		
8 0336 1.9 / 0913 0.2 / SU 1545 2.1 / 2147 0.0	**23** 0401 1.8 / 0943 0.3 / M 1609 2.0 / 2207 0.3		
9 0417 1.9 / 0957 0.1 / M 1626 2.1 / 2227 0.0	**24** 0425 1.8 / 1012 0.3 / TU 1633 1.9 / 2235 0.3		
10 0457 1.9 / 1040 0.1 / TU 1708 2.1 / 2310 0.0	**25** 0446 1.8 / 1043 0.3 / W 1655 1.9 / 2301 0.3		
11 0534 1.9 / 1122 0.1 / W 1751 2.1 / 2354 0.1	**26** 0507 1.8 / 1111 0.3 / TH 1720 1.9 / 2332 0.3		
12 0612 1.8 / 1206 0.1 / TH 1835 2.0	**27** 0536 1.8 / 1146 0.3 / F 1754 1.9		
13 0039 0.2 / 0655 1.8 / F 1255 0.2 / 1925 1.9	**28** 0004 0.4 / 0609 1.9 / SA 1223 0.3 / 1835 1.9		
14 0126 0.4 / 0745 1.8 / SA 1350 0.4 / 2026 1.8	**29** 0044 0.4 / 0653 1.9 / SU 1307 0.4 / 1924 1.8		
15 0222 0.5 / 0846 1.7 / SU 1455 0.4 / 2142 1.7	**30** 0131 0.5 / 0745 1.8 / M 1401 0.4 / 2023 1.7		

OCTOBER

Time m	Time m
1 0227 0.6 / 0846 1.8 / TU 1509 0.5 / 2139 1.7	**16** 0421 0.7 / 1051 1.8 / W 1716 0.5 / 2348 1.7
2 0340 0.6 / 1001 1.8 / W 1636 0.5 / 2309 1.7	**17** 0533 0.6 / 1200 1.9 / TH 1818 0.4
3 0504 0.6 / 1127 1.8 / TH 1756 0.4	**18** 0047 1.8 / 0631 0.5 / F 1259 2.0 / 1910 0.3
4 0029 1.8 / 0616 0.5 / F 1241 1.9 / 1858 0.3	**19** 0138 1.8 / 0719 0.4 / SA 1351 2.0 / 1955 0.3
5 0132 1.8 / 0713 0.4 / SA 1342 2.0 / 1951 0.2	**20** 0221 1.9 / 0803 0.4 / SU 1435 2.0 / 2032 0.3
6 0223 1.9 / 0804 0.3 / SU 1434 2.1 / ● 2037 0.1	**21** 0300 1.9 / 0842 0.3 / M 1511 2.0 / ○ 2107 0.3
7 0310 2.0 / 0851 0.2 / M 1520 2.2 / 2120 0.1	**22** 0333 1.9 / 0915 0.3 / TU 1543 2.0 / 2137 0.3
8 0352 2.0 / 0934 0.1 / TU 1605 2.2 / 2203 0.1	**23** 0359 1.9 / 0948 0.3 / W 1608 1.9 / 2204 0.4
9 0429 2.0 / 1016 0.1 / W 1648 2.1 / 2246 0.1	**24** 0421 1.9 / 1016 0.3 / TH 1632 1.9 / 2233 0.4
10 0507 2.0 / 1101 0.1 / TH 1729 2.1 / 2327 0.2	**25** 0445 1.9 / 1049 0.3 / F 1659 1.9 / 2303 0.4
11 0545 1.9 / 1147 0.1 / F 1814 2.0	**26** 0511 1.9 / 1123 0.3 / SA 1733 1.9 / 2339 0.4
12 0010 0.4 / 0626 1.9 / SA 1235 0.2 / 1905 1.9	**27** 0546 1.9 / 1202 0.3 / SU 1813 1.8
13 0058 0.5 / 0714 1.9 / SU 1329 0.4 / 2006 1.8	**28** 0018 0.4 / 0628 1.9 / M 1250 0.4 / 1904 1.8
14 0153 0.6 / 0814 1.8 / M 1437 0.4 / 2122 1.7	**29** 0106 0.5 / 0717 1.9 / TU 1345 0.4 / 2005 1.7
15 0301 0.7 / 0932 1.8 / TU 1559 0.5 / 2240 1.7	**30** 0203 0.6 / 0818 1.9 / W 1453 0.5 / 2118 1.7
	31 0314 0.6 / 0930 1.9 / TH 1611 0.5 / 2243 1.7

NOVEMBER

Time m	Time m
1 0434 0.6 / 1053 1.9 / F 1726 0.4 / 2359 1.8	**16** 0005 1.7 / 0553 0.6 / SA 1219 1.9 / 1834 0.4
2 0545 0.5 / 1208 2.0 / SA 1828 0.3	**17** 0058 1.8 / 0646 0.5 / SU 1311 2.0 / 1918 0.3
3 0101 1.8 / 0645 0.4 / SU 1311 2.1 / 1921 0.2	**18** 0145 1.9 / 0730 0.4 / M 1358 2.0 / 2000 0.3
4 0155 1.9 / 0737 0.3 / M 1407 2.1 / ● 2010 0.1	**19** 0226 1.9 / 0811 0.4 / TU 1439 2.0 / 2035 0.4
5 0242 2.0 / 0824 0.2 / TU 1458 2.1 / 2056 0.1	**20** 0302 1.9 / 0849 0.4 / W 1514 1.9 / ○ 2107 0.4
6 0324 2.0 / 0911 0.1 / W 1545 2.1 / 2140 0.2	**21** 0334 1.9 / 0922 0.4 / TH 1546 1.9 / 2139 0.4
7 0405 2.0 / 0957 0.1 / TH 1628 2.1 / 2220 0.2	**22** 0401 1.9 / 0956 0.4 / F 1615 1.9 / 2209 0.4
8 0443 2.0 / 1043 0.1 / F 1712 2.0 / 2303 0.3	**23** 0427 1.9 / 1031 0.4 / SA 1647 1.8 / 2244 0.4
9 0521 2.0 / 1128 0.2 / SA 1757 1.9 / 2348 0.4	**24** 0457 1.9 / 1108 0.3 / SU 1721 1.6 / 2320 0.4
10 0602 1.9 / 1217 0.3 / SU 1846 1.8	**25** 0532 1.9 / 1151 0.3 / M 1804 1.8
11 0033 0.5 / 0649 1.9 / M 1312 0.4 / 1942 1.7	**26** 0003 0.4 / 0612 2.0 / TU 1240 0.3 / 1854 1.7
12 0125 0.6 / 0746 1.9 / TU 1415 0.5 / 2049 1.6	**27** 0052 0.5 / 0702 2.0 / W 1334 0.4 / 1953 1.7
13 0227 0.7 / 0855 1.9 / W 1529 0.5 / 2201 1.6	**28** 0148 0.5 / 0801 2.0 / TH 1437 0.4 / 2101 1.7
14 0341 0.7 / 1010 1.9 / TH 1642 0.5 / 2307 1.7	**29** 0252 0.5 / 0909 1.9 / F 1547 0.4 / 2215 1.7
15 0452 0.7 / 1120 1.9 / F 1743 0.4	**30** 0402 0.5 / 1025 1.9 / SA 1655 0.3 / 2327 1.7

DECEMBER

Time m	Time m
1 0510 0.5 / 1139 2.0 / SU 1758 0.3	**16** 0008 1.7 / 0601 0.5 / M 1226 1.8 / 1837 0.4
2 0030 1.8 / 0613 0.4 / M 1245 2.0 / 1854 0.2	**17** 0100 1.8 / 0654 0.5 / TU 1317 1.9 / 1921 0.4
3 0125 1.9 / 0710 0.3 / TU 1345 2.0 / 1946 0.2	**18** 0149 1.8 / 0740 0.4 / W 1404 1.9 / 2002 0.4
4 0216 1.9 / 0803 0.2 / W 1439 2.0 / ● 2032 0.2	**19** 0232 1.9 / 0821 0.4 / TH 1448 1.8 / ○ 2040 0.4
5 0302 1.9 / 0854 0.2 / TH 1528 2.0 / 2117 0.3	**20** 0309 1.9 / 0902 0.4 / F 1527 1.8 / 2115 0.4
6 0345 2.0 / 0942 0.2 / F 1615 1.9 / 2201 0.3	**21** 0344 1.9 / 0941 0.3 / SA 1604 1.8 / 2152 0.4
7 0425 2.0 / 1028 0.2 / SA 1700 1.8 / 2245 0.4	**22** 0415 1.9 / 1018 0.3 / SU 1641 1.8 / 2230 0.3
8 0504 2.0 / 1115 0.2 / SU 1743 1.7 / 2326 0.4	**23** 0449 1.9 / 1059 0.2 / M 1718 1.7 / 2308 0.3
9 0545 1.9 / 1203 0.3 / M 1826 1.7	**24** 0524 1.9 / 1143 0.2 / TU 1800 1.7 / 2352 0.3
10 0010 0.5 / 0628 1.9 / TU 1254 0.4 / 1913 1.6	**25** 0605 2.0 / 1229 0.2 / W 1847 1.7
11 0058 0.5 / 0713 1.9 / W 1349 0.4 / 2007 1.6	**26** 0040 0.3 / 0653 2.0 / TH 1320 0.2 / 1939 1.7
12 0151 0.6 / 0813 1.9 / TH 1448 0.5 / 2107 1.6	**27** 0132 0.4 / 0747 2.0 / F 1416 0.3 / 2037 1.7
13 0251 0.6 / 0917 1.9 / F 1550 0.5 / 2210 1.6	**28** 0229 0.4 / 0849 1.9 / SA 1517 0.3 / 2143 1.6
14 0356 0.6 / 1025 1.8 / SA 1652 0.5 / 2311 1.7	**29** 0333 0.4 / 0958 1.9 / SU 1622 0.3 / 2252 1.7
15 0501 0.6 / 1129 1.8 / SU 1748 0.5	**30** 0441 0.4 / 1112 1.9 / M 1726 0.3 / 2358 1.7
	31 0548 0.3 / 1223 1.9 / TU 1827 0.3

Chart Datum: 0·69 metres below Dansk Normal Null
Register for your FREE weekly weather email service from Macmillan Reeds
at www.nauticaldata.com – NOW!
》》 weekend weather reports sent to your email address, every Thursday 《《

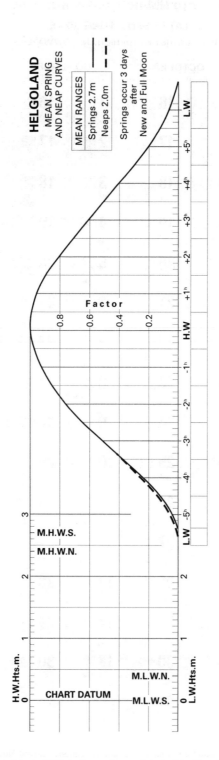

HELGOLAND
MEAN SPRING
AND NEAP CURVES

MEAN RANGES
Springs 2.7m
Neaps 2.0m

Springs occur 3 days
after
New and Full Moon

Factor

0.8 0.6 0.4 0.2

TIME ZONE -0100
(German Standard Time)
Subtract 1 hour for UT
For German Summer Time add ONE hour in **non-shaded areas**

GERMANY – HELGOLAND

LAT 54°11'N   LONG 7°53'E

TIMES AND HEIGHTS OF HIGH AND LOW WATERS

YEAR 2002

JANUARY

Day	Time m	Time m	Time m	Time m
1 TU	0040 2.8	0734 0.0	1310 2.7	1950 0.1
2 W	0128 2.8	0824 0.0	1359 2.7	2035 0.1
3 TH	0214 2.9	0910 0.0	1447 2.6	2119 0.1
4 F	0258 2.9	0957 0.1	1535 2.5	2206 0.2
5 SA	0345 2.9	1047 0.1	1628 2.5	2259 0.3
6 SU	0438 2.9	1139 0.1	1725 2.5	2354 0.4
7 M	0537 2.8	1234 0.2	1822 2.4	
8 TU	0055 0.4	0640 2.7	1337 0.2	1925 2.4
9 W	0206 0.3	0751 2.6	1448 0.3	2032 2.4
10 TH	0322 0.3	0904 0.2	1557 0.2	2139 2.5
11 F	0430 0.2	1012 0.2	1657 0.3	2239 2.6
12 SA	0527 0.2	1109 2.7	1747 0.3	2329 2.7
13 SU	0616 0.2	1155 2.7	1830 0.3	
14 M	0012 2.8	0656 0.2	1234 2.8	1908 0.3
15 TU	0049 2.9	0733 0.2	1312 2.8	1944 0.3
16 W	0124 2.9	0810 0.2	1349 2.7	2019 0.3
17 TH	0158 2.9	0846 0.2	1424 2.6	2051 0.2
18 F	0232 2.8	0919 0.2	1457 2.5	2122 0.2
19 SA	0305 2.8	0953 0.2	1531 2.5	2156 0.3
20 SU	0341 2.8	1029 0.3	1606 2.4	2231 0.3
21 M	0419 2.7	1102 0.3	1642 2.4	2308 0.4
22 TU	0500 2.6	1139 0.4	1726 2.3	2356 0.5
23 W	0550 2.5	1232 0.4	1825 2.3	
24 TH	0104 0.5	0656 2.4	1343 0.4	1938 2.3
25 F	0223 0.4	0811 2.4	1459 0.4	2052 2.4
26 SA	0338 0.4	0922 2.5	1609 0.3	2156 2.6
27 SU	0443 0.2	1025 2.6	1710 0.2	2250 2.7
28 M ○	0541 0.1	1121 2.7	1804 0.2	2339 2.8
29 TU	0634 0.0	1212 2.7	1854 0.1	
30 W	0027 2.9	0726 -0.1	1301 2.7	1942 0.0
31 TH	0117 2.9	0816 -0.2	1349 2.6	2029 0.0

FEBRUARY

Day	Time m	Time m	Time m	Time m
1 F	0204 2.9	0903 -0.2	1436 2.6	2112 -0.1
2 SA	0247 2.9	0946 -0.2	1522 2.6	2156 0.0
3 SU	0331 2.9	1030 -0.1	1608 2.5	2241 0.1
4 M	0418 2.9	1114 0.1	1655 2.5	2327 0.2
5 TU	0508 2.8	1158 0.2	1743 2.5	
6 W	0018 0.2	0604 2.6	1253 0.3	1840 2.4
7 TH	0126 0.2	0714 2.4	1406 0.3	1952 2.3
8 F	0250 0.2	0837 2.4	1527 0.3	2112 2.4
9 SA	0412 0.2	0956 2.4	1639 0.3	2222 2.5
10 SU	0516 0.1	1059 2.5	1734 0.3	2316 2.7
11 M	0605 0.1	1145 2.6	1817 0.3	2358 2.8
12 TU ●	0645 0.1	1222 2.7	1855 0.2	
13 W	0034 2.8	0721 0.1	1256 2.7	1931 0.1
14 TH	0107 2.8	0754 0.1	1330 2.7	2003 0.1
15 F	0138 2.8	0826 0.1	1401 2.6	2032 0.1
16 SA	0208 2.8	0856 0.1	1431 2.5	2101 0.1
17 SU	0240 2.8	0928 0.1	1502 2.5	2132 0.1
18 M	0312 2.7	0959 0.1	1532 2.5	2203 0.1
19 TU	0344 2.7	1026 0.1	1600 2.4	2229 0.1
20 W	0414 2.6	1049 0.2	1630 2.4	2302 0.2
21 TH	0453 2.4	1129 0.3	1719 2.3	
22 F	0001 0.4	0556 2.3	1240 0.4	1835 2.3
23 SA	0127 0.4	0721 2.3	1411 0.4	2005 2.4
24 SU	0300 0.3	0850 2.4	1537 0.4	2126 2.5
25 M	0422 0.2	1007 2.5	1651 0.3	2316 2.7
26 TU	0529 0.0	1108 2.6	1751 0.1	2324 2.8
27 W ○	0605 -0.2	1200 2.6	1843 0.0	
28 TH	0013 2.8	0715 -0.3	1247 2.6	1930 -0.1

MARCH

Day	Time m	Time m	Time m	Time m
1 F	0100 2.9	0802 -0.3	1332 2.6	2015 -0.2
2 SA	0147 2.9	0846 -0.3	1417 2.6	2058 -0.2
3 SU	0230 2.9	0927 -0.2	1500 2.6	2138 -0.2
4 M	0312 2.9	1006 -0.1	1540 2.6	2218 -0.1
5 TU	0355 2.8	1044 0.0	1620 2.6	2258 0.0
6 W	0439 2.6	1122 0.2	1702 2.5	2345 0.1
7 TH	0530 2.4	1212 0.3	1758 2.3	
8 F	0050 0.1	0641 2.2	1326 0.4	1915 2.3
9 SA	0219 0.2	0810 2.2	1457 0.4	2044 2.3
10 SU	0352 0.2	0938 2.2	1620 0.3	2203 2.5
11 M	0503 0.1	1045 2.4	1719 0.2	2258 2.6
12 TU	0550 0.0	1128 2.5	1801 0.1	2337 2.7
13 W	0627 0.0	1202 2.5	1837 0.0	
14 TH ●	0012 2.7	0702 -0.1	1234 2.6	1911 0.0
15 F	0045 2.7	0733 -0.1	1306 2.6	1942 0.0
16 SA	0115 2.7	0802 -0.1	1335 2.6	2011 -0.1
17 SU	0144 2.8	0830 -0.1	1403 2.6	2039 -0.1
18 M	0213 2.7	0900 -0.1	1431 2.5	2108 -0.1
19 TU	0243 2.6	0929 -0.1	1500 2.5	2137 -0.1
20 W	0313 2.6	0954 0.0	1525 2.5	2200 0.0
21 TH	0341 2.5	1015 0.1	1553 2.4	2229 0.1
22 F	0419 2.4	1051 0.2	1639 2.3	2325 0.2
23 SA	0521 2.3	1201 0.4	1755 2.3	
24 SU	0054 0.3	0650 2.2	1338 0.4	1931 2.4
25 M	0236 0.2	0827 2.3	1514 0.4	2101 2.5
26 TU	0405 0.1	0949 2.4	1631 0.2	2211 2.6
27 W	0514 -0.1	1051 2.5	1733 0.0	2306 2.8
28 TH ○	0610 -0.3	1142 2.6	1826 -0.1	2354 2.8
29 F	0658 -0.4	1228 2.6	1913 -0.2	
30 SA	0040 2.9	0741 -0.4	1309 2.6	1956 -0.3
31 SU	0124 2.9	0823 -0.3	1350 2.7	2037 -0.3

APRIL

Day	Time m	Time m	Time m	Time m
1 M	0207 2.8	0902 -0.2	1431 2.6	2116 -0.3
2 TU	0249 2.8	0939 -0.1	1509 2.6	2154 -0.2
3 W	0331 2.7	1014 0.0	1547 2.5	2233 -0.1
4 TH	0414 2.5	1051 0.1	1630 2.5	2320 0.0
5 F	0505 2.3	1140 0.3	1726 2.4	
6 SA	0022 0.1	0612 2.1	1250 0.4	1841 2.3
7 SU	0147 0.2	0738 2.1	1421 0.4	2009 2.3
8 M	0321 0.1	0906 2.1	1548 0.3	2130 2.4
9 TU	0435 0.0	1015 2.3	1651 0.2	2228 2.5
10 W	0523 -0.1	1059 2.4	1733 0.1	2307 2.6
11 TH	0558 -0.1	1133 2.4	1809 0.0	2342 2.6
12 F ●	0632 -0.2	1206 2.5	1845 -0.1	
13 SA	0017 2.7	0705 -0.2	1238 2.6	1917 -0.1
14 SU	0048 2.7	0734 -0.1	1306 2.6	1946 -0.1
15 M	0116 2.7	0802 -0.1	1333 2.6	2015 -0.2
16 TU	0145 2.6	0830 -0.1	1400 2.6	2044 -0.2
17 W	0216 2.6	0859 -0.1	1430 2.5	2114 -0.1
18 TH	0248 2.5	0928 0.0	1502 2.5	2145 -0.1
19 F	0324 2.5	0958 0.1	1537 2.5	2222 0.0
20 SA	0409 2.3	1039 0.2	1626 2.4	2320 0.1
21 SU	0512 2.2	1147 0.3	1739 2.4	
22 M	0044 0.2	0636 2.2	1319 0.4	1908 2.5
23 TU	0220 0.1	0807 2.3	1452 0.4	2035 2.6
24 W	0345 -0.1	0925 2.4	1608 0.2	2145 2.7
25 TH	0450 -0.2	1026 2.6	1709 0.0	2242 2.7
26 F	0545 -0.3	1117 2.6	1804 -0.2	2333 2.8
27 SA ○	0634 -0.4	1203 2.6	1852 -0.3	
28 SU	0019 2.8	0717 -0.3	1244 2.7	1934 -0.3
29 M	0101 2.8	0756 -0.2	1322 2.7	2013 -0.3
30 TU	0143 2.8	0833 -0.1	1401 2.7	2053 -0.2

Chart Datum: 1·68 metres below Normal Null (German reference level)

TIME ZONE -0100
(German Standard Time)
Subtract 1 hour for UT
For German Summer Time add
ONE hour in **non-shaded areas**

GERMANY – HELGOLAND

LAT 54°11′N LONG 7°53′E

TIMES AND HEIGHTS OF HIGH AND LOW WATERS

YEAR **2002**

MAY

Time m	Time m
1 W 0226 2.7 / 0911 -0.1 / 1442 2.7 / 2133 -0.2	**16** TH 0156 2.6 / 0837 -0.1 / 1411 2.6 / 2100 -0.1
2 TH 0310 2.5 / 0947 0.0 / 1523 2.6 / 2215 -0.1	**17** F 0235 2.5 / 0913 0.0 / 1450 2.6 / 2142 -0.1
3 F 0355 2.4 / 1027 0.2 / 1607 2.5 / 2302 0.0	**18** SA 0319 2.4 / 0954 0.1 / 1534 2.6 / 2230 0.0
4 SA 0445 2.3 / 1114 0.3 / 1700 2.5 / 2358 0.1	**19** SU 0411 2.4 / 1044 0.2 / 1628 2.6 / 2329 0.0
5 SU 0545 2.1 / 1216 0.4 / 1806 2.4	**20** M 0514 2.3 / 1147 0.3 / 1734 2.6
6 M 0110 0.2 / 0659 2.1 / 1335 0.4 / 1924 2.4	**21** TU 0041 0.0 / 0628 2.3 / 1306 0.3 / 1850 2.6
7 TU 0232 0.2 / 0818 2.1 / 1457 0.3 / 2041 2.4	**22** W 0201 0.0 / 0745 2.4 / 1429 0.2 / 2007 2.6
8 W 0346 0.1 / 0926 2.2 / 1605 0.2 / 2143 2.5	**23** TH 0317 -0.1 / 0856 2.4 / 1541 0.1 / 2115 2.7
9 TH 0438 -0.1 / 1016 2.3 / 1653 0.1 / 2228 2.5	**24** F 0420 -0.2 / 0956 2.5 / 1642 0.1 / 2214 2.7
10 F 0517 -0.1 / 1055 2.4 / 1733 0.0 / 2306 2.6	**25** SA 0515 -0.3 / 1048 2.5 / 1738 -0.1 / 2309 2.7
11 SA 0554 -0.1 / 1131 2.5 / 1812 0.0 / 2343 2.6	**26** SU 0607 -0.2 / 1137 2.6 / 1829 -0.2 / ○ 2358 2.8
12 SU 0630 -0.1 / 1205 2.6 / 1847 -0.1 ●	**27** M 0651 -0.2 / 1221 2.7 / 1912 -0.2
13 M 0017 2.6 / 0702 -0.1 / 1234 2.6 / 1918 -0.1	**28** TU 0041 2.8 / 0729 -0.1 / 1259 2.8 / 1951 -0.2
14 TU 0048 2.6 / 0732 -0.1 / 1303 2.7 / 1950 -0.1	**29** W 0122 2.7 / 0807 0.0 / 1339 2.8 / 2033 -0.1
15 W 0120 2.6 / 0804 -0.1 / 1335 2.6 / 2024 -0.1	**30** TH 0207 2.6 / 0847 0.0 / 1422 2.8 / 2117 -0.1
	31 F 0253 2.5 / 0927 0.1 / 1505 2.7 / 2159 0.0

JUNE

Time m	Time m
1 SA 0338 2.4 / 1007 0.2 / 1548 2.7 / 2243 0.1	**16** SU 0318 2.5 / 0953 0.1 / 1532 2.7 / 2234 -0.1
2 SU 0424 2.3 / 1050 0.3 / 1634 2.6 / 2331 0.2	**17** M 0412 2.4 / 1047 0.1 / 1627 2.7 / 2331 0.0
3 M 0514 2.3 / 1141 0.4 / 1728 2.6	**18** TU 0512 2.4 / 1145 0.2 / 1726 2.7
4 TU 0026 0.2 / 0612 2.2 / 1241 0.4 / 1832 2.5	**19** W 0030 0.0 / 0614 2.4 / 1249 0.2 / 1831 2.7
5 W 0131 0.2 / 0717 2.2 / 1353 0.4 / 1941 2.5	**20** TH 0135 0.0 / 0719 2.4 / 1400 0.2 / 1938 2.7
6 TH 0239 0.2 / 0823 2.2 / 1503 0.3 / 2046 2.5	**21** F 0243 0.0 / 0823 2.5 / 1511 0.1 / 2046 2.7
7 F 0339 0.1 / 0922 2.3 / 1603 0.2 / 2139 2.5	**22** SA 0348 -0.1 / 0925 2.5 / 1615 0.0 / 2150 2.7
8 SA 0427 0.0 / 1010 2.4 / 1651 0.1 / 2224 2.6	**23** SU 0446 -0.1 / 1022 2.6 / 1714 -0.1 / 2249 2.7
9 SU 0511 0.0 / 1052 2.5 / 1734 0.1 / 2305 2.6	**24** M 0540 0.0 / 1115 2.7 / 1808 -0.1 / ○ 2342 2.7
10 M 0552 0.0 / 1129 2.6 / 1814 0.0 / 2344 2.6	**25** TU 0628 0.0 / 1203 2.8 / 1854 -0.1
11 TU 0630 0.0 / 1203 2.7 / 1851 -0.1 ●	**26** W 0027 2.7 / 0709 0.1 / 1244 2.8 / 1936 0.0
12 W 0023 2.6 / 0707 0.0 / 1239 2.7 / 1931 -0.1	**27** TH 0109 2.7 / 0749 0.1 / 1325 2.9 / 2018 0.0
13 TH 0103 2.6 / 0746 0.0 / 1319 2.7 / 2013 -0.1	**28** F 0152 2.7 / 0830 0.2 / 1406 2.9 / 2101 0.1
14 F 0146 2.6 / 0826 0.0 / 1400 2.7 / 2057 -0.1	**29** SA 0236 2.6 / 0908 0.2 / 1447 2.8 / 2141 0.1
15 SA 0230 2.5 / 0907 0.0 / 1444 2.7 / 2143 -0.1	**30** SU 0317 2.5 / 0945 0.2 / 1525 2.8 / 2219 0.2

JULY

Time m	Time m
1 M 0357 2.4 / 1023 0.3 / 1606 2.7 / 2259 0.2	**16** TU 0402 2.5 / 1038 0.1 / 1615 2.8 / 2317 0.0
2 TU 0439 2.4 / 1104 0.3 / 1650 2.7 / 2341 0.3	**17** W 0456 2.5 / 1130 0.2 / 1710 2.8
3 W 0523 2.3 / 1149 0.4 / 1739 2.6	**18** TH 0008 0.1 / 0550 2.5 / 1224 0.2 / 1806 2.7
4 TH 0027 0.3 / 0613 2.3 / 1245 0.4 / 1835 2.5	**19** F 0102 0.1 / 0645 2.5 / 1327 0.2 / 1909 2.7
5 F 0125 0.3 / 0713 2.3 / 1353 0.4 / 1939 2.5	**20** SA 0207 0.2 / 0749 2.5 / 1441 0.2 / 2021 2.6
6 SA 0230 0.3 / 0817 2.4 / 1502 0.3 / 2043 2.5	**21** SU 0319 0.2 / 0858 2.5 / 1555 0.1 / 2133 2.6
7 SU 0331 0.2 / 0918 2.4 / 1603 0.2 / 2139 2.5	**22** M 0425 0.2 / 1004 2.6 / 1659 0.0 / 2238 2.6
8 M 0426 0.1 / 1011 2.5 / 1656 0.2 / 2230 2.6	**23** TU 0522 0.2 / 1101 2.7 / 1754 0.1 / 2333 2.7
9 TU 0518 0.1 / 1057 2.6 / 1744 0.1 / 2319 2.7	**24** W 0611 0.2 / 1150 2.8 / 1842 0.1 / ○
10 W 0605 0.1 / 1139 2.7 / 1831 0.0 ●	**25** TH 0018 2.7 / 0655 0.2 / 1233 2.9 / 1924 0.1
11 TH 0006 2.7 / 0650 0.1 / 1223 2.8 / 1919 0.0	**26** F 0059 2.7 / 0735 0.2 / 1311 2.9 / 2004 0.1
12 F 0052 2.7 / 0734 0.1 / 1308 2.8 / 2007 -0.1	**27** SA 0138 2.7 / 0814 0.2 / 1348 2.9 / 2042 0.2
13 SA 0139 2.7 / 0819 0.0 / 1353 2.8 / 2053 -0.1	**28** SU 0215 2.7 / 0848 0.2 / 1424 2.9 / 2116 0.2
14 SU 0224 2.6 / 0902 0.0 / 1436 2.8 / 2137 -0.2	**29** M 0249 2.6 / 0919 0.2 / 1459 2.8 / 2149 0.2
15 M 0311 2.5 / 0947 0.0 / 1522 2.8 / 2226 -0.1	**30** TU 0324 2.5 / 0953 0.2 / 1534 2.8 / 2223 0.3
	31 W 0400 2.5 / 1028 0.3 / 1612 2.7 / 2256 0.3

AUGUST

Time m	Time m
1 TH 0436 2.4 / 1102 0.3 / 1649 2.6 / 2329 0.4	**16** F 0515 2.5 / 1152 0.2 / 1737 2.7
2 F 0513 2.4 / 1143 0.4 / 1733 2.5	**17** SA 0025 0.3 / 0608 2.5 / 1253 0.3 / 1842 2.5
3 SA 0013 0.4 / 0602 2.4 / 1241 0.5 / 1832 2.4	**18** SU 0132 0.4 / 0716 2.4 / 1413 0.3 / 2002 2.4
4 SU 0118 0.4 / 0709 2.3 / 1357 0.5 / 1945 2.4	**19** M 0254 0.4 / 0837 2.5 / 1541 0.2 / 2125 2.4
5 M 0234 0.4 / 0825 2.4 / 1514 0.4 / 2058 2.5	**20** TU 0412 0.4 / 0954 2.6 / 1653 0.1 / 2235 2.5
6 TU 0346 0.3 / 0934 2.5 / 1623 0.3 / 2204 2.6	**21** W 0513 0.3 / 1053 2.7 / 1747 0.1 / 2327 2.6
7 W 0450 0.3 / 1032 2.7 / 1723 0.2 / 2301 2.7	**22** TH 0600 0.3 / 1138 2.8 / 1830 0.1 / ○
8 TH 0546 0.2 / 1122 2.8 / 1818 0.1 / ● 2353 2.7	**23** F 0007 2.7 / 0641 0.3 / 1218 2.9 / 1909 0.1
9 F 0636 0.2 / 1209 2.9 / 1908 0.0	**24** SA 0044 2.7 / 0719 0.2 / 1254 2.9 / 1945 0.2
10 SA 0041 2.7 / 0723 0.1 / 1255 2.9 / 1956 -0.1	**25** SU 0118 2.7 / 0754 0.2 / 1327 2.9 / 2017 0.2
11 SU 0127 2.7 / 0808 0.0 / 1340 2.9 / 2041 -0.2	**26** M 0150 2.7 / 0824 0.2 / 1359 2.9 / 2047 0.2
12 M 0212 2.7 / 0851 -0.1 / 1422 2.9 / 2123 -0.2	**27** TU 0220 2.6 / 0852 0.2 / 1429 2.8 / 2116 0.2
13 TU 0256 2.6 / 0933 0.0 / 1505 2.9 / 2206 -0.1	**28** W 0249 2.6 / 0922 0.2 / 1501 2.8 / 2146 0.2
14 W 0341 2.6 / 1018 0.1 / 1554 2.9 / 2251 0.1	**29** TH 0321 2.6 / 0953 0.2 / 1533 2.7 / 2214 0.3
15 TH 0428 2.6 / 1105 0.2 / 1644 2.8 / 2335 0.2	**30** F 0350 2.5 / 1021 0.3 / 1604 2.6 / 2238 0.4
	31 SA 0420 2.5 / 1051 0.4 / 1640 2.5 / 2312 0.5

Chart Datum: 1·68 metres below Normal Null (German reference level)

TIME ZONE -0100
(German Standard Time)
Subtract 1 hour for UT
For German Summer Time add
ONE hour in **non-shaded areas**

LAT 54°11′N   LONG 7°53′E

TIMES AND HEIGHTS OF HIGH AND LOW WATERS

Section 1

SEPTEMBER

Day	Time	m	Time	m	Time	m	Time	m
1 SU	0502	2.4	1141	0.5	1736	2.4		
2 M	0015	0.6	0611	2.3	1301	0.6	1857	2.4
3 TU	0143	0.6	0739	2.4	1435	0.5	2026	2.4
4 W	0313	0.5	0903	2.5	1600	0.4	2145	2.5
5 TH	0428	0.4	1011	2.7	1708	0.2	2247	2.6
6 F	0529	0.3	1105	2.8	1804	0.0	2339	2.7
7 SA ●	0620	0.2	1152	2.9	1853	-0.1		
8 SU	0025	2.7	0706	0.1	1238	3.0	1938	-0.1
9 M	0109	2.7	0750	0.0	1322	3.0	2021	-0.1
10 TU	0151	2.7	0832	0.0	1404	3.0	2101	-0.1
11 W	0233	2.7	0913	0.0	1445	2.9	2140	0.0
12 TH	0313	2.7	0953	0.0	1529	2.9	2219	0.2
13 F	0354	2.6	1035	0.1	1615	2.7	2300	0.3
14 SA	0439	2.6	1122	0.2	1709	2.6	2349	0.5
15 SU	0534	2.5	1223	0.3	1817	2.4		
16 M	0058	0.6	0648	2.4	1349	0.3	1944	2.3
17 TU	0229	0.6	0817	2.4	1525	0.3	2115	2.3
18 W	0357	0.5	0940	2.5	1644	0.2	2228	2.4
19 TH	0502	0.4	1041	2.6	1735	0.2	2315	2.5
20 F	0545	0.3	1121	2.8	1811	0.1	2348	2.6
21 SA ○	0620	0.2	1156	2.8	1845	0.1		
22 SU	0021	2.6	0655	0.2	1231	2.8	1918	0.1
23 TU	0053	2.7	0729	0.2	1303	2.8	1948	0.1
24 TU	0123	2.7	0758	0.1	1332	2.8	2015	0.2
25 W	0149	2.7	0825	0.1	1359	2.8	2041	0.2
26 TH	0215	2.6	0852	0.1	1428	2.7	2108	0.2
27 F	0242	2.6	0919	0.2	1458	2.6	2134	0.3
28 SA	0310	2.6	0946	0.2	1529	2.6	2158	0.4
29 SU	0340	2.5	1015	0.4	1606	2.5	2232	0.5
30 M	0423	2.4	1104	0.5	1702	2.3	2333	0.7

OCTOBER

Day	Time	m	Time	m	Time	m	Time	m
1 TU	0533	2.4	1226	0.6	1825	2.3		
2 W	0105	0.7	0705	2.4	1406	0.5	2000	2.4
3 TH	0244	0.6	0836	2.6	1538	0.4	2124	2.5
4 F	0405	0.5	0948	2.6	1648	0.2	2228	2.6
5 SA	0507	0.3	1043	2.8	1744	0.0	2319	2.7
6 SU ●	0559	0.2	1131	2.9	1831	-0.1		
7 M	0004	2.7	0645	0.1	1217	3.0	1915	-0.1
8 TU	0045	2.7	0727	0.0	1300	3.0	1955	-0.1
9 W	0124	2.8	0809	0.0	1342	3.0	2035	0.0
10 TH	0204	2.8	0849	0.0	1423	2.9	2112	0.1
11 F	0244	2.7	0929	0.0	1506	2.8	2149	0.2
12 SA	0325	2.7	1010	0.1	1552	2.6	2229	0.4
13 SU	0410	2.6	1059	0.2	1645	2.4	2319	0.5
14 M	0506	2.5	1200	0.3	1753	2.2		
15 TU	0027	0.6	0619	2.4	1321	0.4	1918	2.2
16 W	0155	0.7	0746	2.4	1455	0.4	2048	2.2
17 TH	0326	0.6	0911	2.5	1616	0.3	2202	2.3
18 F	0435	0.4	1015	2.6	1709	0.2	2249	2.5
19 SA	0519	0.3	1055	2.7	1742	0.1	2321	2.6
20 SU	0552	0.3	1128	2.8	1814	0.1	2352	2.6
21 M ○	0627	0.2	1203	2.8	1847	0.1		
22 TU	0024	2.7	0700	0.2	1235	2.8	1916	0.1
23 W	0053	2.7	0730	0.1	1303	2.8	1942	0.2
24 TH	0119	2.7	0757	0.1	1330	2.7	2009	0.2
25 F	0144	2.7	0824	0.1	1400	2.6	2036	0.2
26 SA	0212	2.7	0852	0.2	1432	2.6	2104	0.3
27 SU	0242	2.6	0924	0.2	1507	2.5	2135	0.4
28 M	0318	2.6	1001	0.3	1550	2.4	2214	0.5
29 TU	0405	2.5	1053	0.3	1648	2.3	2314	0.6
30 W	0512	2.5	1209	0.5	1805	2.3		
31 TH	0040	0.7	0637	2.5	1342	0.4	1935	2.4

NOVEMBER

Day	Time	m	Time	m	Time	m	Time	m
1 F	0214	0.6	0805	2.6	1510	0.3	2057	2.5
2 SA	0335	0.5	0918	2.7	1620	0.1	2201	2.6
3 SU	0438	0.3	1016	2.8	1715	0.0	2252	2.6
4 M ●	0533	0.1	1107	2.9	1804	-0.1	2338	2.7
5 TU	0621	0.0	1154	2.9	1848	-0.1		
6 W	0019	2.8	0704	0.0	1237	2.9	1928	0.0
7 TH	0057	2.8	0744	0.0	1320	2.9	2007	0.1
8 F	0138	2.8	0824	0.0	1404	2.8	2046	0.2
9 SA	0221	2.8	0910	0.0	1449	2.7	2125	0.2
10 SU	0304	2.7	0954	0.1	1535	2.5	2206	0.4
11 M	0350	2.7	1042	0.2	1626	2.4	2254	0.5
12 TU	0442	2.6	1138	0.3	1726	2.2	2354	0.6
13 W	0546	2.5	1246	0.4	1839	2.2		
14 TH	0109	0.7	0702	2.5	1405	0.5	1959	2.4
15 F	0231	0.6	0822	2.5	1523	0.4	2111	2.3
16 SA	0345	0.5	0930	2.6	1622	0.3	2206	2.4
17 SU	0438	0.4	1018	2.6	1702	0.2	2245	2.5
18 M	0518	0.3	1055	2.7	1736	0.2	2319	2.6
19 TU	0555	0.3	1130	2.7	1811	0.2	2352	2.7
20 W ○	0629	0.2	1204	2.7	1843	0.2		
21 TH	0022	0.2	0700	0.2	1234	2.7	1912	0.2
22 F	0050	0.2	0731	0.1	1306	2.7	1943	0.2
23 SA	0121	0.1	0804	0.1	1341	2.6	2015	0.2
24 SU	0154	2.7	0839	0.1	1418	2.6	2048	0.2
25 M	0229	2.7	0917	0.2	1458	2.5	2126	0.3
26 TU	0310	2.7	1001	0.2	1545	2.4	2212	0.4
27 W	0359	2.6	1059	0.2	1643	2.3	2308	0.5
28 TH	0459	2.4	1159	0.3	1750	2.3		
29 F	0020	0.6	0612	2.6	1315	0.3	1906	2.4
30 SA	0142	0.5	0730	2.7	1433	0.2	2021	2.5

DECEMBER

Day	Time	m	Time	m	Time	m	Time	m
1 SU	0300	0.4	0842	2.7	1543	0.1	2125	2.5
2 M	0406	0.3	0945	2.8	1642	0.0	2221	2.6
3 TU	0505	0.1	1041	2.8	1735	0.0	2311	2.7
4 W ●	0558	0.0	1132	2.8	1822	0.0	2356	2.7
5 TH	0643	0.0	1218	2.9	1903	0.1		
6 F	0037	2.8	0725	0.0	1303	2.8	1944	0.2
7 SA	0119	2.9	0810	0.1	1350	2.7	2027	0.3
8 SU	0204	2.9	0857	0.1	1437	2.6	2109	0.3
9 M	0249	2.8	0942	0.1	1521	2.5	2149	0.3
10 TU	0332	2.8	1025	0.2	1606	2.4	2231	0.4
11 W	0417	2.7	1111	0.3	1654	2.3	2318	0.5
12 TH	0508	2.6	1203	0.4	1749	2.2		
13 F	0014	0.6	0609	2.6	1302	0.5	1853	2.2
14 SA	0122	0.6	0717	2.5	1409	0.5	2001	2.3
15 SU	0236	0.6	0827	2.5	1515	0.4	2105	2.4
16 M	0342	0.5	0927	2.5	1609	0.3	2158	2.5
17 TU	0435	0.4	1015	2.6	1654	0.3	2241	2.6
18 W	0519	0.3	1055	2.7	1735	0.2	2318	2.7
19 TH ○	0558	0.2	1134	2.7	1813	0.2	2352	2.7
20 F	0634	0.2	1211	2.7	1849	0.2		
21 SA	0027	2.7	0713	0.1	1249	2.6	1927	0.2
22 SU	0106	2.8	0754	0.1	1330	2.6	2006	0.2
23 M	0145	2.8	0836	0.1	1412	2.6	2044	0.1
24 TU	0223	2.8	0916	0.0	1454	2.5	2124	0.2
25 W	0304	2.8	1001	0.1	1541	2.4	2211	0.2
26 TH	0352	2.7	1051	0.1	1635	2.4	2303	0.3
27 F	0446	2.7	1144	0.1	1732	2.4		
28 SA	0000	0.3	0545	2.7	1243	0.2	1833	2.4
29 SU	0106	0.4	0652	2.7	1351	0.2	1939	2.4
30 M	0221	0.3	0804	2.6	1503	0.2	2047	2.5
31 TU	0334	0.2	0915	2.6	1610	0.1	2151	2.5

Chart Datum: 1·68 metres below Normal Null (German reference level)

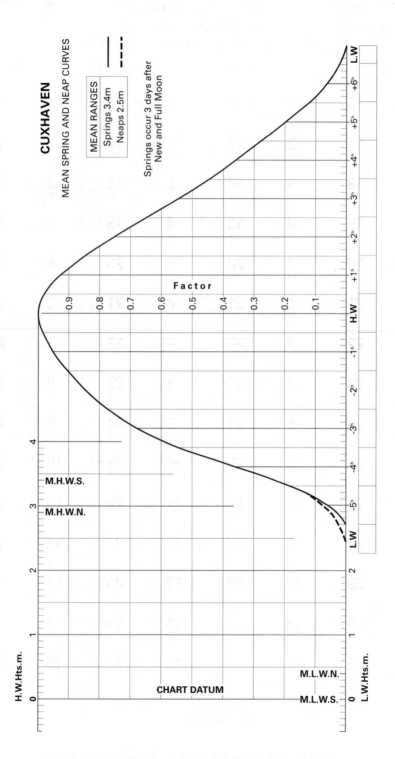

CUXHAVEN

MEAN SPRING AND NEAP CURVES

MEAN RANGES
Springs 3.4m
Neaps 2.5m

Springs occur 3 days after
New and Full Moon

TIME ZONE -0100
(German Standard Time)
Subtract 1 hour for UT
For German Summer Time add
ONE hour in **non-shaded areas**

GERMANY – CUXHAVEN

LAT 53°52'N   LONG 8°43'E

TIMES AND HEIGHTS OF HIGH AND LOW WATERS

YEAR **2002**

JANUARY

Day	Time m	Time m	Time m	Time m
1 TU	0156 3.4	0901 0.1	1425 3.3	2119 0.2
16 W	0233 3.5	0937 0.3	1501 3.3	2150 0.3
2 W	0241 3.5	0951 0.0	1514 3.2	2205 0.1
17 TH	0308 3.5	1013 0.2	1535 3.2	2221 0.3
3 TH	0325 3.5	1037 0.0	1602 3.1	2248 0.2
18 F	0342 3.5	1046 0.2	1608 3.1	2249 0.3
4 F	0409 3.5	1120 0.0	1650 3.1	2333 0.3
19 SA	0416 3.4	1119 0.2	1642 3.0	2321 0.3
5 SA	0457 3.5	1207 0.1	1742 3.1	
20 SU	0452 3.3	1153 0.3	1717 3.0	2354 0.3
6 SU	0024 0.4	0551 3.5	1259 0.2	1836 3.0
21 M	0528 3.2	1225 0.3	1754 2.9	
7 M	0117 0.4	0648 3.4	1355 0.3	1933 3.0
22 TU	0028 0.4	0607 3.1	1258 0.4	1837 2.8
8 TU	0216 0.4	0750 3.3	1457 0.3	2036 2.9
23 W	0113 0.5	0658 3.0	1348 0.5	1937 2.8
9 W	0324 0.4	0901 3.2	1608 0.4	2145 3.0
24 TH	0219 0.5	0806 2.9	1458 0.6	2049 2.9
10 TH	0438 0.3	1015 3.1	1719 0.3	2253 3.0
25 F	0340 0.5	0922 3.0	1616 0.4	2204 3.0
11 F	0548 0.2	1124 3.1	1822 0.3	2352 3.2
26 SA	0459 0.4	1035 3.1	1730 0.3	2309 3.2
12 SA	0649 0.2	1222 3.2	1915 0.3	
27 SU	0608 0.3	1137 3.2	1835 0.3	
13 SU	0041 3.3	0741 0.2	1309 3.3	● 2000 0.3
28 M	0004 3.3	0707 0.2	1233 3.3	○ 1931 0.2
14 M	0122 3.4	0823 0.3	1348 3.4	2039 0.3
29 TU	0054 3.4	0800 0.0	1326 3.3	2021 0.1
15 TU	0158 3.5	0900 0.3	1425 3.3	2115 0.3
30 W	0141 3.5	0852 -0.1	1416 3.3	2111 0.0
31 TH	0228 3.5	0943 -0.1	1505 3.3	2158 0.0

FEBRUARY

Day	Time m	Time m	Time m	Time m
1 F	0313 3.5	1029 -0.2	1551 3.2	2240 0.0
16 SA	0319 3.5	1022 0.1	1542 3.1	2228 0.1
2 SA	0357 3.5	1111 -0.2	1635 3.1	2322 0.0
17 SU	0350 3.4	1053 0.1	1613 3.1	2258 0.1
3 SU	0443 3.5	1153 0.0	1721 3.1	
18 M	0424 3.3	1124 0.1	1645 3.0	2328 0.1
4 M	0006 0.2	0530 3.5	1237 0.1	1806 3.1
19 TU	0455 3.3	1149 0.1	1713 3.0	2352 0.1
5 TU	0049 0.2	0619 3.4	1320 0.2	1853 3.0
20 W	0524 3.1	1210 0.2	1743 2.9	
6 W	0136 0.2	0713 3.2	1411 0.3	1950 2.9
21 TH	0020 0.3	0602 3.0	1245 0.3	1832 2.8
7 TH	0238 0.3	0824 3.0	1520 0.3	2104 2.9
22 F	0114 0.4	0705 2.9	1352 0.4	1947 2.8
8 F	0359 0.2	0947 2.9	1644 0.3	2224 2.9
23 SA	0240 0.4	0832 2.9	1524 0.5	2115 2.9
9 SA	0524 0.2	1108 3.0	1801 0.3	2334 3.1
24 SU	0417 0.4	1001 3.0	1656 0.4	2236 3.1
10 SU	0634 0.1	1212 3.1	1900 0.4	
25 M	0543 0.2	1117 3.2	1814 0.3	2342 3.3
11 M	0027 3.3	0727 0.2	1258 3.2	1946 0.3
26 TU	0652 0.1	1220 3.3	1917 0.1	
12 TU	0108 3.4	0809 0.2	1335 3.2	● 2024 0.2
27 W	0036 3.4	0749 -0.1	1314 3.3	○ 2010 0.0
13 W	0144 3.4	0845 0.2	1409 3.3	2059 0.2
28 TH	0125 3.5	0839 -0.3	1403 3.3	2057 -0.1
14 TH	0217 3.5	0919 0.1	1442 3.3	2131 0.1
15 F	0248 3.5	0952 0.1	1512 3.2	2200 0.1

MARCH

Day	Time m	Time m	Time m	Time m
1 F	0211 3.6	0926 -0.3	1448 3.3	2142 -0.2
16 SA	0226 3.4	0926 0.0	1447 3.2	2138 -0.1
2 SA	0256 3.6	1011 -0.3	1532 3.2	2224 -0.2
17 SU	0254 3.4	0955 -0.1	1514 3.2	2205 -0.1
3 SU	0340 3.6	1053 -0.3	1613 3.2	2303 -0.2
18 M	0323 3.3	1024 -0.1	1543 3.1	2234 -0.1
4 M	0423 3.5	1132 -0.1	1653 3.2	2342 0.0
19 TU	0355 3.3	1053 -0.1	1613 3.1	2302 -0.1
5 TU	0507 3.4	1208 0.0	1732 3.1	
20 W	0425 3.2	1117 0.0	1639 3.1	2324 0.0
6 W	0019 0.1	0550 3.3	1243 0.2	1814 3.0
21 TH	0453 3.1	1136 0.1	1707 3.0	2349 0.1
7 TH	0059 0.1	0641 3.0	1326 0.3	1909 2.9
22 F	0529 2.9	1207 0.2	1752 2.9	
8 F	0158 0.1	0752 2.8	1435 0.4	2026 2.8
23 SA	0038 0.2	0631 2.8	1313 0.4	1907 2.8
9 SA	0324 0.2	0921 2.7	1608 0.4	2156 2.9
24 SU	0204 0.3	0801 2.8	1450 0.5	2041 3.0
10 SU	0500 0.2	1049 2.8	1738 0.3	2314 3.1
25 M	0349 0.3	0938 2.9	1630 0.4	2210 3.2
11 M	0618 0.1	1156 3.0	1843 0.2	
26 TU	0522 0.1	1100 3.1	1753 0.2	2320 3.4
12 TU	0009 3.2	0710 0.0	1241 3.1	1926 0.2
27 W	0633 -0.1	1203 3.2	1858 0.0	
13 W	0048 3.3	0748 0.0	1315 3.1	2002 0.1
28 TH	0016 3.4	0729 -0.3	1256 3.3	○ 1951 -0.2
14 TH	0122 3.4	0823 0.0	1348 3.2	● 2037 0.0
29 F	0105 3.5	0819 -0.4	1343 3.3	2037 -0.3
15 F	0156 3.4	0855 -0.1	1419 3.2	2109 0.0
30 SA	0152 3.5	0904 -0.4	1427 3.3	2120 -0.3
31 SU	0236 3.6	0946 -0.4	1507 3.3	2200 -0.3

APRIL

Day	Time m	Time m	Time m	Time m
1 M	0319 3.5	1026 -0.3	1545 3.3	2239 -0.3
16 TU	0257 3.3	0953 -0.1	1514 3.2	2208 -0.2
2 TU	0402 3.4	1103 -0.2	1623 3.2	2316 -0.2
17 W	0328 3.2	1022 -0.1	1544 3.2	2237 -0.1
3 W	0444 3.3	1136 0.0	1701 3.1	2352 -0.1
18 TH	0402 3.1	1050 0.0	1616 3.1	2306 -0.1
4 TH	0527 3.1	1209 0.1	1742 3.1	
19 F	0437 3.1	1118 0.1	1651 3.1	2341 0.0
5 F	0032 0.0	0617 2.9	1251 0.3	1837 2.9
20 SA	0521 2.9	1157 0.2	1739 3.0	
6 SA	0129 0.1	0724 2.7	1357 0.4	1952 2.8
21 SU	0033 0.1	0624 2.8	1302 0.3	1852 3.0
7 SU	0251 0.2	0850 2.6	1528 0.4	2121 2.9
22 M	0153 0.2	0749 2.8	1433 0.4	2020 3.1
8 M	0427 0.2	1018 2.7	1702 0.3	2243 3.0
23 TU	0329 0.1	0920 2.9	1609 0.3	2146 3.2
9 TU	0548 0.0	1127 2.9	1811 0.2	2339 3.2
24 W	0458 0.0	1039 3.1	1728 0.1	2256 3.4
10 W	0640 -0.1	1212 3.0	1855 0.1	
25 TH	0606 -0.2	1141 3.2	1831 -0.1	2353 3.4
11 TH	0018 3.2	0716 -0.1	1246 3.1	1931 0.0
26 F	0703 -0.3	1233 3.2	1926 -0.2	
12 F	0053 3.3	0751 -0.2	1319 3.1	2007 -0.1
27 SA	0044 3.5	0754 -0.4	1320 3.3	○ 2014 -0.3
13 SA	0128 3.3	0825 -0.2	1352 3.2	2042 -0.1
28 SU	0132 3.5	0839 -0.4	1402 3.3	2055 -0.3
14 SU	0200 3.3	0857 -0.1	1420 3.3	2112 -0.1
29 M	0216 3.5	0918 -0.3	1440 3.4	2135 -0.3
15 M	0228 3.4	0925 -0.1	1446 3.3	2140 -0.2
30 TU	0259 3.5	0956 -0.2	1518 3.4	2214 -0.2

Chart Datum: 1·66 metres below Normal Null (German reference level)

TIME ZONE -0100
(German Standard Time)
Subtract 1 hour for UT
For German Summer Time add
ONE hour in **non-shaded areas**

GERMANY – CUXHAVEN
LAT 53°52'N   LONG 8°43'E
TIMES AND HEIGHTS OF HIGH AND LOW WATERS

YEAR 2002

MAY

Time m	Time m
1 0342 3.3 / 1033 -0.1 / W 1556 3.3 / 2254 -0.2	**16** 0310 3.2 / 1000 -0.1 / TH 1526 3.3 / 2222 -0.1
2 0425 3.2 / 1109 0.0 / TH 1636 3.2 / 2333 -0.1	**17** 0350 3.1 / 1035 0.0 / F 1604 3.2 / 2301 -0.1
3 0509 3.0 / 1145 0.2 / F 1720 3.2	**18** 0435 3.1 / 1115 0.1 / SA 1648 3.2 / 2346 0.0
4 0016 0.0 / 0558 2.8 / SA 1227 0.3 / 1812 3.1	**19** 0527 3.0 / 1203 0.2 / SU 1742 3.2
5 0108 0.1 / 0657 2.7 / SU 1325 0.4 / 1918 3.0	**20** 0042 0.0 / 0629 2.9 / M 1305 0.3 / 1848 3.2
6 0217 0.2 / 0811 2.6 / M 1443 0.4 / 2036 3.0	**21** 0151 0.1 / 0743 2.9 / TU 1423 0.3 / 2005 3.2
7 0340 0.2 / 0930 2.7 / TU 1609 0.1 / 2153 3.0	**22** 0312 0.0 / 0901 3.0 / W 1546 0.3 / 2121 3.3
8 0458 0.1 / 1039 2.8 / W 1721 0.2 / 2254 3.1	**23** 0429 -0.1 / 1013 3.1 / TH 1659 0.1 / 2229 3.3
9 0554 -0.1 / 1129 2.9 / TH 1812 0.1 / 2339 3.2	**24** 0535 -0.2 / 1113 3.2 / F 1801 -0.1 / 2328 3.4
10 0634 -0.1 / 1209 3.1 / F 1853 0.0	**25** 0633 -0.2 / 1206 3.2 / SA 1858 -0.2
11 0018 3.2 / 0713 -0.2 / SA 1245 3.2 / 1933 0.0	**26** 0023 3.4 / 0727 -0.3 / SU 1255 3.3 / O 1949 -0.2
12 0056 3.2 / 0750 -0.1 / SU 1320 3.2 / ● 2010 -0.1	**27** 0114 3.4 / 0814 -0.2 / M 1338 3.3 / 2032 -0.2
13 0131 3.3 / 0823 -0.1 / M 1350 3.3 / 2042 -0.1	**28** 0159 3.5 / 0853 -0.1 / TU 1417 3.4 / 2113 -0.2
14 0202 3.3 / 0854 -0.1 / TU 1419 3.3 / 2114 -0.1	**29** 0241 3.4 / 0931 0.0 / W 1455 3.5 / 2155 -0.1
15 0234 3.3 / 0926 -0.1 / W 1451 3.3 / 2147 -0.2	**30** 0325 3.3 / 1010 0.0 / TH 1536 3.4 / 2237 -0.1
	31 0409 3.2 / 1049 0.1 / F 1618 3.4 / 2319 0.0

JUNE

Time m	Time m
1 0452 3.0 / 1127 0.2 / SA 1701 3.3	**16** 0436 3.1 / 1116 0.1 / SU 1647 3.4 / 2351 0.0
2 0001 0.1 / 0537 2.9 / SU 1207 0.3 / 1747 3.2	**17** 0529 3.0 / 1208 0.2 / M 1742 3.4
3 0046 0.2 / 0626 2.8 / M 1254 0.4 / 1841 3.2	**18** 0046 0.0 / 0628 3.0 / TU 1305 0.2 / 1842 3.4
4 0139 0.2 / 0724 2.7 / TU 1353 0.4 / 1944 3.1	**19** 0145 0.0 / 0731 3.0 / W 1409 0.3 / 1946 3.4
5 0243 0.2 / 0830 2.8 / W 1504 0.4 / 2052 3.1	**20** 0250 0.1 / 0836 3.0 / TH 1518 0.2 / 2054 3.3
6 0352 0.2 / 0937 2.8 / TH 1617 0.3 / 2157 3.1	**21** 0359 0.0 / 0942 3.1 / F 1628 0.1 / 2202 3.3
7 0454 0.1 / 1036 3.0 / F 1719 0.2 / 2252 3.1	**22** 0505 0.0 / 1044 3.1 / SA 1732 0.0 / 2306 3.3
8 0544 0.0 / 1125 3.1 / SA 1810 0.1 / 2339 3.2	**23** 0606 0.0 / 1140 3.2 / SU 1832 -0.1
9 0630 0.0 / 1208 3.2 / SU 1855 0.1	**24** 0006 3.3 / 0702 0.0 / M 1232 3.3 / O 1928 -0.1
10 0022 3.3 / 0713 0.0 / M 1247 3.3 / 1936 0.0	**25** 0100 3.4 / 0753 0.0 / TU 1319 3.4 / 2015 0.0
11 0101 3.3 / 0752 0.0 / TU 1322 3.3 / ● 2014 0.0	**26** 0146 3.4 / 0835 0.1 / W 1400 3.5 / 2058 0.0
12 0139 3.3 / 0829 0.0 / W 1358 3.4 / 2053 -0.1	**27** 0229 3.4 / 0915 0.1 / TH 1440 3.5 / 2141 0.1
13 0219 3.3 / 0909 0.0 / TH 1436 3.4 / 2136 -0.1	**28** 0311 3.3 / 0955 0.2 / F 1521 3.6 / 2224 0.1
14 0303 3.2 / 0950 0.0 / F 1516 3.4 / 2218 -0.1	**29** 0352 3.2 / 1033 0.2 / SA 1600 3.5 / 2303 0.1
15 0347 3.2 / 1031 0.0 / SA 1559 3.4 / 2301 -0.1	**30** 0432 3.1 / 1108 0.2 / SU 1639 3.4 / 2341 0.2

JULY

Time m	Time m
1 0511 3.0 / 1143 0.3 / M 1720 3.4	**16** 0520 3.1 / 1201 0.1 / TU 1731 3.5
2 0020 0.2 / 0552 3.0 / TU 1222 0.4 / 1803 3.3	**17** 0036 0.0 / 0613 3.1 / W 1253 0.2 / 1825 3.5
3 0100 0.3 / 0636 2.9 / W 1306 0.4 / 1851 3.2	**18** 0128 0.1 / 0706 3.1 / TH 1345 0.2 / 1921 3.4
4 0144 0.3 / 0728 2.9 / TH 1400 0.4 / 1947 3.1	**19** 0222 0.2 / 0803 3.0 / F 1445 0.3 / 2025 3.3
5 0240 0.3 / 0828 2.9 / F 1506 0.4 / 2052 3.1	**20** 0325 0.2 / 0907 3.0 / SA 1556 0.2 / 2138 3.2
6 0344 0.3 / 0934 3.0 / SA 1617 0.3 / 2158 3.1	**21** 0436 0.2 / 1017 3.1 / SU 1709 0.1 / 2252 3.2
7 0447 0.2 / 1035 3.1 / SU 1721 0.2 / 2257 3.1	**22** 0545 0.2 / 1122 3.2 / M 1817 0.0 / 2358 3.2
8 0545 0.1 / 1129 3.2 / M 1817 0.2 / 2349 3.2	**23** 0647 0.2 / 1218 3.3 / TU 1915 0.1
9 0639 0.1 / 1216 3.3 / TU 1907 0.1	**24** 0052 3.3 / 0739 0.2 / W 1306 3.4 / O 2004 0.1
10 0037 3.3 / 0727 0.1 / W 1259 3.4 / ● 1954 0.1	**25** 0137 3.3 / 0824 0.2 / TH 1348 3.5 / 2047 0.1
11 0124 3.3 / 0814 0.1 / TH 1343 3.5 / 2042 0.0	**26** 0218 3.4 / 0904 0.2 / F 1427 3.6 / 2128 0.2
12 0211 3.3 / 0900 0.1 / F 1426 3.5 / 2131 -0.1	**27** 0257 3.4 / 0941 0.2 / SA 1505 3.6 / 2207 0.2
13 0258 3.3 / 0946 0.0 / SA 1509 3.5 / 2216 -0.1	**28** 0333 3.3 / 1015 0.2 / SU 1540 3.6 / 2241 0.2
14 0343 3.2 / 1028 0.0 / SU 1551 3.5 / 2258 -0.1	**29** 0406 3.2 / 1044 0.2 / M 1614 3.5 / 2314 0.2
15 0429 3.1 / 1111 0.0 / M 1638 3.5 / 2345 -0.1	**30** 0440 3.1 / 1116 0.2 / TU 1650 3.4 / 2348 0.3
	31 0515 3.1 / 1150 0.3 / W 1726 3.4

AUGUST

Time m	Time m
1 0021 0.3 / 0550 3.0 / TH 1224 0.4 / 1802 3.2	**16** 0059 0.3 / 0632 3.1 / F 1314 0.3 / 1852 3.3
2 0050 0.4 / 0628 3.0 / F 1301 0.5 / 1846 3.1	**17** 0146 0.4 / 0725 3.0 / SA 1410 0.3 / 1957 3.1
3 0130 0.5 / 0719 2.9 / SA 1356 0.5 / 1947 3.0	**18** 0248 0.4 / 0834 2.9 / SU 1526 0.3 / 2119 3.0
4 0232 0.5 / 0828 2.9 / SU 1512 0.5 / 2102 3.0	**19** 0409 0.5 / 0955 3.0 / M 1654 0.2 / 2244 3.0
5 0349 0.4 / 0943 3.0 / M 1633 0.4 / 2218 3.1	**20** 0533 0.4 / 1112 3.1 / TU 1811 0.2 / 2355 3.1
6 0505 0.4 / 1052 3.1 / TU 1745 0.3 / 2323 3.2	**21** 0639 0.4 / 1211 3.3 / W 1909 0.2
7 0613 0.3 / 1150 3.3 / W 1847 0.2	**22** 0047 3.2 / 0730 0.3 / TH 1255 3.4 / O 1954 0.2
8 0020 3.3 / 0712 0.3 / TH 1241 3.4 / ● 1942 0.1	**23** 0126 3.3 / 0811 0.3 / F 1334 3.5 / 2033 0.2
9 0113 3.3 / 0804 0.2 / F 1328 3.5 / 2033 0.0	**24** 0202 3.3 / 0849 0.2 / SA 1410 3.5 / 2110 0.2
10 0202 3.4 / 0852 0.1 / SA 1413 3.6 / 2121 -0.1	**25** 0237 3.3 / 0923 0.2 / SU 1444 3.6 / 2144 0.2
11 0248 3.3 / 0937 0.0 / SU 1456 3.6 / 2206 -0.1	**26** 0309 3.3 / 0953 0.2 / M 1515 3.6 / 2215 0.2
12 0331 3.3 / 1019 0.0 / M 1537 3.6 / 2247 -0.2	**27** 0337 3.2 / 1020 0.2 / TU 1545 3.5 / 2244 0.2
13 0414 3.2 / 1059 0.0 / TU 1622 3.6 / 2329 -0.1	**28** 0406 3.2 / 1048 0.2 / W 1617 3.4 / 2314 0.3
14 0459 3.2 / 1143 0.1 / W 1710 3.5	**29** 0437 3.1 / 1118 0.2 / TH 1649 3.3 / 2341 0.3
15 0015 0.1 / 0545 3.2 / TH 1229 0.2 / 1759 3.5	**30** 0506 3.1 / 1146 0.3 / F 1719 3.2
	31 0003 0.4 / 0536 3.0 / SA 1212 0.4 / 1754 3.0

Chart Datum: 1·66 metres below Normal Null (German reference level)

TIME ZONE -0100
(German Standard Time)
Subtract 1 hour for UT
For German Summer Time add
ONE hour in **non-shaded areas**

GERMANY–CUXHAVEN

LAT 53°52'N   LONG 8°43'E

TIMES AND HEIGHTS OF HIGH AND LOW WATERS

YEAR **2002**

SEPTEMBER

#	Time	m		#	Time	m
1 SU	0033	0.5		**16** M	0213	0.6
	0619	2.9			0803	2.9
	1851	2.9			1500	0.4
					2059	2.8
2 M	0131	0.6		**17** TU	0343	0.6
	0729	2.9			0934	2.9
	1416	0.6			1638	0.4
	2013	2.9			2232	2.8
3 TU	0259	0.7		**18** W	0517	0.6
	0856	2.9			1058	3.1
	1553	0.5			1803	0.3
	2144	3.0			2346	3.0
4 W	0433	0.6		**19** TH	0629	0.4
	1020	3.1			1159	3.3
	1722	0.4			1900	0.2
	2303	3.1				
5 TH	0553	0.5		**20** F	0034	3.1
	1128	3.3			0715	0.3
	1832	0.3			1238	3.4
					1937	0.2
6 F	0006	3.3		**21** SA	0107	3.2
	0658	0.4			0750	0.3
	1222	3.5			1312	3.4
	1929	0.1		O	2011	0.2
7 SA	0058	3.3		**22** SU	0139	3.2
	0751	0.2			0825	0.2
	1309	3.6			1346	3.4
●	2018	0.0			2045	0.2
8 SU	0146	3.4		**23** M	0211	3.3
	0837	0.1			0859	0.2
	1354	3.6			1419	3.5
	2104	-0.1			2117	0.2
9 M	0230	3.4		**24** TU	0240	3.3
	0921	0.0			0929	0.2
	1437	3.6			1448	3.5
	2148	-0.1			2145	0.2
10 TU	0311	3.4		**25** W	0305	3.3
	1002	0.0			0955	0.2
	1519	3.6			1515	3.4
	2228	-0.1			2212	0.2
11 W	0351	3.3		**26** TH	0331	3.2
	1040	0.0			1020	0.2
	1601	3.6			1544	3.3
	2307	0.0			2238	0.2
12 TH	0431	3.2		**27** F	0359	3.2
	1119	0.1			1046	0.2
	1646	3.5			1614	3.2
	2345	0.2			2303	0.3
13 F	0512	3.2		**28** SA	0427	3.1
	1159	0.2			1112	0.3
	1732	3.3			1643	3.1
					2325	0.4
14 SA	0024	0.4		**29** SU	0456	3.0
	0556	3.1			1139	0.4
	1242	0.3			1719	3.0
	1824	3.1			2355	0.6
15 SU	0108	0.5		**30** M	0538	2.9
	0649	3.0			1224	0.5
	1338	0.3			1815	2.8
	1932	2.9				

OCTOBER

#	Time	m		#	Time	m
1 TU	0053	0.7		**16** W	0309	0.7
	0647	2.9			0902	2.9
	1342	0.6			1609	0.5
	1940	2.8			2202	2.7
2 W	0224	0.8		**17** TH	0444	0.7
	0818	3.0			1027	3.1
	1524	0.6			1736	0.4
	2117	2.9			2317	2.9
3 TH	0405	0.7		**18** F	0600	0.5
	0949	3.2			1130	3.2
	1659	0.4			1834	0.2
	2242	3.1				
4 F	0531	0.5		**19** SA	0005	3.0
	1102	3.3			0647	0.4
	1812	0.2			1210	3.3
	2346	3.2			1909	0.2
5 SA	0637	0.4		**20** SU	0038	3.1
	1158	3.5			0721	0.3
	1908	0.0			1242	3.3
					1941	0.1
6 SU	0038	3.3		**21** M	0109	3.2
	0730	0.2			0756	0.2
	1246	3.5			1317	3.4
●	1957	-0.1		O	2014	0.2
7 M	0123	3.3		**22** TU	0140	3.2
	0817	0.1			0831	0.2
	1332	3.6			1350	3.4
	2041	-0.1			2045	0.2
8 TU	0205	3.4		**23** W	0208	3.3
	0858	0.0			0901	0.2
	1415	3.6			1418	3.4
	2123	-0.1			2113	0.2
9 W	0245	3.4		**24** TH	0233	3.3
	0938	0.0			0928	0.2
	1457	3.6			1445	3.3
	2203	0.0			2139	0.2
10 TH	0323	3.4		**25** F	0259	3.3
	1018	0.0			0953	0.2
	1540	3.5			1515	3.2
	2241	0.1			2206	0.2
11 F	0402	3.3		**26** SA	0327	3.2
	1056	0.1			1020	0.2
	1624	3.4			1547	3.1
	2316	0.2			2233	0.3
12 SA	0442	3.2		**27** SU	0359	3.2
	1135	0.2			1050	0.3
	1710	3.2			1622	3.0
	2353	0.4			2302	0.4
13 SU	0525	3.1		**28** M	0433	3.1
	1218	0.3			1124	0.4
	1801	2.9			1703	2.9
					2339	0.4
14 M	0037	0.6		**29** TU	0519	3.0
	0620	3.0			1213	0.4
	1314	0.4			1800	2.8
	1907	2.7				
15 TU	0141	0.7		**30** W	0037	0.7
	0733	2.9			0625	3.0
	1433	0.5			1325	0.5
	2031	2.6			1919	2.8
				31 TH	0201	0.8
					0749	0.5
					1458	0.5
					2050	2.9

NOVEMBER

#	Time	m		#	Time	m
1 F	0337	0.7		**16** SA	0507	0.6
	0917	3.2			1040	3.1
	1629	0.4			1745	0.3
	2213	3.0			2319	2.9
2 SA	0501	0.5		**17** SU	0604	0.4
	1033	3.3			1129	3.2
	1742	0.2			1828	0.2
	2318	3.2			2359	3.1
3 SU	0608	0.3		**18** M	0645	0.3
	1130	3.4			1207	3.2
	1839	0.0			1904	0.2
4 M	0011	3.3		**19** TU	0033	3.3
	0703	0.2			0722	0.3
	1221	3.5			1244	3.3
●	1930	0.0			1939	0.2
5 TU	0057	3.3		**20** W	0106	3.2
	0751	0.1			0759	0.2
	1308	3.5			1318	3.3
	2016	-0.1		O	2012	0.2
6 W	0138	3.3		**21** TH	0136	3.3
	0834	0.0			0831	0.1
	1353	3.5			1349	3.3
	2056	0.0			2042	0.2
7 TH	0217	3.4		**22** F	0205	3.3
	0913	0.0			0902	0.2
	1437	3.5			1421	3.2
	2136	0.1			2113	0.2
8 F	0256	3.4		**23** SA	0235	3.3
	0955	0.1			0934	0.2
	1521	3.4			1455	3.2
	2215	0.2			2145	0.2
9 SA	0337	3.4		**24** SU	0308	3.3
	1038	0.1			1007	0.2
	1607	3.2			1533	3.1
	2254	0.3			2218	0.3
10 SU	0419	3.3		**25** M	0344	3.2
	1119	0.2			1042	0.2
	1652	3.0			1613	3.0
	2331	0.4			2254	0.4
11 M	0503	3.2		**26** TU	0424	3.2
	1203	0.3			1123	0.3
	1741	2.9			1700	2.9
					2338	0.5
12 TU	0014	0.5		**27** W	0512	3.2
	0555	3.1			1213	0.3
	1255	0.4			1755	2.9
	1839	2.7				
13 W	0110	0.7		**28** TH	0032	0.5
	0658	3.0			0612	3.1
	1400	0.5			1316	0.3
	1950	2.6			1903	2.8
14 TH	0223	0.7		**29** F	0143	0.6
	0815	3.0			0724	3.2
	1521	0.5			1432	0.4
	2110	2.6			2020	2.9
15 F	0348	0.7		**30** SA	0304	0.6
	0934	3.0			0841	3.2
	1642	0.5			1552	0.3
	2223	2.8			2136	3.0

DECEMBER

#	Time	m		#	Time	m
1 SU	0423	0.5		**16** M	0503	0.5
	0953	3.3			1035	3.0
	1704	0.2			1732	0.4
	2242	3.1			2310	3.0
2 M	0532	0.3		**17** TU	0559	0.4
	1057	3.3			1126	3.1
	1806	0.1			1820	0.3
	2338	3.2			2354	3.2
3 TU	0631	0.2		**18** W	0644	0.3
	1155	3.4			1209	3.2
	1901	0.0			1902	0.3
4 W	0028	3.2		**19** TH	0032	3.2
	0725	0.1			0725	0.3
	1247	3.4			1248	3.2
●	1950	0.0		O	1941	0.2
5 TH	0113	3.3		**20** F	0107	3.3
	0811	0.1			0803	0.2
	1335	3.4			1326	3.2
	2033	0.1			2017	0.2
6 F	0153	3.4		**21** SA	0142	3.3
	0853	0.1			0841	0.1
	1420	3.4			1405	3.2
	2113	0.2			2056	0.2
7 SA	0234	3.4		**22** SU	0220	3.4
	0938	0.1			0923	0.1
	1507	3.3			1446	3.2
	2157	0.3			2136	0.2
8 SU	0317	3.5		**23** M	0258	3.4
	1025	0.1			1004	0.1
	1553	3.2			1527	3.1
	2238	0.3			2213	0.2
9 M	0401	3.4		**24** TU	0336	3.3
	1108	0.2			1041	0.1
	1636	3.0			1609	3.0
	2316	0.4			2252	0.2
10 TU	0444	3.3		**25** W	0418	3.3
	1149	0.3			1122	0.1
	1720	2.9			1656	3.0
	2354	0.4			2337	0.2
11 W	0529	3.3		**26** TH	0506	3.3
	1232	0.4			1210	0.1
	1806	2.8			1748	2.9
12 TH	0037	0.5		**27** F	0027	0.3
	0619	3.2			0559	3.3
	1321	0.4			1303	0.2
	1900	2.7			1844	2.9
13 F	0131	0.6		**28** SA	0123	0.4
	0718	3.1			0657	3.3
	1419	0.5			1403	0.2
	2003	2.7			1945	2.9
14 SA	0238	0.6		**29** SU	0228	0.5
	0825	3.0			0803	3.2
	1527	0.5			1511	0.3
	2111	2.7			2052	3.0
15 SU	0354	0.6		**30** M	0341	0.4
	0934	3.0			0914	3.2
	1635	0.6			1623	0.3
	2215	2.9			2202	3.0
				31 TU	0454	0.3
					1026	3.2
					1732	0.2
					2306	3.1

Chart Datum: 1·66 metres below Normal Null (German reference level)

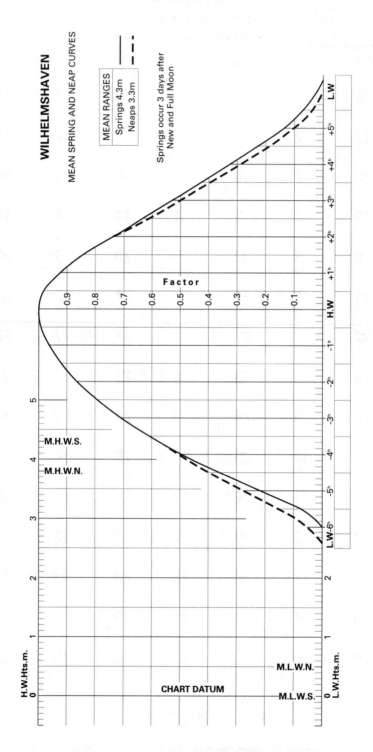

WILHELMSHAVEN

MEAN SPRING AND NEAP CURVES

MEAN RANGES
Springs 4.3m
Neaps 3.3m

Springs occur 3 days after
New and Full Moon

Factor

0.9 0.8 0.7 0.6 0.5 0.4 0.3 0.2 0.1

M.H.W.S.
M.H.W.N.

H.W.Hts.m.

CHART DATUM

M.L.W.N.
M.L.W.S.

L.W.Hts.m.

TIME ZONE -0100
(German Standard Time)
Subtract 1 hour for UT
For German Summer Time add
ONE hour in **non-shaded areas**

GERMANY – WILHELMSHAVEN

LAT 53°31′N   LONG 8°09′E

TIMES AND HEIGHTS OF HIGH AND LOW WATERS

YEAR **2002**

JANUARY

Day	Time m	Time m	Time m	Time m
1 TU	0145 4.4	0807 0.1	1414 4.2	2026 0.2
16 W	0221 4.4	0847 0.3	1450 4.2	2058 0.3
2 W	0231 4.4	0856 0.0	1504 4.1	2112 0.1
17 TH	0257 4.5	0923 0.3	1524 4.1	2129 0.3
3 TH	0316 4.4	0941 0.0	1551 4.1	2155 0.2
18 F	0331 4.4	0955 0.2	1556 4.0	2158 0.3
4 F	0400 4.4	1024 0.0	1639 4.0	2239 0.3
19 SA	0405 4.3	1026 0.3	1629 3.9	2228 0.3
5 SA	0448 4.4	1112 0.1	1730 3.9	2328 0.4
20 SU	0440 4.2	1058 0.3	1703 3.8	2300 0.4
6 SU	0540 4.4	1204 0.2	1822 3.9	
21 M	0515 4.1	1129 0.4	1737 3.8	2333 0.5
7 M	0021 0.5	0636 4.3	1257 0.3	1917 3.8
22 TU	0551 4.0	1203 0.4	1819 3.7	
8 TU	0118 0.5	0738 4.2	1358 0.4	2019 3.8
23 W	0016 0.6	0640 3.9	1252 0.6	1916 3.7
9 W	0225 0.5	0848 4.1	1507 0.4	2130 3.8
24 TH	0119 0.7	0748 3.8	1359 0.6	2030 3.7
10 TH	0338 0.4	1002 4.0	1619 0.4	2239 3.9
25 F	0237 0.7	0906 3.9	1516 0.5	2146 3.8
11 F	0448 0.3	1111 4.1	1725 0.4	2338 4.1
26 SA	0356 0.5	1020 4.0	1631 0.4	2254 4.0
12 SA	0551 0.2	1209 4.1	1822 0.4	
27 SU	0507 0.4	1124 4.1	1738 0.4	2352 4.2
13 SU	0027 4.2	0645 0.2	1256 4.2	● 1908 0.3
28 M	0610 0.2	1222 4.2	1836 0.3	○
14 M	0108 4.3	0730 0.3	1336 4.2	1947 0.3
29 TU	0043 4.3	0705 0.0	1316 4.2	1929 0.2
15 TU	0145 4.4	0809 0.3	1414 4.2	2023 0.3
30 W	0133 4.4	0758 -0.1	1408 4.2	2020 0.1
31 TH	0222 4.5	0850 -0.1	1458 4.2	2107 0.0

FEBRUARY

Day	Time m	Time m	Time m	Time m
1 F	0309 4.5	0936 -0.2	1545 4.1	2149 -0.1
16 SA	0311 4.4	0931 0.1	1534 4.0	2136 0.1
2 SA	0353 4.5	1019 -0.2	1629 4.1	2229 0.0
17 SU	0343 4.3	1000 0.1	1604 4.0	2206 0.1
3 SU	0438 4.5	1101 0.0	1712 4.0	2312 0.2
18 M	0416 4.3	1030 0.1	1634 4.0	2234 0.1
4 M	0524 4.4	1144 0.1	1754 3.9	2354 0.3
19 TU	0445 4.2	1055 0.1	1700 3.9	2257 0.2
5 TU	0610 4.3	1225 0.3	1838 3.9	
20 W	0511 4.0	1116 0.2	1728 3.8	2322 0.3
6 W	0039 0.3	0704 4.1	1313 0.4	1935 3.8
21 TH	0547 3.8	1149 0.4	1815 3.7	
7 TH	0139 0.4	0813 3.9	1421 0.5	2049 3.7
22 F	0013 0.5	0649 3.7	1254 0.6	1930 3.6
8 F	0258 0.4	0936 3.8	1544 0.5	2211 3.8
23 SA	0135 0.6	0817 3.7	1423 0.6	2059 3.7
9 SA	0422 0.3	1056 3.9	1703 0.4	2320 4.0
24 SU	0311 0.5	0948 3.9	1555 0.5	2223 4.0
10 SU	0535 0.2	1159 4.0	1805 0.4	
25 M	0440 0.3	1106 4.0	1716 0.4	2333 4.2
11 M	0013 4.2	0631 0.2	1246 4.1	1852 0.3
26 TU	0553 0.1	1211 4.2	1823 0.2	
12 TU	0055 4.3	0716 0.2	1325 4.1	● 1931 0.3
27 W	0030 4.4	0653 -0.1	1308 4.2	○ 1918 0.0
13 W	0133 4.4	0755 0.2	1401 4.2	2007 0.2
28 TH	0121 4.5	0746 -0.3	1400 4.2	2007 -0.1
14 TH	0208 4.4	0830 0.1	1435 4.2	2040 0.2
15 F	0240 4.4	0903 0.1	1505 4.1	2109 0.1

MARCH

Day	Time m	Time m	Time m	Time m
1 F	0209 4.5	0835 -0.3	1446 4.2	2053 -0.2
16 SA	0221 4.3	0836 -0.1	1443 4.1	2046 -0.1
2 SA	0256 4.5	0921 -0.4	1530 4.2	2134 -0.2
17 SU	0250 4.3	0904 -0.1	1510 4.1	2113 -0.1
3 SU	0340 4.5	1002 -0.3	1610 4.1	2212 -0.2
18 M	0320 4.3	0931 -0.1	1538 4.1	2140 -0.1
4 M	0422 4.5	1040 -0.1	1647 4.1	2248 0.0
19 TU	0350 4.2	0958 0.0	1606 4.0	2207 -0.1
5 TU	0503 4.4	1116 0.1	1723 4.0	2323 0.1
20 W	0418 4.1	1021 0.0	1629 4.0	2228 0.0
6 W	0544 4.2	1149 0.2	1802 3.9	
21 TH	0442 4.0	1040 0.1	1654 3.8	2250 0.1
7 TH	0002 0.2	0633 3.9	1230 0.4	1856 3.8
22 F	0516 3.8	1110 0.3	1738 3.7	2336 0.3
8 F	0059 0.3	0741 3.7	1338 0.5	2014 3.7
23 SA	0617 3.6	1214 0.5	1853 3.7	
9 SA	0222 0.4	0910 3.6	1509 0.6	2144 3.8
24 SU	0059 0.5	0748 3.7	1349 0.6	2028 3.8
10 SU	0358 0.3	1039 3.7	1639 0.5	2303 3.9
25 M	0243 0.4	0927 3.8	1530 0.5	2200 4.0
11 M	0518 0.2	1147 3.8	1745 0.3	2358 4.1
26 TU	0418 0.2	1052 4.0	1656 0.3	2315 4.2
12 TU	0613 0.1	1232 4.0	1831 0.2	
27 W	0534 -0.1	1159 4.1	1805 0.1	
13 W	0038 4.2	0654 0.0	1308 4.0	1908 0.1
28 TH	0014 4.4	0635 -0.3	1245 4.2	○ 1900 -0.1
14 TH	0115 4.3	0731 0.0	1342 4.1	● 1944 0.0
29 F	0106 4.4	0728 -0.4	1345 4.2	1948 -0.3
15 F	0150 4.3	0805 -0.1	1414 4.1	2017 0.0
30 SA	0154 4.5	0814 -0.5	1428 4.2	2031 -0.3
31 SU	0238 4.5	0858 -0.4	1507 4.2	2112 -0.3

APRIL

Day	Time m	Time m	Time m	Time m
1 M	0321 4.5	0937 -0.3	1544 4.2	2148 -0.3
16 TU	0255 4.2	0900 -0.1	1511 4.1	2114 -0.2
2 TU	0402 4.4	1012 -0.2	1619 4.1	2222 -0.2
17 W	0325 4.1	0927 -0.1	1540 4.1	2142 -0.1
3 W	0442 4.2	1044 0.0	1654 4.1	2256 -0.1
18 TH	0356 4.1	0954 0.0	1608 4.0	2210 -0.1
4 TH	0522 4.0	1117 0.2	1733 4.0	2335 0.1
19 F	0429 4.0	1022 0.0	1641 4.0	2242 0.0
5 F	0609 3.8	1157 0.4	1826 3.8	
20 SA	0511 3.8	1100 0.4	1729 3.9	2331 0.2
6 SA	0031 0.2	0714 3.5	1301 0.5	1941 3.7
21 SU	0613 3.7	1204 0.5	1841 3.9	
7 SU	0151 0.3	0840 3.5	1430 0.6	2111 3.8
22 M	0050 0.3	0738 3.7	1335 0.6	2011 3.9
8 M	0326 0.3	1009 3.6	1603 0.5	2234 3.9
23 TU	0227 0.2	0912 3.8	1511 0.5	2139 4.1
9 TU	0448 0.2	1119 3.7	1713 0.3	2331 4.1
24 W	0357 0.0	1034 3.9	1633 0.2	2253 4.2
10 W	0542 0.0	1205 3.9	1759 0.1	
25 TH	0509 -0.2	1139 4.1	1739 0.0	2353 4.3
11 TH	0011 4.2	0621 -0.1	1240 4.0	1837 0.0
26 F	0610 -0.4	1234 4.1	1836 -0.2	
12 F	0048 4.2	0657 -0.1	1315 4.0	● 1915 0.0
27 SA	0047 4.4	0704 -0.4	1323 4.2	○ 1925 -0.3
13 SA	0124 4.2	0733 -0.2	1348 4.1	1950 -0.1
28 SU	0135 4.5	0750 -0.4	1404 4.3	2007 -0.3
14 SU	0157 4.3	0805 -0.1	1417 4.2	2020 -0.2
29 M	0218 4.5	0831 -0.3	1440 4.3	2045 -0.3
15 M	0226 4.3	0833 -0.1	1444 4.2	2047 -0.2
30 TU	0259 4.4	0908 -0.2	1516 4.3	2123 -0.3

Chart Datum: 2·26 metres below Normal Null (German reference level)

TIME ZONE -0100
(German Standard Time)
Subtract 1 hour for UT
For German Summer Time add
ONE hour in **non-shaded areas**

GERMANY – WILHELMSHAVEN

LAT 53°31'N   LONG 8°09'E

TIMES AND HEIGHTS OF HIGH AND LOW WATERS

YEAR **2002**

MAY

Time m	Time m
1 0341 4.2 / 0943 -0.1 / W 1553 4.2 / 2200 -0.2	**16** 0307 4.1 / 0906 -0.1 / TH 1522 4.2 / 2128 -0.1
2 0422 4.1 / 1018 0.0 / TH 1631 4.1 / 2238 -0.1	**17** 0345 4.0 / 0941 0.0 / F 1559 4.2 / 2205 -0.1
3 0503 3.9 / 1053 0.2 / F 1712 4.1 / 2320 0.0	**18** 0428 4.0 / 1020 0.1 / SA 1641 4.1 / 2249 0.0
4 0549 3.7 / 1135 0.4 / SA 1803 4.0	**19** 0519 3.8 / 1108 0.3 / SU 1734 4.1 / 2343 0.0
5 0012 0.2 / 0648 3.6 / SU 1230 0.5 / 1908 3.9	**20** 0620 3.8 / 1209 0.4 / M 1840 4.1
6 0120 0.3 / 0801 3.5 / M 1346 0.6 / 2027 3.9	**21** 0053 0.1 / 0734 3.8 / TU 1327 0.4 / 1957 4.1
7 0241 0.3 / 0921 3.5 / TU 1511 0.5 / 2146 3.9	**22** 0214 0.1 / 0854 3.9 / W 1450 0.3 / 2116 4.2
8 0359 0.2 / 1031 3.7 / W 1624 0.3 / 2248 4.0	**23** 0333 0.0 / 1008 4.0 / TH 1605 0.2 / 2226 4.3
9 0457 0.0 / 1123 3.9 / TH 1717 0.1 / 2334 4.1	**24** 0440 -0.2 / 1111 4.0 / F 1709 0.0 / 2328 4.3
10 0540 -0.1 / 1203 4.0 / F 1800 0.1	**25** 0540 -0.3 / 1206 4.1 / SA 1807 0.0
11 0013 4.2 / 0620 -0.1 / SA 1241 4.1 / 1842 0.0	**26** 0024 4.3 / 0637 -0.3 / SU 1256 4.2 / O 1900 -0.2
12 0052 4.2 / 0658 -0.1 / SU 1317 4.2 / ● 1919 -0.1	**27** 0114 4.4 / 0726 -0.3 / M 1338 4.3 / 1943 -0.2
13 0128 4.2 / 0732 -0.1 / M 1348 4.2 / 1952 -0.1	**28** 0158 4.4 / 0806 -0.2 / TU 1415 4.4 / 2023 -0.2
14 0200 4.2 / 0802 -0.1 / TU 1417 4.3 / 2022 -0.2	**29** 0239 4.3 / 0843 0.0 / W 1452 4.4 / 2104 -0.1
15 0232 4.2 / 0834 -0.1 / W 1448 4.2 / 2054 -0.2	**30** 0322 4.2 / 0921 0.0 / TH 1532 4.3 / 2145 -0.1
	31 0405 4.0 / 0959 0.1 / F 1613 4.3 / 2226 0.0

JUNE

Time m	Time m
1 0446 3.9 / 1036 0.2 / SA 1654 4.1 / 2308 0.1	**16** 0430 4.0 / 1024 0.1 / SU 1642 4.3 / 2257 0.1
2 0529 3.8 / 1116 0.3 / SU 1739 4.1 / 2353 0.2	**17** 0523 3.9 / 1115 0.2 / M 1736 4.3 / 2352 0.0
3 0617 3.7 / 1201 0.5 / M 1832 4.1	**18** 0621 3.9 / 1212 0.3 / TU 1835 4.3
4 0045 0.3 / 0714 3.6 / TU 1259 0.5 / 1935 4.0	**19** 0052 0.0 / 0722 3.9 / W 1315 0.3 / 1939 4.3
5 0147 0.3 / 0820 3.6 / W 1410 0.5 / 2044 4.0	**20** 0157 0.1 / 0827 3.9 / TH 1424 0.3 / 2048 4.2
6 0256 0.3 / 0927 3.7 / TH 1523 0.4 / 2151 4.0	**21** 0304 0.0 / 0934 4.0 / F 1534 0.2 / 2157 4.2
7 0359 0.2 / 1027 3.9 / F 1625 0.3 / 2246 4.1	**22** 0410 0.0 / 1038 4.0 / SA 1639 0.0 / 2303 4.2
8 0452 0.1 / 1117 4.0 / SA 1717 0.2 / 2333 4.1	**23** 0513 0.0 / 1136 4.1 / SU 1741 -0.1
9 0538 0.0 / 1202 4.1 / SU 1804 0.1	**24** 0003 4.3 / 0613 0.0 / M 1229 4.2 / O 1838 -0.1
10 0016 4.2 / 0622 0.0 / M 1241 4.2 / 1846 0.0	**25** 0056 4.3 / 0706 0.0 / TU 1315 4.3 / 1926 -0.1
11 0057 4.2 / 0700 0.0 / TU 1318 4.3 / ● 1924 -0.1	**26** 0142 4.3 / 0749 0.0 / W 1355 4.4 / 2009 0.0
12 0136 4.2 / 0738 0.0 / W 1354 4.3 / 2004 -0.1	**27** 0224 4.3 / 0828 0.1 / TH 1434 4.5 / 2052 0.0
13 0216 4.2 / 0818 0.0 / TH 1433 4.3 / 2045 -0.1	**28** 0306 4.2 / 0908 0.2 / F 1515 4.5 / 2135 0.0
14 0259 4.1 / 0859 0.0 / F 1513 4.3 / 2125 -0.1	**29** 0347 4.1 / 0945 0.2 / SA 1555 4.4 / 2215 0.1
15 0342 4.1 / 0940 0.0 / SA 1555 4.3 / 2208 -0.1	**30** 0425 4.0 / 1019 0.2 / SU 1633 4.4 / 2252 0.2

JULY

Time m	Time m
1 0503 3.9 / 1054 0.3 / M 1713 4.3 / 2330 0.3	**16** 0515 4.0 / 1110 0.1 / TU 1726 4.4 / 2346 0.0
2 0542 3.8 / 1132 0.4 / TU 1754 4.2	**17** 0605 4.0 / 1201 0.2 / W 1818 4.4
3 0009 0.3 / 0625 3.8 / W 1214 0.5 / 1840 4.1	**18** 0037 0.1 / 0655 4.0 / TH 1252 0.3 / 1913 4.3
4 0052 0.4 / 0714 3.7 / TH 1308 0.5 / 1936 4.0	**19** 0130 0.2 / 0750 3.9 / F 1351 0.3 / 2016 4.2
5 0148 0.4 / 0814 3.8 / F 1414 0.5 / 2042 4.0	**20** 0231 0.3 / 0856 3.9 / SA 1500 0.3 / 2129 4.1
6 0252 0.4 / 0920 3.8 / SA 1524 0.5 / 2149 4.0	**21** 0342 0.3 / 1007 4.0 / SU 1614 0.2 / 2243 4.1
7 0356 0.3 / 1023 3.9 / SU 1628 0.3 / 2248 4.1	**22** 0453 0.2 / 1114 4.1 / M 1723 0.1 / 2349 4.2
8 0454 0.2 / 1119 4.1 / M 1725 0.2 / 2341 4.2	**23** 0557 0.2 / 1210 4.2 / TU 1824 0.1
9 0548 0.2 / 1207 4.2 / TU 1816 0.1	**24** 0044 4.2 / 0652 0.2 / W 1257 4.4 / O 1916 0.1
10 0030 4.2 / 0637 0.1 / W 1252 4.3 / ● 1905 0.0	**25** 0130 4.2 / 0737 0.2 / TH 1340 4.4 / 2000 0.1
11 0118 4.2 / 0724 0.1 / TH 1337 4.4 / 1953 0.0	**26** 0212 4.3 / 0817 0.2 / F 1420 4.5 / 2042 0.1
12 0206 4.2 / 0811 0.1 / F 1422 4.5 / 2041 -0.1	**27** 0250 4.2 / 0855 0.2 / SA 1457 4.5 / 2121 0.1
13 0253 4.2 / 0858 0.0 / SA 1506 4.5 / 2125 -0.2	**28** 0326 4.2 / 0928 0.2 / SU 1533 4.5 / 2155 0.1
14 0339 4.1 / 0940 0.0 / SU 1549 4.5 / 2207 -0.2	**29** 0358 4.1 / 0957 0.2 / M 1608 4.4 / 2227 0.2
15 0425 4.1 / 1022 0.0 / M 1635 4.4 / 2254 -0.1	**30** 0431 4.0 / 1028 0.2 / TU 1642 4.4 / 2259 0.3
	31 0504 3.9 / 1101 0.3 / W 1717 4.3 / 2331 0.3

AUGUST

Time m	Time m
1 0537 3.9 / 1133 0.4 / TH 1750 4.1	**16** 0008 0.3 / 0619 4.0 / F 1220 0.3 / 1841 4.2
2 0000 0.4 / 0612 3.8 / F 1210 0.5 / 1831 4.0	**17** 0053 0.4 / 0709 3.9 / SA 1314 0.4 / 1944 4.0
3 0040 0.5 / 0701 3.8 / SA 1303 0.6 / 1932 3.9	**18** 0154 0.5 / 0819 3.9 / SU 1428 0.4 / 2105 3.9
4 0140 0.6 / 0809 3.8 / SU 1417 0.6 / 2048 3.9	**19** 0315 0.6 / 0942 3.9 / M 1555 0.4 / 2231 3.9
5 0256 0.5 / 0926 3.8 / M 1537 0.5 / 2204 3.9	**20** 0439 0.5 / 1059 4.0 / TU 1715 0.2 / 2342 4.0
6 0412 0.4 / 1038 4.0 / TU 1650 0.4 / 2312 4.1	**21** 0548 0.4 / 1158 4.2 / W 1817 0.2
7 0520 0.4 / 1138 4.2 / W 1755 0.2	**22** 0035 4.1 / 0640 0.3 / TH 1243 4.4 / O 1906 0.2
8 0011 4.2 / 0621 0.3 / TH 1232 4.3 / ● 1851 0.1	**23** 0117 4.2 / 0722 0.3 / F 1324 4.4 / 1947 0.2
9 0105 4.3 / 0715 0.2 / F 1321 4.5 / 1944 0.0	**24** 0155 4.2 / 0801 0.2 / SA 1402 4.5 / 2024 0.1
10 0156 4.3 / 0804 0.1 / SA 1408 4.5 / 2033 -0.1	**25** 0229 4.2 / 0836 0.2 / SU 1436 4.5 / 2058 0.1
11 0243 4.3 / 0851 0.0 / SU 1453 4.6 / 2118 -0.2	**26** 0300 4.2 / 0906 0.2 / M 1507 4.5 / 2128 0.1
12 0328 4.2 / 0932 -0.1 / M 1535 4.5 / 2159 -0.2	**27** 0328 4.1 / 0932 0.1 / TU 1538 4.4 / 2155 0.2
13 0410 4.1 / 1012 -0.1 / TU 1619 4.5 / 2240 -0.1	**28** 0355 4.1 / 0959 0.2 / W 1609 4.3 / 2223 0.2
14 0453 4.1 / 1053 0.1 / W 1705 4.5 / 2325 0.1	**29** 0424 4.0 / 1028 0.2 / TH 1639 4.2 / 2250 0.3
15 0536 4.1 / 1137 0.2 / TH 1752 4.4	**30** 0451 4.0 / 1054 0.3 / F 1704 4.1 / 2312 0.4
	31 0518 3.9 / 1119 0.4 / SA 1736 3.9 / 2340 0.5

Chart Datum: 2·26 metres below Normal Null (German reference level)

TIME ZONE -0100
(German Standard Time)
Subtract 1 hour for UT
For German Summer Time add
ONE hour in **non-shaded areas**

GERMANY – WILHELMSHAVEN

LAT 53°31′N   LONG 8°09′E

TIMES AND HEIGHTS OF HIGH AND LOW WATERS

YEAR **2002**

SEPTEMBER

#	Day	Time m	Time m	#	Day	Time m	Time m
1	SU	0559 3.8	1202 0.6 / 1831 3.8	16	M	0118 0.8 / 0746 3.8	1359 0.5 / 2042 3.7
2	M	0036 0.7 / 0707 3.7	1318 0.8 / 1955 3.7	17	TU	0246 0.8 / 0917 3.8	1536 0.5 / 2215 3.7
3	TU	0202 0.8 / 0835 3.8	1453 0.7 / 2127 3.8	18	W	0421 0.7 / 1043 4.0	1704 0.4 / 2330 3.9
4	W	0335 0.7 / 1002 4.0	1623 0.5 / 2249 4.0	19	TH	0534 0.5	1144 4.2 / 1804 0.2
5	TH	0458 0.5 / 1113 4.2	1737 0.3 / 2354 4.2	20	F	0020 4.0 / 0621 0.4	1225 4.3 / 1846 0.2
6	F	0606 0.4	1211 4.4 / 1837 0.1	21	SA	0055 4.1 / 0658 0.3	1300 4.4 / ○ 1922 0.1
7	SA	0050 4.2 / 0702 0.2	1302 4.5 / ● 1929 -0.1	22	SU	0129 4.1 / 0734 0.2	1336 4.4 / 1956 0.1
8	SU	0140 4.3 / 0750 0.1	1349 4.6 / 2016 -0.2	23	M	0201 4.1 / 0809 0.2	1410 4.4 / 2028 0.1
9	M	0225 4.3 / 0834 0.0	1433 4.6 / 2100 -0.2	24	TU	0230 4.2 / 0839 0.2	1439 4.4 / 2055 0.2
10	TU	0307 4.3 / 0915 -0.1	1516 4.6 / 2140 -0.2	25	W	0255 4.2 / 0904 0.1	1506 4.3 / 2119 0.2
11	W	0347 4.2 / 0952 -0.1	1558 4.5 / 2218 0.0	26	TH	0320 4.1 / 0928 0.1	1535 4.2 / 2144 0.2
12	TH	0424 4.2 / 1029 0.0	1640 4.4 / 2255 0.2	27	F	0346 4.1 / 0953 0.2	1602 4.1 / 2208 0.3
13	F	0501 4.1 / 1106 0.2	1722 4.1 / 2332 0.4	28	SA	0411 4.0 / 1017 0.3	1628 4.0 / 2230 0.4
14	SA	0541 4.0 / 1146 0.3	1811 4.0	29	SU	0437 3.9 / 1041 0.4	1700 3.8 / 2259 0.6
15	SU	0014 0.6 / 0632 3.9	1240 0.4 / 1915 3.8	30	M	0517 3.8 / 1123 0.6	1754 3.7 / 2354 0.8

OCTOBER

#	Day	Time m	Time m	#	Day	Time m	Time m
1	TU	0625 3.7 / 1239 0.8	1919 3.6	16	W	0209 0.9 / 0843 3.8	1505 0.6 / 2143 3.6
2	W	0123 0.9 / 0757 3.8	1420 0.7 / 2058 3.8	17	TH	0344 0.8 / 1010 4.0	1633 0.5 / 2259 3.7
3	TH	0305 0.9 / 0930 4.0	1557 0.5 / 2226 3.9	18	F	0501 0.6 / 1115 4.1	1734 0.3 / 2349 3.9
4	F	0434 0.6 / 1047 4.2	1714 0.2 / 2334 4.1	19	SA	0550 0.4	1156 4.2 / 1813 0.2
5	SA	0544 0.4 / 1147 4.4	1814 0.0	20	SU	0024 4.0 / 0626 0.3	1230 4.3 / 1848 0.1
6	SU	0029 4.2 / 0640 0.2	1239 4.5 / ● 1906 -0.1	21	M	0056 4.1 / 0702 0.3	1305 4.3 / 1922 0.2
7	M	0118 4.3 / 0728 0.0	1325 4.5 / 1952 -0.2	22	TU	0128 4.1 / 0739 0.2	1339 4.3 / 1953 0.2
8	TU	0201 4.3 / 0810 0.0	1409 4.6 / 2035 -0.1	23	W	0157 4.2 / 0809 0.2	1408 4.3 / 2020 0.2
9	W	0240 4.3 / 0850 -0.1	1452 4.6 / 2114 -0.1	24	TH	0222 4.2 / 0835 0.2	1435 4.2 / 2044 0.2
10	TH	0317 4.3 / 0927 0.0	1534 4.4 / 2150 0.1	25	F	0247 4.2 / 0900 0.1	1504 4.1 / 2109 0.2
11	F	0353 4.2 / 1003 0.0	1616 4.3 / 2224 0.2	26	SA	0314 4.1 / 0925 0.2	1533 4.0 / 2135 0.3
12	SA	0429 4.1 / 1039 0.2	1658 4.1 / 2259 0.5	27	SU	0342 4.1 / 0952 0.2	1605 3.9 / 2204 0.5
13	SU	0510 4.0 / 1120 0.3	1746 3.8 / 2342 0.7	28	M	0415 4.0 / 1024 0.4	1644 3.8 / 2241 0.6
14	M	0602 3.9 / 1215 0.5	1849 3.6	29	TU	0459 3.9 / 1110 0.5	1740 3.6 / 2337 0.8
15	TU	0043 0.9 / 0714 3.8	1331 0.6 / 2012 3.5	30	W	0604 3.8 / 1221 0.6	1859 3.6
				31	TH	0100 0.9 / 0729 3.9	1354 0.6 / 2031 3.7

NOVEMBER

#	Day	Time m	Time m	#	Day	Time m	Time m
1	F	0236 0.9 / 0859 4.0	1527 0.5 / 2157 3.9	16	SA	0405 0.7 / 1025 4.0	1643 0.4 / 2301 3.8
2	SA	0403 0.6 / 1015 4.2	1642 0.4 / 2306 4.0	17	SU	0504 0.5 / 1114 4.1	1729 0.3 / 2342 4.0
3	SU	0512 0.4 / 1118 4.3	1743 0.0	18	M	0548 0.4 / 1153 4.2	1808 0.2
4	M	0001 4.1 / 0610 0.2	1212 4.4 / ● 1837 -0.1	19	TU	0018 4.1 / 0628 0.4	1230 4.2 / 1845 0.2
5	TU	0050 4.1 / 0700 0.1	1300 4.5 / 1925 -0.1	20	W	0052 4.2 / 0705 0.3	1306 4.2 / ○ 1918 0.2
6	W	0132 4.3 / 0743 0.0	1345 4.5 / 2006 0.0	21	TH	0123 4.2 / 0738 0.2	1338 4.2 / 1947 0.2
7	TH	0209 4.3 / 0822 0.0	1428 4.4 / 2045 0.1	22	F	0152 4.3 / 0808 0.2	1409 4.1 / 2016 0.2
8	F	0246 4.3 / 0902 0.0	1512 4.3 / 2123 0.2	23	SA	0222 4.2 / 0839 0.2	1443 4.1 / 2048 0.2
9	SA	0326 4.3 / 0942 0.1	1556 4.1 / 2200 0.3	24	SU	0255 4.2 / 0910 0.2	1519 4.0 / 2120 0.3
10	SU	0406 4.2 / 1022 0.2	1639 3.9 / 2237 0.4	25	M	0329 4.2 / 0944 0.2	1558 3.9 / 2156 0.4
11	M	0448 4.1 / 1105 0.3	1725 3.7 / 2318 0.6	26	TU	0408 4.1 / 1022 0.3	1643 3.8 / 2239 0.6
12	TU	0538 4.0 / 1155 0.5	1821 3.6	27	W	0455 4.1 / 1111 0.3	1738 3.7 / 2333 0.7
13	W	0011 0.8 / 0640 3.9	1259 0.6 / 1931 3.5	28	TH	0555 4.0 / 1213 0.6	1845 3.7
14	TH	0122 0.9 / 0756 3.9	1418 0.7 / 2050 3.5	29	F	0043 0.7 / 0707 4.0	1329 0.5 / 2002 3.7
15	F	0247 0.9 / 0917 3.9	1538 0.6 / 2204 3.6	30	SA	0204 0.7 / 0824 4.1	1450 0.4 / 2119 3.9

DECEMBER

#	Day	Time m	Time m	#	Day	Time m	Time m
1	SU	0324 0.6 / 0939 4.2	1604 0.2 / 2228 4.0	16	M	0403 0.7 / 1020 4.0	1633 0.5 / 2251 3.9
2	M	0433 0.4 / 1045 4.3	1707 0.1 / 2326 4.1	17	TU	0501 0.5 / 1110 4.1	1723 0.4 / 2337 4.1
3	TU	0535 0.2 / 1144 4.3	1806 0.1	18	W	0549 0.4 / 1153 4.1	1807 0.3
4	W	0018 4.2 / 0631 0.1	1237 4.3 / ● 1858 0.0	19	TH	0017 4.2 / 0631 0.3	1234 4.2 / ○ 1846 0.3
5	TH	0103 4.2 / 0718 0.1	1324 4.4 / 1941 0.1	20	F	0053 4.2 / 0709 0.2	1313 4.2 / 1922 0.3
6	F	0143 4.3 / 0800 0.1	1409 4.3 / 2022 0.2	21	SA	0130 4.3 / 0748 0.2	1353 4.1 / 2000 0.3
7	SA	0222 4.4 / 0843 0.1	1455 4.2 / 2104 0.3	22	SU	0208 4.3 / 0829 0.2	1433 4.1 / 2040 0.2
8	SU	0305 4.4 / 0929 0.1	1541 4.1 / 2144 0.4	23	M	0246 4.3 / 0907 0.1	1514 4.0 / 2117 0.2
9	M	0349 4.3 / 1012 0.2	1624 3.9 / 2222 0.4	24	TU	0324 4.3 / 0944 0.1	1556 3.9 / 2155 0.3
10	TU	0431 4.3 / 1053 0.3	1705 3.8 / 2258 0.5	25	W	0405 4.3 / 1024 0.1	1643 3.9 / 2239 0.4
11	W	0514 4.2 / 1136 0.4	1750 3.7 / 2340 0.7	26	TH	0453 4.2 / 1112 0.2	1734 3.8 / 2329 0.4
12	TH	0604 4.1 / 1223 0.5	1842 3.5	27	F	0546 4.2 / 1204 0.2	1828 3.8
13	F	0032 0.8 / 0702 3.9	1319 0.6 / 1944 3.5	28	SA	0025 0.5 / 0643 4.2	1303 0.3 / 1928 3.8
14	SA	0138 0.8 / 0808 3.9	1426 0.7 / 2051 3.6	29	SU	0129 0.6 / 0749 4.1	1410 0.4 / 2035 3.8
15	SU	0253 0.8 / 0918 3.9	1534 0.6 / 2155 3.8	30	M	0241 0.5 / 0901 4.1	1522 0.3 / 2146 3.9
				31	TU	0354 0.4 / 1014 4.1	1632 0.3 / 2252 4.0

Chart Datum: 2·26 metres below Normal Null (German reference level)

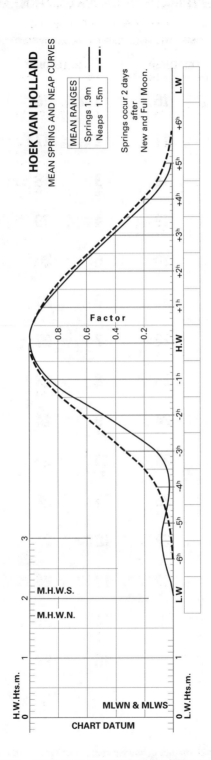

HOEK VAN HOLLAND
MEAN SPRING AND NEAP CURVES

MEAN RANGES	
Springs	1.9m
Neaps	1.5m

Springs occur 2 days after New and Full Moon.

TIME ZONE -0100
(Dutch Standard Time)
Subtract 1 hour for UT
For Dutch Summer Time add ONE hour in **non-shaded areas**

NETHERLANDS – HOEK VAN HOLLAND

LAT 51°59'N   LONG 4°06'E

TIMES AND HEIGHTS OF HIGH AND LOW WATERS

YEAR 2002

Note - Double LWs often occur. The predictions are for the lower LW which is usually the first.

JANUARY

Time	m		Time	m
1 TU 0346	2.1	**16** W 0007	0.5
0900	0.2	0435	1.9
1602	2.3	0939	0.1
2345	0.4	1644	2.1
2 W 0431	2.0	**17** TH 0044	0.5
0940	0.1	0504	1.9
1647	2.3	1015	0.1
		1725	2.1
3 TH 0046	0.4	**18** F 0124	0.5
0515	1.9	0539	1.9
1026	0.1	1100	0.1
1735	2.2	1801	2.0
4 F 0136	0.4	**19** SA 0124	0.5
0605	1.9	0615	1.9
1115	0.1	1135	0.1
1825	2.2	1839	1.9
5 SA 0205	0.4	**20** SU 0127	0.4
0655	1.8	0656	1.9
1213	0.0	1225	0.1
1925	2.1	1925	1.9
6 SU 0307	0.5	**21** M 0200	0.4
0800	1.8	0740	1.8
1324	0.0	1325	0.1
2025	2.0	2015	1.8
7 M 0410	0.5	**22** TU 0230	0.4
0905	1.8	0847	1.7
1435	0.1	1414	0.1
2145	1.9	2116	1.8
8 TU 0524	0.5	**23** W 0324	0.4
1015	1.8	0945	1.7
1539	0.1	1520	0.2
2244	1.9	2226	1.8
9 W 0630	0.5	**24** TH 0440	0.4
1115	1.8	1056	1.7
1650	0.2	1625	0.2
2355	1.9	2319	1.8
10 TH 0740	0.4	**25** F 0540	0.4
1220	1.9	1156	1.7
2000	0.2	1740	0.3
11 F 0056	1.9	**26** SA 0025	1.8
0850	0.4	0620	0.3
1311	2.0	1245	1.9
2040	0.3	1825	0.3
12 SA 0145	1.9	**27** SU 0120	1.9
0937	0.3	0644	0.3
1405	2.0	1335	2.0
2130	0.4	1904	0.3
13 SU 0234	1.9	**28** M 0205	1.9
1030	0.3	0724	0.3
1449	2.1	1241	2.1
2240	0.4	O 1945	0.3
14 M 0325	2.0	**29** TU 0249	2.0
0824	0.2	0754	0.2
1531	2.1	1505	2.2
2330	0.4	2255	0.4
15 TU 0405	2.0	**30** W 0330	2.0
0859	0.2	0840	0.1
1615	2.1	1547	2.3
		2350	0.4
		31 TH 0415	2.0
		0919	0.0
		1636	2.3

FEBRUARY

Time	m		Time	m
1 F 0035	0.4	**16** SA 0050	0.4
0501	2.0	0518	2.0
1006	0.0	1014	0.1
1718	2.3	1736	2.0
2 SA 0115	0.4	**17** SU 0116	0.4
0545	2.0	0545	2.0
1051	0.0	1054	0.1
1807	2.2	1806	2.0
3 SU 0200	0.4	**18** M 0134	0.3
0635	1.9	0619	1.9
1144	0.0	1145	0.0
1906	2.1	1840	2.0
4 M 0240	0.4	**19** TU 0050	0.3
0725	1.9	0655	1.9
1305	0.0	1224	0.0
2005	2.0	1915	1.9
5 TU 0230	0.4	**20** W 0134	0.3
0830	1.9	0734	1.8
1414	0.1	1345	0.1
2111	1.9	2003	1.8
6 W 0310	0.4	**21** TH 0215	0.3
0936	1.8	0845	1.8
1515	0.1	1434	0.1
2213	1.7	2126	1.7
7 TH 0410	0.4	**22** F 0315	0.3
1050	1.8	1006	1.7
1634	0.2	1544	0.2
2346	1.7	2246	1.6
8 F 0514	0.3	**23** SA 0450	0.3
1205	1.8	1125	1.7
1744	0.3	1705	0.3
9 SA 0056	1.7	**24** SU 0000	1.6
0604	0.3	0550	0.3
1305	1.8	1230	1.8
2125	0.3	1820	0.3
10 SU 0135	1.8	**25** M 0059	1.7
0940	0.3	0625	0.2
1354	2.0	1326	2.0
2210	0.3	2115	0.3
11 M 0234	1.9	**26** TU 0149	1.8
1030	0.2	0655	0.2
1445	2.0	1405	2.1
2255	0.4	2214	0.4
12 TU 0320	1.9	**27** W 0236	1.9
0814	0.2	0735	0.1
1519	2.1	1447	2.2
● 2320	0.4	O 2245	0.3
13 W 0349	1.9	**28** TH 0315	2.0
0845	0.1	0818	0.0
1556	2.1	1531	2.3
2355	0.4	2335	0.4
14 TH 0415	1.9		
0915	0.1		
1629	2.1		
15 F 0030	0.4		
0445	2.0		
0945	0.1		
1706	2.1		

MARCH

Time	m		Time	m
1 F 0355	2.0	**16** SA 0419	2.0
0856	-0.1	1154	0.1
1613	2.3	1631	2.1
2 SA 0026	0.3	**17** SU 0005	0.3
0438	2.0	0444	2.0
0939	-0.1	1224	0.1
1657	2.3	1701	2.0
3 SU 0054	0.3	**18** M 0044	0.3
0525	2.1	0519	2.0
1029	-0.1	1026	0.1
1746	2.2	1731	2.0
4 M 0145	0.3	**19** TU 0105	0.3
0607	2.1	0550	2.0
1123	0.0	1054	0.1
1835	2.0	1801	2.0
5 TU 0225	0.3	**20** W 0145	0.2
0655	2.0	0625	2.0
1300	0.0	1133	0.1
1930	1.9	1842	2.0
6 W 0130	0.3	**21** TH 0000	0.2
0756	1.9	0705	2.0
1354	0.1	1235	0.1
2030	1.7	1925	1.8
7 TH 0230	0.2	**22** F 0120	0.2
0854	1.8	0744	1.8
1504	0.1	1436	0.1
2150	1.6	2035	1.7
8 F 0335	0.2	**23** SA 0245	0.2
1025	1.7	0904	1.7
1624	0.2	1546	0.2
2319	1.5	2205	1.5
9 SA 0445	0.2	**24** SU 0400	0.2
1144	1.7	1044	1.7
1724	0.3	1700	0.3
		2336	1.5
10 SU 0036	1.6	**25** M 0504	0.2
0555	0.2	1203	1.8
1300	1.9	2006	0.3
2104	0.3		
11 M 0130	1.7	**26** TU 0040	1.6
0914	0.1	0555	0.1
1356	2.0	1305	2.0
2200	0.3	2110	0.2
12 TU 0213	1.8	**27** W 0125	1.7
1005	0.1	0636	0.1
1429	2.0	1345	2.1
2225	0.3	2206	0.2
13 W 0255	1.9	**28** TH 0215	1.9
1055	0.1	0716	0.0
1459	2.0	1447	2.2
2257	0.3	O 2225	0.3
14 TH 0325	1.9	**29** F 0250	2.0
0830	0.1	0749	-0.1
1529	2.1	1507	2.3
● 2336	0.3	2315	0.3
15 F 0344	1.9	**30** SA 0332	2.0
0843	0.1	0836	-0.1
1558	2.1	1552	2.3
2350	0.3		
		31 SU 0000	0.3
		0416	2.1
		0918	-0.1
		1636	2.2

APRIL

Time	m		Time	m
1 M 0045	0.2	**16** TU 0449	2.0
0457	2.1	1234	0.1
1005	0.0	1705	2.0
1721	2.1	2215	0.2
2 TU 0135	0.2	**17** W 0521	2.0
0541	2.1	1024	0.1
1105	0.1	1738	2.0
1807	2.0	2250	0.1
3 W 0215	0.2	**18** TH 0555	2.0
0625	2.1	1115	0.1
1300	0.1	1815	1.9
1855	1.8	2335	0.1
4 TH 0035	0.1	**19** F 0636	2.0
0725	2.0	1350	0.2
1354	0.1	1906	1.8
1955	1.6		
5 F 0154	0.1	**20** SA 0034	0.1
0823	1.8	0730	1.9
1454	0.2	1424	0.2
2114	1.5	2010	1.6
6 SA 0315	0.1	**21** SU 0205	0.1
1005	1.7	0844	1.8
1616	0.3	1530	0.2
2254	1.4	2145	1.5
7 SU 0434	0.1	**22** M 0325	0.1
1135	1.7	1023	1.8
1720	0.3	1750	0.3
		2305	1.5
8 M 0004	1.5	**23** TU 0424	0.1
0524	0.1	1139	1.9
1240	1.8	1940	0.3
2020	0.3		
9 TU 0106	1.7	**24** W 0015	1.6
0613	0.1	0526	0.1
1325	1.9	1235	2.0
2115	0.2	2056	0.2
10 W 0155	1.8	**25** TH 0101	1.7
0945	0.1	0606	0.0
1405	2.0	1321	2.1
2216	0.2	2125	0.2
11 TH 0223	1.8	**26** F 0148	1.9
0739	0.1	0648	0.0
1436	2.0	1406	2.2
2240	0.2	2216	0.2
12 F 0256	1.9	**27** SA 0229	2.0
0810	0.1	0725	0.0
1458	2.0	1447	2.2
● 2304	0.3	O 2255	0.3
13 SA 0319	2.1	**28** SU 0309	2.1
1030	0.1	0812	0.1
1531	2.1	1531	2.2
2310	0.3	2031	0.2
14 SU 0349	2.0	**29** M 0350	2.1
1115	0.1	0855	0.0
1606	2.1	1615	2.1
2335	0.2	2118	0.2
15 M 0419	2.0	**30** TU 0436	2.1
1205	0.1	1306	0.1
1631	2.0	1658	2.0
2135	0.2	2205	0.1

Chart Datum: 0·84 metres below NAP Datum

Register for your **FREE** weekly weather email service from Macmillan Reeds
》》 at **www.nauticaldata.com – NOW!**
weekend weather reports sent to your email address, every Thursday **《《**

NETHERLANDS – HOEK VAN HOLLAND

LAT 51°59′N   LONG 4°06′E

TIMES AND HEIGHTS OF HIGH AND LOW WATERS

YEAR 2002

TIME ZONE -0100
(Dutch Standard Time)
Subtract 1 hour for UT
For Dutch Summer Time add
ONE hour in **non-shaded areas**

Note - Double LWs often occur. The predictions are for the lower LW which is usually the first.

MAY

Day	Time	m	Time	m
1 W	0519 / 1334 / 1745 / 2300	2.1 / 0.1 / 1.9 / 0.1		
16 TH	0459 / 1244 / 1720 / 2229	2.0 / 0.2 / 1.9 / 0.1		
2 TH	0606 / 1425 / 1835	2.1 / 0.2 / 1.7		
17 F	0538 / 1315 / 1759 / 2319	2.1 / 0.2 / 1.8 / 0.0		
3 F	0005 / 0654 / 1344 / 1925	0.0 / 1.9 / 0.2 / 1.6		
18 SA	0626 / 1400 / 1849	2.0 / 0.2 / 1.7		
4 SA	0115 / 0805 / 1435 / 2035	0.0 / 1.8 / 0.3 / 1.5		
19 SU	0025 / 0716 / 1440 / 1955	0.0 / 1.9 / 0.3 / 1.5		
5 SU	0257 / 0930 / 1550 / 2215	0.0 / 1.7 / 0.3 / 1.4		
20 M	0144 / 0840 / 1557 / 2125	0.0 / 1.8 / 0.3 / 1.5		
6 M	0404 / 1054 / 1650 / 2336	0.0 / 1.7 / 0.3 / 1.5		
21 TU	0255 / 1006 / 1737 / 2240	0.0 / 1.9 / 0.3 / 1.5		
7 TU	0510 / 1159 / 1830	0.0 / 1.8 / 0.3		
22 W	0345 / 1116 / 1855 / 2346	0.0 / 1.9 / 0.3 / 1.6		
8 W	0024 / 0554 / 1250 / 2030	1.6 / 0.0 / 1.9 / 0.3		
23 TH	0450 / 1204 / 2005	0.0 / 2.0 / 0.3		
9 TH	0115 / 0634 / 1325 / 2115	1.7 / 0.1 / 1.9 / 0.2		
24 F	0038 / 0534 / 1256 / 2105	1.7 / 0.0 / 2.1 / 0.3		
10 F	0144 / 0730 / 1354 / 2215	1.8 / 0.1 / 2.0 / 0.2		
25 SA	0125 / 0626 / 1345 / 2145	1.9 / 0.0 / 2.1 / 0.3		
11 SA	0215 / 0830 / 1429 / 2240	1.8 / 0.2 / 2.0 / 0.2		
26 SU	0205 / 0709 / 1427 / ○1936	2.0 / 0.1 / 2.1 / 0.2		
12 SU	0248 / 1000 / 1459 / ●2250	1.9 / 0.2 / 2.0 / 0.2		
27 M	0248 / 0755 / 1512 / 2015	2.1 / 0.1 / 2.0 / 0.2		
13 M	0320 / 1047 / 1531 / 2320	2.0 / 0.2 / 2.0 / 0.2		
28 TU	0336 / 1134 / 1558 / 2059	2.1 / 0.2 / 2.0 / 0.1		
14 TU	0356 / 1125 / 1605 / 2354	2.0 / 0.2 / 2.0 / 0.2		
29 W	0417 / 1235 / 1645 / 2150	2.1 / 0.2 / 1.9 / 0.1		
15 W	0425 / 1215 / 1641 / 2155	2.0 / 0.2 / 2.0 / 0.2		
30 TH	0501 / 1335 / 1725 / 2239	2.1 / 0.2 / 1.8 / 0.0		
31 F	0545 / 1416 / 1815 / 2334	2.0 / 0.2 / 1.7 / 0.0		

JUNE

Day	Time	m
1 SA	0634 / 1455 / 1906	1.9 / 0.3 / 1.6
16 SU	0611 / 1410 / 1845	2.0 / 0.3 / 1.7
2 SU	0045 / 0740 / 1430 / 1955	0.0 / 1.8 / 0.4 / 1.5
17 M	0005 / 0705 / 1457 / 1945	0.0 / 2.0 / 0.3 / 1.6
3 M	0220 / 0846 / 1517 / 2106	0.0 / 1.7 / 0.4 / 1.5
18 TU	0120 / 0856 / 1557 / 2100	0.0 / 1.7 / 0.3 / 1.6
4 TU	0334 / 0955 / 1620 / 2245	0.0 / 1.7 / 0.3 / 1.4
19 W	0215 / 0935 / 1705 / 2210	0.0 / 1.9 / 0.3 / 1.6
5 W	0435 / 1105 / 1710 / 2346	0.0 / 1.7 / 0.3 / 1.5
20 TH	0325 / 1035 / 1835 / 2316	0.0 / 1.9 / 0.3 / 1.7
6 TH	0524 / 1206 / 1744	0.1 / 1.8 / 0.3
21 F	0425 / 1145 / 1930	0.0 / 2.0 / 0.3
7 F	0025 / 0620 / 1256 / 1824	1.6 / 0.1 / 1.9 / 0.3
22 SA	0005 / 0525 / 1238 / 2030	1.8 / 0.1 / 2.0 / 0.3
8 SA	0105 / 0700 / 1326 / 1915	1.7 / 0.1 / 1.9 / 0.2
23 SU	0102 / 0614 / 1329 / 2120	1.9 / 0.1 / 2.0 / 0.3
9 SU	0135 / 0730 / 1354 / 1940	1.8 / 0.2 / 1.9 / 0.2
24 M	0149 / 0704 / 1416 / ○1925	2.0 / 0.2 / 2.0 / 0.2
10 M	0215 / 0734 / 1428 / 1955	1.9 / 0.2 / 2.0 / 0.2
25 TU	0235 / 0734 / 1505 / 2004	2.0 / 0.2 / 1.9 / 0.2
11 TU	0249 / 0805 / 1509 / ●2029	2.0 / 0.3 / 2.0 / 0.2
26 W	0318 / 1125 / 1548 / 2056	2.1 / 0.3 / 1.9 / 0.1
12 W	0325 / 1107 / 1548 / 2105	2.0 / 0.3 / 2.0 / 0.2
27 TH	0406 / 1226 / 1635 / 2135	2.1 / 0.3 / 1.9 / 0.1
13 TH	0406 / 1145 / 1625 / 2134	2.1 / 0.3 / 1.9 / 0.1
28 F	0449 / 1316 / 1715 / 2225	2.1 / 0.4 / 1.8 / 0.0
14 F	0445 / 1224 / 1705 / 2225	2.1 / 0.3 / 1.8 / 0.1
29 SA	0531 / 1355 / 1751 / 2314	2.0 / 0.4 / 1.8 / 0.0
15 SA	0526 / 1326 / 1749 / 2315	2.1 / 0.3 / 1.8 / 0.0
30 SU	0614 / 1435 / 1836	1.9 / 0.4 / 1.7

JULY

Day	Time	m
1 M	0004 / 0705 / 1420 / 1926	0.0 / 1.9 / 0.4 / 1.7
16 TU	0656 / 1456 / 1925	2.1 / 0.4 / 1.7
2 TU	0110 / 0800 / 1450 / 2005	0.0 / 1.9 / 0.4 / 1.6
17 W	0049 / 0755 / 1525 / 2030	0.0 / 2.0 / 0.4 / 1.7
3 W	0230 / 0856 / 1534 / 2104	0.1 / 1.7 / 0.3 / 1.6
18 TH	0154 / 0905 / 1627 / 2136	0.0 / 1.9 / 0.4 / 1.7
4 TH	0406 / 0944 / 1624 / 2215	0.1 / 1.7 / 0.3 / 1.6
19 F	0255 / 1004 / 1730 / 2246	0.0 / 1.9 / 0.4 / 1.7
5 F	0445 / 1100 / 1704 / 2315	0.1 / 1.7 / 0.3 / 1.6
20 SA	0409 / 1120 / 1844 / 2348	0.1 / 1.9 / 0.4 / 1.8
6 SA	0544 / 1205 / 1755	0.2 / 1.8 / 0.3
21 SU	0520 / 1226 / 2000	0.2 / 1.9 / 0.3
7 SU	0015 / 0620 / 1246 / 1835	1.7 / 0.2 / 1.8 / 0.3
22 M	0046 / 0814 / 1319 / 1835	1.9 / 0.3 / 1.9 / 0.3
8 M	0101 / 0650 / 1325 / 1914	1.8 / 0.3 / 1.9 / 0.3
23 TU	0139 / 0920 / 1415 / 1924	2.0 / 0.3 / 1.9 / 0.2
9 TU	0146 / 0715 / 1405 / 1939	1.9 / 0.3 / 1.9 / 0.2
24 W	0224 / 1030 / 1459 / ○2005	2.0 / 0.4 / 1.9 / 0.2
10 W	0226 / 0745 / 1449 / ●2010	2.0 / 0.3 / 1.9 / 0.2
25 TH	0315 / 1105 / 1545 / 2045	2.1 / 0.4 / 1.9 / 0.1
11 TH	0305 / 0824 / 1528 / 2045	2.1 / 0.4 / 1.9 / 0.1
26 F	0350 / 1154 / 1614 / 2119	2.1 / 0.5 / 1.9 / 0.1
12 F	0347 / 1140 / 1611 / 2114	2.1 / 0.4 / 1.9 / 0.1
27 SA	0435 / 1256 / 1655 / 2200	2.1 / 0.5 / 1.9 / 0.1
13 SA	0429 / 1230 / 1655 / 2159	2.2 / 0.3 / 1.9 / 0.0
28 SU	0508 / 1336 / 1738 / 2235	2.1 / 0.5 / 1.9 / 0.1
14 SU	0515 / 1304 / 1738 / 2245	2.2 / 0.3 / 1.8 / 0.0
29 M	0549 / 1405 / 1805 / 2325	2.0 / 0.5 / 1.9 / 0.1
15 M	0601 / 1354 / 1829 / 2339	2.1 / 0.3 / 1.8 / 0.1
30 TU	0629 / 1400 / 1845	1.9 / 0.5 / 1.8
31 W	0015 / 0709 / 1400 / 1925	0.1 / 1.9 / 0.4 / 1.8

AUGUST

Day	Time	m
1 TH	0104 / 0806 / 1440 / 2026	0.1 / 1.8 / 0.4 / 1.7
16 F	0145 / 0830 / 1450 / 2100	0.1 / 1.9 / 0.4 / 1.8
2 F	0154 / 0845 / 1520 / 2115	0.1 / 1.8 / 0.4 / 1.7
17 SA	0255 / 0940 / 1540 / 2215	0.1 / 1.9 / 0.4 / 1.8
3 SA	0255 / 0950 / 1640 / 2226	0.2 / 1.7 / 0.4 / 1.6
18 SU	0405 / 1054 / 1650 / 2325	0.2 / 1.7 / 0.4 / 1.8
4 SU	0430 / 1055 / 1734 / 2329	0.3 / 1.7 / 0.3 / 1.7
19 M	0514 / 1216 / 1745	0.3 / 1.7 / 0.3
5 M	0550 / 1205 / 1814	0.3 / 1.7 / 0.3
20 TU	0035 / 0850 / 1313 / 2116	1.9 / 0.4 / 1.8 / 0.3
6 TU	0031 / 0630 / 1306 / 1845	1.8 / 0.3 / 1.8 / 0.3
21 W	0140 / 0945 / 1409 / 2205	2.0 / 0.4 / 1.9 / 0.2
7 W	0125 / 0700 / 1349 / 1915	1.9 / 0.3 / 1.9 / 0.3
22 TH	0223 / 1034 / 1455 / ○1955	2.1 / 0.4 / 1.9 / 0.2
8 TH	0208 / 0729 / 1431 / ●1945	2.0 / 0.4 / 1.9 / 0.2
23 F	0305 / 1055 / 1524 / 2025	2.1 / 0.5 / 1.9 / 0.2
9 F	0249 / 0805 / 1515 / 2019	2.2 / 0.4 / 2.0 / 0.1
24 SA	0339 / 1145 / 1606 / 2100	2.1 / 0.5 / 2.0 / 0.1
10 SA	0332 / 1130 / 1555 / 2058	2.2 / 0.4 / 2.0 / 0.0
25 SU	0411 / 1220 / 1635 / 2124	2.1 / 0.5 / 2.0 / 0.1
11 SU	0412 / 1204 / 1635 / 2139	2.3 / 0.4 / 2.0 / 0.0
26 M	0445 / 1245 / 1705 / 2159	2.1 / 0.5 / 2.0 / 0.1
12 M	0455 / 1255 / 1721 / 2225	2.3 / 0.4 / 2.0 / 0.0
27 TU	0519 / 1320 / 1735 / 2239	2.1 / 0.5 / 2.0 / 0.2
13 TU	0541 / 1334 / 1808 / 2315	2.2 / 0.4 / 1.9 / 0.0
28 W	0555 / 1340 / 1808 / 2325	2.0 / 0.5 / 2.0 / 0.2
14 W	0635 / 1415 / 1855	2.1 / 0.4 / 1.9
29 TH	0626 / 1200 / 1839	2.0 / 0.4 / 1.9
15 TH	0025 / 0725 / 1510 / 1956	0.0 / 2.0 / 0.4 / 1.9
30 F	0004 / 0700 / 1304 / 1913	0.2 / 1.9 / 0.4 / 1.9
31 SA	0114 / 0739 / 1400 / 2010	0.2 / 1.9 / 0.4 / 1.8

Chart Datum: 0·84 metres below NAP Datum

TIME ZONE -0100
(Dutch Standard Time)
Subtract 1 hour for UT
For Dutch Summer Time add
ONE hour in **non-shaded areas**

NETHERLANDS – HOEK VAN HOLLAND

LAT 51°59'N   LONG 4°06'E

TIMES AND HEIGHTS OF HIGH AND LOW WATERS

YEAR 2002

Note - Double LWs often
occur. The predictions are
for the lower LW which is
usually the first.

SEPTEMBER

Day	Time m	Time m	Time m	Time m
1 SU	0220 0.2	0856 1.8	1455 0.4	2124 1.7
2 M	0325 0.3	1010 1.7	1700 0.4	2255 1.7
3 TU	0510 0.4	1124 1.6	1754 0.4	
4 W	0010 1.8	0620 0.4	1240 1.7	1815 0.3
5 TH	0105 2.0	0905 0.4	1324 1.8	1844 0.3
6 F	0145 2.1	1006 0.4	1408 1.9	1919 0.2
7 SA	0225 2.3	1025 0.4	1451 2.0	●1955 0.1
8 SU	0308 2.4	1105 0.5	1536 2.1	2031 0.0
9 M	0351 2.4	1155 0.5	1613 2.1	2116 0.0
10 TU	0436 2.3	1246 0.5	1657 2.1	2159 0.0
11 W	0517 2.3	1314 0.5	1741 2.1	2249 0.1
12 TH	0605 2.1	1355 0.4	1826 2.1	2355 0.2
13 F	0655 2.0	1420 0.4	1919 2.0	
14 SA	0145 0.2	0800 1.9	1400 0.4	2026 1.9
15 SU	0240 0.3	0910 1.8	1505 0.4	2155 1.8
16 M	0345 0.4	1050 1.6	1630 0.4	2326 1.8
17 TU	0640 0.4	1206 1.7	1724 0.3	
18 W	0035 1.9	0827 0.4	1306 1.8	2045 0.2
19 TH	0123 2.1	0945 0.4	1356 1.9	2155 0.2
20 F	0204 2.1	1024 0.4	1433 2.0	2234 0.2
21 SA	0245 2.2	1050 0.5	1504 2.0	○2004 0.2
22 SU	0315 2.2	1114 0.5	1535 2.0	2035 0.2
23 M	0348 2.2	1150 0.5	1605 2.1	2054 0.2
24 TU	0419 2.2	1220 0.5	1635 2.1	2124 0.2
25 W	0449 2.1	1250 0.4	1705 2.1	2206 0.3
26 TH	0520 2.1	1019 0.4	1731 2.1	2240 0.3
27 F	0545 2.1	1100 0.4	1801 2.1	2315 0.3
28 SA	0619 2.0	1134 0.3	1840 2.0	
29 SU	0004 0.3	0659 2.0	1240 0.3	1925 1.9
30 M	0154 0.3	0756 1.8	1407 0.4	2024 1.8

OCTOBER

Day	Time m	Time m	Time m	Time m
1 TU	0310 0.4	0915 1.6	1525 0.4	2214 1.7
2 W	0440 0.4	1106 1.6	1710 0.4	2334 1.9
3 TH	0630 0.5	1215 1.7	1746 0.3	
4 F	0039 2.1	0837 0.4	1305 1.8	1816 0.2
5 SA	0125 2.2	0946 0.4	1348 2.0	1856 0.1
6 SU	0205 2.3	1026 0.5	1427 2.1	●1930 0.1
7 M	0246 2.4	0755 0.5	1509 2.2	2010 0.0
8 TU	0328 2.4	0829 0.5	1549 2.2	2049 0.1
9 W	0410 2.4	0915 0.4	1632 2.3	2135 0.1
10 TH	0455 2.2	0955 0.4	1716 2.3	2230 0.2
11 F	0541 2.1	1049 0.4	1801 2.2	2334 0.3
12 SA	0629 2.0	1145 0.3	1855 2.1	
13 SU	0136 0.3	0725 1.8	1320 0.3	2006 1.9
14 M	0214 0.4	0834 1.6	1444 0.4	2115 1.8
15 TU	0334 0.5	1025 1.6	1605 0.3	2315 1.8
16 W	0625 0.5	1146 1.7	1704 0.3	
17 TH	0004 2.0	0750 0.5	1234 1.8	2007 0.2
18 F	0105 2.1	0916 0.4	1330 1.9	2125 0.2
19 SA	0146 2.1	0956 0.4	1404 2.0	2216 0.2
20 SU	0215 2.2	1015 0.4	1439 2.0	1945 0.3
21 M	0249 2.2	1047 0.5	1505 2.1	○2004 0.3
22 TU	0319 2.2	1126 0.5	1535 2.1	2035 0.3
23 W	0345 2.2	0855 0.4	1605 2.1	2059 0.1
24 TH	0419 2.2	1210 0.4	1635 2.1	2136 0.3
25 F	0449 2.1	0953 0.4	1705 2.1	2210 0.3
26 SA	0522 2.1	1036 0.3	1738 2.1	2245 0.3
27 SU	0555 2.0	1104 0.3	1816 2.1	2324 0.4
28 M	0638 1.9	1155 0.3	1900 2.0	
29 TU	0147 0.4	0730 1.8	1334 0.3	1959 1.9
30 W	0245 0.5	0906 1.6	1456 0.3	2156 1.8
31 TH	0440 0.5	1025 1.6	1606 0.3	2316 2.0

NOVEMBER

Day	Time m	Time m	Time m	Time m
1 F	0654 0.5	1139 1.7	1644 0.3	
2 SA	0015 2.1	0825 0.4	1235 1.8	1739 0.2
3 SU	0055 2.2	0904 0.4	1322 2.0	1825 0.1
4 M	0142 2.3	0956 0.5	1400 2.1	●1905 0.1
5 TU	0226 2.4	0729 0.4	1445 2.2	1945 0.1
6 W	0307 2.3	0809 0.4	1527 2.3	2032 0.2
7 TH	0351 2.3	0855 0.3	1611 2.3	2118 0.3
8 F	0435 2.2	0939 0.3	1656 2.3	2150 0.4
9 SA	0126 0.4	0521 0.4	1029 0.3	1738 2.2
10 SU	0157 0.4	0605 1.9	1125 0.2	1828 2.1
11 M	0110 0.5	0706 1.8	1234 0.2	1935 2.0
12 TU	0155 0.5	0804 1.6	1355 0.2	2054 1.8
13 W	0320 0.6	0956 1.6	1540 0.2	2235 1.8
14 TH	0537 0.5	1105 1.6	1634 0.2	2335 1.9
15 F	0700 0.5	1205 1.7	1746 0.2	
16 SA	0029 2.0	0807 0.4	1256 1.8	1830 0.2
17 SU	0116 2.1	0910 0.4	1336 1.9	1920 0.3
18 M	0150 2.1	0945 0.4	1406 2.0	1957 0.3
19 TU	0214 2.1	1036 0.4	1435 2.0	2120 0.3
20 W	0249 2.1	0815 0.4	1501 2.1	○2220 0.4
21 TH	0326 2.1	0834 0.4	1535 2.1	2310 0.4
22 F	0355 2.1	0905 0.4	1608 2.2	2356 0.4
23 SA	0425 2.1	0945 0.3	1641 2.2	2150 0.4
24 SU	0501 2.0	1014 0.3	1718 2.2	2235 0.4
25 M	0539 2.0	1055 0.2	1758 2.1	
26 TU	0140 0.4	0626 1.9	1155 0.2	1845 2.1
27 W	0207 0.5	0720 1.8	1254 0.2	1949 2.0
28 TH	0310 0.5	0835 1.6	1426 0.2	2126 1.9
29 F	0450 0.5	0955 1.6	1515 0.2	2235 2.0
30 SA	0617 0.5	1110 1.7	1620 0.2	2340 2.1

DECEMBER

Day	Time m	Time m	Time m	Time m
1 SU	0735 0.5	1206 1.8	1709 0.2	
2 M	0029 2.2	0846 0.4	1256 2.0	1755 0.2
3 TU	0117 2.2	0915 0.4	1338 2.1	1845 0.2
4 W	0205 2.2	0715 0.4	1426 2.2	●1935 0.2
5 TH	0251 2.2	0756 0.3	1509 2.3	2014 0.3
6 F	0335 2.1	0835 0.3	1556 2.3	
7 SA	0005 0.4	0421 2.1	0925 0.2	1638 2.3
8 SU	0106 0.4	0509 2.0	1015 0.2	1728 2.2
9 M	0156 0.5	0556 1.9	1115 0.1	1815 2.1
10 TU	0227 0.5	0639 1.8	1205 0.1	1916 2.0
11 W	0140 0.5	0735 1.7	1324 0.1	2014 1.9
12 TH	0235 0.5	0835 1.6	1450 0.2	2124 1.8
13 F	0350 0.5	1000 1.6	1610 0.2	2244 1.8
14 SA	0435 0.5	1125 1.6	1716 0.2	2350 1.9
15 SU	0524 0.5	1205 1.7	1755 0.2	
16 M	0029 1.9	0614 0.4	1249 1.8	1850 0.3
17 TU	0116 2.0	0654 0.4	1330 1.9	1950 0.3
18 W	0149 2.0	0724 0.4	1406 1.9	2050 0.3
19 TH	0226 2.0	0804 0.4	1435 2.0	○2150 0.4
20 F	0255 2.1	0824 0.3	1511 2.1	2240 0.4
21 SA	0335 2.1	0835 0.3	1549 2.2	2330 0.4
22 SU	0408 2.0	0925 0.2	1626 2.2	
23 M	0010 0.4	0449 2.0	1006 0.2	1706 2.2
24 TU	0044 0.4	0529 1.9	1045 0.1	1745 2.2
25 W	0146 0.4	0616 1.8	1136 0.1	1838 2.1
26 TH	0230 0.4	0710 1.8	1246 0.1	1934 2.0
27 F	0307 0.5	0816 1.7	1335 0.1	2055 2.0
28 SA	0407 0.5	0919 1.7	1456 0.1	2205 2.0
29 SU	0527 0.5	1030 1.8	1556 0.1	2305 2.0
30 M	0650 0.5	1136 1.8	1650 0.2	
31 TU	0010 2.0	0800 0.5	1229 1.9	1750 0.2

Chart Datum: 0·84 metres below NAP Datum

Register for your **FREE** weekly weather email service from Macmillan Reeds
》 at **www.nauticaldata.com – NOW!** 《
weekend weather reports sent to your email address, every Thursday

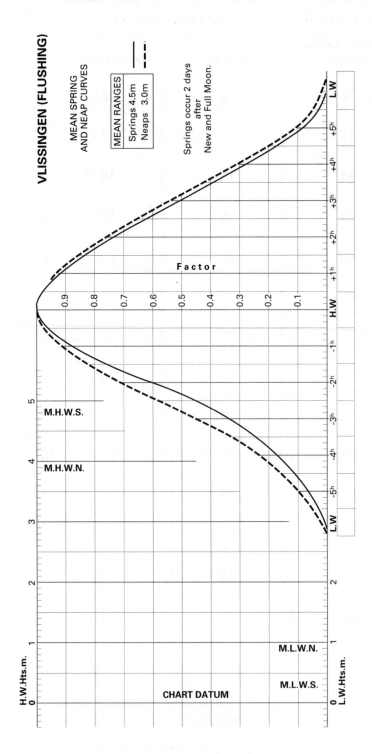

VLISSINGEN (FLUSHING)

MEAN SPRING
AND NEAP CURVES

MEAN RANGES
Springs 4.5m
Neaps 3.0m

Springs occur 2 days
after
New and Full Moon.

Factor

0.9 0.8 0.7 0.6 0.5 0.4 0.3 0.2 0.1

H.W

M.H.W.S.

M.H.W.N.

M.L.W.N.

M.L.W.S.

CHART DATUM

H.W.Hts.m.

L.W.Hts.m.

Register for your **FREE** weekly weather email service from Macmillan Reeds
at **www.nauticaldata.com – NOW!**
weekend weather reports sent to your email address, every Thursday

154

NETHERLANDS – VLISSINGEN

LAT 51°27′N   LONG 3°36′E

TIMES AND HEIGHTS OF HIGH AND LOW WATERS

YEAR 2002

TIME ZONE -0100
(Dutch Standard Time)
Subtract 1 hour for UT
For Dutch Summer Time add
ONE hour in **non-shaded areas**

JANUARY

Day	Time	m	Time	m	Time	m	Time	m
1 TU	0302	4.7	0928	0.3	1519	4.9	2146	0.4
2 W	0345	4.7	1016	0.2	1606	4.9	2230	0.5
3 TH	0429	4.6	1105	0.2	1650	4.8	2318	0.6
4 F	0517	4.5	1151	0.2	1742	4.6		
5 SA	0006	0.7	0611	4.3	1246	0.2	1846	4.5
6 SU	0100	0.8	0709	4.2	1346	0.3	1948	4.3
7 M	0154	0.9	0816	4.1	1445	0.5	2055	4.2
8 TU	0310	1.0	0925	4.1	1606	0.6	2205	4.1
9 W	0425	1.0	1036	4.1	1710	0.6	2312	4.2
10 TH	0545	0.9	1136	4.2	1816	0.6		
11 F	0008	4.3	0635	0.7	1236	4.4	1900	0.5
12 SA	0105	4.4	0721	0.5	1325	4.5	1941	0.5
13 SU	0151	4.4	0809	0.4	1411	4.6	●2026	0.6
14 M	0236	4.5	0856	0.3	1451	4.7	2102	0.6
15 TU	0311	4.5	0936	0.3	1529	4.6	2135	0.7
16 W	0346	4.5	1009	0.3	1606	4.6	2216	0.7
17 TH	0421	4.5	1048	0.3	1638	4.5	2248	0.7
18 F	0457	4.4	1126	0.4	1715	4.4	2320	0.8
19 SA	0529	4.3	1156	0.5	1749	4.3	2349	0.8
20 SU	0610	4.2	1226	0.5	1835	4.1		
21 M	0036	0.9	0649	4.1	1306	0.6	1920	4.0
22 TU	0116	1.0	0745	3.9	1355	0.7	2021	3.9
23 W	0215	1.1	0850	3.8	1506	0.8	2126	3.8
24 TH	0340	1.1	0955	3.8	1620	0.8	2235	3.9
25 F	0455	1.0	1105	4.0	1719	0.7	2340	4.0
26 SA	0555	0.8	1201	4.2	1826	0.6		
27 SU	0035	4.2	0645	0.7	1256	4.4	1912	0.6
28 M	0119	4.4	0740	0.4	1337	4.7	○2000	0.4
29 TU	0206	4.6	0830	0.3	1422	4.9	2046	0.4
30 W	0247	4.7	0915	0.1	1506	5.0	2129	0.4
31 TH	0330	4.7	1005	0.0	1550	5.0	2215	0.4

FEBRUARY

Day	Time	m	Time	m	Time	m	Time	m
1 F	0415	4.8	1052	-0.1	1636	4.9	2306	0.4
2 SA	0501	4.7	1135	-0.1	1726	4.8	2348	0.5
3 SU	0548	4.6	1226	0.1	1819	4.6		
4 M	0035	0.6	0641	4.4	1316	0.2	1916	4.3
5 TU	0125	0.7	0742	4.2	1410	0.4	2020	4.1
6 W	0224	0.9	0850	4.1	1526	0.7	2129	3.9
7 TH	0350	0.9	1006	3.9	1640	0.8	2250	3.8
8 F	0516	0.9	1119	4.0	1756	0.8		
9 SA	0000	4.0	0619	0.7	1225	4.2	1845	0.7
10 SU	0056	4.1	0716	0.5	1326	4.4	1929	0.7
11 M	0141	4.3	0806	0.3	1405	4.5	2010	0.7
12 TU	0221	4.4	0839	0.3	1438	4.6	●2041	0.6
13 W	0255	4.5	0916	0.3	1515	4.6	2118	0.6
14 TH	0325	4.5	0950	0.2	1546	4.6	2156	0.6
15 F	0357	4.6	1022	0.2	1616	4.6	2226	0.6
16 SA	0427	4.6	1052	0.3	1646	4.5	2256	0.6
17 SU	0459	4.5	1120	0.3	1716	4.4	2315	0.6
18 M	0531	4.4	1151	0.4	1748	4.4	2350	0.6
19 TU	0605	4.3	1226	0.4	1826	4.2		
20 W	0030	0.7	0646	4.2	1305	0.5	1916	4.0
21 TH	0120	0.8	0751	3.9	1406	0.7	2031	3.8
22 F	0223	1.0	0905	3.8	1526	0.9	2148	3.7
23 SA	0406	1.0	1030	3.8	1645	0.8	2311	3.8
24 SU	0526	0.8	1140	4.1	1801	0.7		
25 M	0016	4.0	0630	0.6	1236	4.4	1856	0.6
26 TU	0106	4.3	0725	0.3	1322	4.7	1945	0.4
27 W	0147	4.6	0816	0.1	1404	4.9	○2030	0.3
28 TH	0229	4.7	0859	-0.1	1449	5.1	2113	0.3

MARCH

Day	Time	m	Time	m	Time	m	Time	m
1 F	0310	4.9	0946	-0.2	1533	5.1	2158	0.2
2 SA	0353	4.9	1029	-0.2	1616	5.0	2242	0.3
3 SU	0438	4.7	1115	-0.1	1703	4.9	2325	0.3
4 M	0522	4.8	1156	0.0	1751	4.6		
5 TU	0005	0.4	0611	4.6	1246	0.2	1846	4.3
6 W	0056	0.6	0708	4.3	1329	0.5	1941	4.0
7 TH	0200	0.7	0819	4.0	1435	0.8	2100	3.7
8 F	0315	0.9	0934	3.8	1604	1.0	2230	3.6
9 SA	0456	0.9	1105	3.8	1724	0.9	2338	3.8
10 SU	0605	0.7	1215	4.1	1829	0.8		
11 M	0039	4.0	0706	0.5	1306	4.3	1916	0.7
12 TU	0128	4.2	0748	0.3	1350	4.5	1949	0.7
13 W	0201	4.4	0819	0.3	1426	4.5	2026	0.6
14 TH	0231	4.5	0856	0.2	1449	4.6	●2056	0.5
15 F	0259	4.6	0925	0.2	1517	4.6	2125	0.5
16 SA	0329	4.6	0955	0.2	1548	4.6	2200	0.4
17 SU	0357	4.6	1025	0.2	1615	4.6	2228	0.4
18 M	0429	4.6	1052	0.3	1642	4.6	2252	0.5
19 TU	0500	4.6	1116	0.3	1716	4.5	2326	0.5
20 W	0532	4.5	1150	0.4	1751	4.4		
21 TH	0000	0.5	0609	4.3	1236	0.5	1838	4.1
22 F	0051	0.6	0702	4.1	1325	0.7	1946	3.8
23 SA	0155	0.8	0826	3.8	1445	0.9	2104	3.6
24 SU	0323	0.9	0954	3.8	1614	0.9	2234	3.7
25 M	0500	0.7	1115	4.1	1736	0.8	2350	4.0
26 TU	0616	0.5	1216	4.4	1836	0.6		
27 W	0039	4.3	0708	0.2	1305	4.7	1926	0.4
28 TH	0126	4.6	0755	0.0	1346	5.0	○2012	0.3
29 F	0206	4.8	0839	-0.1	1428	5.1	●2056	0.2
30 SA	0247	4.9	0925	-0.2	1510	5.1	2135	0.2
31 SU	0328	5.0	1006	-0.2	1556	5.0	2220	0.2

APRIL

Day	Time	m	Time	m	Time	m	Time	m
1 M	0413	5.0	1051	-0.1	1639	4.8	2259	0.2
2 TU	0456	4.8	1130	0.1	1726	4.6	2346	0.3
3 W	0545	4.6	1209	0.3	1816	4.2		
4 TH	0029	0.4	0640	4.3	1300	0.6	1915	3.9
5 F	0124	0.6	0746	3.9	1405	0.9	2025	3.6
6 SA	0256	0.8	0916	3.7	1546	1.1	2206	3.5
7 SU	0426	0.8	1046	3.8	1655	1.0	2320	3.7
8 M	0540	0.6	1149	4.0	1805	0.9		
9 TU	0015	3.9	0641	0.5	1239	4.3	1855	0.7
10 W	0058	4.2	0720	0.3	1319	4.4	1926	0.6
11 TH	0136	4.3	0755	0.3	1351	4.5	1956	0.5
12 F	0206	4.4	0822	0.2	1418	4.6	●2031	0.4
13 SA	0228	4.5	0852	0.2	1446	4.6	2059	0.4
14 SU	0259	4.6	0921	0.2	1517	4.7	2136	0.4
15 M	0329	4.7	0956	0.2	1547	4.7	2206	0.4
16 TU	0401	4.7	1026	0.3	1617	4.6	2236	0.4
17 W	0433	4.6	1059	0.3	1652	4.6	2306	0.4
18 TH	0507	4.5	1135	0.4	1727	4.4	2347	0.4
19 F	0545	4.4	1216	0.5	1815	4.1		
20 SA	0036	0.5	0639	4.2	1310	0.7	1920	3.8
21 SU	0146	0.7	0805	3.9	1425	0.9	2050	3.6
22 M	0316	0.7	0938	3.9	1555	0.9	2212	3.7
23 TU	0446	0.6	1051	4.1	1716	0.8	2321	4.0
24 W	0550	0.4	1151	4.5	1816	0.6		
25 TH	0016	4.3	0648	0.1	1239	4.7	1906	0.4
26 F	0059	4.6	0735	0.0	1326	4.9	1950	0.3
27 SA	0141	4.8	0821	-0.1	1406	5.0	○2033	0.2
28 SU	0226	4.9	0902	-0.1	1449	5.0	2115	0.1
29 M	0307	5.0	0943	0.0	1533	4.9	2200	0.1
30 TU	0353	4.9	1022	0.1	1616	4.7	2242	0.2

Chart Datum: 2·32 metres below NAP Datum
Register for your **FREE** weekly weather email service from Macmillan Reeds
at **www.nauticaldata.com – NOW!**
》》 weekend weather reports sent to your email address, every Thursday 《《

TIME ZONE -0100
(Dutch Standard Time)
Subtract 1 hour for UT
For Dutch Summer Time add
ONE hour in **non-shaded areas**

NETHERLANDS – VLISSINGEN

LAT 51°27′N   LONG 3°36′E

TIMES AND HEIGHTS OF HIGH AND LOW WATERS

YEAR 2002

MAY

Day	Time m	Time m	Time m	Time m	Day	Time m	Time m	Time m	Time m
1 W	0435 4.8	1105 0.3	1702 4.5	2326 0.3	16 TH	0410 4.6	1041 0.4	1632 4.4	2258 0.3
2 TH	0522 4.5	1146 0.5	1749 4.2		17 F	0451 4.6	1116 0.5	1712 4.3	2346 0.4
3 F	0016 0.4	0616 4.2	1235 0.8	1841 3.9	18 SA	0536 4.4	1206 0.6	1806 4.1	
4 SA	0116 0.5	0719 3.9	1346 1.0	1945 3.6	19 SU	0036 0.4	0636 4.2	1254 0.8	1909 3.8
5 SU	0226 0.7	0846 3.7	1500 1.1	2127 3.5	20 M	0145 0.5	0756 4.0	1404 0.9	2024 3.7
6 M	0340 0.7	1010 3.7	1625 1.1	2234 3.6	21 TU	0255 0.5	0916 4.1	1536 0.9	2146 3.8
7 TU	0454 0.6	1115 3.9	1715 0.9	2336 3.8	22 W	0416 0.4	1026 4.2	1656 0.8	2251 4.0
8 W	0555 0.5	1201 4.1	1804 0.8		23 TH	0525 0.3	1126 4.4	1756 0.6	2345 4.3
9 TH	0018 4.1	0640 0.4	1245 4.3	1844 0.6	24 F	0626 0.2	1218 4.6	1842 0.5	
10 F	0057 4.2	0715 0.4	1316 4.4	1925 0.5	25 SA	0035 4.5	0715 0.1	1305 4.7	1930 0.3
11 SA	0126 4.4	0745 0.3	1348 4.5	2001 0.4	26 SU	0123 4.7	0757 0.0	1347 4.8	O 2015 0.2
12 SU	0157 4.5	0815 0.3	1417 4.6	● 2036 0.4	27 M	0205 4.8	0839 0.1	1433 4.8	2100 0.2
13 M	0227 4.6	0856 0.2	1447 4.7	2108 0.3	28 TU	0249 4.8	0926 0.2	1515 4.7	2146 0.1
14 TU	0302 4.7	0928 0.3	1521 4.6	2146 0.3	29 W	0335 4.8	1006 0.3	1602 4.6	2230 0.2
15 W	0337 4.7	1006 0.3	1555 4.6	2220 0.3	30 TH	0421 4.7	1041 0.5	1646 4.4	2316 0.2
					31 F	0505 4.5	1126 0.6	1731 4.2	2355 0.3

JUNE

Day	Time m	Time m	Time m	Time m	Day	Time m	Time m	Time m	Time m
1 SA	0600 4.3	1205 0.8	1814 4.0		16 SU	0528 4.5	1156 0.7	1758 4.2	
2 SU	0044 0.5	0656 4.0	1306 1.0	1909 3.8	17 M	0035 0.3	0626 4.3	1250 0.8	1859 4.0
3 M	0150 0.6	0755 3.8	1416 1.1	2016 3.6	18 TU	0136 0.3	0740 4.2	1356 0.8	2010 4.0
4 TU	0255 0.6	0916 3.7	1514 1.1	2141 3.6	19 W	0240 0.3	0850 4.2	1506 0.9	2116 4.0
5 W	0355 0.7	1025 3.8	1619 1.0	2246 3.7	20 TH	0346 0.4	0956 4.2	1615 0.8	2226 4.1
6 TH	0500 0.6	1118 4.0	1714 0.8	2332 3.9	21 F	0506 0.4	1059 4.3	1726 0.7	2321 4.3
7 F	0545 0.5	1206 4.2	1805 0.7		22 SA	0600 0.3	1156 4.4	1826 0.6	
8 SA	0016 4.1	0636 0.5	1238 4.3	1845 0.6	23 SU	0016 4.4	0649 0.3	1247 4.5	1915 0.4
9 SU	0052 4.3	0705 0.4	1312 4.5	1928 0.5	24 M	0106 4.6	0735 0.3	1336 4.6	O 1959 0.3
10 M	0128 4.4	0745 0.4	1349 4.5	2006 0.4	25 TU	0155 4.7	0822 0.3	1420 4.6	2045 0.2
11 TU	0205 4.5	0826 0.3	1425 4.6	● 2046 0.4	26 W	0241 4.7	0901 0.4	1505 4.6	2132 0.2
12 W	0242 4.6	0906 0.4	1500 4.6	2125 0.3	27 TH	0325 4.7	0945 0.5	1548 4.5	2216 0.2
13 TH	0316 4.7	0946 0.4	1541 4.5	2208 0.3	28 F	0408 4.6	1021 0.6	1631 4.4	2255 0.2
14 F	0356 4.7	1026 0.5	1621 4.4	2252 0.3	29 SA	0456 4.5	1102 0.7	1716 4.3	2334 0.3
15 SA	0441 4.6	1111 0.5	1705 4.3	2339 0.3	30 SU	0536 4.3	1146 0.8	1756 4.2	

JULY

Day	Time m	Time m	Time m	Time m	Day	Time m	Time m	Time m	Time m
1 M	0026 0.4	0626 4.1	1236 0.9	1835 4.0	16 TU	0026 0.1	0612 4.5	1236 0.7	1839 4.3
2 TU	0105 0.5	0705 4.0	1315 1.0	1928 3.9	17 W	0116 0.2	0716 4.4	1329 0.8	1942 4.2
3 W	0200 0.6	0805 3.8	1425 1.0	2025 3.8	18 TH	0216 0.3	0819 4.3	1435 0.8	2049 4.1
4 TH	0301 0.7	0905 3.8	1536 1.0	2130 3.7	19 F	0316 0.4	0925 4.2	1539 0.9	2151 4.1
5 F	0355 0.7	1004 3.8	1625 1.0	2236 3.8	20 SA	0436 0.5	1036 4.1	1706 0.8	2302 4.2
6 SA	0449 0.7	1116 4.0	1725 0.9	2329 4.0	21 SU	0541 0.5	1139 4.2	1806 0.7	
7 SU	0550 0.6	1202 4.1	1812 0.7		22 M	0001 4.3	0635 0.5	1238 4.3	1906 0.5
8 M	0016 4.1	0635 0.6	1245 4.3	1900 0.6	23 TU	0101 4.5	0726 0.5	1325 4.4	1952 0.3
9 TU	0058 4.3	0718 0.5	1326 4.4	1946 0.5	24 W	0151 4.6	0805 0.5	1416 4.5	O 2038 0.3
10 W	0143 4.5	0800 0.5	1406 4.5	● 2026 0.4	25 TH	0236 4.6	0845 0.6	1455 4.5	2120 0.2
11 TH	0222 4.7	0846 0.4	1447 4.6	2112 0.3	26 F	0316 4.7	0925 0.6	1535 4.5	2200 0.2
12 F	0302 4.7	0928 0.4	1527 4.6	2158 0.2	27 SA	0355 4.6	1002 0.7	1608 4.5	2238 0.2
13 SA	0346 4.8	1012 0.5	1609 4.5	2245 0.1	28 SU	0431 4.6	1040 0.7	1646 4.5	2316 0.3
14 SU	0431 4.8	1058 0.5	1657 4.5	2336 0.1	29 M	0508 4.4	1116 0.8	1718 4.4	2351 0.4
15 M	0518 4.7	1145 0.6	1746 4.4		30 TU	0546 4.3	1150 0.8	1758 4.3	
					31 W	0026 0.5	0626 4.2	1225 0.9	1840 4.1

AUGUST

Day	Time m	Time m	Time m	Time m	Day	Time m	Time m	Time m	Time m
1 TH	0106 0.6	0706 4.0	1305 1.0	1925 4.0	16 F	0146 0.4	0748 4.2	1405 0.8	2011 4.2
2 F	0134 0.7	0800 3.9	1359 1.1	2026 3.8	17 SA	0245 0.6	0855 4.0	1516 0.9	2126 4.0
3 SA	0250 0.8	0854 3.8	1530 1.1	2136 3.7	18 SU	0400 0.8	1016 3.9	1646 0.9	2246 4.0
4 SU	0400 0.9	1015 3.8	1635 1.0	2246 3.8	19 M	0526 0.8	1130 4.0	1755 0.7	2354 4.2
5 M	0506 0.8	1119 3.9	1746 0.9	2345 4.0	20 TU	0626 0.7	1229 4.2	1855 0.5	
6 TU	0606 0.7	1220 4.1	1835 0.7		21 W	0055 4.4	0709 0.7	1318 4.4	1942 0.4
7 W	0042 4.3	0655 0.6	1305 4.3	1926 0.5	22 TH	0146 4.6	0755 0.7	1406 4.5	O 2025 0.3
8 TH	0125 4.6	0746 0.5	1347 4.5	● 2012 0.3	23 F	0225 4.7	0832 0.7	1442 4.6	2101 0.2
9 F	0207 4.8	0828 0.5	1429 4.7	2055 0.2	24 SA	0258 4.7	0905 0.7	1516 4.6	2138 0.2
10 SA	0246 4.9	0909 0.4	1510 4.7	2142 0.0	25 SU	0331 4.7	0940 0.7	1546 4.6	2209 0.3
11 SU	0330 5.0	0955 0.4	1553 4.8	2230 0.0	26 M	0406 4.6	1015 0.7	1617 4.6	2246 0.3
12 M	0415 5.0	1039 0.5	1636 4.7	2315 0.0	27 TU	0436 4.6	1046 0.7	1646 4.6	2309 0.4
13 TU	0501 4.9	1125 0.5	1726 4.6		28 W	0508 4.5	1116 0.7	1719 4.5	2335 0.5
14 W	0002 0.1	0551 4.7	1215 0.6	1810 4.5	29 TH	0538 4.4	1140 0.8	1751 4.3	
15 TH	0050 0.2	0645 4.5	1301 0.7	1909 4.4	30 F	0008 0.6	0616 4.2	1216 0.8	1829 4.2
					31 SA	0045 0.7	0656 4.1	1300 0.9	1920 4.0

Chart Datum: 2·32 metres below NAP Datum

TIME ZONE -0100
(Dutch Standard Time)
Subtract 1 hour for UT
For Dutch Summer Time add
ONE hour in **non-shaded areas**

NETHERLANDS – VLISSINGEN

YEAR **2002**

LAT 51°27′N   LONG 3°36′E

TIMES AND HEIGHTS OF HIGH AND LOW WATERS

SEPTEMBER

Day	Time m	Day	Time m
1 SU	0140 0.9 / 0800 3.8 / 1359 1.1 / 2046 3.8	**16 M**	0335 1.0 / 0952 3.7 / 1615 0.9 / 2236 3.9
2 M	0305 1.0 / 0920 3.7 / 1556 1.1 / 2206 3.8	**17 TU**	0505 1.0 / 1116 3.9 / 1745 0.9 / 2344 4.2
3 TU	0430 1.0 / 1046 3.8 / 1705 1.0 / 2319 4.0	**18 W**	0615 0.9 / 1218 4.1 / 1846 0.5
4 W	0546 0.9 / 1155 4.0 / 1810 0.7	**19 TH**	0045 4.5 / 0706 0.8 / 1305 4.4 / 1930 0.4
5 TH	0015 4.3 / 0635 0.7 / 1246 4.3 / 1905 0.5	**20 F**	0129 4.6 / 0740 0.7 / 1345 4.5 / 2006 0.3
6 F	0106 4.7 / 0722 0.6 / 1327 4.6 / 1955 0.3	**21 SA**	0206 4.7 / 0809 0.7 / 1418 4.6 / 2040 0.3
7 SA ●	0147 4.9 / 0808 0.5 / 1406 4.8 / 2041 0.1	**22 SU**	0238 4.7 / 0846 0.7 / 1445 4.7 / 2110 0.3
8 SU	0226 5.1 / 0852 0.4 / 1448 4.9 / 2126 0.0	**23 M**	0306 4.7 / 0916 0.6 / 1516 4.7 / 2139 0.3
9 M	0309 5.2 / 0935 0.4 / 1530 5.0 / 2207 -0.1	**24 TU**	0332 4.7 / 0946 0.6 / 1546 4.7 / 2212 0.4
10 TU	0353 5.1 / 1018 0.4 / 1612 5.0 / 2252 0.0	**25 W**	0400 4.7 / 1019 0.6 / 1616 4.7 / 2235 0.5
11 W	0436 5.0 / 1102 0.5 / 1655 4.9 / 2335 0.1	**26 TH**	0431 4.6 / 1040 0.7 / 1643 4.6 / 2306 0.5
12 TH	0525 4.8 / 1148 0.5 / 1746 4.7	**27 F**	0502 4.5 / 1108 0.7 / 1716 4.5 / 2330 0.6
13 F	0015 0.3 / 0616 4.5 / 1235 0.7 / 1838 4.5	**28 SA**	0536 4.4 / 1135 0.7 / 1749 4.4
14 SA	0106 0.6 / 0715 4.2 / 1336 0.8 / 1945 4.2	**29 SU**	0008 0.7 / 0616 4.2 / 1226 0.8 / 1836 4.1
15 SU	0204 0.8 / 0826 3.9 / 1443 0.9 / 2106 3.9	**30 M**	0055 0.9 / 0705 3.9 / 1325 1.0 / 1951 3.9

OCTOBER

Day	Time m	Day	Time m
1 TU	0210 1.1 / 0835 3.7 / 1454 1.1 / 2130 3.8	**16 W**	0445 1.2 / 1049 3.8 / 1726 0.7 / 2325 4.1
2 W	0356 1.1 / 1010 3.7 / 1636 1.0 / 2255 4.0	**17 TH**	0550 1.0 / 1156 4.1 / 1826 0.5
3 TH	0504 1.0 / 1125 4.0 / 1745 0.7 / 2355 4.4	**18 F**	0019 4.4 / 0635 0.9 / 1235 4.3 / 1906 0.4
4 F	0609 0.8 / 1217 4.3 / 1846 0.4	**19 SA**	0106 4.6 / 0716 0.8 / 1318 4.5 / 1940 0.4
5 SA	0045 4.8 / 0700 0.6 / 1303 4.6 / 1929 0.2	**20 SU**	0138 4.7 / 0745 0.7 / 1350 4.6 / 2010 0.4
6 SU ●	0123 5.0 / 0747 0.5 / 1342 4.9 / 2016 0.0	**21 M ○**	0206 4.7 / 0816 0.6 / 1415 4.7 / 2041 0.4
7 M	0205 5.2 / 0831 0.4 / 1426 5.0 / 2100 0.0	**22 TU**	0237 4.7 / 0848 0.6 / 1446 4.7 / 2111 0.4
8 TU	0246 5.2 / 0912 0.3 / 1506 5.1 / 2143 0.0	**23 W**	0306 4.7 / 0915 0.6 / 1515 4.8 / 2140 0.4
9 W	0329 5.1 / 0957 0.3 / 1546 5.1 / 2226 0.1	**24 TH**	0332 4.7 / 0951 0.6 / 1546 4.7 / 2208 0.5
10 TH	0413 5.0 / 1040 0.4 / 1632 5.0 / 2305 0.2	**25 F**	0403 4.6 / 1016 0.6 / 1617 4.7 / 2235 0.6
11 F	0459 4.7 / 1126 0.5 / 1717 4.8 / 2348 0.5	**26 SA**	0432 4.6 / 1046 0.6 / 1648 4.6 / 2306 0.6
12 SA	0547 4.4 / 1210 0.6 / 1812 4.5	**27 SU**	0507 4.4 / 1114 0.7 / 1726 4.5 / 2346 0.7
13 SU	0038 0.7 / 0646 4.1 / 1305 0.8 / 1915 4.1	**28 M**	0547 4.3 / 1206 0.7 / 1816 4.4
14 M	0135 1.0 / 0755 3.8 / 1425 0.9 / 2046 3.9	**29 TU**	0035 0.9 / 0646 4.0 / 1305 0.9 / 1920 4.0
15 TU	0304 1.2 / 0930 3.6 / 1600 0.9 / 2215 3.9	**30 W**	0146 1.1 / 0810 3.7 / 1424 0.9 / 2106 3.9
		31 TH	0320 1.2 / 0941 3.7 / 1606 0.8 / 2226 4.1

NOVEMBER

Day	Time m	Day	Time m
1 F	0440 1.0 / 1049 4.0 / 1726 0.6 / 2325 4.4	**16 SA**	0605 1.0 / 1201 4.2 / 1830 0.6
2 SA	0546 0.8 / 1148 4.3 / 1818 0.4	**17 SU**	0028 4.4 / 0635 0.8 / 1238 4.3 / 1906 0.5
3 SU	0016 4.7 / 0636 0.7 / 1235 4.6 / 1908 0.2	**18 M**	0106 4.5 / 0716 0.7 / 1316 4.4 / 1936 0.5
4 M ●	0056 5.0 / 0722 0.5 / 1318 4.9 / 1952 0.1	**19 TU**	0136 4.6 / 0746 0.6 / 1346 4.6 / 2006 0.5
5 TU	0141 5.1 / 0808 0.4 / 1359 5.0 / 2036 0.0	**20 W ○**	0205 4.6 / 0815 0.6 / 1414 4.7 / 2038 0.5
6 W	0226 5.1 / 0852 0.3 / 1443 5.1 / 2120 0.1	**21 TH**	0236 4.7 / 0852 0.5 / 1447 4.7 / 2110 0.5
7 TH	0308 5.0 / 0937 0.3 / 1526 5.1 / 2202 0.2	**22 F**	0307 4.7 / 0926 0.5 / 1521 4.7 / 2146 0.5
8 F	0353 4.9 / 1019 0.3 / 1612 4.9 / 2242 0.4	**23 SA**	0338 4.6 / 1000 0.5 / 1555 4.7 / 2219 0.6
9 SA	0439 4.6 / 1106 0.4 / 1658 4.7 / 2326 0.6	**24 SU**	0416 4.5 / 1035 0.6 / 1631 4.6 / 2256 0.7
10 SU	0527 4.4 / 1156 0.5 / 1755 4.5	**25 M**	0453 4.4 / 1111 0.6 / 1711 4.5 / 2336 0.8
11 M	0010 0.9 / 0619 4.1 / 1245 0.7 / 1856 4.1	**26 TU**	0538 4.2 / 1200 0.6 / 1802 4.4
12 TU	0110 1.1 / 0728 3.8 / 1400 0.8 / 2016 3.9	**27 W**	0026 0.9 / 0636 4.0 / 1300 0.7 / 1910 4.1
13 W	0225 1.3 / 0845 3.7 / 1515 0.9 / 2146 3.8	**28 TH**	0130 1.0 / 0748 3.9 / 1416 0.7 / 2029 4.1
14 TH	0355 1.3 / 1016 3.7 / 1640 0.8 / 2256 4.0	**29 F**	0245 1.1 / 0906 3.9 / 1537 0.7 / 2148 4.2
15 F	0510 1.1 / 1116 3.9 / 1745 0.7 / 2346 4.2	**30 SA**	0359 1.0 / 1015 4.0 / 1646 0.6 / 2251 4.4

DECEMBER

Day	Time m	Day	Time m
1 SU	0516 0.9 / 1116 4.3 / 1750 0.4 / 2347 4.6	**16 M**	0544 1.0 / 1159 4.1 / 1820 0.7
2 M	0615 0.7 / 1207 4.5 / 1846 0.3	**17 TU**	0025 4.2 / 0638 0.8 / 1240 4.2 / 1901 0.6
3 TU	0037 4.8 / 0702 0.6 / 1256 4.8 / 1930 0.2	**18 W**	0106 4.4 / 0716 0.7 / 1316 4.4 / 1936 0.6
4 W ●	0126 4.8 / 0750 0.4 / 1340 4.9 / 2016 0.2	**19 TH ○**	0137 4.5 / 0752 0.6 / 1348 4.5 / 2005 0.5
5 TH	0208 4.9 / 0837 0.3 / 1425 5.0 / 2058 0.3	**20 F**	0212 4.6 / 0830 0.5 / 1428 4.6 / 2046 0.5
6 F	0253 4.8 / 0922 0.3 / 1512 4.9 / 2142 0.4	**21 SA**	0247 4.6 / 0905 0.5 / 1502 4.7 / 2126 0.5
7 SA	0339 4.7 / 1008 0.3 / 1557 4.9 / 2222 0.5	**22 SU**	0326 4.6 / 0948 0.4 / 1539 4.7 / 2200 0.6
8 SU	0426 4.6 / 1049 0.3 / 1648 4.7 / 2306 0.7	**23 M**	0402 4.5 / 1030 0.4 / 1619 4.7 / 2239 0.6
9 M	0511 4.4 / 1135 0.4 / 1735 4.5 / 2348 0.9	**24 TU**	0442 4.4 / 1112 0.4 / 1706 4.6 / 2327 0.7
10 TU	0559 4.2 / 1230 0.5 / 1829 4.2	**25 W**	0529 4.3 / 1206 0.4 / 1750 4.5
11 W	0036 1.0 / 0656 4.0 / 1314 0.7 / 1930 4.0	**26 TH**	0016 0.8 / 0626 4.2 / 1256 0.4 / 1856 4.3
12 TH	0140 1.2 / 0756 3.8 / 1426 0.8 / 2034 3.8	**27 F**	0110 0.9 / 0725 4.1 / 1356 0.5 / 2006 4.2
13 F	0250 1.2 / 0906 3.7 / 1525 0.8 / 2155 3.8	**28 SA**	0209 1.0 / 0836 4.0 / 1500 0.5 / 2111 4.2
14 SA	0406 1.2 / 1020 3.8 / 1634 0.8 / 2301 3.9	**29 SU**	0326 1.0 / 0946 4.1 / 1604 0.6 / 2219 4.2
15 SU	0455 1.1 / 1117 3.9 / 1735 0.8 / 2346 4.1	**30 M**	0435 0.9 / 1045 4.2 / 1727 0.5 / 2325 4.3
		31 TU	0551 0.8 / 1145 4.4 / 1826 0.5

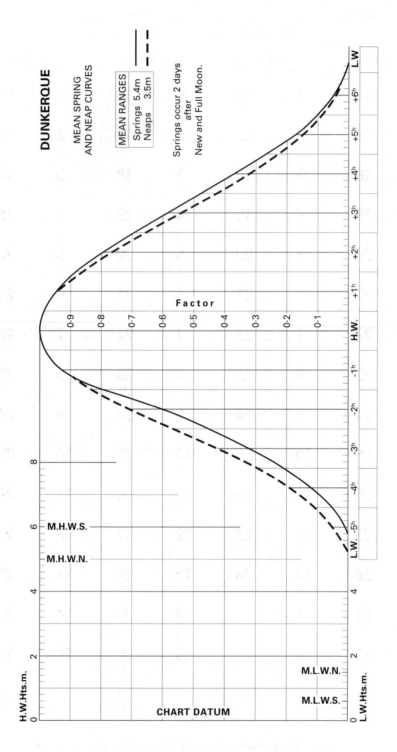

DUNKERQUE

MEAN SPRING
AND NEAP CURVES

MEAN RANGES	
Springs	5.4m
Neaps	3.5m

Springs occur 2 days
after
New and Full Moon.

Factor

0·9 0·8 0·7 0·6 0·5 0·4 0·3 0·2 0·1

H.W.Hts.m.

M.H.W.S.
M.H.W.N.

CHART DATUM

L.W.Hts.m.

M.L.W.N.
M.L.W.S.

L.W.
+6ʰ +5ʰ +4ʰ +3ʰ +2ʰ +1ʰ H.W. -1ʰ -2ʰ -3ʰ -4ʰ -5ʰ L.W.

Register for your **FREE** weekly weather email service from Macmillan Reeds
》 at **www.nauticaldata.com – NOW!** 《
weekend weather reports sent to your email address, every Thursday

158

TIME ZONE -0100
(French Standard Time)
Subtract 1 hour for UT
For French Summer Time add
ONE hour in **non-shaded areas**

FRANCE – DUNKERQUE

LAT 51°03′N   LONG 2°22′E

TIMES AND HEIGHTS OF HIGH AND LOW WATERS

YEAR 2002

JANUARY

Day	Time	m	Day	Time	m
1 TU	0138 / 0839 / 1358 / 2059	6.0 / 0.6 / 6.1 / 0.7	**16** W	0219 / 0917 / 1443 / 2129	5.7 / 0.8 / 5.8 / 1.0
2 W	0223 / 0926 / 1446 / 2146	6.0 / 0.6 / 6.1 / 0.8	**17** TH	0252 / 0951 / 1516 / 2201	5.7 / 0.8 / 5.7 / 1.1
3 TH	0310 / 1013 / 1536 / 2233	5.9 / 0.6 / 6.0 / 0.9	**18** F	0326 / 1023 / 1550 / 2234	5.6 / 0.9 / 5.5 / 1.2
4 F	0359 / 1101 / 1627 / 2322	5.6 / 0.7 / 5.6 / 1.1	**19** SA	0401 / 1055 / 1626 / 2308	5.5 / 1.0 / 5.4 / 1.3
5 SA	0450 / 1153 / 1723	5.6 / 0.8 / 5.6	**20** SU	0439 / 1130 / 1707 / 2345	5.3 / 1.2 / 5.2 / 1.4
6 SU	0020 / 0546 / 1252 / 1826	1.2 / 5.5 / 0.9 / 5.4	**21** M	0521 / 1210 / 1755	5.2 / 1.3 / 5.0
7 M	0122 / 0650 / 1356 / 1939	1.4 / 5.3 / 1.1 / 5.3	**22** TU	0031 / 0614 / 1300 / 1852	1.6 / 5.0 / 1.5 / 4.8
8 TU	0230 / 0804 / 1504 / 2052	1.5 / 5.2 / 1.1 / 5.2	**23** W	0128 / 0716 / 1407 / 1957	1.8 / 4.8 / 1.6 / 4.8
9 W	0339 / 0915 / 1613 / 2157	1.5 / 5.2 / 1.1 / 5.3	**24** TH	0245 / 0824 / 1526 / 2110	1.8 / 4.8 / 1.6 / 4.8
10 TH	0449 / 1017 / 1719 / 2257	1.4 / 5.4 / 1.1 / 5.4	**25** F	0401 / 0935 / 1635 / 2219	1.7 / 4.9 / 1.4 / 5.0
11 F	0550 / 1113 / 1814 / 2349	1.2 / 5.5 / 1.0 / 5.5	**26** SA	0506 / 1039 / 1735 / 2315	1.4 / 5.2 / 1.2 / 5.3
12 SA	0640 / 1203 / 1900	1.0 / 5.6 / 1.0	**27** SU	0604 / 1131 / 1829	1.1 / 5.5 / 1.0
13 SU ●	0027 / 0724 / 1247 / 1941	5.6 / 0.9 / 5.8 / 0.9	**28** M ○	0010 / 0655 / 1218 / 1917	5.6 / 0.9 / 5.8 / 0.8
14 M	0108 / 0803 / 1328 / 2019	5.7 / 0.8 / 5.8 / 0.9	**29** TU	0043 / 0743 / 1303 / 2003	5.9 / 0.6 / 6.1 / 0.6
15 TU	0145 / 0841 / 1407 / 2055	5.7 / 0.8 / 5.8 / 0.9	**30** W	0127 / 0829 / 1348 / 2049	6.0 / 0.4 / 6.2 / 0.6
			31 TH	0210 / 0915 / 1434 / 2134	6.1 / 0.3 / 6.2 / 0.6

FEBRUARY

Day	Time	m	Day	Time	m
1 F	0255 / 1001 / 1521 / 2218	6.1 / 0.2 / 6.1 / 0.6	**16** SA	0259 / 0957 / 1520 / 2207	5.8 / 0.7 / 5.7 / 0.9
2 SA	0339 / 1047 / 1609 / 2303	6.0 / 0.3 / 6.0 / 0.8	**17** SU	0329 / 1025 / 1550 / 2236	5.7 / 0.8 / 5.6 / 1.0
3 SU	0426 / 1134 / 1658 / 2350	5.9 / 0.5 / 5.8 / 1.0	**18** M	0358 / 1055 / 1621 / 2307	5.6 / 0.9 / 5.4 / 1.2
4 M	0517 / 1224 / 1753	5.7 / 0.7 / 5.5	**19** TU	0428 / 1129 / 1656 / 2343	5.4 / 1.1 / 5.2 / 1.3
5 TU	0047 / 0615 / 1322 / 1858	1.2 / 5.4 / 1.0 / 5.2	**20** W	0509 / 1210 / 1747	5.2 / 1.3 / 4.9
6 W	0150 / 0726 / 1428 / 2016	1.5 / 5.2 / 1.3 / 4.9	**21** TH	0033 / 0611 / 1306 / 1902	1.6 / 4.9 / 1.5 / 4.7
7 TH	0302 / 0846 / 1544 / 2133	1.6 / 5.0 / 1.4 / 4.9	**22** F	0141 / 0732 / 1428 / 2023	1.8 / 4.8 / 1.7 / 4.6
8 F	0426 / 1000 / 1704 / 2244	1.6 / 5.1 / 1.4 / 5.0	**23** SA	0312 / 0857 / 1557 / 2149	1.8 / 4.8 / 1.6 / 4.8
9 SA	0537 / 1106 / 1803 / 2341	1.3 / 5.2 / 1.2 / 5.2	**24** SU	0435 / 1017 / 1713 / 2257	1.5 / 5.1 / 1.3 / 5.2
10 SU	0630 / 1158 / 1848	1.1 / 5.5 / 1.1	**25** M	0545 / 1117 / 1814 / 2349	1.1 / 5.5 / 1.0 / 5.5
11 M	0019 / 0712 / 1239 / 1927	5.4 / 0.9 / 5.6 / 1.0	**26** TU	0641 / 1205 / 1904	0.7 / 5.9 / 0.7
12 TU ●	0056 / 0750 / 1316 / 2003	5.6 / 0.7 / 5.8 / 0.9	**27** W ○	0027 / 0729 / 1249 / 1949	5.9 / 0.4 / 6.1 / 0.5
13 W	0130 / 0824 / 1351 / 2035	5.7 / 0.7 / 5.8 / 0.8	**28** TH	0109 / 0814 / 1333 / 2032	6.1 / 0.2 / 6.3 / 0.4
14 TH	0200 / 0857 / 1422 / 2107	5.8 / 0.6 / 5.8 / 0.8			
15 F	0229 / 0928 / 1451 / 2137	5.8 / 0.6 / 5.8 / 0.9			

MARCH

Day	Time	m	Day	Time	m
1 F	0151 / 0858 / 1416 / 2115	6.2 / 0.1 / 6.3 / 0.4	**16** SA	0202 / 0900 / 1422 / 2110	5.8 / 0.6 / 5.8 / 0.7
2 SA	0233 / 0942 / 1500 / 2157	6.2 / 0.0 / 6.2 / 0.5	**17** SU	0229 / 0929 / 1449 / 2139	5.8 / 0.6 / 5.8 / 0.8
3 SU	0316 / 1025 / 1544 / 2239	6.2 / 0.2 / 6.1 / 0.6	**18** M	0256 / 0956 / 1515 / 2207	5.8 / 0.7 / 5.7 / 0.8
4 M	0401 / 1108 / 1630 / 2322	6.0 / 0.4 / 5.8 / 0.8	**19** TU	0322 / 1024 / 1541 / 2236	5.7 / 0.8 / 5.5 / 1.0
5 TU	0449 / 1154 / 1720	5.8 / 0.7 / 5.5	**20** W	0350 / 1056 / 1611 / 2311	5.6 / 1.0 / 5.3 / 1.2
6 W	0003 / 0543 / 1246 / 1820	1.1 / 5.5 / 1.1 / 5.1	**21** TH	0429 / 1135 / 1654 / 2359	5.4 / 1.2 / 5.0 / 1.4
7 TH	0111 / 0653 / 1352 / 1940	1.4 / 5.1 / 1.5 / 4.7	**22** F	0525 / 1229 / 1814	5.1 / 1.5 / 4.7
8 F	0227 / 0820 / 1516 / 2109	1.7 / 4.8 / 1.7 / 4.6	**23** SA	0104 / 0655 / 1350 / 1951	1.6 / 4.8 / 1.7 / 4.6
9 SA	0402 / 0944 / 1645 / 2226	1.7 / 4.8 / 1.6 / 4.8	**24** SU	0236 / 0830 / 1528 / 2125	1.7 / 4.8 / 1.6 / 4.7
10 SU	0520 / 1053 / 1745 / 2324	1.4 / 5.1 / 1.3 / 5.1	**25** M	0409 / 0958 / 1652 / 2236	1.5 / 5.1 / 1.3 / 5.1
11 M	0612 / 1144 / 1830	1.1 / 5.4 / 1.1	**26** TU	0525 / 1059 / 1755 / 2328	1.0 / 5.5 / 0.9 / 5.5
12 TU	0006 / 0654 / 1222 / 1907	5.4 / 0.8 / 5.6 / 0.9	**27** W	0621 / 1147 / 1844	0.6 / 5.9 / 0.6
13 W	0036 / 0728 / 1257 / 1940	5.6 / 0.7 / 5.7 / 0.8	**28** TH ○	0013 / 0709 / 1230 / 1928	5.9 / 0.3 / 6.2 / 0.5
14 TH ●	0107 / 0800 / 1328 / 2010	5.7 / 0.6 / 5.8 / 0.8	**29** F	0047 / 0753 / 1311 / 2010	6.1 / 0.1 / 6.3 / 0.4
15 F	0135 / 0830 / 1357 / 2040	5.8 / 0.6 / 5.8 / 0.7	**30** SA	0128 / 0836 / 1353 / 2051	6.2 / 0.0 / 6.3 / 0.4
			31 SU	0209 / 0918 / 1435 / 2133	6.3 / 0.1 / 6.2 / 0.4

APRIL

Day	Time	m	Day	Time	m
1 M	0252 / 1000 / 1518 / 2214	6.2 / 0.2 / 6.0 / 0.5	**16** TU	0227 / 0929 / 1446 / 2142	5.8 / 0.7 / 5.7 / 0.8
2 TU	0337 / 1042 / 1603 / 2256	6.1 / 0.5 / 5.8 / 0.8	**17** W	0256 / 0959 / 1514 / 2214	5.8 / 0.8 / 5.6 / 0.9
3 W	0424 / 1124 / 1651 / 2341	5.8 / 0.8 / 5.4 / 1.1	**18** TH	0329 / 1033 / 1548 / 2252	5.6 / 1.0 / 5.4 / 1.1
4 TH	0518 / 1214 / 1749	5.4 / 1.3 / 5.0	**19** F	0411 / 1115 / 1635 / 2339	5.4 / 1.2 / 5.1 / 1.3
5 F	0038 / 0625 / 1317 / 1905	1.4 / 5.0 / 1.6 / 4.6	**20** SA	0513 / 1212 / 1803	5.1 / 1.5 / 4.7
6 SA	0153 / 0753 / 1444 / 2038	1.7 / 4.7 / 1.7 / 4.5	**21** SU	0049 / 0642 / 1333 / 1930	1.5 / 4.9 / 1.6 / 4.6
7 SU	0330 / 0920 / 1613 / 2156	1.7 / 4.7 / 1.7 / 4.7	**22** M	0216 / 0810 / 1507 / 2101	1.5 / 4.9 / 1.5 / 4.8
8 M	0449 / 1027 / 1716 / 2252	1.4 / 5.0 / 1.4 / 5.0	**23** TU	0346 / 0935 / 1627 / 2211	1.3 / 5.2 / 1.2 / 5.2
9 TU	0544 / 1116 / 1802 / 2333	1.1 / 5.3 / 1.1 / 5.3	**24** W	0459 / 1036 / 1729 / 2303	0.9 / 5.6 / 0.9 / 5.6
10 W	0625 / 1154 / 1839	0.9 / 5.5 / 1.0	**25** TH	0557 / 1124 / 1819 / 2347	0.5 / 5.9 / 0.7 / 5.8
11 TH	0010 / 0658 / 1229 / 1910	5.5 / 0.7 / 5.7 / 0.9	**26** F	0645 / 1206 / 1904	0.3 / 6.1 / 0.5
12 F ●	0038 / 0728 / 1300 / 1939	5.7 / 0.7 / 5.8 / 0.8	**27** SA ○	0022 / 0729 / 1247 / 1946	6.1 / 0.2 / 6.2 / 0.5
13 SA	0106 / 0758 / 1327 / 2009	5.8 / 0.6 / 5.8 / 0.7	**28** SU	0104 / 0812 / 1328 / 2028	6.2 / 0.2 / 6.2 / 0.4
14 SU	0132 / 0829 / 1352 / 2041	5.8 / 0.6 / 5.8 / 0.7	**29** M	0146 / 0854 / 1412 / 2110	6.2 / 0.3 / 6.1 / 0.5
15 M	0159 / 0900 / 1418 / 2112	5.8 / 0.6 / 5.8 / 0.7	**30** TU	0231 / 0936 / 1456 / 2151	6.2 / 0.4 / 5.9 / 0.6

Chart Datum: 2·69 metres below IGN Datum
Register for your **FREE** weekly weather email service from Macmillan Reeds
at **www.nauticaldata.com – NOW!**
weekend weather reports sent to your email address, every Thursday

TIME ZONE -0100
(French Standard Time)
Subtract 1 hour for UT
For French Summer Time add
ONE hour in non-shaded areas

FRANCE – DUNKERQUE

LAT 51°03′N   LONG 2°22′E

TIMES AND HEIGHTS OF HIGH AND LOW WATERS

YEAR **2002**

MAY

Time	m		Time	m
1 0317	6.0	**16**	0243	5.8
1017	0.7		0944	0.9
W 1542	5.7	TH	1505	5.6
2234	0.8		2203	0.8
2 0405	5.7	**17**	0324	5.6
1059	1.0		1023	1.0
TH 1630	5.3	F	1549	5.3
2318	1.0		2245	1.0
3 0458	5.4	**18**	0414	5.4
1146	1.3		1110	1.2
F 1723	5.0	SA	1650	5.1
			2336	1.1
4 0003	1.3	**19**	0520	5.2
0559	5.0		1208	1.4
SA 1244	1.7	SU	1759	4.9
1829	4.7			
5 0119	1.6	**20**	0044	1.3
0716	4.7		0631	5.1
SU 1402	1.8	M	1323	1.5
1955	4.5		1910	4.9
6 0244	1.6	**21**	0202	1.2
0841	4.7		0747	5.1
M 1525	1.7	TU	1445	1.4
2111	4.6		2031	5.0
7 0401	1.4	**22**	0321	1.1
0946	4.9		0907	5.3
TU 1631	1.5	W	1557	1.2
2207	4.9		2140	5.3
8 0459	1.2	**23**	0430	0.8
1036	5.2		1009	5.6
W 1721	1.3	TH	1659	1.0
2252	5.2		2234	5.5
9 0543	1.0	**24**	0529	0.6
1118	5.4		1058	5.8
TH 1801	1.1	F	1752	0.8
2331	5.4		2320	5.8
10 0619	0.9	**25**	0620	0.5
1155	5.6		1143	5.9
F 1834	0.9	SA	1840	0.7
11 0004	5.6	**26**	0011	6.0
0652	0.8		0706	0.4
SA 1227	5.7	SU	1226	6.0
1906	0.9	○	1925	0.6
12 0033	5.7	**27**	0044	6.1
0725	0.7		0750	0.5
SU 1255	5.7	M	1309	6.0
● 1939	0.8		2008	0.6
13 0102	5.7	**28**	0130	6.1
0759	0.7		0833	0.5
M 1322	5.8	TU	1355	5.9
2014	0.7		2051	0.6
14 0133	5.8	**29**	0216	6.0
0834	0.7		0916	0.7
TU 1354	5.8	W	1441	5.8
2049	0.7		2134	0.6
15 0207	5.8	**30**	0304	5.9
0908	0.8		0957	0.8
W 1428	5.7	TH	1527	5.6
2125	0.7		2217	0.8
		31	0351	5.6
			1039	1.1
		F	1612	5.4
			2300	1.0

JUNE

Time	m		Time	m
1 0438	5.4	**16**	0417	5.6
1122	1.3		1110	1.1
SA 1658	5.1	SU	1648	5.3
2346	1.2		2335	0.9
2 0530	5.1	**17**	0513	5.5
1211	1.6		1204	1.2
SU 1750	4.9	M	1743	5.2
3 0041	1.4	**18**	0036	1.0
0629	4.9		0614	5.4
M 1312	1.7	TU	1308	1.0
1854	4.7		1845	5.2
4 0148	1.5	**19**	0144	1.0
0741	4.8		0721	5.3
TU 1424	1.7	W	1418	1.3
2009	4.7		1956	5.2
5 0259	1.5	**20**	0254	0.9
0851	4.8		0834	5.3
W 1531	1.6	TH	1526	1.2
2113	4.8		2106	5.3
6 0401	1.3	**21**	0400	0.9
0947	5.0		0940	5.5
TH 1627	1.4	F	1630	1.1
2205	5.0		2206	5.5
7 0452	1.2	**22**	0503	0.8
1034	5.2		1036	5.6
F 1715	1.2	SA	1729	1.0
2250	5.2		2300	5.6
8 0536	1.0	**23**	0559	0.7
1116	5.4		1127	5.6
SA 1756	1.1	SU	1822	0.9
2330	5.4		2350	5.7
9 0616	1.0	**24**	0650	0.7
1152	5.5		1215	5.7
SU 1834	1.0	M	1910	0.8
		○		
10 0009	5.5	**25**	0033	5.9
0655	0.9		0736	0.7
M 1226	5.6	TU	1301	5.7
1913	0.9		1955	0.7
11 0037	5.7	**26**	0120	5.9
0734	0.8		0819	0.8
TU 1300	5.7	W	1346	5.8
● 1952	0.8		2039	0.6
12 0114	5.8	**27**	0207	5.9
0814	0.8		0900	0.8
W 1338	5.7	TH	1430	5.7
2033	0.7		2121	0.6
13 0155	5.8	**28**	0251	5.8
0855	0.8		0940	0.9
TH 1420	5.7	F	1511	5.6
2115	0.7		2201	0.7
14 0238	5.8	**29**	0334	5.6
0937	0.9		1018	1.1
F 1506	5.6	SA	1550	5.5
2158	0.7		2240	0.9
15 0326	5.7	**30**	0414	5.5
1022	1.0		1057	1.2
SA 1556	5.5	SU	1629	5.3
2244	0.8		2319	1.0

JULY

Time	m		Time	m
1 0456	5.3	**16**	0455	5.7
1137	1.4		1149	1.0
M 1710	5.1	TU	1719	5.5
2 0001	1.2	**17**	0020	0.7
0542	5.1		0550	5.6
TU 1222	1.5	W	1244	1.2
1758	5.0		1815	5.4
3 0051	1.3	**18**	0119	0.8
0634	4.9		0652	5.4
W 1318	1.6	TH	1347	1.3
1854	4.9		1921	5.3
4 0150	1.4	**19**	0225	1.0
0734	4.8		0802	5.3
TH 1425	1.7	F	1455	1.3
1958	4.8		2034	5.2
5 0257	1.5	**20**	0333	1.1
0839	4.8		0915	5.2
F 1529	1.6	SA	1604	1.3
2105	4.9		2145	5.3
6 0358	1.4	**21**	0443	1.1
0941	4.9		1021	5.3
SA 1627	1.5	SU	1714	1.2
2204	5.0		2249	5.4
7 0454	1.3	**22**	0548	1.0
1035	5.1		1121	5.4
SU 1720	1.3	M	1812	1.0
2255	5.2		2346	5.6
8 0544	1.2	**23**	0641	1.0
1122	5.3		1213	5.5
M 1807	1.1	TU	1902	0.8
2341	5.4			
9 0630	1.0	**24**	0029	5.7
1204	5.5		0726	0.9
TU 1852	1.0	W	1256	5.6
		○	1946	0.7
10 0019	5.6	**25**	0114	5.8
0715	0.9		0807	0.9
W 1245	5.6	TH	1336	5.7
● 1936	0.8		2027	0.6
11 0101	5.8	**26**	0155	5.8
0800	0.8		0845	0.9
TH 1326	5.8	F	1414	5.7
2020	0.6		2106	0.6
12 0144	5.9	**27**	0234	5.8
0845	0.8		0921	0.9
F 1410	5.8	SA	1449	5.7
2105	0.5		2142	0.7
13 0229	6.0	**28**	0310	5.7
0930	0.8		0955	1.0
SA 1455	5.8	SU	1522	5.6
2151	0.5		2216	0.8
14 0316	5.9	**29**	0345	5.6
1015	0.8		1028	1.1
SU 1541	5.7	M	1555	5.5
2237	0.5		2248	0.9
15 0404	5.9	**30**	0420	5.5
1101	0.9		1101	1.2
M 1629	5.6	TU	1630	5.4
2324	0.6		2322	1.0
		31	0458	5.3
			1136	1.3
		W	1710	5.2

AUGUST

Time	m		Time	m
1 0000	1.2	**16**	0049	0.9
0541	5.1		0622	5.4
TH 1217	1.5	F	1315	1.4
1758	5.0		1849	5.3
2 0045	1.4	**17**	0154	1.2
0633	4.9		0733	5.1
F 1309	1.7	SA	1426	1.5
1855	4.9		2009	5.1
3 0145	1.6	**18**	0309	1.4
0735	4.8		0855	4.9
SA 1422	1.8	SU	1546	1.5
2003	4.7		2133	5.1
4 0300	1.7	**19**	0433	1.4
0845	4.7		1013	5.0
SU 1538	1.8	M	1705	1.3
2117	4.8		2245	5.3
5 0412	1.6	**20**	0542	1.3
0957	4.9		1117	5.2
M 1645	1.6	TU	1804	1.1
2225	5.0		2342	5.5
6 0517	1.4	**21**	0632	1.1
1057	5.2		1206	5.3
TU 1745	1.3	W	1851	0.8
2320	5.4			
7 0612	1.2	**22**	0022	5.7
1146	5.4		0713	1.0
W 1836	1.0	TH	1244	5.6
		○	1932	0.7
8 0012	5.7	**23**	0101	5.8
0701	1.0		0750	0.9
TH 1230	5.7	F	1318	5.8
● 1922	0.7		2009	0.6
9 0046	5.9	**24**	0137	5.9
0747	0.8		0823	0.9
F 1311	5.9	SA	1350	5.8
2006	0.5		2043	0.6
10 0129	6.1	**25**	0210	5.9
0831	0.7		0856	0.9
SA 1352	6.0	SU	1421	5.8
2051	0.4		2116	0.6
11 0212	6.2	**26**	0241	5.8
0915	0.6		0927	0.9
SU 1434	6.0	M	1449	5.8
2135	0.3		2146	0.7
12 0257	6.2	**27**	0310	5.8
0958	0.7		0957	1.0
M 1516	6.0	TU	1517	5.7
2219	0.3		2215	0.8
13 0343	6.1	**28**	0340	5.6
1041	0.8		1025	1.1
TU 1601	5.9	W	1548	5.6
2304	0.4		2243	1.0
14 0431	5.8	**29**	0410	5.5
1126	0.9		1055	1.2
W 1649	5.8	TH	1620	5.4
2352	0.6		2314	1.2
15 0523	5.7	**30**	0442	5.3
1215	1.1		1129	1.4
TH 1743	5.6	F	1656	5.2
			2351	1.4
		31	0526	5.0
			1213	1.7
		SA	1753	4.9

Chart Datum: 2·69 metres below IGN Datum

TIME ZONE -0100
(French Standard Time)
Subtract 1 hour for UT
For French Summer Time add
ONE hour in **non-shaded areas**

FRANCE – DUNKERQUE

LAT 51°03′N   LONG 2°22′E

TIMES AND HEIGHTS OF HIGH AND LOW WATERS

YEAR **2002**

SEPTEMBER

Day	Time m	Day	Time m
1 SU	0044 1.7 / 0638 4.7 / 1315 1.9 / 1913 4.7	**16** M	0250 1.8 / 0837 4.7 / 1531 1.7 / 2123 5.0
2 M	0201 1.9 / 0800 4.6 / 1445 1.9 / 2038 4.7	**17** TU	0422 1.7 / 1001 4.9 / 1653 1.4 / 2236 5.2
3 TU	0333 1.8 / 0925 4.7 / 1613 1.7 / 2200 5.0	**18** W	0528 1.4 / 1104 5.2 / 1750 1.1 / 2330 5.5
4 W	0453 1.5 / 1035 5.1 / 1724 1.3 / 2301 5.4	**19** TH	0615 1.2 / 1149 5.5 / 1834 0.8
5 TH	0556 1.2 / 1128 5.5 / 1819 0.9 / 2350 5.8	**20** F	0009 5.7 / 0653 1.0 / 1222 5.7 / 1912 0.7
6 F	0645 0.9 / 1211 5.8 / 1905 0.6	**21** SA	0041 5.9 / 0726 1.0 / 1252 5.8 / ○ 1945 0.7
7 SA	0027 6.1 / 0729 0.7 / 1249 6.0 / ● 1948 0.4	**22** SU	0113 5.9 / 0756 0.9 / 1322 5.9 / 2015 0.7
8 SU	0108 6.3 / 0811 0.6 / 1327 6.1 / 2031 0.2	**23** M	0141 5.9 / 0826 0.9 / 1349 5.9 / 2044 0.7
9 M	0150 6.3 / 0853 0.6 / 1407 6.2 / 2113 0.2	**24** TU	0207 5.9 / 0856 0.9 / 1415 5.9 / 2113 0.8
10 TU	0232 6.3 / 0935 0.6 / 1448 6.2 / 2156 0.2	**25** W	0233 5.9 / 0925 1.0 / 1441 5.8 / 2141 0.9
11 W	0317 6.2 / 1017 0.7 / 1532 6.1 / 2239 0.4	**26** TH	0300 5.8 / 0952 1.1 / 1508 5.7 / 2208 1.0
12 TH	0403 6.0 / 1059 0.9 / 1619 5.9 / 2324 0.7	**27** F	0325 5.6 / 1020 1.2 / 1535 5.6 / 2237 1.2
13 F	0454 5.7 / 1146 1.2 / 1715 5.6	**28** SA	0353 5.4 / 1053 1.4 / 1607 5.4 / 2312 1.4
14 SA	0018 1.1 / 0553 5.3 / 1244 1.5 / 1823 5.2	**29** SU	0431 5.1 / 1135 1.6 / 1651 5.0
15 SU	0125 1.5 / 0707 4.9 / 1400 1.7 / 1950 4.9	**30** M	0004 1.7 / 0536 4.8 / 1235 1.9 / 1832 4.7

OCTOBER

Day	Time m	Day	Time m
1 TU	0119 2.0 / 0724 4.6 / 1403 2.0 / 2007 4.7	**16** W	0357 1.8 / 0935 4.8 / 1628 1.5 / 2211 5.1
2 W	0259 1.9 / 0855 4.7 / 1541 1.7 / 2135 5.0	**17** TH	0502 1.6 / 1034 5.1 / 1725 1.1 / 2303 5.4
3 TH	0429 1.6 / 1011 5.1 / 1658 1.3 / 2239 5.5	**18** F	0549 1.3 / 1117 5.4 / 1808 0.9 / 2342 5.7
4 F	0534 1.2 / 1104 5.5 / 1755 0.8 / 2327 5.9	**19** SA	0626 1.1 / 1151 5.6 / 1844 0.8
5 SA	0623 0.9 / 1145 5.9 / 1842 0.5	**20** SU	0014 5.8 / 0657 1.0 / 1223 5.8 / 1915 0.8
6 SU	0012 6.2 / 0706 0.7 / 1222 6.1 / ● 1925 0.3	**21** M	0043 5.9 / 0725 1.0 / 1252 5.9 / ○ 1943 0.8
7 M	0044 6.4 / 0747 0.6 / 1259 6.3 / 2007 0.2	**22** TU	0110 5.9 / 0755 0.9 / 1318 5.9 / 2012 0.8
8 TU	0125 6.4 / 0828 0.6 / 1339 6.3 / 2049 0.3	**23** W	0134 5.9 / 0826 0.9 / 1343 5.9 / 2042 0.8
9 W	0207 6.3 / 0910 0.6 / 1421 6.3 / 2131 0.4	**24** TH	0201 5.9 / 0856 1.0 / 1410 5.9 / 2111 0.9
10 TH	0252 6.2 / 0952 0.7 / 1506 6.2 / 2214 0.6	**25** F	0228 5.8 / 0924 1.0 / 1439 5.8 / 2140 1.1
11 F	0338 5.9 / 1034 0.9 / 1555 5.9 / 2258 0.9	**26** SA	0256 5.7 / 0955 1.2 / 1509 5.6 / 2211 1.3
12 SA	0428 5.6 / 1121 1.2 / 1652 5.6 / 2348 1.4	**27** SU	0328 5.5 / 1030 1.3 / 1544 5.4 / 2249 1.5
13 SU	0526 5.2 / 1217 1.5 / 1801 5.2	**28** M	0409 5.2 / 1114 1.5 / 1633 5.1 / 2340 1.7
14 M	0056 1.8 / 0640 4.8 / 1334 1.8 / 1929 4.9	**29** TU	0515 4.8 / 1216 1.7 / 1812 4.8
15 TU	0226 2.0 / 0813 4.6 / 1508 1.8 / 2102 4.9	**30** W	0057 1.9 / 0654 4.7 / 1337 1.8 / 1939 4.8
		31 TH	0231 1.9 / 0820 4.8 / 1510 1.6 / 2105 5.1

NOVEMBER

Day	Time m	Day	Time m
1 F	0358 1.6 / 0938 5.1 / 1627 1.2 / 2211 5.5	**16** SA	0507 1.5 / 1035 5.3 / 1730 1.1 / 2304 5.5
2 SA	0503 1.2 / 1032 5.5 / 1726 0.8 / 2301 5.9	**17** SU	0548 1.3 / 1115 5.5 / 1809 1.0 / 2340 5.6
3 SU	0555 0.9 / 1115 5.9 / 1816 0.5 / 2344 6.1	**18** M	0622 1.1 / 1150 5.6 / 1841 0.9
4 M	0640 0.6 / 1154 6.1 / 1900 0.4 / ●	**19** TU	0011 5.7 / 0653 1.1 / 1222 5.7 / 1910 0.9
5 TU	0020 6.3 / 0723 0.7 / 1234 6.3 / 1943 0.3	**20** W	0039 5.8 / 0726 1.0 / 1249 5.8 / ○ 1942 0.9
6 W	0102 6.3 / 0805 0.6 / 1316 6.3 / 2026 0.4	**21** TH	0107 5.8 / 0759 1.0 / 1318 5.9 / 2015 0.9
7 TH	0146 6.3 / 0847 0.6 / 1401 6.3 / 2109 0.6	**22** F	0136 5.9 / 0833 1.0 / 1349 5.9 / 2049 1.0
8 F	0231 6.1 / 0931 0.7 / 1449 6.1 / 2152 0.8	**23** SA	0209 5.8 / 0907 1.0 / 1424 5.8 / 2123 1.1
9 SA	0318 5.8 / 1015 0.9 / 1539 5.9 / 2237 1.1	**24** SU	0244 5.7 / 0942 1.1 / 1501 5.7 / 2159 1.3
10 SU	0407 5.5 / 1101 1.2 / 1635 5.5 / 2325 1.5	**25** M	0322 5.5 / 1022 1.2 / 1544 5.5 / 2241 1.4
11 M	0502 5.2 / 1154 1.5 / 1738 5.2	**26** TU	0409 5.2 / 1109 1.3 / 1642 5.2 / 2332 1.6
12 TU	0026 1.8 / 0606 4.8 / 1302 1.7 / 1857 4.9	**27** W	0514 5.0 / 1207 1.5 / 1756 5.1
13 W	0144 2.0 / 0730 4.7 / 1426 1.7 / 2024 4.8	**28** TH	0041 1.7 / 0626 4.9 / 1317 1.5 / 1909 5.1
14 TH	0308 2.0 / 0857 4.7 / 1543 1.6 / 2130 5.0	**29** F	0201 1.7 / 0740 5.0 / 1438 1.4 / 2028 5.2
15 F	0416 1.7 / 0949 5.0 / 1643 1.3 / 2221 5.3	**30** SA	0321 1.6 / 0855 5.2 / 1552 1.1 / 2137 5.5

DECEMBER

Day	Time m	Day	Time m
1 SU	0428 1.3 / 0956 5.5 / 1654 0.9 / 2232 5.8	**16** M	0500 1.5 / 1034 5.2 / 1724 1.0 / 2302 5.3
2 M	0525 1.1 / 1046 5.8 / 1749 0.7 / 2320 5.9	**17** TU	0544 1.3 / 1116 5.4 / 1805 1.2 / 2341 5.5
3 TU	0616 0.9 / 1131 6.0 / 1838 0.6	**18** W	0623 1.2 / 1153 5.5 / 1842 1.1
4 W	0011 6.1 / 0702 0.8 / 1216 6.1 / ● 1924 0.6	**19** TH	0015 5.6 / 0701 1.1 / 1227 5.7 / ○ 1918 1.0
5 TH	0046 6.1 / 0747 0.7 / 1302 6.2 / 2009 0.6	**20** F	0047 5.7 / 0739 1.0 / 1301 5.8 / 1956 1.0
6 F	0131 6.1 / 0832 0.7 / 1350 6.2 / 2053 0.7	**21** SA	0122 5.8 / 0818 0.9 / 1338 5.8 / 2035 1.0
7 SA	0218 6.0 / 0917 0.7 / 1440 6.0 / 2137 0.9	**22** SU	0159 5.8 / 0857 0.9 / 1418 5.9 / 2115 1.0
8 SU	0304 5.8 / 1001 0.9 / 1529 5.8 / 2220 1.2	**23** M	0239 5.7 / 0938 0.9 / 1501 5.8 / 2156 1.1
9 M	0350 5.5 / 1045 1.0 / 1619 5.5 / 2304 1.4	**24** TU	0321 5.6 / 1020 0.9 / 1546 5.7 / 2239 1.2
10 TU	0436 5.3 / 1131 1.3 / 1710 5.2 / 2352 1.7	**25** W	0407 5.5 / 1106 1.0 / 1637 5.5 / 2326 1.3
11 W	0527 5.0 / 1224 1.5 / 1810 5.0	**26** TH	0459 5.3 / 1157 1.1 / 1734 5.4
12 TH	0050 1.8 / 0626 4.8 / 1327 1.6 / 1922 4.8	**27** F	0023 1.4 / 0558 5.2 / 1256 1.2 / 1837 5.3
13 F	0159 1.9 / 0740 4.7 / 1436 1.6 / 2032 4.8	**28** SA	0128 1.5 / 0702 5.2 / 1406 1.2 / 1948 5.2
14 SA	0308 1.8 / 0850 4.8 / 1540 1.5 / 2129 5.0	**29** SU	0242 1.5 / 0813 5.2 / 1517 1.1 / 2102 5.3
15 SU	0408 1.7 / 0946 5.0 / 1636 1.4 / 2219 5.2	**30** M	0352 1.4 / 0923 5.4 / 1624 1.0 / 2207 5.5
		31 TU	0458 1.3 / 1024 5.6 / 1727 0.9 / 2305 5.6

Chart Datum: 2·69 metres below IGN Datum
Register for your **FREE** weekly weather email service from Macmillan Reeds
at **www.nauticaldata.com – NOW!**
》 weekend weather reports sent to your email address, every Thursday 《

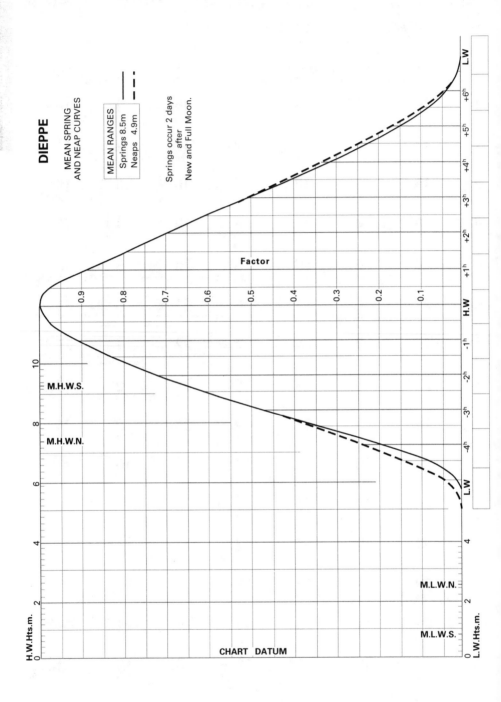

DIEPPE

MEAN SPRING
AND NEAP CURVES

MEAN RANGES
Springs 8.5m
Neaps 4.9m

Springs occur 2 days
after
New and Full Moon.

Factor

M.H.W.S.

M.H.W.N.

M.L.W.N.

M.L.W.S.

CHART DATUM

H.W.Hts.m.

L.W.Hts.m.

<table>
<tr><td>TIME ZONE -0100
(French Standard Time)
Subtract 1 hour for UT
For French Summer Time add
ONE hour in non-shaded areas</td><td>FRANCE – DIEPPE
LAT 49°56'N   LONG 1°05'E
TIMES AND HEIGHTS OF HIGH AND LOW WATERS</td><td>YEAR 2002</td></tr>
</table>

JANUARY

Day	Time m	Time m	Time m	Time m	Day	Time m	Time m	Time m	Time m
1 TU	0039 9.2	0732 1.1	1256 9.3	2000 0.8	**16** W	0115 8.8	0804 1.4	1328 8.8	2024 1.2
2 W	0125 9.2	0818 1.1	1342 9.3	2046 0.8	**17** TH	0149 8.7	0837 1.6	1403 8.7	2056 1.4
3 TH	0212 9.1	0905 1.2	1429 9.1	2132 1.0	**18** F	0223 8.8	0907 1.8	1437 8.4	2125 1.6
4 F	0300 8.9	0952 1.4	1518 8.8	2219 1.2	**19** SA	0255 8.3	0937 2.0	1510 8.1	2155 1.9
5 SA	0351 8.6	1042 1.6	1611 8.5	2309 1.5	**20** SU	0327 8.0	1010 2.2	1544 7.8	2229 2.2
6 SU	0445 8.3	1136 1.9	1708 8.1	2359 1.8	**21** M	0404 7.7	1051 2.5	1625 7.4	2312 2.5
7 M	0546 8.0	1238 2.1	1813 7.8		**22** TU	0450 7.4	1141 2.7	1717 7.1	
8 TU	0108 2.1	0655 7.8	1348 2.2	1925 7.7	**23** W	0002 2.7	0550 7.1	1243 2.9	1828 6.9
9 W	0220 2.2	0807 7.9	1459 2.1	2035 7.8	**24** TH	0112 2.9	0710 7.1	1358 2.8	1951 7.1
10 TH	0330 2.1	0912 8.1	1605 1.8	2138 8.1	**25** F	0232 2.7	0827 7.4	1516 2.4	2100 7.5
11 F	0431 1.9	1008 8.4	1702 1.6	2232 8.3	**26** SA	0346 2.3	0929 7.9	1621 1.9	2157 8.0
12 SA	0523 1.7	1056 8.6	1750 1.4	2318 8.6	**27** SU	0447 1.8	1022 8.4	1718 1.4	2249 8.6
13 SU	0608 1.5	1138 8.8	1833 1.2		**28** M	0542 1.4	1112 8.9	1812 1.0	○ 2339 9.0
14 M	0000 8.7	0649 1.4	1216 8.9	1912 1.2	**29** TU	0636 1.1	1200 9.3	1905 0.7	
15 TU	0039 8.8	0728 1.4	1253 8.9	1949 1.1	**30** W	0030 9.3	0727 0.8	1248 9.5	1955 0.4
					31 TH	0117 9.5	0816 0.7	1334 9.6	2042 0.3

FEBRUARY

Day	Time m	Time m	Time m	Time m	Day	Time m	Time m	Time m	Time m
1 F	0202 9.5	0901 0.7	1419 9.6	2125 0.4	**16** SA	0157 8.8	0845 1.4	1410 8.8	2100 1.2
2 SA	0246 9.4	0944 0.8	1504 9.3	2207 0.7	**17** SU	0225 8.6	0910 1.5	1439 8.5	2126 1.5
3 SU	0330 9.0	1025 1.1	1549 8.9	2248 1.1	**18** M	0253 8.4	0939 1.8	1509 8.2	2154 1.8
4 M	0416 8.6	1109 1.5	1638 8.3	2333 1.7	**19** TU	0324 8.1	1012 2.1	1543 7.8	2229 2.1
5 TU	0508 8.1	1200 2.0	1736 7.8		**20** W	0401 7.7	1053 2.4	1626 7.4	2314 2.6
6 W	0025 2.2	0613 7.6	1306 2.4	1849 7.3	**21** TH	0450 7.3	1148 2.8	1725 7.0	
7 TH	0138 2.6	0733 7.4	1426 2.5	2012 7.3	**22** F	0016 2.9	0603 7.0	1302 2.9	1856 6.8
8 F	0301 2.6	0854 7.5	1543 2.2	2127 7.6	**23** SA	0141 3.0	0743 7.0	1435 2.7	2029 7.2
9 SA	0414 2.3	0957 7.9	1648 1.9	2224 8.0	**24** SU	0314 2.5	0903 7.6	1554 2.1	2137 7.9
10 SU	0513 2.0	1047 8.3	1740 1.5	2309 8.4	**25** M	0425 1.9	1004 8.3	1659 1.4	2234 8.5
11 M	0559 1.7	1128 8.6	1822 1.3	2348 8.6	**26** TU	0527 1.3	1058 8.9	1758 0.9	2325 9.1
12 TU	0638 1.4	1203 8.8	1859 1.1	●	**27** W	0625 0.9	1147 9.4	1853 0.4	○
13 W	0023 8.8	0714 1.3	1236 8.9	1933 1.0	**28** TH	0016 9.5	0717 0.5	1234 9.7	1943 0.1
14 TH	0055 8.9	0747 1.2	1309 9.0	2005 1.0					
15 F	0127 8.9	0817 1.3	1340 8.9	2034 1.1					

MARCH

Day	Time m	Time m	Time m	Time m	Day	Time m	Time m	Time m	Time m
1 F	0101 9.8	0804 0.3	1318 9.9	2027 0.0	**16** SA	0100 9.0	0753 1.1	1314 9.0	2007 0.9
2 SA	0144 9.8	0847 0.3	1401 9.9	2108 0.1	**17** SU	0128 9.0	0820 1.1	1343 9.0	2033 1.1
3 SU	0225 9.4	0926 0.5	1442 9.6	2145 0.5	**18** M	0155 8.9	0845 1.3	1411 8.8	2058 1.3
4 M	0305 9.3	1002 0.9	1524 9.1	2221 1.1	**19** TU	0223 8.7	0912 1.5	1440 8.5	2125 1.6
5 TU	0345 8.7	1040 1.4	1608 8.4	2259 1.7	**20** W	0253 8.4	0942 1.8	1513 8.1	2157 2.0
6 W	0430 8.0	1125 2.0	1701 7.6	2348 2.4	**21** TH	0328 8.0	1019 2.2	1554 7.6	2240 2.5
7 TH	0531 7.3	1226 2.6	1814 7.0		**22** F	0413 7.4	1112 2.6	1650 7.1	2341 2.9
8 F	0059 2.9	0700 6.9	1352 2.8	1951 6.8	**23** SA	0523 7.0	1226 2.9	1820 6.8	
9 SA	0234 3.0	0837 7.1	1522 2.5	2114 7.3	**24** SU	0108 3.0	0711 6.9	1404 2.7	2004 7.1
10 SU	0400 2.6	0943 7.6	1632 2.0	2209 7.8	**25** M	0249 2.6	0840 7.5	1531 2.0	2118 7.9
11 M	0500 2.0	1031 8.1	1723 1.6	2251 8.3	**26** TU	0405 1.9	0945 8.3	1639 1.3	2215 8.6
12 TU	0544 1.6	1109 8.5	1803 1.3	2327 8.6	**27** W	0510 1.2	1040 9.0	1740 0.7	2305 9.2
13 W	0620 1.4	1143 8.8	1838 1.1		**28** TH	0607 0.7	1128 9.5	1834 0.3	○ 2351 9.7
14 TH	0000 8.8	0653 1.2	1214 8.9	● 1910 1.0	**29** F	0659 0.4	1214 9.8	1922 0.0	
15 F	0030 8.9	0724 1.1	1244 9.0	1940 0.9	**30** SA	0039 9.9	0744 0.2	1257 10.0	2005 0.0
					31 SU	0120 9.8	0825 0.3	1339 9.9	2044 0.2

APRIL

Day	Time m	Time m	Time m	Time m	Day	Time m	Time m	Time m	Time m
1 M	0159 9.6	0902 0.5	1419 9.5	2119 0.6	**16** TU	0128 8.9	0822 1.2	1346 8.8	2034 1.3
2 TU	0237 9.2	0936 0.9	1459 9.0	2153 1.2	**17** W	0158 8.8	0851 1.4	1418 8.5	2104 1.6
3 W	0316 8.6	1012 1.4	1541 8.3	2229 1.9	**18** TH	0231 8.5	0923 1.7	1454 8.2	2139 2.0
4 TH	0359 7.9	1055 2.1	1631 7.5	2316 2.6	**19** F	0308 8.0	1002 2.0	1538 7.7	2224 2.4
5 F	0456 7.2	1153 2.7	1742 6.8		**20** SA	0356 7.5	1055 2.4	1636 7.2	2325 2.7
6 SA	0027 3.1	0623 6.7	1317 2.9	1921 6.7	**21** SU	0507 7.1	1209 2.7	1805 7.0	
7 SU	0203 3.1	0807 6.8	1447 2.7	2046 7.1	**22** M	0051 2.8	0650 7.1	1344 2.5	1941 7.3
8 M	0328 2.7	0915 7.3	1558 2.2	2140 7.7	**23** TU	0227 2.4	0815 7.6	1508 1.9	2053 8.0
9 TU	0427 2.1	1002 7.9	1649 1.7	2221 8.2	**24** W	0342 1.7	0921 8.3	1615 1.2	2150 8.7
10 W	0511 1.7	1040 8.3	1730 1.4	2256 8.5	**25** TH	0445 1.2	1016 9.0	1715 0.7	2241 9.2
11 TH	0549 1.4	1113 8.7	1806 1.2	2328 8.8	**26** F	0543 0.8	1105 9.4	1808 0.4	2327 9.6
12 F	0623 1.2	1145 8.9	1839 1.0	●	**27** SA	0633 0.5	1151 9.7	1856 0.3	○
13 SA	0000 8.9	0655 1.1	1216 9.0	1909 1.0	**28** SU	0008 9.7	0719 0.4	1234 9.7	1939 0.3
14 SU	0030 9.0	0725 1.1	1246 9.0	1939 1.0	**29** M	0054 9.7	0800 0.4	1315 9.6	2017 0.5
15 M	0059 9.0	0753 1.0	1316 9.0	2006 1.1	**30** TU	0134 9.4	0837 0.7	1356 9.3	2053 0.9

Chart Datum: 4·43 metres below IGN Datum
Register for your **FREE** weekly weather email service from Macmillan Reeds
at **www.nauticaldata.com – NOW!**
》 weekend weather reports sent to your email address, every Thursday 《

TIME ZONE -0100
(French Standard Time)
Subtract 1 hour for UT
For French Summer Time add
ONE hour in **non-shaded areas**

FRANCE – DIEPPE

YEAR **2002**

LAT 49°56'N   LONG 1°05'E

TIMES AND HEIGHTS OF HIGH AND LOW WATERS

MAY

Day	Time m	Day	Time m
1 W	0213 9.1 / 0912 1.0 / 1436 8.8 / 2128 1.4	16 TH	0140 8.8 / 0837 1.3 / 1404 8.6 / 2051 1.5
2 TH	0252 8.5 / 0949 1.5 / 1519 8.2 / 2205 2.0	17 F	0218 8.5 / 0915 1.5 / 1445 8.3 / 2131 1.9
3 F	0335 7.9 / 1030 2.1 / 1607 7.5 / 2251 2.6	18 SA	0300 8.1 / 0958 1.8 / 1533 7.9 / 2220 2.2
4 SA	0429 7.2 / 1125 2.6 / 1711 7.0 / 2356 3.0	19 SU	0353 7.7 / 1052 2.1 / 1635 7.5 / 2321 2.4
5 SU	0543 6.8 / 1237 2.8 / 1831 6.8	20 M	0504 7.4 / 1202 2.3 / 1754 7.4
6 M	0119 3.1 / 0711 6.7 / 1355 2.7 / 1953 7.0	21 TU	0039 2.5 / 0629 7.4 / 1325 2.1 / 1913 7.7
7 TU	0235 2.8 / 0825 7.1 / 1503 2.4 / 2054 7.5	22 W	0202 2.1 / 0746 7.8 / 1441 1.7 / 2022 8.2
8 W	0335 2.3 / 0918 7.6 / 1558 2.0 / 2139 7.9	23 TH	0313 1.7 / 0852 8.3 / 1546 1.3 / 2121 8.6
9 TH	0425 1.9 / 1000 8.1 / 1645 1.6 / 2217 8.3	24 F	0416 1.3 / 0950 8.8 / 1646 1.0 / 2214 9.0
10 F	0507 1.6 / 1037 8.4 / 1725 1.4 / 2253 8.6	25 SA	0513 1.0 / 1041 9.1 / 1739 0.8 / 2301 9.3
11 SA	0546 1.4 / 1112 8.6 / 1802 1.2 / 2326 8.8	26 SU	0605 0.8 / 1128 9.3 / 1828 0.7 / ○ 2346 9.4
12 SU	0622 1.3 / 1146 8.8 / ● 1837 1.2	27 M	0652 0.7 / 1212 9.3 / 1911 0.8
13 M	0000 8.9 / 0656 1.2 / 1219 8.8 / 1910 1.1	28 TU	0031 9.3 / 0735 0.7 / 1255 9.2 / 1952 0.9
14 TU	0032 8.9 / 0729 1.1 / 1252 8.9 / 1942 1.2	29 W	0112 9.2 / 0814 0.9 / 1337 9.0 / 2030 1.2
15 W	0105 8.9 / 0802 1.1 / 1327 8.8 / 2016 1.3	30 TH	0152 8.9 / 0852 1.1 / 1418 8.7 / 2107 1.6
		31 F	0233 8.5 / 0930 1.5 / 1500 8.2 / 2146 2.0

JUNE

Day	Time m	Day	Time m
1 SA	0316 8.0 / 1010 1.9 / 1546 7.8 / 2229 2.4	16 SU	0300 8.4 / 1000 1.5 / 1534 8.3 / 2220 1.8
2 SU	0404 7.5 / 1056 2.3 / 1637 7.3 / 2321 2.7	17 M	0353 8.1 / 1053 1.7 / 1630 8.0 / 2317 2.0
3 M	0501 7.1 / 1152 2.6 / 1737 7.1	18 TU	0455 7.9 / 1152 1.8 / 1734 7.9
4 TU	0024 2.9 / 0608 6.9 / 1256 2.7 / 1844 7.0	19 W	0021 2.1 / 0603 7.8 / 1259 1.8 / 1842 7.9
5 W	0132 2.8 / 0717 7.0 / 1401 2.5 / 1950 7.6	20 TH	0132 2.0 / 0715 7.9 / 1409 1.7 / 1949 8.1
6 TH	0235 2.5 / 0820 7.3 / 1500 2.3 / 2046 7.6	21 F	0242 1.5 / 0823 8.1 / 1516 1.6 / 2052 8.4
7 F	0331 2.2 / 0912 7.7 / 1554 2.0 / 2133 8.0	22 SA	0347 1.5 / 0925 8.4 / 1617 1.4 / 2149 8.6
8 SA	0421 1.9 / 0958 8.0 / 1642 1.7 / 2215 8.3	23 SU	0446 1.3 / 1020 8.6 / 1713 1.3 / 2240 8.8
9 SU	0506 1.6 / 1039 8.3 / 1725 1.5 / 2254 8.5	24 M	0540 1.2 / 1110 8.8 / 1803 1.2 / ○ 2328 8.9
10 M	0548 1.4 / 1118 8.5 / 1806 1.4 / 2331 8.7	25 TU	0629 1.1 / 1157 8.9 / 1849 1.2
11 TU	0629 1.3 / 1156 8.7 / ● 1845 1.3	26 W	0010 9.0 / 0714 1.0 / 1240 8.9 / 1931 1.2
12 W	0010 8.8 / 0708 1.2 / 1235 8.8 / 1924 1.3	27 TH	0056 8.9 / 0756 1.1 / 1321 8.8 / 2012 1.3
13 TH	0049 8.9 / 0749 1.1 / 1315 8.8 / 2004 1.3	28 F	0136 8.8 / 0836 1.2 / 1401 8.7 / 2050 1.5
14 F	0129 8.8 / 0830 1.2 / 1358 8.7 / 2046 1.4	29 SA	0216 8.5 / 0913 1.4 / 1441 8.4 / 2127 1.8
15 SA	0213 8.7 / 0914 1.3 / 1444 8.5 / 2131 1.6	30 SU	0255 8.2 / 0948 1.7 / 1520 8.1 / 2203 2.1

JULY

Day	Time m	Day	Time m
1 M	0335 7.9 / 1024 2.0 / 1600 7.8 / 2242 2.4	16 TU	0343 8.7 / 1044 1.2 / 1613 8.5 / 2304 1.5
2 TU	0418 7.5 / 1104 2.3 / 1645 7.5 / 2328 2.6	17 W	0435 8.3 / 1133 1.5 / 1706 8.2 / 2357 1.8
3 W	0507 7.2 / 1153 2.5 / 1737 7.2	18 TH	0534 8.0 / 1229 1.8 / 1808 8.0
4 TH	0022 2.7 / 0606 7.0 / 1250 2.6 / 1839 7.1	19 F	0059 2.0 / 0643 7.8 / 1335 2.0 / 1917 7.9
5 F	0125 2.8 / 0715 7.0 / 1355 2.6 / 1946 7.3	20 SA	0211 2.1 / 0757 7.7 / 1447 2.0 / 2028 7.9
6 SA	0232 2.6 / 0821 7.3 / 1500 2.4 / 2046 7.6	21 SU	0323 1.9 / 0908 7.9 / 1555 1.9 / 2133 8.2
7 SU	0334 2.3 / 0918 7.6 / 1600 2.1 / 2138 7.9	22 M	0428 1.7 / 1010 8.2 / 1655 1.7 / 2229 8.4
8 M	0429 1.9 / 1008 8.0 / 1652 1.8 / 2225 8.2	23 TU	0525 1.5 / 1102 8.4 / 1748 1.5 / 2318 8.6
9 TU	0519 1.6 / 1054 8.3 / 1740 1.6 / ○ 2309 8.5	24 W	0615 1.3 / 1148 8.7 / ○ 1835 1.4
10 W	0607 1.4 / 1138 8.6 / 1826 1.4 / ● 2352 8.7	25 TH	0000 8.8 / 0700 1.2 / 1229 8.8 / 1917 1.3
11 TH	0654 1.1 / 1222 8.8 / 1912 1.2	26 F	0043 8.9 / 0741 1.1 / 1306 8.8 / 1956 1.3
12 F	0038 9.0 / 0741 1.0 / 1307 9.0 / 1959 1.1	27 SA	0120 8.8 / 0818 1.1 / 1342 8.8 / 2031 1.4
13 SA	0123 9.1 / 0828 0.9 / 1352 9.0 / 2044 1.1	28 SU	0155 8.7 / 0851 1.3 / 1416 8.7 / 2103 1.6
14 SU	0209 9.0 / 0914 0.9 / 1438 9.0 / 2130 1.2	29 M	0229 8.5 / 0921 1.5 / 1449 8.4 / 2133 1.8
15 M	0256 8.9 / 0958 1.1 / 1524 8.8 / 2216 1.3	30 TU	0302 8.3 / 0958 1.7 / 1522 8.2 / 2202 2.0
		31 W	0334 7.9 / 1020 2.0 / 1555 7.8 / 2237 2.3

AUGUST

Day	Time m	Day	Time m
1 TH	0411 7.6 / 1058 2.3 / 1634 7.5 / 2321 2.6	16 F	0503 8.0 / 1156 2.0 / 1734 7.8
2 F	0457 7.2 / 1146 2.7 / 1725 7.2	17 SA	0028 2.2 / 0612 7.5 / 1303 2.4 / 1849 7.5
3 SA	0017 2.9 / 0600 6.9 / 1247 2.9 / 1836 7.0	18 SU	0145 2.4 / 0738 7.3 / 1426 2.6 / 2013 7.5
4 SU	0128 2.9 / 0725 6.9 / 1404 2.9 / 1959 7.1	19 M	0308 2.3 / 0902 7.5 / 1544 2.3 / 2127 7.8
5 M	0249 2.7 / 0842 7.2 / 1522 2.6 / 2106 7.5	20 TU	0420 2.0 / 1006 8.0 / 1649 2.0 / 2224 8.2
6 TU	0358 2.2 / 0943 7.7 / 1624 2.1 / 2201 8.0	21 W	0520 1.6 / 1055 8.4 / 1742 1.6 / 2310 8.6
7 W	0456 1.7 / 1035 8.2 / 1719 1.7 / 2251 8.5	22 TH	0607 1.3 / 1137 8.7 / 1825 1.4 / ○ 2349 8.8
8 TH	0551 1.3 / 1124 8.7 / 1812 1.3 / ● 2338 8.9	23 F	0647 1.2 / 1213 8.9 / 1902 1.3
9 F	0644 1.0 / 1210 9.1 / 1903 1.0	24 SA	0025 8.9 / 0722 1.0 / 1245 9.0 / 1936 1.2
10 SA	0028 9.2 / 0735 0.7 / 1255 9.3 / 1951 0.8	25 SU	0058 9.0 / 0755 1.1 / 1316 8.9 / 2007 1.3
11 SU	0113 9.4 / 0821 0.5 / 1339 9.5 / 2037 0.7	26 M	0129 8.9 / 0824 1.1 / 1347 8.9 / 2035 1.4
12 M	0157 9.5 / 0905 0.5 / 1422 9.4 / 2120 0.7	27 TU	0159 8.8 / 0850 1.3 / 1416 8.7 / 2101 1.6
13 TU	0240 9.3 / 0945 0.6 / 1505 9.2 / 2201 1.0	28 W	0227 8.5 / 0914 1.5 / 1443 8.4 / 2126 1.8
14 W	0324 9.0 / 1024 1.0 / 1549 8.9 / 2243 1.3	29 TH	0255 8.2 / 0940 1.8 / 1511 8.1 / 2155 2.1
15 TH	0409 8.6 / 1106 1.5 / 1636 8.4 / 2330 1.8	30 F	0327 7.8 / 1012 2.2 / 1544 7.7 / 2232 2.5
		31 SA	0406 7.4 / 1054 2.7 / 1628 7.3 / 2322 2.9

FRANCE – DIEPPE

LAT 49°56′N   LONG 1°05′E

TIMES AND HEIGHTS OF HIGH AND LOW WATERS

YEAR 2002

TIME ZONE -0100
(French Standard Time)
Subtract 1 hour for UT
For French Summer Time add
ONE hour in **non-shaded areas**

SEPTEMBER

Time	m	Time	m
1 0501	6.9	**16** 0124	2.8
1152	3.1	0725	7.0
SU 1732	6.8	M 1410	3.0
		2002	7.1
2 0033	3.1	**17** 0257	2.6
0628	6.6	0855	7.0
M 1315	3.2	TU 1536	2.5
1912	6.8	2118	7.6
3 0208	3.0	**18** 0412	2.1
0811	7.0	0953	8.0
TU 1450	2.9	W 1639	2.0
2039	7.3	2210	8.2
4 0333	2.4	**19** 0506	1.6
0921	7.6	1038	8.5
W 1602	2.2	TH 1727	1.6
2141	8.0	2251	8.6
5 0437	1.7	**20** 0548	1.3
1017	8.3	1115	8.8
TH 1701	1.6	F 1806	1.3
2233	8.6	2327	8.9
6 0535	1.2	**21** 0624	1.2
1106	9.0	1148	9.0
F 1756	1.1	SA 1839	1.2
2321	9.2	○	
7 0630	0.7	**22** 0000	9.0
1152	9.4	0655	1.1
SA 1848	0.7	SU 1218	9.0
●		1909	1.2
8 0010	9.6	**23** 0030	9.1
0704	0.4	0725	1.0
SU 1236	9.7	M 1246	9.1
1936	0.5	1938	1.2
9 0054	9.8	**24** 0100	9.0
0804	0.3	0753	1.1
M 1318	9.8	TU 1315	9.0
2020	0.4	2005	1.3
10 0137	9.8	**25** 0128	8.9
0845	0.3	0818	1.3
TU 1400	9.7	W 1342	8.9
2101	0.5	2030	1.5
11 0218	9.6	**26** 0155	8.7
0922	0.6	0842	1.5
W 1440	9.4	TH 1408	8.6
2140	0.8	2055	1.7
12 0300	9.2	**27** 0223	8.4
0958	1.1	0907	1.8
TH 1521	8.9	F 1436	8.3
2218	1.3	2122	2.0
13 0343	8.6	**28** 0254	8.0
1037	1.7	0935	2.3
F 1606	8.3	SA 1508	7.9
2302	1.9	2156	2.4
14 0434	7.8	**29** 0331	7.5
1125	2.3	1014	2.7
SA 1703	7.6	SU 1550	7.4
2358	2.5	2244	2.8
15 0546	7.2	**30** 0424	7.0
1235	2.9	1113	3.2
SU 1825	7.1	M 1652	6.9
		2353	3.2

OCTOBER

Time	m	Time	m
1 0550	6.6	**16** 0231	2.8
1239	3.4	0829	7.3
TU 1834	6.7	W 1511	2.7
		2052	7.5
2 0135	3.1	**17** 0342	2.3
0743	7.0	0926	7.8
W 1423	3.0	TH 1610	2.1
2012	7.2	2142	8.0
3 0309	2.4	**18** 0434	1.8
0857	7.7	1008	8.4
TH 1539	2.2	F 1656	1.7
2117	8.0	2223	8.5
4 0415	1.7	**19** 0515	1.5
0953	8.5	1044	8.7
F 1639	1.5	SA 1733	1.4
2211	8.8	2257	8.8
5 0513	1.0	**20** 0550	1.3
1042	9.2	1116	8.9
SA 1735	0.9	SU 1807	1.3
2259	9.3	2329	8.9
6 0607	0.6	**21** 0622	1.2
1128	9.6	1146	9.0
SU 1826	0.6	M 1838	1.2
● 2344	9.7	○	
7 0656	0.3	**22** 0000	9.0
1212	9.9	0652	1.2
M 1914	0.4	TU 1215	9.0
		1908	1.2
8 0031	9.9	**23** 0030	9.0
0740	0.3	0721	1.2
TU 1254	9.9	W 1243	9.0
1958	0.4	1937	1.3
9 0114	9.9	**24** 0059	8.9
0820	0.4	0748	1.4
W 1334	9.8	TH 1311	8.9
2038	0.5	2004	1.4
10 0155	9.6	**25** 0128	8.8
0857	0.8	0814	1.6
TH 1414	9.4	F 1339	8.7
2116	0.9	2031	1.6
11 0236	9.1	**26** 0158	8.5
0932	1.3	0842	1.9
F 1455	8.9	SA 1410	8.4
2154	1.4	2101	1.9
12 0319	8.4	**27** 0232	8.1
1010	1.9	0913	2.3
SA 1540	8.2	SU 1446	8.0
2237	2.1	2137	2.3
13 0410	7.7	**28** 0312	7.7
1059	2.6	0955	2.7
SU 1637	7.4	M 1530	7.5
2334	2.7	2225	2.7
14 0522	7.0	**29** 0406	7.2
1211	3.1	1054	3.1
M 1759	6.9	TU 1633	7.0
		2332	3.0
15 0058	3.0	**30** 0531	6.9
0702	6.8	1217	3.2
TU 1348	3.2	W 1808	6.9
1938	7.0		
		31 0107	2.9
		0713	7.2
		TH 1355	2.8
		1940	7.4

NOVEMBER

Time	m	Time	m
1 0239	2.3	**16** 0344	2.2
0826	7.9	0926	8.0
F 1511	2.1	SA 1610	2.0
2047	8.1	2144	8.1
2 0347	1.6	**17** 0430	1.8
0924	8.6	1005	8.4
SA 1612	1.4	SU 1652	1.7
2143	8.8	2221	8.4
3 0445	1.1	**18** 0510	1.6
1015	9.2	1040	8.7
SU 1708	0.9	M 1731	1.5
2233	9.3	2256	8.6
4 0539	0.7	**19** 0546	1.6
1101	9.6	1113	8.8
M 1800	0.6	TU 1806	1.4
● 2319	9.6	2329	8.8
5 0628	0.5	**20** 0620	1.4
1146	9.8	1145	8.9
TU 1849	0.5	W 1839	1.3
		○	
6 0003	9.8	**21** 0001	8.8
0712	0.5	0652	1.4
W 1228	9.8	TH 1216	8.9
1933	0.5	1911	1.3
7 0051	9.7	**22** 0035	8.8
0753	0.7	0723	1.5
TH 1310	9.7	F 1247	8.9
2014	0.7	1943	1.4
8 0133	9.4	**23** 0108	8.7
0832	1.0	0755	1.6
F 1352	9.3	SA 1320	8.8
2054	1.0	2016	1.5
9 0216	8.9	**24** 0143	8.6
0909	1.5	0828	1.8
SA 1434	8.8	SU 1356	8.5
2133	1.5	2051	1.8
10 0300	8.4	**25** 0222	8.3
0949	2.1	0906	2.1
SU 1519	8.1	M 1436	8.2
2216	2.1	2131	2.1
11 0351	7.7	**26** 0306	7.9
1038	2.7	0951	2.4
M 1614	7.5	TU 1524	7.8
2309	2.6	2220	2.3
12 0455	7.2	**27** 0401	7.5
1143	3.1	1048	2.7
TU 1725	7.0	W 1625	7.4
		2322	2.5
13 0020	3.0	**28** 0515	7.0
0614	6.9	1200	2.8
W 1304	3.2	TH 1744	7.3
1847	6.9		
14 0140	2.9	**29** 0040	2.5
0736	7.1	0637	7.5
TH 1420	2.8	F 1322	2.6
2004	7.2	1903	7.6
15 0249	2.6	**30** 0202	2.2
0840	7.5	0749	8.0
F 1521	2.4	SA 1437	2.1
2100	7.7	2012	8.1

DECEMBER

Time	m	Time	m
1 0312	1.7	**16** 0339	2.3
0851	8.5	0920	7.9
SU 1542	1.6	M 1608	2.1
2113	8.6	2142	7.9
2 0414	1.3	**17** 0428	2.0
0946	9.0	1003	8.2
M 1640	1.2	TU 1654	1.8
2207	9.0	2223	8.2
3 0509	1.1	**18** 0511	1.8
1036	9.3	1042	8.5
TU 1734	0.9	W 1735	1.6
2257	9.3	2302	8.4
4 0600	0.9	**19** 0551	1.7
1123	9.5	1119	8.7
W 1824	0.7	TH 1814	1.5
● 2344	9.4	○ 2340	8.6
5 0646	0.9	**20** 0629	1.6
1208	9.5	1155	8.8
TH 1911	0.7	F 1852	1.3
6 0033	9.3	**21** 0018	8.7
0730	1.0	0706	1.5
F 1251	9.4	SA 1232	8.9
1954	0.8	1930	1.3
7 0117	9.2	**22** 0056	8.8
0812	1.2	0744	1.5
SA 1334	9.2	SU 1310	8.9
2036	1.1	2009	1.3
8 0201	8.9	**23** 0136	8.7
0852	1.6	0824	1.6
SU 1417	8.8	M 1351	8.7
2116	1.4	2049	1.5
9 0244	8.4	**24** 0219	8.6
0932	2.0	0906	1.7
M 1502	8.3	TU 1434	8.5
2157	1.9	2132	1.6
10 0330	8.0	**25** 0305	8.3
1016	2.4	0951	1.9
TU 1550	7.8	W 1522	8.3
2242	2.3	2219	1.8
11 0420	7.5	**26** 0355	8.1
1107	2.7	1042	2.1
W 1643	7.4	TH 1615	8.0
2333	2.6	2311	2.0
12 0517	7.2	**27** 0452	7.9
1206	3.0	1140	2.2
TH 1745	7.1	F 1716	7.8
13 0033	2.8	**28** 0004	2.1
0622	7.1	0559	7.8
F 1311	3.0	SA 1246	2.3
1852	7.0	1825	7.8
14 0138	2.8	**29** 0119	2.1
0730	7.2	0710	7.9
SA 1416	2.8	SU 1400	2.1
1958	7.2	1938	7.9
15 0242	2.6	**30** 0233	2.0
0830	7.5	0819	8.2
SU 1516	2.5	M 1511	1.8
2054	7.5	2045	8.2
		31 0343	1.8
		0921	8.5
		TU 1616	1.5
		2146	8.5

Chart Datum: 4·43 metres below IGN Datum
Register for your **FREE** weekly weather email service from Macmillan Reeds
》 at **www.nauticaldata.com – NOW !** 《
weekend weather reports sent to your email address, every Thursday

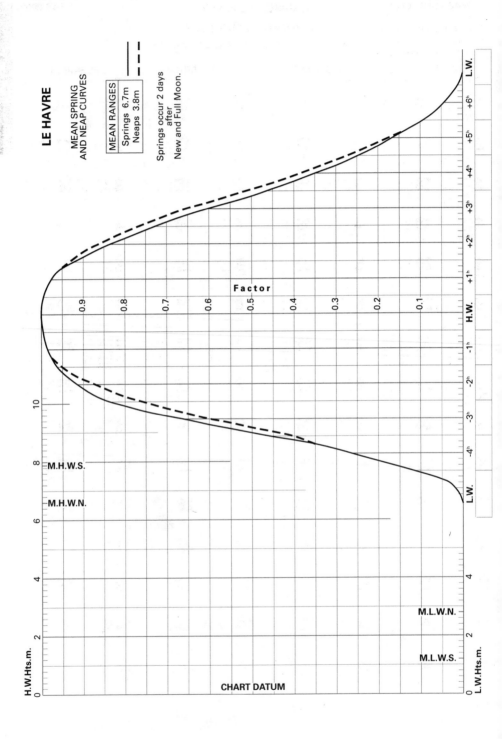

LE HAVRE

MEAN SPRING
AND NEAP CURVES

MEAN RANGES
Springs 6.7m
Neaps 3.8m

Springs occur 2 days
after
New and Full Moon.

Factor

0.9 0.8 0.7 0.6 0.5 0.4 0.3 0.2 0.1

H.W.

L.W.

+6ʰ +5ʰ +4ʰ +3ʰ +2ʰ +1ʰ H.W. -1ʰ -2ʰ -3ʰ -4ʰ L.W.

M.H.W.S.

M.H.W.N.

H.W.Hts.m.

M.L.W.N.

M.L.W.S.

L.W.Hts.m.

CHART DATUM

TIME ZONE -0100
(French Standard Time)
Subtract 1 hour for UT
For French Summer Time add ONE hour in **non-shaded areas**

FRANCE – LE HAVRE

LAT 49°29′N LONG 0°07′E

YEAR 2002

TIMES AND HEIGHTS OF HIGH AND LOW WATERS

JANUARY

#	Day	Time	m		#	Day	Time	m
1	TU	0643	1.5		16	W	0018	7.5
		1153	7.9				0713	1.8
		1912	1.2				1227	7.6
							1933	1.6
2	W	0026	7.8		17	TH	0052	7.4
		0730	1.5				0747	1.9
		1239	7.9				1301	7.5
		1958	1.2				2005	1.8
3	TH	0114	7.7		18	F	0125	7.3
		0816	1.6				0819	2.1
		1327	7.8				1334	7.3
		2044	1.3				2035	2.0
4	F	0203	7.6		19	SA	0158	7.1
		0902	1.8				0849	2.3
		1417	7.6				1406	7.2
		2130	1.6				2104	2.2
5	SA	0255	7.4		20	SU	0230	7.0
		0950	2.0				0920	2.6
		1510	7.4				1441	6.9
		2218	1.9				2136	2.5
6	SU	0353	7.2		21	M	0307	6.8
		1042	2.3				0957	2.8
		1611	7.1				1523	6.7
		2312	2.2				2217	2.8
7	M	0455	7.1		22	TU	0354	6.6
		1142	2.5				1045	3.1
		1719	7.0				1618	6.5
							2310	3.0
8	TU	0015	2.4		23	W	0457	6.5
		0604	7.0				1145	3.2
		1252	2.6				1730	6.4
		1832	6.9					
9	W	0128	2.5		24	TH	0016	3.1
		0712	7.1				0617	6.5
		1408	2.5				1300	3.2
		1944	7.0				1856	6.4
10	TH	0239	2.4		25	F	0136	3.0
		0816	7.2				0731	6.7
		1514	2.3				1423	2.8
		2048	7.1				2010	6.7
11	F	0340	2.2		26	SA	0254	2.7
		0910	7.4				0830	7.0
		1611	2.0				1532	2.3
		2140	7.3				2105	7.1
12	SA	0432	2.1		27	SU	0356	2.2
		0957	7.5				0922	7.3
		1701	1.8				1630	1.8
		2226	7.5				2155	7.4
13	SU ●	0518	2.0		28	M ○	0453	1.8
		1039	7.6				1011	7.6
		1743	1.7				1725	1.4
		2306	7.5				2243	7.7
14	M	0559	1.9		29	TU	0548	1.4
		1116	7.7				1057	7.9
		1822	1.6				1818	1.0
		2343	7.6				2330	7.9
15	TU	0637	1.8		30	W	0639	1.2
		1152	7.7				1144	8.1
		1858	1.5				1908	0.8
					31	TH	0017	8.0
							0728	1.0
							1231	8.1
							1954	0.7

FEBRUARY

#	Day	Time	m		#	Day	Time	m
1	F	0102	8.0		16	SA	0057	7.5
		0812	1.0				0756	1.7
		1316	8.1				1307	7.6
		2037	0.8				2010	1.6
2	SA	0148	7.9		17	SU	0126	7.4
		0854	1.2				0822	1.9
		1402	7.9				1336	7.4
		2117	1.1				2035	1.9
3	SU	0234	7.7		18	M	0155	7.2
		0934	1.5				0849	2.1
		1448	7.6				1407	7.2
		2157	1.5				2102	2.1
4	M	0321	7.4		19	TU	0226	7.0
		1015	2.0				0919	2.4
		1538	7.2				1443	6.9
		2239	2.0				2134	2.5
5	TU	0414	7.1		20	W	0305	6.8
		1104	2.4				0957	2.8
		1640	6.9				1528	6.6
		2332	2.5				2218	2.9
6	W	0517	6.8		21	TH	0356	6.5
		1208	2.8				1050	3.1
		1758	6.6				1631	6.3
							2320	3.2
7	TH	0045	2.9		22	F	0511	6.3
		0641	6.7				1204	3.2
		1332	2.9				1807	6.2
		1926	6.6					
8	F	0209	2.9		23	SA	0047	3.2
		0759	6.8				0650	6.4
		1451	2.7				1343	3.0
		2038	6.8				1944	6.5
9	SA	0322	2.7		24	SU	0224	2.9
		0859	7.0				0805	6.6
		1558	2.3				1506	2.4
		2132	7.0				2045	7.0
10	SU	0423	2.4		25	M	0336	2.3
		0946	7.2				0904	7.2
		1652	2.0				1612	1.8
		2215	7.3				2140	7.4
11	M	0510	2.1		26	TU	0440	1.7
		1025	7.4				0956	7.6
		1734	1.7				1713	1.2
		2251	7.4				2251	7.8
12	TU	0549	1.9		27	W ○	0538	1.2
		1100	7.6				1044	8.0
		1810	1.5				1808	0.8
		2324	7.5				2314	8.0
13	W	0624	1.7		28	TH	0630	0.8
		1132	7.7				1130	8.2
		1843	1.4				1856	0.5
		2355	7.6				2359	8.2
14	TH	0658	1.6					
		1205	7.7					
		1915	1.4					
15	F	0026	7.5					
		0728	1.6					
		1237	7.7					
		1943	1.5					

MARCH

#	Day	Time	m		#	Day	Time	m
1	F	0715	0.6		16	SA	0704	1.4
		1215	8.3				1210	7.7
		1940	0.4				1917	1.3
2	SA	0043	8.2		17	SU	0028	7.6
		0757	0.6				0730	1.5
		1259	8.2				1240	7.6
		2019	0.5				1942	1.5
3	SU	0126	8.1		18	M	0056	7.5
		0835	0.9				0756	1.6
		1342	8.0				1310	7.5
		2056	0.9				2008	1.7
4	M	0207	7.8		19	TU	0125	7.4
		0911	1.3				0823	1.8
		1424	7.7				1341	7.3
		2130	1.5				2035	2.0
5	TU	0248	7.4		20	W	0155	7.2
		0947	1.8				0852	2.1
		1508	7.2				1416	7.0
		2206	2.1				2104	2.4
6	W	0334	7.0		21	TH	0230	6.9
		1029	2.4				0926	2.5
		1604	6.7				1458	6.6
		2253	2.7				2143	2.8
7	TH	0437	6.6		22	F	0318	6.6
		1127	2.9				1014	2.9
		1726	6.3				1600	6.3
							2243	3.2
8	F	0003	3.2		23	SA	0432	6.3
		0608	6.3				1127	3.1
		1255	3.1				1739	6.0
		1910	6.3					
9	SA	0141	3.3		24	SU	0016	3.3
		0740	6.4				0620	6.3
		1427	2.9				1315	3.0
		2025	6.5				1920	6.5
10	SU	0308	2.9		25	M	0202	2.9
		0843	6.7				0743	6.7
		1546	2.5				1444	2.4
		2117	6.8				2026	7.0
11	M	0414	2.5		26	TU	0317	2.2
		0929	7.0				0845	7.2
		1638	2.1				1553	1.7
		2156	7.1				2120	7.5
12	TU	0457	2.0		27	W	0423	1.6
		1005	7.3				0937	7.6
		1716	1.7				1655	1.1
		2229	7.4				2208	7.9
13	W	0533	1.7		28	TH	0521	1.1
		1037	7.5				1024	8.0
		1750	1.5				1748	0.6
		2258	7.5				2253	8.1
14	TH ●	0605	1.5		29	F ○	0611	0.7
		1108	7.7				1110	8.2
		1822	1.3				1835	0.4
		2328	7.6				2337	8.3
15	F	0636	1.4		30	SA	0655	0.5
		1139	7.7				1154	8.3
		1850	1.3				1917	0.4
		2358	7.6		31	SU	0020	8.3
							0735	0.6
							1237	8.2
							1955	0.6

APRIL

#	Day	Time	m		#	Day	Time	m
1	M	0100	8.1		16	TU	0029	7.6
		0812	0.8				0732	1.5
		1319	8.0				1247	7.5
		2030	1.0				1944	1.6
2	TU	0140	7.8		17	W	0100	7.4
		0846	1.3				0802	1.7
		1400	7.6				1323	7.3
		2102	1.6				2014	1.9
3	W	0219	7.4		18	TH	0134	7.2
		0920	1.8				0834	2.0
		1444	7.1				1402	7.0
		2136	2.3				2046	2.3
4	TH	0302	7.0		19	F	0213	7.0
		0958	2.4				0909	2.3
		1537	6.6				1448	6.7
		2220	2.9				2127	2.7
5	F	0401	6.5		20	SA	0304	6.6
		1054	2.9				0958	2.7
		1658	6.2				1551	6.4
		2331	3.4				2228	3.1
6	SA	0533	6.2		21	SU	0417	6.4
		1219	3.2				1112	2.9
		1840	6.2				1727	6.4
7	SU	0108	3.4		22	M	0002	3.1
		0708	6.2				0559	6.4
		1348	3.0				1255	2.7
		1958	6.4				1856	6.7
8	M	0233	3.0		23	TU	0139	2.7
		0815	6.5				0718	6.8
		1503	2.6				1419	2.2
		2049	6.8				2001	7.1
9	TU	0337	2.5		24	W	0253	2.1
		0900	6.9				0820	7.2
		1558	2.2				1526	1.6
		2126	7.1				2055	7.6
10	W	0423	2.1		25	TH	0357	1.5
		0936	7.2				0913	7.6
		1641	1.8				1627	1.1
		2157	7.3				2143	7.9
11	TH	0502	1.7		26	F	0455	1.1
		1008	7.4				1001	7.9
		1718	1.6				1721	0.8
		2227	7.5				2229	8.1
12	F	0536	1.5		27	SA ○	0546	0.8
		1039	7.6				1047	8.1
		1751	1.4				1809	0.6
		2257	7.6				2312	8.2
13	SA	0607	1.4		28	SU	0630	0.7
		1111	7.6				1132	8.1
		1820	1.4				1851	0.7
		2328	7.6				2355	8.1
14	SU	0635	1.4		29	M	0711	0.7
		1143	7.7				1216	8.0
		1847	1.4				1929	0.9
		2359	7.6					
15	M	0703	1.4		30	TU	0035	8.0
		1215	7.6				0748	1.0
		1915	1.5				1259	7.8
							2004	1.3

Chart Datum: 4·38 metres below IGN Datum

TIME ZONE -0100
(French Standard Time)
Subtract 1 hour for UT
For French Summer Time add
ONE hour in **non-shaded areas**

FRANCE – LE HAVRE

LAT 49°29′N   LONG 0°07′E

TIMES AND HEIGHTS OF HIGH AND LOW WATERS

YEAR **2002**

MAY

Day	Time m	Time m	Time m	Time m
1 W	0116 7.7 / 0822 1.4 / 1341 7.5 / 2037 1.8	16 TH 0042 7.5 / 0747 1.6 / 1310 7.3 / 1959 1.9		
2 TH	0156 7.3 / 0857 1.8 / 1425 7.0 / 2112 2.4	17 F 0122 7.3 / 0823 1.8 / 1354 7.1 / 2037 2.2		
3 F	0239 6.9 / 0935 2.4 / 1516 6.6 / 2157 2.9	18 SA 0206 7.1 / 0903 2.1 / 1444 6.9 / 2123 2.6		
4 SA	0334 6.5 / 1028 2.8 / 1626 6.3 / 2304 3.3	19 SU 0259 6.8 / 0956 2.4 / 1548 6.7 / 2227 2.8		
5 SU	0448 6.2 / 1142 3.1 / 1750 6.2	20 M 0409 6.6 / 1108 2.6 / 1711 6.7 / 2351 2.8		
6 M	0026 3.3 / 0615 6.2 / 1258 3.0 / 1907 6.4	21 TU 0536 6.7 / 1233 2.4 / 1828 6.9		
7 TU	0140 3.0 / 0726 6.4 / 1405 2.7 / 2004 6.7	22 W 0112 2.5 / 0649 6.9 / 1348 2.1 / 1931 7.2		
8 W	0242 2.6 / 0818 6.7 / 1503 2.3 / 2045 7.0	23 TH 0223 2.0 / 0751 7.2 / 1455 1.7 / 2027 7.5		
9 TH	0334 2.2 / 0858 7.0 / 1554 2.0 / 2119 7.2	24 F 0327 1.6 / 0848 7.5 / 1556 1.4 / 2117 7.8		
10 F	0420 1.9 / 0933 7.3 / 1637 1.8 / 2153 7.4	25 SA 0425 1.3 / 0939 7.7 / 1651 1.2 / 2204 7.9		
11 SA	0459 1.7 / 1008 7.4 / 1714 1.6 / 2226 7.5	26 SU 0518 1.1 / 1027 7.8 / 1740 1.1 / ○2249 8.0		
12 SU	0534 1.6 / 1043 7.5 / 1746 1.6 / ●2259 7.6	27 M 0604 1.0 / 1113 7.9 / 1823 1.2 / 2332 7.9		
13 M	0605 1.5 / 1118 7.5 / 1817 1.5 / 2331 7.6	28 TU 0646 1.0 / 1158 7.8 / 1903 1.3		
14 TU	0638 1.4 / 1153 7.5 / 1850 1.6	29 W 0014 7.8 / 0724 1.2 / 1242 7.6 / 1940 1.6		
15 W	0005 7.6 / 0712 1.5 / 1230 7.5 / 1924 1.7	30 TH 0054 7.6 / 0801 1.5 / 1324 7.4 / 2016 2.0		
		31 F 0136 7.3 / 0837 1.8 / 1407 7.1 / 2054 2.4		

JUNE

Day	Time m	Day	Time m
1 SA	0219 7.0 / 0916 2.2 / 1454 6.7 / 2137 2.7	16 SU	0201 7.3 / 0908 1.8 / 1440 7.1 / 2128 2.2
2 SU	0307 6.7 / 1002 2.6 / 1549 6.5 / 2232 3.0	17 M	0254 7.1 / 0959 2.0 / 1539 7.0 / 2226 2.4
3 M	0407 6.4 / 1100 2.8 / 1654 6.4 / 2336 3.2	18 TU	0356 7.0 / 1059 2.1 / 1646 7.0 / 2331 2.4
4 TU	0517 6.3 / 1203 2.9 / 1801 6.4	19 W	0508 6.9 / 1205 2.2 / 1756 7.0
5 W	0041 3.1 / 0623 6.4 / 1306 2.8 / 1902 6.6	20 TH	0040 2.3 / 0618 7.0 / 1315 2.1 / 1859 7.2
6 TH	0143 2.8 / 0723 6.6 / 1406 2.6 / 1953 6.8	21 F	0151 2.2 / 0724 7.1 / 1423 1.9 / 2000 7.4
7 F	0241 2.5 / 0813 6.8 / 1501 2.3 / 2037 7.1	22 SA	0257 1.9 / 0826 7.3 / 1526 1.8 / 2055 7.5
8 SA	0332 2.3 / 0857 7.0 / 1550 2.1 / 2117 7.3	23 SU	0357 1.7 / 0923 7.5 / 1622 1.7 / 2146 7.7
9 SU	0418 2.0 / 0938 7.2 / 1634 1.9 / 2155 7.4	24 M	0452 1.5 / 1014 7.6 / 1713 1.6 / ○2232 7.7
10 M	0459 1.8 / 1017 7.3 / 1713 1.8 / 2232 7.5	25 TU	0541 1.4 / 1101 7.6 / 1759 1.6 / 2316 7.7
11 TU	0538 1.6 / 1057 7.4 / 1752 1.7 / ●2309 7.6	26 W	0624 1.3 / 1145 7.6 / 1841 1.6 / 2357 7.7
12 W	0617 1.5 / 1136 7.5 / 1832 1.6 / 2348 7.6	27 TH	0705 1.4 / 1227 7.5 / 1921 1.7
13 TH	0658 1.4 / 1218 7.5 / 1913 1.7	28 F	0037 7.6 / 0743 1.5 / 1307 7.4 / 1959 1.9
14 F	0029 7.6 / 0739 1.5 / 1302 7.4 / 1955 1.8	29 SA	0116 7.4 / 0820 1.7 / 1346 7.2 / 2036 2.2
15 SA	0114 7.5 / 0822 1.6 / 1349 7.3 / 2039 2.0	30 SU	0156 7.2 / 0857 2.0 / 1426 7.0 / 2113 2.4

JULY

Day	Time m	Day	Time m
1 M	0236 6.9 / 0932 2.3 / 1507 6.8 / 2153 2.7	16 TU	0242 7.5 / 0952 1.6 / 1519 7.3 / 2212 1.9
2 TU	0319 6.7 / 1012 2.6 / 1553 6.6 / 2238 2.9	17 W	0335 7.3 / 1039 1.8 / 1615 7.2 / 2304 2.2
3 W	0410 6.5 / 1059 2.8 / 1649 6.5 / 2331 3.1	18 TH	0436 7.1 / 1133 2.1 / 1718 7.0
4 TH	0512 6.4 / 1154 2.9 / 1753 6.5	19 F	0007 2.4 / 0546 6.9 / 1240 2.4 / 1828 7.0
5 F	0032 3.1 / 0621 6.4 / 1257 2.9 / 1856 6.6	20 SA	0120 2.4 / 0701 6.9 / 1354 2.4 / 1938 7.1
6 SA	0138 2.9 / 0726 6.5 / 1404 2.8 / 1952 6.8	21 SU	0232 2.3 / 0814 7.0 / 1502 2.3 / 2041 7.3
7 SU	0243 2.6 / 0821 6.7 / 1505 2.5 / 2042 7.0	22 M	0336 2.1 / 0915 7.2 / 1602 2.1 / 2135 7.4
8 M	0338 2.3 / 0910 7.0 / 1558 2.2 / 2127 7.2	23 TU	0434 1.8 / 1007 7.4 / 1656 1.9 / 2222 7.6
9 TU	0428 2.0 / 0956 7.2 / 1647 2.0 / 2210 7.4	24 W	0526 1.7 / 1052 7.5 / 1745 1.9 / ○2303 7.6
10 W	0516 1.7 / 1040 7.4 / 1734 1.8 / ●2252 7.6	25 TH	0610 1.5 / 1132 7.5 / 1827 1.8 / 2341 7.7
11 TH	0604 1.4 / 1124 7.5 / 1822 1.6 / 2335 7.7	26 F	0650 1.5 / 1209 7.5 / 1905 1.7
12 F	0651 1.3 / 1208 7.6 / 1910 1.5	27 SA	0018 7.6 / 0725 1.5 / 1244 7.5 / 1941 1.8
13 SA	0020 7.8 / 0738 1.2 / 1254 7.6 / 1956 1.5	28 SU	0053 7.6 / 0759 1.6 / 1319 7.4 / 2013 1.9
14 SU	0106 7.7 / 0824 1.2 / 1340 7.6 / 2041 1.6	29 M	0128 7.4 / 0833 1.8 / 1352 7.2 / 2043 2.1
15 M	0153 7.6 / 0907 1.3 / 1429 7.5 / 2126 1.7	30 TU	0201 7.2 / 0907 2.0 / 1425 7.0 / 2112 2.4
		31 W	0234 7.0 / 0926 2.3 / 1457 6.9 / 2144 2.7

AUGUST

Day	Time m	Day	Time m
1 TH	0311 6.8 / 1000 2.6 / 1537 6.7 / 2225 2.9	16 F	0406 7.0 / 1101 2.3 / 1643 6.9 / 2334 2.6
2 F	0358 6.5 / 1046 2.9 / 1631 6.5 / 2320 3.2	17 SA	0519 6.7 / 1206 2.8 / 1801 6.7
3 SA	0503 6.3 / 1147 3.2 / 1745 6.4	18 SU	0054 2.8 / 0649 6.5 / 1332 2.9 / 1925 6.8
4 SU	0031 3.2 / 0630 6.3 / 1306 3.2 / 1906 6.5	19 M	0216 2.6 / 0811 6.8 / 1449 2.7 / 2035 7.0
5 M	0156 3.0 / 0750 6.5 / 1428 2.9 / 2011 6.8	20 TU	0327 2.3 / 0911 7.0 / 1557 2.4 / 2127 7.2
6 TU	0307 2.5 / 0847 6.8 / 1532 2.5 / 2105 7.1	21 W	0431 2.0 / 0958 7.3 / 1654 2.1 / 2210 7.5
7 W	0405 2.1 / 0938 7.2 / 1628 2.1 / 2153 7.4	22 TH	0520 1.7 / 1038 7.5 / 1737 1.9 / ○2247 7.6
8 TH	0500 1.6 / 1025 7.5 / 1723 1.7 / ●2238 7.7	23 F	0558 1.5 / 1113 7.6 / 1813 1.7 / 2321 7.7
9 F	0554 1.3 / 1111 7.7 / 1816 1.4 / 2323 7.9	24 SA	0631 1.4 / 1145 7.6 / 1846 1.6 / 2353 7.7
10 SA	0645 1.0 / 1156 7.9 / 1904 1.2	25 SU	0703 1.4 / 1216 7.6 / 1917 1.6
11 SU	0008 8.0 / 0731 0.8 / 1240 8.0 / 1949 1.1	26 M	0025 7.7 / 0732 1.5 / 1247 7.5 / 1945 1.7
12 M	0053 8.0 / 0814 0.8 / 1324 7.9 / 2030 1.1	27 TU	0057 7.6 / 0758 1.6 / 1317 7.4 / 2011 1.9
13 TU	0138 7.9 / 0854 1.0 / 1409 7.8 / 2110 1.4	28 W	0126 7.4 / 0822 1.9 / 1344 7.3 / 2036 2.2
14 W	0223 7.7 / 0932 1.3 / 1454 7.5 / 2150 1.7	29 TH	0155 7.2 / 0847 2.2 / 1413 7.1 / 2104 2.5
15 TH	0310 7.4 / 1013 1.8 / 1542 7.2 / 2236 2.2	30 F	0228 6.9 / 0909 2.5 / 1448 6.8 / 2138 2.8
		31 SA	0310 6.6 / 0956 2.9 / 1535 6.5 / 2226 3.1

Chart Datum: 4·38 metres below IGN Datum

TIME ZONE -0100
(French Standard Time)
Subtract 1 hour for UT
For French Summer Time add
ONE hour in **non-shaded areas**

FRANCE – LE HAVRE

LAT 49°29′N   LONG 0°07′E

TIMES AND HEIGHTS OF HIGH AND LOW WATERS

YEAR **2002**

SEPTEMBER

Time m	Time m
1 0409 6.3 / 1052 3.3 / SU 1643 6.3 / 2335 3.4	**16** 0033 3.1 / 0642 6.4 / M 1318 3.3 / 1914 6.5
2 0540 6.1 / 1216 3.5 / M 1824 6.3	**17** 0205 2.9 / 0804 6.6 / TU 1444 2.9 / 2023 6.8
3 0117 3.2 / 0724 6.3 / TU 1400 3.2 / 1945 6.6	**18** 0321 2.4 / 0859 7.0 / W 1552 2.5 / 2112 7.1
4 0244 2.7 / 0827 6.8 / W 1513 2.6 / 2045 7.1	**19** 0419 2.0 / 0941 7.3 / TH 1641 2.1 / 2151 7.4
5 0347 2.0 / 0920 7.3 / TH 1614 2.0 / 2135 7.5	**20** 0501 1.7 / 1015 7.5 / F 1718 1.8 / 2224 7.6
6 0445 1.5 / 1007 7.7 / F 1710 1.5 / 2221 7.8	**21** 0534 1.5 / 1046 7.6 / SA 1750 1.5 / ○ 2254 7.8
7 0540 1.0 / 1051 7.9 / SA 1802 1.1 / ● 2305 8.1	**22** 0605 1.4 / 1115 7.7 / SU 1820 1.5 / 2325 7.8
8 0629 0.7 / 1135 8.1 / SU 1849 0.8 / 2350 8.2	**23** 0635 1.4 / 1144 7.7 / M 1849 1.6 / 2355 7.8
9 0713 0.5 / 1219 8.2 / M 1931 0.8	**24** 0701 1.5 / 1214 7.6 / TU 1915 1.7
10 0034 8.3 / 0754 0.6 / TU 1301 8.1 / 2011 0.9	**25** 0025 7.6 / 0726 1.6 / W 1242 7.5 / 1940 1.8
11 0117 8.1 / 0832 0.9 / W 1344 7.9 / 2049 1.2	**26** 0054 7.5 / 0751 1.9 / TH 1308 7.4 / 2006 2.0
12 0200 7.8 / 0908 1.4 / TH 1426 7.6 / 2126 1.7	**27** 0122 7.2 / 0816 2.2 / F 1336 7.2 / 2033 2.3
13 0245 7.4 / 0945 2.0 / F 1511 7.2 / 2207 2.3	**28** 0155 6.9 / 0844 2.6 / SA 1410 6.9 / 2105 2.7
14 0339 6.9 / 1030 2.6 / SA 1610 6.8 / 2304 2.8	**29** 0237 6.6 / 0921 3.0 / SU 1456 6.5 / 2149 3.1
15 0458 6.5 / 1138 3.2 / SU 1739 6.5	**30** 0337 6.3 / 1014 3.4 / M 1605 6.3 / 2256 3.4

OCTOBER

Time m	Time m
1 0509 6.1 / 1140 3.6 / TU 1751 6.2	**16** 0140 3.0 / 0742 6.6 / W 1420 3.0 / 1959 6.7
2 0047 3.3 / 0659 6.4 / W 1338 3.2 / 1920 6.6	**17** 0249 2.6 / 0835 6.9 / TH 1520 2.5 / 2046 7.0
3 0221 2.7 / 0804 6.9 / TH 1452 2.5 / 2021 7.1	**18** 0342 2.2 / 0913 7.3 / F 1606 2.1 / 2123 7.3
4 0325 2.0 / 0857 7.4 / F 1553 1.9 / 2112 7.6	**19** 0423 1.9 / 0945 7.5 / SA 1643 1.8 / 2155 7.6
5 0423 1.4 / 0943 7.8 / SA 1649 1.3 / 2158 8.0	**20** 0459 1.6 / 1014 7.6 / SU 1718 1.7 / 2225 7.7
6 0516 0.9 / 1027 8.1 / SU 1740 1.0 / ● 2243 8.2	**21** 0533 1.5 / 1042 7.7 / M 1750 1.6 / ○ 2255 7.7
7 0605 0.6 / 1112 8.3 / M 1826 0.7 / 2327 8.3	**22** 0603 1.5 / 1112 7.7 / TU 1819 1.6 / 2327 7.7
8 0649 0.5 / 1154 8.3 / TU 1908 0.7	**23** 0630 1.6 / 1141 7.7 / W 1846 1.7 / 2357 7.6
9 0011 8.3 / 0729 0.7 / W 1236 8.2 / 1948 0.9	**24** 0656 1.7 / 1210 7.6 / TH 1913 1.8
10 0055 8.1 / 0807 1.1 / TH 1317 7.9 / 2025 1.3	**25** 0028 7.5 / 0724 1.9 / F 1238 7.5 / 1942 2.0
11 0138 7.7 / 0842 1.6 / F 1359 7.6 / 2102 1.8	**26** 0100 7.3 / 0753 2.2 / SA 1311 7.3 / 2013 2.2
12 0224 7.3 / 0918 2.3 / SA 1444 7.1 / 2142 2.4	**27** 0138 7.0 / 0824 2.6 / SU 1348 7.0 / 2046 2.6
13 0319 6.8 / 1003 2.9 / SU 1543 6.7 / 2239 3.0	**28** 0223 6.7 / 0902 3.0 / M 1437 6.6 / 2130 2.9
14 0439 6.4 / 1115 3.4 / M 1713 6.3	**29** 0323 6.4 / 0956 3.3 / TU 1545 6.4 / 2236 3.2
15 0008 3.2 / 0621 6.3 / TU 1258 3.4 / 1848 6.4	**30** 0450 6.3 / 1122 3.5 / W 1723 6.4
	31 0021 3.1 / 0630 6.6 / TH 1309 3.1 / 1849 6.7

NOVEMBER

Time m	Time m
1 0150 2.6 / 0734 7.0 / F 1424 2.4 / 1952 7.2	**16** 0250 2.5 / 0833 7.1 / SA 1519 2.4 / 2046 7.1
2 0256 1.9 / 0828 7.5 / SA 1525 1.8 / 2045 7.6	**17** 0338 2.2 / 0907 7.3 / SU 1603 2.1 / 2121 7.3
3 0354 1.4 / 0915 7.9 / SU 1621 1.4 / 2133 8.0	**18** 0420 1.9 / 0939 7.5 / M 1643 1.9 / 2155 7.5
4 0448 1.0 / 1001 8.1 / M 1714 1.0 / ● 2220 8.2	**19** 0457 1.8 / 1010 7.6 / TU 1718 1.8 / 2228 7.6
5 0538 0.8 / 1045 8.3 / TU 1801 0.9 / 2305 8.2	**20** 0530 1.8 / 1042 7.7 / W 1750 1.7 / ○ 2302 7.6
6 0623 0.8 / 1129 8.3 / W 1845 0.9 / 2351 8.2	**21** 0601 1.8 / 1114 7.7 / TH 1820 1.7 / 2335 7.6
7 0704 1.0 / 1211 8.1 / TH 1925 1.0	**22** 0631 1.8 / 1145 7.7 / F 1852 1.7
8 0036 8.0 / 0743 1.4 / F 1254 7.9 / 2004 1.4	**23** 0009 7.5 / 0704 2.0 / SA 1219 7.6 / 1926 1.8
9 0121 7.6 / 0820 1.9 / SA 1337 7.5 / 2041 1.9	**24** 0047 7.3 / 0738 2.2 / SU 1257 7.4 / 2001 2.1
10 0207 7.2 / 0858 2.4 / SU 1422 7.1 / 2122 2.4	**25** 0129 7.1 / 0815 2.5 / M 1340 7.1 / 2039 2.3
11 0301 6.8 / 0944 3.0 / M 1518 6.7 / 2215 2.9	**26** 0216 6.9 / 0857 2.7 / TU 1429 6.9 / 2126 2.6
12 0411 6.4 / 1050 3.3 / TU 1631 6.4 / 2329 3.1	**27** 0313 6.7 / 0952 3.0 / W 1531 6.7 / 2229 2.8
13 0534 6.3 / 1213 3.4 / W 1758 6.3	**28** 0429 6.6 / 1109 3.1 / TH 1653 6.6 / 2351 2.8
14 0047 3.1 / 0652 6.5 / TH 1327 3.2 / 1911 6.5	**29** 0557 6.8 / 1232 2.9 / F 1813 6.8
15 0154 2.8 / 0745 6.8 / F 1428 2.8 / 2005 6.8	**30** 0111 2.5 / 0658 7.1 / SA 1347 2.4 / 1918 7.1

DECEMBER

Time m	Time m
1 0221 2.0 / 0755 7.5 / SU 1453 2.0 / 2016 7.5	**16** 0248 2.6 / 0824 7.0 / M 1520 2.5 / 2045 7.0
2 0323 1.7 / 0847 7.8 / M 1553 1.6 / 2110 7.8	**17** 0338 2.4 / 0904 7.2 / TU 1606 2.3 / 2126 7.2
3 0419 1.4 / 0936 8.0 / TU 1647 1.3 / 2200 7.9	**18** 0421 2.2 / 0941 7.4 / W 1646 2.0 / 2204 7.3
4 0511 1.2 / 1023 8.1 / W 1737 1.1 / ● 2249 8.0	**19** 0500 2.1 / 1017 7.5 / TH 1724 1.9 / ○ 2242 7.4
5 0558 1.2 / 1108 8.1 / TH 1823 1.1 / 2336 8.0	**20** 0537 1.9 / 1053 7.6 / F 1801 1.7 / 2319 7.5
6 0641 1.4 / 1153 8.0 / F 1905 1.2	**21** 0614 1.9 / 1129 7.7 / SA 1839 1.6 / 2358 7.5
7 0022 7.8 / 0722 1.6 / SA 1235 7.8 / 1945 1.4	**22** 0653 1.9 / 1207 7.7 / SU 1919 1.6
8 0107 7.6 / 0802 1.9 / SU 1319 7.6 / 2025 1.8	**23** 0038 7.5 / 0733 2.0 / M 1249 7.6 / 2000 1.7
9 0151 7.3 / 0842 2.3 / M 1403 7.2 / 2105 2.2	**24** 0122 7.4 / 0815 2.1 / TU 1333 7.4 / 2042 1.9
10 0238 7.0 / 0925 2.7 / TU 1451 6.9 / 2149 2.6	**25** 0209 7.2 / 0900 2.3 / W 1421 7.3 / 2128 2.1
11 0331 6.6 / 1016 3.0 / W 1548 6.6 / 2241 2.9	**26** 0301 7.1 / 0950 2.5 / TH 1515 7.1 / 2220 2.3
12 0433 6.5 / 1115 3.2 / TH 1653 6.4 / 2341 3.0	**27** 0401 7.0 / 1048 2.6 / F 1620 7.0 / 2320 2.4
13 0539 6.5 / 1218 3.3 / F 1802 6.4	**28** 0510 7.0 / 1153 2.6 / SA 1733 6.9
14 0045 3.0 / 0643 6.6 / SA 1324 3.1 / 1906 6.5	**29** 0028 2.4 / 0621 7.1 / SU 1306 2.5 / 1844 7.0
15 0149 2.9 / 0738 6.8 / SU 1426 2.8 / 2000 6.8	**30** 0142 2.3 / 0724 7.2 / M 1421 2.3 / 1952 7.2
	31 0253 2.1 / 0838 7.5 / TU 1527 2.0 / 2054 7.4

Chart Datum: 4·38 metres below IGN Datum

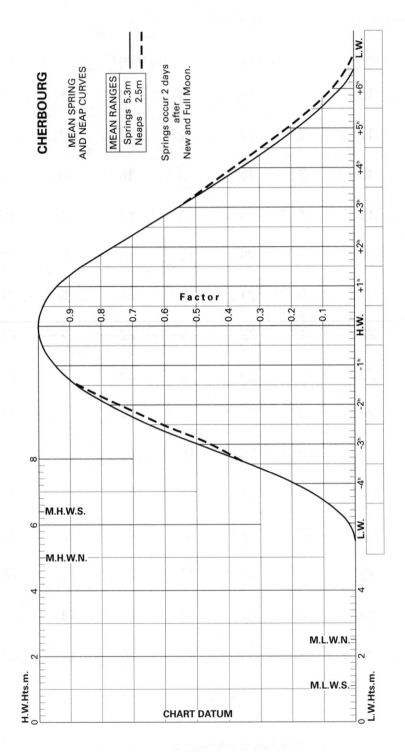

CHERBOURG

MEAN SPRING
AND NEAP CURVES

MEAN RANGES
Springs 5.3m
Neaps 2.5m

Springs occur 2 days
after
New and Full Moon.

Factor

0.9 0.8 0.7 0.6 0.5 0.4 0.3 0.2 0.1

H.W.Hts.m.

M.H.W.S.

M.H.W.N.

CHART DATUM

M.L.W.N.

M.L.W.S.

L.W.Hts.m.

L.W.   H.W.   L.W.

TIME ZONE -0100
(French Standard Time)
Subtract 1 hour for UT
For French Summer Time add
ONE hour in **non-shaded areas**

FRANCE – CHERBOURG

LAT 49°39'N   LONG 1°38'W

TIMES AND HEIGHTS OF HIGH AND LOW WATERS

YEAR **2002**

JANUARY

Day	Time m	Time m	Time m	Time m		Day	Time m	Time m	Time m	Time m
1 TU	0425 1.3	0956 6.5	1651 1.0	2228 6.3		**16** W	0500 1.7	1030 6.1	1719 1.4	2252 5.9
2 W	0510 1.3	1041 6.5	1737 1.1	2315 6.2		**17** TH	0534 1.8	1104 6.0	1752 1.5	2325 5.7
3 TH	0557 1.4	1128 6.3	1825 1.2			**18** F	0606 1.9	1136 5.8	1825 1.7	2357 5.5
4 F	0000 6.0	0646 1.6	1217 6.1	1915 1.4		**19** SA	0639 2.1	1209 5.6	1858 1.9	
5 SA	0054 5.8	0738 1.9	1309 5.9	2008 1.6		**20** SU	0030 5.3	0714 2.3	1244 5.4	1934 2.2
6 SU	0150 5.6	0835 2.1	1407 5.6	2108 1.9		**21** M	0108 5.1	0755 2.5	1327 5.1	2017 2.4
7 M	0254 5.4	0940 2.3	1515 5.4	2216 2.1		**22** TU	0157 5.0	0847 2.7	1421 4.9	2112 2.6
8 TU	0404 5.3	1052 2.3	1628 5.3	2327 2.2		**23** W	0300 4.9	0955 2.8	1532 4.8	2223 2.7
9 W	0513 5.4	1204 2.2	1740 5.4			**24** TH	0416 4.9	1113 2.7	1653 4.9	2340 2.5
10 TH	0036 2.1	0616 5.6	1307 2.0	1844 5.5		**25** F	0531 5.1	1224 2.4	1805 5.1	
11 F	0133 2.2	0710 5.8	1401 1.8	1939 5.7		**26** SA	0051 2.3	0633 5.5	1325 2.0	1905 5.5
12 SA	0224 1.8	0758 6.0	1449 1.6	2026 5.8		**27** SU	0148 1.9	0726 5.8	1418 1.6	1957 5.8
13 SU	0308 1.7	0840 6.1	1526 1.5	●2107 5.9		**28** M	0240 1.6	0815 6.2	1508 1.2	○2046 6.2
14 M	0348 1.7	0919 6.2	1609 1.4	2144 6.0		**29** TU	0329 1.3	0902 6.4	1556 0.9	2134 6.4
15 TU	0425 1.7	0955 6.2	1645 1.4	2218 5.9		**30** W	0417 1.1	0949 6.6	1643 0.7	2221 6.5
						31 TH	0503 1.0	1035 6.7	1728 0.6	2306 6.5

FEBRUARY

Day	Time m	Time m	Time m	Time m		Day	Time m	Time m	Time m	Time m
1 F	0548 1.0	1120 6.7	1813 0.7	2351 6.4		**16** SA	0542 1.6	1111 6.0	1757 1.4	2327 5.8
2 SA	0632 1.1	1204 6.5	1858 1.0			**17** SU	0610 1.7	1139 5.9	1825 1.6	2356 5.6
3 SU	0034 6.1	0718 1.4	1249 6.1	1944 1.4		**18** M	0640 1.9	1209 5.6	1856 1.9	
4 M	0120 5.8	0806 1.8	1336 5.7	2034 1.8		**19** TU	0024 5.4	0714 2.2	1241 5.3	1931 2.2
5 TU	0211 5.4	0902 2.2	1434 5.3	2134 2.3		**20** W	0101 5.2	0756 2.4	1324 5.0	2017 2.5
6 W	0317 5.1	1013 2.5	1552 5.0	2251 2.5		**21** TH	0153 4.9	0854 2.7	1429 4.8	2124 2.7
7 TH	0438 5.1	1136 2.5	1720 5.0			**22** F	0311 4.8	1017 2.7	1605 4.7	2253 2.7
8 F	0003 2.5	0555 5.2	1251 2.3	1837 5.1		**23** SA	0450 4.9	1148 2.5	1740 4.9	
9 SA	0122 2.3	0658 5.4	1351 2.0	1934 5.4		**24** SU	0023 2.5	0608 5.2	1301 2.1	1848 5.4
10 SU	0215 2.1	0748 5.7	1439 1.7	2018 5.7		**25** M	0130 2.0	0708 5.7	1401 1.6	1943 5.8
11 M	0259 1.9	0830 5.9	1520 1.5	2056 5.8		**26** TU	0226 1.5	0801 6.1	1454 1.1	2033 6.2
12 TU	0337 1.7	0907 6.1	1555 1.4	●2129 6.0		**27** W	0316 1.1	0850 6.5	1542 0.7	○2121 6.5
13 W	0412 1.5	0941 6.2	1628 1.3	2201 6.0		**28** TH	0403 0.8	0937 6.8	1628 0.4	2207 6.7
14 TH	0443 1.5	1013 6.2	1700 1.2	2231 6.0						
15 F	0513 1.5	1043 6.2	1729 1.3	2259 5.9						

MARCH

Day	Time m	Time m	Time m	Time m		Day	Time m	Time m	Time m	Time m
1 F	0448 0.6	1022 6.9	1712 0.3	2250 6.7		**16** SA	0448 1.3	1018 6.2	1701 1.2	2231 6.0
2 SA	0530 0.6	1105 6.9	1754 0.5	2331 6.6		**17** SU	0515 1.4	1045 6.1	1728 1.3	2257 6.0
3 SU	0612 0.8	1145 6.6	1835 0.8			**18** M	0543 1.5	1112 6.0	1755 1.5	2324 5.8
4 M	0002 6.3	0653 1.2	1225 6.2	1916 1.3		**19** TU	0611 1.6	1140 5.7	1824 1.7	2352 5.6
5 TU	0047 5.9	0736 1.7	1306 5.7	2000 1.9		**20** W	0643 1.9	1210 5.4	1858 2.0	
6 W	0131 5.4	0826 2.2	1358 5.1	2054 2.5		**21** TH	0023 5.3	0723 2.2	1249 5.1	1942 2.4
7 TH	0232 5.0	0933 2.6	1519 4.7	2214 2.8		**22** F	0110 5.0	0817 2.5	1350 4.8	2047 2.7
8 F	0403 4.8	1107 2.7	1707 4.7	2351 2.8		**23** SA	0226 4.8	0938 2.7	1536 4.6	2222 2.8
9 SA	0536 4.9	1234 2.5	1830 4.9			**24** SU	0417 4.8	1119 2.5	1723 4.9	
10 SU	0110 2.5	0644 5.2	1336 2.1	1922 5.3		**25** M	0010 2.5	0546 5.1	1239 2.0	1832 5.4
11 M	0203 2.2	0732 5.5	1423 1.8	2001 5.6		**26** TU	0111 2.0	0649 5.7	1341 1.5	1926 5.9
12 TU	0244 1.9	0812 5.8	1501 1.5	2035 5.8		**27** W	0208 1.5	0743 6.2	1434 1.0	2015 6.3
13 W	0319 1.6	0847 6.0	1534 1.3	2107 6.0		**28** TH	0258 1.0	0832 6.6	1522 0.6	○2101 6.6
14 TH	0351 1.4	0919 6.2	1605 1.2	●2137 6.1		**29** F	0344 0.7	0919 6.8	1607 0.3	2145 6.8
15 F	0420 1.3	0950 6.2	1634 1.1	2205 6.1		**30** SA	0427 0.5	1003 6.9	1649 0.3	2227 6.8
						31 SU	0509 0.5	1044 6.8	1730 0.5	2306 6.6

APRIL

Day	Time m	Time m	Time m	Time m		Day	Time m	Time m	Time m	Time m
1 M	0548 0.8	1123 6.5	1808 0.9	2343 6.3		**16** TU	0518 1.3	1049 6.0	1729 1.4	2300 5.9
2 TU	0628 1.2	1201 6.1	1847 1.5			**17** W	0549 1.5	1121 5.8	1801 1.7	2331 5.7
3 W	0017 5.9	0708 1.6	1240 5.6	1929 2.1		**18** TH	0623 1.7	1155 5.5	1837 2.0	
4 TH	0058 5.4	0755 2.2	1329 5.0	2020 2.6		**19** F	0010 5.4	0705 2.0	1239 5.1	1925 2.4
5 F	0156 4.9	0858 2.6	1450 4.6	2140 3.0		**20** SA	0056 5.1	0801 2.3	1343 4.8	2033 2.7
6 SA	0329 4.7	1031 2.7	1643 4.6	2322 3.0		**21** SU	0211 4.9	0921 2.5	1525 4.7	2205 2.7
7 SU	0506 4.8	1201 2.6	1804 4.9			**22** M	0353 4.9	1056 2.3	1703 5.0	2335 2.4
8 M	0041 2.6	0614 5.1	1304 2.2	1853 5.2		**23** TU	0520 5.2	1214 1.9	1808 5.5	
9 TU	0134 2.2	0702 5.4	1351 1.9	1930 5.5		**24** W	0047 1.9	0624 5.7	1316 1.4	1902 5.9
10 W	0215 1.9	0742 5.7	1429 1.6	2004 5.8		**25** TH	0143 1.4	0718 6.1	1409 1.0	1951 6.3
11 TH	0250 1.7	0818 5.9	1503 1.4	2037 6.0		**26** F	0234 1.0	0809 6.5	1457 0.7	2037 6.6
12 F	0322 1.5	0851 6.1	1534 1.3	●2107 6.1		**27** SA	0320 0.8	0856 6.7	1542 0.5	○2120 6.7
13 SA	0351 1.3	0922 6.2	1603 1.2	2136 6.1		**28** SU	0404 0.6	0940 6.7	1625 0.6	2201 6.7
14 SU	0420 1.3	0951 6.2	1631 1.2	2203 6.1		**29** M	0446 0.7	1022 6.6	1705 0.8	2240 6.5
15 M	0449 1.3	1019 6.1	1700 1.3	2231 6.1		**30** TU	0526 1.0	1101 6.3	1743 1.2	2317 6.2

FRANCE – CHERBOURG — YEAR 2002

TIME ZONE -0100
(French Standard Time)
Subtract 1 hour for UT
For French Summer Time add
ONE hour in **non-shaded areas**

LAT 49°39′N   LONG 1°38′W

TIMES AND HEIGHTS OF HIGH AND LOW WATERS

MAY

Day	Time	m	Day	Time	m
1 W	0605 / 1140 / 1822 / 2355	1.2 / 5.9 / 1.7 / 5.8	**16** TH	0534 / 1111 / 1747 / 2322	1.4 / 5.8 / 1.7 / 5.8
2 TH	0646 / 1221 / 1904	1.7 / 5.5 / 2.2	**17** F	0614 / 1153 / 1830	1.6 / 5.5 / 2.0
3 F	0035 / 0731 / 1310 / 1955	5.4 / 2.1 / 5.0 / 2.6	**18** SA	0006 / 0700 / 1242 / 1922	5.6 / 1.9 / 5.3 / 2.3
4 SA	0130 / 0829 / 1421 / 2107	5.0 / 2.5 / 4.7 / 2.9	**19** SU	0057 / 0759 / 1346 / 2030	5.3 / 2.1 / 5.0 / 2.5
5 SU	0250 / 0948 / 1555 / 2236	4.7 / 2.6 / 4.6 / 2.9	**20** M	0206 / 0912 / 1511 / 2150	5.1 / 2.2 / 5.0 / 2.5
6 M	0417 / 1109 / 1712 / 2350	4.7 / 2.6 / 4.8 / 2.7	**21** TU	0330 / 1033 / 1633 / 2308	5.1 / 2.1 / 5.2 / 2.2
7 TU	0525 / 1214 / 1806	4.9 / 2.3 / 5.1	**22** W	0449 / 1145 / 1738	5.4 / 1.8 / 5.5
8 W	0048 / 0618 / 1305 / 1848	2.4 / 5.2 / 2.0 / 5.4	**23** TH	0018 / 0554 / 1247 / 1833	1.9 / 5.7 / 1.4 / 5.9
9 TH	0133 / 0702 / 1347 / 1926	2.1 / 5.5 / 1.8 / 5.7	**24** F	0116 / 0651 / 1342 / 1924	1.5 / 6.0 / 1.2 / 6.2
10 F	0212 / 0742 / 1424 / 2001	1.8 / 5.7 / 1.6 / 5.9	**25** SA	0209 / 0745 / 1432 / 2011	1.2 / 6.2 / 1.0 / 6.4
11 SA	0247 / 0818 / 1458 / 2035	1.6 / 5.9 / 1.4 / 6.0	**26** SU	0257 / 0834 / 1518 / ○2056	1.0 / 6.4 / 0.9 / 6.5
12 SU	0320 / 0852 / 1530 / ●2106	1.4 / 6.0 / 1.3 / 6.1	**27** M	0343 / 0920 / 1602 / 2138	0.9 / 6.4 / 1.0 / 6.4
13 M	0352 / 0925 / 1603 / 2137	1.3 / 6.0 / 1.3 / 6.1	**28** TU	0426 / 1003 / 1643 / 2218	1.0 / 6.3 / 1.2 / 6.3
14 TU	0425 / 0958 / 1636 / 2209	1.3 / 6.0 / 1.4 / 6.1	**29** W	0507 / 1043 / 1723 / 2257	1.1 / 6.1 / 1.5 / 6.1
15 W	0459 / 1033 / 1710 / 2244	1.3 / 5.9 / 1.5 / 6.0	**30** TH	0547 / 1124 / 1803 / 2336	1.3 / 5.8 / 1.8 / 5.8
			31 F	0628 / 1205 / 1845	1.6 / 5.5 / 2.1

JUNE

Day	Time	m	Day	Time	m
1 SA	0018 / 0711 / 1250 / 1932	5.5 / 2.0 / 5.2 / 2.5	**16** SU	0004 / 0700 / 1242 / 1922	5.8 / 1.5 / 5.4 / 2.0
2 SU	0107 / 0801 / 1346 / 2030	5.2 / 2.2 / 4.9 / 2.7	**17** M	0055 / 0755 / 1340 / 2022	5.6 / 1.7 / 5.4 / 2.1
3 M	0207 / 0900 / 1453 / 2139	5.0 / 2.4 / 4.8 / 2.8	**18** TU	0155 / 0858 / 1447 / 2129	5.5 / 1.8 / 5.3 / 2.2
4 TU	0316 / 1007 / 1603 / 2248	4.8 / 2.5 / 4.8 / 2.7	**19** W	0303 / 1005 / 1558 / 2239	5.4 / 1.9 / 5.3 / 2.1
5 W	0423 / 1112 / 1705 / 2349	4.9 / 2.4 / 5.0 / 2.5	**20** TH	0415 / 1114 / 1704 / 2346	5.4 / 1.8 / 5.5 / 2.0
6 TH	0522 / 1209 / 1757	5.0 / 2.2 / 5.2	**21** F	0524 / 1218 / 1804	5.5 / 1.7 / 5.7
7 F	0043 / 0615 / 1258 / 1842	2.3 / 5.2 / 2.0 / 5.4	**22** SA	0050 / 0627 / 1317 / 1859	1.7 / 5.7 / 1.5 / 5.9
8 SA	0129 / 0701 / 1342 / 1923	2.0 / 5.4 / 1.8 / 5.7	**23** SU	0147 / 0725 / 1410 / 1950	1.5 / 5.9 / 1.4 / 6.1
9 SU	0210 / 0744 / 1422 / 2002	1.8 / 5.6 / 1.7 / 5.9	**24** M	0239 / 0818 / 1459 / ○2037	1.4 / 6.0 / 1.4 / 6.2
10 M	0249 / 0825 / 1501 / 2039	1.6 / 5.8 / 1.5 / 6.0	**25** TU	0327 / 0906 / 1544 / 2120	1.2 / 6.0 / 1.4 / 6.2
11 TU	0328 / 0903 / 1540 / ●2116	1.4 / 5.9 / 1.5 / 6.1	**26** W	0411 / 0949 / 1627 / 2201	1.2 / 6.0 / 1.5 / 6.2
12 W	0407 / 0942 / 1619 / 2154	1.3 / 6.0 / 1.5 / 6.1	**27** TH	0452 / 1029 / 1707 / 2241	1.3 / 5.9 / 1.6 / 6.1
13 TH	0446 / 1022 / 1659 / 2234	1.3 / 5.9 / 1.5 / 6.1	**28** F	0532 / 1108 / 1746 / 2320	1.4 / 5.8 / 1.8 / 5.9
14 F	0527 / 1105 / 1742 / 2317	1.3 / 5.9 / 1.6 / 6.0	**29** SA	0610 / 1147 / 1825 / 2359	1.5 / 5.6 / 2.0 / 5.7
15 SA	0612 / 1151 / 1829	1.4 / 5.7 / 1.8	**30** SU	0648 / 1226 / 1906	1.7 / 5.4 / 2.2

JULY

Day	Time	m	Day	Time	m
1 M	0040 / 0728 / 1306 / 1949	5.5 / 2.0 / 5.2 / 2.4	**16** TU	0045 / 0741 / 1322 / 2004	6.0 / 1.4 / 5.7 / 1.8
2 TU	0123 / 0812 / 1352 / 2040	5.2 / 2.2 / 5.0 / 2.6	**17** W	0136 / 0834 / 1416 / 2102	5.8 / 1.6 / 5.5 / 2.0
3 W	0212 / 0903 / 1447 / 2139	5.0 / 2.4 / 4.9 / 2.7	**18** TH	0234 / 0935 / 1519 / 2208	5.5 / 1.9 / 5.4 / 2.1
4 TH	0311 / 1002 / 1550 / 2244	4.9 / 2.5 / 4.9 / 2.7	**19** F	0343 / 1043 / 1630 / 2319	5.3 / 2.0 / 5.3 / 2.2
5 F	0416 / 1106 / 1656 / 2347	4.8 / 2.5 / 5.0 / 2.5	**20** SA	0459 / 1154 / 1740	5.3 / 2.1 / 5.4
6 SA	0522 / 1208 / 1755	4.9 / 2.4 / 5.2	**21** SU	0031 / 0612 / 1259 / 1842	2.0 / 5.4 / 2.0 / 5.6
7 SU	0045 / 0622 / 1302 / 1847	2.3 / 5.2 / 2.2 / 5.4	**22** M	0133 / 0717 / 1357 / 1938	1.8 / 5.5 / 1.9 / 5.8
8 M	0136 / 0714 / 1351 / 1933	2.0 / 5.4 / 1.9 / 5.7	**23** TU	0228 / 0811 / 1448 / 2026	1.6 / 5.7 / 1.7 / 6.0
9 TU	0223 / 0802 / 1437 / 2017	1.7 / 5.6 / 1.7 / 5.9	**24** W	0316 / 0858 / 1533 / ○2109	1.4 / 5.9 / 1.6 / 6.1
10 W	0308 / 0846 / 1522 / ●2059	1.5 / 5.9 / 1.5 / 6.1	**25** TH	0359 / 0938 / 1614 / 2148	1.3 / 5.9 / 1.6 / 6.2
11 TH	0352 / 0930 / 1607 / 2142	1.3 / 6.0 / 1.4 / 6.2	**26** F	0437 / 1014 / 1652 / 2225	1.3 / 5.9 / 1.6 / 6.2
12 F	0437 / 1015 / 1652 / 2226	1.1 / 6.1 / 1.3 / 6.3	**27** SA	0514 / 1049 / 1727 / 2300	1.3 / 5.9 / 1.6 / 6.1
13 SA	0521 / 1100 / 1737 / 2311	1.0 / 6.1 / 1.3 / 6.3	**28** SU	0547 / 1122 / 1801 / 2334	1.4 / 5.8 / 1.8 / 5.9
14 SU	0606 / 1146 / 1823 / 2358	1.0 / 6.0 / 1.4 / 6.2	**29** M	0620 / 1154 / 1833	1.5 / 5.6 / 1.9
15 M	0653 / 1233 / 1912	1.2 / 5.9 / 1.6	**30** TU	0003 / 0652 / 1226 / 1907	5.7 / 1.6 / 5.4 / 2.2
			31 W	0039 / 0725 / 1259 / 1945	5.4 / 2.0 / 5.2 / 2.4

AUGUST

Day	Time	m	Day	Time	m
1 TH	0117 / 0804 / 1340 / 2032	5.2 / 2.3 / 5.0 / 2.6	**16** F	0204 / 0902 / 1441 / 2137	5.5 / 2.1 / 5.3 / 2.3
2 F	0204 / 0853 / 1434 / 2133	4.9 / 2.5 / 4.9 / 2.8	**17** SA	0314 / 1014 / 1600 / 2258	5.1 / 2.4 / 5.1 / 2.4
3 SA	0307 / 0959 / 1546 / 2249	4.7 / 2.7 / 4.8 / 2.8	**18** SU	0445 / 1137 / 1724	5.0 / 2.5 / 5.0
4 SU	0429 / 1117 / 1708	4.7 / 2.7 / 4.9	**19** M	0021 / 0610 / 1251 / 1835	2.3 / 5.1 / 2.4 / 5.4
5 M	0010 / 0549 / 1228 / 1816	2.5 / 4.9 / 2.5 / 5.2	**20** TU	0127 / 0716 / 1352 / 1930	2.0 / 5.4 / 2.1 / 5.7
6 TU	0108 / 0651 / 1327 / 1910	2.2 / 5.2 / 2.1 / 5.6	**21** W	0220 / 0805 / 1441 / 2016	1.7 / 5.7 / 1.9 / 6.0
7 W	0201 / 0744 / 1419 / 1958	1.8 / 5.6 / 1.8 / 5.9	**22** TH	0305 / 0845 / 1522 / ○2055	1.5 / 5.9 / 1.7 / 6.1
8 TH	0251 / 0832 / 1508 / ●2044	1.4 / 5.9 / 1.5 / 6.2	**23** F	0343 / 0921 / 1558 / 2130	1.3 / 6.0 / 1.5 / 6.2
9 F	0338 / 0918 / 1555 / 2130	1.1 / 6.2 / 1.2 / 6.5	**24** SA	0417 / 0953 / 1631 / 2203	1.3 / 6.0 / 1.5 / 6.3
10 SA	0424 / 1004 / 1640 / 2215	0.8 / 6.4 / 1.1 / 6.6	**25** SU	0449 / 1023 / 1702 / 2234	1.2 / 6.0 / 1.5 / 6.2
11 SU	0508 / 1048 / 1724 / 2259	0.7 / 6.4 / 1.0 / 6.6	**26** M	0519 / 1052 / 1731 / 2303	1.3 / 6.0 / 1.6 / 6.1
12 M	0551 / 1131 / 1808 / 2343	0.7 / 6.4 / 1.1 / 6.5	**27** TU	0547 / 1119 / 1759 / 2331	1.4 / 5.8 / 1.7 / 5.9
13 TU	0634 / 1213 / 1852	0.9 / 6.2 / 1.3	**28** W	0614 / 1145 / 1827 / 2359	1.6 / 5.7 / 2.0 / 5.6
14 W	0025 / 0718 / 1256 / 1939	6.3 / 1.2 / 5.9 / 1.6	**29** TH	0643 / 1212 / 1858	1.9 / 5.5 / 2.2
15 TH	0111 / 0806 / 1342 / 2032	5.9 / 1.6 / 5.6 / 2.0	**30** F	0028 / 0715 / 1245 / 1937	5.3 / 2.2 / 5.2 / 2.5
			31 SA	0108 / 0756 / 1331 / 2030	5.0 / 2.6 / 4.9 / 2.8

Chart Datum: 3·33 metres below IGN Datum

TIME ZONE -0100
(French Standard Time)
Subtract 1 hour for UT
For French Summer Time add ONE hour in **non-shaded areas**

FRANCE – CHERBOURG

YEAR 2002

LAT 49°39′N   LONG 1°38′W

TIMES AND HEIGHTS OF HIGH AND LOW WATERS

SEPTEMBER

Day	Time m	Time m	Time m	Time m
1 SU	0207 4.7	0858 2.8	1442 4.7	2152 2.9
2 M	0341 4.6	1031 2.9	1625 4.8	2327 2.7
3 TU	0525 4.8	1201 2.7	1750 5.1	
4 W	0045 2.3	0633 5.2	1308 2.3	1849 5.5
5 TH	0142 1.8	0726 5.7	1402 1.8	1939 6.0
6 F	0232 1.3	0815 6.1	1451 1.3	2026 6.4
7 SA	0319 0.9	0900 6.4	1537 1.0	● 2112 6.7
8 SU	0404 0.6	0945 6.6	1621 0.8	2157 6.9
9 M	0447 0.5	1027 6.7	1704 0.7	2240 6.9
10 TU	0529 0.5	1108 6.6	1746 0.8	2322 6.7
11 W	0610 0.8	1147 6.4	1827 1.1	
12 TH	0000 6.3	0651 1.3	1226 6.0	1911 1.6
13 F	0044 5.9	0735 1.8	1308 5.7	2002 2.1
14 SA	0135 5.3	0829 2.4	1404 5.2	2108 2.5
15 SU	0251 4.9	0948 2.8	1533 4.9	2241 2.7
16 M	0441 4.8	1128 2.9	1713 5.0	
17 TU	0005 2.5	0611 5.0	1245 2.6	1825 5.3
18 W	0116 2.1	0706 5.4	1341 2.2	1916 5.6
19 TH	0205 1.8	0747 5.7	1424 1.9	1956 6.0
20 F	0244 1.5	0822 5.9	1501 1.7	2032 6.2
21 SA	0319 1.4	0854 6.1	1534 1.5	O 2105 6.3
22 SU	0350 1.3	0924 6.1	1604 1.4	2135 6.3
23 M	0419 1.3	0952 6.1	1632 1.4	2204 6.3
24 TU	0447 1.3	1018 6.1	1659 1.5	2230 6.1
25 W	0513 1.4	1042 6.0	1726 1.6	2256 6.0
26 TH	0539 1.6	1107 5.8	1753 1.8	2322 5.7
27 F	0606 1.9	1133 5.6	1822 2.1	2351 5.4
28 SA	0637 2.2	1203 5.4	1858 2.4	
29 SU	0027 5.1	0717 2.6	1245 5.1	1948 2.7
30 M	0126 4.8	0817 2.9	1355 4.8	2107 2.9

OCTOBER

Day	Time m	Time m	Time m	Time m
1 TU	0308 4.6	0954 3.1	1548 4.7	2255 2.8
2 W	0504 4.8	1136 2.8	1724 5.1	
3 TH	0020 2.3	0612 5.3	1245 2.3	1825 5.6
4 F	0118 1.7	0703 5.8	1339 1.7	1915 6.1
5 SA	0208 1.2	0750 6.3	1428 1.2	2003 6.5
6 SU	0255 0.8	0836 6.6	1514 0.9	● 2049 6.8
7 M	0340 0.5	0919 6.8	1558 0.7	2134 7.0
8 TU	0422 0.5	1001 6.8	1640 0.7	2217 6.9
9 W	0503 0.6	1041 6.7	1722 0.8	2258 6.7
10 TH	0544 1.0	1119 6.5	1803 1.2	2339 6.3
11 F	0624 1.5	1157 6.1	1846 1.7	
12 SA	0020 5.7	0707 2.1	1238 5.6	1935 2.2
13 SU	0112 5.2	0801 2.7	1334 5.1	2041 2.6
14 M	0231 4.8	0924 3.1	1505 4.9	2218 2.8
15 TU	0425 4.7	1108 3.0	1648 4.9	2345 2.6
16 W	0548 5.0	1222 2.7	1758 5.2	
17 TH	0048 2.3	0638 5.3	1314 2.3	1846 5.5
18 F	0134 1.9	0715 5.7	1355 2.0	1925 5.9
19 SA	0213 1.7	0749 5.9	1431 1.7	2000 6.1
20 SU	0246 1.5	0821 6.1	1504 1.6	2033 6.2
21 M	0317 1.4	0851 6.2	1533 1.5	O 2104 6.3
22 TU	0346 1.4	0919 6.2	1602 1.5	2133 6.2
23 W	0414 1.4	0944 6.2	1630 1.5	2200 6.1
24 TH	0442 1.5	1010 6.1	1658 1.6	2227 6.0
25 F	0510 1.7	1037 6.0	1727 1.8	2257 5.8
26 SA	0539 2.0	1107 5.8	1759 2.0	2330 5.5
27 SU	0613 2.3	1140 5.5	1836 2.3	
28 M	0012 5.2	0656 2.6	1225 5.2	1928 2.6
29 TU	0111 4.9	0758 2.9	1335 4.9	2044 2.8
30 W	0248 4.7	0930 3.0	1517 4.9	2223 2.6
31 TH	0433 4.9	1106 2.7	1649 5.2	2345 2.2

NOVEMBER

Day	Time m	Time m	Time m	Time m
1 F	0541 5.4	1216 2.2	1753 5.6	
2 SA	0049 1.7	0634 5.9	1312 1.7	1846 6.1
3 SU	0140 1.2	0721 6.3	1402 1.3	1936 6.5
4 M	0228 0.9	0807 6.6	1449 1.0	● 2024 6.6
5 TU	0314 0.7	0851 6.8	1534 0.8	2110 6.8
6 W	0357 0.7	0933 6.8	1618 0.8	2154 6.8
7 TH	0439 0.9	1014 6.7	1700 1.0	2237 6.5
8 F	0520 1.3	1053 6.4	1742 1.3	2319 6.1
9 SA	0601 1.7	1133 6.1	1825 1.7	2359 5.7
10 SU	0645 2.3	1216 5.6	1913 2.2	
11 M	0053 5.2	0738 2.7	1310 5.2	2013 2.5
12 TU	0203 4.9	0850 3.0	1428 4.9	2133 2.8
13 W	0335 4.8	1022 3.0	1556 4.9	2255 2.7
14 TH	0454 4.9	1135 2.8	1708 5.0	2307 2.5
15 F	0000 2.5	0550 5.2	1231 2.5	1801 5.3
16 SA	0051 2.2	0632 5.5	1316 2.2	1845 5.6
17 SU	0132 1.9	0710 5.7	1355 2.0	1923 5.8
18 M	0209 1.8	0745 5.9	1430 1.8	2000 6.0
19 TU	0243 1.6	0817 6.1	1502 1.6	2034 6.1
20 W	0315 1.6	0847 6.1	1534 1.5	O 2106 6.1
21 TH	0346 1.6	0916 6.2	1605 1.5	2137 6.1
22 F	0418 1.6	0947 6.1	1638 1.6	2209 6.0
23 SA	0450 1.8	1019 6.1	1711 1.7	2244 5.8
24 SU	0524 1.9	1055 5.9	1748 1.8	2324 5.6
25 M	0603 2.2	1135 5.7	1830 2.0	
26 TU	0010 5.3	0650 2.4	1224 5.4	1923 2.3
27 W	0109 5.1	0751 2.6	1326 5.2	2030 2.4
28 TH	0226 5.0	0908 2.7	1446 5.1	2150 2.4
29 F	0352 5.1	1030 2.6	1608 5.3	2307 2.2
30 SA	0502 5.4	1141 2.2	1717 5.6	

DECEMBER

Day	Time m	Time m	Time m	Time m
1 SU	0015 1.8	0600 5.8	1242 1.8	1816 6.0
2 M	0111 1.4	0652 6.2	1336 1.5	1910 6.3
3 TU	0203 1.2	0740 6.4	1427 1.2	2002 6.5
4 W	0251 1.1	0827 6.6	1514 1.0	● 2050 6.5
5 TH	0337 1.1	0911 6.6	1600 1.0	2137 6.5
6 F	0420 1.3	0953 6.5	1644 1.1	2221 6.3
7 SA	0503 1.5	1035 6.3	1727 1.3	2304 6.0
8 SU	0545 1.8	1116 6.1	1809 1.6	2347 5.7
9 M	0628 2.2	1200 5.8	1854 2.0	
10 TU	0032 5.4	0715 2.5	1248 5.4	1942 2.3
11 W	0125 5.1	0809 2.8	1344 5.1	2038 2.5
12 TH	0229 4.9	0914 2.9	1450 5.0	2143 2.6
13 F	0338 4.9	1026 2.9	1558 4.9	2250 2.6
14 SA	0443 5.0	1131 2.7	1701 5.0	2351 2.5
15 SU	0538 5.2	1227 2.5	1756 5.2	
16 M	0045 2.3	0626 5.4	1314 2.3	1844 5.4
17 TU	0129 2.1	0707 5.6	1356 2.0	1928 5.6
18 W	0210 1.9	0746 5.8	1434 1.8	2007 5.8
19 TH	0247 1.8	0822 6.0	1511 1.6	O 2045 5.9
20 F	0325 1.7	0857 6.1	1548 1.5	2121 6.0
21 SA	0402 1.7	0932 6.2	1625 1.5	2159 6.0
22 SU	0440 1.7	1010 6.2	1704 1.5	2239 5.9
23 M	0520 1.7	1051 6.1	1745 1.5	2322 5.7
24 TU	0602 1.9	1134 6.0	1829 1.6	
25 W	0006 5.6	0649 2.0	1221 5.8	1918 1.8
26 TH	0100 5.5	0742 2.2	1314 5.6	2014 2.0
27 F	0159 5.3	0843 2.3	1416 5.4	2117 2.1
28 SA	0308 5.3	0952 2.4	1527 5.4	2227 2.1
29 SU	0420 5.4	1104 2.2	1641 5.5	2338 2.0
30 M	0526 5.6	1213 2.0	1750 5.6	
31 TU	0045 1.8	0626 5.8	1315 1.7	1852 5.8

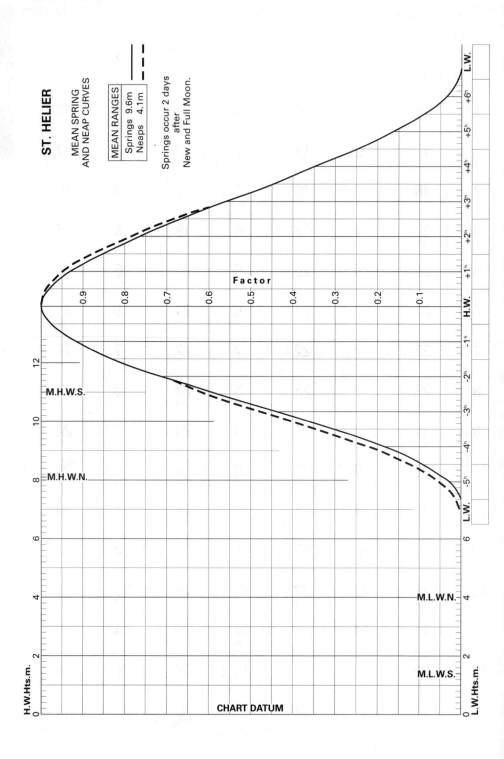

ST. HELIER

MEAN SPRING AND NEAP CURVES

MEAN RANGES
Springs 9.6m Neaps 4.1m

Springs occur 2 days after New and Full Moon.

Factor

0.9 0.8 0.7 0.6 0.5 0.4 0.3 0.2 0.1

L.W. +6ʰ +5ʰ +4ʰ +3ʰ +2ʰ +1ʰ H.W. -1ʰ -2ʰ -3ʰ -4ʰ -5ʰ L.W.

M.H.W.S.

M.H.W.N.

H.W.Hts.m.

M.L.W.N.

M.L.W.S.

L.W.Hts.m.

CHART DATUM

TIME ZONE (UTC)
For Summer Time add ONE hour in **non-shaded areas**

CHANNEL ISLES – ST HELIER

LAT 49°11′N   LONG 2°07′W

TIMES AND HEIGHTS OF HIGH AND LOW WATERS

YEAR **2002**

JANUARY

Day	Time	m	Time	m	Time	m	Time	m
1 TU	0155	1.6	0732	11.0	1422	1.5	2001	10.7
2 W	0241	1.7	0816	11.0	1509	1.6	2046	10.6
3 TH	0326	1.8	0902	10.8	1556	1.7	2133	10.3
4 F	0413	2.1	0950	10.5	1644	2.0	2223	9.9
5 SA	0502	2.5	1042	10.0	1735	2.4	2316	9.4
6 SU	0557	2.9	1139	9.5	1831	2.8		
7 M	0016	9.0	0658	3.2	1246	9.1	1933	3.1
8 TU	0128	8.7	0804	3.4	1400	8.9	2043	3.3
9 W	0245	8.8	0913	3.3	1512	8.9	2154	3.2
10 TH	0351	9.1	1021	3.1	1616	9.2	2256	2.9
11 F	0447	9.5	1121	2.8	1711	9.5	2349	2.6
12 SA	0535	9.9	1214	2.4	1759	9.8		
13 SU ●	0036	2.4	0617	10.2	1301	2.1	1841	10.1
14 M	0118	2.2	0657	10.5	1342	2.0	1921	10.2
15 TU	0155	2.1	0733	10.5	1420	2.0	1957	10.2
16 W	0228	2.2	0807	10.4	1454	2.1	2030	10.0
17 TH	0300	2.4	0840	10.2	1525	2.3	2101	9.7
18 F	0330	2.6	0912	9.8	1554	2.6	2131	9.4
19 SA	0400	2.9	0942	9.4	1624	2.9	2202	9.0
20 SU	0431	3.3	1014	9.0	1657	3.3	2236	8.6
21 M	0507	3.7	1052	8.5	1738	3.6	2320	8.3
22 TU	0556	4.0	1143	8.2	1835	3.9		
23 W	0020	8.0	0707	4.2	1256	7.9	1949	4.0
24 TH	0138	8.0	0830	4.1	1421	8.1	2108	3.8
25 F	0259	8.3	0942	3.6	1536	8.5	2217	3.3
26 SA	0407	9.0	1045	3.0	1638	9.2	2316	2.7
27 SU	0503	9.7	1143	2.4	1733	9.8		
28 M ○	0010	2.1	0553	10.4	1238	1.7	1824	10.4
29 TU	0101	1.5	0641	11.0	1330	1.2	1911	10.9
30 W	0150	1.2	0728	11.4	1419	0.9	1957	11.2
31 TH	0236	1.0	0812	11.6	1505	0.7	2040	11.3

FEBRUARY

Day	Time	m	Time	m	Time	m	Time	m
1 F	0321	0.9	0856	11.5	1548	0.8	2123	11.1
2 SA	0404	1.2	0939	11.2	1630	1.2	2205	10.6
3 SU	0446	1.7	1022	10.6	1712	1.8	2248	9.9
4 M	0531	2.3	1108	9.8	1758	2.6	2335	9.2
5 TU	0622	3.0	1202	9.0	1852	3.3		
6 W	0035	8.5	0724	3.6	1314	8.3	2000	3.8
7 TH	0204	8.1	0840	3.9	1444	8.1	2125	3.9
8 F	0330	8.3	1003	3.7	1605	8.4	2240	3.6
9 SA	0434	8.8	1103	3.2	1704	8.9	2337	3.1
10 SU	0524	9.4	1203	2.6	1750	9.4		
11 M	0023	2.6	0605	9.9	1247	2.2	1829	9.9
12 TU ●	0104	2.2	0643	10.3	1327	1.8	1906	10.2
13 W	0140	1.9	0718	10.5	1403	1.6	1940	10.3
14 TH	0214	1.8	0752	10.6	1436	1.6	2011	10.3
15 F	0245	1.8	0823	10.4	1506	1.7	2041	10.2
16 SA	0313	2.0	0852	10.2	1534	1.9	2107	9.9
17 SU	0340	2.3	0918	9.8	1558	2.3	2132	9.5
18 M	0403	2.6	0942	9.4	1623	2.7	2158	9.2
19 TU	0429	3.0	1011	9.0	1653	3.1	2232	8.8
20 W	0504	3.5	1051	8.5	1735	3.6	2320	8.3
21 TH	0558	3.9	1150	8.0	1842	4.0		
22 F	0032	7.9	0730	4.1	1328	7.7	2020	4.1
23 SA	0215	7.9	0909	3.8	1509	8.1	2151	3.6
24 SU	0346	8.6	1027	3.1	1625	8.8	2258	2.8
25 M	0450	9.5	1131	2.2	1724	9.7	2356	1.9
26 TU	0543	10.4	1227	1.4	1814	10.6		
27 W ○	0049	1.2	0632	11.2	1319	0.7	1900	11.3
28 TH	0139	0.6	0717	11.8	1406	0.2	1944	11.7

MARCH

Day	Time	m	Time	m	Time	m	Time	m
1 F	0224	0.2	0800	12.1	1450	0.0	2025	11.8
2 SA	0306	0.2	0841	12.0	1530	0.2	2103	11.6
3 SU	0346	0.5	0920	11.5	1608	0.7	2141	11.0
4 M	0423	1.2	0958	10.8	1644	1.6	2218	10.2
5 TU	0501	2.0	1038	9.8	1722	2.5	2258	9.3
6 W	0545	3.0	1125	8.8	1808	3.5	2349	8.3
7 TH	0645	3.8	1232	7.9	1917	4.3		
8 F	0113	7.7	0808	4.2	1419	7.5	2057	4.4
9 SA	0308	7.8	0948	4.0	1554	7.9	2225	3.9
10 SU	0417	8.4	1056	3.3	1650	8.6	2321	3.3
11 M	0506	9.1	1144	2.7	1732	9.2		
12 TU	0004	2.6	0545	9.7	1225	2.1	1808	9.8
13 W	0042	2.1	0621	10.2	1303	1.7	1842	10.2
14 TH ●	0118	1.7	0656	10.5	1338	1.4	1915	10.5
15 F	0151	1.5	0729	10.7	1411	1.3	1946	10.6
16 SA	0223	1.4	0800	10.6	1441	1.4	2015	10.4
17 SU	0251	1.6	0828	10.3	1508	1.6	2040	10.2
18 M	0316	1.9	0852	10.0	1532	1.9	2103	9.9
19 TU	0338	2.2	0914	9.7	1554	2.4	2127	9.6
20 W	0401	2.6	0942	9.3	1621	2.8	2159	9.1
21 TH	0433	3.1	1020	8.7	1659	3.4	2244	8.6
22 F	0522	3.6	1117	8.1	1800	3.9	2353	8.0
23 SA	0645	4.0	1257	7.6	1940	4.1		
24 SU	0144	7.8	0841	3.8	1449	8.0	2126	3.6
25 M	0325	8.5	1008	3.0	1609	8.8	2239	2.7
26 TU	0431	9.5	1113	2.0	1707	9.8	2338	1.7
27 W	0526	10.5	1209	1.1	1756	10.7		
28 TH ○	0030	0.9	0613	11.3	1259	0.4	1841	11.5
29 F	0120	0.3	0658	11.9	1346	-0.1	1923	11.9
30 SA	0204	-0.1	0740	12.1	1428	-0.2	2002	12.0
31 SU	0245	0.0	0820	12.0	1506	0.1	2039	11.7

APRIL

Day	Time	m	Time	m	Time	m	Time	m
1 M	0323	0.4	0857	11.5	1542	0.8	2114	11.1
2 TU	0359	1.1	0933	10.7	1615	1.7	2149	10.2
3 W	0433	2.0	1011	9.6	1648	2.7	2227	9.2
4 TH	0512	3.0	1056	8.6	1728	3.7	2315	8.3
5 F	0608	3.9	1201	7.7	1833	4.4		
6 SA	0033	7.6	0736	4.3	1347	7.3	2020	4.6
7 SU	0232	7.6	0917	4.1	1525	7.7	2154	4.1
8 M	0345	8.2	1025	3.4	1619	8.4	2249	3.4
9 TU	0434	8.8	1111	2.7	1700	9.1	2331	2.7
10 W	0514	9.5	1152	2.2	1736	9.7		
11 TH	0010	2.1	0550	10.0	1231	1.7	1811	10.2
12 F ●	0047	1.7	0626	10.4	1307	1.4	1844	10.5
13 SA	0122	1.5	0701	10.5	1341	1.3	1916	10.6
14 SU	0155	1.4	0733	10.5	1412	1.4	1945	10.5
15 M	0225	1.5	0801	10.4	1440	1.6	2011	10.4
16 TU	0251	1.7	0826	10.1	1506	1.9	2036	10.1
17 W	0315	2.1	0851	9.8	1530	2.3	2104	9.8
18 TH	0341	2.4	0923	9.4	1600	2.7	2140	9.3
19 F	0418	2.9	1005	8.8	1643	3.2	2228	8.7
20 SA	0510	3.4	1108	8.2	1745	3.7	2341	8.2
21 SU	0630	3.7	1246	7.9	1919	3.9		
22 M	0125	8.1	0817	3.5	1426	8.2	2059	3.4
23 TU	0258	8.7	0942	2.7	1543	9.0	2212	2.6
24 W	0404	9.6	1047	1.9	1649	9.9	2311	1.7
25 TH	0500	10.4	1143	1.0	1730	10.7		
26 F	0005	1.0	0548	11.2	1233	0.5	1815	11.4
27 SA ○	0054	0.5	0634	11.6	1320	0.2	1857	11.7
28 SU	0140	0.2	0716	11.8	1403	0.2	1936	11.7
29 M	0222	0.3	0757	11.6	1441	0.6	2014	11.5
30 TU	0300	0.7	0835	11.2	1517	1.2	2050	10.9

Chart Datum: 5·88 metres below Ordnance Datum (Local)

CHANNEL ISLES – ST HELIER
LAT 49°11′N   LONG 2°07′W
TIMES AND HEIGHTS OF HIGH AND LOW WATERS

YEAR 2002

TIME ZONE (UTC)
For Summer Time add ONE hour in **non-shaded areas**

MAY

#	Day	Time m	Time m	Time m	Time m	#	Day	Time m	Time m	Time m	Time m
1	W	0336 1.4	0912 10.3	1549 2.0	2125 10.1	16	TH	0258 2.0	0837 9.9	1515 2.3	2051 10.0
2	TH	0410 2.2	0950 9.4	1621 2.9	2203 9.2	17	F	0332 2.3	0917 9.5	1552 2.7	2134 9.5
3	F	0448 3.1	1035 8.5	1700 3.7	2250 8.4	18	SA	0414 2.7	1006 9.0	1639 3.1	2227 9.1
4	SA	0540 3.8	1136 7.8	1759 4.3		19	SU	0511 3.1	1112 8.5	1743 3.4	2338 8.7
5	SU	0000 7.8	0657 4.2	1303 7.5	1928 4.6	20	M	0627 3.3	1232 8.4	1905 3.5	
6	M	0139 7.6	0824 4.1	1432 7.7	2057 4.2	21	TU	0104 8.6	0753 3.1	1355 8.6	2029 3.1
7	TU	0254 8.0	0935 3.6	1532 8.3	2159 3.6	22	W	0224 9.0	0910 2.6	1508 9.1	2139 2.6
8	W	0348 8.6	1026 3.0	1617 8.9	2246 3.0	23	TH	0331 9.6	1015 2.1	1609 9.8	2240 1.9
9	TH	0433 9.2	1110 2.5	1657 9.5	2328 2.5	24	F	0430 10.2	1113 1.5	1701 10.4	2336 1.4
10	F	0514 9.6	1151 2.1	1734 9.9		25	SA	0522 10.7	1205 1.2	1748 10.9	
11	SA	0008 2.1	0552 10.0	1230 1.8	1809 10.3	26	SU	0027 1.1	0609 11.0	1254 1.0	○1832 11.2
12	SU	0046 1.8	0628 10.2	1306 1.6	●1842 10.4	27	M	0116 0.9	0654 11.1	1339 1.0	1913 11.2
13	M	0123 1.7	0702 10.3	1341 1.6	1914 10.5	28	TU	0200 1.0	0737 11.0	1419 1.3	1952 11.0
14	TU	0156 1.7	0733 10.3	1413 1.7	1944 10.4	29	W	0241 1.3	0817 10.6	1456 1.7	2030 10.6
15	W	0228 1.8	0804 10.1	1444 2.0	2016 10.3	30	TH	0319 1.8	0856 10.0	1529 2.3	2106 10.0
						31	F	0355 2.4	0935 9.4	1603 3.0	2145 9.3

JUNE

#	Day	Time m	Time m	Time m	Time m	#	Day	Time m	Time m	Time m	Time m
1	SA	0432 3.0	1017 8.7	1640 3.5	2228 8.7	16	SU	0422 2.3	1010 9.5	1642 2.7	2227 9.6
2	SU	0516 3.5	1106 8.2	1729 4.0	2323 8.2	17	M	0516 2.6	1107 9.2	1740 2.9	2328 9.3
3	M	0612 3.9	1208 7.8	1833 4.3		18	TU	0618 2.8	1211 8.9	1847 3.1	
4	TU	0034 7.9	0719 4.0	1321 7.8	1947 4.2	19	W	0037 9.1	0725 2.8	1321 8.9	1957 3.0
5	W	0150 7.9	0826 3.8	1431 8.1	2053 3.9	20	TH	0150 9.1	0834 2.8	1432 9.1	2105 2.8
6	TH	0253 8.3	0926 3.4	1526 8.5	2150 3.4	21	F	0258 9.3	0942 2.6	1538 9.4	2209 2.5
7	F	0345 8.7	1019 3.0	1612 9.0	2240 3.0	22	SA	0401 9.6	1045 2.3	1635 9.9	2310 2.1
8	SA	0432 9.1	1106 2.6	1654 9.5	2326 2.5	23	SU	0459 9.9	1141 2.0	1726 10.3	
9	SU	0515 9.6	1151 2.3	1733 9.9		24	M	0006 1.8	0551 10.2	1233 1.8	○1812 10.5
10	M	0010 2.2	0555 9.9	1233 2.0	●1811 10.3	25	TU	0058 1.6	0638 10.4	1320 1.8	1856 10.7
11	TU	0052 2.0	0634 10.1	1313 1.9	1848 10.5	26	W	0145 1.6	0723 10.4	1403 1.8	1937 10.7
12	W	0133 1.8	0713 10.2	1353 1.9	1926 10.5	27	TH	0228 1.7	0804 10.3	1441 2.1	2015 10.4
13	TH	0212 1.8	0752 10.2	1431 2.0	2005 10.5	28	F	0306 1.9	0843 10.0	1515 2.4	2052 10.1
14	F	0252 1.9	0833 10.1	1510 2.1	2047 10.3	29	SA	0342 2.3	0919 9.6	1547 2.7	2128 9.6
15	SA	0335 2.1	0919 9.8	1553 2.4	2134 10.0	30	SU	0415 2.7	0955 9.2	1620 3.1	2205 9.2

JULY

#	Day	Time m	Time m	Time m	Time m	#	Day	Time m	Time m	Time m	Time m
1	M	0448 3.1	1033 8.7	1657 3.5	2246 8.7	16	TU	0508 2.0	1050 9.8	1727 2.4	2309 9.9
2	TU	0527 3.4	1116 8.3	1742 3.8	2334 8.3	17	W	0558 2.4	1143 9.4	1821 2.8	
3	W	0615 3.7	1207 8.1	1839 4.1		18	TH	0006 9.4	0654 2.8	1244 9.0	1923 3.1
4	TH	0035 8.0	0714 3.9	1310 8.0	1947 4.1	19	F	0114 9.0	0759 3.2	1357 8.8	2033 3.3
5	F	0144 8.0	0821 3.8	1418 8.1	2054 3.9	20	SA	0228 8.8	0913 3.3	1512 8.9	2147 3.2
6	SA	0250 8.2	0926 3.6	1521 8.5	2155 3.5	21	SU	0341 8.9	1024 3.1	1618 9.2	2256 2.8
7	SU	0349 8.6	1025 3.2	1615 9.1	2251 3.0	22	M	0447 9.2	1126 2.8	1713 9.6	2355 2.4
8	M	0441 9.1	1118 2.7	1703 9.6	2342 2.5	23	TU	0541 9.6	1220 2.5	1801 10.1	
9	TU	0530 9.6	1207 2.3	1749 10.1		24	W	0046 2.1	0628 9.9	1308 2.2	○1844 10.4
10	W	0030 2.1	0616 10.0	1254 2.0	●1832 10.5	25	TH	0132 1.8	0711 10.2	1349 2.0	1924 10.6
11	TH	0119 1.8	0701 10.3	1340 1.8	1916 10.8	26	F	0214 1.7	0750 10.3	1426 2.0	2001 10.5
12	F	0206 1.6	0746 10.5	1425 1.7	2000 10.9	27	SA	0250 1.8	0826 10.2	1459 2.1	2035 10.4
13	SA	0252 1.5	0831 10.5	1509 1.7	2045 10.9	28	SU	0322 2.0	0858 10.0	1528 2.3	2107 10.1
14	SU	0337 1.5	0916 10.4	1553 1.8	2130 10.7	29	M	0351 2.2	0929 9.6	1556 2.6	2139 9.6
15	M	0422 1.7	1002 10.2	1638 2.0	2218 10.3	30	TU	0418 2.6	0959 9.3	1624 3.0	2209 9.2
						31	W	0446 3.0	1029 8.8	1656 3.4	2242 8.7

AUGUST

#	Day	Time m	Time m	Time m	Time m	#	Day	Time m	Time m	Time m	Time m
1	TH	0520 3.4	1106 8.4	1736 3.8	2325 8.2	16	F	0619 3.1	1205 8.8	1849 3.4	
2	F	0606 3.8	1157 8.1	1834 4.1		17	SA	0038 8.6	0723 3.7	1323 8.3	2005 3.9
3	SA	0028 7.9	0712 4.1	1309 7.9	1956 4.2	18	SU	0204 8.1	0850 4.0	1456 8.3	2136 3.8
4	SU	0154 7.8	0835 4.0	1433 8.1	2116 3.9	19	M	0334 8.2	1016 3.8	1609 8.7	2252 3.3
5	M	0312 8.2	0951 3.7	1545 8.6	2224 3.4	20	TU	0442 8.7	1119 3.2	1704 9.3	2347 2.7
6	TU	0417 8.7	1054 3.1	1643 9.3	2323 2.7	21	W	0533 9.3	1209 2.7	1750 9.9	
7	W	0514 9.4	1148 2.5	1734 10.0		22	TH	0033 2.2	0615 9.8	1257 2.2	○1829 10.4
8	TH	0017 2.1	0604 10.1	1240 1.9	●1822 10.7	23	F	0115 1.8	0653 10.2	1331 1.9	1906 10.7
9	F	0109 1.5	0652 10.6	1329 1.4	1908 11.2	24	SA	0152 1.6	0728 10.4	1405 1.8	1940 10.8
10	SA	0158 1.1	0738 11.0	1416 1.1	1953 11.5	25	SU	0226 1.5	0801 10.5	1435 1.8	2012 10.7
11	SU	0244 0.8	0821 11.2	1500 1.0	2035 11.5	26	M	0256 1.7	0831 10.3	1503 1.9	2043 10.4
12	M	0327 0.8	0903 11.1	1542 1.1	2117 11.3	27	TU	0322 1.9	0859 10.0	1528 2.2	2110 10.0
13	TU	0408 1.1	0944 10.8	1622 1.4	2159 10.9	28	W	0346 2.3	0923 9.6	1552 2.6	2133 9.5
14	W	0448 1.6	1026 10.3	1704 2.0	2243 10.2	29	TH	0409 2.7	0946 9.2	1617 3.0	2156 9.0
15	TH	0530 2.3	1111 9.6	1750 2.7	2333 9.3	30	F	0436 3.2	1014 8.8	1649 3.5	2229 8.5
						31	SA	0514 3.7	1055 8.3	1735 4.0	2321 7.9

Chart Datum: 5·88 metres below Ordnance Datum (Local)

TIME ZONE (UTC)
For Summer Time add ONE hour in **non-shaded areas**

CHANNEL ISLES – ST HELIER

LAT 49°11′N   LONG 2°07′W

TIMES AND HEIGHTS OF HIGH AND LOW WATERS

YEAR 2002

SEPTEMBER

Time	m		Time	m
1 SU	0612 4.2 / 1202 7.8 / 1853 4.4	**16** M	0149 7.7 / 0835 4.6 / 1444 7.9 / 2133 4.1
2 M	0058 7.6 / 0744 4.4 / 1351 7.8 / 2040 4.2	**17** TU	0331 8.0 / 1009 4.1 / 1557 8.5 / 2242 3.5
3 TU	0247 7.9 / 0923 4.0 / 1524 8.4 / 2204 3.5	**18** W	0431 8.6 / 1106 3.4 / 1648 9.2 / 2330 2.8
4 W	0402 8.6 / 1034 3.2 / 1627 9.2 / 2308 2.7	**19** TH	0514 9.3 / 1150 2.7 / 1728 9.9
5 TH	0500 9.5 / 1131 2.4 / 1720 10.1	**20** F	0010 2.2 / 0551 9.9 / 1228 2.2 / 1805 10.4
6 F	0003 1.8 / 0550 10.3 / 1224 1.6 / 1808 11.0	**21** SA	0048 1.8 / 0626 10.4 / 1303 1.8 / ○ 1839 10.7
7 SA	0054 1.1 / 0637 11.0 / 1313 1.0 / ● 1853 11.6	**22** SU	0123 1.5 / 0659 10.6 / 1336 1.6 / 1913 10.9
8 SU	0141 0.6 / 0720 11.5 / 1359 0.6 / 1936 12.0	**23** M	0155 1.5 / 0731 10.7 / 1406 1.6 / 1945 10.8
9 M	0225 0.3 / 0802 11.7 / 1442 0.4 / 2017 12.0	**24** TU	0225 1.6 / 0800 10.5 / 1434 1.8 / 2014 10.5
10 TU	0306 0.4 / 0841 11.6 / 1521 0.6 / 2056 11.7	**25** W	0251 1.8 / 0826 10.3 / 1459 2.1 / 2038 10.1
11 W	0344 0.8 / 0919 11.2 / 1559 1.2 / 2135 11.1	**26** TH	0314 2.2 / 0846 9.9 / 1522 2.4 / 2057 9.7
12 TH	0420 1.5 / 0956 10.4 / 1636 2.0 / 2215 10.2	**27** F	0336 2.7 / 0907 9.5 / 1546 2.9 / 2120 9.2
13 F	0458 2.5 / 1037 9.5 / 1718 2.9 / 2301 9.1	**28** SA	0402 3.2 / 0935 9.1 / 1616 3.4 / 2153 8.7
14 SA	0541 3.5 / 1128 8.6 / 1814 3.8	**29** SU	0436 3.7 / 1015 8.5 / 1659 3.9 / 2243 8.1
15 SU	0007 8.1 / 0647 4.3 / 1252 7.9 / 1940 4.3	**30** M	0532 4.2 / 1118 7.9 / 1811 4.3

OCTOBER

Time	m		Time	m
1 TU	0020 7.5 / 0703 4.5 / 1316 7.7 / 2006 4.3	**16** W	0307 7.9 / 0945 4.3 / 1529 8.4 / 2215 3.6
2 W	0225 7.8 / 0856 4.1 / 1502 8.4 / 2142 3.5	**17** TH	0402 8.6 / 1038 3.6 / 1617 9.1 / 2259 2.9
3 TH	0343 8.7 / 1011 3.2 / 1606 9.3 / 2247 2.5	**18** F	0443 9.3 / 1118 2.9 / 1657 9.7 / 2337 2.4
4 F	0440 9.6 / 1109 2.3 / 1659 10.3 / 2341 1.6	**19** SA	0518 9.9 / 1153 2.4 / 1733 10.2
5 SA	0528 10.5 / 1201 1.4 / 1746 11.2	**20** SU	0013 2.0 / 0552 10.3 / 1228 2.0 / 1808 10.6
6 SU	0030 0.9 / 0613 11.3 / 1250 0.8 / ● 1831 11.8	**21** M	0048 1.7 / 0626 10.6 / 1301 1.8 / ○ 1842 10.7
7 M	0117 0.4 / 0655 11.8 / 1335 0.4 / 1913 12.1	**22** TU	0120 1.6 / 0657 10.7 / 1333 1.8 / 1914 10.7
8 TU	0200 0.2 / 0736 11.9 / 1417 0.4 / 1953 12.1	**23** W	0151 1.7 / 0726 10.6 / 1402 1.9 / 1943 10.5
9 W	0240 0.4 / 0814 11.7 / 1456 0.6 / 2032 11.7	**24** TH	0219 2.0 / 0751 10.4 / 1429 2.1 / 2007 10.1
10 TH	0317 1.0 / 0851 11.2 / 1533 1.3 / 2110 10.9	**25** F	0244 2.3 / 0814 10.1 / 1455 2.5 / 2029 9.8
11 F	0352 1.8 / 0927 10.4 / 1610 2.1 / 2149 9.9	**26** SA	0309 2.7 / 0839 9.7 / 1522 2.9 / 2057 9.2
12 SA	0427 2.8 / 1007 9.5 / 1650 3.1 / 2235 8.9	**27** SU	0337 3.2 / 0911 9.3 / 1556 3.3 / 2134 8.8
13 SU	0508 3.8 / 1057 8.5 / 1745 4.0 / 2342 7.9	**28** M	0415 3.7 / 0955 8.8 / 1643 3.8 / 2229 8.2
14 M	0614 4.6 / 1224 7.8 / 1916 4.5	**29** TU	0513 4.1 / 1101 8.2 / 1753 4.1
15 TU	0130 7.5 / 0810 4.8 / 1419 7.8 / 2110 4.3	**30** W	0004 7.8 / 0639 4.3 / 1248 8.0 / 1936 4.0
		31 TH	0154 8.0 / 0823 4.0 / 1429 8.6 / 2109 3.4

NOVEMBER

Time	m		Time	m
1 F	0313 8.8 / 0939 3.1 / 1535 9.4 / 2216 2.5	**16** SA	0402 9.0 / 1032 3.3 / 1618 9.3 / 2255 2.8
2 SA	0411 9.7 / 1038 2.3 / 1630 10.3 / 2311 1.7	**17** SU	0441 9.5 / 1110 2.8 / 1657 9.8 / 2333 2.4
3 SU	0500 10.6 / 1131 1.5 / 1719 11.1	**18** M	0517 10.0 / 1147 2.4 / 1735 10.1
4 M	0001 1.1 / 0545 11.2 / 1221 1.0 / ● 1804 11.6	**19** TU	0009 2.1 / 0551 10.3 / 1224 2.2 / 1810 10.3
5 TU	0049 0.7 / 0628 11.7 / 1308 0.7 / 1848 11.8	**20** W	0045 2.0 / 0624 10.5 / 1259 2.1 / ○ 1843 10.4
6 W	0133 0.6 / 0709 11.8 / 1352 0.7 / 1930 11.7	**21** TH	0119 2.0 / 0654 10.5 / 1333 2.1 / 1914 10.3
7 TH	0214 0.9 / 0749 11.6 / 1433 1.0 / 2010 11.3	**22** F	0151 2.1 / 0723 10.4 / 1405 2.2 / 1943 10.1
8 F	0252 1.4 / 0827 11.1 / 1512 1.6 / 2049 10.6	**23** SA	0221 2.4 / 0753 10.2 / 1437 2.5 / 2014 9.9
9 SA	0328 2.2 / 0904 10.3 / 1550 2.4 / 2130 9.7	**24** SU	0252 2.7 / 0825 10.0 / 1510 2.8 / 2049 9.5
10 SU	0404 3.1 / 0944 9.5 / 1632 3.2 / 2216 8.8	**25** M	0325 3.1 / 0904 9.6 / 1549 3.1 / 2133 9.0
11 M	0446 3.9 / 1033 8.6 / 1725 3.9 / 2318 8.0	**26** TU	0409 3.4 / 0952 9.1 / 1640 3.4 / 2231 8.6
12 TU	0546 4.5 / 1148 8.0 / 1841 4.4	**27** W	0506 3.8 / 1056 8.7 / 1747 3.6 / 2348 8.3
13 W	0047 7.7 / 0716 4.8 / 1331 7.9 / 2012 4.3	**28** TH	0622 3.9 / 1220 8.6 / 1909 3.6
14 TH	0218 7.9 / 0847 4.5 / 1442 8.3 / 2124 3.9	**29** F	0113 8.4 / 0747 3.7 / 1347 8.8 / 2029 3.2
15 F	0318 8.4 / 0948 3.9 / 1535 8.8 / 2214 3.3	**30** SA	0232 8.9 / 0900 3.1 / 1457 9.4 / 2138 2.6

DECEMBER

Time	m		Time	m
1 SU	0336 9.6 / 1003 2.5 / 1557 10.0 / 2238 2.1	**16** M	0359 8.9 / 1021 3.4 / 1618 9.1 / 2249 3.0
2 M	0430 10.2 / 1100 2.0 / 1651 10.6 / 2333 1.6	**17** TU	0440 9.4 / 1107 3.0 / 1700 9.5 / 2332 2.7
3 TU	0520 10.8 / 1154 1.5 / 1741 11.0	**18** W	0518 9.8 / 1150 2.6 / 1740 9.8
4 W	0023 1.4 / 0605 11.2 / 1245 1.3 / ● 1828 11.2	**19** TH	0013 2.4 / 0554 10.1 / 1232 2.4 / ○ 1818 10.0
5 TH	0110 1.3 / 0649 11.3 / 1333 1.2 / 1912 11.1	**20** F	0053 2.2 / 0630 10.4 / 1312 2.2 / 1854 10.2
6 F	0154 1.5 / 0730 11.2 / 1418 1.4 / 1955 10.8	**21** SA	0132 2.2 / 0706 10.5 / 1352 2.2 / 1932 10.3
7 SA	0235 1.8 / 0810 10.9 / 1500 1.8 / 2036 10.4	**22** SU	0209 2.3 / 0743 10.4 / 1431 2.2 / 2010 10.0
8 SU	0313 2.4 / 0849 10.3 / 1540 2.4 / 2117 9.7	**23** M	0247 2.4 / 0822 10.3 / 1511 2.4 / 2051 9.8
9 M	0350 3.0 / 0929 9.7 / 1621 3.0 / 2200 9.1	**24** TU	0327 2.6 / 0905 10.1 / 1555 2.5 / 2136 9.6
10 TU	0429 3.6 / 1013 9.0 / 1705 3.5 / 2248 8.5	**25** W	0411 2.8 / 0953 9.8 / 1643 2.7 / 2228 9.2
11 W	0517 4.1 / 1106 8.5 / 1758 3.9 / 2346 8.0	**26** TH	0502 3.1 / 1047 9.5 / 1738 3.0 / 2326 9.0
12 TH	0617 4.4 / 1215 8.1 / 1900 4.1	**27** F	0603 3.3 / 1150 9.2 / 1841 3.1
13 F	0059 7.8 / 0725 4.5 / 1334 8.0 / 2005 4.1	**28** SA	0032 8.8 / 0712 3.4 / 1303 9.0 / 1949 3.1
14 SA	0215 8.0 / 0832 4.2 / 1438 8.3 / 2107 3.8	**29** SU	0147 8.8 / 0822 3.2 / 1418 9.1 / 2100 3.0
15 SU	0313 8.4 / 0930 3.8 / 1532 8.6 / 2202 3.4	**30** M	0301 9.1 / 0930 3.0 / 1527 9.4 / 2209 2.7
		31 TU	0405 9.6 / 1035 2.6 / 1630 9.7 / 2310 2.4

Chart Datum: 5·88 metres below Ordnance Datum (Local)

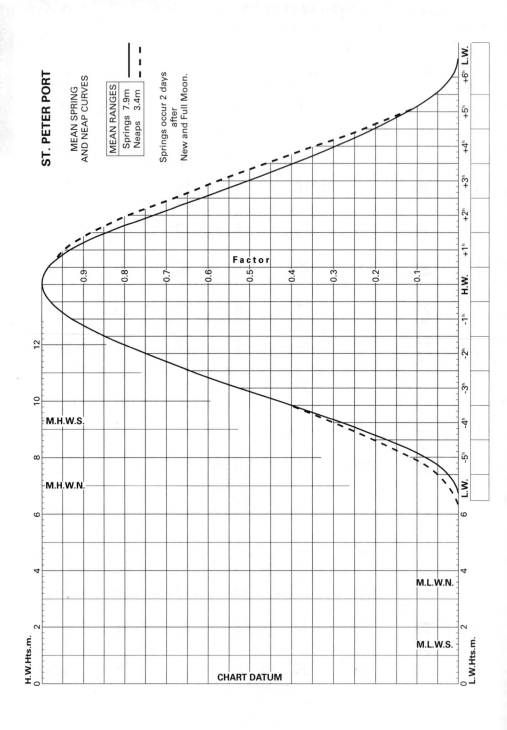

ST. PETER PORT

MEAN SPRING
AND NEAP CURVES

MEAN RANGES
Springs 7.9m
Neaps 3.4m

Springs occur 2 days
after
New and Full Moon.

TIME ZONE (UTC)
For Summer Time add ONE hour in **non-shaded areas**

CHANNEL ISLES – ST PETER PORT

LAT 49°27'N   LONG 2°31'W

YEAR 2002

TIMES AND HEIGHTS OF HIGH AND LOW WATERS

JANUARY

Time	m	Time	m
1 0141	1.4	**16** 0217	2.0
0739	9.3	0813	8.8
TU 1410	1.2	W 1440	1.9
2008	9.1	2034	8.4
2 0226	1.4	**17** 0248	2.2
0824	9.4	0846	8.6
W 1455	1.3	TH 1512	2.1
2053	9.0	2106	8.2
3 0311	1.6	**18** 0317	2.4
0909	9.2	0918	8.3
TH 1541	1.5	F 1542	2.3
2139	8.8	2137	7.9
4 0357	1.9	**19** 0348	2.7
0957	8.9	0950	8.0
F 1628	1.8	SA 1613	2.7
2227	8.4	2209	7.6
5 0446	2.3	**20** 0420	3.0
1047	8.5	1025	7.6
SA 1720	2.2	SU 1647	3.0
2321	8.0	2245	7.3
6 0542	2.7	**21** 0458	3.4
1144	8.1	1105	7.3
SU 1818	2.6	M 1728	3.3
		2328	7.0
7 0022	7.7	**22** 0547	3.6
0647	3.0	1157	7.0
M 1251	7.7	TU 1822	3.5
1926	2.9		
8 0136	7.5	**23** 0026	6.9
0804	3.1	0656	3.8
TU 1406	7.5	W 1305	6.8
2041	3.0	1935	3.6
9 0249	7.6	**24** 0143	6.9
0919	3.0	0820	3.7
W 1517	7.6	TH 1425	6.9
2150	2.8	2053	3.4
10 0353	7.8	**25** 0301	7.1
1021	2.7	0933	3.3
TH 1618	7.8	F 1537	7.3
2247	2.4	2200	3.0
11 0447	8.1	**26** 0407	7.6
1116	2.4	1036	2.7
F 1712	8.0	SA 1640	7.7
2338	2.4	2300	2.5
12 0536	8.4	**27** 0503	8.1
1204	2.1	1133	2.1
SA 1800	8.3	SU 1736	8.3
		2354	2.0
13 0024	2.1	**28** 0556	8.8
0619	8.7	1226	1.6
SU 1249	1.9	M 1827	8.8
● 1843	8.5	○	
14 0106	2.0	**29** 0045	1.5
0700	9.0	0644	9.3
M 1330	1.8	TU 1316	1.1
1923	8.6	1915	9.2
15 0143	1.9	**30** 0134	1.1
0738	8.9	0731	9.6
TU 1406	1.7	W 1403	0.7
2000	8.5	2000	9.4
		31 0219	0.8
		0816	9.8
		TH 1448	0.6
		2044	9.5

FEBRUARY

Time	m	Time	m
1 0303	0.8	**16** 0255	1.9
0900	9.8	0855	8.6
F 1531	0.7	SA 1515	1.9
2127	9.3	2110	8.3
2 0345	1.1	**17** 0322	2.1
0943	9.4	0922	8.3
SA 1612	1.1	SU 1542	2.2
2209	8.9	2137	8.0
3 0428	1.6	**18** 0350	2.5
1027	8.9	0951	8.0
SU 1655	1.7	M 1610	2.6
2253	8.3	2206	7.7
4 0513	2.2	**19** 0420	2.9
1114	8.2	1024	7.6
M 1742	2.4	TU 1643	2.9
2343	7.7	2241	7.4
5 0606	2.8	**20** 0458	3.2
1211	7.5	1106	7.2
TU 1838	3.0	W 1725	3.3
		2329	7.0
6 0048	7.2	**21** 0552	3.6
0715	3.3	1206	6.8
W 1325	7.0	TH 1828	3.6
1955	3.4		
7 0213	7.0	**22** 0038	6.8
0847	3.5	0717	3.7
TH 1453	6.9	F 1333	6.7
2125	3.5	2003	3.7
8 0333	7.2	**23** 0215	6.9
1006	3.2	0859	3.5
F 1606	7.1	SA 1509	6.9
2235	3.2	2132	3.3
9 0434	7.6	**24** 0341	7.3
1106	2.8	1016	2.9
SA 1702	7.5	SU 1623	7.5
2328	2.8	2242	2.7
10 0523	8.0	**25** 0447	8.0
1154	2.4	1119	2.1
SU 1749	7.9	M 1723	8.2
		2341	1.9
11 0013	2.4	**26** 0542	8.8
0606	8.4	1213	1.3
M 1237	2.0	TU 1815	8.9
1830	8.3		
12 0053	2.0	**27** 0033	1.2
0646	8.7	0631	9.5
TU 1315	1.7	W 1303	0.7
● 1908	8.6	○ 1901	9.5
13 0128	1.8	**28** 0121	0.6
0722	8.9	0718	10.0
W 1349	1.5	TH 1349	0.2
1943	8.7	1945	9.8
14 0200	1.7		
0755	9.0		
TH 1420	1.5		
2014	8.7		
15 0228	1.7		
0826	8.9		
F 1449	1.6		
2043	8.6		

MARCH

Time	m	Time	m
1 0205	0.3	**16** 0203	1.4
0801	10.2	0801	9.0
F 1431	0.1	SA 1421	1.4
2027	9.9	2017	8.8
2 0247	0.3	**17** 0230	1.5
0842	10.1	0829	8.8
SA 1511	0.3	SU 1447	1.6
2106	9.7	2042	8.6
3 0326	0.6	**18** 0256	1.8
0922	9.7	0855	8.6
SU 1549	0.8	M 1513	1.9
2145	9.2	2107	8.4
4 0405	1.2	**19** 0322	2.1
1002	9.0	0922	8.2
M 1627	1.5	TU 1539	2.3
2223	8.5	2134	8.0
5 0444	1.9	**20** 0350	2.5
1043	8.2	0953	7.8
TU 1707	2.4	W 1609	2.7
2305	7.8	2207	7.6
6 0530	2.8	**21** 0424	3.0
1131	7.3	1033	7.3
W 1755	3.3	TH 1649	3.2
		2252	7.2
7 0000	7.0	**22** 0515	3.4
0631	3.5	1132	6.9
TH 1243	6.6	F 1750	3.6
1906	3.8		
8 0130	6.6	**23** 0001	6.9
0811	3.8	0639	3.7
F 1433	6.4	SA 1301	6.6
2103	4.0	1927	3.8
9 0314	6.7	**24** 0140	6.8
0953	3.5	0835	3.5
SA 1554	6.8	SU 1449	6.5
2222	3.5	2110	3.4
10 0418	7.2	**25** 0319	7.3
1052	3.0	0958	2.8
SU 1648	7.3	M 1608	7.5
2313	3.0	2224	2.7
11 0506	7.8	**26** 0428	8.1
1137	2.4	1101	1.9
M 1732	7.8	TU 1706	8.3
2354	2.4	2323	1.8
12 0547	8.3	**27** 0523	8.9
1216	2.0	1154	1.1
TU 1810	8.3	W 1755	9.1
13 0032	2.0	**28** 0014	1.0
0624	8.7	0612	9.6
W 1252	1.6	TH 1242	0.5
1845	8.6	○ 1840	9.7
14 0106	1.6	**29** 0101	0.5
0659	9.0	0657	10.1
TH 1325	1.4	F 1327	0.1
● 1918	8.9	1923	10.0
15 0136	1.5	**30** 0145	0.1
0732	9.1	0740	10.2
F 1354	1.3	SA 1408	0.0
1949	8.9	2003	10.1
		31 0225	0.1
		0820	10.1
		SU 1447	0.2
		2042	9.8

APRIL

Time	m	Time	m
1 0304	0.5	**16** 0231	1.7
0859	9.6	0830	8.6
M 1524	0.8	TU 1447	1.8
2118	9.3	2041	8.5
2 0341	1.1	**17** 0259	2.0
0937	8.9	0859	8.3
TU 1559	1.6	W 1515	2.2
2154	8.6	2110	8.2
3 0418	1.9	**18** 0330	2.4
1015	8.1	0933	7.9
W 1636	2.5	TH 1548	2.7
2233	7.8	2146	7.8
4 0501	2.8	**19** 0407	2.8
1100	7.2	1017	7.4
TH 1720	3.4	F 1630	3.2
2321	7.0	2234	7.4
5 0600	3.5	**20** 0501	3.3
1205	6.5	1118	7.0
F 1828	4.0	SA 1734	3.6
		2345	7.1
6 0043	6.5	**21** 0626	3.5
0731	3.9	1245	6.8
SA 1404	6.3	SU 1909	3.7
2024	4.2		
7 0242	6.6	**22** 0118	7.0
0924	3.7	0814	3.3
SU 1529	6.6	M 1427	7.1
2154	3.7	2048	3.3
8 0350	7.0	**23** 0253	7.5
1023	3.1	0934	2.6
M 1621	7.2	TU 1543	7.7
2244	3.1	2200	2.6
9 0437	7.6	**24** 0402	8.2
1106	2.6	1035	1.8
TU 1703	7.7	W 1639	8.5
2325	2.6	2258	1.8
10 0518	8.1	**25** 0457	8.9
1145	2.1	1128	1.2
W 1740	8.2	TH 1729	9.1
		2349	1.1
11 0001	2.1	**26** 0547	9.5
0555	8.6	1216	0.6
TH 1220	1.7	F 1815	9.6
1815	8.6		
12 0034	1.7	**27** 0036	0.6
0630	8.8	0632	9.8
F 1252	1.4	SA 1301	0.4
● 1848	8.9	○ 1857	9.9
13 0105	1.5	**28** 0120	0.4
0703	9.0	0716	9.9
SA 1322	1.3	SU 1343	0.4
1919	9.0	1938	9.9
14 0134	1.4	**29** 0202	0.4
0733	9.0	0757	9.8
SU 1351	1.3	M 1423	0.6
1947	8.9	2017	9.7
15 0203	1.4	**30** 0241	0.7
0802	8.9	0837	9.3
M 1419	1.5	TU 1500	1.2
2014	8.8	2054	9.2

Chart Datum: 5·06 metres below Ordnance Datum (Local)
Register for your **FREE** weekly weather email service from Macmillan Reeds
》》 at **www.nauticaldata.com – NOW!** 《《
weekend weather reports sent to your email address, every Thursday

TIME ZONE (UTC)
For Summer Time add ONE hour in **non-shaded areas**

CHANNEL ISLES – ST PETER PORT

YEAR **2002**

LAT 49°27'N LONG 2°31'W

TIMES AND HEIGHTS OF HIGH AND LOW WATERS

MAY

Day	Time	m	Time	m	Time	m	Time	m
1 W	0319	1.3	0915	8.7	1536	1.9	2130	8.5
2 TH	0357	2.0	0954	7.9	1612	2.7	2209	7.8
3 F	0440	2.8	1038	7.2	1655	3.4	2255	7.2
4 SA	0536	3.4	1138	6.6	1758	4.0		
5 SU	0003	6.7	0652	3.8	1308	6.4	1925	4.2
6 M	0144	6.6	0825	3.7	1441	6.6	2101	3.9
7 TU	0303	6.9	0934	3.3	1538	7.0	2159	3.4
8 W	0356	7.4	1022	2.8	1622	7.6	2242	2.8
9 TH	0439	7.8	1102	2.3	1701	8.0	2320	2.3
10 F	0518	8.2	1139	2.0	1738	8.4	2356	2.0
11 SA	0555	8.5	1214	1.7	1814	8.7		
12 SU	0030	1.7	0630	8.7	1248	1.5	●1847	8.8
13 M	0104	1.5	0705	8.8	1321	1.5	1919	8.9
14 TU	0137	1.5	0737	8.8	1354	1.6	1949	8.8
15 W	0210	1.6	0810	8.6	1426	1.8	2021	8.7
16 TH	0244	1.9	0845	8.3	1501	2.2	2057	8.4
17 F	0321	2.2	0925	8.0	1539	2.6	2139	8.1
18 SA	0405	2.6	1013	7.6	1627	3.0	2231	7.7
19 SU	0503	2.9	1115	7.3	1731	3.3	2338	7.4
20 M	0620	3.1	1231	7.1	1853	3.4		
21 TU	0057	7.4	0747	2.9	1357	7.4	2019	3.1
22 W	0221	7.7	0903	2.5	1510	7.8	2130	2.5
23 TH	0330	8.2	1005	1.9	1608	8.4	2229	1.9
24 F	0428	8.7	1057	1.5	1700	8.9	2322	1.4
25 SA	0520	9.1	1149	1.1	1747	9.2		
26 SU	0011	1.1	0608	9.3	1236	1.0	○1832	9.5
27 M	0057	0.9	0654	9.4	1320	1.0	1915	9.5
28 TU	0141	0.9	0737	9.2	1401	1.2	1956	9.3
29 W	0222	1.2	0819	8.9	1440	1.6	2034	9.0
30 TH	0302	1.6	0858	8.5	1518	2.1	2112	8.5
31 F	0341	2.1	0938	7.9	1555	2.7	2151	8.0

JUNE

Day	Time	m	Time	m	Time	m	Time	m
1 SA	0423	2.7	1021	7.4	1636	3.2	2234	7.4
2 SU	0512	3.2	1111	7.0	1727	3.7	2328	7.0
3 M	0611	3.5	1213	6.7	1832	3.9		
4 TU	0036	6.8	0717	3.6	1326	6.7	1944	3.9
5 W	0151	6.8	0824	3.4	1434	6.9	2051	3.6
6 TH	0256	7.1	0922	3.1	1528	7.2	2145	3.2
7 F	0348	7.4	1011	2.8	1615	7.6	2232	2.7
8 SA	0434	7.8	1054	2.4	1657	8.0	2314	2.3
9 SU	0517	8.1	1136	2.1	1738	8.3	2356	2.0
10 M	0559	8.4	1216	1.9	1816	8.6 ●		
11 TU	0036	1.8	0638	8.5	1256	1.7	1854	8.8
12 W	0116	1.6	0718	8.6	1335	1.7	1931	8.9
13 TH	0156	1.6	0758	8.6	1414	1.8	2010	8.8
14 F	0237	1.7	0839	8.5	1455	1.9	2052	8.7
15 SA	0320	1.9	0923	8.3	1538	2.2	2137	8.5
16 SU	0407	2.1	1012	8.0	1627	2.5	2228	8.2
17 M	0502	2.4	1108	7.8	1724	2.8	2327	7.9
18 TU	0605	2.6	1212	7.6	1831	2.9		
19 W	0034	7.8	0716	2.7	1323	7.6	1945	2.9
20 TH	0148	7.8	0828	2.5	1434	7.8	2058	2.6
21 F	0259	8.0	0934	2.3	1538	8.1	2202	2.3
22 SA	0401	8.2	1033	2.0	1634	8.4	2258	1.9
23 SU	0458	8.5	1126	1.8	1725	8.7	2350	1.7
24 M	0550	8.6	1216	1.7	1813	8.9 ○		
25 TU	0039	1.5	0638	8.6	1302	1.6	●1857	9.0
26 W	0125	1.4	0723	8.6	1345	1.7	1939	9.0
27 TH	0208	1.5	0805	8.6	1425	1.8	2019	8.8
28 F	0248	1.7	0845	8.4	1502	2.1	2056	8.6
29 SA	0326	2.0	0922	8.1	1538	2.5	2133	8.2
30 SU	0403	2.4	0959	7.7	1613	2.9	2210	7.8

JULY

Day	Time	m	Time	m	Time	m	Time	m
1 M	0441	2.8	1039	7.4	1651	3.2	2251	7.4
2 TU	0524	3.2	1123	7.1	1736	3.5	2339	7.1
3 W	0616	3.4	1216	6.9	1834	3.7		
4 TH	0037	6.9	0716	3.5	1319	6.8	1940	3.7
5 F	0146	6.9	0818	3.4	1424	6.9	2045	3.5
6 SA	0251	7.0	0917	3.2	1524	7.2	2144	3.2
7 SU	0350	7.3	1011	2.9	1616	7.6	2237	2.7
8 M	0442	7.7	1102	2.5	1705	8.0	2327	2.3
9 TU	0532	8.1	1150	2.2	1751	8.4		
10 W	0015	1.9	0619	8.4	1237	1.9	●1836	8.8
11 TH	0102	1.6	0705	8.7	1323	1.6	1920	9.0
12 F	0148	1.4	0750	8.8	1407	1.5	2003	9.2
13 SA	0233	1.3	0834	8.9	1451	1.5	2047	9.2
14 SU	0317	1.3	0918	8.8	1535	1.6	2132	9.0
15 M	0402	1.5	1003	8.6	1620	1.9	2218	8.7
16 TU	0449	1.8	1052	8.3	1708	2.2	2309	8.3
17 W	0541	2.2	1145	7.9	1803	2.6		
18 TH	0006	7.9	0641	2.6	1249	7.6	1909	2.9
19 F	0115	7.6	0752	2.9	1401	7.5	2026	3.0
20 SA	0232	7.5	0907	2.9	1513	7.6	2141	2.8
21 SU	0343	7.6	1015	2.7	1616	7.9	2244	2.5
22 M	0445	7.9	1113	2.5	1711	8.2	2339	2.2
23 TU	0539	8.1	1204	2.2	1800	8.5		
24 W	0028	1.9	0627	8.4	1251	2.0	○1845	8.8
25 TH	0114	1.7	0711	8.6	1333	1.8	1926	8.9
26 F	0154	1.6	0751	8.6	1411	1.8	2003	8.9
27 SA	0231	1.6	0827	8.6	1444	1.9	2038	8.8
28 SU	0304	1.8	0900	8.4	1515	2.1	2110	8.5
29 M	0335	2.1	0936	8.1	1544	2.4	2141	8.2
30 TU	0405	2.5	1003	7.8	1614	2.8	2213	7.8
31 W	0436	2.8	1036	7.4	1646	3.2	2248	7.4

AUGUST

Day	Time	m	Time	m	Time	m	Time	m
1 TH	0512	3.2	1114	7.1	1727	3.5	2332	7.0
2 F	0600	3.5	1204	6.9	1823	3.7		
3 SA	0031	6.8	0708	3.7	1313	6.8	1944	3.8
4 SU	0152	6.8	0827	3.6	1433	6.9	2102	3.5
5 M	0311	7.0	0936	3.3	1542	7.3	2208	3.1
6 TU	0416	7.4	1036	2.9	1641	7.8	2307	2.5
7 W	0514	7.9	1132	2.3	1734	8.4		
8 TH	0001	1.9	0605	8.5	1224	1.8	●1822	8.9
9 F	0051	1.4	0653	8.9	1312	1.3	1909	9.4
10 SA	0138	1.0	0739	9.3	1357	1.0	1953	9.7
11 SU	0223	0.7	0822	9.4	1440	0.9	2036	9.8
12 M	0305	0.7	0904	9.4	1522	1.0	2118	9.6
13 TU	0346	1.0	0945	9.1	1603	1.3	2200	9.2
14 W	0428	1.5	1028	8.6	1645	1.9	2244	8.5
15 TH	0513	2.1	1115	8.0	1733	2.5	2335	7.9
16 F	0606	2.8	1213	7.5	1834	3.1		
17 SA	0042	7.3	0716	3.4	1331	7.1	1958	3.5
18 SU	0213	7.0	0850	3.5	1459	7.1	2132	3.4
19 M	0338	7.1	1009	3.3	1608	7.5	2240	3.0
20 TU	0441	7.5	1107	2.9	1703	8.0	2333	2.5
21 W	0532	8.0	1155	2.4	1749	8.4		
22 TH	0018	2.1	0615	8.4	1238	2.0	○1830	8.8
23 F	0059	1.7	0654	8.6	1316	1.8	1908	9.0
24 SA	0135	1.5	0730	8.8	1350	1.7	1942	9.1
25 SU	0208	1.5	0803	8.8	1420	1.7	2014	9.0
26 M	0237	1.6	0832	8.7	1447	1.8	2042	8.8
27 TU	0303	1.9	0900	8.5	1513	2.1	2109	8.5
28 W	0328	2.2	0926	8.1	1538	2.5	2136	8.1
29 TH	0354	2.6	0952	7.8	1605	2.9	2205	7.7
30 F	0423	3.1	1024	7.4	1637	3.3	2242	7.2
31 SA	0501	3.5	1106	7.0	1723	3.7	2334	6.8

Chart Datum: 5·06 metres below Ordnance Datum (Local)
Register for your FREE weekly weather email service from Macmillan Reeds
》 at **www.nauticaldata.com – NOW!** 《
weekend weather reports sent to your email address, every Thursday

TIME ZONE (UTC)
For Summer Time add ONE hour in **non-shaded areas**

CHANNEL ISLES – ST PETER PORT
LAT 49°27′N   LONG 2°31′W
TIMES AND HEIGHTS OF HIGH AND LOW WATERS

YEAR 2002

SEPTEMBER

Day	Time m	Time m		Day	Time m	Time m
1 SU	0600 3.9 / 1210 6.7 / 1839 4.0			**16** M	0206 6.6 / 0843 4.0 / 1449 6.9 / 2129 3.7	
2 M	0057 6.6 / 0738 4.0 / 1345 6.7 / 2029 3.8			**17** TU	0335 6.9 / 1004 3.6 / 1558 7.3 / 2232 3.1	
3 TU	0242 6.8 / 0910 3.7 / 1516 7.1 / 2149 3.3			**18** W	0432 7.5 / 1056 3.0 / 1648 7.9 / 2318 2.6	
4 W	0400 7.0 / 1019 3.0 / 1623 7.8 / 2252 2.5			**19** TH	0515 8.0 / 1138 2.5 / 1730 8.4 / 2358 2.1	
5 TH	0459 8.0 / 1117 2.3 / 1718 8.6 / 2346 1.8			**20** F	0554 8.5 / 1216 2.0 / 1808 8.8	
6 F	0550 8.7 / 1208 1.6 / 1807 9.2			**21** SA	0034 1.7 / 0629 8.8 / 1252 1.7 / ○ 1843 9.1	
7 SA	0035 1.1 / 0636 9.3 / 1256 1.0 / ● 1852 9.8			**22** SU	0108 1.5 / 0702 9.0 / 1323 1.6 / 1916 9.2	
8 SU	0121 0.6 / 0720 9.7 / 1341 0.6 / 1936 10.1			**23** M	0138 1.4 / 0733 9.1 / 1351 1.5 / 1946 9.2	
9 M	0204 0.3 / 0802 9.9 / 1422 0.4 / 2017 10.2			**24** TU	0205 1.5 / 0801 8.9 / 1417 1.7 / 2013 9.0	
10 TU	0245 0.4 / 0842 9.8 / 1502 0.6 / 2057 9.9			**25** W	0230 1.8 / 0827 8.7 / 1442 2.0 / 2038 8.7	
11 W	0323 0.8 / 0921 9.4 / 1541 1.1 / 2136 9.3			**26** TH	0255 2.1 / 0851 8.4 / 1507 2.3 / 2104 8.3	
12 TH	0402 1.5 / 1000 8.8 / 1620 1.8 / 2217 8.5			**27** F	0319 2.6 / 0916 8.0 / 1532 2.8 / 2131 7.9	
13 F	0442 2.3 / 1043 8.1 / 1704 2.7 / 2304 7.7			**28** SA	0346 3.0 / 0945 7.6 / 1602 3.2 / 2206 7.4	
14 SA	0532 3.2 / 1137 7.3 / 1803 3.4			**29** SU	0421 3.5 / 1026 7.2 / 1645 3.7 / 2258 6.9	
15 SU	0011 6.9 / 0645 3.9 / 1303 6.8 / 1937 3.9			**30** M	0518 4.0 / 1131 6.8 / 1759 4.0	

OCTOBER

Day	Time m		Day	Time m
1 TU	0023 6.6 / 0658 4.2 / 1310 6.7 / 2003 3.9		**16** W	0314 6.8 / 0941 3.8 / 1533 7.2 / 2207 3.3
2 W	0220 6.8 / 0848 3.8 / 1452 7.2 / 2131 3.3		**17** TH	0407 7.4 / 1030 3.2 / 1621 7.8 / 2250 2.7
3 TH	0343 7.5 / 1000 3.1 / 1602 7.9 / 2233 2.4		**18** F	0448 8.0 / 1110 2.6 / 1702 8.3 / 2328 2.2
4 F	0439 8.2 / 1057 2.2 / 1656 8.8 / 2325 1.6		**19** SA	0524 8.4 / 1147 2.2 / 1738 8.7
5 SA	0528 9.0 / 1147 1.4 / 1745 9.5		**20** SU	0003 1.9 / 0557 8.8 / 1221 1.8 / 1813 9.0
6 SU	0013 0.9 / 0613 9.6 / 1234 0.8 / ● 1830 10.0		**21** M	0035 1.7 / 0630 9.0 / 1251 1.7 / ○ 1845 9.1
7 M	0058 0.5 / 0656 10.0 / 1308 0.4 / 1913 10.3		**22** TU	0104 1.6 / 0701 9.1 / 1319 1.6 / 1916 9.1
8 TU	0140 0.3 / 0737 10.1 / 1400 0.3 / 1954 10.2		**23** W	0132 1.6 / 0729 9.0 / 1347 1.7 / 1944 8.9
9 W	0221 0.4 / 0817 10.0 / 1440 0.6 / 2034 9.9		**24** TH	0159 1.8 / 0756 8.8 / 1415 1.9 / 2011 8.7
10 TH	0259 0.9 / 0856 9.5 / 1519 1.1 / 2113 9.2		**25** F	0226 2.1 / 0821 8.6 / 1442 2.3 / 2039 8.4
11 F	0337 1.7 / 0934 8.9 / 1558 1.9 / 2153 8.4		**26** SA	0253 2.5 / 0849 8.2 / 1510 2.7 / 2109 8.0
12 SA	0416 2.6 / 1016 8.1 / 1642 2.8 / 2239 7.5		**27** SU	0323 3.0 / 0922 7.9 / 1543 3.1 / 2147 7.5
13 SU	0504 3.5 / 1108 7.3 / 1740 3.6 / 2345 6.8		**28** M	0401 3.5 / 1006 7.4 / 1630 3.6 / 2243 7.0
14 M	0618 4.2 / 1233 6.7 / 1914 4.1		**29** TU	0459 3.9 / 1114 7.0 / 1745 3.9
15 TU	0148 6.5 / 0824 4.3 / 1426 6.8 / 2108 3.8		**30** W	0006 6.8 / 0634 4.1 / 1245 7.0 / 1936 3.7
			31 TH	0151 7.0 / 0821 3.7 / 1420 7.4 / 2103 3.1

NOVEMBER

Day	Time m		Day	Time m
1 F	0313 7.6 / 0934 3.0 / 1532 8.1 / 2206 2.4		**16** SA	0409 7.7 / 1033 3.0 / 1624 7.9 / 2249 2.6
2 SA	0410 8.4 / 1031 2.2 / 1628 8.8 / 2258 1.6		**17** SU	0447 8.1 / 1110 2.5 / 1702 8.3 / 2325 2.3
3 SU	0500 9.0 / 1121 1.5 / 1718 9.4 / 2346 1.1		**18** M	0522 8.5 / 1144 2.2 / 1739 8.6 / 2358 2.0
4 M	0546 9.6 / 1209 1.0 / 1805 9.8 ●		**19** TU	0556 8.8 / 1217 2.0 / 1814 8.7
5 TU	0032 0.7 / 0630 9.9 / 1255 0.6 / 1849 10.0		**20** W	0030 1.9 / 0629 8.9 / 1249 1.8 / ○ 1847 8.8
6 W	0116 0.6 / 0712 10.0 / 1338 0.6 / 1932 9.9		**21** TH	0102 1.8 / 0701 8.9 / 1321 1.8 / 1920 8.8
7 TH	0158 0.8 / 0753 9.9 / 1420 0.8 / 2014 9.6		**22** F	0134 1.9 / 0731 8.9 / 1354 2.0 / 1951 8.6
8 F	0237 1.3 / 0833 9.4 / 1501 1.4 / 2055 9.0		**23** SA	0206 2.1 / 0802 8.7 / 1426 2.2 / 2024 8.4
9 SA	0316 1.9 / 0913 8.8 / 1542 2.0 / 2136 8.3		**24** SU	0238 2.4 / 0835 8.4 / 1501 2.5 / 2100 8.1
10 SU	0357 2.7 / 0956 8.1 / 1627 2.8 / 2222 7.5		**25** M	0314 2.8 / 0914 8.1 / 1541 2.8 / 2144 7.7
11 M	0444 3.5 / 1046 7.4 / 1722 3.5 / 2321 6.9		**26** TU	0358 3.2 / 1003 7.8 / 1631 3.2 / 2240 7.4
12 TU	0550 4.1 / 1156 6.9 / 1837 3.9		**27** W	0456 3.6 / 1106 7.5 / 1739 3.4 / 2350 7.2
13 W	0053 6.6 / 0726 4.3 / 1334 6.8 / 2013 3.9		**28** TH	0614 3.7 / 1221 7.4 / 1903 3.3
14 TH	0228 6.8 / 0856 4.0 / 1449 7.1 / 2121 3.5		**29** F	0113 7.3 / 0743 3.5 / 1343 7.6 / 2025 3.0
15 F	0325 7.2 / 0950 3.5 / 1541 7.5 / 2209 3.1		**30** SA	0233 7.7 / 0859 3.0 / 1456 8.1 / 2132 2.4

DECEMBER

Day	Time m		Day	Time m
1 SU	0336 8.2 / 1001 2.4 / 1557 8.5 / 2228 1.9		**16** M	0401 7.6 / 1024 3.1 / 1620 7.7 / 2240 2.8
2 M	0430 8.8 / 1055 1.8 / 1651 9.0 / 2320 1.5		**17** TU	0443 8.0 / 1105 2.9 / 1703 8.0 / 2321 2.5
3 TU	0520 9.2 / 1146 1.4 / 1742 9.3		**18** W	0523 8.3 / 1144 2.3 / 1744 8.3
4 W	0009 1.3 / 0607 9.5 / 1234 1.1 / ● 1829 9.4		**19** TH	0000 2.2 / 0601 8.6 / 1223 2.1 / ○ 1823 8.5
5 TH	0056 1.2 / 0652 9.6 / 1321 1.0 / 1916 9.4		**20** F	0038 2.0 / 0638 8.7 / 1302 1.9 / 1902 8.6
6 F	0140 1.3 / 0735 9.5 / 1405 1.2 / 2000 9.2		**21** SA	0116 2.0 / 0715 8.8 / 1341 1.9 / 1940 8.6
7 SA	0222 1.6 / 0818 9.3 / 1448 1.5 / 2042 8.8		**22** SU	0154 2.0 / 0752 8.8 / 1420 1.9 / 2018 8.5
8 SU	0303 2.1 / 0859 8.8 / 1530 2.0 / 2124 8.3		**23** M	0233 2.1 / 0831 8.7 / 1500 2.0 / 2059 8.4
9 M	0343 2.6 / 0940 8.3 / 1613 2.5 / 2206 7.7		**24** TU	0314 2.3 / 0913 8.5 / 1543 2.2 / 2143 8.1
10 TU	0426 3.2 / 1025 7.8 / 1700 3.1 / 2254 7.2		**25** W	0358 2.6 / 1001 8.3 / 1630 2.5 / 2232 7.9
11 W	0516 3.7 / 1117 7.3 / 1754 3.5 / 2352 6.9		**26** TH	0449 2.9 / 1054 8.0 / 1725 2.7 / 2329 7.7
12 TH	0618 4.0 / 1221 7.0 / 1857 3.7		**27** F	0550 3.1 / 1155 7.8 / 1828 2.9
13 F	0103 6.7 / 0731 4.0 / 1334 6.9 / 2004 3.7		**28** SA	0035 7.5 / 0701 3.1 / 1305 7.7 / 1940 2.9
14 SA	0216 6.9 / 0842 3.8 / 1440 7.0 / 2106 3.5		**29** SU	0150 7.6 / 0819 3.0 / 1419 7.8 / 2054 2.7
15 SU	0314 7.2 / 0938 3.5 / 1534 7.3 / 2157 3.1		**30** M	0302 7.9 / 0930 2.7 / 1528 8.0 / 2201 2.5
			31 TU	0405 8.2 / 1032 2.3 / 1630 8.3 / 2259 2.2

Chart Datum: 5·06 metres below Ordnance Datum (Local)

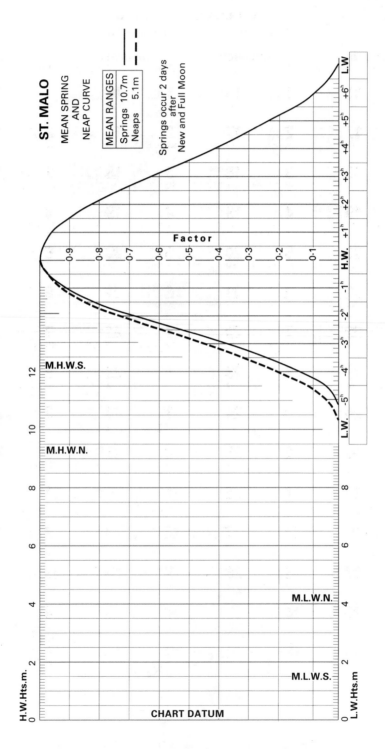

ST. MALO

MEAN SPRING
AND
NEAP CURVE

MEAN RANGES
Springs 10.7m
Neaps 5.1m

Springs occur 2 days
after
New and Full Moon

Factor

0.9
0.8
0.7
0.6
0.5
0.4
0.3
0.2
0.1

M.H.W.S.

M.H.W.N.

M.L.W.N.

M.L.W.S.

H.W.Hts.m.

L.W.Hts.m

CHART DATUM

TIME ZONE -0100
(French Standard Time)
Subtract 1 hour for UT
For French Summer Time add ONE hour in **non-shaded areas**

FRANCE – ST MALO

LAT 48°38′N   LONG 2°02′W

TIMES AND HEIGHTS OF HIGH AND LOW WATERS

YEAR 2002

JANUARY

Time	m	Time	m
1 0253	1.9	**16** 0318	2.7
0816	12.3	0849	11.5
TU 1520	1.7	W 1540	2.5
2046	11.9	2109	11.1
2 0338	1.9	**17** 0349	2.8
0901	12.2	0920	11.3
W 1606	1.7	TH 1610	2.7
2131	11.8	2139	10.9
3 0422	2.1	**18** 0417	3.0
0946	12.0	0950	11.0
TH 1652	2.0	F 1640	3.0
2216	11.5	2209	10.6
4 0507	2.4	**19** 0445	3.4
1032	11.6	1020	10.6
F 1738	2.3	SA 1709	3.4
2303	11.0	2239	10.2
5 0553	2.9	**20** 0514	3.7
1120	11.1	1052	10.1
SA 1825	2.8	SU 1741	3.7
2353	10.5	2313	9.8
6 0642	3.3	**21** 0549	4.1
1213	10.5	1129	9.7
SU 1917	3.3	M 1820	4.1
7 0053	10.1	**22** 0006	9.4
0740	3.7	0636	4.5
M 1318	10.1	TU 1221	9.2
2017	3.6	1913	4.5
8 0203	9.8	**23** 0057	9.1
0849	3.9	0742	4.7
TU 1433	9.9	W 1334	9.0
2129	3.7	2023	4.6
9 0318	9.9	**24** 0217	9.1
1006	3.8	0906	4.7
W 1547	10.1	TH 1500	9.1
2242	3.6	2145	4.4
10 0426	10.3	**25** 0337	9.4
1116	3.4	1028	4.2
TH 1653	10.4	F 1616	9.6
2346	3.2	2258	3.9
11 0525	10.7	**26** 0444	10.1
1217	3.0	1135	3.5
F 1750	10.8	SA 1718	10.2
12 0044	3.0	**27** 0008	3.2
0616	11.1	0541	10.8
SA 1309	2.7	SU 1234	2.8
1840	11.0	1813	11.0
13 0130	2.7	**28** 0101	2.6
0701	11.4	0633	11.5
SU 1353	2.5	M 1330	2.1
● 1923	11.2	○ 1904	11.6
14 0210	2.6	**29** 0154	2.0
0740	11.5	0722	12.2
M 1432	2.4	TU 1423	1.5
2002	11.3	1953	12.1
15 0245	2.6	**30** 0245	1.5
0816	11.6	0809	12.6
TU 1507	2.4	W 1513	1.1
2037	11.3	2039	12.4
		31 0332	1.3
		0854	12.8
		TH 1600	0.9
		2122	12.5

FEBRUARY

Time	m	Time	m
1 0416	1.3	**16** 0358	2.3
0937	12.7	0926	11.5
F 1643	1.1	SA 1617	2.3
2204	12.2	2141	11.3
2 0457	1.5	**17** 0424	2.6
1019	12.4	0953	11.2
SA 1724	1.5	SU 1643	2.7
2245	11.8	2208	10.9
3 0537	2.0	**18** 0449	2.9
1100	11.8	1021	10.8
SU 1803	2.2	M 1710	3.1
2326	11.1	2237	10.5
4 0617	2.7	**19** 0518	3.4
1144	11.0	1051	10.2
M 1845	2.9	TU 1741	3.6
		2310	10.0
5 0014	10.4	**20** 0555	3.9
0703	3.4	1130	9.6
TU 1237	10.1	W 1823	4.2
1935	3.7	2354	9.4
6 0116	9.7	**21** 0646	4.5
0804	4.1	1227	9.0
W 1350	9.5	TH 1923	4.7
2045	4.3		
7 0240	9.3	**22** 0108	8.9
0930	4.4	0806	4.8
TH 1520	9.3	F 1402	8.7
2212	4.3	2052	4.8
8 0406	9.5	**23** 0249	8.6
1056	4.1	0946	4.5
F 1641	9.6	SA 1547	9.0
2328	4.0	2224	4.3
9 0513	10.0	**24** 0419	9.6
1203	3.5	1108	3.8
SA 1742	10.1	SU 1702	9.9
		2337	3.5
10 0030	3.5	**25** 0525	10.5
0606	10.6	1215	2.8
SU 1256	3.0	M 1801	10.8
1830	10.6		
11 0117	3.0	**26** 0045	2.6
0649	11.0	0620	11.5
M 1339	2.7	TU 1316	1.9
1910	11.0	1852	11.7
12 0156	2.7	**27** 0141	1.7
0725	11.4	0710	12.4
TU 1416	2.4	W 1411	1.1
1945	11.3	○ 1939	12.3
13 0230	2.5	**28** 0233	1.0
0759	11.6	0756	13.0
W 1449	2.2	TH 1501	0.5
2017	11.4	2023	12.9
14 0301	2.3		
0829	11.7		
TH 1520	2.1		
2046	11.5		
15 0331	2.3		
0858	11.7		
F 1550	2.1		
2114	11.4		

MARCH

Time	m	Time	m
1 0320	0.6	**16** 0309	1.8
0839	13.3	0833	11.9
F 1545	0.3	SA 1525	1.7
2105	13.0	2047	11.8
2 0402	0.6	**17** 0336	1.9
0920	13.3	0900	11.9
SA 1626	0.5	SU 1553	1.9
2144	12.8	2114	11.7
3 0440	0.9	**18** 0402	2.1
0959	12.8	0928	11.6
SU 1703	1.0	M 1618	2.2
2221	12.2	2141	11.4
4 0516	1.5	**19** 0428	2.5
1037	12.1	0955	11.1
M 1738	1.9	TU 1644	2.7
2258	11.4	2208	10.9
5 0551	2.4	**20** 0455	3.0
1116	11.1	1024	10.5
TU 1813	2.9	W 1713	3.3
2339	10.5	2239	10.3
6 0631	3.4	**21** 0528	3.6
1203	10.0	1059	9.8
W 1856	3.9	TH 1751	4.0
		2318	9.6
7 0036	9.5	**22** 0614	4.3
0725	4.3	1149	9.1
TH 1314	9.0	F 1847	4.6
2002	4.7		
8 0207	8.8	**23** 0025	8.9
0858	4.8	0729	4.7
F 1501	8.6	SA 1322	8.5
2147	4.9	2018	4.9
9 0349	8.9	**24** 0216	8.7
1038	4.5	0917	4.6
SA 1632	9.0	SU 1529	8.8
2313	4.4	2200	4.4
10 0500	9.6	**25** 0400	9.4
1147	3.8	1047	3.7
SU 1729	9.7	M 1647	9.8
		2317	3.5
11 0012	3.7	**26** 0508	10.4
0549	10.2	1156	2.6
M 1237	3.1	TU 1743	10.9
1812	10.4		
12 0058	3.1	**27** 0026	2.4
0628	10.8	0602	11.5
TU 1317	2.6	W 1257	1.6
1847	10.9	1833	11.9
13 0135	2.6	**28** 0123	1.4
0702	11.3	0650	12.5
W 1353	2.2	TH 1352	0.8
1920	11.3	○ 1918	12.7
14 0209	2.2	**29** 0214	0.7
0734	11.6	0735	13.2
TH 1426	1.9	F 1441	0.2
● 1950	11.6	2001	13.1
15 0240	2.0	**30** 0300	0.4
0804	11.9	0818	13.4
F 1456	1.8	SA 1524	0.1
2019	11.8	2041	13.2
		31 0341	0.3
		0859	13.3
		SU 1603	0.4
		2119	13.0

APRIL

Time	m	Time	m
1 0419	0.7	**16** 0342	1.9
0937	12.8	0905	11.6
M 1638	1.1	TU 1555	2.1
2156	12.3	2116	11.6
2 0453	1.5	**17** 0410	2.3
1014	11.9	0935	11.2
TU 1711	2.0	W 1624	2.6
2232	11.4	2146	11.1
3 0527	2.4	**18** 0440	2.8
1052	10.8	1007	10.5
W 1744	3.1	TH 1655	3.2
2311	10.4	2220	10.4
4 0604	3.4	**19** 0515	3.4
1137	9.7	1045	9.8
TH 1823	4.1	F 1735	3.9
		2303	9.7
5 0000	9.3	**20** 0603	4.1
0656	4.4	1139	9.1
F 1246	8.7	SA 1833	4.5
1927	5.0		
6 0136	8.6	**21** 0015	9.1
0826	4.9	0718	4.5
SA 1436	8.3	SU 1313	8.6
2118	5.2	2002	4.7
7 0321	8.6	**22** 0158	8.9
1008	4.6	0858	4.3
SU 1607	8.7	M 1509	9.0
2245	4.6	2138	4.2
8 0431	9.2	**23** 0335	9.5
1114	4.0	1023	3.5
M 1701	9.5	TU 1622	9.9
2341	3.8	2253	3.3
9 0518	9.9	**24** 0442	10.5
1202	3.3	1132	2.5
TU 1740	10.2	W 1718	11.0
10 0025	3.1	**25** 0007	2.3
0556	10.6	0536	11.5
W 1243	2.7	TH 1232	1.6
1815	10.8	1806	11.9
11 0103	2.6	**26** 0058	1.5
0631	11.1	0625	12.3
TH 1320	2.2	F 1327	0.9
1848	11.3	1852	12.6
12 0138	2.2	**27** 0150	0.9
0704	11.5	0711	12.9
F 1355	1.9	SA 1415	0.5
● 1920	11.6	○ 1935	12.9
13 0212	1.9	**28** 0236	0.6
0736	11.8	0755	13.1
SA 1428	1.7	SU 1459	0.5
1950	11.8	2016	13.0
14 0243	1.7	**29** 0318	0.7
0806	11.9	0836	12.9
SU 1458	1.6	M 1538	0.8
2019	11.9	2055	12.7
15 0313	1.7	**30** 0356	1.0
0835	11.8	0916	12.3
M 1528	1.8	TU 1613	1.5
2048	11.8	2133	12.1

Chart Datum: 6·29 metres below IGN Datum

FRANCE – ST MALO

TIME ZONE -0100
(French Standard Time)
Subtract 1 hour for UT
For French Summer Time add
ONE hour in **non-shaded areas**

YEAR 2002

LAT 48°38'N   LONG 2°02'W

TIMES AND HEIGHTS OF HIGH AND LOW WATERS

MAY

Time	m	Time	m
1 0431	1.7	**16** 0356	2.3
0954	11.5	0922	11.1
W 1646	2.4	TH 1610	2.6
2210	11.2	2134	11.2
2 0506	2.6	**17** 0433	2.7
1034	10.5	1001	10.6
TH 1718	3.3	F 1648	3.1
2250	10.3	2214	10.6
3 0543	3.5	**18** 0514	3.2
1119	9.5	1046	10.0
F 1757	4.2	SA 1733	3.7
2341	9.3	2304	9.9
4 0632	4.3	**19** 0606	3.7
1221	8.7	1145	9.4
SA 1855	5.0	SU 1832	4.1
5 0057	8.6	**20** 0015	9.5
0746	4.8	0715	4.0
SU 1347	8.3	M 1306	9.1
2029	5.2	1950	4.3
6 0227	8.5	**21** 0139	9.4
0913	4.7	0836	3.8
M 1512	8.6	TU 1436	9.4
2152	4.8	2111	3.9
7 0339	8.9	**22** 0302	9.8
1020	4.2	0954	3.3
TU 1611	9.2	W 1547	10.0
2250	4.1	2223	3.2
8 0431	9.5	**23** 0409	10.5
1112	3.5	1102	2.6
W 1656	9.9	TH 1646	10.8
2337	3.4	2327	2.5
9 0514	10.2	**24** 0506	11.3
1158	2.9	1203	2.0
TH 1734	10.5	F 1737	11.6
10 0022	2.8	**25** 0029	1.9
0553	10.8	0558	11.9
F 1240	2.4	SA 1259	1.5
1811	11.1	1825	12.1
11 0102	2.4	**26** 0123	1.4
0630	11.2	0647	12.2
SA 1320	2.1	SU 1349	1.3
1846	11.4	○ 1911	12.4
12 0139	2.1	**27** 0211	1.3
0705	11.5	0733	12.3
SU 1356	1.9	M 1433	1.3
● 1920	11.7	1954	12.4
13 0215	1.9	**28** 0255	1.3
0739	11.6	0817	12.1
M 1431	1.9	TU 1513	1.6
1953	11.8	2035	12.2
14 0249	1.9	**29** 0334	1.6
0813	11.6	0858	11.7
TU 1504	1.9	W 1549	2.1
2025	11.8	2114	11.7
15 0323	2.0	**30** 0411	2.1
0846	11.5	0939	11.1
W 1536	2.2	TH 1623	2.7
2058	11.6	2153	11.1
		31 0447	2.7
		1019	10.4
		F 1657	3.4
		2233	10.4

JUNE

Time	m	Time	m
1 0524	3.4	**16** 0517	2.7
1101	9.7	1049	10.5
SA 1734	4.0	SU 1734	3.1
2318	9.6	2305	10.6
2 0606	4.0	**17** 0608	3.0
1148	9.1	1143	10.1
SU 1821	4.6	M 1828	3.5
3 0010	9.0	**18** 0009	10.2
0659	4.4	0704	3.3
M 1245	8.7	TU 1245	9.8
1926	4.9	1930	3.6
4 0116	8.7	**19** 0111	10.0
0805	4.5	0809	3.4
TU 1352	8.7	W 1356	9.8
2040	4.8	2038	3.6
5 0225	8.8	**20** 0224	10.0
0912	4.3	0919	3.3
W 1459	8.9	TH 1507	10.0
2146	4.4	2149	3.3
6 0328	9.2	**21** 0335	10.3
1013	3.9	1029	3.0
TH 1558	9.5	F 1612	10.5
2242	3.9	2257	2.9
7 0422	9.7	**22** 0438	10.8
1107	3.4	1134	2.6
F 1647	10.1	SA 1711	11.0
2333	3.3	2359	2.5
8 0510	10.3	**23** 0536	11.1
1157	2.9	1233	2.3
SA 1732	10.6	SU 1804	11.4
9 0022	2.8	**24** 0059	2.2
0554	10.7	0629	11.4
SU 1242	2.6	M 1325	2.1
1813	11.1	○ 1853	11.7
10 0106	2.5	**25** 0150	2.0
0636	11.0	0718	11.5
M 1325	2.3	TU 1411	2.1
1852	11.4	1938	11.8
11 0148	2.2	**26** 0235	2.0
0716	11.3	0803	11.5
TU 1405	2.2	W 1453	2.2
● 1930	11.6	2020	11.7
12 0228	2.1	**27** 0315	2.1
0755	11.4	0845	11.3
W 1444	2.1	TH 1530	2.4
2008	11.7	2059	11.5
13 0308	2.0	**28** 0353	2.3
0835	11.4	0924	11.0
TH 1523	2.2	F 1604	2.7
2048	11.6	2136	11.2
14 0349	2.1	**29** 0427	2.6
0917	11.2	1000	10.6
F 1604	2.4	SA 1637	3.1
2130	11.4	2212	10.7
15 0432	2.4	**30** 0501	3.1
1001	10.9	1035	10.2
SA 1647	2.7	SU 1710	3.6
2215	11.0	2248	10.2

JULY

Time	m	Time	m
1 0535	3.5	**16** 0558	2.3
1111	9.7	1127	10.9
M 1745	4.0	TU 1814	2.7
2326	9.7	2343	10.9
2 0612	3.9	**17** 0644	2.7
1150	9.4	1217	10.4
TU 1827	4.3	W 1904	3.2
3 0014	9.3	**18** 0040	10.4
0659	4.2	0737	3.2
W 1239	9.1	TH 1317	10.0
1922	4.6	2004	3.5
4 0109	9.0	**19** 0147	10.0
0757	4.3	0842	3.5
TH 1340	9.0	F 1429	9.9
2030	4.6	2117	3.7
5 0217	9.0	**20** 0304	9.9
0905	4.3	0958	3.6
F 1450	9.1	SA 1544	10.0
2142	4.3	2234	3.5
6 0326	9.3	**21** 0418	10.1
1012	4.0	1112	3.4
SA 1556	9.6	SU 1653	10.4
2246	3.9	2342	3.1
7 0428	9.7	**22** 0523	10.4
1120	3.6	1215	3.0
SU 1654	10.1	M 1753	10.8
2342	3.4		
8 0522	10.2	**23** 0045	2.7
1207	3.1	0620	10.8
M 1744	10.6	TU 1310	2.7
		1843	11.2
9 0036	2.9	**24** 0136	2.5
0612	10.6	0709	11.0
TU 1257	2.7	W 1357	2.6
1830	11.1	○ 1928	11.5
10 0125	2.5	**25** 0220	2.3
0658	11.0	0752	11.2
W 1344	2.4	TH 1437	2.5
● 1915	11.5	2007	11.6
11 0212	2.1	**26** 0259	2.2
0744	11.3	0829	11.2
TH 1431	2.1	F 1513	2.5
1958	11.8	2042	11.6
12 0259	1.9	**27** 0333	2.3
0828	11.6	0903	11.2
F 1516	2.0	SA 1545	2.5
2042	11.9	2115	11.4
13 0345	1.7	**28** 0405	2.4
0913	11.6	0934	11.0
SA 1601	1.9	SU 1614	2.7
2126	11.9	2146	11.2
14 0430	1.8	**29** 0435	2.6
0957	11.5	1004	10.8
SU 1645	2.0	M 1642	3.0
2210	11.7	2215	10.8
15 0514	1.9	**30** 0502	3.0
1041	11.3	1033	10.4
M 1728	2.3	TU 1710	3.3
2255	11.4	2245	10.4
		31 0531	3.4
		1104	10.0
		W 1740	3.8
		2319	9.8

AUGUST

Time	m	Time	m
1 0606	3.8	**16** 0008	10.5
1141	9.6	0704	3.3
TH 1820	4.2	F 1241	10.0
		1932	3.7
2 0009	9.3	**17** 0114	9.7
0651	4.2	0806	4.0
F 1231	9.2	SA 1357	9.5
1916	4.6	2050	4.2
3 0107	8.9	**18** 0242	9.3
0753	4.6	0935	4.3
SA 1342	8.9	SU 1528	9.5
2035	4.8	2220	4.0
4 0230	8.8	**19** 0410	9.5
0915	4.6	1100	4.0
SU 1507	9.1	M 1647	9.9
2200	4.5	2334	3.5
5 0351	9.1	**20** 0520	10.0
1033	4.2	1206	3.5
M 1622	9.6	TU 1747	10.6
2310	3.8		
6 0458	9.7	**21** 0036	3.0
1138	3.6	0613	10.6
TU 1722	10.3	W 1259	3.0
		1833	11.1
7 0013	3.1	**22** 0124	2.5
0554	10.4	0656	11.0
W 1236	3.0	TH 1343	2.6
1814	11.0	○ 1913	11.5
8 0107	2.5	**23** 0204	2.3
0645	11.1	0733	11.3
TH 1329	2.3	F 1420	2.4
● 1902	11.6	1947	11.7
9 0200	1.9	**24** 0239	2.1
0732	11.6	0806	11.4
F 1420	1.8	SA 1453	2.2
1948	12.2	2019	11.6
10 0250	1.4	**25** 0310	2.0
0818	12.1	0836	11.5
SA 1508	1.4	SU 1522	2.2
2032	12.5	2048	11.8
11 0337	1.1	**26** 0339	2.1
0901	12.3	0903	11.5
SU 1552	1.2	M 1549	2.3
2114	12.7	2116	11.6
12 0420	1.0	**27** 0406	2.2
0943	12.3	0930	11.3
M 1634	1.3	TU 1615	2.5
2156	12.5	2142	11.3
13 0500	1.3	**28** 0431	2.6
1023	12.0	0957	11.0
TU 1714	1.7	W 1639	2.9
2236	12.0	2209	10.9
14 0539	1.8	**29** 0456	3.0
1103	11.5	1024	10.5
W 1754	2.3	TH 1705	3.4
2318	11.3	2237	10.3
15 0618	2.5	**30** 0524	3.6
1147	10.8	1054	10.0
TH 1837	3.0	F 1737	4.0
		2311	9.6
		31 0601	4.2
		1134	9.4
		SA 1823	4.6

Chart Datum: 6·29 metres below IGN Datum

Register for your **FREE** weekly weather email service from Macmillan Reeds
》 at **www.nauticaldata.com – NOW!** 《
weekend weather reports sent to your email address, every Thursday

<table>
<tr><td colspan="2">

TIME ZONE -0100
(French Standard Time)
Subtract 1 hour for UT
For French Summer Time add
ONE hour in **non-shaded areas**

</td><td colspan="2">

FRANCE – ST MALO

LAT 48°38′N   LONG 2°02′W

TIMES AND HEIGHTS OF HIGH AND LOW WATERS

</td><td>YEAR **2002**</td></tr>
</table>

Section 1

SEPTEMBER

Time	m	Time	m
1 0010 8.9 0655 4.8 SU 1237 8.8 1936 5.0		**16** 0231 8.8 0922 4.9 M 1521 9.1 2213 4.4	
2 0136 8.5 0822 5.0 M 1422 8.6 2119 4.9		**17** 0407 9.1 1053 4.4 TU 1640 9.7 2325 3.7	
3 0326 8.7 1002 4.7 TU 1600 9.0 2245 4.1		**18** 0511 9.8 1155 3.6 W 1733 10.4	
4 0442 9.5 1117 3.8 W 1706 10.1 2350 3.2		**19** 0020 3.0 0556 10.5 TH 1242 2.9 1813 11.1	
5 0539 10.5 1218 2.9 TH 1759 11.1		**20** 0102 2.5 0633 11.1 F 1321 2.5 1849 11.5	
6 0051 2.2 0629 11.4 F 1313 2.1 1847 12.0		**21** 0139 2.2 0704 11.7 SA 1355 2.2 ○ 1921 11.8	
7 0145 1.4 0716 12.1 SA 1405 1.3 ● 1932 12.7		**22** 0212 2.0 0736 11.7 SU 1426 2.0 1951 12.0	
8 0235 0.8 0759 12.7 SU 1453 0.9 2015 13.1		**23** 0242 1.8 0805 11.8 M 1455 1.9 2019 12.0	
9 0321 0.5 0841 13.0 M 1537 0.7 2056 13.2		**24** 0310 1.9 0832 11.8 TU 1522 2.0 2045 11.9	
10 0402 0.5 0921 12.9 TU 1617 0.6 2135 13.0		**25** 0337 2.0 0858 11.7 W 1548 2.3 2111 11.6	
11 0440 1.0 0959 12.4 W 1654 1.3 2214 12.3		**26** 0401 2.4 0924 11.4 TH 1612 2.7 2137 11.1	
12 0516 1.7 1037 11.7 TH 1731 2.2 2253 11.4		**27** 0425 2.9 0950 10.9 F 1637 3.2 2205 10.5	
13 0551 2.7 1118 10.8 F 1812 3.1 2339 10.3		**28** 0452 3.5 1023 9.6 SA 1707 3.8 2236 9.7	
14 0633 3.7 1210 9.8 SA 1905 4.1		**29** 0525 4.2 1053 9.6 SU 1749 4.5 2320 8.9	
15 0049 9.3 0736 4.6 SU 1334 9.1 2032 4.6		**30** 0616 4.9 1149 8.8 M 1858 5.1	

OCTOBER

Time	m	Time	m
1 0053 8.4 0745 5.3 TU 1346 8.5 2047 5.0		**16** 0347 8.9 1031 4.6 W 1616 9.5 2259 3.9	
2 0307 8.6 0936 4.9 W 1541 9.1 2222 4.2		**17** 0444 9.7 1127 3.8 TH 1704 10.2 2347 3.2	
3 0424 9.6 1055 3.9 TH 1646 10.1 2329 3.1		**18** 0525 10.4 1209 3.1 F 1742 10.8	
4 0519 10.7 1156 2.8 F 1737 11.3		**19** 0028 2.7 0600 11.0 SA 1247 2.6 1816 11.3	
5 0031 2.0 0607 11.7 SA 1252 1.8 1824 12.2		**20** 0105 2.3 0633 11.4 SU 1322 2.2 1849 11.7	
6 0124 1.1 0652 12.5 SU 1344 1.0 ● 1909 13.0		**21** 0139 2.0 0704 11.7 M 1355 2.0 ○ 1920 11.9	
7 0213 0.6 0735 13.1 M 1432 0.6 1952 13.4		**22** 0211 1.9 0733 11.9 TU 1426 2.0 1949 11.9	
8 0258 0.4 0816 13.3 TU 1516 0.5 2033 13.4		**23** 0241 1.9 0801 11.9 W 1456 2.0 2018 11.8	
9 0339 0.5 0856 13.1 W 1556 0.8 2113 13.0		**24** 0309 2.1 0829 11.8 TH 1524 2.3 2045 11.4	
10 0416 1.1 0934 12.5 TH 1634 1.4 2152 12.2		**25** 0335 2.4 0856 11.5 F 1551 2.7 2113 11.1	
11 0451 2.0 1012 11.7 F 1711 2.3 2232 11.2		**26** 0402 2.9 0924 11.1 SA 1618 3.2 2143 10.5	
12 0525 3.0 1053 10.7 SA 1751 3.3 2318 10.0		**27** 0430 3.5 0955 10.5 SU 1651 3.6 2218 9.8	
13 0606 4.1 1146 9.6 SU 1845 4.3		**28** 0506 4.2 1033 9.7 M 1735 4.4 2306 9.1	
14 0030 8.9 0711 5.0 M 1314 8.9 2014 4.9		**29** 0559 4.8 1132 9.0 TU 1843 4.9	
15 0201 8.6 0903 5.2 TU 1502 8.9 2152 4.6		**30** 0035 8.6 0725 5.1 W 1319 8.7 2021 4.8	
		31 0238 8.8 0907 4.7 TH 1509 9.2 2152 4.1	

NOVEMBER

Time	m	Time	m
1 0354 9.7 1026 3.8 F 1615 10.2 2300 3.0		**16** 0441 9.9 1124 3.6 SA 1701 10.3 2343 3.1	
2 0450 10.8 1129 2.7 SA 1708 11.3		**17** 0520 10.6 1206 3.0 SU 1738 10.9	
3 0009 2.0 0538 11.8 SU 1225 1.8 1757 12.2		**18** 0025 2.7 0556 11.1 M 1245 2.6 1814 11.3	
4 0057 1.3 0624 12.5 M 1318 1.2 ● 1843 12.9		**19** 0103 2.4 0630 11.5 TU 1323 2.4 1849 11.5	
5 0147 0.8 0709 13.0 TU 1407 0.8 1928 13.2		**20** 0139 2.2 0703 11.7 W 1358 2.2 ○ 1923 11.6	
6 0233 0.7 0751 13.1 W 1453 0.8 2011 13.1		**21** 0212 2.2 0735 11.8 TH 1431 2.2 1955 11.6	
7 0315 1.0 0832 12.9 TH 1535 1.1 2053 12.6		**22** 0244 2.3 0806 11.7 F 1503 2.4 2027 11.4	
8 0353 1.6 0913 12.3 F 1614 1.7 2134 11.9		**23** 0315 2.6 0837 11.5 SA 1536 2.7 2100 11.1	
9 0428 2.4 0953 11.6 SA 1653 2.5 2216 10.9		**24** 0347 2.9 0910 11.2 SU 1610 3.1 2135 10.6	
10 0504 3.3 1035 10.6 SU 1734 3.5 2304 9.9		**25** 0421 3.4 0948 10.7 M 1648 3.5 2217 10.0	
11 0545 4.3 1128 9.7 M 1825 4.3		**26** 0503 3.9 1032 10.1 TU 1735 4.0 2309 9.5	
12 0001 9.0 0644 5.0 TU 1241 9.0 1938 4.8		**27** 0557 4.4 1131 9.5 W 1837 4.3	
13 0129 8.6 0739 5.2 W 1411 8.8 2100 4.8		**28** 0023 9.1 0708 4.6 TH 1252 9.3 1954 4.3	
14 0254 8.7 0939 4.9 TH 1527 9.1 2207 4.3		**29** 0154 9.2 0831 4.4 F 1423 9.5 2114 3.9	
15 0356 9.3 1038 4.2 F 1619 9.7 2259 3.7		**30** 0312 9.8 0949 3.8 SA 1535 10.2 2225 3.2	

DECEMBER

Time	m	Time	m
1 0414 10.6 1056 3.0 SU 1635 11.0 2328 2.5		**16** 0432 9.9 1119 3.7 M 1656 10.1 2340 3.4	
2 0508 11.4 1156 2.3 M 1728 11.8		**17** 0517 10.5 1207 3.2 TU 1740 10.6	
3 0029 1.9 0558 12.1 TU 1252 1.7 1819 12.3		**18** 0027 3.0 0559 11.0 W 1251 2.8 1822 11.0	
4 0122 1.5 0646 12.5 W 1344 1.4 ● 1908 12.5		**19** 0109 2.7 0638 11.3 TH 1331 2.6 ○ 1901 11.2	
5 0210 1.4 0731 12.6 TH 1432 1.3 1954 12.4		**20** 0148 2.6 0715 11.5 F 1410 2.4 1939 11.3	
6 0253 1.6 0815 12.5 F 1517 1.5 2039 12.1		**21** 0226 2.5 0751 11.6 SA 1449 2.4 2017 11.3	
7 0333 2.1 0858 12.1 SA 1558 2.0 2122 11.5		**22** 0303 2.5 0828 11.6 SU 1528 2.5 2055 11.2	
8 0410 2.7 0939 11.5 SU 1638 2.6 2204 10.8		**23** 0342 2.7 0907 11.5 M 1608 2.6 2136 11.0	
9 0447 3.3 1021 10.9 M 1717 3.3 2247 10.1		**24** 0422 2.9 0949 11.2 TU 1651 2.9 2219 10.6	
10 0525 4.0 1105 10.0 TU 1759 3.9 2332 9.4		**25** 0505 3.2 1034 10.8 W 1736 3.2 2307 10.3	
11 0609 4.6 1155 9.4 W 1848 4.5		**26** 0553 3.6 1124 10.4 TH 1827 3.5	
12 0026 8.9 0707 5.0 TH 1255 9.0 1947 4.7		**27** 0009 9.9 0648 3.9 F 1224 10.0 1925 3.7	
13 0129 8.7 0816 5.0 F 1404 8.9 2051 4.7		**28** 0110 9.7 0753 4.0 SA 1336 9.9 2031 3.7	
14 0238 8.9 0925 4.7 SA 1511 9.1 2153 4.3		**29** 0225 9.8 0906 3.8 SU 1452 10.1 2145 3.5	
15 0340 9.3 1026 4.3 SU 1608 9.6 2249 3.8		**30** 0336 10.0 1021 3.5 M 1603 10.5 2256 3.1	
		31 0440 10.4 1130 2.9 TU 1706 11.0	

Chart Datum: 6·29 metres below IGN Datum
Register for your **FREE** weekly weather email service from Macmillan Reeds
》》 at **www.nauticaldata.com – NOW!** **《《**
weekend weather reports sent to your email address, every Thursday

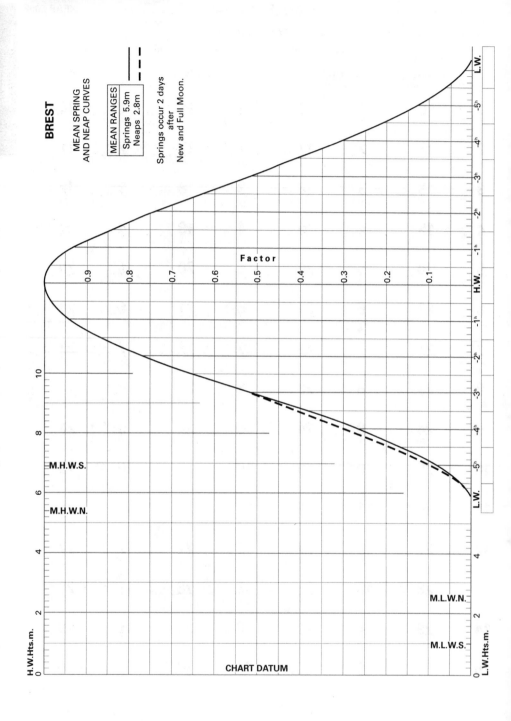

BREST

MEAN SPRING AND NEAP CURVES

MEAN RANGES
Springs 5.9m
Neaps 2.8m

Springs occur 2 days after New and Full Moon.

Factor

0.9 0.8 0.7 0.6 0.5 0.4 0.3 0.2 0.1

H.W.

M.H.W.S.

M.H.W.N.

M.L.W.N.

M.L.W.S.

CHART DATUM

L.W.

H.W.Hts.m.

L.W.Hts.m.

TIME ZONE -0100
(French Standard Time)
Subtract 1 hour for UT
For French Summer Time add
ONE hour in **non-shaded areas**

FRANCE – BREST

LAT 48°23′N   LONG 4°30′W

TIMES AND HEIGHTS OF HIGH AND LOW WATERS

YEAR **2002**

Section 1

JANUARY

Time	m		Time	m
1 TU 0004 / 0605 / 1230 / 1830	1.2 / 7.0 / 1.0 / 6.8		**16** W 0041 / 0638 / 1301 / 1854	1.6 / 6.6 / 1.5 / 6.3
2 W 0050 / 0651 / 1317 / 1917	1.2 / 7.0 / 1.0 / 6.7		**17** TH 0115 / 0712 / 1335 / 1927	1.7 / 6.5 / 1.6 / 6.1
3 TH 0137 / 0738 / 1406 / 2006	1.3 / 6.9 / 1.2 / 6.3		**18** F 0148 / 0746 / 1408 / 2000	1.9 / 6.3 / 1.8 / 5.9
4 F 0226 / 0828 / 1457 / 2058	1.5 / 6.7 / 1.4 / 6.3		**19** SA 0223 / 0820 / 1443 / 2035	2.1 / 6.0 / 2.1 / 5.7
5 SA 0319 / 0922 / 1552 / 2155	1.7 / 6.4 / 1.7 / 6.0		**20** SU 0259 / 0857 / 1522 / 2115	2.3 / 5.8 / 2.3 / 5.5
6 SU 0417 / 1022 / 1653 / 2258	2.0 / 6.1 / 2.0 / 5.8		**21** M 0342 / 0941 / 1607 / 2205	2.6 / 5.5 / 2.6 / 5.2
7 M 0521 / 1128 / 1758	2.2 / 5.9 / 2.2		**22** TU 0434 / 1038 / 1703 / 2310	2.8 / 5.3 / 2.7 / 5.1
8 TU 0005 / 0629 / 1240 / 1907	5.7 / 2.3 / 5.8 / 2.2		**23** W 0539 / 1147 / 1811	2.9 / 5.2 / 2.8
9 W 0120 / 0739 / 1350 / 2013	5.8 / 2.2 / 5.8 / 2.1		**24** TH 0028 / 0652 / 1303 / 1923	5.2 / 2.8 / 5.3 / 2.6
10 TH 0224 / 0844 / 1451 / 2112	6.0 / 2.0 / 6.0 / 1.9		**25** F 0140 / 0803 / 1411 / 2028	5.4 / 2.5 / 5.6 / 2.3
11 F 0319 / 0940 / 1543 / 2202	6.2 / 1.8 / 6.0 / 1.8		**26** SA 0241 / 0903 / 1509 / 2124	5.8 / 2.1 / 5.9 / 1.9
12 SA 0406 / 1028 / 1629 / 2246	6.4 / 1.6 / 6.3 / 1.6		**27** SU 0334 / 0956 / 1601 / 2215	6.2 / 1.7 / 6.3 / 1.5
13 SU ● 0448 / 1111 / 1709 / 2327	6.6 / 1.5 / 6.4 / 1.6		**28** M ○ 0423 / 1046 / 1649 / 2303	6.7 / 1.2 / 6.7 / 1.2
14 M 0527 / 1149 / 1746	6.7 / 1.4 / 6.4		**29** TU 0510 / 1133 / 1735 / 2349	7.0 / 0.9 / 7.0 / 0.9
15 TU 0002 / 0603 / 1226 / 1821	1.5 / 6.7 / 1.4 / 6.4		**30** W 0555 / 1220 / 1820	7.3 / 0.6 / 7.1
			31 TH 0039 / 0641 / 1306 / 1905	0.8 / 7.4 / 0.6 / 7.1

FEBRUARY

Time	m		Time	m
1 F 0125 / 0726 / 1352 / 1950	0.8 / 7.3 / 0.7 / 6.9		**16** SA 0121 / 0717 / 1337 / 1929	1.6 / 6.5 / 1.6 / 6.2
2 SA 0211 / 0811 / 1439 / 2036	1.0 / 7.1 / 1.0 / 6.6		**17** SU 0151 / 0747 / 1408 / 1958	1.7 / 6.3 / 1.8 / 6.0
3 SU 0259 / 0858 / 1527 / 2124	1.3 / 6.7 / 1.4 / 6.2		**18** M 0223 / 0818 / 1441 / 2031	2.0 / 6.1 / 2.0 / 5.8
4 M 0349 / 0949 / 1620 / 2219	1.7 / 6.2 / 1.9 / 5.8		**19** TU 0300 / 0854 / 1520 / 2112	2.3 / 5.7 / 2.3 / 5.5
5 TU 0447 / 1049 / 1721 / 2325	2.1 / 5.7 / 2.3 / 5.5		**20** W 0344 / 0941 / 1609 / 2207	2.5 / 5.4 / 2.6 / 5.2
6 W 0554 / 1203 / 1832	2.4 / 5.4 / 2.6		**21** TH 0442 / 1047 / 1713 / 2323	2.8 / 5.2 / 2.8 / 5.1
7 TH 0048 / 0712 / 1328 / 1951	5.4 / 2.5 / 5.4 / 2.5		**22** F 0558 / 1213 / 1834	2.9 / 5.1 / 2.8
8 F 0207 / 0829 / 1441 / 2058	5.6 / 2.4 / 5.5 / 2.3		**23** SA 0058 / 0725 / 1342 / 1957	5.2 / 2.7 / 5.3 / 2.6
9 SA 0308 / 0929 / 1535 / 2151	5.9 / 2.1 / 5.8 / 2.0		**24** SU 0216 / 0840 / 1450 / 2103	5.6 / 2.2 / 5.8 / 2.1
10 SU 0356 / 1017 / 1619 / 2235	6.2 / 1.8 / 6.1 / 1.8		**25** M 0316 / 0938 / 1545 / 2158	6.2 / 1.6 / 6.3 / 1.5
11 M 0437 / 1058 / 1657 / 2313	6.4 / 1.6 / 6.3 / 1.6		**26** TU 0408 / 1030 / 1634 / 2247	6.7 / 1.1 / 6.8 / 1.0
12 TU 0513 / 1134 / 1730 / 2347	6.6 / 1.4 / 6.4 / 1.4		**27** W ○ 0455 / 1118 / 1720 / 2334	7.2 / 0.6 / 7.2 / 0.6
13 W 0545 / 1206 / 1801	6.7 / 1.3 / 6.5		**28** TH 0540 / 1204 / 1804	7.5 / 0.3 / 7.4
14 TH 0020 / 0617 / 1237 / 1831	1.4 / 6.7 / 1.3 / 6.5			
15 F 0051 / 0647 / 1308 / 1900	1.5 / 6.7 / 1.4 / 6.4			

MARCH

Time	m		Time	m
1 F 0023 / 0624 / 1248 / 1846	0.4 / 7.7 / 0.3 / 7.4		**16** SA 0025 / 0620 / 1239 / 1831	1.3 / 6.8 / 1.3 / 6.6
2 SA 0107 / 0706 / 1332 / 1928	0.5 / 7.5 / 0.5 / 7.2		**17** SU 0053 / 0648 / 1307 / 1859	1.4 / 6.7 / 1.4 / 6.5
3 SU 0150 / 0748 / 1415 / 2009	0.7 / 7.2 / 0.9 / 6.8		**18** M 0122 / 0716 / 1336 / 1927	1.5 / 6.5 / 1.6 / 6.3
4 M 0235 / 0831 / 1500 / 2053	1.1 / 6.7 / 1.4 / 6.3		**19** TU 0153 / 0747 / 1408 / 1959	1.7 / 6.2 / 1.9 / 6.0
5 TU 0322 / 0917 / 1548 / 2143	1.6 / 6.1 / 2.0 / 5.8		**20** W 0229 / 0822 / 1446 / 2037	2.0 / 5.9 / 2.2 / 5.7
6 W 0415 / 1013 / 1645 / 2246	2.2 / 5.5 / 2.5 / 5.4		**21** TH 0312 / 0906 / 1534 / 2129	2.4 / 5.5 / 2.5 / 5.4
7 TH 0521 / 1129 / 1758	2.6 / 5.1 / 2.8		**22** F 0408 / 1010 / 1636 / 2244	2.7 / 5.2 / 2.8 / 5.1
8 F 0005 / 0646 / 1309 / 1929	5.2 / 2.8 / 5.0 / 2.8		**23** SA 0523 / 1142 / 1801	2.8 / 5.0 / 2.9
9 SA 0150 / 0813 / 1430 / 2043	5.3 / 2.6 / 5.3 / 2.5		**24** SU 0027 / 0658 / 1320 / 1932	5.2 / 2.7 / 5.3 / 2.6
10 SU 0253 / 0914 / 1522 / 2135	5.7 / 2.2 / 5.7 / 2.2		**25** M 0153 / 0818 / 1431 / 2043	5.6 / 2.2 / 5.8 / 2.0
11 M 0340 / 1000 / 1603 / 2217	6.0 / 1.9 / 6.0 / 1.8		**26** TU 0256 / 0919 / 1526 / 2138	6.2 / 1.5 / 6.4 / 1.4
12 TU 0418 / 1037 / 1637 / 2253	6.3 / 1.6 / 6.2 / 1.6		**27** W 0348 / 1010 / 1614 / 2228	6.8 / 0.9 / 6.9 / 0.9
13 W 0451 / 1111 / 1708 / 2325	6.5 / 1.4 / 6.4 / 1.4		**28** TH ○ 0435 / 1058 / 1659 / 2314	7.3 / 0.5 / 7.3 / 0.5
14 TH ● 0521 / 1141 / 1736 / 2356	6.7 / 1.3 / 6.6 / 1.3		**29** F 0520 / 1143 / 1742	7.6 / 0.3 / 7.5
15 F 0551 / 1210 / 1804	6.8 / 1.2 / 6.6		**30** SA 0000 / 0603 / 1226 / 1823	0.3 / 7.7 / 0.3 / 7.5
			31 SU 0045 / 0644 / 1308 / 1903	0.4 / 7.5 / 0.5 / 7.3

APRIL

Time	m		Time	m
1 M 0128 / 0724 / 1350 / 1943	0.7 / 7.1 / 1.0 / 6.9		**16** TU 0057 / 0651 / 1310 / 1903	1.4 / 6.5 / 1.6 / 6.4
2 TU 0211 / 0805 / 1432 / 2025	1.1 / 6.6 / 1.5 / 6.4		**17** W 0130 / 0724 / 1344 / 1937	1.6 / 6.2 / 1.8 / 6.2
3 W 0256 / 0849 / 1519 / 2112	1.7 / 6.0 / 2.1 / 5.8		**18** TH 0208 / 0802 / 1424 / 2018	1.9 / 5.9 / 2.1 / 5.8
4 TH 0348 / 0943 / 1614 / 2215	2.2 / 5.4 / 2.6 / 5.3		**19** F 0254 / 0850 / 1514 / 2112	2.2 / 5.5 / 2.5 / 5.5
5 F 0451 / 1059 / 1726 / 2340	2.7 / 5.0 / 3.0 / 5.1		**20** SA 0351 / 0957 / 1618 / 2227	2.5 / 5.2 / 2.7 / 5.3
6 SA 0615 / 1241 / 1859	2.9 / 4.9 / 3.0		**21** SU 0507 / 1127 / 1742	2.6 / 5.1 / 2.8
7 SU 0119 / 0744 / 1404 / 2016	5.2 / 2.7 / 5.2 / 2.7		**22** M 0012 / 0637 / 1258 / 1909	5.4 / 2.5 / 5.4 / 2.5
8 M 0224 / 0845 / 1455 / 2108	5.5 / 2.3 / 5.6 / 2.3		**23** TU 0128 / 0755 / 1406 / 2018	5.7 / 2.0 / 5.9 / 2.0
9 TU 0310 / 0930 / 1534 / 2148	5.9 / 2.0 / 5.9 / 1.9		**24** W 0231 / 0855 / 1501 / 2114	6.3 / 1.4 / 6.4 / 1.4
10 W 0347 / 1007 / 1607 / 2223	6.2 / 1.7 / 6.2 / 1.7		**25** TH 0324 / 0947 / 1550 / 2204	6.8 / 0.9 / 6.9 / 0.9
11 TH 0421 / 1040 / 1637 / 2255	6.4 / 1.5 / 6.4 / 1.5		**26** F 0412 / 1034 / 1635 / 2251	7.2 / 0.6 / 7.2 / 0.6
12 F ● 0452 / 1110 / 1706 / 2326	6.6 / 1.3 / 6.6 / 1.4		**27** SA ○ 0457 / 1119 / 1718 / 2336	7.4 / 0.5 / 7.4 / 0.5
13 SA 0522 / 1140 / 1735 / 2357	6.7 / 1.3 / 6.6 / 1.3		**28** SU 0540 / 1202 / 1759	7.4 / 0.5 / 7.3
14 SU 0551 / 1210 / 1803	6.7 / 1.3 / 6.7		**29** M 0023 / 0621 / 1244 / 1839	0.6 / 7.2 / 0.8 / 7.1
15 M 0026 / 0621 / 1239 / 1832	1.3 / 6.7 / 1.4 / 6.6		**30** TU 0106 / 0702 / 1326 / 1920	0.9 / 6.9 / 1.2 / 6.8

TIME ZONE -0100
(French Standard Time)
Subtract 1 hour for UT
For French Summer Time add
ONE hour in **non-shaded areas**

FRANCE – BREST
LAT 48°23'N   LONG 4°30'W
TIMES AND HEIGHTS OF HIGH AND LOW WATERS

YEAR **2002**

MAY

Time	m	Time	m
1 W 0149 / 0743 / 1408 / 2002	1.3 / 6.4 / 1.7 / 6.3	**16** TH 0115 / 0711 / 1329 / 1926	1.6 / 6.2 / 1.8 / 6.3
2 TH 0234 / 0827 / 1454 / 2050	1.7 / 5.9 / 2.2 / 5.8	**17** F 0158 / 0755 / 1414 / 2012	1.8 / 5.9 / 2.0 / 6.0
3 F 0324 / 0920 / 1547 / 2149	2.2 / 5.4 / 2.6 / 5.4	**18** SA 0247 / 0848 / 1506 / 2109	2.0 / 5.6 / 2.3 / 5.7
4 SA 0423 / 1028 / 1653 / 2303	2.6 / 5.0 / 2.9 / 5.2	**19** SU 0345 / 0954 / 1610 / 2220	2.2 / 5.4 / 2.5 / 5.6
5 SU 0535 / 1153 / 1813	2.8 / 4.9 / 3.0	**20** M 0457 / 1113 / 1726 / 2340	2.3 / 5.4 / 2.5 / 5.6
6 M 0028 / 0654 / 1314 / 1929	5.2 / 2.7 / 5.1 / 2.8	**21** TU 0615 / 1230 / 1842	2.2 / 5.6 / 2.3
7 TU 0136 / 0759 / 1410 / 2024	5.4 / 2.5 / 5.4 / 2.4	**22** W 0059 / 0727 / 1337 / 1949	5.9 / 1.9 / 6.0 / 1.9
8 W 0226 / 0847 / 1452 / 2108	5.7 / 2.2 / 5.7 / 2.1	**23** TH 0202 / 0827 / 1433 / 2048	6.3 / 1.5 / 6.4 / 1.5
9 TH 0307 / 0927 / 1529 / 2146	6.0 / 1.9 / 6.0 / 1.9	**24** F 0258 / 0921 / 1524 / 2140	6.6 / 1.2 / 6.7 / 1.1
10 F 0344 / 1003 / 1602 / 2221	6.2 / 1.7 / 6.3 / 1.6	**25** SA 0348 / 1010 / 1611 / 2229	6.9 / 1.0 / 6.9 / 0.9
11 SA 0419 / 1037 / 1634 / 2255	6.4 / 1.5 / 6.4 / 1.5	**26** SU 0435 / 1056 / 1655 / ○ 2316	7.0 / 0.9 / 7.1 / 0.8
12 SU 0452 / 1110 / 1706 / ● 2328	6.5 / 1.4 / 6.6 / 1.4	**27** M 0520 / 1141 / 1738	7.0 / 1.0 / 7.0
13 M 0524 / 1142 / 1738	6.6 / 1.4 / 6.6	**28** TU 0000 / 0602 / 1223 / 1820	0.9 / 6.8 / 1.1 / 6.9
14 TU 0002 / 0557 / 1215 / 1810	1.4 / 6.6 / 1.4 / 6.6	**29** W 0047 / 0644 / 1305 / 1902	1.1 / 6.5 / 1.4 / 6.6
15 W 0037 / 0632 / 1250 / 1846	1.4 / 6.4 / 1.6 / 6.5	**30** TH 0130 / 0725 / 1348 / 1944	1.4 / 6.2 / 1.8 / 6.3
		31 F 0214 / 0809 / 1432 / 2030	1.7 / 5.8 / 2.1 / 5.9

JUNE

Time	m	Time	m
1 SA 0300 / 0856 / 1520 / 2121	2.1 / 5.5 / 2.5 / 5.6	**16** SU 0243 / 0846 / 1501 / 2105	1.7 / 5.9 / 1.9 / 6.1
2 SU 0351 / 0951 / 1614 / 2220	2.4 / 5.2 / 2.7 / 5.4	**17** M 0338 / 0945 / 1559 / 2206	1.8 / 5.8 / 2.1 / 5.9
3 M 0448 / 1055 / 1717 / 2325	2.6 / 5.0 / 2.8 / 5.2	**18** TU 0441 / 1050 / 1705 / 2314	2.0 / 5.7 / 2.2 / 5.9
4 TU 0551 / 1204 / 1825	2.7 / 5.1 / 2.8	**19** W 0549 / 1158 / 1813	2.0 / 5.7 / 2.1
5 W 0032 / 0655 / 1308 / 1927	5.3 / 2.6 / 5.2 / 2.6	**20** TH 0027 / 0656 / 1304 / 1920	5.9 / 1.9 / 5.9 / 1.9
6 TH 0131 / 0752 / 1400 / 2019	5.5 / 2.4 / 5.5 / 2.4	**21** F 0133 / 0759 / 1405 / 2022	6.0 / 1.7 / 6.1 / 1.7
7 F 0221 / 0840 / 1445 / 2104	5.7 / 2.2 / 5.8 / 2.1	**22** SA 0234 / 0857 / 1501 / 2120	6.2 / 1.6 / 6.4 / 1.5
8 SA 0305 / 0923 / 1525 / 2145	5.9 / 1.9 / 6.0 / 1.9	**23** SU 0329 / 0950 / 1552 / 2212	6.4 / 1.4 / 6.6 / 1.3
9 SU 0345 / 1002 / 1603 / 2225	6.1 / 1.7 / 6.3 / 1.7	**24** M 0419 / 1039 / 1639 / ○ 2301	6.5 / 1.3 / 6.7 / 1.2
10 M 0424 / 1041 / 1640 / 2303	6.3 / 1.6 / 6.4 / 1.5	**25** TU 0505 / 1124 / 1723 / 2346	6.5 / 1.3 / 6.7 / 1.2
11 TU 0502 / 1119 / 1717 / ● 2342	6.4 / 1.5 / 6.5 / 1.4	**26** W 0548 / 1207 / 1805	6.5 / 1.4 / 6.5
12 W 0541 / 1157 / 1756	6.4 / 1.5 / 6.6	**27** TH 0031 / 0629 / 1248 / 1846	1.3 / 6.4 / 1.5 / 6.6
13 TH 0024 / 0622 / 1238 / 1837	1.4 / 6.4 / 1.5 / 6.6	**28** F 0112 / 0708 / 1328 / 1926	1.4 / 6.2 / 1.7 / 6.4
14 F 0107 / 0705 / 1321 / 1921	1.4 / 6.3 / 1.6 / 6.5	**29** SA 0152 / 0747 / 1408 / 2006	1.6 / 5.9 / 1.9 / 6.1
15 SA 0152 / 0753 / 1409 / 2010	1.5 / 6.1 / 1.8 / 6.3	**30** SU 0232 / 0826 / 1448 / 2048	1.9 / 5.7 / 2.2 / 5.9

JULY

Time	m	Time	m
1 M 0314 / 0909 / 1532 / 2133	2.1 / 5.5 / 2.4 / 5.6	**16** TU 0323 / 0924 / 1541 / 2144	1.5 / 6.1 / 1.7 / 6.2
2 TU 0359 / 0957 / 1622 / 2224	2.4 / 5.2 / 2.6 / 5.4	**17** W 0418 / 1021 / 1640 / 2244	1.7 / 5.9 / 1.9 / 6.0
3 W 0450 / 1054 / 1719 / 2323	2.6 / 5.1 / 2.8 / 5.2	**18** TH 0519 / 1125 / 1744 / 2351	2.0 / 5.7 / 2.1 / 5.8
4 TH 0548 / 1158 / 1821	2.7 / 5.1 / 2.8	**19** F 0625 / 1233 / 1853	2.1 / 5.7 / 2.2
5 F 0028 / 0650 / 1302 / 1924	5.3 / 2.6 / 5.2 / 2.6	**20** SA 0108 / 0734 / 1343 / 2003	5.7 / 2.1 / 5.8 / 2.1
6 SA 0130 / 0750 / 1359 / 2021	5.4 / 2.5 / 5.5 / 2.4	**21** SU 0218 / 0840 / 1446 / 2107	5.8 / 2.0 / 6.0 / 1.9
7 SU 0226 / 0843 / 1450 / 2111	5.6 / 2.2 / 5.8 / 2.1	**22** M 0319 / 0937 / 1541 / 2202	6.0 / 1.8 / 6.3 / 1.6
8 M 0315 / 0931 / 1535 / 2158	5.8 / 2.0 / 6.1 / 1.8	**23** TU 0410 / 1027 / 1629 / 2251	6.1 / 1.7 / 6.5 / 1.5
9 TU 0401 / 1016 / 1619 / 2242	6.1 / 1.7 / 6.3 / 1.6	**24** W 0455 / 1112 / 1712 / ○ 2334	6.3 / 1.5 / 6.6 / 1.3
10 W 0445 / 1100 / 1702 / ● 2326	6.3 / 1.5 / 6.6 / 1.3	**25** TH 0535 / 1152 / 1751	6.3 / 1.5 / 6.7
11 TH 0529 / 1144 / 1745	6.5 / 1.4 / 6.7	**26** F 0013 / 0612 / 1230 / 1828	1.3 / 6.3 / 1.5 / 6.6
12 F 0013 / 0613 / 1228 / 1829	1.2 / 6.6 / 1.3 / 6.8	**27** SA 0051 / 0646 / 1305 / 1903	1.4 / 6.3 / 1.6 / 6.5
13 SA 0058 / 0658 / 1313 / 1914	1.1 / 6.6 / 1.2 / 6.8	**28** SU 0126 / 0719 / 1340 / 1936	1.5 / 6.2 / 1.7 / 6.3
14 SU 0144 / 0744 / 1400 / 2001	1.1 / 6.5 / 1.3 / 6.7	**29** M 0200 / 0752 / 1414 / 2010	1.7 / 6.0 / 1.9 / 6.1
15 M 0232 / 0833 / 1449 / 2051	1.2 / 6.3 / 1.5 / 6.5	**30** TU 0234 / 0826 / 1449 / 2046	1.9 / 5.7 / 2.2 / 5.8
		31 W 0310 / 0902 / 1529 / 2126	2.2 / 5.5 / 2.4 / 5.5

AUGUST

Time	m	Time	m
1 TH 0352 / 0947 / 1616 / 2216	2.5 / 5.3 / 2.7 / 5.3	**16** F 0449 / 1052 / 1716 / 2322	2.2 / 5.6 / 2.3 / 5.5
2 F 0443 / 1046 / 1715 / 2321	2.7 / 5.1 / 2.8 / 5.1	**17** SA 0557 / 1207 / 1831	2.5 / 5.5 / 2.5
3 SA 0547 / 1159 / 1826	2.8 / 5.1 / 2.9	**18** SU 0051 / 0716 / 1329 / 1952	5.3 / 2.5 / 5.5 / 2.4
4 SU 0038 / 0659 / 1314 / 1939	5.1 / 2.8 / 5.2 / 2.7	**19** M 0213 / 0831 / 1439 / 2101	5.5 / 2.4 / 5.8 / 2.1
5 M 0151 / 0808 / 1418 / 2042	5.3 / 2.5 / 5.5 / 2.3	**20** TU 0315 / 0930 / 1533 / 2155	5.8 / 2.1 / 6.1 / 1.8
6 TU 0252 / 0906 / 1513 / 2136	5.6 / 2.2 / 5.9 / 1.9	**21** W 0403 / 1017 / 1618 / 2239	6.0 / 1.8 / 6.4 / 1.5
7 W 0343 / 0956 / 1602 / 2225	6.0 / 1.8 / 6.3 / 1.5	**22** TH 0443 / 1058 / 1657 / ○ 2318	6.3 / 1.6 / 6.6 / 1.4
8 TH 0431 / 1044 / 1647 / ● 2311	6.4 / 1.4 / 6.7 / 1.1	**23** F 0518 / 1135 / 1732 / 2353	6.4 / 1.5 / 6.7 / 1.4
9 F 0516 / 1129 / 1732	6.7 / 1.1 / 7.0	**24** SA 0550 / 1208 / 1804	6.5 / 1.4 / 6.7
10 SA 0001 / 0600 / 1214 / 1816	0.8 / 6.9 / 0.9 / 7.2	**25** SU 0026 / 0619 / 1239 / 1834	1.3 / 6.5 / 1.5 / 6.7
11 SU 0044 / 0643 / 1258 / 1859	0.7 / 7.0 / 0.8 / 7.2	**26** M 0056 / 0648 / 1309 / 1904	1.4 / 6.4 / 1.6 / 6.5
12 M 0128 / 0726 / 1343 / 1943	0.7 / 6.9 / 0.9 / 7.1	**27** TU 0126 / 0717 / 1339 / 1933	1.6 / 6.2 / 1.8 / 6.3
13 TU 0213 / 0811 / 1429 / 2029	0.9 / 6.7 / 1.2 / 6.8	**28** W 0155 / 0745 / 1410 / 2004	1.8 / 6.0 / 2.0 / 6.0
14 W 0300 / 0857 / 1518 / 2118	1.3 / 6.4 / 1.5 / 6.4	**29** TH 0227 / 0816 / 1444 / 2037	2.1 / 5.8 / 2.3 / 5.7
15 TH 0351 / 0949 / 1613 / 2214	1.7 / 6.0 / 1.9 / 5.9	**30** F 0303 / 0854 / 1525 / 2120	2.4 / 5.5 / 2.6 / 5.4
		31 SA 0349 / 0945 / 1619 / 2221	2.7 / 5.2 / 2.9 / 5.1

Chart Datum: 3·64 metres below IGN Datum

TIME ZONE -0100
(French Standard Time)
Subtract 1 hour for UT
For French Summer Time add ONE hour in **non-shaded areas**

FRANCE – BREST

LAT 48°23′N   LONG 4°30′W

TIMES AND HEIGHTS OF HIGH AND LOW WATERS

YEAR 2002

SEPTEMBER

Day	Time m	Time m	Time m	Time m
1 SU	0451 2.9	1100 5.0	1732 3.0	2348 4.9
2 M	0612 3.0	1233 5.1	1902 2.9	
3 TU	0124 5.2	0738 2.7	1353 5.4	2019 2.6
4 W	0233 5.6	0844 2.3	1453 6.0	2117 1.9
5 TH	0326 6.1	0937 1.8	1543 6.5	2206 1.3
6 F	0413 6.6	1025 1.2	1629 7.0	2252 0.9
7 SA	0457 7.0	1111 0.8	1713 7.4	● 2337 0.5
8 SU	0540 7.3	1155 0.6	1756 7.6	
9 M	0024 0.4	0622 7.4	1239 0.5	1839 7.6
10 TU	0107 0.5	0703 7.2	1322 0.7	1921 7.4
11 W	0150 0.8	0745 6.9	1407 1.0	2004 6.9
12 TH	0235 1.3	0829 6.5	1454 1.5	2050 6.3
13 F	0323 1.9	0919 6.0	1548 2.0	2145 5.7
14 SA	0420 2.4	1023 5.5	1652 2.5	2259 5.2
15 SU	0533 2.8	1147 5.3	1814 2.7	
16 M	0043 5.1	0703 2.8	1320 5.4	1944 2.6
17 TU	0209 5.4	0821 2.5	1429 5.8	2050 2.2
18 W	0304 5.7	0916 2.2	1519 6.1	2139 1.8
19 TH	0346 6.1	1000 1.8	1559 6.4	2219 1.6
20 F	0422 6.3	1037 1.6	1635 6.6	2255 1.4
21 SA	0453 6.5	1110 1.5	1706 6.8	○ 2326 1.3
22 SU	0522 6.6	1141 1.4	1736 6.8	2356 1.3
23 M	0549 6.6	1210 1.4	1804 6.8	
24 TU	0024 1.4	0617 6.6	1238 1.5	1832 6.6
25 W	0052 1.5	0643 6.4	1306 1.7	1900 6.4
26 TH	0120 1.7	0711 6.3	1336 1.9	1928 6.2
27 F	0151 2.0	0740 6.0	1409 2.2	2001 5.8
28 SA	0226 2.4	0816 5.7	1450 2.5	2042 5.4
29 SU	0312 2.7	0905 5.3	1543 2.9	2142 5.1
30 M	0413 3.0	1020 5.1	1655 3.0	2314 4.9

OCTOBER

Day	Time m	Time m	Time m	Time m
1 TU	0537 3.1	1200 5.1	1832 2.9	
2 W	0102 5.2	0711 2.8	1328 5.5	1955 2.4
3 TH	0211 5.7	0821 2.3	1429 6.1	2054 1.8
4 F	0304 6.3	0915 1.7	1520 6.7	2143 1.2
5 SA	0350 6.8	1003 1.1	1607 7.2	2229 0.7
6 SU	0434 7.2	1048 0.7	1651 7.5	● 2314 0.4
7 M	0516 7.5	1133 0.5	1734 7.7	2358 0.4
8 TU	0557 7.5	1217 0.4	1816 7.6	
9 W	0043 0.5	0638 7.4	1300 0.7	1838 7.3
10 TH	0126 0.9	0720 7.0	1345 1.1	1940 6.8
11 F	0210 1.5	0803 6.5	1432 1.6	2027 6.2
12 SA	0258 2.1	0849 6.0	1526 2.2	2123 5.6
13 SU	0355 2.6	0959 5.5	1630 2.6	2239 5.1
14 M	0509 3.0	1125 5.3	1753 2.8	
15 TU	0025 5.0	0641 3.0	1257 5.4	1922 2.7
16 W	0147 5.3	0758 2.7	1404 5.7	2025 2.3
17 TH	0238 5.7	0850 2.3	1452 6.0	2111 2.1
18 F	0318 6.0	0932 2.0	1531 6.3	2150 1.7
19 SA	0352 6.3	1008 1.7	1605 6.5	2224 1.5
20 SU	0423 6.5	1041 1.5	1636 6.7	2255 1.4
21 M	0451 6.6	1111 1.4	1706 6.7	○ 2324 1.4
22 TU	0519 6.7	1141 1.5	1735 6.7	2353 1.4
23 W	0547 6.7	1210 1.5	1803 6.6	
24 TH	0022 1.6	0615 6.6	1240 1.7	1832 6.5
25 F	0052 1.8	0644 6.4	1311 1.9	1903 6.2
26 SA	0124 2.0	0716 6.2	1346 2.1	1938 5.9
27 SU	0202 2.3	0754 5.8	1429 2.4	2022 5.5
28 M	0250 2.6	0845 5.5	1523 2.7	2125 5.2
29 TU	0351 2.9	0959 5.3	1634 2.9	2254 5.0
30 W	0513 3.0	1132 5.3	1804 2.8	
31 TH	0033 5.3	0642 2.7	1257 5.6	1925 2.3

NOVEMBER

Day	Time m	Time m	Time m	Time m
1 F	0142 5.8	0752 2.2	1400 6.2	2025 1.8
2 SA	0236 6.4	0848 1.6	1453 6.7	2116 1.2
3 SU	0324 6.9	0938 1.1	1541 7.2	2204 0.8
4 M	0409 7.2	1025 0.8	1627 7.4	● 2249 0.6
5 TU	0452 7.4	1111 0.6	1712 7.5	2334 0.6
6 W	0534 7.5	1156 0.6	1755 7.4	
7 TH	0020 0.8	0617 7.3	1241 0.8	1838 7.1
8 F	0104 1.2	0659 7.0	1326 1.2	1922 6.6
9 SA	0148 1.7	0744 6.5	1414 1.7	2009 6.1
10 SU	0236 2.2	0834 6.0	1505 2.2	2103 5.6
11 M	0331 2.6	0935 5.6	1605 2.6	2211 5.2
12 TU	0438 2.9	1049 5.3	1717 2.9	2334 5.0
13 W	0557 3.0	1210 5.3	1836 2.7	
14 TH	0059 5.2	0713 2.8	1319 5.5	1941 2.5
15 F	0156 5.5	0810 2.5	1411 5.8	2031 2.2
16 SA	0239 5.8	0855 2.2	1453 6.1	2112 2.0
17 SU	0316 6.1	0933 2.0	1530 6.3	2148 1.8
18 M	0349 6.3	1008 1.8	1604 6.4	2222 1.6
19 TU	0421 6.5	1042 1.6	1637 6.5	2254 1.6
20 W	0452 6.6	1114 1.6	1709 6.5	○ 2326 1.6
21 TH	0523 6.6	1147 1.6	1741 6.5	2359 1.6
22 F	0554 6.6	1220 1.6	1814 6.4	
23 SA	0033 1.7	0627 6.5	1255 1.8	1850 6.2
24 SU	0109 1.9	0704 6.3	1334 2.0	1930 6.0
25 M	0151 2.2	0747 6.0	1419 2.2	2018 5.7
26 TU	0240 2.4	0840 5.8	1513 2.4	2118 5.4
27 W	0339 2.6	0945 5.6	1618 2.6	2232 5.3
28 TH	0450 2.7	1103 5.6	1734 2.5	2352 5.5
29 F	0608 2.5	1220 5.8	1848 2.2	
30 SA	0106 5.8	0718 2.2	1326 6.1	1952 1.8

DECEMBER

Day	Time m	Time m	Time m	Time m
1 SU	0204 6.3	0818 1.7	1425 6.5	2048 1.4
2 M	0257 6.7	0913 1.3	1517 6.8	2139 1.1
3 TU	0345 7.0	1004 1.0	1607 7.1	2228 1.0
4 W	0432 7.2	1052 0.9	1654 7.1	● 2314 1.0
5 TH	0517 7.2	1139 0.9	1739 7.0	2359 1.1
6 F	0601 7.1	1225 1.0	1824 6.8	
7 SA	0046 1.4	0645 6.9	1311 1.3	1908 6.5
8 SU	0131 1.7	0729 6.6	1356 1.6	1952 6.1
9 M	0216 2.0	0815 6.2	1443 2.0	2040 5.7
10 TU	0304 2.4	0905 5.8	1533 2.3	2132 5.4
11 W	0357 2.7	1001 5.5	1628 2.6	2233 5.2
12 TH	0458 2.9	1105 5.4	1730 2.7	2342 5.1
13 F	0605 2.9	1212 5.3	1836 2.7	
14 SA	0051 5.2	0710 2.8	1314 5.4	1936 2.6
15 SU	0148 5.5	0806 2.6	1406 5.6	2027 2.4
16 M	0234 5.7	0853 2.3	1452 5.9	2110 2.1
17 TU	0315 6.0	0935 2.1	1533 6.1	2150 1.9
18 W	0352 6.2	1014 1.9	1611 6.3	2228 1.8
19 TH	0429 6.4	1052 1.6	1648 6.4	○ 2304 1.7
20 F	0505 6.5	1129 1.6	1726 6.4	2341 1.6
21 SA	0541 6.6	1207 1.5	1804 6.4	
22 SU	0021 1.6	0619 6.6	1246 1.5	1844 6.4
23 M	0101 1.7	0700 6.5	1328 1.6	1926 6.2
24 TU	0145 1.8	0745 6.4	1413 1.7	2013 6.1
25 W	0232 2.0	0833 6.2	1503 1.9	2106 5.9
26 TH	0325 2.1	0928 6.0	1559 2.1	2205 5.7
27 F	0424 2.3	1031 5.9	1702 2.2	2312 5.7
28 SA	0532 2.3	1140 5.8	1811 2.2	
29 SU	0025 5.8	0642 2.2	1251 5.9	1919 2.0
30 M	0132 6.0	0750 2.0	1358 6.1	2022 1.8
31 TU	0233 6.3	0852 1.7	1459 6.3	2120 1.6

Chart Datum: 3·64 metres below IGN Datum

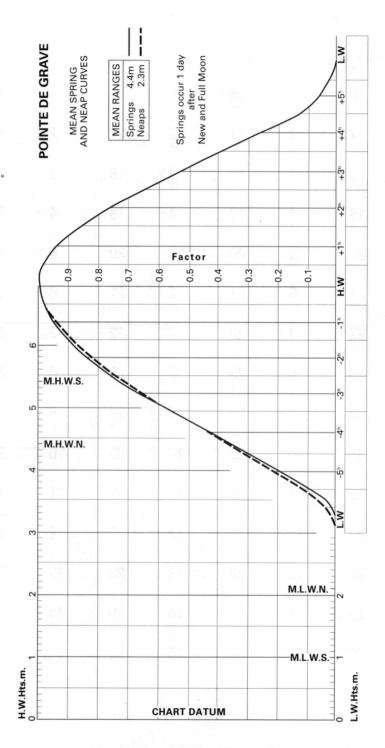

POINTE DE GRAVE

MEAN SPRING
AND NEAP CURVES

MEAN RANGES	
Springs	4.4m
Neaps	2.3m

Springs occur 1 day
after
New and Full Moon

Factor

0.9 0.8 0.7 0.6 0.5 0.4 0.3 0.2 0.1

L.W +5ʰ +4ʰ +3ʰ +2ʰ +1ʰ H.W -1ʰ -2ʰ -3ʰ -4ʰ -5ʰ L.W

H.W.Hts.m.

M.H.W.S.

M.H.W.N.

M.L.W.N.

M.L.W.S.

CHART DATUM

L.W.Hts.m.

TIME ZONE -0100
(French Standard Time)
Subtract 1 hour for UT
For French Summer Time add
ONE hour in **non-shaded areas**

FRANCE – POINTE DE GRAVE

LAT 45°34′N   LONG 1°04′W

TIMES AND HEIGHTS OF HIGH AND LOW WATERS

YEAR **2002**

JANUARY

Day	Time m	Time m	Time m	Time m
1 TU	0612 5.5	1223 1.1	1842 5.4	
2 W	0039 1.2	0659 5.5	1309 1.1	1931 5.3
3 TH	0125 1.3	0749 5.4	1357 1.2	2022 5.1
4 F	0213 1.4	0841 5.3	1446 1.3	2118 5.0
5 SA	0305 1.5	0939 5.1	1540 1.5	2219 4.8
6 SU	0403 1.7	1045 4.9	1640 1.7	2327 4.7
7 M	0507 1.8	1157 4.8	1747 1.8	
8 TU	0039 4.7	0616 1.9	1310 4.8	1856 1.9
9 W	0143 4.8	0726 1.8	1416 4.9	2001 1.8
10 TH	0240 4.9	0830 1.7	1513 4.9	2058 1.7
11 F	0330 5.0	0927 1.6	1602 5.0	2148 1.5
12 SA	0414 5.2	1016 1.5	1644 5.1	2233 1.5
13 SU	0454 5.3	1100 1.4	1722 5.1	● 2314 1.4
14 M	0532 5.3	1139 1.3	1757 5.1	2352 1.4
15 TU	0608 5.3	1216 1.3	1829 5.0	
16 W	0028 1.5	0641 5.3	1250 1.4	1900 5.0
17 TH	0103 1.5	0715 5.2	1324 1.5	1931 4.8
18 F	0137 1.6	0749 5.0	1358 1.6	2004 4.7
19 SA	0213 1.7	0826 4.9	1435 1.7	2041 4.5
20 SU	0252 1.9	0907 4.7	1514 1.9	2127 4.4
21 M	0336 2.1	0957 4.5	1601 2.1	2226 4.2
22 TU	0430 2.2	1059 4.4	1659 2.2	2342 4.2
23 W	0537 2.3	1212 4.3	1809 2.3	
24 TH	0058 4.3	0648 2.2	1325 4.4	1918 2.1
25 F	0202 4.5	0753 2.0	1429 4.6	2018 1.9
26 SA	0256 4.8	0851 1.8	1524 4.9	2113 1.7
27 SU	0345 5.1	0946 1.5	1614 5.2	2204 1.4
28 M	0432 5.4	1037 1.2	1701 5.4	○ 2253 1.2
29 TU	0518 5.6	1126 1.0	1747 5.5	2340 1.0
30 W	0604 5.7	1214 0.8	1833 5.6	
31 TH	0030 0.9	0650 5.8	1259 0.8	1918 5.6

FEBRUARY

Day	Time m	Time m	Time m	Time m
1 F	0115 0.9	0737 5.7	1344 0.9	2004 5.4
2 SA	0159 1.0	0824 5.5	1429 1.1	2052 5.2
3 SU	0246 1.2	0913 5.3	1515 1.3	2143 4.9
4 M	0336 1.5	1010 4.9	1608 1.6	2245 4.7
5 TU	0435 1.7	1122 4.7	1710 1.9	2358 4.5
6 W	0545 2.0	1245 4.5	1824 2.1	
7 TH	0119 4.5	0703 2.0	1402 4.5	1940 2.1
8 F	0227 4.6	0816 1.9	1507 4.6	2044 1.9
9 SA	0321 4.8	0916 1.7	1556 4.8	2137 1.7
10 SU	0406 5.0	1005 1.6	1636 4.9	2221 1.5
11 M	0443 5.2	1047 1.4	1709 5.0	2301 1.4
12 TU	0517 5.3	1124 1.3	1739 5.1	● 2336 1.3
13 W	0549 5.3	1157 1.3	1808 5.1	
14 TH	0008 1.3	0619 5.3	1228 1.3	1835 5.1
15 F	0041 1.3	0649 5.3	1258 1.3	1902 5.0
16 SA	0111 1.4	0719 5.2	1328 1.4	1930 4.9
17 SU	0142 1.5	0750 5.0	1359 1.5	2000 4.8
18 M	0214 1.6	0824 4.8	1431 1.7	2036 4.6
19 TU	0251 1.8	0904 4.6	1510 1.9	2121 4.4
20 W	0335 2.0	0958 4.4	1558 2.1	2227 4.2
21 TH	0436 2.2	1114 4.2	1706 2.3	
22 F	0008 4.2	0557 2.3	1245 4.3	1831 2.3
23 SA	0126 4.4	0718 2.1	1405 4.5	1948 2.1
24 SU	0233 4.7	0828 1.8	1507 4.8	2052 1.8
25 M	0328 5.1	0929 1.4	1559 5.2	2148 1.4
26 TU	0417 5.4	1022 1.1	1647 5.5	2238 1.1
27 W	0504 5.7	1111 0.8	1732 5.7	○ 2325 0.8
28 TH	0549 5.9	1157 0.6	1815 5.8	

MARCH

Day	Time m	Time m	Time m	Time m
1 F	0013 0.7	0633 6.0	1241 0.6	1858 5.7
2 SA	0057 0.7	0717 5.9	1323 0.7	1940 5.6
3 SU	0139 0.8	0800 5.6	1405 0.9	2022 5.3
4 M	0222 1.0	0844 5.3	1447 1.3	2106 5.0
5 TU	0309 1.4	0934 4.9	1535 1.7	2201 4.6
6 W	0403 1.7	1043 4.5	1634 2.0	2320 4.4
7 TH	0513 2.1	1220 4.3	1751 2.3	
8 F	0053 4.3	0640 2.2	1348 4.3	1918 2.3
9 SA	0210 4.5	0800 2.1	1455 4.5	2028 2.1
10 SU	0307 4.7	0900 1.8	1542 4.7	2120 1.8
11 M	0349 4.9	0946 1.6	1618 4.9	2203 1.6
12 TU	0424 5.1	1025 1.4	1648 5.0	2240 1.4
13 W	0455 5.3	1100 1.3	1715 5.1	2314 1.3
14 TH	0524 5.3	1131 1.2	1741 5.2	● 2345 1.2
15 F	0553 5.4	1201 1.2	1807 5.2	
16 SA	0015 1.2	0621 5.3	1230 1.2	1833 5.1
17 SU	0044 1.2	0649 5.3	1257 1.3	1859 5.1
18 M	0112 1.3	0718 5.1	1326 1.4	1928 4.9
19 TU	0143 1.4	0750 4.9	1357 1.5	2000 4.8
20 W	0217 1.6	0828 4.7	1433 1.7	2041 4.5
21 TH	0259 1.8	0919 4.4	1519 2.0	2141 4.3
22 F	0355 2.1	1036 4.2	1623 2.2	2312 4.2
23 SA	0517 2.2	1218 4.2	1754 2.3	
24 SU	0054 4.4	0650 2.1	1343 4.5	1921 2.1
25 M	0209 4.7	0807 1.8	1447 4.9	2030 1.8
26 TU	0308 5.1	0909 1.4	1540 5.2	2127 1.4
27 W	0358 5.5	1002 1.0	1626 5.5	2218 1.0
28 TH	0445 5.8	1050 0.7	1710 5.7	○ 2305 0.8
29 F	0529 5.9	1135 0.6	1752 5.8	2349 0.6
30 SA	0612 6.0	1217 0.6	1833 5.8	
31 SU	0035 0.6	0654 5.8	1258 0.7	1914 5.6

APRIL

Day	Time m	Time m	Time m	Time m
1 M	0116 0.8	0736 5.5	1338 1.0	1953 5.3
2 TU	0158 1.0	0817 5.2	1419 1.3	2035 5.0
3 W	0242 1.4	0903 4.7	1505 1.7	2124 4.7
4 TH	0334 1.8	1007 4.4	1601 2.1	2239 4.4
5 F	0442 2.1	1149 4.1	1718 2.4	
6 SA	0003 4.3	0609 2.3	1322 4.2	1848 2.4
7 SU	0138 4.4	0731 2.2	1427 4.4	2000 2.2
8 M	0236 4.6	0831 1.9	1513 4.6	2052 1.9
9 TU	0319 4.8	0916 1.7	1548 4.8	2134 1.7
10 W	0354 5.0	0954 1.5	1617 5.0	2211 1.5
11 TH	0425 5.2	1028 1.4	1644 5.1	2244 1.4
12 F	0455 5.3	1100 1.3	1711 5.2	● 2316 1.3
13 SA	0524 5.3	1130 1.2	1738 5.2	2347 1.2
14 SU	0553 5.3	1200 1.2	1805 5.2	
15 M	0017 1.2	0622 5.3	1228 1.3	1834 5.1
16 TU	0047 1.2	0653 5.1	1258 1.3	1904 5.0
17 W	0119 1.3	0727 4.9	1331 1.5	1939 4.9
18 TH	0155 1.5	0807 4.7	1409 1.7	2023 4.7
19 F	0238 1.7	0903 4.5	1457 1.9	2124 4.5
20 SA	0335 1.9	1022 4.3	1602 2.2	2249 4.4
21 SU	0456 2.1	1158 4.3	1730 2.2	
22 M	0026 4.5	0627 2.0	1319 4.6	1854 2.0
23 TU	0142 4.8	0743 1.7	1422 4.9	2003 1.7
24 W	0243 5.1	0844 1.3	1514 5.2	2101 1.3
25 TH	0335 5.5	0937 1.0	1601 5.5	2153 1.0
26 F	0422 5.7	1024 0.8	1645 5.7	2241 0.8
27 SA	0507 5.8	1109 0.7	1727 5.7	○ 2326 0.7
28 SU	0550 5.8	1152 0.7	1809 5.7	
29 M	0005 0.7	0632 5.6	1233 0.9	1849 5.5
30 TU	0054 0.9	0714 5.3	1312 1.1	1930 5.3

Chart Datum: 2·83 metres below IGN Datum

TIME ZONE -0100
(French Standard Time)
Subtract 1 hour for UT
For French Summer Time add
ONE hour in **non-shaded areas**

FRANCE – POINTE DE GRAVE
LAT 45°34′N   LONG 1°04′W
TIMES AND HEIGHTS OF HIGH AND LOW WATERS

YEAR **2002**

MAY

Day	Time m	Time m	Time m	Time m
1 W	0135 1.1	0754 5.0	1353 1.5	2011 5.0
16 TH	0103 1.3	0716 4.9	1314 1.5	1931 5.0
2 TH	0219 1.4	0839 4.6	1438 1.8	2059 4.7
17 F	0142 1.4	0803 4.7	1357 1.7	2020 4.8
3 F	0309 1.8	0936 4.3	1532 2.1	2203 4.5
18 SA	0230 1.6	0901 4.5	1448 1.8	2121 4.6
4 SA	0410 2.1	1101 4.1	1641 2.4	2326 4.3
19 SU	0329 1.8	1015 4.4	1554 2.0	2236 4.6
5 SU	0526 2.2	1233 4.1	1803 2.4	
20 M	0443 1.9	1137 4.5	1710 2.0	
6 M	0045 4.3	0644 2.2	1341 4.3	1915 2.3
21 TU	0000 4.6	0602 1.8	1251 4.6	1825 1.9
7 TU	0148 4.5	0747 2.0	1429 4.5	2010 2.0
22 W	0113 4.8	0713 1.6	1353 4.9	1933 1.6
8 W	0236 4.7	0835 1.8	1507 4.7	2055 1.8
23 TH	0216 5.1	0815 1.3	1447 5.1	2033 1.4
9 TH	0316 4.9	0915 1.6	1540 4.9	2134 1.6
24 F	0311 5.3	0910 1.1	1536 5.3	2127 1.1
10 F	0351 5.0	0951 1.5	1610 5.0	2210 1.5
25 SA	0401 5.4	0959 1.0	1621 5.4	2218 1.0
11 SA	0424 5.1	1025 1.4	1640 5.1	2244 1.4
26 SU	0447 5.5	1045 0.9	1705 5.5	O 2305 0.9
12 SU	0456 5.2	1059 1.3	1711 5.2	● 2318 1.3
27 M	0532 5.4	1128 1.0	1748 5.5	2350 0.9
13 M	0528 5.2	1131 1.3	1742 5.2	2352 1.2
28 TU	0615 5.3	1210 1.1	1830 5.4	
14 TU	0602 5.2	1204 1.3	1814 5.2	
29 W	0035 1.1	0656 5.1	1250 1.3	1912 5.2
15 W	0027 1.3	0637 5.1	1238 1.4	1850 5.1
30 TH	0116 1.2	0737 4.9	1331 1.5	1953 5.0
31 F	0159 1.5	0818 4.6	1415 1.8	2038 4.8

JUNE

Day	Time m	Time m	Time m	Time m
1 SA	0244 1.7	0905 4.4	1504 2.0	2129 4.6
16 SU	0228 1.4	0858 4.7	1445 1.6	2116 4.9
2 SU	0336 1.9	1006 4.2	1602 2.2	2230 4.4
17 M	0324 1.5	1002 4.6	1544 1.7	2221 4.8
3 M	0436 2.1	1120 4.1	1708 2.3	2339 4.3
18 TU	0427 1.6	1111 4.6	1649 1.8	2331 4.8
4 TU	0543 2.1	1233 4.2	1816 2.2	
19 W	0535 1.6	1220 4.6	1757 1.7	
5 W	0046 4.4	0648 2.1	1332 4.3	1916 2.1
20 TH	0044 4.8	0643 1.6	1324 4.8	1904 1.6
6 TH	0143 4.5	0743 1.9	1419 4.5	2007 2.0
21 F	0150 4.9	0747 1.5	1422 4.9	2008 1.5
7 F	0231 4.6	0830 1.8	1459 4.7	2052 1.8
22 SA	0250 5.0	0845 1.3	1515 5.1	2106 1.3
8 SA	0313 4.8	0912 1.6	1536 4.8	2134 1.6
23 SU	0344 5.1	0938 1.3	1603 5.2	2200 1.2
9 SU	0353 4.9	0951 1.5	1611 5.0	2213 1.5
24 M	0433 5.1	1026 1.2	1649 5.3	O 2249 1.1
10 M	0431 5.0	1030 1.4	1647 5.1	2253 1.3
25 TU	0519 5.1	1111 1.2	1733 5.3	2335 1.1
11 TU	0509 5.1	1108 1.3	1723 5.2	● 2332 1.3
26 W	0601 5.1	1153 1.3	1814 5.3	
12 W	0548 5.1	1146 1.3	1802 5.2	
27 TH	0019 1.2	0641 5.0	1233 1.3	1854 5.2
13 TH	0014 1.2	0630 5.0	1225 1.3	1844 5.1
28 F	0059 1.3	0718 4.8	1313 1.5	1933 5.0
14 F	0055 1.3	0714 5.0	1307 1.4	1929 5.1
29 SA	0139 1.4	0754 4.7	1352 1.6	2012 4.9
15 SA	0139 1.3	0803 4.8	1353 1.5	2019 5.0
30 SU	0219 1.6	0832 4.5	1434 1.8	2053 4.7

JULY

Day	Time m	Time m	Time m	Time m
1 M	0301 1.7	0915 4.3	1521 2.0	2140 4.5
16 TU	0310 1.3	0939 4.8	1526 1.5	2200 4.9
2 TU	0348 1.9	1009 4.2	1613 2.1	2235 4.4
17 W	0404 1.4	1040 4.6	1624 1.6	2305 4.8
3 W	0441 2.0	1115 4.1	1713 2.2	2337 4.3
18 TH	0505 1.6	1149 4.6	1729 1.7	
4 TH	0542 2.1	1224 4.2	1816 2.2	
19 F	0018 4.6	0613 1.7	1259 4.6	1840 1.7
5 F	0042 4.3	0644 2.1	1326 4.3	1916 2.1
20 SA	0131 4.6	0723 1.7	1405 4.7	1950 1.7
6 SA	0143 4.4	0742 2.0	1418 4.5	2010 1.9
21 SU	0239 4.7	0828 1.6	1503 4.8	2054 1.5
7 SU	0237 4.5	0833 1.8	1504 4.7	2059 1.7
22 M	0337 4.8	0924 1.5	1554 5.0	2150 1.4
8 M	0325 4.7	0920 1.6	1546 4.8	2146 1.6
23 TU	0427 4.9	1014 1.4	1639 5.1	2239 1.3
9 TU	0411 4.9	1005 1.5	1628 5.0	2232 1.4
24 W	0510 4.9	1059 1.3	1720 5.2	O 2323 1.2
10 W	0455 5.0	1049 1.3	1709 5.2	● 2317 1.2
25 TH	0548 4.9	1140 1.3	1758 5.2	
11 TH	0539 5.1	1133 1.2	1752 5.3	
26 F	0001 1.2	0622 4.9	1218 1.3	1833 5.2
12 F	0006 1.1	0623 5.1	1217 1.2	1837 5.3
27 SA	0041 1.3	0654 4.9	1253 1.4	1907 5.1
13 SA	0050 1.1	0709 5.1	1302 1.2	1923 5.3
28 SU	0115 1.3	0724 4.8	1327 1.5	1940 5.0
14 SU	0135 1.1	0756 5.1	1347 1.2	2012 5.2
29 M	0149 1.4	0755 4.6	1402 1.6	2015 4.8
15 M	0221 1.2	0845 4.9	1435 1.3	2103 5.1
30 TU	0224 1.6	0829 4.5	1439 1.7	2053 4.6
31 W	0300 1.7	0910 4.3	1520 1.9	2138 4.4

AUGUST

Day	Time m	Time m	Time m	Time m
1 TH	0342 1.9	1001 4.2	1609 2.1	2233 4.2
16 F	0435 1.7	1119 4.5	1703 1.8	2357 4.4
2 F	0434 2.1	1109 4.1	1712 2.2	2340 4.1
17 SA	0545 2.0	1241 4.4	1821 1.9	
3 SA	0541 2.2	1228 4.1	1824 2.2	
18 SU	0124 4.4	0705 2.0	1356 4.5	1941 1.9
4 SU	0056 4.2	0654 2.2	1338 4.3	1931 2.1
19 M	0237 4.5	0818 1.9	1458 4.7	2048 1.7
5 M	0205 4.3	0758 2.0	1435 4.5	2031 1.9
20 TU	0335 4.6	0916 1.7	1548 4.9	2142 1.5
6 TU	0303 4.6	0854 1.8	1525 4.8	2124 1.6
21 W	0420 4.8	1004 1.5	1629 5.1	2227 1.4
7 W	0354 4.8	0945 1.5	1611 5.1	2215 1.3
22 TH	0456 4.9	1046 1.4	1704 5.2	O 2307 1.3
8 TH	0441 5.0	1034 1.3	1655 5.3	● 2303 1.1
23 F	0528 5.0	1123 1.3	1736 5.2	2343 1.2
9 F	0526 5.2	1120 1.1	1740 5.5	2349 0.9
24 SA	0557 5.0	1157 1.2	1807 5.2	
10 SA	0610 5.3	1205 1.0	1824 5.6	
25 SU	0016 1.2	0624 4.9	1229 1.3	1836 5.2
11 SU	0037 0.8	0654 5.4	1249 0.9	1909 5.6
26 M	0047 1.3	0650 4.9	1259 1.4	1905 5.1
12 M	0121 0.8	0738 5.3	1333 1.0	1955 5.4
27 TU	0116 1.4	0717 4.8	1328 1.5	1935 4.9
13 TU	0204 1.0	0823 5.1	1417 1.1	2043 5.2
28 W	0145 1.5	0745 4.7	1359 1.6	2007 4.7
14 W	0248 1.2	0911 4.9	1504 1.3	2136 4.9
29 TH	0216 1.6	0818 4.5	1433 1.8	2045 4.5
15 TH	0337 1.4	1007 4.6	1558 1.6	2240 4.6
30 F	0251 1.9	0859 4.3	1513 2.0	2134 4.2
31 SA	0335 2.1	0959 4.1	1608 2.2	2245 4.1

Chart Datum: 2·83 metres below IGN Datum

TIME ZONE -0100
(French Standard Time)
Subtract 1 hour for UT
For French Summer Time add ONE hour in **non-shaded areas**

FRANCE – POINTE DE GRAVE

LAT 45°34'N   LONG 1°04'W

TIMES AND HEIGHTS OF HIGH AND LOW WATERS

YEAR 2002

SEPTEMBER

Time m	Time m
1 SU 0438 2.3 / 1129 4.0 / 1729 2.4	**16** M 0120 4.2 / 0651 2.3 / 1347 4.5 / 1933 2.1
2 M 0018 4.0 / 0606 2.3 / 1301 4.2 / 1857 2.2	**17** TU 0232 4.4 / 0806 2.1 / 1449 4.7 / 2038 1.8
3 TU 0140 4.2 / 0726 2.2 / 1410 4.5 / 2007 2.0	**18** W 0324 4.6 / 0901 1.9 / 1534 4.9 / 2126 1.6
4 W 0243 4.6 / 0831 1.9 / 1504 4.8 / 2105 1.6	**19** TH 0403 4.8 / 0946 1.6 / 1610 5.1 / 2207 1.4
5 TH 0336 4.9 / 0925 1.5 / 1552 5.2 / 2157 1.3	**20** F 0433 4.9 / 1025 1.4 / 1640 5.2 / 2243 1.3
6 F 0423 5.2 / 1015 1.2 / 1637 5.5 / 2244 1.0	**21** SA 0500 5.0 / 1059 1.3 / 1709 5.3 / ○2316 1.3
7 SA 0507 5.4 / 1102 1.0 / ●2330 0.8	**22** SU 0526 5.1 / 1131 1.3 / 1736 5.3 / 2346 1.3
8 SU 0549 5.6 / 1147 0.8 / 1805 5.8	**23** M 0551 5.1 / 1200 1.3 / 1804 5.3
9 M 0017 0.7 / 0632 5.6 / 1230 0.7 / 1849 5.8	**24** TU 0014 1.3 / 0616 5.0 / 1229 1.3 / 1831 5.2
10 TU 0059 0.7 / 0714 5.5 / 1312 0.8 / 1933 5.6	**25** W 0042 1.4 / 0641 4.9 / 1256 1.6 / 1859 5.0
11 W 0140 0.9 / 0756 5.2 / 1355 1.0 / 2020 5.3	**26** TH 0109 1.5 / 0708 4.8 / 1325 1.6 / 1929 4.8
12 TH 0223 1.2 / 0841 5.0 / 1440 1.3 / 2111 4.9	**27** F 0139 1.6 / 0738 4.7 / 1356 1.7 / 2003 4.6
13 F 0309 1.6 / 0936 4.7 / 1533 1.7 / 2217 4.5	**28** SA 0213 1.8 / 0815 4.5 / 1435 2.0 / 2050 4.3
14 SA 0406 2.0 / 1053 4.4 / 1639 2.0 / 2347 4.3	**29** SU 0256 2.1 / 0911 4.2 / 1525 2.2 / 2206 4.1
15 SU 0521 2.2 / 1227 4.3 / 1806 2.2	**30** M 0355 2.3 / 1044 4.1 / 1643 2.4 / 2348 4.1

OCTOBER

Time m	Time m
1 TU 0526 2.4 / 1227 4.2 / 1826 2.3	**16** W 0210 4.4 / 0741 2.2 / 1423 4.7 / 2013 2.0
2 W 0118 4.3 / 0656 2.3 / 1343 4.6 / 1943 2.0	**17** TH 0258 4.6 / 0835 1.9 / 1507 4.9 / 2059 1.7
3 TH 0221 4.7 / 0804 1.9 / 1440 5.0 / 2042 1.6	**18** F 0333 4.8 / 0918 1.7 / 1541 5.1 / 2137 1.5
4 F 0312 5.0 / 0901 1.5 / 1530 5.3 / 2133 1.2	**19** SA 0401 5.0 / 0956 1.6 / 1610 5.2 / 2212 1.4
5 SA 0358 5.4 / 0951 1.2 / 1615 5.7 / 2220 0.9	**20** SU 0427 5.1 / 1030 1.4 / 1638 5.3 / 2244 1.4
6 SU 0442 5.6 / 1038 0.9 / 1659 5.9 / ●2305 0.7	**21** M 0454 5.1 / 1101 1.4 / 1707 5.3 / ○2313 1.3
7 M 0524 5.7 / 1124 0.7 / 1743 5.9 / 2348 0.7	**22** TU 0520 5.2 / 1131 1.4 / 1735 5.3 / 2342 1.4
8 TU 0606 5.7 / 1207 0.7 / 1826 5.8	**23** W 0546 5.1 / 1200 1.4 / 1803 5.2
9 W 0034 0.8 / 0648 5.6 / 1250 0.8 / 1911 5.6	**24** TH 0011 1.4 / 0613 5.1 / 1229 1.5 / 1832 5.0
10 TU 0115 1.0 / 0730 5.3 / 1333 1.1 / 1957 5.2	**25** F 0040 1.5 / 0642 5.0 / 1259 1.6 / 1903 4.9
11 F 0157 1.4 / 0815 5.0 / 1418 1.4 / 2049 4.8	**26** SA 0112 1.7 / 0714 4.8 / 1333 1.7 / 1940 4.6
12 SA 0243 1.8 / 0910 4.7 / 1510 1.8 / 2158 4.4	**27** SU 0148 1.9 / 0754 4.6 / 1412 1.9 / 2031 4.4
13 SU 0340 2.1 / 1029 4.4 / 1616 2.1 / 2333 4.2	**28** M 0233 2.1 / 0853 4.4 / 1504 2.2 / 2149 4.2
14 M 0456 2.4 / 1205 4.4 / 1744 2.3	**29** TU 0334 2.3 / 1019 4.3 / 1619 2.3 / 2326 4.2
15 TU 0104 4.2 / 0627 2.4 / 1324 4.5 / 1911 2.2	**30** W 0459 2.4 / 1155 4.4 / 1755 2.2
	31 TH 0051 4.5 / 0624 2.2 / 1312 4.7 / 1912 1.9

NOVEMBER

Time m	Time m
1 F 0153 4.8 / 0733 1.9 / 1412 5.1 / 2013 1.6	**16** SA 0253 4.7 / 0841 1.9 / 1503 4.9 / 2100 1.7
2 SA 0245 5.1 / 0831 1.5 / 1504 5.4 / 2105 1.2	**17** SU 0325 4.9 / 0920 1.7 / 1537 5.1 / 2136 1.6
3 SU 0332 5.4 / 0924 1.2 / 1552 5.7 / 2153 1.0	**18** M 0355 5.0 / 0956 1.6 / 1609 5.2 / 2210 1.5
4 M 0416 5.6 / 1013 1.0 / 1637 5.8 / ●2239 0.8	**19** TU 0424 5.1 / 1030 1.5 / 1640 5.2 / 2242 1.5
5 TU 0459 5.7 / 1100 0.8 / 1722 5.8 / 2323 0.8	**20** W 0453 5.2 / 1104 1.5 / 1712 5.2 / ○2314 1.5
6 W 0542 5.7 / 1146 0.8 / 1807 5.7	**21** TH 0524 5.2 / 1136 1.4 / 1744 5.2 / 2346 1.5
7 TH 0003 1.0 / 0625 5.6 / 1230 0.9 / 1852 5.5	**22** F 0555 5.2 / 1210 1.5 / 1817 5.0
8 F 0051 1.2 / 0710 5.4 / 1313 1.2 / 1939 5.1	**23** SA 0020 1.6 / 0628 5.1 / 1244 1.5 / 1853 4.9
9 SA 0134 1.5 / 0756 5.1 / 1359 1.5 / 2030 4.8	**24** SU 0056 1.7 / 0706 5.0 / 1321 1.7 / 1936 4.7
10 SU 0220 1.9 / 0849 4.8 / 1449 1.8 / 2134 4.4	**25** M 0136 1.8 / 0751 4.8 / 1404 1.8 / 2030 4.5
11 M 0315 2.2 / 0957 4.6 / 1550 2.1 / 2258 4.2	**26** TU 0223 2.0 / 0849 4.7 / 1457 2.0 / 2139 4.4
12 TU 0424 2.4 / 1120 4.5 / 1706 2.3	**27** W 0323 2.1 / 1002 4.6 / 1605 2.1 / 2300 4.4
13 W 0022 4.2 / 0544 2.4 / 1237 4.5 / 1826 2.3	**28** TH 0436 2.2 / 1123 4.6 / 1723 2.0
14 TH 0127 4.4 / 0658 2.3 / 1338 4.6 / 1930 2.1	**29** F 0018 4.6 / 0551 2.1 / 1238 4.8 / 1836 1.9
15 F 0216 4.6 / 0755 2.1 / 1426 4.8 / 2019 1.9	**30** SA 0121 4.8 / 0659 1.8 / 1342 5.1 / 1940 1.6

DECEMBER

Time m	Time m
1 SU 0216 5.1 / 0801 1.6 / 1439 5.3 / 2036 1.4	**16** M 0247 4.7 / 0840 2.0 / 1503 4.8 / 2059 1.8
2 M 0306 5.3 / 0858 1.3 / 1531 5.5 / 2127 1.2	**17** TU 0324 4.9 / 0922 1.8 / 1542 4.9 / 2138 1.7
3 TU 0353 5.5 / 0951 1.1 / 1620 5.6 / 2215 1.1	**18** W 0359 5.0 / 1002 1.7 / 1619 5.0 / 2215 1.6
4 W 0439 5.6 / 1041 1.0 / 1707 5.6 / ●2302 1.1	**19** TH 0433 5.1 / 1040 1.5 / 1655 5.1 / ○2252 1.5
5 TH 0524 5.6 / 1128 1.0 / 1753 5.5 / 2347 1.2	**20** F 0508 5.2 / 1119 1.5 / 1732 5.1 / 2329 1.5
6 F 0610 5.6 / 1214 1.1 / 1839 5.3	**21** SA 0544 5.2 / 1157 1.4 / 1810 5.1
7 SA 0033 1.3 / 0655 5.4 / 1258 1.2 / 1924 5.1	**22** SU 0009 1.5 / 0623 5.2 / 1237 1.4 / 1851 5.0
8 SU 0116 1.5 / 0740 5.2 / 1343 1.5 / 2010 4.8	**23** M 0049 1.5 / 0704 5.2 / 1318 1.5 / 1935 4.9
9 M 0201 1.8 / 0826 5.0 / 1429 1.7 / 2059 4.5	**24** TU 0131 1.6 / 0750 5.1 / 1402 1.6 / 2025 4.8
10 TU 0250 2.0 / 0917 4.8 / 1519 2.0 / 2158 4.3	**25** W 0218 1.7 / 0842 5.0 / 1451 1.7 / 2122 4.7
11 W 0346 2.2 / 1017 4.6 / 1617 2.2 / 2309 4.2	**26** TH 0311 1.8 / 0942 4.9 / 1547 1.8 / 2227 4.6
12 TH 0449 2.3 / 1125 4.5 / 1723 2.3	**27** F 0412 1.9 / 1050 4.8 / 1651 1.8 / 2338 4.6
13 F 0019 4.3 / 0557 2.4 / 1232 4.5 / 1829 2.2	**28** SA 0518 1.9 / 1204 4.8 / 1759 1.8
14 SA 0118 4.4 / 0700 2.3 / 1331 4.6 / 1928 2.1	**29** SU 0048 4.7 / 0627 1.8 / 1314 4.9 / 1907 1.7
15 SU 0206 4.5 / 0754 2.1 / 1420 4.7 / 2017 2.0	**30** M 0150 4.9 / 0734 1.7 / 1419 5.0 / 2010 1.6
	31 TU 0247 5.1 / 0838 1.5 / 1517 5.2 / 2107 1.5

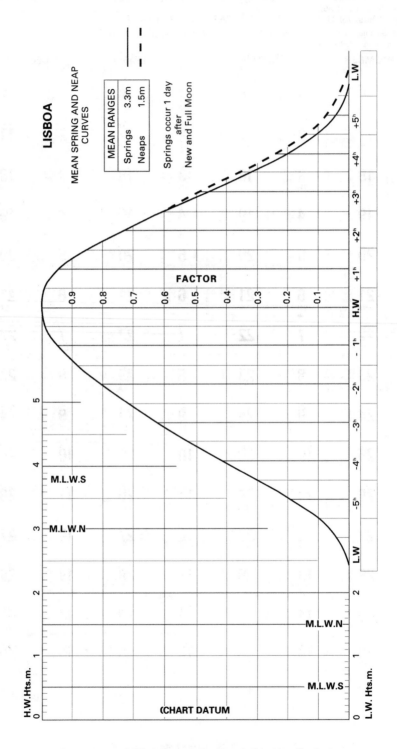

LISBOA

MEAN SPRING AND NEAP CURVES

MEAN RANGES	
Springs	3.3m
Neaps	1.5m

Springs occur 1 day after New and Full Moon

FACTOR

M.L.W.S
M.L.W.N
L.W

H.W.Hts.m.
L.W. Hts.m.

M.L.W.N
M.L.W.S

(CHART DATUM

TIME ZONE (UTC)
For Summer Time add ONE hour in **non-shaded areas**

PORTUGAL – LISBOA

LAT 38°42'N LONG 9°08'W

TIMES AND HEIGHTS OF HIGH AND LOW WATERS

YEAR 2002

JANUARY

Time	m		Time	m
1 TU 0423	3.8	**16** 0451	3.5
1016	0.4	1045	0.7
1650	3.6	W 1712	3.3
2230	0.6	2251	0.9
2 W 0509	3.8	**17** 0522	3.5
1103	0.5	1117	0.8
1738	3.6	TH 1742	3.2
2317	0.6	2325	0.9
3 TH 0557	3.8	**18** 0554	3.4
1152	0.6	1152	0.9
1828	3.5	F 1815	3.1
4 F 0007	0.8	**19** 0000	1.0
0648	3.7	0629	3.3
1244	0.7	SA 1229	1.0
1921	3.3	1853	3.0
5 SA 0101	0.9	**20** 0040	1.2
0743	3.5	0709	3.1
1341	0.9	SU 1312	1.1
2019	3.2	1938	2.9
6 SU 0201	1.0	**21** 0128	1.3
0844	3.3	0758	3.0
1445	1.0	M 1405	1.3
2125	3.1	2035	2.8
7 M 0310	1.1	**22** 0228	1.4
0953	3.2	0900	2.9
1554	1.1	TU 1509	1.4
2234	3.1	2144	2.7
8 TU 0423	1.1	**23** 0341	1.5
1104	3.2	1012	2.8
1703	1.1	W 1620	1.4
2339	3.2	2255	2.8
9 W 0534	1.1	**24** 0455	1.4
1209	3.2	1123	2.9
1805	1.0	TH 1726	1.3
		2359	3.0
10 TH 0039	3.3	**25** 0600	1.2
0636	1.0	1227	3.0
1308	3.3	F 1823	1.1
1900	0.9		
11 F 0132	3.4	**26** 0056	3.2
0730	0.9	0656	1.0
1400	3.3	SA 1324	3.2
1947	0.9	1915	0.9
12 SA 0220	3.5	**27** 0148	3.4
0817	0.8	0747	0.7
1447	3.3	SU 1416	3.4
2030	0.8	2003	0.7
13 SU 0303	3.6	**28** 0238	3.7
0859	0.7	0835	0.5
1529	3.3	M 1505	3.6
● 2109	0.8	O 2050	0.5
14 M 0343	3.6	**29** 0325	3.9
0937	0.7	0921	0.3
1606	3.3	TU 1553	3.7
2144	0.8	2135	0.4
15 TU 0419	3.6	**30** 0412	4.0
1011	0.7	1006	0.2
1640	3.3	W 1639	3.8
2218	0.8	2220	0.3
		31 0458	4.0
		1051	0.2
		TH 1724	3.8
		2305	0.4

FEBRUARY

Time	m		Time	m
1 F 0543	4.0	**16** 0528	3.5
1136	0.3	1121	0.7
1809	3.7	SA 1746	3.3
2350	0.5	2330	0.9
2 SA 0629	3.8	**17** 0600	3.4
1222	0.5	1153	0.9
1856	3.5	SU 1818	3.2
3 SU 0038	0.7	**18** 0004	1.0
0718	3.6	0635	3.3
1311	0.7	M 1228	1.0
1947	3.3	1855	3.1
4 M 0130	0.9	**19** 0042	1.1
0812	3.3	0715	3.1
1407	1.0	TU 1308	1.2
2045	3.1	1941	2.9
5 TU 0233	1.1	**20** 0130	1.3
0918	3.1	0806	2.9
1513	1.2	W 1402	1.4
2156	3.0	2041	2.8
6 W 0350	1.2	**21** 0238	1.5
1035	3.0	0915	2.8
1631	1.3	TH 1517	1.5
2312	3.0	2158	2.8
7 TH 0515	1.2	**22** 0406	1.5
1153	2.9	1040	2.8
1747	1.3	F 1642	1.4
		2321	2.9
8 F 0022	3.1	**23** 0530	1.3
0629	1.1	1201	3.0
1259	3.0	SA 1757	1.2
1850	1.1		
9 SA 0120	3.3	**24** 0032	3.2
0725	1.0	0637	1.0
1352	3.1	SU 1307	3.2
1938	1.0	1857	1.0
10 SU 0209	3.4	**25** 0131	3.5
0809	0.9	0732	0.7
1436	3.3	M 1402	3.5
2019	0.9	1949	0.7
11 M 0250	3.5	**26** 0223	3.8
0847	0.8	0820	0.4
1514	3.3	TU 1451	3.7
2055	0.8	2036	0.5
12 TU 0326	3.6	**27** 0311	4.0
0920	0.7	0906	0.2
1548	3.4	W 1537	3.9
● 2127	0.8	O 2121	0.3
13 W 0359	3.6	**28** 0356	4.2
0950	0.6	0949	0.1
1618	3.4	TH 1641	4.0
2158	0.6	2204	0.2
14 TH 0429	3.6		
1020	0.6		
1647	3.4		
2228	0.7		
15 F 0458	3.6		
1050	0.7		
1716	3.4		
2259	0.8		

MARCH

Time	m		Time	m
1 F 0440	4.2	**16** 0433	3.7
1032	0.1	1022	0.7
1704	4.0	SA 1648	3.6
2246	0.2	2233	0.7
2 SA 0524	4.2	**17** 0503	3.7
1114	0.3	1051	0.7
1746	3.9	SU 1718	3.5
2329	0.4	2303	0.8
3 SU 0607	4.0	**18** 0534	3.5
1156	0.5	1121	0.9
1829	3.7	M 1749	3.4
		2335	0.9
4 M 0013	0.6	**19** 0607	3.4
0652	3.7	1152	1.0
1240	0.8	TU 1824	3.3
1915	3.5		
5 TU 0102	0.9	**20** 0010	1.1
0742	3.3	0644	3.2
1331	1.1	W 1229	1.2
2009	3.2	1905	3.1
6 W 0202	1.2	**21** 0055	1.3
0845	3.0	0731	3.0
1435	1.4	TH 1318	1.4
2119	3.0	2000	3.0
7 TH 0323	1.4	**22** 0200	1.5
1010	2.8	0839	2.8
1602	1.5	F 1433	1.5
2246	3.0	2118	2.9
8 F 0502	1.4	**23** 0333	1.5
1140	2.8	1013	2.8
1733	1.5	SA 1610	1.5
		2252	3.0
9 SA 0006	3.0	**24** 0507	1.3
0620	1.3	1143	3.0
1249	3.0	SU 1735	1.3
1837	1.3		
10 SU 0105	3.2	**25** 0011	3.3
0712	1.1	0617	1.0
1338	3.1	M 1250	3.3
1924	1.2	1838	1.0
11 M 0151	3.4	**26** 0112	3.6
0752	0.9	0713	0.7
1417	3.3	TU 1344	3.6
2001	1.0	1931	0.7
12 TU 0229	3.5	**27** 0203	3.9
0825	0.8	0801	0.4
1451	3.4	W 1432	3.9
2034	0.9	2017	0.5
13 W 0302	3.6	**28** 0251	4.2
0855	0.7	0845	0.3
1522	3.5	TH 1516	4.1
2104	0.8	O 2101	0.3
14 TH 0333	3.7	**29** 0335	4.3
0924	0.6	0927	0.2
1551	3.6	F 1559	4.2
● 2134	0.7	2143	0.2
15 F 0403	3.8	**30** 0419	4.3
0953	0.6	1008	0.2
1620	3.6	SA 1640	4.1
2203	0.7	2225	0.3
		31 0501	4.2
		1049	0.4
		SU 1721	4.0
		2307	0.4

APRIL

Time	m		Time	m
1 M 0544	4.0	**16** 0510	3.6
1129	0.6	1053	0.9
1803	3.8	TU 1726	3.5
2351	0.7	2313	0.9
2 TU 0628	3.6	**17** 0545	3.4
1212	0.9	1126	1.0
1847	3.5	W 1802	3.4
		2351	1.1
3 W 0039	1.0	**18** 0625	3.3
0717	3.3	1205	1.2
1300	1.2	TH 1844	3.3
1938	3.3		
4 TH 0138	1.3	**19** 0039	1.3
0818	3.0	0715	3.1
1402	1.5	F 1257	1.4
2046	3.0	1940	3.1
5 F 0259	1.5	**20** 0145	1.4
0945	2.8	0825	2.9
1532	1.7	SA 1413	1.5
2216	3.0	2058	3.1
6 SA 0438	1.5	**21** 0316	1.4
1118	2.8	0958	2.9
1706	1.7	SU 1549	1.5
2338	3.0	2231	3.2
7 SU 0553	1.4	**22** 0444	1.3
1225	3.0	1124	3.1
1811	1.5	M 1712	1.4
		2348	3.4
8 M 0037	3.2	**23** 0553	1.0
0643	1.2	1228	3.4
1311	3.2	TU 1815	1.1
1856	1.3		
9 TU 0121	3.4	**24** 0048	3.7
0721	1.1	0648	0.7
1348	3.3	W 1320	3.7
1933	1.1	1907	0.8
10 W 0158	3.5	**25** 0140	3.9
0754	0.9	0736	0.5
1420	3.5	TH 1407	3.9
2006	1.0	1954	0.6
11 TH 0231	3.7	**26** 0227	4.1
0824	0.8	0821	0.4
1451	3.6	F 1452	4.1
2037	0.8	2039	0.4
12 F 0303	3.7	**27** 0313	4.2
0854	0.7	0903	0.3
1521	3.7	SA 1535	4.2
● 2107	0.8	O 2122	0.3
13 SA 0335	3.8	**28** 0357	4.2
0924	0.7	0944	0.4
1552	3.7	SU 1617	4.1
2138	0.8	2204	0.4
14 SU 0406	3.8	**29** 0440	4.0
0953	0.7	1025	0.5
1622	3.7	M 1659	4.0
2208	0.8	2247	0.5
15 M 0438	3.7	**30** 0523	3.8
1023	0.8	1105	0.8
1653	3.6	TU 1741	3.8
2239	0.9	2332	0.8

PORTUGAL – LISBOA

TIME ZONE (UTC)
For Summer Time add ONE hour in **non-shaded areas**

LAT 38°42′N   LONG 9°08′W

TIMES AND HEIGHTS OF HIGH AND LOW WATERS

MAY

Day	Time m	Time m	Time m	Time m		Day	Time m	Time m	Time m	Time m
1 W	0607 3.5	1147 1.0	1824 3.6			16 TH	0532 3.4	1110 1.0	1749 3.5	2342 1.0
2 TH	0020 1.0	0655 3.2	1234 1.3	1912 3.3		17 F	0617 3.3	1155 1.2	1836 3.4	
3 F	0116 1.3	0752 2.9	1332 1.6	2012 3.1		18 SA	0034 1.1	0711 3.1	1251 1.3	1934 3.3
4 SA	0228 1.5	0909 2.8	1452 1.7	2131 3.0		19 SU	0140 1.2	0820 3.0	1403 1.4	2047 3.2
5 SU	0352 1.5	1035 2.8	1618 1.7	2251 3.0		20 M	0259 1.3	0942 3.1	1527 1.4	2208 3.3
6 M	0504 1.5	1141 2.9	1725 1.6	2352 3.1		21 TU	0417 1.2	1057 3.2	1643 1.3	2320 3.4
7 TU	0557 1.3	1230 3.1	1815 1.4			22 W	0524 1.0	1200 3.4	1747 1.1	
8 W	0039 3.3	0640 1.1	1309 3.3	1856 1.2		23 TH	0021 3.6	0620 0.8	1253 3.6	1841 0.8
9 TH	0119 3.4	0716 1.0	1344 3.5	1932 1.1		24 F	0114 3.8	0710 0.6	1342 3.8	1931 0.6
10 F	0156 3.5	0750 0.9	1417 3.6	2006 0.9		25 SA	0204 3.9	0756 0.5	1428 3.9	2018 0.5
11 SA	0231 3.6	0822 0.8	1450 3.7	2039 0.9		26 SU	0251 3.9	0840 0.5	1513 4.0	○2103 0.5
12 SU	0306 3.7	0854 0.8	1523 3.7	●2112 0.8		27 M	0337 3.9	0922 0.6	1557 4.0	2148 0.5
13 M	0340 3.7	0926 0.8	1557 3.7	2146 0.8		28 TU	0422 3.8	1004 0.7	1640 3.9	2232 0.6
14 TU	0416 3.6	0958 0.8	1632 3.7	2221 0.9		29 W	0506 3.6	1045 0.9	1722 3.7	2316 0.8
15 W	0452 3.5	1032 0.9	1709 3.6	2259 0.9		30 TH	0550 3.4	1126 1.1	1804 3.5	
						31 F	0001 1.0	0633 3.1	1210 1.3	1847 3.3

JUNE

Day	Time m	Time m	Time m	Time m		Day	Time m	Time m	Time m	Time m
1 SA	0050 1.2	0721 3.0	1300 1.5	1935 3.1		16 SU	0030 0.9	0707 3.2	1245 1.1	1927 3.4
2 SU	0146 1.4	0819 2.8	1402 1.6	2033 3.0		17 M	0129 1.0	0808 3.2	1348 1.2	2031 3.4
3 M	0251 1.4	0928 2.8	1514 1.6	2143 3.0		18 TU	0236 1.0	0916 3.1	1459 1.2	2140 3.3
4 TU	0358 1.4	1037 2.8	1623 1.6	2250 3.0		19 W	0345 1.0	1025 3.2	1610 1.2	2250 3.4
5 W	0459 1.3	1135 3.0	1722 1.5	2347 3.1		20 TH	0452 1.0	1129 3.3	1717 1.1	2353 3.5
6 TH	0550 1.2	1222 3.1	1812 1.3			21 F	0552 0.9	1226 3.5	1817 0.9	
7 F	0035 3.2	0634 1.1	1303 3.3	1855 1.1		22 SA	0051 3.5	0646 0.8	1319 3.6	1912 0.8
8 SA	0117 3.3	0713 1.0	1342 3.4	1934 1.0		23 SU	0145 3.6	0735 0.7	1409 3.7	2003 0.7
9 SU	0158 3.4	0750 0.9	1419 3.6	2012 0.9		24 M	0235 3.6	0821 0.7	1456 3.8	○2050 0.6
10 M	0237 3.5	0826 0.9	1457 3.6	●2049 0.8		25 TU	0323 3.6	0905 0.7	1541 3.8	2135 0.6
11 TU	0317 3.5	0902 0.8	1536 3.7	2128 0.8		26 W	0408 3.5	0947 0.8	1624 3.7	2218 0.7
12 W	0358 3.5	0939 0.8	1616 3.7	2208 0.8		27 TH	0450 3.4	1027 0.9	1704 3.7	2258 0.8
13 TH	0440 3.5	1019 0.8	1658 3.7	2251 0.8		28 F	0530 3.3	1105 1.0	1741 3.5	2337 0.9
14 F	0525 3.4	1102 0.9	1743 3.6	2338 0.8		29 SA	0607 3.2	1144 1.1	1818 3.4	
15 SA	0613 3.3	1150 1.0	1832 3.5			30 SU	0017 1.0	0645 3.0	1225 1.2	1856 3.2

JULY

Day	Time m	Time m	Time m	Time m		Day	Time m	Time m	Time m	Time m
1 M	0101 1.2	0727 2.9	1312 1.4	1940 3.1		16 TU	0109 0.8	0745 3.3	1326 1.0	2008 3.5
2 TU	0151 1.3	0818 2.8	1408 1.5	2034 3.0		17 W	0206 0.9	0845 3.2	1428 1.1	2111 3.3
3 W	0249 1.3	0920 2.8	1514 1.5	2139 2.9		18 TH	0311 1.0	0951 3.2	1538 1.1	2220 3.3
4 TH	0353 1.4	1027 2.8	1621 1.5	2245 3.0		19 F	0420 1.1	1059 3.2	1652 1.1	2330 3.2
5 F	0455 1.3	1127 3.0	1723 1.4	2345 3.0		20 SA	0527 1.1	1204 3.3	1801 1.0	
6 SA	0549 1.2	1219 3.1	1816 1.3			21 SU	0035 3.3	0629 1.0	1303 3.4	1903 0.9
7 SU	0038 3.1	0636 1.1	1306 3.2	1904 1.1		22 M	0134 3.3	0722 0.9	1356 3.6	1955 0.8
8 M	0127 3.2	0719 1.0	1350 3.4	1948 0.9		23 TU	0226 3.4	0810 0.9	1444 3.7	2042 0.7
9 TU	0213 3.3	0801 0.9	1434 3.5	2031 0.8		24 W	0312 3.4	0852 0.8	1528 3.7	○2123 0.7
10 W	0259 3.4	0843 0.8	1519 3.7	●2114 0.7		25 TH	0353 3.5	0931 0.8	1607 3.7	2200 0.7
11 TH	0344 3.5	0926 0.7	1603 3.8	2157 0.6		26 F	0431 3.4	1007 0.8	1643 3.7	2235 0.7
12 F	0430 3.6	1009 0.7	1649 3.8	2242 0.5		27 SA	0504 3.4	1041 0.9	1715 3.6	2308 0.8
13 SA	0516 3.6	1054 0.7	1734 3.8	2328 0.6		28 SU	0536 3.3	1115 0.9	1746 3.5	2342 0.9
14 SU	0603 3.5	1141 0.7	1822 3.8			29 M	0607 3.2	1150 1.0	1819 3.4	
15 M	0017 0.6	0652 3.4	1231 0.8	1912 3.6		30 TU	0017 1.0	0642 3.1	1228 1.2	1856 3.2
						31 W	0058 1.1	0723 3.0	1312 1.3	1940 3.1

AUGUST

Day	Time m	Time m	Time m	Time m		Day	Time m	Time m	Time m	Time m
1 TH	0145 1.3	0814 2.9	1407 1.5	2035 2.9		16 F	0237 1.2	0919 3.2	1511 1.2	2156 3.1
2 F	0245 1.4	0917 2.8	1516 1.5	2143 2.9		17 SA	0352 1.3	1034 3.1	1636 1.3	2316 3.1
3 SA	0354 1.5	1028 2.8	1632 1.5	2256 2.9		18 SU	0512 1.3	1149 3.2	1757 1.2	
4 SU	0502 1.4	1135 3.0	1740 1.4			19 M	0029 3.1	0621 1.2	1253 3.4	1900 1.1
5 M	0003 3.0	0602 1.3	1234 3.2	1837 1.2		20 TU	0127 3.2	0715 1.0	1346 3.5	1948 0.9
6 TU	0101 3.1	0654 1.1	1326 3.4	1928 1.0		21 W	0216 3.4	0759 1.0	1431 3.7	2029 0.8
7 W	0154 3.3	0742 0.9	1416 3.6	2014 0.7		22 TH	0257 3.5	0838 0.9	1510 3.7	○2104 0.7
8 TH	0243 3.5	0828 0.7	1503 3.8	●2059 0.5		23 F	0333 3.5	0912 0.8	1545 3.8	2136 0.7
9 F	0330 3.7	0912 0.6	1549 4.0	2143 0.4		24 SA	0405 3.5	0944 0.8	1616 3.8	2206 0.7
10 SA	0415 3.8	0956 0.5	1634 4.1	2227 0.3		25 SU	0435 3.5	1015 0.8	1646 3.7	2236 0.7
11 SU	0500 3.8	1040 0.5	1719 4.1	2311 0.4		26 M	0503 3.5	1045 0.8	1715 3.6	2307 0.8
12 M	0544 3.8	1124 0.5	1804 4.0	2355 0.5		27 TU	0532 3.4	1117 0.9	1746 3.5	2338 0.9
13 TU	0630 3.7	1210 0.7	1851 3.8			28 W	0604 3.3	1150 1.1	1819 3.4	
14 W	0043 0.7	0718 3.5	1301 0.9	1942 3.5		29 TH	0012 1.1	0640 3.2	1227 1.3	1858 3.2
15 TH	0135 0.9	0813 3.3	1359 1.1	2042 3.3		30 F	0051 1.3	0723 3.0	1312 1.4	1946 3.0
						31 SA	0141 1.5	0818 2.9	1416 1.6	2050 2.9

TIME ZONE (UTC)
For Summer Time add ONE hour in **non-shaded areas**

PORTUGAL – LISBOA
LAT 38°42'N   LONG 9°08'W
TIMES AND HEIGHTS OF HIGH AND LOW WATERS

YEAR 2002

SEPTEMBER

Time m	Time m
1 0252 1.6 / 0933 2.9 / SU 1543 1.6 / 2213 2.8	**16** 0503 1.5 / 1137 3.2 / M 1753 1.3
2 0418 1.6 / 1055 3.0 / M 1709 1.5 / 2336 3.0	**17** 0022 3.1 / 0613 1.4 / TU 1240 3.4 / 1850 1.2
3 0534 1.4 / 1207 3.2 / TU 1815 1.2	**18** 0115 3.3 / 0702 1.2 / W 1329 3.5 / 1932 1.0
4 0042 3.2 / 0633 1.2 / W 1306 3.5 / 1909 0.9	**19** 0157 3.4 / 0742 1.1 / TH 1410 3.7 / 2007 0.9
5 0137 3.5 / 0724 0.9 / TH 1357 3.8 / 1956 0.7	**20** 0233 3.6 / 0816 0.9 / F 1445 3.8 / 2038 0.8
6 0226 3.7 / 0811 0.7 / F 1445 4.0 / 2041 0.4	**21** 0305 3.7 / 0848 0.8 / SA 1517 3.8 / ○ 2107 0.8
7 0311 3.9 / 0855 0.5 / SA 1530 4.2 / ● 2124 0.3	**22** 0335 3.7 / 0918 0.8 / SU 1547 3.8 / 2136 0.7
8 0355 4.0 / 0938 0.4 / SU 1614 4.3 / 2206 0.3	**23** 0404 3.7 / 0947 0.8 / M 1616 3.8 / 2205 0.8
9 0438 4.1 / 1020 0.3 / M 1658 4.3 / 2248 0.3	**24** 0432 3.7 / 1017 0.8 / TU 1646 3.7 / 2234 0.9
10 0521 4.0 / 1103 0.4 / TU 1742 4.1 / 2330 0.5	**25** 0501 3.6 / 1047 0.9 / W 1716 3.6 / 2303 1.0
11 0604 3.9 / 1147 0.6 / W 1827 3.9	**26** 0532 3.5 / 1118 1.1 / TH 1749 3.5 / 2334 1.1
12 0015 0.8 / 0650 3.6 / TH 1236 0.9 / 1917 3.6	**27** 0605 3.3 / 1152 1.2 / F 1825 3.3
13 0105 1.1 / 0743 3.4 / F 1334 1.1 / 2018 3.2	**28** 0009 1.3 / 0645 3.2 / SA 1234 1.4 / 1910 3.1
14 0207 1.4 / 0850 3.2 / SA 1452 1.4 / 2138 3.0	**29** 0055 1.5 / 0737 3.0 / SU 1335 1.6 / 2013 2.9
15 0331 1.6 / 1015 3.1 / SU 1629 1.5 / 2308 3.0	**30** 0204 1.7 / 0851 3.0 / M 1506 1.7 / 2143 2.9

OCTOBER

Time m	Time m
1 0342 1.7 / 1023 3.0 / TU 1642 1.6 / 2315 3.0	**16** 0001 3.1 / 0550 1.5 / W 1215 3.3 / 1823 1.3
2 0509 1.5 / 1143 3.3 / W 1753 1.3	**17** 0050 3.3 / 0637 1.3 / TH 1302 3.5 / 1903 1.1
3 0023 3.3 / 0612 1.2 / TH 1244 3.6 / 1847 0.9	**18** 0129 3.5 / 0715 1.2 / F 1340 3.6 / 1936 1.0
4 0117 3.6 / 0704 0.9 / F 1336 3.9 / 1934 0.6	**19** 0203 3.6 / 0749 1.0 / SA 1415 3.7 / 2007 0.9
5 0204 3.9 / 0750 0.6 / SA 1423 4.2 / 2018 0.4	**20** 0234 3.7 / 0820 0.9 / SU 1447 3.8 / 2037 0.8
6 0248 4.1 / 0834 0.4 / SU 1508 4.3 / ● 2100 0.3	**21** 0305 3.8 / 0851 0.8 / M 1518 3.8 / ○ 2107 0.8
7 0332 4.2 / 0916 0.3 / M 1552 4.4 / 2142 0.3	**22** 0334 3.8 / 0921 0.8 / TU 1548 3.8 / 2136 0.8
8 0414 4.2 / 0959 0.3 / TU 1636 4.3 / 2223 0.4	**23** 0404 3.7 / 0951 0.9 / W 1619 3.7 / 2205 0.9
9 0456 4.1 / 1042 0.4 / W 1720 4.1 / 2305 0.6	**24** 0434 3.7 / 1022 0.9 / TH 1651 3.6 / 2234 1.0
10 0540 4.0 / 1127 0.6 / TH 1805 3.8 / 2349 0.9	**25** 0506 3.6 / 1054 1.0 / F 1725 3.4 / 2306 1.1
11 0626 3.7 / 1216 0.9 / F 1856 3.5	**26** 0541 3.5 / 1130 1.2 / SA 1803 3.3 / 2342 1.3
12 0038 1.2 / 0718 3.5 / SA 1315 1.2 / 1957 3.2	**27** 0621 3.3 / 1214 1.4 / SU 1849 3.1
13 0140 1.5 / 0825 3.2 / SU 1435 1.5 / 2120 3.0	**28** 0029 1.5 / 0713 3.2 / M 1315 1.5 / 1954 2.9
14 0308 1.7 / 0951 3.1 / M 1613 1.5 / 2252 3.0	**29** 0138 1.6 / 0826 3.1 / TU 1441 1.6 / 2123 2.9
15 0442 1.7 / 1114 3.2 / TU 1731 1.4	**30** 0313 1.6 / 0957 3.1 / W 1613 1.4 / 2251 3.1
	31 0440 1.5 / 1117 3.3 / TH 1724 1.2 / 2358 3.4

NOVEMBER

Time m	Time m
1 0545 1.2 / 1218 3.6 / F 1820 0.9	**16** 0052 3.3 / 0640 1.2 / SA 1304 3.4 / 1901 1.0
2 0051 3.7 / 0639 0.9 / SA 1311 3.9 / 1909 0.6	**17** 0129 3.5 / 0717 1.1 / SU 1341 3.5 / 1935 0.9
3 0139 3.9 / 0726 0.6 / SU 1359 4.1 / 1953 0.4	**18** 0202 3.6 / 0751 1.0 / M 1416 3.6 / 2007 0.9
4 0224 4.1 / 0811 0.5 / M 1445 4.2 / ● 2037 0.4	**19** 0235 3.6 / 0824 0.9 / TU 1449 3.6 / 2039 0.8
5 0308 4.2 / 0856 0.4 / TU 1530 4.2 / 2119 0.4	**20** 0307 3.7 / 0857 0.9 / W 1523 3.6 / ○ 2110 0.8
6 0352 4.2 / 0939 0.4 / W 1615 4.1 / 2201 0.5	**21** 0339 3.7 / 0930 0.9 / TH 1557 3.6 / 2141 0.9
7 0435 4.1 / 1024 0.5 / TH 1701 3.9 / 2243 0.7	**22** 0413 3.7 / 1003 0.9 / F 1633 3.5 / 2213 0.9
8 0519 3.7 / 1110 0.7 / F 1747 3.7 / 2327 1.0	**23** 0448 3.6 / 1039 0.9 / SA 1710 3.4 / 2249 1.0
9 0605 3.7 / 1200 0.9 / SA 1837 3.4	**24** 0527 3.5 / 1119 1.0 / SU 1752 3.3 / 2329 1.2
10 0015 1.3 / 0656 3.5 / SU 1256 1.2 / 1935 3.1	**25** 0610 3.4 / 1206 1.2 / M 1841 3.1
11 0113 1.5 / 0756 3.2 / M 1407 1.4 / 2049 2.9	**26** 0019 1.3 / 0703 3.3 / TU 1305 1.3 / 1943 3.0
12 0230 1.7 / 0912 3.1 / TU 1529 1.5 / 2211 2.9	**27** 0124 1.4 / 0809 3.2 / W 1419 1.3 / 2100 3.0
13 0355 1.7 / 1030 3.1 / W 1644 1.5 / 2320 3.0	**28** 0244 1.5 / 0928 3.2 / TH 1538 1.3 / 2219 3.1
14 0505 1.6 / 1134 3.2 / TH 1740 1.3	**29** 0405 1.4 / 1044 3.3 / F 1650 1.1 / 2326 3.3
15 0011 3.2 / 0558 1.4 / F 1223 3.3 / 1824 1.2	**30** 0513 1.1 / 1149 3.5 / SA 1749 0.9

DECEMBER

Time m	Time m
1 0023 3.5 / 0611 0.9 / SU 1245 3.7 / 1842 0.7	**16** 0050 3.2 / 0643 1.2 / M 1305 3.3 / 1901 1.0
2 0114 3.7 / 0703 0.7 / M 1336 3.9 / 1930 0.6	**17** 0129 3.3 / 0723 1.0 / TU 1345 3.3 / 1938 0.9
3 0201 3.9 / 0752 0.5 / TU 1425 3.9 / 2015 0.5	**18** 0206 3.4 / 0801 0.9 / W 1424 3.4 / 2013 0.9
4 0248 4.0 / 0839 0.4 / W 1513 3.9 / ● 2100 0.5	**19** 0243 3.5 / 0837 0.9 / TH 1502 3.4 / ○ 2048 0.8
5 0334 4.0 / 0925 0.4 / TH 1600 3.8 / 2143 0.6	**20** 0320 3.6 / 0914 0.8 / F 1541 3.4 / 2124 0.8
6 0419 4.0 / 1011 0.5 / F 1647 3.7 / 2226 0.7	**21** 0358 3.6 / 0951 0.7 / SA 1621 3.4 / 2201 0.8
7 0504 3.8 / 1057 0.7 / SA 1732 3.5 / 2310 0.9	**22** 0438 3.6 / 1031 0.7 / SU 1702 3.4 / 2240 0.8
8 0548 3.7 / 1143 0.9 / SU 1818 3.3 / 2354 1.1	**23** 0519 3.6 / 1113 0.8 / M 1746 3.3 / 2324 0.9
9 0633 3.4 / 1232 1.1 / M 1906 3.0	**24** 0604 3.5 / 1200 0.9 / TU 1834 3.2
10 0043 1.3 / 0721 3.2 / TU 1325 1.2 / 2000 2.9	**25** 0012 1.0 / 0654 3.4 / W 1252 0.9 / 1929 3.1
11 0140 1.5 / 0817 3.0 / W 1427 1.4 / 2105 2.8	**26** 0108 1.1 / 0751 3.3 / TH 1353 1.0 / 2032 3.1
12 0248 1.6 / 0923 3.0 / TH 1534 1.4 / 2214 2.8	**27** 0214 1.2 / 0857 3.2 / F 1501 1.1 / 2142 3.1
13 0400 1.5 / 1031 3.0 / F 1638 1.4 / 2316 2.9	**28** 0326 1.2 / 1009 3.2 / SA 1611 1.0 / 2251 3.2
14 0504 1.5 / 1131 3.0 / SA 1734 1.3	**29** 0438 1.1 / 1118 3.3 / SU 1734 0.9 / 2354 3.3
15 0007 3.1 / 0558 1.3 / SU 1221 3.1 / 1821 1.1	**30** 0545 0.9 / 1221 3.4 / M 1817 0.8
	31 0051 3.5 / 0645 0.8 / TU 1319 3.5 / 1911 0.7

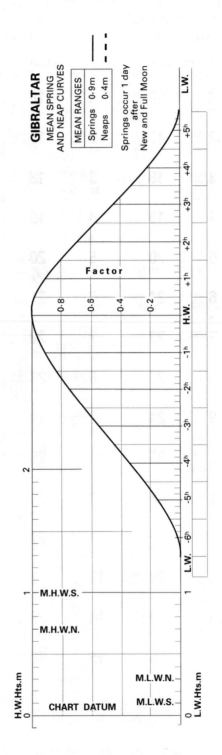

GIBRALTAR
MEAN SPRING AND NEAP CURVES

MEAN RANGES	
Springs	0·9m
Neaps	0·4m

Springs occur 1 day after New and Full Moon

TIME ZONE (UTC)
For Summer Time add ONE hour in **non-shaded areas**

GIBRALTAR

LAT 36°08'N LONG 5°21'W

TIMES AND HEIGHTS OF HIGH AND LOW WATERS

YEAR 2002

JANUARY

Time	m	Time	m
1 TU 0419 / 0953 / 1713 / 2218	1.0 / 0.1 / 1.0 / 0.1	**16** W 0454 / 1027 / 1713 / 2251	0.9 / 0.1 / 1.0 / 0.1
2 W 0504 / 1040 / 1723 / 2303	1.0 / 0.1 / 1.0 / 0.1	**17** TH 0528 / 1103 / 1748 / 2324	0.8 / 0.2 / 0.8 / 0.1
3 TH 0552 / 1130 / 1812 / 2352	1.0 / 0.2 / 0.9 / 0.1	**18** F 0602 / 1138 / 1824 / 2358	0.8 / 0.2 / 0.8 / 0.2
4 F 0643 / 1226 / 1905	0.9 / 0.2 / 0.9	**19** SA 0639 / 1217 / 1903	0.8 / 0.2 / 0.7
5 SA 0047 / 0740 / 1331 / 2004	0.2 / 0.9 / 0.2 / 0.8	**20** SU 0036 / 0720 / 1302 / 1946	0.2 / 0.7 / 0.3 / 0.7
6 SU 0152 / 0843 / 1443 / 2109	0.2 / 0.9 / 0.2 / 0.8	**21** M 0122 / 0808 / 1357 / 2037	0.3 / 0.7 / 0.3 / 0.6
7 M 0306 / 0951 / 1558 / 2223	0.3 / 0.8 / 0.2 / 0.7	**22** TU 0223 / 0904 / 1505 / 2139	0.3 / 0.7 / 0.3 / 0.6
8 TU 0425 / 1102 / 1712 / 2338	0.3 / 0.8 / 0.2 / 0.8	**23** W 0343 / 1009 / 1627 / 2256	0.3 / 0.7 / 0.3 / 0.6
9 W 0536 / 1206 / 1814	0.2 / 0.8 / 0.1	**24** TH 0503 / 1119 / 1739	0.3 / 0.7 / 0.2
10 TH 0041 / 0630 / 1301 / 1904	0.8 / 0.2 / 0.9 / 0.1	**25** F 0007 / 0602 / 1221 / 1832	0.7 / 0.2 / 0.8 / 0.2
11 F 0134 / 0716 / 1349 / 1948	0.8 / 0.2 / 0.9 / 0.1	**26** SA 0104 / 0649 / 1315 / 1918	0.8 / 0.2 / 0.8 / 0.1
12 SA 0220 / 0758 / 1435 / 2029	0.8 / 0.1 / 0.9 / 0.1	**27** SU 0153 / 0733 / 1405 / 2002	0.8 / 0.1 / 0.9 / 0.1
13 SU 0303 / 0837 / 1518 / ●2107	0.1 / 0.1 / 0.9 / 0.1	**28** M 0240 / 0817 / 1452 / ○2046	0.9 / 0.1 / 0.9 / 0.1
14 M 0343 / 0915 / 1558 / 2143	0.9 / 0.1 / 1.0 / 0.1	**29** TU 0326 / 0903 / 1542 / 2130	1.0 / 0.0 / 1.0 / 0.0
15 TU 0420 / 0952 / 1637 / 2218	0.9 / 0.1 / 1.0 / 0.1	**30** W 0410 / 0948 / 1628 / 2213	1.0 / 0.0 / 1.0 / 0.0
		31 TH 0454 / 1034 / 1714 / 2255	1.0 / 0.0 / 1.0 / 0.0

FEBRUARY

Time	m	Time	m
1 F 0539 / 1121 / 1801 / 2338	1.0 / 0.0 / 1.0 / 0.0	**16** SA 0532 / 1111 / 1754 / 2327	0.8 / 0.1 / 0.8 / 0.1
2 SA 0627 / 1209 / 1850	1.0 / 0.1 / 0.9	**17** SU 0602 / 1141 / 1826 / 2356	0.8 / 0.1 / 0.8 / 0.2
3 SU 0024 / 0718 / 1303 / 1943	0.1 / 0.9 / 0.1 / 0.8	**18** M 0638 / 1215 / 1905	0.8 / 0.2 / 0.7
4 M 0117 / 0815 / 1405 / 2041	0.1 / 0.8 / 0.2 / 0.8	**19** TU 0029 / 0720 / 1257 / 1951	0.2 / 0.7 / 0.2 / 0.7
5 TU 0220 / 0918 / 1520 / 2150	0.2 / 0.8 / 0.2 / 0.7	**20** W 0113 / 0812 / 1356 / 2050	0.3 / 0.7 / 0.2 / 0.6
6 W 0345 / 1033 / 1653 / 2314	0.3 / 0.8 / 0.2 / 0.7	**21** TH 0223 / 0917 / 1527 / 2206	0.3 / 0.7 / 0.3 / 0.6
7 TH 0522 / 1150 / 1810	0.3 / 0.7 / 0.2	**22** F 0418 / 1039 / 1716 / 2336	0.3 / 0.7 / 0.2 / 0.6
8 F 0032 / 0627 / 1255 / 1902	0.7 / 0.2 / 0.8 / 0.2	**23** SA 0544 / 1159 / 1821	0.3 / 0.7 / 0.1
9 SA 0131 / 0714 / 1346 / 1944	0.7 / 0.2 / 0.8 / 0.1	**24** SU 0045 / 0638 / 1301 / 1909	0.7 / 0.2 / 0.8 / 0.1
10 SU 0218 / 0754 / 1431 / 2022	0.8 / 0.1 / 0.8 / 0.1	**25** M 0139 / 0725 / 1354 / 1953	0.8 / 0.1 / 0.9 / 0.1
11 M 0257 / 0830 / 1511 / 2057	0.8 / 0.1 / 0.8 / 0.1	**26** TU 0226 / 0809 / 1443 / 2036	0.9 / 0.0 / 0.9 / 0.0
12 TU 0332 / 0905 / 1547 / ●2130	0.8 / 0.1 / 0.9 / 0.0	**27** W 0311 / 0854 / 1530 / ○2118	1.0 / 0.0 / 1.0 / -0.1
13 W 0404 / 0939 / 1621 / 2201	0.9 / 0.1 / 0.9 / 0.0	**28** TH 0355 / 0938 / 1615 / 2159	1.0 / -0.1 / 1.0 / -0.1
14 TH 0434 / 1010 / 1652 / 2231	0.9 / 0.1 / 0.9 / 0.1		
15 F 0503 / 1041 / 1723 / 2259	0.9 / 0.1 / 0.8 / 0.1		

MARCH

Time	m	Time	m
1 F 0438 / 1022 / 1700 / 2239	1.0 / -0.1 / 1.0 / -0.1	**16** SA 0433 / 1015 / 1656 / 2231	0.9 / 0.1 / 0.9 / 0.1
2 SA 0522 / 1104 / 1745 / 2318	1.0 / 0.0 / 1.0 / 0.0	**17** SU 0501 / 1043 / 1725 / 2258	0.9 / 0.1 / 0.8 / 0.1
3 SU 0606 / 1147 / 1831 / 2359	1.0 / 0.0 / 0.9 / 0.1	**18** M 0531 / 1111 / 1757 / 2325	0.8 / 0.1 / 0.8 / 0.2
4 M 0654 / 1234 / 1921	0.9 / 0.1 / 0.8	**19** TU 0605 / 1142 / 1835 / 2357	0.8 / 0.2 / 0.8 / 0.2
5 TU 0044 / 0747 / 1329 / 2016	0.2 / 0.8 / 0.2 / 0.8	**20** W 0645 / 1219 / 1922	0.8 / 0.2 / 0.7
6 W 0140 / 0848 / 1442 / 2121	0.2 / 0.7 / 0.3 / 0.7	**21** TH 0037 / 0736 / 1312 / 2020	0.3 / 0.7 / 0.3 / 0.7
7 TH 0306 / 1005 / 1634 / 2248	0.3 / 0.7 / 0.3 / 0.7	**22** F 0141 / 0842 / 1446 / 2135	0.3 / 0.7 / 0.3 / 0.6
8 F 0513 / 1137 / 1801	0.3 / 0.7 / 0.3	**23** SA 0346 / 1008 / 1655 / 2309	0.3 / 0.7 / 0.3 / 0.7
9 SA 0020 / 0624 / 1248 / 1851	0.7 / 0.3 / 0.7 / 0.2	**24** SU 0527 / 1139 / 1804	0.3 / 0.7 / 0.2
10 SU 0120 / 0707 / 1338 / 1929	0.7 / 0.2 / 0.8 / 0.1	**25** M 0024 / 0624 / 1246 / 1852	0.7 / 0.2 / 0.8 / 0.1
11 M 0203 / 0742 / 1419 / 2003	0.8 / 0.2 / 0.8 / 0.1	**26** TU 0119 / 0711 / 1338 / 1935	0.8 / 0.1 / 0.9 / 0.0
12 TU 0238 / 0814 / 1454 / 2036	0.8 / 0.1 / 0.8 / 0.1	**27** W 0206 / 0755 / 1426 / 2016	0.9 / 0.0 / 0.9 / 0.0
13 W 0310 / 0846 / 1527 / 2107	0.9 / 0.1 / 0.9 / 0.1	**28** TH 0251 / 0839 / 1512 / ○2057	1.0 / -0.1 / 1.0 / 0.0
14 TH 0338 / 0917 / 1557 / ●2136	0.9 / 0.1 / 0.9 / 0.1	**29** F 0334 / 0921 / 1557 / 2137	1.0 / -0.1 / 1.0 / -0.1
15 F 0406 / 0947 / 1627 / 2204	0.9 / 0.1 / 0.9 / 0.1	**30** SA 0417 / 1003 / 1641 / 2216	1.1 / -0.1 / 1.0 / 0.0
		31 SU 0500 / 1043 / 1725 / 2254	1.0 / 0.0 / 1.0 / 0.0

APRIL

Time	m	Time	m
1 M 0543 / 1124 / 1810 / 2333	1.0 / 0.0 / 0.9 / 0.1	**16** TU 0505 / 1046 / 1735 / 2301	0.9 / 0.1 / 0.8 / 0.2
2 TU 0629 / 1206 / 1859	0.9 / 0.1 / 0.8	**17** W 0540 / 1119 / 1815 / 2336	0.8 / 0.2 / 0.8 / 0.2
3 W 0016 / 0721 / 1256 / 1953	0.2 / 0.8 / 0.2 / 0.8	**18** TH 0622 / 1157 / 1903	0.8 / 0.2 / 0.8
4 TH 0108 / 0821 / 1405 / 2056	0.3 / 0.7 / 0.2 / 0.7	**19** F 0020 / 0715 / 1252 / 2003	0.3 / 0.7 / 0.3 / 0.7
5 F 0231 / 0936 / 1556 / 2217	0.3 / 0.7 / 0.3 / 0.7	**20** SA 0130 / 0822 / 1429 / 2116	0.3 / 0.7 / 0.3 / 0.7
6 SA 0448 / 1111 / 1729 / 2348	0.4 / 0.7 / 0.3 / 0.7	**21** SU 0324 / 0946 / 1624 / 2242	0.3 / 0.7 / 0.3 / 0.7
7 SU 0602 / 1225 / 1820	0.3 / 0.7 / 0.3	**22** M 0500 / 1116 / 1734 / 2356	0.3 / 0.7 / 0.2 / 0.8
8 M 0048 / 0642 / 1314 / 1857	0.7 / 0.2 / 0.8 / 0.2	**23** TU 0601 / 1223 / 1824	0.2 / 0.8 / 0.1
9 TU 0130 / 0715 / 1352 / 1931	0.8 / 0.2 / 0.8 / 0.2	**24** W 0051 / 0649 / 1316 / 1908	0.9 / 0.1 / 0.9 / 0.1
10 W 0204 / 0747 / 1426 / 2003	0.8 / 0.1 / 0.8 / 0.1	**25** TH 0139 / 0734 / 1403 / 1949	0.9 / 0.0 / 0.9 / 0.0
11 TH 0234 / 0818 / 1457 / 2034	0.9 / 0.1 / 0.9 / 0.1	**26** F 0224 / 0817 / 1449 / 2030	1.0 / 0.0 / 1.0 / 0.0
12 F 0304 / 0848 / 1528 / ●2104	0.9 / 0.1 / 0.9 / 0.1	**27** SA 0309 / 0900 / 1534 / ○2111	1.0 / -0.1 / 1.0 / 0.0
13 SA 0333 / 0918 / 1558 / 2133	0.9 / 0.1 / 0.9 / 0.1	**28** SU 0352 / 0941 / 1619 / 2151	1.0 / 0.0 / 1.0 / 0.0
14 SU 0402 / 0948 / 1629 / 2202	0.9 / 0.1 / 0.9 / 0.1	**29** M 0436 / 1021 / 1703 / 2230	1.0 / 0.0 / 1.0 / 0.1
15 M 0433 / 1017 / 1700 / 2231	0.9 / 0.1 / 0.9 / 0.1	**30** TU 0520 / 1101 / 1749 / 2310	0.9 / 0.1 / 0.9 / 0.1

Chart Datum: 0·25 metres below Alicante Datum (Mean Sea Level, Alicante)
Register for your **FREE** weekly weather email service from Macmillan Reeds
at **www.nauticaldata.com – NOW!**
》 weekend weather reports sent to your email address, every Thursday 《

GIBRALTAR

YEAR 2002

LAT 36°08′N   LONG 5°21′W

TIMES AND HEIGHTS OF HIGH AND LOW WATERS

TIME ZONE (UTC)
For Summer Time add ONE hour in **non-shaded areas**

MAY

Day	Time m	Time m	Time m	Time m	Day	Time m	Time m	Time m	Time m
1 W	0606 0.9	1142 0.1	1837 0.8	2352 0.2	16 TH	0524 0.9	1104 0.2	1800 0.8	2324 0.2
2 TH	0657 0.8	1229 0.2	1931 0.8		17 F	0609 0.8	1148 0.2	1850 0.8	
3 F	0044 0.3	0755 0.7	1334 0.3	2030 0.7	18 SA	0015 0.3	0702 0.8	1247 0.3	1949 0.8
4 SA	0159 0.3	0903 0.7	1503 0.3	2138 0.7	19 SU	0127 0.3	0808 0.7	1412 0.3	2057 0.8
5 SU	0342 0.4	1024 0.7	1630 0.3	2254 0.7	20 M	0258 0.3	0924 0.7	1542 0.3	2212 0.8
6 M	0510 0.3	1140 0.7	1730 0.3	2357 0.7	21 TU	0423 0.3	1045 0.7	1654 0.3	2323 0.8
7 TU	0600 0.3	1232 0.7	1813 0.3		22 W	0530 0.2	1154 0.8	1750 0.2	
8 W	0042 0.8	0637 0.2	1313 0.8	1850 0.2	23 TH	0020 0.9	0623 0.1	1250 0.9	1837 0.1
9 TH	0119 0.8	0711 0.2	1349 0.8	1924 0.2	24 F	0110 0.9	0710 0.1	1339 0.9	1921 0.1
10 F	0152 0.9	0744 0.2	1422 0.9	1957 0.2	25 SA	0157 1.0	0755 0.0	1425 0.9	2004 0.1
11 SA	0225 0.9	0816 0.1	1455 0.9	2029 0.2	26 SU	0243 1.0	0839 0.0	1512 0.9	○ 2047 0.1
12 SU	0258 0.9	0849 0.1	1529 0.9	● 2101 0.2	27 M	0329 1.0	0921 0.0	1558 0.9	2128 0.1
13 M	0332 0.9	0921 0.1	1603 0.9	2134 0.2	28 TU	0414 1.0	1002 0.0	1643 0.9	2210 0.1
14 TU	0407 0.9	0953 0.1	1639 0.9	2207 0.2	29 W	0459 0.9	1042 0.1	1729 0.9	2251 0.2
15 W	0444 0.9	1027 0.1	1717 0.9	2243 0.2	30 TH	0545 0.9	1123 0.1	1816 0.8	2334 0.2
					31 F	0635 0.8	1207 0.2	1906 0.8	

JUNE

Day	Time m	Time m	Time m	Time m	Day	Time m	Time m	Time m	Time m
1 SA	0023 0.3	0728 0.7	1302 0.3	1959 0.8	16 SU	0010 0.2	0652 0.8	1237 0.2	1932 0.9
2 SU	0124 0.3	0826 0.7	1409 0.3	2054 0.7	17 M	0115 0.3	0753 0.8	1345 0.2	2033 0.8
3 M	0237 0.3	0928 0.7	1520 0.3	2152 0.7	18 TU	0228 0.3	0859 0.8	1458 0.2	2139 0.8
4 TU	0352 0.3	1036 0.7	1625 0.3	2252 0.7	19 W	0342 0.2	1012 0.8	1610 0.2	2247 0.9
5 W	0459 0.3	1138 0.7	1720 0.3	2344 0.8	20 TH	0456 0.2	1124 0.8	1716 0.2	2350 0.9
6 TH	0551 0.3	1227 0.7	1806 0.3		21 F	0559 0.2	1225 0.8	1812 0.2	
7 F	0028 0.8	0632 0.2	1308 0.8	1844 0.2	22 SA	0044 0.9	0652 0.1	1318 0.9	1901 0.2
8 SA	0108 0.8	0709 0.2	1346 0.8	1921 0.2	23 SU	0135 0.9	0739 0.1	1407 0.9	1946 0.1
9 SU	0146 0.9	0745 0.2	1423 0.9	1956 0.2	24 M	0223 0.9	0824 0.1	1456 0.9	○ 2030 0.1
10 M	0225 0.9	0821 0.1	1501 0.9	2033 0.2	25 TU	0311 0.9	0907 0.1	1542 0.9	2113 0.1
11 TU	0305 0.9	0857 0.1	1540 0.9	● 2111 0.2	26 W	0357 0.9	0947 0.1	1626 0.9	2155 0.1
12 W	0347 0.9	0935 0.1	1620 0.9	2150 0.2	27 TH	0442 0.9	1026 0.1	1709 0.9	2235 0.2
13 TH	0429 0.9	1014 0.1	1702 0.9	2232 0.2	28 F	0525 0.9	1104 0.1	1751 0.9	2315 0.2
14 F	0512 0.9	1055 0.2	1747 0.9	2318 0.2	29 SA	0609 0.8	1143 0.2	1834 0.8	2358 0.2
15 SA	0559 0.9	1141 0.2	1837 0.9		30 SU	0655 0.8	1225 0.2	1918 0.8	

JULY

Day	Time m	Time m	Time m	Time m	Day	Time m	Time m	Time m	Time m
1 M	0044 0.3	0742 0.7	1314 0.3	2003 0.8	16 TU	0053 0.2	0733 0.9	1313 0.2	2006 0.9
2 TU	0138 0.3	0832 0.7	1410 0.3	2050 0.7	17 W	0156 0.2	0834 0.8	1417 0.2	2107 0.9
3 W	0237 0.3	0927 0.7	1512 0.3	2142 0.7	18 TH	0305 0.2	0942 0.8	1529 0.3	2214 0.8
4 TH	0343 0.3	1030 0.7	1618 0.3	2239 0.7	19 F	0425 0.2	1056 0.8	1648 0.3	2324 0.8
5 F	0452 0.3	1133 0.7	1719 0.3	2335 0.8	20 SA	0543 0.2	1207 0.8	1757 0.3	
6 SA	0552 0.3	1226 0.7	1809 0.3		21 SU	0027 0.9	0642 0.2	1307 0.8	1851 0.2
7 SU	0026 0.8	0638 0.2	1313 0.8	1851 0.3	22 M	0123 0.9	0731 0.1	1359 0.9	1938 0.2
8 M	0113 0.9	0719 0.2	1356 0.8	1931 0.2	23 TU	0213 0.9	0814 0.1	1446 0.9	2021 0.2
9 TU	0159 0.9	0759 0.2	1439 0.9	2012 0.2	24 W	0300 0.9	0854 0.1	1530 0.9	○ 2101 0.1
10 W	0245 0.9	0839 0.1	1522 0.9	● 2054 0.2	25 TH	0344 0.9	0931 0.1	1609 0.9	2140 0.1
11 TH	0331 1.0	0920 0.1	1604 1.0	2138 0.1	26 F	0424 0.9	1006 0.1	1646 0.9	2216 0.1
12 F	0416 1.0	1002 0.1	1648 1.0	2222 0.1	27 SA	0502 0.9	1039 0.1	1721 0.9	2252 0.2
13 SA	0501 1.0	1044 0.1	1732 1.0	2309 0.1	28 SU	0538 0.9	1112 0.2	1755 0.9	2327 0.2
14 SU	0548 1.0	1129 0.1	1819 0.9	2358 0.2	29 M	0615 0.8	1145 0.2	1829	
15 M	0638 0.9	1217 0.2	1910 0.9		30 TU	0003 0.2	0652 0.8	1222 0.2	1906 0.8
					31 W	0042 0.3	0735 0.7	1302 0.3	1947 0.8

AUGUST

Day	Time m	Time m	Time m	Time m	Day	Time m	Time m	Time m	Time m
1 TH	0128 0.3	0823 0.7	1354 0.3	2035 0.8	16 F	0230 0.3	0914 0.8	1452 0.3	2143 0.8
2 F	0226 0.3	0921 0.7	1503 0.4	2132 0.7	17 SA	0400 0.3	1033 0.8	1630 0.4	2305 0.8
3 SA	0344 0.3	1032 0.7	1628 0.4	2240 0.7	18 SU	0536 0.3	1157 0.8	1753 0.3	
4 SU	0512 0.3	1146 0.7	1738 0.3	2349 0.8	19 M	0021 0.8	0637 0.3	1303 0.8	1847 0.3
5 M	0614 0.3	1244 0.8	1830 0.3		20 TU	0120 0.9	0722 0.2	1353 0.9	1930 0.2
6 TU	0048 0.8	0659 0.2	1334 0.9	1914 0.2	21 W	0208 0.9	0800 0.2	1435 0.9	2008 0.2
7 W	0140 0.9	0741 0.1	1419 0.9	1957 0.2	22 TH	0249 0.9	0835 0.1	1512 0.9	○ 2044 0.2
8 TH	0229 1.0	0822 0.1	1504 1.0	● 2040 0.1	23 F	0326 0.9	0908 0.1	1546 1.0	2118 0.1
9 F	0316 1.0	0904 0.1	1547 1.1	2125 0.1	24 SA	0401 0.9	0939 0.1	1616 1.0	2151 0.1
10 SA	0402 1.0	0946 0.1	1630 1.1	2209 0.1	25 SU	0433 0.9	1009 0.1	1645 1.0	2222 0.1
11 SU	0447 1.1	1027 0.1	1713 1.1	2253 0.1	26 M	0503 0.9	1038 0.2	1714 0.9	2253 0.2
12 M	0532 1.0	1109 0.1	1757 1.1	2339 0.1	27 TU	0533 0.9	1107 0.2	1742 0.9	2323 0.2
13 TU	0619 1.0	1152 0.1	1845 1.0		28 W	0605 0.9	1136 0.2	1814 0.9	2355 0.2
14 W	0027 0.2	0711 0.9	1241 0.2	1937 1.0	29 TH	0641 0.8	1209 0.3	1852 0.8	
15 TH	0123 0.2	0808 0.9	1338 0.3	2035 0.9	30 F	0032 0.3	0727 0.8	1249 0.4	1939 0.8
					31 SA	0122 0.3	0826 0.8	1353 0.4	2038 0.8

Chart Datum: 0·25 metres below Alicante Datum (Mean Sea Level, Alicante)

TIME ZONE (UTC)

For Summer Time add ONE hour in **non-shaded areas**

GIBRALTAR

YEAR **2002**

LAT 36°08'N   LONG 5°21'W

TIMES AND HEIGHTS OF HIGH AND LOW WATERS

SEPTEMBER

Day	Time	m	Time	m	Time	m	Time	m
1 SU	0241	0.4	0940	0.7	1541	0.7	2153	0.7
2 M	0441	0.4	1109	0.7	1715	0.4	2320	0.8
3 TU	0555	0.3	1220	0.8	1812	0.3		
4 W	0029	0.8	0642	0.2	1313	0.9	1857	0.2
5 TH	0124	0.9	0723	0.1	1359	1.0	1940	0.1
6 F	0212	1.0	0803	0.1	1443	1.1	2023	0.1
7 SA	0259	1.1	0844	0.1	1526	1.1	●2107	0.0
8 SU	0343	1.1	0924	0.0	1608	1.2	2150	0.0
9 M	0427	1.1	1005	0.0	1650	1.2	2232	0.0
10 TU	0511	1.1	1045	0.1	1733	1.1	2315	0.1
11 W	0557	1.0	1125	0.2	1819	1.1	2359	0.2
12 TH	0646	1.0	1209	0.2	1909	1.0		
13 F	0049	0.3	0742	0.9	1303	0.3	2006	0.9
14 SA	0155	0.3	0848	0.8	1420	0.4	2117	0.8
15 SU	0339	0.4	1013	0.8	1619	0.4	2253	0.8
16 M	0527	0.4	1148	0.8	1748	0.4		
17 TU	0018	0.8	0624	0.3	1252	0.9	1836	0.3
18 W	0113	0.9	0703	0.3	1336	0.9	1913	0.3
19 TH	0154	0.9	0737	0.2	1412	1.0	1946	0.2
20 F	0229	0.9	0808	0.2	1444	1.0	2018	0.2
21 SA	0301	1.0	0838	0.2	1514	1.0	○2050	0.2
22 SU	0331	1.0	0907	0.1	1542	1.0	2121	0.1
23 M	0400	1.0	0936	0.2	1609	1.0	2151	0.1
24 TU	0428	1.0	1005	0.2	1636	1.0	2219	0.2
25 W	0456	1.0	1032	0.2	1704	1.0	2248	0.2
26 TH	0526	0.9	1100	0.3	1735	0.9	2317	0.2
27 F	0602	0.9	1131	0.4	1812	0.9	2351	0.4
28 SA	0648	0.8	1208	0.4	1859	0.8		
29 SU	0035	0.4	0747	0.8	1307	0.4	2001	0.8
30 M	0156	0.4	0903	0.7	1509	0.5	2119	0.8

OCTOBER

Day	Time	m	Time	m	Time	m	Time	m
1 TU	0418	0.4	1035	0.8	1652	0.4	2255	0.8
2 W	0533	0.3	1154	0.8	1751	0.3		
3 TH	0011	0.9	0620	0.2	1249	0.9	1837	0.2
4 F	0106	1.0	0701	0.1	1334	1.0	1920	0.1
5 SA	0152	1.0	0740	0.1	1418	1.1	2002	0.1
6 SU	0237	1.1	0819	0.1	1501	1.2	●2045	0.1
7 M	0321	1.1	0859	0.1	1543	1.2	2127	0.0
8 TU	0405	1.1	0939	0.1	1626	1.2	2208	0.0
9 W	0448	1.1	1019	0.1	1709	1.1	2249	0.1
10 TH	0533	1.0	1059	0.2	1753	1.0	2331	0.2
11 F	0621	1.0	1141	0.3	1843	0.9		
12 SA	0017	0.3	0716	0.9	1233	0.4	1940	0.9
13 SU	0121	0.4	0823	0.8	1352	0.5	2054	0.8
14 M	0310	0.4	0946	0.8	1556	0.5	2232	0.8
15 TU	0458	0.4	1120	0.8	1723	0.4	2359	0.8
16 W	0554	0.4	1223	0.9	1810	0.4		
17 TH	0050	0.9	0632	0.3	1305	0.9	1844	0.3
18 F	0128	0.9	0704	0.3	1339	1.0	1916	0.2
19 SA	0200	0.9	0735	0.2	1409	1.0	1947	0.2
20 SU	0230	1.0	0805	0.2	1437	1.0	2019	0.2
21 M	0259	1.0	0835	0.2	1506	1.0	○2050	0.2
22 TU	0328	1.0	0905	0.2	1535	1.0	2120	0.2
23 W	0357	1.0	0934	0.2	1605	1.0	2150	0.2
24 TH	0427	1.0	1003	0.2	1636	1.0	2219	0.2
25 F	0459	1.0	1033	0.3	1709	0.9	2250	0.3
26 SA	0537	0.9	1106	0.3	1748	0.9	2324	0.3
27 SU	0623	0.9	1146	0.4	1836	0.8		
28 M	0009	0.4	0722	0.8	1249	0.4	1938	0.8
29 TU	0130	0.4	0836	0.8	1445	0.4	2055	0.8
30 W	0344	0.4	1002	0.8	1621	0.4	2227	0.8
31 TH	0501	0.3	1122	0.9	1724	0.3	2346	0.9

NOVEMBER

Day	Time	m	Time	m	Time	m	Time	m
1 F	0552	0.2	1219	0.9	1813	0.2		
2 SA	0042	0.9	0634	0.2	1307	1.0	1856	0.1
3 SU	0129	1.0	0714	0.1	1351	1.1	1939	0.1
4 M	0214	1.1	0754	0.1	1434	1.1	●2022	0.0
5 TU	0258	1.1	0834	0.1	1518	1.1	2104	0.0
6 W	0342	1.1	0915	0.1	1602	1.1	2146	0.1
7 TH	0426	1.1	0956	0.1	1646	1.1	2227	0.1
8 F	0511	1.0	1037	0.2	1732	1.0	2308	0.2
9 SA	0559	0.9	1121	0.3	1822	0.9	2354	0.3
10 SU	0653	0.9	1213	0.4	1920	0.8		
11 M	0054	0.4	0756	0.8	1328	0.4	2027	0.8
12 TU	0225	0.4	0909	0.8	1508	0.4	2148	0.7
13 W	0400	0.4	1029	0.8	1633	0.4	2313	0.8
14 TH	0506	0.4	1135	0.9	1728	0.4		
15 F	0012	0.8	0551	0.3	1222	0.9	1808	0.3
16 SA	0053	0.9	0628	0.3	1258	0.9	1844	0.2
17 SU	0128	0.9	0702	0.2	1331	0.9	1917	0.2
18 M	0159	0.9	0734	0.2	1402	1.0	1950	0.2
19 TU	0230	1.0	0806	0.2	1434	1.0	2023	0.2
20 W	0301	1.0	0838	0.2	1507	1.0	○2055	0.2
21 TH	0333	1.0	0909	0.2	1541	1.0	2127	0.2
22 F	0407	1.0	0942	0.2	1617	1.0	2200	0.2
23 SA	0443	0.9	1016	0.3	1655	0.9	2234	0.2
24 SU	0523	0.9	1053	0.3	1736	0.9	2312	0.3
25 M	0609	0.9	1139	0.3	1825	0.8		
26 TU	0001	0.3	0705	0.8	1244	0.4	1924	0.8
27 W	0114	0.3	0812	0.8	1416	0.4	2033	0.8
28 TH	0255	0.3	0927	0.8	1542	0.3	2153	0.8
29 F	0416	0.3	1043	0.9	1650	0.3	2312	0.8
30 SA	0517	0.2	1147	0.9	1746	0.2		

DECEMBER

Day	Time	m	Time	m	Time	m	Time	m
1 SU	0014	0.9	0607	0.2	1239	1.0	1834	0.1
2 M	0106	0.9	0651	0.1	1326	1.0	1920	0.1
3 TU	0153	1.0	0733	0.1	1412	1.0	2005	0.1
4 W	0239	1.0	0816	0.1	1458	1.0	●2048	0.0
5 TH	0325	1.0	0858	0.1	1544	1.0	2131	0.1
6 F	0411	0.9	0941	0.1	1631	1.0	2213	0.1
7 SA	0456	0.9	1024	0.2	1717	0.9	2255	0.2
8 SU	0543	0.9	1109	0.2	1806	0.9	2339	0.2
9 M	0633	0.9	1159	0.3	1858	0.9		
10 TU	0030	0.3	0727	0.8	1300	0.3	1955	0.8
11 W	0136	0.3	0826	0.8	1413	0.4	2057	0.7
12 TH	0250	0.4	0928	0.8	1527	0.4	2205	0.7
13 F	0402	0.4	1031	0.8	1633	0.3	2314	0.7
14 SA	0503	0.3	1128	0.8	1728	0.3		
15 SU	0010	0.8	0551	0.3	1215	0.8	1812	0.3
16 M	0053	0.8	0632	0.3	1255	0.9	1851	0.2
17 TU	0131	0.8	0709	0.2	1332	0.9	1928	0.2
18 W	0206	0.9	0743	0.2	1409	0.9	2003	0.2
19 TH	0241	0.9	0817	0.2	1447	0.9	○2038	0.1
20 F	0318	0.9	0852	0.2	1527	0.9	2114	0.1
21 SA	0355	0.9	0929	0.2	1607	0.9	2151	0.1
22 SU	0434	0.9	1008	0.2	1648	0.9	2229	0.2
23 M	0515	0.9	1050	0.2	1731	0.9	2309	0.2
24 TU	0600	0.9	1137	0.2	1818	0.9	2356	0.2
25 W	0651	0.9	1235	0.3	1911	0.8		
26 TH	0054	0.2	0749	0.8	1345	0.3	2011	0.8
27 F	0207	0.3	0854	0.8	1500	0.3	2120	0.8
28 SA	0325	0.3	1005	0.8	1614	0.2	2236	0.8
29 SU	0440	0.2	1115	0.9	1725	0.2	2348	0.8
30 M	0544	0.2	1215	0.9	1821	0.1		
31 TU	0048	0.8	0637	0.2	1309	0.9	1912	0.1

Chart Datum: 0·25 metres below Alicante Datum (Mean Sea Level, Alicante)

TIDAL CURVES -
BOURNEMOUTH TO CHRISTCHURCH

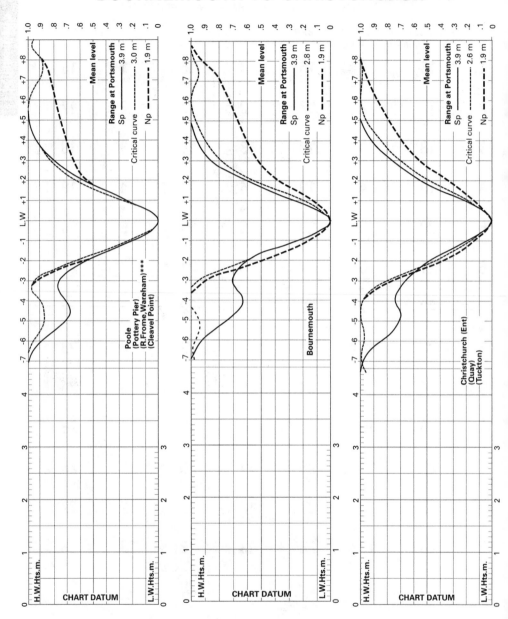

TIDAL CURVES - LYMINGTON TO COWES

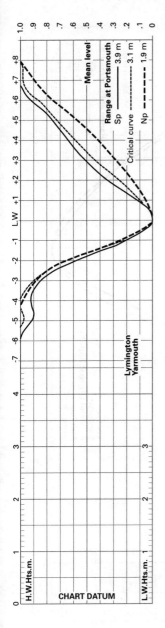

Mean level
Range at Portsmouth
Sp — 3.9 m
——— 3.1 m
Np — — — 1.9 m
Critical curve

Lymington
Yarmouth

H.W.Hts.m.
L.W.Hts.m.
CHART DATUM

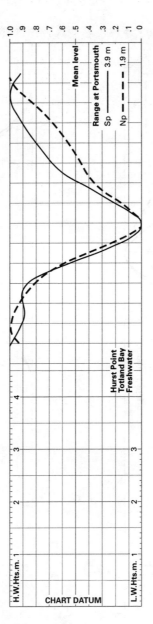

Mean level
Range at Portsmouth
Sp — 3.9 m
Np — — — 1.9 m

Hurst Point
Totland Bay
Freshwater

H.W.Hts.m.
L.W.Hts.m.
CHART DATUM

H.W.Hts at Secondary Ports

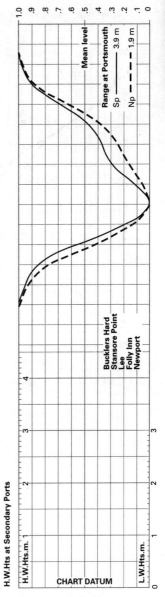

Mean level
Range at Portsmouth
Sp — 3.9 m
Np — — — 1.9 m

Bucklers Hard
Stansore Point
Lee
Folly Inn
Newport

H.W.Hts.m.
L.W.Hts.m.
CHART DATUM

TIDAL CURVES - RYDE TO SELSEY

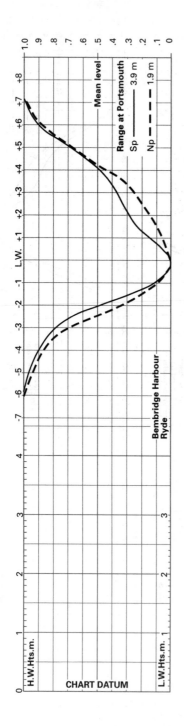

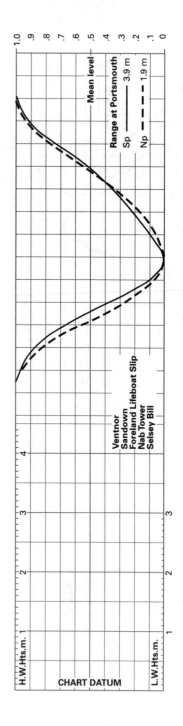

BREST TIDAL COEFFICIENTS 2002

Date	Jan am	Jan pm	Feb am	Feb pm	Mar am	Mar pm	Apr am	Apr pm	May am	May pm	June am	June pm	July am	July pm	Aug am	Aug pm	Sept am	Sept pm	Oct am	Oct pm	Nov am	Nov pm	Dec am	Dec pm
1	92	92	102	99	115	115	102	94	80	72	53	49	53	49	44	41	31	31		32	57	66	72	78
2	92	90	95	90	112	108	85	76	64	56	44	41	45	43	38	36		33	37	45	75	83	84	89
3	88	85	83	76	102	95	66	57	49	43	39	38	40	39	35		38	45	54	64	91	98	94	97
4	81	77	69	62	87	79	49	41	38	35		39	39		37	40	53	61	73	83	104	108	99	100
5	72	68	55	50	69	60	36	33	35		40	43	40	42	44	49	70	78	91	99	110	111	99	98
6	64	60		47	51	44		34	36	40	46	50	45	49	55	62	86	94	106	111	110	107	95	91
7	58		45	47	39		37	42	44	49	54	58	53	57	68	74	100	106	114	116	103	98	87	81
8	56	56	49	53	37	38	48	54	54	59	62	66	62	66	80	86	109	112	115	113	91	83	76	70
9	57	59	58	62	41	46	59	65	63	67	70	73	70	74	91	96	113	111	109	103	76	67	64	58
10	62	65	67	71	52	58	69	74	71	75	76	78	78	81	99	101	109	104	96	88	59	51	53	48
11	68	72	75	78	63	68	77	80	77	80	80	81	84	86	102	102	98	91	79	69	45	40	43	40
12	74	77	80	82	73	77	83	85	82	83	82	82	88	88	100	97	83	73	60	51	36	36	38	38
13	79	80	83	84	80	83	86	87	84	84	81	80	89	88	93	88	64	55	43	37		37		39
14	81	81	84	83	85	86	87	86	83	82	78	76	87	84	82	75	48	41	34		40	44	41	43
15	81	80	82	80	87	87	85	83	80	77	73	70	82	78	68	61	38		35	38	49	53	47	50
16	79	77	78	75	87	85	80	76	74	69	68	65	75	70	55	50	38	41	43	49	58	62	54	58
17	75	72	72	68	84	81	73	68	65	61	62	60	66	63		47	46	52	55	60	66	70	62	65
18	69	65	64	59	78	74	63	57	57	53	59	59	60	58	46	48	58	63	66	70	73	75	69	71
19	62	57	54	49	70	65	51	46	50	48	60			57	51	55	69	73	74	77	78	79	74	76
20	54	49	44	40	60	54	41	39	48	51	61	64	57	59	60	65	77	80	80	82	80	81	78	79
21	46	42	36	34	49	43	38			54	67	70	61	64	70	74	83	85	84	85	81	80	79	79
22	39	37		35	38	34	42	47	60	66	74	77	68	71	77	80	86	86	85	84	79	77	79	77
23	37		38	43	34		55	63	72	78	80	83	74	77	82	84	86	85	83	82	74	71	76	74
24	38	41	51	59	37	42	72	81	84	89	85	86	79	80	84	84	84	82	80	77	67	64	71	69
25	45	50	68	77	51	60	89	96	93	97	86	86	82	82	84	83	79	76	73	69	59	55	66	63
26	57	63	85	93	70	79	103	107	99	99	85	84	82	81	81	78	72	68	64	59	51	48	60	58
27	70	76	101	106	89	97	110	112	99	97	82	79	80	78	75	72	62	57	54	48	45	45	57	56
28	83	89	111	114	105	111	111	109	95	91	76	73	75	72	68	63	51	45	43	38	46	48	56	
29	94	98			115	117	106	101	87	82	69	65	69	65	58	54	39	34	35	34		53	58	60
30	102	104			118	116	95	88	76	71	61	57	61	57	48	43	30	29	36		59	65	63	67
31	105	104			113	108			65	59			52	48	38	34			41	49			71	76

These tidal coefficients indicate at a glance the magnitude of the tide on any particular day by assigning a non-dimensional coefficient to the twice-daily range of tide. The coefficient is based on a scale of 45 for mean neap (morte eau) and 100 for mean spring (vive eau) ranges at Brest. The coefficient is 70 for an average tide. A very small neap tide may have a coefficient of only 20, whilst a very big spring tide might be as high as 120. The ratio of the coefficients of different tides equals the ratio of their ranges; the range, for example, of the largest spring tide (120) is six times that of the smallest neap tide (20). The table above is for Brest, but holds good elsewhere along the Channel and Atlantic coasts of France.

French translations of common tidal terms are as follows:

HW	Pleine mer (PM)		MHWS	Pleine mer moyenne de VE
LW	Basse mer (BM)		MHWN	Pleine mer moyenne de ME
Springs	Vive eau (VE)		MLWN	Basse mer moyenne de ME
Neaps	Morte eau (ME)		MLWS	Basse mer moyenne de VE

TIDAL CALCULATIONS

The worked examples in this section make use of a method introduced by The Hydrographer to the Navy and now adopted by other nautical almanacs. Form NP 204, an example of which is published on page 214, is available in booklet form from Admiralty Chart agents and larger chandlers.

TO FIND THE HEIGHT OF TIDE AT TIMES
BETWEEN HIGH AND LOW WATER

Standard Ports

Intermediate times and heights may best be predicted by the use of the Mean Spring and Neap curves which are given before the daily predictions for each port.

Secondary Ports

For Secondary Ports on a stretch of coast where there is little change of shape between adjacent Standard Port curves and where the duration of rise or fall at the Secondary Port is not markedly different from that of the appropriate Standard Port (i.e. where H.W. and L.W. time differences are nearly the same) intermediate times and heights may be obtained by using the Mean Spring and Neap Curves for the appropriate Standard Port.
Between Swanage and Selsey the tide is of considerable complexity and justifies the inclusion of individual curves.

CURVE INTERPOLATION

Mean Spring and Neap Curves for Standard Ports show the factor of the range attained at given time intervals relative to that of H.W.: thus by definition H.W. = 1 and L.W. = 0.

The Spring curve is shown in solid line and the Neap curve, where it differs from the Spring, in pecked. Interpolation can be made by eye using the plotted positions of the predicted heights with reference to the levels of M.H.W.S. etc. No attempt should be made to extrapolate beyond the Spring or Neap curves: for ranges greater than Springs the Spring curve should be used, while for ranges less than Neaps the Neap curve should be used.
Where there is an appreciable change in duration between Spring and Neap tides the results obtained may have a slight error, this being greatest near L.W.

To find the time and height of H.W. and L.W. at a Secondary Port

EXAMPLE:

Find the time and height of the afternoon H.W. and L.W. at ST MARY's (Isles of Scilly) on 14th July (BST)

Note: *The data used in this example do not refer to the year of these tables.*

Section 1

from tables	JULY		
PLYMOUTH (DEVONPORT)	**14**	0309	1.0
		0927	5.3
		1532	1.1
	SA	2149	5.0

from tables

Location	Lat	Long	High Water		Low Water		MHWS	MHWN	MLWN	MLWS
PLYMOUTH, DEVONPORT *standard port*	50 22N	4 11W	0000 and 1200	0600 and 1800	0000 and 1200	0600 and 1800	5.5	4.4	2.2	0.8
Isles of Scilly, St. Mary's	49 55N	6 19W	-0030	-0110	-0100	-0020	+0.2	-0.1	-0.2	-0.1

TIDAL PREDICTION FORM

STANDARD PORT ..... *Devonport* ..... TIME/HEIGHT REQUIRED ..... *pm*

SECONDARY PORT ..... *St Mary's* ..... DATE *14 July* TIME ZONE ..... *B.S.T*

	TIME		HEIGHT		
	HW	**LW**	**HW**	**LW**	**RANGE**
STANDARD PORT	¹ *2149*	² *1532*	³ *5.0*	⁴ *1.1*	⁵ *3.9*
Seasonal change	Standard Ports -		⁶ *0.0*	⁶ *0.0*	
DIFFERENCES	⁷* *-0044*	⁸ *-0036*	⁹ *+0.1*	¹⁰ *-0.1*	
Seasonal change *	Secondary Ports +		¹¹ *0.0*	¹¹ *0.0*	
SECONDARY PORT	¹² *2105*	¹³ *1456*	¹⁴ *5.1*	¹⁵ *1.0*	
Duration	¹⁶ *0609*		*LW 1456 GMT = 1556 BST* *HW 2105 GMT = 2205 BST*		

* The seasonal changes are generally less than ± 0.1m and for most purposes can be ignored. See Admiraly Tide Tables Vol 1. for details

207

SECONDARY PORT TIME AND HEIGHT DIFFERENCE INTERPOLATION

In most cases interpolation can be carried out by eye. For complex examples, or where greater accuracy is required, the use of a pocket calculator may be preferred. These interpolations can also be shown graphically at any convenient scale.

Plot the two high water differences A (-0110 at 1800) and B (-0030 at 0000) and join AB. Read off the Time Difference for St Mary's corresponding to a HW time at Devonport of 2149 = -0044.

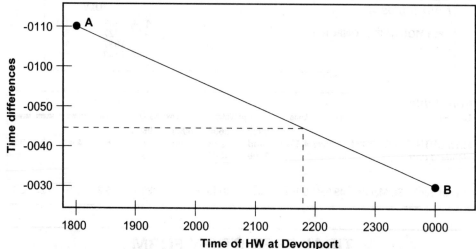

The height differences can be plotted in the same way. Plot A (MHWS of 5.5 and +0.2) and B (MHWN of 4.4 and -0.1). Draw a line through A and B. Read off the height difference for St. Mary's corresponding to a height at Devonport of 5.0 = +0.1m

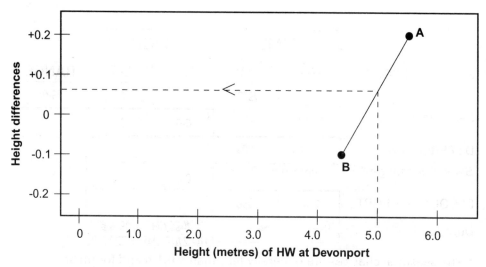

Similarly plot the low water time and differences.

To find the height at a given time (STANDARD PORT)

1. On Standard Curve diagram, plot heights of H.W. and L.W. occuring either side of required time and join by sloping line.
2. Enter H.W. Time and sufficient others to bracket required time.
3. From required time, proceed vertically to curves, using heights plotted in (1) to help interpolation between Spring and Neaps. Do NOT extrapolate.
4. Proceed horizontally to sloping line, thence vertically to Height scale.
5. Read off height.

EXAMPLE:

Find the height of tide at ULLAPOOL at 1900 on 6th January

from tables	JANUARY	
ULLAPOOL	**6** 0420	4.6
	1033	1.6
	1641	4.6
	F 2308	1.2

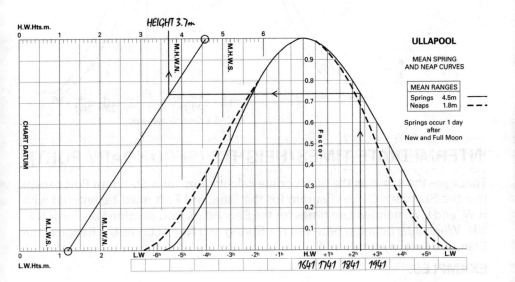

To find the time for a given height (STANDARD PORT)

1. On Standard Curve diagram, plot heights of H.W. and L.W. occurring either side of required event and join by sloping line.
2. Enter H.W. time and those for half-tidal cycle covering required event.
3. From required height, proceed vertically to sloping line, thence horizontally to curves, using heights plotted in (1) to assist interpolation between Spring and Neaps. Do NOT extrapolate.
4. Proceed vertically to Time scale.
5. Read off time.

EXAMPLE:

Find the time at which the afternoon tide at ULLAPOOL falls to 3.7m on 6 January

from tables	JANUARY		
ULLAPOOL	**6**	0420	4.6
		1033	1.6
		1641	4.6
	F	2308	1.2

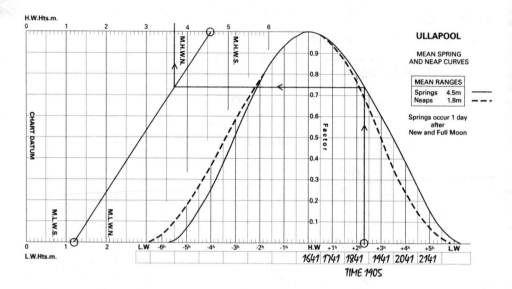

ULLAPOOL

MEAN SPRING
AND NEAP CURVES

MEAN RANGES
Springs 4.5m ——
Neaps 1.8m - - -

Springs occur 1 day
after
New and Full Moon

INTERMEDIATE TIMES/HEIGHTS (SECONDARY PORT)

These are the same as the appropriate calculations for a Standard Port except that the Standard Curve diagram for the Standard Port must be entered with H.W. and L.W. heights and times for the Secondary Port obtained on Form N.P. 204. When interpolating between the Spring and Neap curves the Range at the Standard Port must be used.

EXAMPLES:

Find the height of the tide at PADSTOW at 1100 on 28th February. Find the time at which the morning tide at PADSTOW falls to 4.9m on 28th February.

Notes:
The data in these examples do not refer to the year of these tables.
For instructions on graphical interpolation of differences, see p 208

from tables	FEBRUARY		
MILFORD HAVEN	**28**	0315	1.1
		0922	6.6
		1538	1.3
	TU	2145	6.3

from tables

Location	Lat	Long	High Water		Low Water		MHWS	MHWN	MLWN	MLWS
			0100 and 1300	0700 and 1900	0100 and 1300	0700 and 1900				
MILFORD HAVEN	51 42N	5 03W					7.0	5.2	2.5	0.7
standard port										
Port Isaac	50 35N	4 50W	-0100	-0100	-0100	-0100	+0.5	+0.6	0.0	+0.2
River Camel										
Padstow	50 33N	4 56W	-0055	-0050	-0040	-0050	+0.3	+0.4	+0.1	+0.1
Wadebridge	50 31N	4 50W	-0052	-0052	+0235	+0245	-3.8	-3.8	-2.5	-0.4
Newquay	50 25N	5 05W	-0100	-0110	-0105	-0050	0.0	+0.1	0.0	-0.1

TIDAL PREDICTION FORM

STANDARD PORT ...*Milford Haven*... TIME/HEIGHT REQUIRED ... **1100 : 4.9**

SECONDARY PORT ...*Padstow*... DATE **28 Feb** TIME ZONE **GMT**

	TIME		HEIGHT		
STANDARD PORT	HW	LW	HW	LW	RANGE
	¹ 0922	² 1538	³ 6·6	⁴ 1·3	⁵ 5·3
Seasonal change	Standard Ports +		⁶ 0·0	⁶ 0·0	
DIFFERENCES	⁷* -0052	⁸ –	⁹ +0·3	¹⁰ +0·1	
Seasonal change *	Secondary Ports -		¹¹ 0·0	¹¹ 0·0	
SECONDARY PORT	¹² 0830	¹³ –	¹⁴ 6·9	¹⁵ 1·4	
Duration	¹⁶ –				

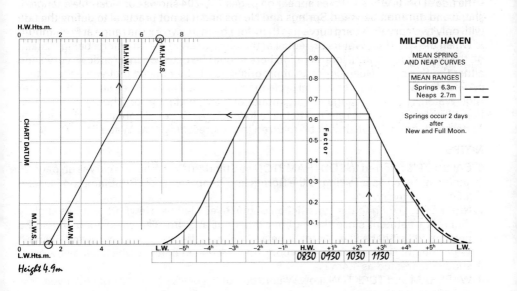

H.W.Hts.m.

MILFORD HAVEN

MEAN SPRING AND NEAP CURVES

MEAN RANGES
Springs 6.3m
Neaps 2.7m

Springs occur 2 days after New and Full Moon.

M.H.W.N. M.H.W.S. M.L.W.S. M.L.W.N.

CHART DATUM

Factor

L.W. −5ʰ −4ʰ −3ʰ −2ʰ −1ʰ H.W. +1ʰ +2ʰ +3ʰ +4ʰ +5ʰ L.W.

0830 0930 1030 1130

L.W.Hts.m.

Height 4.9m

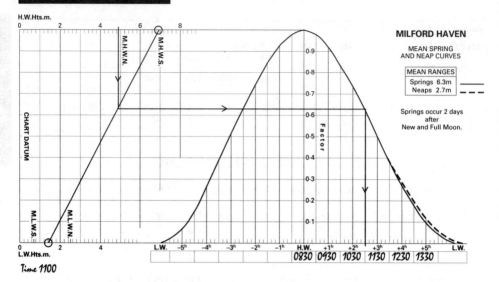

H.W.Hts.m.

MILFORD HAVEN

MEAN SPRING AND NEAP CURVES

MEAN RANGES
Springs 6.3m
Neaps 2.7m

Springs occur 2 days after New and Full Moon.

L.W.Hts.m.

Time 1100

SPECIAL INSTRUCTIONS FOR PLACES BETWEEN SWANAGE AND SELSEY

• Owing to the rapid change of tidal characteristics and distortion of the tidal curve in this area curves are shown for individual ports. It is a characteristic of the tide here that Low Water is more sharply defined than High Water and these curves have therefore been drawn with their times relative to that of Low Water.

• Apart from differences caused by referring the times to Low Water the procedure for obtaining intermediate heights at places whose curves are shown is identical to that used for normal Secondary Ports.

• The height differences for ports between Swanage and Yarmouth always refer to the Higher High Water, i.e. that which is shown as reaching a factor of 1.0 on the curves. Note that the time differences, which are not required for this calculation, also refer to the Higher High Water.

• The tide at ports whose curves appear on pages 202-204 shows considerable change of shape and duration between Springs and Neaps and it is not practical to define the tide with only two curves. A third curve has therefore been drawn for the range at Portsmouth at which the two High Waters are equal at the port concerned – this range being marked on the body of the graph. Interpolation here should be between this "critical" curve and either the Spring or Neap curve as appropriate. It will be noticed that while the critical curve extends throughout the tidal cycle the Spring and Neap curves stop at the Higher High Water. Thus for a range at Portsmouth of 3.5m the factor for 7 hours after L.W. at Poole (Bridge) should be referred to the following Low Water, whereas had the range at Portsmouth been 2.5, it should be referred to the preceding Low Water.

NOTES

1. CALSHOT is referred to SOUTHAMPTON as Standard Port. The two curves on page 26 should be taken as referring to the Spring and Neap Ranges at Southampton (4.0 and 1.9m respectively)

2. NEWPORT. Owing to the constriction of the River Medina, Newport requires slightly different treatment since the harbour dries out at 1.4m. The calculation should be performed using the Low Water Time and Height Differences for Cowes and the High Water Height Differences for Newport. Any calculated heights which fall below 1.4m should be treated as 1.4m

3. WAREHAM and TUCKTON. Low Waters do not fall below 0.7m except under very low river flow conditions.

To find the Height at a given time at a Secondary Port between Swanage and Selsey

1. Complete top section of N.P. 204 (Page 214). Omit H.W. time column (Boxes 1,7,12)
2. On Standard Curve diagram, plot Secondary Port H.W. and L.W. heights and join by sloping line.
3. From the time required, using Secondary Port L.W. time, proceed vertically to curve, interpolating as necessary using Range at Portsmouth. Do NOT extrapolate.
4. Proceed horizontally to sloping line, thence vertically to Height Scale.
5. Read off height.

EXAMPLE:

Find the height of tide at SWANAGE at 0200 on 18th November

from tables		NOVEMBER	
PORTSMOUTH		**18** 0110	4.6
		0613	1.1
		1318	4.6
		SA 1833	1.0

from tables Location	Lat	Long	High Water		Low Water		MHWS	MHWN	MLWN	MLWS
			0000	0600	0500	1100				
PORTSMOUTH standard port	50 48N	1 07W	and 1200	and 1800	and 1700	and 2300	4.7	3.8	1.8	0.6
Swanage	50 37N	1 57W	-0250	+0105	-0105	-0105	-2.7	-2.2	-0.7	-0.3

STANDARD PORT ___Portsmouth___   TIME/HEIGHT REQUIRED ___0200___

SECONDARY PORT ___Swanage___   DATE _18 Nov._ TIME ZONE ___GMT___

	TIME		HEIGHT		
	HW	**LW**	**HW**	**LW**	**RANGE**
STANDARD PORT	1 –	2 0613	3 4.6	4 1.1	5 3.5
Seasonal change	Standard Ports -		6 0.0	6 0.0	
DIFFERENCES	7* –	8 -0105	9 -2.7	10 -0.5	
Seasonal change *	Secondary Ports +		11 0.0	11 0.0	
SECONDARY PORT	12 –	13 0508	14 1.9	15 0.6	
Duration	16 –				

Height 1.7m

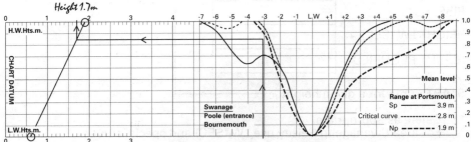

Swanage
Poole (entrance)
Bournemouth

Mean level

Range at Portsmouth
Sp ——— 3.9 m
Critical curve ------------ 2.8 m
Np – – – – – 1.9 m

* *The Seasonal changes are generally less than ± 0.1m and for most purposes can be ignored. See Admiralty Tide Tables Vol 1 for full details.*

TIDAL PREDICTION FORM

STANDARD PORT .... TIME/HEIGHT REQUIRED........................

SECONDARY PORT................................ DATE ....TIME ZONE.................

	TIME		HEIGHT		
STANDARD PORT	HW	LW	HW	LW	RANGE
	1	2	3	4	5
Seasonal change	Standard Ports +		6	6	
DIFFERENCES	7*	8*	9*	10*	
Seasonal change	Secondary Ports -		11	11	
SECONDARY PORT	12	13	14	15	
Duration	16				

Springs/Neaps/Interpolate (Box 21a) **

START - height for a given time

REQUIRED TIME	18
TIME HW (SEC)*	19
INTERVAL (SEC)	20

21a

	FACTOR	STANDARD RANGE
SPRINGS		
NEAPS		
	INTERVAL	RANGE STANDARD

FACTOR	21

RANGE (SEC) x	22
RISE	23
HEIGHT LW (SEC) +	24
HEIGHT REQUIRED	25

START - time for a given height

** Delete as appropriate.

* For area Swanage to Selsey use LW (SEC) and special curves.

SECONDARY PORTS & TIDAL DIFFERENCES
SOUTH COAST ENGLAND *Time Zone UT*

Location	Lat	Long	High Water		Low Water		MHWS	MHWN	MLWN	MLWS
			0000	0600	0000	0600				
PLYMOUTH, DEVONPORT	50 22N	4 11W	and	and	and	and	5.5	4.4	2.2	0.8
standard port			1200	1800	1200	1800				
Isles of Scilly, St. Mary's	49 55N	6 19W	-0035	-0100	-0040	-0025	+0.2	-0.1	-0.2	-0.1
Penzance Newlyn	50 06N	5 33W	-0040	-0105	-0030	-0025	0.0	-0.1	-0.2	0.0
Porthleven	50 05N	5 19W	-0045	-0105	-0030	-0025	0.0	-0.1	-0.2	0.0
Lizard Point	49 57N	5 12W	-0045	-0100	-0030	-0030	-0.2	-0.2	-0.3	-0.2
Coverack	50 01N	5 05W	-0030	-0050	-0020	-0015	-0.2	-0.2	-0.3	-0.2
Helford River (Entrance)	50 05N	5 05W	-0030	-0035	-0015	-0010	-0.2	-0.2	-0.3	-0.2
FALMOUTH	50 09N	5 03W		*standard port*						
Truro	50 16N	5 03W	-0020	-0025	*dries*	*dries*	-2.0	-2.0	*dries*	
Mevagissey	50 16N	4 47W	-0015	-0020	-0010	-0005	-0.1	-0.1	-0.2	-0.1
Par	50 21N	4 42W	-0010	-0015	-0010	-0005	-0.4	-0.4	-0.4	-0.2
Fowey	50 20N	4 38W	-0010	-0015	-0010	-0005	-0.1	-0.1	-0.2	-0.2
Lostwithiel	50 24N	4 40W	+0005	-0010	*dries*	*dries*	-4.1	-4.1	*dries*	
Looe	50 21N	4 27W	-0010	-0010	-0005	-0005	-0.1	-0.2	-0.2	-0.2
Whitsand Bay	50 20N	4 15W	0000	0000	0000	0000	0.0	+0.1	-0.1	+0.2
Saltash	50 24N	4 12W	0000	+0010	0000	-0005	+0.1	+0.1	+0.1	+0.1
Cargreen	50 26N	4 12W	0000	+0010	+0020	+0020	0.0	0.0	-0.1	0.0
Cotehele Quay	50 29N	4 13W	0000	+0020	+0045	+0045	-0.9	-0.9	-0.8	-0.4
Lopwell	50 28N	4 09W	*no data*	*no data*	*dries*	*dries*	-2.6	-2.7	*dries*	
Jupiter Point	50 23N	4 14W	+0010	+0005	0000	-0005	0.0	0.0	+0.1	0.0
St. Germans	50 23N	4 18W	0000	0000	+0020	+0020	-0.3	-0.1	0.0	+0.2
Turnchapel	50 22N	4 07W	0000	0000	+0010	-0015	0.0	+0.1	+0.2	+0.1
Bovisand Pier .	50 20N	4 08W	0000	-0020	0000	-0010	-0.2	-0.1	0.0	+0.1
River Yealm Entrance	50 18N	4 04W	+0006	+0006	+0002	+0002	-0.1	-0.1	-0.1	-0.1
			0100	0600	0100	0600				
PLYMOUTH, DEVONPORT	50 22N	4 11W	and	and	and	and	5.5	4.4	2.2	0.8
standard port			1300	1800	1300	1800				
Salcombe	50 13N	3 47W	0000	+0010	+0005	-0005	-0.2	-0.3	-0.1	-0.1
Start Point	50 13N	3 39W	+0015	+0015	+0005	+0010	-0.1	-0.2	+0.1	+0.2
River Dart										
DARTMOUTH	50 21N	3 34W		*standard port*						
Greenway Quay	50 23N	3 35W	+0030	+0045	+0025	+0005	-0.6	-0.6	-0.2	-0.2
Totnes	50 26N	3 41W	+0030	+0040	+0115	+0030	-2.0	-2.1	*dries*	
Torquay	50 28N	3 31W	+0025	+0045	+0010	0000	-0.6	-0.7	-0.2	-0.1
Teignmouth *Approaches*	50 33N	3 30W	+0025	+0040	0000	0000	-0.7	-0.8	-0.3	-0.2
Teignmouth *Shaldon Bridge*	50 33N	3 31W	+0035	+0050	+0020	+0020	-0.9	-0.9	-0.2	0.0
Exmouth *Approaches*	50 36N	3 23W	+0030	+0050	+0015	+0005	-0.9	-1.0	-0.5	-0.3
River Exe										
Exmouth Dock	50 37N	3 25W	+0035	+0055	+0050	+0020	-1.5	-1.6	-0.9	-0.6
Starcross	50 38N	3 27W	+0040	+0110	+0055	+0025	-1.4	-1.5	-0.8	-0.1
Topsham	50 41N	3 28W	+0045	+0105	*no data*	*no data*	- 1.5	-1.6	*no data*	
Lyme Regis	50 43N	2 56W	+0040	+0100	+0005	-0005	-1.2	-1.3	-0.5	-0.2
Bridport *West Bay*	50 42N	2 45W	+0025	+0040	0000	0000	-1.4	-1.4	-0.6	-0.2
Chesil Beach	50 37N	2 33W	+0040	+0055	-0005	+0010	-1.6	-1.5	-0.5	0.0
Chesil Cove	50 34N	2 28W	+0035	+0050	-0010	+0005	-1.5	-1.6	-0.5	-0.2
			0100	0700	0100	0700				
PORTLAND	50 34N	2 26W	and	and	and	and	2.1	1.4	0.8	0.1
standard port			1300	1900	1300	1900				
Lulworth Cove	50 37N	2 15W	+0005	+0015	-0005	0000	+0.1	+0.1	+0.2	+0.1
Mupe Bay	50 37N	2 13W	+0005	+0015	-0005	0000	+0.1	+0.1	+0.2	+0.1
			0000	0600	0500	1100				
PORTSMOUTH	50 48N	1 07W	and	and	and	and	4.7	3.8	1.9	0.8
standard port			1200	1800	1700	2300				
Swanage	50 37N	1 57W	-0250	+0105	-0105	-0105	-2.7	-2.2	-0.7	-0.3
Poole Harbour Entrance	50 41N	1 57W	-0230	+0115	-0045	-0020	-2.5	-2.1	-0.6	-0.2
POOLE, TOWN QUAY	50 43N	1 59W		*standard port*						
Pottery Pier	50 42N	1 59W	-0150	+0200	-0010	0000	-2.7	-2.1	-0.6	0.0
Wareham *River Frome*	50 41N	2 06W	-0140	+0205	+0110	+0035	-2.5	-2.1	-0.7	+0.1
Cleavel Point	50 40N	2 00W	-0220	+0130	-0025	-0015	-2.6	-2.3	-0.7	-0.3
Bournemouth	50 43N	1 52W	-0240	+0055	-0050	-0030	-2.7	-2.2	-0.8	-0.3
Christchurch *Entrance*	50 43N	1 45W	-0230	+0030	-0035	-0035	-2.9	-2.4	-1.2	-0.2
Christchurch *Quay*	50 44N	1 46W	-0210	+0100	+0105	+0055	-2.9	-2.4	-1.0	0.0
Christchurch *Tuckton*	50 44N	1 47W	-0205	+0110	+0110	+0105	-3.0	-2.5	-1.0	+0.1
Hurst Point	50 42N	1 33W	-0115	-0005	-0030	-0025	-2.0	-1.5	-0.5	-0.1

215

Location	Lat	Long	High Water		Low Water		MHWS	MHWN	MLWN	MLWS
Lymington	50 46N	1 32W	-0110	+0005	-0020	-0020	-1.7	-1.2	-0.5	-0.1
Bucklers Hard	50 48N	1 25W	-0040	-0010	+0010	-0010	-1.0	-0.8	-0.2	-0.3
Stansore Point	50 47N	1 21W	-0050	-0010	-0005	-0010	-0.8	-0.5	-0.3	-0.1
Isle of Wight										
Yarmouth	50 42N	1 30W	-0105	+0005	-0025	-0030	-1.7	-1.2	-0.3	0.0
Totland Bay	50 41N	1 33W	-0130	-0045	-0035	-0045	-2.2	-1.7	-0.4	-0.1
Freshwater	50 40N	1 31W	-0210	+0025	-0040	-0020	-2.1	-1.5	-0.4	0.0
Ventnor	50 36N	1 12W	-0025	-0030	-0025	-0030	-0.8	-0.6	-0.2	+0.2
Sandown	50 39N	1 09W	0000	+0005	+0010	+0025	-0.6	-0.5	-0.2	0.0
Foreland *Lifeboat Slip*	50 41N	1 04W	-0005	0000	+0005	+0010	-0.1	-0.1	0.0	+0.1
Bembridge Harbour	50 42N	1 06W	-0020	0000	+0100	0020	-1.5	-1.4	-1.3	-1.0
Ryde	50 44N	1 07W	-0010	+0010	-0005	-0010	-0.2	-0.1	0.0	+0.1
Medina River										
Cowes	50 46N	1 18W	-0015	+0015	0000	-0020	-0.5	-0.3	-0.1	0.0
Folly Inn	50 44N	1 17W	-0015	+0015	0000	-0020	-0.6	-0.4	-0.1	+0.2
Newport	50 42N	1 17W	no data	no data	no data	no data	-0.6	-0.4	+0.1	+0.8
			0400	**1100**	**0000**	**0600**				
SOUTHAMPTON	50 54N	1 24W	and	and	and	and	4.5	3.7	1.8	0.5
standard port			**1600**	**2300**	**1200**	**1800**				
Calshot Castle	50 49N	1 18W	0000	+0025	0000	0000	0.0	0.0	+0.2	+0.3
Redbridge	50 55N	1 28W	-0020	+0005	0000	-0005	-0.1	-0.1	-0.1	-0.1
River Hamble										
Warsash	50 51N	1 18W	+0020	+0005	+0010	0000	0.0	+0.1	+0.1	+0.3
Bursledon	50 53N	1 18W	+0020	+0020	+0010	+0010	+0.1	+0.1	+0.2	+0.2
			0500	**1000**	**0000**	**0600**				
PORTSMOUTH	50 48N	1 07W	and	and	and	and	4.7	3.8	1.9	0.8
standard port			**1700**	**2200**	**1200**	**1800**				
Lee-on-the-Solent	50 48N	1 12W	-0005	+0005	-0015	-0010	-0.2	-0.1	+0.1	+0.2
Chichester Harbour										
Entrance	50 47N	0 56W	-0010	+0005	+0015	+0020	+0.2	+0.2	0.0	+0.1
Northney	50 50N	0 58W	+0020	+0010	0000	+0005	0.0	-0.2	-0.2	-0.4
Bosham	50 50N	0 52W	+0010	+0005	no data	no data	0.0	-0.1	no data	
Itchenor	50 48N	0 52W	+0005	0000	-0010	+0005	-0.1	-0.2	-0.2	-0.3
Dell Quay	50 49N	0 49W	+0015	+0010	no data	no data	0.0	-0.1	no data	
Selsey Bill	50 43N	0 47W	-0005	-0005	+0035	+0035	+0.6	+0.6	0.0	0.0
Nab Tower	50 40N	0 57W	+0015	0000	+0015	+0015	-0.2	0.0	+0.2	0.0
			0500	**1000**	**0000**	**0600**				
SHOREHAM	50 50N	0 15W	and	and	and	and	6.3	4.8	1.9	0.6
standard port			**1700**	**2200**	**1200**	**1800**				
Pagham	50 46N	0 43W	+0015	0000	-0015	-0025	-0.7	-0.5	-0.1	-0.1
Bognor Regis	50 47N	0 40W	+0010	-0005	-0005	-0020	-0.6	-0.5	-0.2	-0.1
River Arun										
Littlehampton *Entrance*	50 48N	0 32W	+0010	0000	-0005	-0010	-0.4	-0.4	-0.2	-0.2
Littlehampton *Norfolk Wharf*	50 48N	0 33W	+0015	+0005	0000	+0045	-0.7	-0.7	-0.3	+0.2
Arundel	50 51N	0 33W	no data	+0120	no data	no data	-3.1	-2.8	no data	
Worthing	50 48N	0 22W	+0010	0000	-0005	-0010	-0.1	-0.2	0.0	0.0
Brighton	50 49N	0 08W	-0010	-0005	-0005	-0005	+0.3	+0.1	0.0	-0.1
Newhaven	50 47N	0 04E	-0015	-0010	0000	0000	+0.4	+0.2	0.0	-0.2
Eastbourne	50 46N	0 17E	-0010	-0005	+0015	+0020	+1.1	+0.6	+0.2	+0.1
			0000	**0600**	**0100**	**0700**				
DOVER	51 07N	1 19E	and	and	and	and	6.8	5.3	2.1	0.8
standard port			**1200**	**1800**	**1300**	**1900**				
Hastings	50 51N	0 35E	0000	-0010	-0030	-0030	+0.8	+0.5	+0.1	-0.1
Rye *Approaches*	50 55N	0 47E	+0005	-0010	no data	no data	+1.0	+0.7	no data	
Rye *Harbour*	50 56N	0 46E	+0005	-0010	dries	dries	-1.4	-1.7	dries	
Dungeness	50 54N	0 58E	-0010	-0015	-0020	-0010	+1.0	+0.6	+0.4	+0.1
Folkestone	51 05N	1 12E	-0020	-0005	-0010	-0010	+0.4	+0.4	0.0	-0.1
Deal	51 13N	1 25E	+0010	+0020	+0010	+0005	-0.6	-0.3	0.0	0.0
Richborough	51 18N	1 21E	+0015	+0015	+0030	+0030	-3.4	-2.6	-1.7	-0.7
Ramsgate	51 20N	1 25E	+0030	+0030	+0017	+0007	-1.6	-1.3	-0.7	-0.2

EAST COAST ENGLAND *Time Zone UT*

Location	Lat	Long	High Water		Low Water		MHWS	MHWN	MLWN	MLWS
			0200	**0800**	**0200**	**0700**				
SHEERNESS	51 27N	0 45E	and	and	and	and	5.8	4.7	1.5	0.6
standard port			**1400**	**2000**	**1400**	**1900**				
Margate	51 23N	1 23E	-0050	-0040	-0020	-0050	-0.9	-0.9	-0.1	0.0
Herne Bay	51 23N	1 07E	-0025	-0015	0000	-0025	-0.5	-0.5	-0.1	-0.1
Whitstable	51 22N	1 02E	-0008	-0011	+0005	0000	-0.3	-0.3	0.0	-0.1

Location	Lat	Long	High Water		Low Water		MHWS	MHWN	MLWN	MLWS
River Swale										
Grovehurst Jetty	51 22N	0 46E	-0007	0000	0000	+0016	0.0	0.0	0.0	-0.1
Faversham	51 19N	0 54E	*no data*	*no data*	*no data*	*no data*	-0.2	-0.2	*no data*	
River Medway										
Bee Ness	51 25N	0 39E	+0002	+0002	0000	+0005	+0.2	+0.1	0.0	0.0
Bartlett Creek	51 23N	0 38E	+0016	+0008	*no data*	*no data*	+0.1	0.0	*no data*	
Darnett Ness	51 24N	0 36E	+0004	+0004	0000	+0010	+0.2	+0.1	0.0	-0.1
Chatham *Lock approaches*	51 24N	0 33E	+0010	+0012	+0012	+0018	+0.3	+0.1	-0.1	-0.2
Upnor	51 25N	0 32E	+0015	+0015	+0015	+0025	+0.2	+0.2	-0.1	-0.1
Rochester *Strood Pier*	51 24N	0 30E	+0018	+0018	+0018	+0028	+0.2	+0.2	-0.2	-0.3
Wouldham	51 21N	0 27E	+0030	+0025	+0035	+0120	-0.2	-0.3	-1.0	-0.3
New Hythe	51 19N	0 28E	+0035	+0035	+0220	+0240	-1.6	-1.7	-1.2	-0.3
Allington Lock	51 17N	0 30E	+0050	+0035	*no data*	*no data*	-2.1	-2.2	-1.3	-0.4
River Thames										
Southend-on-Sea	51 31N	0 43E	-0005	0000	0000	+0005	0.0	0.0	-0.1	-0.1
Coryton	51 30N	0 31E	+0005	+0010	+0010	+0015	+0.4	+0.3	+0.1	-0.1
			0300	0900	0400	1100				
LONDON BRIDGE	51 30N	0 05W	and	and	and	and	7.1	5.9	1.3	0.5
standard port			1500	2100	1600	2300				
Albert Bridge	51 29N	0 10W	+0025	+0020	+0105	+0110	-0.9	-0.8	-0.7	-0.4
Hammersmith Bridge	51 29N	0 14W	+0040	+0035	+0205	+0155	-1.4	-1.3	-1.0	-0.5
Kew Bridge	51 29N	0 17W	+0055	+0050	+0255	+0235	-1.8	-1.8	-1.2	-0.5
Richmond Lock	51 28N	0 19W	+0105	+0055	+0325	+0305	-2.2	-2.2	-1.3	-0.5
			0200	0700	0100	0700				
SHEERNESS	51 27N	0 45E	and	and	and	and	5.8	4.7	1.5	0.6
standard port			1400	1900	1300	1900				
Thames Estuary Shivering Sand	51 30N	1 05E	-0025	-0019	-0008	-0026	-0.6	-0.6	-0.1	-0.1
			0000	0600	0500	1100				
WALTON-ON-THE-NAZE	51 51N	1 17E	and	and	and	and	4.2	3.4	1.1	0.4
standard port			1200	1800	1700	2300				
Whitaker Beacon	51 40N	1 06E	+0022	+0024	+0033	+0027	+0.6	+0.5	+0.2	+0.1
Holliwell Point	51 38N	0 56E	+0034	+0037	+0100	+0037	+1.1	+0.9	+0.3	+0.1
River Roach Rochford	51 35N	0 43E	+0050	+0040	*dries*	*dries*	-0.8	-1.1	*dries*	
River Crouch										
BURNHAM-ON-CROUCH	51 37N	0 48E		*standard port*						
North Fambridge	51 38N	0 41E	+0115	+0050	+0130	+0100	+1.1	+0.8	0.0	-0.1
Hullbridge	51 38N	0 38E	+0115	+0050	+0135	+0105	+1.1	+0.8	0.0	-0.1
Battlesbridge	51 37N	0 34E	+0120	+0110	*dries*	*dries*	-1.8	-2.0	*dries*	
River Blackwater										
Bradwell Waterside	51 45N	0 53E	+0035	+0023	+0047	+0004	+1.0	+0.8	+0.2	0.0
Osea Island	51 43N	0 46E	+0057	+0045	+0050	+0007	+1.1	+0.9	+0.1	0.0
Maldon	51 44N	0 42E	+0107	+0055	*no data*	*no data*	-1.3	-1.1	*no data*	
West Mersea	51 47N	0 54E	+0035	+0015	+0055	+0010	+0.9	+0.4	+0.1	+0.1
River Colne										
Brightlingsea	51 48N	1 00E	+0025	+0021	+0046	+0004	+0.8	+0.4	+0.1	0.0
Colchester	51 53N	0 56E	+0035	+0025	*dries*	*dries*	0.0	-0.3	*dries*	
Clacton-on-Sea	51 47N	1 09E	+0012	+0010	+0025	+0008	+0.3	+0.1	+0.1	+0.1
Bramble Creek	51 53N	1 14E	+0010	-0007	-0005	+0010	+0.3	+0.3	+0.3	+0.3
Sunk Head	51 46N	1 30E	0000	+0002	-0002	+0002	-0.3	-0.3	-0.1	-0.1
Harwich	51 57N	1 17E	+0007	+0002	-0010	-0012	-0.2	0.0	0.0	0.0
Wrabness	51 57N	1 10E	+0017	+0015	-0010	-0012	-0.1	0.0	0.0	0.0
Mistley	51 57N	1 05E	+0032	+0027	-0010	-0012	0.0	0.0	-0.1	-0.1
Pin Mill	52 00N	1 17E	+0012	+0015	-0008	-0012	-0.1	0.0	0.0	0.0
Ipswich	52 03N	1 10E	+0022	+0027	0000	-0012	0.0	0.0	-0.1	-0.1
			0100	0700	0100	0700				
WALTON-ON-THE-NAZE	51 51N	1 17E	and	and	and	and	4.2	3.4	1.1	0.4
standard port			1300	1900	1300	1900				
Felixstowe Pier	51 57N	1 21E	-0008	-0010	-0020	-0020	-0.4	-0.3	-0.1	0.0
River Deben										
Woodbridge Haven	51 59N	1 24E	0000	-0005	-0020	-0025	-0.5	-0.5	-0.1	+0.1
Woodbridge	52 05N	1 19E	+0045	+0025	+0025	-0020	-0.2	-0.3	-0.2	0.0
Bawdsey	52 00N	1 26E	-0016	-0020	-0030	-0032	-0.8	-0.6	-0.1	-0.1
Orford Haven										
Bar	52 02N	1 28E	-0026	-0030	-0036	-0038	-1.0	-0.8	-0.1	0.0
Orford Quay	52 05N	1 32E	+0040	+0040	+0055	+0055	-1.4	-1.1	0.0	+0.2
Slaughden Quay	52 08N	1 36E	+0105	+0105	+0125	+0125	-1.3	-0.8	-0.1	+0.2
Iken Cliffs	52 09N	1 31E	+0130	+0130	+0155	+0155	-1.3	-1.0	0.0	+0.2

Location	Lat	Long	High Water		Low Water		MHWS	MHWN	MLWN	MLWS
			0300	0900	0200	0800				
LOWESTOFT	52 28N	1 45E	and	and	and	and	2.4	2.1	1.0	0.5
standard port			1500	2100	1400	2000				
Orford Ness	52 05N	1 35E	+0135	+0135	+0135	+0125	+0.4	+0.6	-0.1	0.0
Aldeburgh	52 09N	1 36E	+0130	+0130	+0115	+0120	+0.3	+0.2	-0.1	-0.2
Minsmere Sluice	52 14N	1 38E	+0110	+0110	+0110	+0110	0.0	-0.1	-0.2	-0.2
Southwold	52 19N	1 40E	+0105	+0105	+0055	+0055	0.0	0.0	-0.1	0.0
Great Yarmouth										
Gorleston-on-Sea	52 34N	1 44E	-0035	-0035	-0030	-0030	0.0	0.0	0.0	0.0
Britannia Pier	52 36N	1 45E	-0105	-0100	-0040	-0055	+0.1	+0.1	0.0	0.0
Caister-on-Sea	52 39N	1 44E	-0120	-0120	-0100	-0100	0.0	-0.1	0.0	0.0
Winterton-on-Sea	52 43N	1 42E	-0225	-0215	-0135	-0135	+0.8	+0.5	+0.2	+0.1
			0100	0700	0100	0700				
IMMINGHAM	53 38N	0 11E	and	and	and	and	7.3	5.8	2.6	0.9
standard port			1300	1900	1300	1900				
Cromer	52 56N	1 18E	+0050	+0030	+0050	+0130	-2.1	-1.7	-0.5	-0.1
Blakeney Bar	52 59N	0 59E	+0035	+0025	+0030	+0040	-1.6	-1.3	*no data*	
Blakeney	52 57N	1 01E	+0115	+0055	*no data*	*no data*	-3.9	-3.8	*no data*	
Wells Bar	52 59N	0 49E	+0020	+0020	+0020	+0020	-1.3	-1.0	*no data*	
Wells	52 57N	0 51E	+0035	+0045	+0340	+0310	-3.8	-3.8	*not below CD*	
Burnham *Overy Staithe*	52 58N	0 48E	+0045	+0055	*no data*	*no data*	-5.0	-4.9	*no data*	
The Wash										
Hunstanton	52 56N	0 29E	+0010	+0020	+0105	+0025	+0.1	-0.2	-0.1	0.0
West Stones	52 50N	0 21E	+0025	+0025	+0115	+0040	-0.3	-0.4	-0.3	+0.2
King's Lynn	52 45N	0 24E	+0030	+0030	+0305	+0140	-0.5	-0.8	-0.8	+0.1
Wisbech Cut	52 48N	0 13E	+0020	+0025	+0200	+0030	-0.3	-0.7	-0.4	*no data*
Lawyer's Creek	52 53N	0 05E	+0010	+0020	*no data*	*no data*	-0.3	-0.6	*no data*	
Tabs Head	52 56N	0 05E	0000	+0005	+0125	+0020	+0.2	-0.2	-0.2	-0.2
Boston	52 58N	0 01W	0000	+0010	+0140	+0050	-0.5	-1.0	-0.9	-0.5
Skegness	53 09N	0 21E	+0010	+0015	+0030	+0020	-0.4	-0.5	-0.1	0.0
Inner Dowsing Light Tower	53 20N	0 34E	0000	0000	+0010	+0010	-0.9	-0.7	-0.1	+0.3
River Humber										
Bull Sand Fort	53 34N	0 04E	-0020	-0030	-0035	-0015	-0.4	-0.3	+0.1	+0.2
Grimsby	53 35N	0 04W	-0010	-0010	-0012	-0012	-0.2	-0.1	0.0	+0.2
Hull *King George Dock*	53 44N	0 16W	+0010	+0010	+0021	+0017	+0.3	+0.2	-0.1	-0.2
Hull *Albert Dock*	53 44N	0 21W	+0019	+0019	+0033	+0027	+0.3	+0.1	-0.1	-0.2
Humber Bridge	53 43N	0 27W	+0027	+0022	+0049	+0039	-0.1	-0.4	-0.7	-0.6
River Trent										
Burton Stather	53 39N	0 42W	+0105	+0045	+0335	+0305	-2.1	-2.3	-2.3	*dries*
Flixborough Wharf	53 37N	0 42W	+0120	+0100	+0400	+0340	-2.3	-2.6	*dries*	
Keadby	53 36N	0 44W	+0135	+0120	+0425	+0410	-2.5	-2.8	*dries*	
Owston Ferry	53 29N	0 46W	+0155	+0145	*dries*	*dries*	-3.5	-3.9	*dries*	
River Ouse										
Blacktoft	53 42N	0 43W	+0100	+0055	+0325	+0255	-1.6	-1.8	-2.2	-1.1
Goole	53 42N	0 52W	+0130	+0115	+0355	+0350	-1.6	-2.1	-1.9	-0.6
			0200	0800	0100	0800				
R. TYNE, N. SHIELDS	55 01N	1 26W	and	and	and	and	5.0	3.9	1.8	0.7
standard port			1400	2000	1300	2000				
Bridlington	55 47N	2 00W	+0119	+0109	+0109	+0104	+1.1	+0.8	+0.5	+0.4
Filey Bay	54 13N	0 16W	+0101	+0101	+0101	+0048	+0.8	+1.0	+0.6	+0.3
Scarborough	55 17N	0 23W	+0059	+0059	+0044	+0044	+0.7	+0.7	+0.5	+0.2
Whitby	55 29N	0 37W	+0034	+0049	+0034	+0019	+0.6	+0.4	+0.1	+0.1
Middlesborough	55 35N	1 13W	+0019	+0021	+0014	+0011	+0.6	+0.6	+0.3	+0.1
Hartlepool	55 41N	1 11W	+0015	+0015	+0008	+0008	+0.4	+0.3	0.0	+0.1
Seaham	54 50N	1 19W	+0004	+0004	-0001	-0001	+0.2	+0.2	+0.2	0.0
Sunderland	45 55N	1 21W	+0002	-0002	-0002	-0002	+0.2	+0.3	+0.2	+0.1
Newcastle-upon-Tyne	54 58N	1 36W	+0003	+0003	+0008	+0008	+0.3	+0.2	+0.1	+0.1
Blyth	55 07N	1 29W	+0005	-0007	-0001	+0009	0.0	0.0	-0.1	+0.1
Coquet Island	55 20N	1 32W	-0010	-0010	-0020	-0020	+0.1	+0.1	0.0	+0.1
Amble	55 20N	1 34W	-0013	-0013	-0016	-0020	0.0	0.0	+0.1	+0.1
North Sunderland	55 34N	1 38W	-0048	-0044	-0058	-0102	-0.2	-0.2	-0.2	0.0
Holy Island	55 40N	1 47W	-0043	-0039	-0105	-0110	-0.2	-0.2	-0.3	-0.1
Berwick	55 47N	2 00W	-0053	-0053	-0109	-0109	-0.3	-0.1	-0.5	-0.1
			0300	0900	0300	0900				
SCOTLAND *Time Zone UT*										
LEITH	55 59N	3 11W	and	and	and	and	5.6	4.4	2.0	0.8
standard port			1500	2100	1500	2100				
Eyemouth	55 52N	2 05W	-0015	-0025	-0014	-0004	-0.9	-0.8	*no data*	
Dunbar	56 00N	2 31W	-0005	-0010	+0010	+0017	-0.4	-0.3	-0.1	-0.1
Fidra	56 04N	2 47W	-0001	0000	-0002	+0001	-0.2	-0.2	0.0	0.0

Location	Lat	Long	High Water		Low Water		MHWS	MHWN	MLWN	MLWS
Cockenzie	55 58N	2 57W	-0007	-0015	-0013	-0005	-0.2	0.0	no data	
Granton	55 59N	3 13W	0000	0000	0000	0000	0.0	0.0	0.0	0.0
Grangemouth	56 02N	3 41W	+0025	+0010	-0052	-0015	-0.1	-0.2	-0.3	-0.3
Kincardine	56 04N	3 43W	+0015	+0030	-0030	-0030	0.0	-0.2	-0.5	-0.3
Alloa	56 07N	3 48W	+0040	+0040	+0025	+0025	-0.2	-0.5	No data	-0.7
Stirling	56 07N	3 56W	+0100	+0100		No data	-2.9	-3.1	-2.3	-0.7
Firth of Forth										
Burntisland	56 03N	3 14W	+0013	+0004	-0002	+0007	+0.1	0.0	+0.1	+0.2
Kirkcaldy	56 09N	3 09W	+0005	0000	-0004	-0001	-0.3	-0.3	-0.2	-0.2
Methil	56 11N	3 00W	-0005	-0001	-0001	-0001	-0.1	-0.1	-0.1	-0.1
Anstruther Easter	56 13N	2 42W	-0018	-0012	-0006	-0008	-0.3	-0.2	0.0	0.0
			0000	0600	0100	0700				
ABERDEEN	57 09N	2 05W	and	and	and	and	4.3	3.4	1.6	0.6
standard port			1200	1800	1300	1900				
River Tay										
Bar	56 27N	2 38W	+0100	+0100	+0050	+0110	+0.9	+0.8	+0.3	+0.1
Dundee	56 27N	2 58W	+0140	+0120	+0055	+0145	+1.1	+0.9	+0.3	+0.1
Newburgh	56 21N	3 14W	+0215	+0200	+0250	+0335	-0.2	-0.4	-1.1	-0.5
Perth	56 24N	3 27W	+0220	+0225	+0510	+0530	-0.9	-1.4	-1.2	-0.3
Arbroath	56 33N	2 35W	+0056	+0037	+0034	+0055	+0.7	+0.7	+0.2	+0.1
Montrose	56 42N	2 27W	+0055	+0055	+0030	+0040	+0.5	+0.4	+0.2	0.0
Stonehaven	56 58N	2 12W	+0013	+0008	+0013	+0009	+0.2	+0.2	+0.1	0.0
Peterhead	57 30N	1 46W	-0035	-0045	-0035	-0040	-0.5	-0.3	-0.1	-0.1
Fraserburgh	57 41N	2 00W	-0105	-0115	-0120	-0110	-0.6	-0.5	-0.2	0.0
			0200	0900	0400	0900				
ABERDEEN	57 09N	2 05W	and	and	and	and	4.3	3.4	1.6	0.6
standard port			1400	2100	1600	2100				
Banff	57 40N	2 31W	-0100	-0150	-0150	-0050	-0.4	-0.2	-0.1	+0.2
Whitehills	57 41N	2 35W	-0122	-0137	-0117	-0127	-0.4	-0.3	+0.1	+0.1
Buckie	57 40N	2 58W	-0130	-0145	-0125	-0140	-0.2	-0.2	0.0	+0.1
Lossiemouth	57 43N	3 18W	-0125	-0200	-0130	-0130	-0.2	-0.2	0.0	0.0
Burghead	57 42N	3 29W	-0120	-0150	-0135	-0120	-0.2	-0.2	0.0	0.0
Nairn	57 36N	3 52W	-0120	-0150	-0135	-0130	0.0	-0.1	0.0	+0.1
McDermott Base	57 36N	3 59W	-0110	-0140	-0120	-0115	-0.1	-0.1	+0.1	+0.3
			0300	1000	0000	0700				
ABERDEEN	57 09N	2 05W	and	and	and	and	4.3	3.4	1.6	0.6
standard port			1500	2200	1200	1900				
Inverness Firth										
Fortrose	57 35N	4 08W	-0125	-0125	-0125	-0125	0.0	0.0	no data	
Inverness	57 30N	4 15W	-0115	-0120	-0115	-0105	+0.4	+0.2	+0.1	+0.1
Cromarty Firth										
Cromarty	57 42N	4 03W	-0130	-0135	-0135	-0120	0.0	-0.1	0.0	+0.1
Invergordon	57 41N	4 10W	-0125	-0135	-0135	-0115	0.0	-0.1	-0.1	0.0
Dingwall	57 36N	4 25W	-0105	-0120	no data	no data	0.0	0.0	no data	
			0300	0800	0200	0800				
ABERDEEN	57 09N	2 05W	and	and	and	and	4.3	3.4	1.6	0.6
standard port			1500	2000	1400	2000				
Dornoch Firth										
Portmahomack	57 50N	3 50W	-0120	-0210	-0140	-0110	-0.2	-0.1	+0.1	+0.1
Meikle Ferry	57 51N	4 08W	-0100	-0140	-0120	-0055	+0.1	0.0	-0.1	0.0
Golspie	57 58N	3 59W	-0130	-0215	-0155	-0130	-0.3	-0.3	-0.1	0.0
			0000	0700	0200	0700				
WICK	58 26N	3 05W	and	and	and	and	3.5	2.8	1.4	0.7
standard port			1200	1900	1400	1900				
Helmsdale	58 07N	3 39W	+0025	+0015	+0035	+0030	+0.4	+0.3	+0.1	0.0
Duncansby Head	58 39N	3 02W	-0115	-0115	-0110	-0110	-0.4	-0.4	no data	
Orkney Islands										
Muckle Skerry	58 41N	2 55W	-0025	-0025	-0020	-0020	-0.9	-0.8	-0.4	-0.3
Burray Ness	58 51N	2 52W	+0005	+0005	+0015	+0015	-0.2	-0.3	-0.1	-0.1
Deer Sound	58 58N	2 50W	-0040	-0040	-0035	-0035	-0.3	-0.3	-0.1	-0.1
Kirkwall	58 59N	2 58W	-0042	-0042	-0041	-0041	-0.5	-0.4	-0.1	-0.1
Loth	59 12N	2 42W	-0052	-0052	-0058	-0058	-0.1	0.0	+0.3	+0.4
Kettletoft Pier	59 14N	2 36W	-0025	-0025	-0015	-0015	0.0	0.0	+0.2	+0.2
Rapness	59 15N	2 52W	-0205	-0205	-0205	-0205	+0.1	0.0	+0.2	0.0
Pierowall	59 19N	2 58W	-0150	-0150	-0145	-0145	+0.2	0.0	0.0	-0.1

219

Location	Lat	Long	High Water		Low Water		MHWS	MHWN	MLWN	MLWS
Tingwall	59 05N	3 02W	-0200	-0125	-0145	-0125	-0.4	-0.4	-0.1	-0.1
Stromness	58 58N	3 18W	-0225	-0135	-0205	-0205	+0.1	-0.1	0.0	0.0
St. Mary's	58 54N	2 55W	-0140	-0140	-0140	-0140	-0.2	-0.2	0.0	-0.1
Widewall Bay	58 49N	3 01W	-0155	-0155	-0150	-0150	+0.1	-0.1	-0.1	-0.3
Bur Wick	58 44N	2 58W	-0100	-0100	-0150	-0150	-0.1	-0.1	+0.2	+0.1
			0000	**0600**	**0100**	**0800**				
LERWICK	60 09N	1 08W	and	and	and	and	2.1	1.7	0.9	0.5
standard port			**1200**	**1800**	**1300**	**2000**				
Fair Isle	59 32N	1 36W	-0006	-0015	-0031	-0037	+0.1	0.0	+0.1	+0.1
Shetland Islands										
Sumburgh *Grutness Voe*	59 53N	1 17W	+0006	+0008	+0004	-0002	-0.3	-0.3	-0.2	-0.1
Dury Voe	60 21N	1 10W	-0015	-0015	-0010	-0010	0.0	-0.1	0.0	-0.2
Out Skerries	60 25N	0 45W	-0025	-0025	-0010	-0010	+0.1	0.0	0.0	0.0
Toft Pier	60 28N	1 12W	-0105	-0100	-0125	-0115	+0.2	+0.1	-0.1	-0.1
Burra Voe *Yell Sound*	60 30N	1 03W	-0025	-0025	-0025	-0025	+0.2	+0.1	0.0	-0.1
Mid Yell	60 36N	1 03W	-0030	-0020	-0035	-0025	+0.3	+0.2	+0.2	+0.1
Balta Sound	60 45N	0 50W	-0055	-0055	-0045	-0045	+0.2	+0.1	0.0	-0.1
Burra Firth	60 48N	0 52W	-0110	-0110	-0115	-0115	+0.4	+0.2	0.0	0.0
Bluemull Sound	60 42N	1 00W	-0135	-0135	-0155	-0155	+0.5	+0.2	+0.1	0.0
Sullom Voe	60 27N	1 18W	-0135	-0125	-0135	-0120	0.0	0.0	-0.2	-0.2
Hillswick	60 29N	1 29W	-0220	-0220	-0200	-0200	-0.1	-0.1	-0.1	-0.1
Scalloway	60 08N	1 16W	-0150	-0150	-0150	-0150	-0.5	-0.4	-0.3	0.0
Bay of Quendale	59 54N	1 20W	-0025	-0025	-0030	-0030	-0.4	-0.3	0.0	+0.1
Foula	60 07N	2 03W	-0140	-0130	-0140	-0120	-0.1	-0.1	0.0	0.0
			0200	**0700**	**0100**	**0700**				
WICK	58 26N	3 05W	and	and	and	and	3.5	2.8	1.4	0.7
Standard port			**1400**	**1900**	**1300**	**1900**				
Stroma	58 40N	3 08W	-0115	-0115	-0110	-0110	-0.4	-0.5	-0.1	-0.2
Gills Bay	58 38N	3 10W	-0150	-0150	-0202	-0202	+0.7	+0.7	+0.6	+0.3
Scrabster	58 37N	3 33W	-0255	-0225	-0240	-0230	+1.5	+1.2	+0.8	+0.3
Sule Skerry	59 05N	4 24W	-0320	-0255	-0315	-0250	+0.4	+0.3	+0.2	+0.1
Loch Eriboll Portnancon	58 30N	4 42W	-0340	-0255	-0315	-0255	+1.6	+1.3	+0.8	+0.4
Kyle of Durness	58 36N	4 47W	-0350	-0350	-0315	-0315	+1.1	+0.7	+0.4	-0.1
Rona	59 08N	5 49W	-0410	-0345	-0330	-0340	-0.1	-0.2	-0.2	-0.1
			0100	**0700**	**0300**	**0900**				
STORNOWAY	58 12N	6 23W	and	and	and	and	4.8	3.7	2.0	0.7
standard port			**1300**	**1900**	**1500**	**2100**				
Outer Hebrides										
Loch Shell	58 00N	6 25W	-0013	-0000	0000	-0017	0.0	-0.1	-0.1	0.0
E. Loch Tarbert	57 54N	6 48W	-0025	-0010	-0010	-0020	+0.2	0.0	+0.1	+0.1
Loch Maddy	57 36N	7 06W	-0044	-0014	-0016	-0030	0.0	-0.1	-0.1	0.0
Loch Carnan	57 22N	7 16W	-0050	-0010	-0020	-0040	-0.3	-0.5	-0.1	-0.1
Loch Skiport	57 20N	7 16W	-0100	-0025	-0024	-0024	-0.2	-0.4	-0.3	-0.2
Loch Boisdale	57 09N	7 16W	-0055	-0030	-0020	-0040	-0.7	-0.7	-0.3	-0.2
Barra *North Bay*	57 00N	7 24W	-0103	-0031	-0034	-0048	-0.6	-0.5	-0.2	-0.1
Castle Bay	56 57N	7 29W	-0115	-0040	-0045	-0100	-0.5	-0.6	-0.3	-0.1
Barra Head	56 47N	7 38W	-0115	-0040	-0045	-0055	-0.8	-0.7	-0.2	+0.1
Shillay	57 31N	7 41W	-0103	-0043	-0047	-0107	-0.6	-0.7	-0.7	-0.3
Balivanich	57 29N	7 23W	-0103	-0017	-0031	-0045	-0.7	-0.6	-0.5	-0.2
Scolpaig	57 39N	7 29W	-0033	-0033	-0040	-0040	-1.0	-0.9	-0.5	0.0
Leverburgh	57 46N	7 01W	-0025	-0025	-0015	-0025	-0.2	-0.2	-0.1	-0.1
W. Loch Tarbert	57 55N	6 55W	-0015	-0025	-0056	-0056	-1.5	-1.1	-0.6	0.0
Little Bernera	58 16N	6 52W	-0021	-0011	-0017	-0027	-0.5	-0.6	-0.4	-0.2
Carloway	58 17N	6 47W	-0040	+0020	-0035	-0015	-0.6	-0.5	-0.4	-0.1
St Kilda Village Bay	57 48N	8 34W	-0040	-0040	-0045	-0045	-1.4	-1.2	-0.8	-0.3
Flannan Isles	58 16N	7 36W	-0026	-0016	-0016	-0026	-0.9	-0.7	-0.6	-0.2
Rockall	57 36N	13 41W	-0055	-0055	-0105	-0105	-1.8	-1.5	-0.9	-0.2
			0000	**0600**	**0300**	**0900**				
ULLAPOOL	57 54N	5 10W	and	and	and	and	5.2	3.9	2.1	0.7
standard port			**1200**	**1800**	**1500**	**2100**				
Loch Bervie	58 27N	5 03W	+0030	+0010	+0010	+0020	-0.3	-0.3	-0.2	0.0
Loch Laxford	58 24N	5 05W	+0015	+0015	+0005	+0005	-0.3	-0.4	-0.2	0.0
Eddrachillis Bay										
Badcall Bay	58 19N	5 08W	+0005	+0005	+0005	+0005	-0.7	-0.5	-0.5	+0.2
Loch Nedd	58 14N	5 10W	0000	0000	0000	0000	-0.3	-0.2	-0.2	0.0
Loch Inver	58 09N	5 18W	-0005	-0005	-0005	-0005	-0.2	0.0	0.0	+0.1

Location	Lat	Long	High Water		Low Water		MHWS	MHWN	MLWN	MLWS
Summer Isles Tanera Mor	58 01N	5 24W	-0005	-0005	-0010	-0010	-0.1	+0.1	0.0	+0.1
Loch Ewe Mellon Charles	57 51N	5 38W	-0010	-0010	-0010	-0010	-0.1	-0.1	-0.1	0.0
Loch Gairloch Gairloch	57 43N	5 41W	-0020	-0020	-0010	-0010	0.0	+0.1	-0.3	-0.1
Loch Torridon Shieldaig	57 31N	5 39W	-0020	-0020	-0015	-0015	+0.4	+0.3	+0.1	0.0
Inner Sound Applecross	57 26N	5 49W	-0010	-0015	-0010	-0010	0.0	0.0	0.0	+0.1
Loch Carron Plockton	57 20N	5 39W	+0005	-0025	-0005	-0010	+0.5	+0.5	+0.5	+0.2
Rona Loch a' Bhraige	57 35N	5 58W	-0020	0000	-0010	0000	-0.1	-0.1	-0.1	-0.2
Skye										
Broadford Bay	57 15N	5 54W	-0015	-0015	-0010	-0015	+0.2	+0.1	+0.1	0.0
Portree	57 24N	6 11W	-0025	-0025	-0025	-0025	+0.1	-0.2	-0.2	0.0
Loch Snizort (Uig Bay)	57 35N	6 22W	-0045	-0020	-0005	-0025	+0.1	-0.4	-0.2	0.0
Loch Dunvegan	57 27N	6 38W	-0105	-0030	-0020	-0040	0.0	-0.1	0.0	0.0
Loch Harport	57 20N	6 25W	-0115	-0035	-0020	-0100	-0.1	-0.1	0.0	+0.1
Soay Camus nan Gall	57 09N	6 13W	-0055	-0025	-0025	-0045	-0.4	-0.2	no data	
Loch Alsh										
Kyle of Lochalsh	57 17N	5 43W	-0040	-0020	-0005	-0025	0.0	-0.1	-0.2	-0.2
Dornie Bridge	57 17N	5 31W	-0040	-0010	-0005	-0020	+0.1	-0.1	0.0	0.0
Kyle Rhea Glenelg Bay	57 13N	5 38W	-0105	-0035	-0035	-0055	-0.4	-0.4	-0.9	-0.1
Loch Hourn	57 06N	5 34W	-0125	-0050	-0040	-0110	-0.2	-0.1	-0.1	+0.1
			0000	0600	0100	0700				
OBAN	56 25N	5 29W	and	and	and	and	4.0	2.9	1.8	0.7
standard port			1200	1800	1300	1900				
Loch Nevis										
Inverie Bay	57 02N	5 41W	+0030	+0020	+0035	+0020	+1.0	+0.9	+0.2	0.0
Mallaig	57 00N	5 50W	+0017	+0017	+0017	+0017	+1.0	+0.7	+0.3	+0.1
Eigg Bay of Laig	56 55N	6 10 W	+0015	+0030	+0040	+0005	+0.7	+0.6	-0.2	- 0.2
Loch Moidart	56 47N	5 53W	+0015	+0015	+0040	+0020	+0.8	+0.6	- 0.2	-0.2
Coll Loch Eatharna	56 37N	6 31W	+0025	+0010	+0015	+0025	+0.4	+0.3	no data	
Tiree Gott Bay	56 31N	6 48W	0000	+0010	+0005	+0010	0.0	+0.1	0.0	0.0
			0100	0700	0100	0800				
OBAN	56 25N	5 29W	and	and	and	and	4.0	2.9	1.8	0.7
standard port			1300	1900	1300	2000				
Mull										
Carsaig Bay	56 19N	5 59W	-0015	-0005	-0030	+0020	+0.1	+0.2	0.0	-0.1
Iona	56 19N	6 23W	-0010	-0005	-0020	+0015	0.0	+0.1	-0.3	-0.2
Bunessan	56 19N	6 14W	-0015	-0015	-0010	-0015	+0.3	+0.1	0.0	-0.1
Ulva Sound	56 29N	6 08W	-0010	-0015	0000	-0005	+0.4	+0.3	0.0	-0.1
Loch Sunart Salen	56 42N	5 47W	-0015	+0015	+0010	+0005	+0.6	+0.5	-0.1	-0.1
Sound of Mull										
Tobermory	56 37N	6 04W	+0025	+0010	+0015	+0025	+0.4	+0.4	0.0	0.0
Salen	56 31N	5 57W	+0045	+0015	+0020	+0030	+0.2	+0.2	-0.1	0.0
Loch Aline	56 32N	5 46W	+0012	+0012	no data	no data	+0.5	+0.3	no data	
Craignure	56 28N	5 42W	+0030	+0005	+0010	+0015	0.0	+0.1	-0.1	-0.1
Loch Linnhe										
Corran	56 43N	5 14W	+0007	+0007	+0004	+0004	+0.4	+0.4	-0.1	0.0
Corpach	56 50N	5 07W	0000	+0020	+0040	0000	0.0	0.0	-0.2	-0.2
Loch Eil Head	56 51N	5 20W	+0025	+0045	+0105	+0025	no data		no data	
Loch Leven Head	56 43N	5 00W	+0045	+0045	+0045	+0045	no data		no data	
Loch Linnhe Port Appin	56 33N	5 25W	-0005	-0005	-0030	0000	+0.2	+0.2	+0.1	+0.1
Loch Creran										
Barcaldine Pier	56 32N	5 19W	+0010	+0020	+0040	+0015	+0.1	+0.1	0.0	+0.1
Loch Creran Head	56 33N	5 16W	+0015	+0025	+0120	+0020	-0.3	-0.3	-0.4	-0.3
Loch Etive										
Dunstaffnage Bay	56 27N	5 26W	+0005	0000	0000	+0005	+0.1	+0.1	+0.1	+0.1
Connel	56 27N	5 24W	+0020	+0005	+0010	+0015	-0.3	-0.2	-0.1	+0.1
Bonawe	56 27N	5 13W	+0150	+0205	+0240	+0210	-2.0	-1.7	-1.3	-0.5
Seil Sound	56 18N	5 35W	-0035	-0015	-0040	-0015	-1.3	-0.9	-0.7	-0.3
Colonsay Scalasaig	56 04N	6 10W	-0020	-0005	-0015	+0005	-0.1	-0.2	-0.2	-0.2
Jura Glengarrisdale Bay	56 06N	5 47W	-0020	0000	-0010	0000	-0.4	-0.2	0.0	-0.2
Islay										
Rubha A'Mhail	55 56N	6 07W	-0020	0000	+0005	-0015	-0.3	-0.1	-0.3	-0.1
Ardnave Point	55 52N	6 20W	-0035	+0010	0000	-0025	-0.4	-0.2	-0.3	-0.1
Orsay	55 41N	6 31W	-0110	-0110	-0040	-0040	-1.4	-0.6	-0.5	-0.2
Bruichladdich	55 48N	6 22W	-0105	-0035	-0110	-0110	-1.8	-1.3	-0.4	+0.1
Port Ellen	55 38N	6 11W	-0530	-0050	-0340	-0530	-3.1	-2.1	-1.3	-0.4
Port Askaig	55 51N	6 06W	-0110	-0030	-0020	-0020	-1.9	-1.4	-0.8	-0.3
Sound of Jura										
Craighouse	55 50N	5 57W	-0230	-0250	-0150	-0230	-3.0	-2.4	-1.3	-0.6

Location	Lat	Long	High Water		Low Water		MHWS	MHWN	MLWN	MLWS
Loch Melfort	56 15N	5 29W	-0055	-0025	-0040	-0035	-1.2	-0.8	-0.5	-0.1
Loch Beag	56 09N	5 36W	-0110	-0045	-0035	-0045	-1.6	-1.2	-0.8	-0.4
Carsaig Bay	56 02N	5 38W	-0105	-0040	-0050	-0050	-2.1	-1.6	-1.0	-0.4
Sound of Gigha	55 41N	5 44W	-0450	-0210	-0130	-0410	-2.5	-1.6	-1.0	-0.1
Machrihanish	55 25N	5 45W	-0520	-0350	-0340	-0540	Mean range 0.5 metres			
			0000	**0600**	**0000**	**0600**				
GREENOCK	55 57N	4 46W	and	and	and	and	**3.4**	**2.8**	**1.0**	**0.3**
standard port			1200	1800	1200	1800				
Firth of Clyde										
Southend, Kintyre	55 19N	5 38W	-0030	-0010	+0005	+0035	-1.3	-1.2	-0.5	-0.2
Campbeltown	55 25N	5 36W	-0025	-0005	-0015	+0005	-0.5	-0.3	+0.1	+0.2
Carradale	55 36N	5 28W	-0015	-0005	-0005	+0005	-0.3	-0.2	+0.1	+0.1
Loch Ranza	55 43N	5 18W	-0015	-0005	-0010	-0005	-0.4	-0.3	-0.1	0.0
Loch Fyne										
East Loch Tarbert	55 52N	5 24W	-0005	-0005	0000	-0005	+0.2	+0.1	0.0	0.0
Inveraray	56 14N	5 04W	+0011	+0011	+0034	+0034	-0.1	+0.1	-0.5	-0.2
Kyles of Bute										
Rubha Bodach	55 55N	5 09W	-0020	-0010	-0007	-0007	-0.2	-0.1	+0.2	+0.2
Tighnabruich	55 55N	5 13W	+0007	-0010	-0002	-0015	0.0	+0.2	+0.4	+0.5
Firth of Clyde - continued										
Millport	55 45N	4 56W	-0005	-0025	-0025	-0005	0.0	-0.1	0.0	+0.1
Rothesay Bay	55 51N	5 03W	-0020	-0015	-0010	-0002	+0.2	+0.2	+0.2	+0.2
Wemyss Bay	55 53N	4 53W	-0005	-0005	-0005	-0005	0.0	0.0	+0.1	+0.1
Loch Long										
Coulport	56 03N	4 53W	-0011	-0011	-0008	-0008	0.0	0.0	0.0	0.0
Lochgoilhead	56 10N	4 54W	+0015	0000	-0005	-0005	-0.2	-0.3	-0.3	-0.3
Arrochar	56 12N	4 45W	-0005	-0005	-0005	-0005	0.0	0.0	-0.1	-0.1
Gareloch										
Rosneath	56 01N	4 47W	-0005	-0005	-0005	-0005	0.0	-0.1	0.0	0.0
Faslane	56 04N	4 49W	-0010	-0010	-0010	-0010	0.0	0.0	-0.1	-0.2
Garelochhead	56 05N	4 50W	0000	0000	0000	0000	0.0	0.0	0.0	-0.1
River Clyde										
Helensburgh	56 00N	4 44W	0000	0000	0000	0000	0.0	0.0	0.0	0.0
Port Glasgow	55 56N	4 41W	+0010	+0005	+0010	+0020	+0.2	+0.1	0.0	0.0
Bowling	55 56N	4 29W	+0020	+0010	+0030	+0055	+0.6	+0.5	+0.3	+0.1
Rothesay Dock	55 54N	4 24W	+0025	+0015	+0035	+0100	+1.3	+1.2	+0.5	+0.4
Glasgow	55 51N	4 16W	+0025	+0015	+0035	+0105	+1.3	+1.2	+0.6	+0.4
Firth of Clyde - continued										
Brodick Bay	55 35N	5 08W	0000	0000	+0005	+0005	-0.2	-0.2	0.0	0.0
Lamlash	55 32N	5 07W	-0016	-0036	-0024	-0004	-0.2	-0.2	no data	
Ardrossan	55 38N	4 49W	-0020	-0010	-0010	-0010	-0.2	-0.2	+0.1	+0.1
Irvine	55 36N	4 41W	-0020	-0020	-0030	-0010	-0.3	-0.3	-0.1	0.0
Troon	55 33N	4 41W	-0025	-0025	-0020	-0020	-0.2	-0.2	0.0	0.0
Ayr	55 28N	4 39W	-0025	-0025	-0030	-0015	-0.4	-0.3	+0.1	+0.1
Girvan	55 15N	4 52W	-0025	-0040	-0035	-0010	-0.3	-0.3	-0.1	0.0
Loch Ryan Stranraer	54 55N	5 03W	-0020	-0020	-0017	-0017	-0.4	-0.4	-0.4	-0.2

WEST COAST ENGLAND *Time Zone UT*

Location	Lat	Long	High Water		Low Water		MHWS	MHWN	MLWN	MLWS
			0000	**0600**	**0200**	**0800**				
LIVERPOOL	53 24N	3 01W	and	and	and	and	**9.3**	**7.4**	**2.9**	**0.9**
standard port			1200	1800	1400	2000				
Portpatrick	54 50N	5 07W	+0018	+0026	0000	-0035	-5.5	-4.4	-2.0	-0.6
Wigtown Bay										
Drummore	54 41N	4 53W	+0030	+0040	+0015	+0020	-3.4	-2.5	-0.9	-0.3
Port William	54 43N	4 40W	+0030	+0030	+0025	0000	-2.9	-2.2	-0.8	no data
Isle of Whithorn	54 42N	4 22W	+0020	+0025	+0025	+0005	-2.4	-2.0	-0.8	-0.2
Garlieston	54 47N	4 21W	+0025	+0035	+0030	+0005	-2.3	-1.7	-0.5	no data
Solway Firth										
Kirkcudbright Bay	54 48N	4 04W	+0015	+0015	+0010	0000	-1.8	-1.5	-0.5	-0.1
Hestan Islet	54 50N	3 48W	+0025	+0025	+0020	+0025	-1.0	-1.1	-0.5	0.0
Southerness Point	54 52N	3 36W	+0030	+0030	+0030	+0010	-0.7	-0.7	no data	
Annan Waterfoot	54 58N	3 16W	+0050	+0105	+0220	+0310	-2.2	-2.6	-2.7	
Torduff Point	54 58N	3 09W	+0105	+0140	+0520	+0410	-4.1	-4.9		
Redkirk	54 59N	3 06W	+0110	+0215	+0715	+0445	-5.5	-6.2		
Silloth	54 52N	3 24W	+0030	+0040	+0045	+0055	-0.1	-0.3	-0.6	-0.1
Maryport	54 43N	3 30W	+0017	+0032	+0020	+0005	-0.7	-0.8	-0.4	0.0
Workington	54 39N	3 34W	+0020	+0020	+0020	+0010	-1.2	-1.1	-0.3	0.0
Whitehaven	54 33N	3 36W	+0005	+0015	+0010	+0005	-1.3	-1.1	-0.5	+0.1
Tarn Point	54 17N	3 25W	+0005	+0005	+0010	0000	-1.0	-1.0	-0.4	0.0
Duddon Bar	54 09N	3 20W	+0003	+0003	+0008	+0002	-0.8	-0.8	-0.3	0.0

Location	Lat	Long	High Water		Low Water		MHWS	MHWN	MLWN	MLWS
			0000	0600	0200	0700				
LIVERPOOL	53 24N	3 01W	and	and	and	and	9.3	7.4	2.9	0.9
standard port			1200	1800	1400	1900				
Barrow-in-Furness	54 06N	3 12W	+0009	+0015	+0015	+0011	-0.1	-0.1	- 0.1	+0.1
Ulverston	54 11N	3 04W	+0020	+0040	*no data*	*no data*	0.0	-0.1	*no data*	
Arnside	54 12N	2 51W	+0100	+0135	*no data*	*no data*	+0.5	+0.2	*no data*	
Morecambe	54 04N	2 52W	+0005	+0010	+0030	+0015	+0.2	0.0	0.0	+0.2
Heysham	54 02N	2 55W	+0005	+0005	+0015	0000	+0.1	0.0	0.0	+0.2
River Lune Glasson Dock	54 00N	2 51W	+0020	+0030	+0220	+0240	-2.7	-3.0	*no data*	
Lancaster	54 03N	2 49W	+0110	+0030	*dries*	*dries*	-5.0	-4.9	*dries*	
River Wyre										
Wyre Lighthouse	53 57N	3 02W	-0010	-0010	+0005	0000	-0.1	-0.1	*no data*	
Fleetwood	53 56N	3 00W	-0008	-0008	-0003	-0003	-0.1	-0.1	+0.1	+0.3
Blackpool	53 49N	3 04W	-0015	-0005	-0005	-0015	-0.4	-0.4	-0.1	+0.1
River Ribble Preston	53 46N	2 45W	+0010	+0010	+0335	+0310	-4.0	-4.1	-2.8	-0.8
Liverpool Bay										
Southport	53 39N	3 01W	-0020	-0010	*no data*	*no data*	-0.3	-0.3	*no data*	
Formby	53 32N	3 07W	-0015	-0010	-0020	-0020	-0.3	-0.1	0.0	+0.1
River Mersey										
Gladstone Dock	53 27N	3 01W	-0003	-0003	-0003	-0003	-0.1	-0.1	0.0	-0.1
Eastham	53 19N	2 57W	+0010	+0010	+0009	+0009	+0.3	+0.1	-0.1	-0.3
Hale Head	53 19N	2 48W	+0030	+0025	*no data*	*no data*	-2.4	-2.5	*no data*	
Widnes	53 21N	2 44W	+0040	+0045	+0400	+0345	-4.2	-4.4	-2.5	-0.3
Fiddler's Ferry	53 22N	2 39W	+0100	+0115	+0540	+0450	-5.9	-6.3	-2.4	-0.4
River Dee										
Hilbre Island	53 23N	3 13W	-0015	-0012	-0010	-0015	-0.3	-0.2	+0.2	+0.4
Mostyn Docks	53 19N	3 16W	-0020	-0015	-0020	-0020	-0.8	-0.7	*no data*	
Connah's Quay	53 13N	3 03W	0000	+0015	+0355	+0340	-4.6	-4.4	*dries*	
Chester	53 12N	2 54W	+0105	+0105	+0500	+0500	-5.3	-5.4	*dries*	
Isle of Man										
Peel	54 14N	4 42W	+0005	+0005	-0015	-0025	-4.1	-3.1	-1.4	-0.5
Ramsey	54 19N	4 22W	+0005	+0015	-0005	-0015	-1.9	-1.5	-0.6	0.0
Douglas	54 09N	4 28W	+0005	+0015	-0015	-0025	-2.4	-2.0	-0.5	-0.1
Port St. Mary	54 04N	4 44W	+0005	+0015	-0010	-0030	-3.4	-2.6	-1.3	-0.4
Calf Sound	54 04N	4 48W	+0005	+0005	-0015	-0025	-3.2	-2.6	-0.9	-0.3
Port Erin	54 05N	4 46W	-0005	+0015	-0010	-0050	-4.1	-3.2	-1.3	-0.5
WALES *Time Zone UT*										
Colwyn Bay	53 18N	3 43W	-0020	-0020	*no data*	*no data*	-1.5	-1.3	*no data*	
Llandudno	53 20N	3 50W	-0020	-0020	-0035	-0040	-1.7	-1.4	-0.7	-0.3
			0000	0600	0500	1100				
HOLYHEAD	53 19N	4 37W	and	and	and	and	5.6	4.4	2.0	0.7
standard port			1200	1800	1700	2300				
Conwy	53 17N	3 50W	+0025	+0035	+0120	+0105	+2.3	+1.8	+0.6	+0.4
Menai Strait										
Beaumaris	53 16N	4 05W	+0025	+0010	+0055	+0035	+2.0	+1.6	+0.5	+0.1
Menai Bridge	53 13N	4 09W	+0030	+0010	+0100	+0035	+1.7	+1.4	+0.3	0.0
Port Dinorwic	53 11N	4 13W	-0015	-0025	+0030	0000	0.0	0.0	0.0	+0.1
Caernarfon	53 09N	4 16W	-0030	-0030	+0015	-0005	-0.4	-0.4	-0.1	-0.1
Fort Belan	53 07N	4 20W	-0040	-0015	-0025	-0005	-1.0	-0.9	-0.2	-0.1
Trwyn Dinmor	53 19N	4 03W	+0025	+0015	+0050	+0035	+1.9	+1.5	+0.5	+0.2
Moelfre	53 20N	4 14W	+0025	+0020	+0050	+0035	+1.9	+1.4	+0.5	+0.2
Amlwch	53 25N	4 20W	+0020	+0010	+0035	+0025	+1.6	+ 1.3	+0.5	+0.2
Cemaes Bay	53 25N	4 27W	+0020	+0025	+0040	+0035	+1.0	+0.7	+0.3	+0.1
Treardur Bay	53 16N	4 37W	-0045	-0025	-0015	-0015	-0.4	-0.4	0.0	+0.1
Porth Trecastell	53 12N	4 30W	-0045	-0025	-0005	-0015	-0.6	-0.6	0.0	0.0
Llanddwyn Island	53 08N	4 25W	-0115	-0055	-0030	-0020	-0.7	-0.5	-0.1	0.0
Trefor	53 00N	4 25W	-0115	-0100	-0030	-0020	-0.8	-0.9	-0.2	-0.1
Porth Dinllaen	52 57N	4 34W	-0120	-0105	-0035	-0025	-1.0	-1.0	-0.2	-0.2
Porth Ysgaden	52 54N	4 39W	-0125	-0110	-0040	-0035	-1.1	-1.0	-0.1	-0.1
Bardsey Island	52 46N	4 47W	-0220	-0240	-0145	-0140	-1.2	-1.2	-0.5	-0.1
			0100	0800	0100	0700				
MILFORD HAVEN	51 42N	5 03W	and	and	and	and	7.0	5.2	2.5	0.7
standard port			1300	2000	1300	1900				
Cardigan Bay										
Aberdaron	52 48N	4 43W	+0210	+0200	+0240	+0310	-2.4	-1.9	-0.6	-0.2
St. Tudwal's Roads	52 49N	4 29W	+0155	+0145	+0240	+0310	-2.2	-1.9	-0.7	-0.2
Pwllheli	52 53N	4 24W	+0210	+0150	+0245	+0320	-2.0	- 1.8	-0.6	-0.2
Criccieth	52 55N	4 14W	+0210	+0155	+0255	+0320	-2.0	-1.8	-0.7	-0.3
Porthmadog	52 55N	4 08W	+0235	+0210	*no data*	*no data*	-1.9	-1.8	*no data*	
Barmouth	52 43N	4 03W	+0215	+0205	+0310	+0320	-2.0	-1.7	-0.7	0.0

223

Location	Lat	Long	High Water		Low Water		MHWS	MHWN	MLWN	MLWS
Aberdovey	52 32N	4 03W	+0215	+0200	+0230	+0305	-2.0	-1.7	-0.5	0.0
Aberystwyth	52 24N	4 05W	+0145	+0130	+0210	+0245	-2.0	-1.7	-0.7	0.0
New Quay	52 13N	4 21W	+0150	+0125	+0155	+0230	-2.1	-1.8	-0.6	-0.1
Aberporth	52 08N	4 33W	+0135	+0120	+0150	+0220	-2.1	-1.8	-0.6	-0.1
Port Cardigan	52 07N	4 42W	+0140	+0120	+0220	+0130	-2.3	-1.8	-0.5	0.0
Cardigan *Town*	52 05N	4 40W	+0220	+0150	no data	no data	-2.2	-1.6	no data	
Fishguard	52 00N	4 58W	+0115	+0100	+0110	+0135	-2.2	-1.8	-0.5	+0.1
Porthgain	51 57N	5 11W	+0055	+0045	+0045	+0100	-2.5	-1.8	-0.6	0.0
Ramsey Sound	51 53N	5 19W	+0030	+0030	+0030	+0030	-1.9	-1.3	-0.3	0.0
Solva	51 52N	5 12W	+0015	+0010	+0035	+0015	-1.5	-1.0	-0.2	0.0
Little Haven	51 46N	5 06W	+0010	+0010	+0025	+0015	-1.1	-0.8	-0.2	0.0
Martin's Haven	51 44N	5 15W	+0010	+0010	+0015	+0015	-0.8	-0.5	+0.1	+0.1
Skomer Island	51 44N	5 17W	-0005	-0005	+0005	+0005	-0.4	-0.1	0.0	0.0
Dale Roads	51 42N	5 09W	-0005	-0005	-0008	-0008	0.0	0.0	0.0	-0.1
Cleddau River										
Neyland	51 42N	4 57W	+0002	+0010	0000	0000	0.0	0.0	0.0	0.0
Black Tar	51 45N	4 54W	+0010	+0020	+0005	0000	+0.1	+0.1	0.0	-0.1
Haverfordwest	51 48N	4 58W	+0010	+0025	dries	dries	-4.8	-4.9	dries	
Stackpole Quay	51 37N	4 54W	-0005	+0025	-0010	-0010	+0.9	+0.7	+0.2	+0.3
Tenby	51 40N	4 42W	-0015	-0010	-0015	-0020	+1.4	+1.1	+0.5	+0.2
Towy River										
Ferryside	51 46N	4 22W	0000	-0010	+0220	0000	-0.3	-0.7	-1.7	-0.6
Carmarthen	51 51N	4 18W	+0010	0000	dries	dries	-4.4	-4.8	dries	
Burry Inlet										
Burry Port	51 41N	4 15W	+0003	+0003	+0007	+0007	+1.6	+1.4	+0.5	+0.4
Llanelli	51 40N	4 10W	-0003	-0003	+0150	+0020	+0.8	+0.6	no data	
Mumbles	51 34N	3 58W	+0005	+0010	-0020	-0015	+2.3	+1.7	+0.6	+0.2
River Neath Entrance	51 37N	3 51W	+0002	+0011	dries	dries	+2.7	+2.2	dries	
Port Talbot	51 35N	3 49W	+0003	+0005	-0010	-0003	+2.6	+2.2	+1.0	+0.5
Porthcawl	51 28N	3 42W	+0005	+0010	-0010	-0005	+2.9	+2.3	+0.8	+0.3
			0600	**1100**	**0300**	**0800**				
BRISTOL, AVONMOUTH	51 30N	2 44W	and	and	and	and	**13.2**	**9.8**	**3.8**	**1.0**
standard port			**1800**	**2300**	**1500**	**2000**				
Barry	51 23N	3 16W	-0030	-0015	-0125	-0030	-1.8	-1.3	+0.2	0.0
Flat Holm	51 23N	3 07W	-0015	-0015	-0045	-0045	-1.3	-1.1	-0.2	+0.2
Steep Holm	51 20N	3 06W	-0020	-0020	-0050	-0050	-1.6	-1.2	-0.2	-0.2
Cardiff	51 27N	3 09W	-0015	-0015	-0100	-0030	-1.0	-0.6	+0.1	0.0
Newport	51 33N	2 59W	-0020	-0010	0000	-0020	-1.1	-1.0	-0.6	-0.7
River Wye Chepstow	51 39N	2 40W	+0020	+0020	no data	no data	no data		no data	
			0000	**0600**	**0000**	**0700**				
BRISTOL, AVONMOUTH	51 30N	2 44W	and	and	and	and	**13.2**	**9.8**	**3.8**	**1.0**
standard port			**1200**	**1800**	**1200**	**1900**				

WEST COAST ENGLAND *Time Zone UT*

Location	Lat	Long	High Water		Low Water		MHWS	MHWN	MLWN	MLWS
River Severn										
Sudbrook	51 35N	2 43W	+0010	+0010	+0025	+0015	+0.2	+0.1	-0.1	+0.1
Beachley *Aust*	51 36N	2 38W	+0010	+0015	+0040	+0025	-0.2	-0.2	-0.5	-0.3
Inward Rocks	51 39N	2 37W	+0020	+0020	+0105	+0045	-1.0	-1.1	-1.4	-0.6
Narlwood Rocks	51 39N	2 36W	+0025	+0025	+0120	+0100	-1.9	-2.0	-2.3	-0.8
White House	51 40N	2 33W	+0025	+0025	+0145	+0120	-3.0	-3.1	-3.6	-1.0
Berkeley	51 42N	2 30W	+0030	+0045	+0245	+0220	-3.8	-3.9	-3.4	-0.5
Sharpness Dock	51 43N	2 29W	+0035	+0050	+0305	+0245	-3.9	-4.2	-3.3	-0.4
Wellhouse Rock	51 44N	2 29W	+0040	+0055	+0320	+0305	-4.1	-4.4	-3.1	-0.2
Epney	51 42N	2 24W	+0130	no data	no data	no data	-9.4	no data	no data	
Minsterworth	51 50N	2 23W	+0140	no data	no data	no data	-10.1	no data	no data	
Llanthony	51 51N	2 21W	+0215	no data	no data	no data	-10.7	no data	no data	
			0200	**0800**	**0300**	**0800**				
BRISTOL, AVONMOUTH	51 30N	2 44W	and	and	and	and	**13.2**	**9.8**	**3.8**	**1.0**
standard port			**1400**	**2000**	**1500**	**2000**				
River Avon										
Shirehampton	51 29N	2 41W	0000	0000	+0035	+0010	-0.7	-0.7	-0.8	0.0
Sea Mills	51 29N	2 39W	+0005	+0005	+0105	+0030	-1.4	-1.5	-1.7	-0.1
Cumberland Basin *Entrance*	51 27N	2 37W	+0010	+0010	dries	dries	-2.9	-3.0	dries	
Portishead	51 30N	2 45W	-0002	0000	no data	no data	-0.1	-0.1	no data	
Clevedon	51 27N	2 52W	-0010	-0020	-0025	-0015	-0.4	-0.2	+0.2	0.0
St Thomas Head	51 24N	2 56W	0000	0000	-0030	-0030	-0.4	-0.2	+0.1	+0.1
English & Welsh Grounds	51 28N	2 59W	-0008	-0008	-0030	-0030	-0.5	-0.8	-0.3	0.0
Weston-super-Mare	51 21N	2 59W	-0020	-0030	-0130	-0030	-1.2	-1.0	-0.8	-0.2
River Parrett										
Burnham	51 14N	3 00W	-0020	-0025	-0030	0000	-2.3	-1.9	-1.4	-1.1
Bridgwater	51 08N	3 00W	-0015	-0030	+0305	+0455	-8.6	-8.1	dries	

Location	Lat	Long	High Water		Low Water		MHWS	MHWN	MLWN	MLWS
Hinkley Point	51 13N	3 08W	-0020	-0025	-0100	-0040	-1.7	-1.4	-0.2	-0.2
Watchet	51 11N	3 20W	-0035	-0050	-0145	-0040	-1.9	-1.5	+0.1	+0.1
Minehead	51 13N	3 28W	-0037	-0052	-0155	-0045	-2.6	-1.9	-0.2	0.0
Porlock Bay	51 13N	3 38W	-0045	-0055	-0205	-0050	-3.0	-2.2	-0.1	-0.1
Lynmouth	51 14N	3 49W	-0055	-0115	no data	no data	-3.6	-2.7	no data	
			0100	**0700**	**0100**	**0700**				
MILFORD HAVEN	51 42N	5 03W	and	and	and	and	**7.0**	**5.2**	**2.5**	**0.7**
standard port			**1300**	**1900**	**1300**	**1900**				
Ilfracombe	51 13N	4 07W	-0016	-0016	-0041	-0031	+2.3	+1.8	+0.6	+0.3
Rivers Taw & Torridge										
Appledore	51 03N	4 12W	-0020	-0025	+0015	-0045	+0.5	0.0	-0.9	-0.5
Yelland Marsh	51 04N	4 10W	-0010	-0015	+0100	-0015	+0.1	-0.4	-1.2	-0.6
Fremington	51 05N	4 07W	-0010	-0015	+0030	-0030	-1.1	-1.8	-2.2	-0.5
Barnstaple	51 05N	4 04W	0000	-0015	-0155	-0245	-2.9	-3.8	-2.2	-0.4
Bideford	51 01N	4 12W	-0020	-0025	0000	0000	-1.1	-1.6	-2.5	-0.7
Clovelly	51 00N	4 24W	-0030	-0030	-0020	-0040	+1.3	+1.1	+0.2	+0.2
Lundy	51 10N	4 40W	-0025	-0025	-0020	-0035	+1.0	+0.7	+0.2	0.0
Bude	50 50N	4 33W	-0040	-0040	-0035	-0045	+0.7	+0.6	no data	
Boscastle	50 41N	4 42W	-0045	-0010	-0110	-0100	+0.3	+0.4	+0.2	+0.2
Port Isaac	50 35N	4 50W	-0100	-0100	-0100	-0100	+0.5	+0.6	0.0	+0.2
River Camel										
Padstow	50 33N	4 56W	-0055	-0050	-0040	-0050	+0.3	+0.4	+0.1	+0.1
Wadebridge	50 31N	4 50W	-0052	-0052	+0235	+0245	-3.8	-3.8	-2.5	-0.4
Newquay	50 25N	5 05W	-0100	-0110	-0105	-0050	0.0	+0.1	0.0	-0.1
Perranporth	50 21N	5 09W	-0100	-0110	-0110	-0050	-0.1	0.0	0.0	+0.1
St. Ives	50 13N	5 28W	-0050	-0115	-0105	-0040	-0.4	-0.3	-0.1	+0.1
Cape Cornwall	50 08N	5 42 W	-0130	-0145	-0120	-0120	-1.0	-0.9	-0.5	-0.1
Sennen Cove	50 04N	5 42W	-0130	-0145	-0125	-0125	-0.9	-0.4	no data	

IRELAND *Time Zone UT*

Location	Lat	Long	High Water		Low Water		MHWS	MHWN	MLWN	MLWS
			0000	**0700**	**0000**	**0500**				
DUBLIN, NORTH WALL	53 21N	6 13W	and	and	and	and	**4.1**	**3.4**	**1.5**	**0.7**
standard port			**1200**	**1900**	**1200**	**1700**				
Courtown	52 39N	6 13W	-0328	-0242	-0158	-0138	-2.8	-2.4	-0.5	0.0
Arklow	52 47N	6 08W	-0315	-0201	-0140	-0134	-2.7	-2.2	-0.6	-0.1
Wicklow	52 59N	6 02W	-0019	-0019	-0024	-0026	-1.4	-1.1	-0.4	0.0
Greystones	53 09N	6 04W	-0008	-0008	-0008	-0008	-0.5	-0.4	no data	
Dun Laoghaire	53 18N	6 08W	-0006	-0001	-0002	-0003	0.0	0.0	0.0	+0.1
Dublin Bar	53 21N	6 09W	-0006	-0001	-0002	-0003	0.0	0.0	0.0	+0.1
Howth	53 23N	6 04W	-0007	-0005	+0001	+0005	0.0	-0.1	-0.2	-0.2
Malahide	53 27N	6 09W	+0002	+0003	+0009	+0009	+0.1	-0.2	-0.4	-0.2
Balbriggan	53 37N	6 11W	-0021	-0015	+0010	+0002	+0.3	+0.2	no data	
River Boyne Bar	53 43N	6 14W	-0005	0000	+0020	+0030	+0.4	+0.3	-0.1	-0.2
Dunany Point	53 52N	6 14W	-0028	-0018	-0008	-0006	+0.7	+0.9	no data	
Dundalk Soldiers Point	54 00N	6 21W	-0010	-0010	0000	+0045	+1.0	+0.8	+0.1	-0.1

NORTHERN IRELAND *Time Zone UT*

Location	Lat	Long	High Water		Low Water		MHWS	MHWN	MLWN	MLWS
Carlingford Lough										
Cranfield Point	54 01N	6 03W	-0027	-0011	+0005	-0010	+0.7	+0.9	+0.3	+0.2
Warrenpoint	54 06N	6 15W	-0020	-0010	+0025	+0035	+1.0	+0.7	+0.2	+0.0
Newry *Victoria Lock*	54 09N	6 19W	-0010	-0010	+0025	dries	+1.1	+1.0	+0.1	dries
			0100	**0700**	**0000**	**0600**				
BELFAST	54 36N	5 55W	and	and	and	and	**3.5**	**3.0**	**1.1**	**0.4**
standard port			**1300**	**1900**	**1200**	**1800**				
Kilkeel	54 03N	5 59W	+0040	+0030	+0010	+0010	+1.2	+1.1	+0.4	+0.4
Newcastle	54 12N	5 53W	+0025	+0035	+0020	+0040	+1.6	+1.1	+0.4	+0.1
Killough Harbour	54 15N	5 38W	0000	+0020	no data	no data	+1.8	+1.6	no data	
Ardglass	54 16N	5 36W	+0010	+0015	+0005	+0010	+1.7	+1.2	+0.6	+0.3
Strangford Lough										
Killard Point	54 19N	5 31W	+0011	+0021	+0005	+0025	+1.0	+0.8	+0.1	+0.1
Strangford	54 22N	5 33W	+0147	+0157	+0148	+0208	+0.1	+0.1	-0.2	0.0
Quoile Barrier	54 22N	5 41W	+0150	+0200	+0150	+0300	+0.2	+0.2	-0.3	-0.1
Killyleagh	54 24N	5 39W	+0157	+0207	+0211	+0231	+0.3	+0.3	no data	
South Rock	54 24N	5 25W	+0023	+0023	+0025	+0025	+1.0	+0.8	+0.1	+0.1
Portavogie	54 28N	5 26W	+0010	+0020	+0010	+0020	+1.2	+0.9	+0.3	+0.2
Donaghadee	54 38N	5 32W	+0020	+0020	+0023	+0023	+0.5	+0.4	0.0	+0.1
Carrickfergus	54 43N	5 48W	+0005	+0005	+0005	+0005	-0.3	-0.3	-0.2	-0.1
Larne	54 51N	5 47W	+0005	0000	+0010	-0005	-0.7	-0.5	-0.3	0.0
Red Bay	55 04N	6 03W	+0022	-0010	+0007	-0017	-1.9	-1.5	-0.8	-0.2
Cushendun	55 08N	6 02W	+0010	-0030	0000	-0025	-1.7	-1.5	-0.6	-0.2
Portrush	55 12N	6 40W	-0433	-0433	-0433	-0433	-1.6	-1.6	-0.3	0.0
Coleraine	55 08N	6 40W	-0403	-0403	-0403	-0403	-1.3	-1.2	-0.2	0.0

Location	Lat	Long	High Water		Low Water		MHWS	MHWN	MLWN	MLWS
			0200	0900	0200	0800				
GALWAY	53 16N	9 03W	and	and	and	and	5.1	3.9	2.0	0.6
standard port			1400	2100	1400	2000				
Londonderry	55 00N	7 19W	+0254	+0319	+0322	+0321	-2.4	-1.8	-0.8	-0.1
IRELAND *Time Zone UT*										
Inishtrahull	55 26N	7 14W	+0100	+0100	+0115	+0200	-1.8	-1.4	-0.4	-0.2
Portmore	55 22N	7 20W	+0120	+0120	+0135	+0135	-1.3	-1.1	-0.4	-0.1
Trawbreaga Bay	55 19N	7 23W	+0115	+0059	+0109	+0125	-1.1	-0.8	*no data*	
Lough Swilly										
Rathmullan	55 05N	7 31W	+0125	+0050	+0126	+0118	-0.8	-0.7	-0.1	-0.1
Fanad Head	55 16N	7 38W	+0115	+0040	+0125	+0120	-1.1	-0.9	-0.5	-0.1
Mulroy Bay										
Bar	55 15N	7 46W	+0108	+0052	+0102	+0118	-1.2	-1.0	*no data*	
Sheephaven										
Downies Bay	55 11N	7 50W	+0057	+0043	+0053	+0107	-1.1	-0.9	*no data*	
			0600	1100	0000	0700				
GALWAY	53 16N	9 03W	and	and	and	and	5.1	3.9	2.0	0.6
standard port			1800	2300	1200	1900				
Gweedore Harbour	55 04N	8 19W	+0048	+0100	+0055	+0107	-1.3	-1.0	-0.5	-0.1
Burtonport	54 59N	8 26W	+0042	+0055	+0115	+0055	-1.2	-1.0	-0.6	-0.1
Loughros More Bay	54 47N	8 30W	+0042	+0054	+0046	+0058	-1.1	-0.9	*no data*	
Donegal Bay										
Killybegs	54 38N	8 26W	+0040	+0050	+0055	+0035	-1.0	-0.9	-0.5	0.0
Donegal Hbr *Salt Hill Quay*	54 38N	8 13W	+0038	+0050	+0052	+0104	-1.2	-0.9	*no data*	
Mullaghmore	54 28N	8 27W	+0036	+0048	+0047	+0059	-1.4	-1.0	-0.4	-0.2
Sligo Harbour *Oyster Island*	54 18N	8 34W	+0043	+0055	+0042	+0054	-1.0	-0.9	-0.5	-0.1
Ballysadare Bay *Culleenamore*	54 16N	8 36W	+0059	+0111	+0111	+0123	-1.2	-0.9	*no data*	
Killala Bay *Inishcrone*	54 13N	9 06W	+0035	+0055	+0030	+0050	-1.3	-1.2	-0.7	-0.2
Broadhaven	54 16N	9 53W	+0040	+0050	+0040	+0050	-1.4	-1.1	-0.4	-0.1
Blacksod Bay										
Blacksod Quay	54 06N	10 03W	+0025	+0035	+0040	+0040	-1.2	-1.0	-0.6	-0.2
Bull's Mouth	54 02N	9 55W	+0101	+0057	+0109	+0105	-1.5	-1.0	-0.6	-0.1
Clare Island	53 48N	9 57W	+0019	+0013	+0029	+0023	-1.0	-0.7	-0.4	-0.1
Westport Bay										
Inishraher	53 48N	9 38W	+0030	+0012	+0058	+0026	-0.6	-0.5	-0.3	-0.1
Killary Harbour	53 38N	9 53W	+0021	+0015	+0035	+0029	-1.0	-0.8	-0.4	-0.1
Inishbofin Bofin Harbour	53 37N	10 13W	+0013	+0009	+0021	+0017	-1.0	-0.8	-0.4	-0.1
Clifden Bay	53 29N	10 04W	+0005	+0005	+0016	+0016	-0.7	-0.5	*no data*	
Slyne Head	53 24N	10 14W	+0002	+0002	+0010	+0010	-0.7	-0.5	*no data*	
Roundstone Bay	53 23N	9 55W	+0003	+0003	+0008	+0008	-0.7	-0.5	-0.3	-0.1
Kilkieran Cove	53 20N	9 44W	+0005	+0005	+0016	+0016	-0.3	-0.2	-0.1	0.0
Aran Islands Killeany Bay	53 07N	9 39W	-0008	-0008	+0003	+0003	-0.4	-0.3	-0.2	-0.1
Liscannor	52 56N	9 23W	-0003	-0007	+0006	+0002	-0.4	-0.3	*no data*	
Seafield Point	52 48N	9 30W	-0006	-0014	+0004	-0004	-0.5	-0.4	*no data*	
Kilrush	52 38N	9 30W	+0025	+0016	+0046	+0014	-0.1	-0.2	-0.3	-0.1
Limerick Dock	52 40N	8 38W	+0135	+0141	+0141	+0219	+1.0	+0.7	-0.8	-0.2
			0500	1100	0500	1100				
COBH	51 51N	8 18 W	and	and	and	and	4.1	3.2	1.3	0.4
standard port			1700	2300	1700	2300				
Tralee Bay Fenit Pier	52 16N	9 52W	-0057	-0017	-0029	-0109	+0.5	+0.2	+0.3	+0.1
Smerwick Harbour	52 12N	10 24W	-0107	-0027	-0041	-0121	-0.3	-0.4	*no data*	
Dingle Harbour	52 07N	10 15W	-0111	-0041	-0049	-0119	-0.1	0.0	+0.3	+0.4
Castlemaine Hbr										
Cromane Point	52 09N	9 54W	-0026	-0006	-0017	-0037	+0.4	+0.2	+0.4	+0.2
Valentia Harbour										
Knights Town	51 56N	10 18W	-0118	-0038	-0056	-0136	-0.6	-0.4	-0.1	0.0
Ballinskelligs Bay										
Castle	51 49N	10 16W	-0119	-0039	-0054	-0134	-0.5	-0.5	-0.1	0.0
Kenmare River										
West Cove	51 46N	10 03W	-0113	-0033	-0049	-0129	-0.6	-0.5	-0.1	0.0
Dunkerron Harbour	51 52N	9 38W	-0117	-0027	-0050	-0140	-0.2	-0.3	+0.1	0.0
Coulagh Bay										
Ballycrovane Hbr	51 43N	9 57W	-0116	-0036	-0053	-0133	-0.6	-0.5	-0.1	0.0
Black Ball Harbour	51 36N	10 02W	-0115	-0035	-0047	-0127	-0.7	-0.6	-0.1	+0.1
Bantry Bay										
Castletown Bearhaven	51 39N	9 54W	-0048	-0012	-0025	-0101	-0.9	-0.6	-0.1	0.0
Bantry	51 41N	9 28W	-0045	-0025	-0040	-0105	-0.9	-0.8	-0.2	0.0

Location	Lat	Long	High Water		Low Water		MHWS	MHWN	MLWN	MLWS
Dunmanus Bay										
Dunbeacon Harbour	51 37N	9 33W	-0057	-0025	-0032	-0104	-0.8	-0.7	-0.3	-0.1
Dunmanus Harbour	51 32N	9 40W	-0107	-0031	-0044	-0120	-0.7	-0.6	-0.2	0.0
Crookhaven	51 28N	9 43W	-0057	-0033	-0048	-0112	-0.8	-0.6	-0.4	-0.1
Schull	51 31N	9 32W	-0040	-0015	-0015	-0110	-0.9	-0.6	-0.2	0.0
Baltimore	51 29N	9 23W	-0025	-0005	-0010	-0050	-0.6	-0.3	+0.1	+0.2
Castletownshend	51 32N	9 10W	-0020	-0030	-0020	-0050	-0.4	-0.2	+0.1	+0.3
Clonakilty Bay	51 35N	8 50W	-0033	-0011	-0019	-0041	-0.3	-0.2	*no data*	
Courtmacsherry	51 38N	8 42W	-0029	-0007	+0005	-0017	-0.4	-0.3	-0.2	-0.1
Kinsale	51 42N	8 31W	-0019	-0005	-0009	-0023	-0.2	0.0	+0.1	+0.2
Roberts Cove	51 45N	8 19W	-0005	-0005	-0005	-0005	-0.1	0.0	0.0	+0.1
Cork Harbour										
Ringaskiddy	51 50N	8 19W	+0005	+0020	+0007	+0013	+0.1	+0.1	+0.1	+0.1
Marino Point	51 53N	8 20W	0000	+0010	0000	+0010	+0.1	+0.1	0.0	0.0
Cork City	51 54N	8 27W	+0005	+0010	+0020	+0010	+0.4	+0.4	+0.3	+0.2
Ballycotton	51 50N	8 01W	-0011	+0001	+0003	-0009	0.0	0.0	-0.1	0.0
Youghal	51 57N	7 51W	0000	+0010	+0010	0000	-0.2	-0.1	-0.1	-0.1
Dungarvan Harbour	52 05N	7 34W	+0004	+0012	+0007	-0001	0.0	+0.1	-0.2	0.0
Waterford Harbour										
Dunmore East	52 09N	6 59W	+0008	+0003	0000	0000	+0.1	0.0	+0.1	+0.2
Cheekpoint	52 16N	7 00W	+0022	+0020	+0020	+0020	+0.3	+0.2	+0.2	+0.1
Kilmokea Point	52 17N	7 00W	+0026	+0022	+0020	+0020	+0.2	+0.1	+0.1	+0.1
Waterford	52 16N	7 07W	+0057	+0057	+0046	+0046	+0.4	+0.3	-0.1	+0.1
New Ross	52 24N	6 57W	+0100	+0030	+0055	+0130	+0.3	+0.4	+0.3	+0.4
Baginbun Head	52 10N	6 50W	+0003	+0003	-0008	-0008	-0.2	-0.1	+0.2	+0.2
Great Saltee	52 07N	6 38W	+0019	+0009	-0004	+0006	-0.3	-0.4	*no data*	
Carnsore Point	52 10N	6 22W	+0029	+0019	-0002	+0008	-1.1	-1.0	*no data*	
Rosslare Harbour	52 15N	6 21W	+0045	+0035	+0015	-0005	-2.2	-1.8	-0.5	-0.1
Wexford Harbour	52 20N	6 27W	+0126	+0126	+0118	+0108	-2.1	-1.7	-0.3	+0.1

DENMARK *Time Zone -0100*

			0300	0700	0100	0800				
ESBJERG	55 28N	8 27E	and	and	and	and	l.8	1.4	0.4	0.0
standard port			1500	1900	1300	2000				
Hirtshals	57 36N	9 58E	+0055	+0320	+0340	+0100	-1.5	-1.1	-0.3	0.0
Hanstholm	57 08N	8 36E	+0100	+0340	+0340	+0130	-1.5	-1.1	-0.3	0.0
Thyborøn	56 42N	8 13E	+0120	+0230	+0410	+0210	-1.4	-1.1	-0.3	0.0
Torsminde	56 22N	8 07E	+0045	+0050	+0040	+0010	-1.2	-0.9	-0.3	0.0
Hvide Sande	56 00N	8 07E	0000	+0010	-0015	-0025	-1.0	-0.7	-0.3	0.0
Blavandshuk	55 33N	8 05E	-0120	-0110	-0050	-0100	0.0	0.0	-0.1	0.0
Gradyb Bar	55 26N	8 15E	-0130	-0115	*no data*	*no data*	-0.3	-0.2	-0.1	0.0
Rømø Havn	55 05N	8 34E	-0040	-0005	0000	-0020	+0.2	+0.2	-0.1	0.0
Hojer	54 58N	8 40E	-0020	+0015	*no data*	*no data*	+0.6	+0.7	0.0	0.0

GERMANY *Time Zone -0100*

			0100	0600	0100	0800				
HELGOLAND	54 11N	7 53E	and	and	and	and	2.7	2.4	0.4	0.0
standard port			1300	1800	1300	2000				
Lister Tief List	55 01N	8 27E	+0252	+0240	+0201	+0210	-0.8	-0.6	-0.2	0.0
Hörnum	54 46N	8 18E	+0223	+0218	+0131	+0137	-0.5	-0.4	-0.2	0.0
Amrum-Hafen	54 38N	8 23E	+0138	+0137	+0128	+0134	+0.2	+0.2	-0.1	0.0
Dagebüll	54 44N	8 41E	+0226	+0217	+0211	+0225	+0.5	+0.5	-0.1	0.0
Suderoogsand	54 25N	8 30E	+0116	+0102	+0038	+0122	+0.4	+0.3	0.0	0.0
Hever Husum	54 28N	9 02E	+0205	+0152	+0118	+0200	+1.1	+1.0	0.0	0.0
Suederhoeft	54 16N	8 42E	+0103	+0056	+0051	+0112	+0.7	+0.6	0.0	0.0
Eidersperrwerk	54 16N	8 51E	+0120	+0115	+0130	+0155	+0.7	+0.6	0.0	0.0
Linnenplate	54 13N	8 40E	+0047	+0046	+0034	+0046	+0.7	+0.6	0.0	0.0
Büsum	54 07N	8 52E	+0054	+0049	-0001	+0027	+0.9	+0.8	0.0	0.0

			0200	0800	0200	0900				
CUXHAVEN	53 52N	8 43E	and	and	and	and	3.4	2.9	0.4	0.0
standard port			1400	2000	1400	2100				
River Elbe										
Grober Vogelsand	54 00N	8 29E	-0044	-0046	-0101	-0103	0.0	0.0	0.0	0.0
Scharhörn	53 58N	8 28E	-0045	-0047	-0101	-0103	0.0	0.0	0.0	-0.1
Brunsbüttel	53 53N	9 08E	+0057	+0105	+0121	+0112	-0.3	-0.2	-0.2	0.0
Glückstadt	53 47N	9 25E	+0205	+0214	+0220	+0213	-0.3	-0.2	-0.2	0.0
Stadersand	53 38N	9 32E	+0241	+0245	+0300	+0254	-0.1	0.0	-0.2	0.0
Schulau	53 34N	9 42E	+0304	+0315	+0337	+0321	0.0	+0.1	-0.3	-0.1
Seemannshoeft	53 32N	9 53E	+0324	+0332	+0403	+0347	+0.1	+0.2	-0.4	-0.2
Hamburg	53 33N	9 58E	+0338	+0346	+0422	+0406	+0.2	+0.3	-0.4	-0.2

Location	Lat	Long	High Water		Low Water		MHWS	MHWN	MLWN	MLWS
Harburg	53 28N	10 00E	+0344	+0350	+0430	+0416	+0.3	+0.4	-0.4	-0.2
Wangerooge East	53 46N	7 58E	-0108	-0109	-0116	-0023	0.0	0.0	+0.1	0.0
WILHELMSHAVEN			*standard port*							
Bremerhaven	53 33N	8 34E	+0019	+0034	-0024	-0012	+0.7	+0.7	0.0	-0.1
Hooksiel	53 39N	8 05E	-0033	-0038	-0100	-0101	+0.5	+0.4	+0.1	0.0
			0200	**0700**	**0200**	**0800**				
HELGOLAND	54 11N	7 53E	and	and	and	and	**2.7**	**2.4**	**0.4**	**0.0**
standard port			**1400**	**1900**	**1400**	**2000**				
East Frisian islands and coast										
Spiekeroog	53 45N	7 41E	+0003	-0003	-0031	-0012	+0.4	+0.3	0.0	0.0
Neuharlingersiel	53 42N	7 42E	+0014	+0008	-0024	-0013	+0.5	+0.4	0.0	0.0
Langeoog	53 43N	7 30E	+0003	-0001	-0034	-0018	+0.4	+0.2	0.0	0.0
Norderney *Riffgat*	53 42N	7 10E	-0024	-0030	-0056	-0045	+0.1	0.0	0.0	0.0
Norddeich Hafen	53 37N	7 10E	-0018	-0017	-0029	-0012	+0.2	+0.1	0.0	0.0
River Ems										
Memmert	53 38N	6 53E	-0032	-0038	-0114	-0103	+0.1	+0.1	0.0	0.0
Borkum *Fischerbalje*	53 33N	6 45E	-0048	-0052	-0124	-0105	0.0	0.0	0.0	0.0
Emshorn	53 30N	6 51E	-0037	-0041	-0108	-0047	+0.1	+0.1	0.0	0.0
Knock	53 20N	7 02E	+0018	+0005	-0028	+0004	+0.6	+0.6	0.0	0.0
Emden	53 20N	7 11E	+0041	+0028	-0011	+0022	+0.8	+0.8	0.0	0.0

NETHERLANDS *Time Zone -0100*

Location	Lat	Long	High Water		Low Water		MHWS	MHWN	MLWN	MLWS
			0200	**0700**	**0200**	**0800**				
HELGOLAND	54 11N	7 53E	and	and	and	and	**2.7**	**2.4**	**0.4**	**0.0**
standard port			**1400**	**1900**	**1400**	**2000**				
Nieuwe Statenzijl	53 14N	7 13E	+0110	+0135	*no data*	*no data*	+1.1	+1.0	*no data*	
Delfzijl	53 20N	6 56E	+0020	-0005	-0040	0000	+0.9	+0.8	+0.3	+0.3
Eemshaven	53 26N	6 52E	-0025	-0045	-0115	-0045	+0.5	+0.4	+0.3	+0.3
Schiermonnikoog	53 28N	6 12E	-0120	-0130	-0240	-0220	+0.2	+0.2	+0.3	+0.3
Waddenzee										
Lauwersoog	53 25N	6 12E	-0130	-0145	-0235	-0220	+0.2	+0.2	+0.3	+0.3
Nes	53 26N	5 47E	-0135	-0150	-0245	-0225	+0.1	+0.1	+0.2	+0.2
Holwerd	53 24N	5 53E	-0120	-0135	-0155	-0135	+0.3	+0.3	+0.4	+0.4
West Terschelling	53 22N	5 13E	-0220	-0250	-0335	-0310	-0.4	-0.3	+0.1	+0.2
Vlieland-haven	53 18N	5 06E	-0250	-0320	-0355	-0330	-0.3	-0.3	+0.1	+0.2
Harlingen	53 10N	5 25E	-0155	-0245	-0210	-0130	-0.4	-0.4	-0.1	+0.2
Kornwerderzand	53 04N	5 20E	-0210	-0315	-0300	-0215	-0.5	-0.5	-0.1	+0.2
Den Oever	52 56N	5 00E	-0245	-0410	-0400	-0305	-0.8	-0.7	0.0	+0.2
Oude Schild	53 02N	4 51E	-0310	-0420	-0445	-0400	-1.0	-0.9	0.0	+0.2
Den Helder	52 58N	4 45E	-0410	-0520	-0520	-0430	-1.0	-0.9	0.0	+0.2
Noordwinning *Platform K13-a*	53 13N	3 13E	-0420	-0430	-0520	-0530	-1.0	-1.1	+0.1	+0.1
			0300	**0900**	**0400**	**1000**				
VLISSINGEN	51 27N	3 36E	and	and	and	and	**4.8**	**3.9**	**0.9**	**0.3**
standard port			**1500**	**2100**	**1600**	**2200**				
IJmuiden	52 28N	4 35E	+0145	+0140	+0305	+0325	-2.7	-2.2	-0.6	-0.1
Scheveningen	52 06N	4 15E	+0105	+0100	+0220	+0245	-2.6	-2.1	-0.6	-0.1
Europlatform	52 00N	3 17E	+0005	-0005	-0030	-0055	-2.7	-2.2	-0.6	-0.1
Nieuwe Waterweg										
HOEK VAN HOLLAND			*standard port*							
Maassluis	51 55N	4 15E	+0155	+0115	+0100	+0310	-2.7	-2.1	-0.6	0.0
Nieuwe Maas Vlaardingen	51 54N	4 21E	+0150	+0120	+0130	+0330	-2.7	-2.1	-0.6	-0.1
Lek										
Krimpen Aan de Lek	51 55N	4 38E	+0225	+0200	+0325	+0445	-3.1	-2.5	-0.7	-0.I
Schoonhoven	51 57N	4 51E	+0415	+0315	+0435	+0545	-3.1	-2.4	-0.5	+0.1
Oude Maas										
Spijkenisse	51 52N	4 20E	+0145	+0120	+0145	+0310	-2.9	-2.3	-0.7	-0.1
Goidschalxoord	51 50N	4 27E	+0200	+0140	+0240	+0410	-3.4	-2.7	-0.7	-0.1
Merwede										
Dordrecht	51 49N	4 39E	+0220	+0210	+0420	+0510	-3.8	-3.4	-0.8	-0.2
Werkendam	51 49N	4 53E	+0425	+0410	+0550	+0650	-4.1	-3.3	-0.6	0.0
Haringvlietsluizen	51 50N	4 02E	+0015	+0015	+0015	-0020	-1.8	-1.6	-0.5	0.0
Ooster Schelde										
Roompot	51 37N	3 40E	-0015	+0005	+0005	-0020	-1.2	-1.0	-0.3	0.0
Stavenisse	51 36N	4 01E	+0150	+0120	+0055	+0115	-1.3	-0.9	-0.5	0.0
Lodijkse Gat	51 30N	4 12E	+0145	+0125	+0105	+0115	-0.7	-0.4	-0.3	0.0
Zijpe Philipsdam *West*	51 40N	4 11E	+0215	+0125	+0100	+0110	-1.2	-0.8	-0.5	-0.1

Location	Lat	Long	High Water		Low Water		MHWS	MHWN	MLWN	MLWS
Walcheren Westkapelle	51 31N	3 27E	-0025	-0015	-0010	-0025	-0.6	-0.5	-0.1	0.0
Westerschelde										
Terneuzen	51 20N	3 50E	+0020	+0020	+0020	+0030	+0.3	+0.3	0.0	0.0
Hansweert	51 27N	4 00E	+0100	+0050	+0040	+0100	+0.6	+0.6	0.0	0.0
Bath	51 24N	4 13E	+0125	+0115	+0115	+0140	+1.0	+0.9	0.0	0.0

BELGIUM *Time Zone -0100*

Location	Lat	Long	High Water		Low Water		MHWS	MHWN	MLWN	MLWS
Antwerpen			+0128	+0116	+0121	+0144	+1.1	+0.9	0.0	0.0
Zeebrugge	51 21N	3 12E	-0035	-0027	-0015	-0040	0.0	0.0	+0.2	+0.1
Blankenberge	51 19N	3 07E	-0045	-0045	-0018	-0043	+0.1	+0.1	+0.2	+0.1
Oostende	51 14N	2 56E	-0054	-0046	-0023	-0048	+0.2	+0.3	+0.2	+0.1
Nieuwpoort	51 09N	2 43E	-0106	-0058	-0025	-0050	+0.5	+0.4	+0.3	+0.1

FRANCE *Time Zone -0100*

Location	Lat	Long	High Water		Low Water		MHWS	MHWN	MLWN	MLWS
DUNKERQUE	51 03N	2 22E	0200 and 1400	0800 and 2000	0200 and 1400	0900 and 2100	6.0	5.0	1.5	0.6
standard port										
Gravelines	51 01N	2 06E	-0005	-0015	-0005	+0005	+0.3	+0.1	-0.1	-0.1
Sandettie Bank	51 09N	1 47E	-0015	-0025	-0020	-0005	+0.1	-0.1	-0.1	-0.1
Calais	51 58N	1 51E	-0020	-0030	-0015	-0005	+1.2	+0.9	+0.6	+0.3
Wissant	50 53N	1 40E	-0035	-0050	-0030	-0010	+1.8	+1.4	+0.8	+0.4
DIEPPE	49 56N	1 05E	0100 and 1300	0600 and 1800	0100 and 1300	0700 and 1900	9.3	7.4	2.5	0.8
standard port										
Boulogne	50 44N	1 35E	+0014	+0027	+0035	+0033	-0.4	-0.2	+0.1	+0.3
Le Touquet, Étaples	50 31N	1 35E	+0007	+0017	+0032	+0032	+0.2	+0.3	+0.4	+0.4
Berck	50 24N	1 34E	+0007	+0017	+0028	+0028	+0.5	+0.5	+0.4	+0.4
La Somme										
Le Hourdel	50 13N	1 34E	+0020	+0020	no data	no data	+0.8	+0.6	no data	
St Valéry	50 11N	1 37E	+0035	+0035	no data	no data	+0.9	+0.7	no data	
Cayeux	50 11N	1 29E	0000	+0005	+0015	+0010	+0.4	+0.5	+0.5	+0.5
Le Tréport	50 04N	1 22E	+0005	0000	+0007	+0007	+0.1	+0.1	0.0	+0.1
St. Valéry-en-Caux	49 52N	0 42E	-0005	-0005	-0015	-0020	-0.5	-0.4	-0.1	-0.1
Fécamp	49 46N	0 22E	-0015	-0010	-0030	-0040	-1.0	-0.6	+0.3	+0.4
Etretat	49 42N	0 12E	-0020	-0020	-0045	-0050	-1.2	-0.8	+0.3	+0.4
LE HAVRE	49 29N	0 07E	0000 and 1200	0500 and 1700	0000 and 1200	0700 and 1900	7.9	6.6	2.8	1.2
standard port										
Antifer *Le Havre*	49 39N	0 09E	+0025	+0015	+0005	-0007	+0.1	0.0	0.0	0.0
La Seine										
Honfleur	49 25N	0 14E	-0135	-0135	+0015	+0040	+0.1	+0.1	+0.1	+0.3
Tancarville	49 28N	0 28E	-0105	-0100	+0105	+0140	-0.1	-0.1	0.0	+1.0
Quillebeuf	49 28N	0 32E	-0045	-0050	+0120	+0200	0.0	0.0	+0.2	+1.4
Vatteville	49 29N	0 40E	+0005	-0020	+0225	+0250	0.0	-0.1	+0.8	+2.3
Caudebec	49 32N	0 44E	+0020	-0015	+0230	+0300	-0.3	-0.2	+0.9	+2.4
Heurteauville	49 27N	0 49E	+0110	+0025	+0310	+0330	-0.5	-0.2	+1.1	+2.7
Duclair	49 29N	0 53E	+0225	+0150	+0355	+0410	-0.4	-0.3	+1.4	+3.3
Rouen	49 27N	1 06E	+0440	+0415	+0525	+0525	-0.2	-0.1	+1.6	+3.6
Trouville	49 22N	0 05E	-0100	-0010	0000	+0005	+0.4	+0.3	+0.3	+0.1
Dives	49 18N	0 05W	-0100	-0010	0000	0000	+0.3	+0.2	+0.2	+0.1
Ouistreham	49 17N	0 15W	-0045	-0010	-0005	0000	-0.3	-0.3	-0.2	-0.3
Courseulles-sur-Mer	49 20N	0 27W	-0045	-0015	-0020	-0025	-0.5	-0.5	-0.1	-0.1
Arromanches	49 21N	0 37W	-0055	-0025	-0027	-0035	-0.6	-0.6	-0.2	-0.2
Port-en-Bessin	49 21N	0 45W	-0055	-0030	-0030	-0035	-0.7	-0.7	-0.2	-0.1
Alpha-Baie de Seine	49 49N	0 20W	+0030	+0020	-0005	-0020	-1.0	-0.9	-0.4	-0.2
CHERBOURG	49 39N	1 38W	0300 and 1500	1000 and 2200	0400 and 1600	1000 and 2200	6.4	5.0	2.5	1.1
standard port										
Rade de la Capelle	49 25N	1 05W	+0115	+0050	+0130	+0117	+0.8	+0.9	+0.1	+0.1
Iles Saint Marcouf	49 30N	1 08W	+0118	+0052	+0125	+0110	+0.6	+0.7	+0.1	+0.1
St. Vaast-la-Hougue	49 34N	1 16W	+0120	+0050	+0120	+0115	+0.3	+0.5	0.0	-0.1
Barfleur	49 40N	1 15W	+0110	+0055	+0052	+0052	+0.1	+0.3	0.0	0.0
Omonville	49 42N	1 50W	-0010	-0010	-0015	-0015	-0.1	-0.1	0.0	0.0
Goury	49 43N	1 57W	-0100	-0040	-0105	-0120	+1.7	+1.6	+l.0	+0.3

Location	Lat	Long	High Water		Low Water		MHWS	MHWN	MLWN	MLWS
CHANNEL ISLANDS *Time Zone UT*										
			0300	0900	0200	0900				
ST. HELIER	49 11N	2 07W	and	and	and	and	11.0	8.I	4.0	I.4
standard port			1500	2100	1400	2100				
Alderney Braye	49 43N	2 12W	+0050	+0040	+0025	+0105	-4.8	-3.4	-1.5	-0.5
Sark Maseline Pier	49 26N	2 21W	+0005	+0015	+0005	+0010	-2.1	-1.5	-0.6	-0.3
Guernsey **St PETER PORT**	49 27N	2 31W	*standard port*							
Jersey										
St. Catherine Bay	49 13N	2 01W	0000	+0010	+0010	+0010	0.0	-0.1	0.0	+0.1
Bouley Bay	49 14N	2 05W	+0002	+0002	+0004	+0004	-0.3	-0.3	-0.1	-0.1
Les Ecrehou	49 17N	1 56W	+0005	+0009	+0011	+0009	-0.2	+0.1	-0.2	0.0
Les Minquiers	48 57N	2 08W	-0014	-0018	-0001	-0008	+0.5	+0.6	+0.1	+0.1
FRANCE *Time Zone -0100*										
			0100	0800	0300	0800				
ST. MALO	48 38N	2 02W	and	and	and	and	12.2	9.3	4.2	I.5
standard port			1300	2000	1500	2000				
Iles Chausey	48 52N	1 49W	+0005	+0005	+0015	+0015	+0.8	+0.7	+0.6	+0.4
Diélette	49 33N	1 52W	+0045	+0035	+0020	+0035	-2.5	-1.9	-0.7	-0.3
Carteret	49 22N	1 47W	+0030	+0020	+0015	+0030	-1.6	-1.2	-0.5	-0.2
Portbail	49 18N	1 45W	+0030	+0025	+0025	+0030	-0.8	-0.6	-0.2	-0.1
St. Germain sur Ay	49 14N	1 36W	+0025	+0025	+0035	+0035	-0.7	-0.5	0.0	+0.1
Le Sénéquet	49 05N	1 40W	+0015	+0015	+0023	+0023	-0.3	-0.3	+0.1	+0.1
Regnéville sur Mer	49 01N	1 33W	+0010	+0010	+0030	+0020	+0.4	+0.3	+0.2	0.0
Granville	48 50N	1 36W	+0005	+0005	+0020	+0010	+0.7	+0.5	+0.3	+0.1
Cancale	48 40N	1 51W	-0002	-0002	+0010	+0010	+0.8	+0.6	+0.3	+0.1
Ile des Hebihens	48 37N	2 11W	-0002	-0002	-0005	-0005	-0.2	-0.2	-0.1	-0.1
St. Cast	48 38N	2 15W	-0002	-0002	-0005	-0005	-0.2	-0.2	-0.1	-0.1
Erquy	48 38N	2 28W	-0010	-0005	-0023	-0017	-0.6	-0.5	0.0	0.0
Dahouët	48 35N	2 34W	-0010	-0010	-0025	-0020	-0.9	-0.7	-0.2	-0.2
Le Légué *(buoy)*	48 34N	2 41W	-0005	-0005	-0025	-0015	-0.8	-0.5	-0.2	-0.1
Binic	48 36N	2 49W	-0008	-0008	-0030	-0015	-0.8	-0.7	-0.2	-0.2
Portrieux	48 38N	2 49W	-0010	-0005	-0025	-0015	-1.0	-0.7	-0.2	-0.1
Paimpol	48 47N	3 02W	-0005	-0010	-0035	-0025	-1.4	-0.9	-0.4	-0.1
Ile de Bréhat	48 51N	3 00W	-0008	-0013	-0040	-0037	-1.8	-1.3	-0.4	-0.2
Les Héaux de Bréhat	48 55N	3 05W	-0018	-0017	-0050	-0050	-2.4	-1.7	-0.6	-0.2
Lézardrieux	48 47N	3 06W	-0010	-0010	-0047	-0037	-1.7	-1.3	-0.5	-0.2
Port-Béni	48 51N	3 10W	-0017	-0022	-0100	-0045	-2.4	-1.6	-0.5	-0.1
Tréguier	48 47N	3 13W	-0005	-0010	-0055	-0040	-2.3	-1.6	-0.6	-0.2
Perros-Guirec	48 49N	3 28W	-0030	-0040	-0115	-0055	-2.9	-1.9	-0.8	-0.2
Ploumanac'h	48 50N	3 29W	-0023	-0033	-0112	-0053	-2.9	-1.9	-0.6	-0.1
			0000	0600	0000	0600				
BREST	48 23N	4 30W	and	and	and	and	6.9	5.4	2.6	I.0
standard port			1200	1800	1200	1800				
Trébeurden	48 46N	3 35W	+0100	+0110	+0120	+0100	+2.3	+1.9	+0.9	+0.4
Locquirec	48 42N	3 38W	+0058	+0108	+0120	+0100	+2.2	+1.8	+0.8	+0.3
Anse de Primel	48 43N	3 50W	+0100	+0110	+0120	+0100	+2.1	+1.7	+0.8	+0.3
Rade de Morlaix Morlaix	48 41N	3 53W	+0055	+0105	+0115	+0055	+2.0	+1.7	+0.8	+0.3
Roscoff	48 43N	3 58W	+0055	+0105	+0115	+0055	+1.9	+1.6	+0.8	+0.3
Ile de Batz	48 44N	4 00W	+0045	+0100	+0105	+0055	+2.0	+1.6	+0.9	+0.4
Brignogan	48 40N	4 19W	+0040	+0045	+0058	+0038	+1.5	+1.2	+0.6	+0.2
L'Aber Vrac'h Ile Cézon	48 36N	4 34W	+0030	+0030	+0040	+0035	+0.8	+0.7	+0.2	0.0
Aber Benoit	48 35N	4 37W	+0022	+0025	+0035	+0020	+0.9	+0.7	+0.3	+0.1
Portsall	48 34N	4 43W	+0015	+0020	+0025	+0015	+0.6	+0.5	+0.1	0.0
L'Aber Ildut	48 28N	4 45W	+0010	+0010	+0023	+0010	+0.4	+0.3	0.0	0.0
Ouessant Baie de Lampaul	48 27N	5 06W	+0005	+0005	-0005	+0003	0.0	-0.1	-0.1	0.0
Molene	48 24N	4 58W	+0012	+0012	+0017	+0017	+0.4	+0.3	+0.2	+0.1
Le Conquet	48 22N	4 47W	-0005	0000	+0007	+0007	-0.1	-0.1	-0.1	0.0
Le Trez Hir	48 21N	4 42W	-0010	-0005	-0008	-0008	-0.3	-0.3	-0.1	0.0
Camaret	48 16N	4 36W	-0010	-0010	-0013	-0013	-0.3	-0.3	-0.1	0.0
Morgat	48 13N	4 30W	-0008	-0008	-0020	-0010	-0.4	-0.4	-0.2	0.0
Douarnenez	48 06N	4 19W	-0010	-0015	-0018	-0008	-0.5	-0.5	-0.3	-0.1
Ile de Sein	48 02N	4 51W	-0005	-0005	-0010	-0005	-0.7	-0.6	-0.2	-0.1
Audierne	48 01N	4 33W	-0035	-0030	-0035	-0030	-1.7	-1.3	-0.6	-0.2
Le Guilvinec	47 48N	4 17W	-0010	-0025	-0025	-0015	-1.8	-1.4	-0.6	-0.1
Lesconil	47 48N	4 13W	-0008	-0028	-0028	-0018	-1.9	-1.4	-0.6	-0.1
Pont l'Abbe River Loctudy	47 50N	4 10W	-0013	-0033	-0035	-0025	-1.9	-1.5	-0.7	-0.2
Odet River										
Bénodet	47 53N	4 07W	0000	-0020	-0023	-0013	-1.7	-1.3	-0.5	-0.1
Corniguel	47 58N	4 06W	+0015	+0010	-0015	-0010	-2.0	-1.6	-1.0	-0.7

Location	Lat	Long	High Water		Low Water		MHWS	MHWN	MLWN	MLWS
Concarneau	47 52N	3 55W	-0010	-0030	-0030	-0020	-1.9	-1.5	-0.7	-0.2
Iles de Glenan Ile de Penfret	47 44N	3 57W	-0005	-0030	-0028	-0018	-1.9	-1.5	-0.7	-0.2
Port Louis	47 42N	3 21W	+0004	-0021	-0022	-0012	-1.8	-1.4	-0.6	-0.1
Lorient	47 45N	3 21W	+0003	-0022	-0020	-0010	-1.8	-1.4	-0.6	-0.2
Hennebont	47 48N	3 17W	+0015	-0017	+0005	+0003	-1.9	-1.5	-0.8	-0.2
Ile de Groix Port Tudy	47 39N	3 27W	0000	-0025	-0025	-0015	-1.8	-1.4	-0.6	-0.1
Port d'Etel	47 39N	3 12W	+0020	-0010	+0030	+0010	-2.0	-1.3	-0.4	+0.5
Port-Haliguen	47 29N	3 06W	+0015	-0020	-0015	-0010	-1.7	-1.3	-0.6	-0.3
Port Maria	47 29N	3 08W	+0010	-0025	-0025	-0015	-1.6	-1.3	-0.6	-0.1
Belle-Ile Le Palais	47 21N	3 09W	+0007	-0028	-0025	-0020	-1.8	-1.4	-0.7	-0.3
Crac'h River La Trinité	47 35N	3 01W	+0020	-0020	-0015	-0005	-1.5	-1.1	-0.5	-0.2
Morbihan										
Port-Navalo	47 33N	2 55W	+0030	-0005	-0010	-0005	-2.0	-1.5	-0.8	-0.3
Auray	47 40N	2 59W	+0055	0000	+0020	+0005	-2.0	-1.4	-0.8	-0.2
Arradon	47 37N	2 50W	+0155	+0145	+0145	+0130	-3.7	-2.7	-1.6	-0.5
Vannes	47 39N	2 46W	+0220	+0200	+0200	+0125	-3.6	-2.7	-1.6	-0.5
Le Logeo	47 33N	2 51W	+0155	+0140	+0145	+0125	-3.7	-2.7	-1.6	-0.5
Port du Crouesty	47 32N	2 54W	+0013	-0022	-0017	-0012	-1.6	-1.2	-0.6	-0.3
Ile de Houat	47 24N	2 57W	+0010	-0025	-0020	-0015	-1.7	-1.3	-0.6	-0.2
Ile de Hoedic	47 20N	2 52W	+0010	-0035	-0027	-0022	-1.8	-1.4	-0.7	-0.3
Pénerf	47 31N	2 37W	+0020	-0025	-0015	-0015	-1.5	-1.1	-0.6	-0.3
Tréhiguier	47 30N	2 27W	+0035	-0020	-0005	-0010	-1.4	-1.0	-0.5	-0.3
Le Croisic	47 18N	2 31W	+0015	-0040	-0020	-0015	-1.5	-1.1	-0.6	-0.3
Le Pouliguen	47 17N	2 25W	+0020	-0025	-0020	-0025	-1.5	-1.1	-0.6	-0.3
Le Grand-Charpentier	47 13N	2 19W	+0015	-0045	-0025	-0020	-1.5	-1.1	-0.6	-0.3
Pornichet	47 16N	2 21W	+0020	-0045	-0022	-0022	-1.4	-1.0	-0.5	-0.2
La Loire										
St. Nazaire	47 16N	2 12W	+0030	-0040	-0010	-0010	-1.1	-0.8	-0.4	-0.2
Donges	47 18N	2 05W	+0035	-0035	+0005	+0005	-1.0	-0.7	-0.5	-0.4
Cordemais	47 17N	1 54W	+0055	-0005	+0105	+0030	-0.7	-0.5	-0.7	-0.4
Le Pellerin	47 12N	1 46W	+0110	+0010	+0145	+0100	-0.7	-0.5	-0.9	-0.4
Nantes *Chantenay*	47 12N	1 35W	+0135	+0055	+0215	+0125	-0.6	-0.3	-0.8	-0.1
			0500	**1100**	**0500**	**1100**				
BREST	48 23N	4 30W	and	and	and	and	6.9	5.4	2.6	1.0
standard port			**1700**	**2300**	**1700**	**2300**				
Pointe de Saint-Gildas	47 08N	2 15W	-0045	+0025	-0020	-0020	-1.3	-1.0	-0.5	-0.2
Pornic	47 06N	2 07W	-0050	+0030	-0010	-0010	-1.1	-0.8	-0.4	-0.2
Ile de Noirmoutier L'Herbaudière	47 02N	2 18W	-0047	+0023	-0020	-0020	-1.4	-1.0	-0.5	-0.2
Fromentine	46 54N	2 10W	-0050	+0020	-0020	+0010	-1.6	-1.2	-0.7	-0.0
Ile de Yeu Port Joinville	46 44N	2 21W	-0040	+0015	-0030	-0035	-1.9	-1.4	-0.7	-0.3
St. Gilles-Croix-de-Vie	46 41N	1 56W	-0030	+0015	-0032	-0032	-1.8	-1.3	-0.6	-0.3
Les Sables d'Olonne	46 30N	1 48W	-0030	+0015	-0035	-0035	-1.7	-1.3	-0.6	-0.3
			0000	**0600**	**0500**	**1200**				
POINTE DE GRAVE	45 34N	1 04W	and	and	and	and	5.4	4.4	2.1	1.0
standard port			**1200**	**1800**	**1700**	**2400**				
Ile de Ré St Martin	46 12N	1 22W	+0015	-0030	-0025	-0020	+0.6	+0.5	+0.3	-0.1
La Pallice	46 10N	1 13W	+0015	-0030	-0025	-0020	+0.6	+0.5	+0.3	-0.1
La Rochelle	46 09N	1 09W	+0015	-0030	-0025	-0020	+0.6	+0.5	+0.3	-0.1
Ile d'Aix	46 01N	1 10W	+0015	-0040	-0030	-0025	+0.7	+0.5	+0.3	-0.1
La Charente Rochefort	45 57N	0 58W	+0035	-0010	+0030	+0125	+1.1	+0.9	+0.1	-0.2
Le Chapus	45 51N	1 11W	+0015	-0040	-0025	-0015	+0.6	+0.6	+0.4	+0.2
La Cayenne	45 47N	1 08W	+0030	-0015	-0010	-0005	+0.2	+0.2	+0.3	0.0
Pointe de Gatseau	45 48N	1 14W	+0005	-0005	-0015	-0025	-0.1	-0.1	+0.2	+0.2
La Gironde										
Royan	45 37N	1 00W	0000	-0005	-0005	-0005	-0.3	-0.2	0.0	0.0
Richard	45 27N	0 56W	+0018	+0018	+0028	+0033	-0.1	-0.1	-0.4	-0.5
Lamena	45 20N	0 48W	+0035	+0045	+0100	+0125	+0.2	+0.1	-0.5	-0.3
Pauillac	45 12N	0 45W	+0100	+0100	+0135	+0205	+0.1	0.0	-1.0	-0.5
La Reuille	45 03N	0 36W	+0135	+0145	+0230	+0305	-0.2	-0.3	-1.3	-0.7
La Garonne										
Le Marquis	45 00N	0 33W	+0145	+0150	+0247	+0322	-0.3	-0.4	-1.5	-0.9
Bordeaux	44 52N	0 33W	+0200	+0225	+0330	+0405	-0.1	-0.2	-1.7	-1.0
La Dordogne Libourne	44 55N	0 15W	+0250	+0305	+0525	+0540	-0.7	-0.9	-2.0	-0.4
Bassin d' Arcachon										
Cap Ferret	44 37N	1 15W	-0015	+0005	-0005	+0015	-1.4	-1.2	-0.8	-0.5
Arcachon *Eyrac*	44 40N	1 10W	+0010	+0025	0000	+0020	-1.1	-1.0	-0.8	-0.6
L'Adour Boucau	43 31N	1 31W	-0030	-0035	-0025	-0040	-1.2	-1.1	-0.4	-0.3
St Jean de Luz Socoa	43 24N	1 41W	-0040	-0045	-0030	-0045	-1.1	-1.1	-0.6	-0.4

Location	Lat	Long	High Water		Low Water		MHWS	MHWN	MLWN	MLWS
SPAIN *Time Zone -0100*										
Pasajes	43 20N	1 56W	-0050	-0030	-0015	-0045	-1.2	-1.3	-0.5	-0.5
San Sebastian	43 19N	1 59W	-0110	-0030	-0020	-0040	-1.2	-1.2	-0.5	-0.4
Guetaria	43 18N	2 12W	-0110	-0030	-0020	-0040	-1.0	-1.0	-0.5	-0.4
Lequeitio	43 22N	2 30W	-0115	-0035	-0025	-0045	-1.2	-1.2	-0.5	-0.4
Bermeo	43 25N	2 43W	-0055	-0015	-0005	-0025	-0.8	-0.7	-0.5	-0.4
Abra de Bilbao	43 21N	3 02W	-0125	-0045	-0035	-0055	-1.2	-1.2	-0.5	-0.4
Portugalete *Bilbao*	43 20N	3 02W	-0100	-0020	-0010	-0030	-1.2	-1.2	-0.5	-0.4
Castro Urdiales	43 23N	3 13W	-0040	-0120	-0020	-0110	-1.4	-1.5	-0.6	-0.6
Ria de Santona	43 26N	3 28W	-0005	-0045	+0015	-0035	-1.4	-1.4	-0.6	-0.6
Santander	43 28N	3 47W	-0020	-0100	0000	-0050	-1.3	-1.4	-0.6	-0.6
Ria de Suances	43 27N	4 03W	0000	-0030	+0020	-0020	-1.5	-1.5	-0.6	-0.6
San Vicente de la Barquera	43 23N	4 24W	-0020	-0100	0000	-0050	-1.5	-1.5	-0.6	-0.6
Ria de Tina Mayor	43 24N	4 31W	-0020	-0100	0000	-0050	-1.4	-1.5	-0.6	-0.6
Ribadesella	43 28N	5 04W	+0005	-0020	+0020	-0020	-1.4	-1.3	-0.6	-0.4
Gijon	43 34N	5 42W	-0005	-0030	+0010	-0030	-1.4	-1.3	-0.6	-0.4
Luanco	43 37N	5 47W	-0010	-0035	+0005	-0035	-1.4	-1.3	-0.6	-0.4
Aviles	43 35N	5 56W	-0100	-0040	-0015	-0050	-1.5	-1.4	-0.7	-0.5
San Esteban de Pravia	43 34N	6 05W	-0005	-0030	+0010	-0030	-1.4	-1.3	-0.6	-0.4
Luarca	43 33N	6 32W	+0010	-0015	+0025	-0015	-1.2	-1.1	-0.5	-0.3
Ribadeo	43 33N	7 02W	+0010	-0015	+0025	-0015	-1.4	-1.3	-0.6	-0.4
Ria de Vivero	43 43N	7 36W	+0010	-0015	+0025	-0015	-1.4	-1.3	-0.6	-0.4
Santa Marta de Ortigueira	43 41N	7 51W	-0020	0000	+0020	-0010	-1.3	-1.2	-0.6	-0.4
El Ferrol del Caudillo	43 28N	8 16W	-0045	-0100	-0010	-0105	-1.6	-1.4	-0.7	-0.4
La Coruna	43 22N	8 24W	-0110	-0050	-0030	-0100	-1.6	-1.6	-0.6	-0.5
Ria de Corme	43 16N	8 58W	-0025	-0005	+0015	-0015	-1.7	-1.6	-0.6	-0.5
Ria de Camarinas	43 08N	9 11W	-0120	-0055	-0030	-0100	-1.6	-1.6	-0.6	-0.5
LISBOA standard port	38 42N	9 08W	0500 and 1700	1000 and 2200	0300 and 1500	0800 and 2000	3.8	3.0	1.5	0.5
Corcubion	42 57N	9 12W	+0055	+0110	+0120	+0135	-0.5	-0.4	-0.3	0.0
Muros	42 46N	9 03W	+0050	+0105	+0115	+0130	-0.3	-0.3	-0.2	0.0
Ria de Arosa Villagarcia	42 37N	8 47W	+0040	+0100	+0110	+0120	-0.3	-0.2	-0.2	0.0
Ria de Pontevedra Marin	42 24N	8 42W	+0050	+0110	+0120	+0130	-0.5	-0.4	-0.3	0.0
Vigo	42 15N	8 43W	+0040	+0100	+0105	+0125	-0.4	-0.3	-0.2	0.0
Bayona	42 07N	8 51W	+0035	+0050	+0100	+0115	-0.3	-0.3	-0.2	0.0
La Guardia	41 54N	8 53W	+0040	+0055	+0105	+0120	-0.5	-0.4	-0.3	-0.1
LISBOA standard port	38 42N	9 08W	0400 and 1600	0900 and 2100	0400 and 1600	0900 and 2100	3.8	3.0	1.5	0.5
PORTUGAL *Time Zone UT*										
Viana do Castelo	41 41N	8 50W	-0020	0000	+0010	+0015	-0.3	-0.3	-0.1	0.0
Esposende	41 32N	8 47W	-0020	0000	+0010	+0015	-0.6	-0.5	-0.2	0.0
Povoa de Varzim	41 22N	8 46W	-0020	0000	+0010	+0015	-0.3	-0.3	-0.1	0.0
Porto de Leixoes	41 11N	8 42W	-0025	-0010	0000	+0010	-0.3	-0.3	-0.2	0.0
Rio Douro										
Entrance	41 09N	8 40W	-0010	+0005	+0015	+0025	-0.6	-0.5	-0.2	0.0
Oporto *Porto*	41 08N	8 37W	+0002	+0002	+0040	+0040	-0.5	-0.4	-0.2	+0.1
Porto de Aveiro	40 39N	8 45W	+0005	+0010	+0010	+0015	-0.5	-0.4	-0.1	+0.1
Figueira da Foz	40 09N	8 51W	-0015	0000	+0010	+0020	-0.3	-0.3	-0.2	0.0
Nazare *Pederneira*	39 36N	9 05W	-0030	-0015	-0005	+0005	-0.5	-0.4	-0.1	+0.1
Peniche	39 21N	9 22W	-0035	-0015	-0005	0000	-0.3	-0.4	-0.2	0.0
Ericeira	38 58N	9 25W	-0040	-0025	-0010	-0010	-0.4	-0.3	-0.1	+0.1
River Tagus (Rio Tejo)										
Cascais	38 42N	9 25W	-0040	-0025	-0015	-0010	-0.3	-0.3	-0.1	+0.2
Paco de Arcos	38 41N	9 18W	-0020	-0030	-0005	-0005	-0.4	-0.4	-0.2	0.0
Alcochete	38 45N	8 58W	+0010	+0010	+0010	+0010	+0.5	+0.4	+0.1	+0.1
Vila Franca de Xira	38 57N	8 59W	+0045	+0040	+0100	+0140	+0.3	+0.2	-0.2	+0.4
Sesimbra	38 26N	9 07W	-0045	-0030	-0020	-0010	-0.4	-0.4	-0.1	+0.1
Setubal	38 30N	8 54W	-0020	-0015	-0005	+0005	-0.3	-0.3	-0.2	0.0
Porto de Sines	37 57N	8 53W	-0050	-0030	-0020	-0010	-0.4	-0.4	-0.1	+0.1
Milfontes	37 43N	8 47W	-0040	-0030	*no data*	*no data*	-0.1	-0.1	0.0	+0.2
Arrifana	37 17N	8 52W	-0030	-0020	*no data*	*no data*	-0.1	0.0	-0.1	+0.2

Location	Lat	Long	High Water		Low Water		MHWS	MHWN	MLWN	MLWS
Enseada de Belixe	37 01N	8 58W	-0050	-0030	-0020	-0015	+0.3	+0.2	+0.2	+0.3
Lagos	37 06N	8 40W	-0100	-0040	-0030	-0025	-0.4	-0.4	-0.1	+0.1
Portimao	37 07N	8 32W	-0100	-0040	-0030	-0025	-0.5	-0.4	-0.1	+0.2
Ponta do Altar	37 06N	8 31W	-0100	-0040	-0030	-0025	-0.3	-0.3	-0.1	+0.1
Enseada de Albufeira	37 05N	8 15W	-0035	+0015	-0005	0000	-0.2	-0.2	0.0	+0.2
Cabo de Santa Maria	36 58N	7 52W	-0050	-0030	-0015	+0005	-0.4	-0.4	-0.1	+0.1
Rio Guadiana										
Vila Real de Santo António	37 11N	7 25W	-0050	-0015	-0010	0000	-0.4	-0.4	-0.2	+0.2
			0500	**1000**	**0500**	**1100**				
LISBOA	38 42N	9 08W	and	and	and	and	3.8	3.0	1.5	0.5
standard port			**1700**	**2200**	**1700**	**2300**				

SPAIN *Time Zone -0100*

Location	Lat	Long	High Water		Low Water		MHWS	MHWN	MLWN	MLWS
Ayamonte	37 13N	7 25W	+0005	+0015	+0025	+0045	-0.7	-0.6	-0.1	-0.1
Ria de Huelva										
Bar	37 08N	6 52W	0000	+0015	+0035	+0030	-0.6	-0.5	-0.3	-0.1
Huelva, Muelle de Fabrica	37 15N	6 58W	+0010	+0025	+0045	+0040	-0.3	-0.3	-0.3	0.0
Rio Guadalquivir										
Bar	36 45N	6 26W	-0005	+0005	+0020	+0030	-0.6	-0.5	-0.2	-0.1
Bonanza	36 48N	6 20W	+0025	+0040	+0100	+0120	-0.8	-0.6	-0.4	0.0
Corta de los Jerónimos	37 08N	6 06W	+0210	+0230	+0255	+0345	-1.2	-0.9	-0.5	0.0
Sevilla	37 23N	6 00W	+0400	+0430	+0510	+0545	-1.7	-1.2	-0.6	0.0
Rota	36 37N	6 21W	-0010	+0010	+0025	+0015	-0.7	-0.6	-0.3	-0.1
Puerto de Santa Maria	36 36N	6 13W	+0006	+0006	+0027	+0027	-0.6	-0.4	-0.3	-0.1
Cadiz										
Puerto Cadiz	36 32N	6 17W	0000	+0020	+0040	+0025	-0.5	-0.5	-0.2	0.0
La Carraca	36 30N	6 11W	+0020	+0050	+0100	+0040	-0.5	-0.4	-0.1	0.0
Cabo Trafalgar	36 11N	6 02W	-0003	-0003	+0026	+0026	-1.4	-1.1	0.5	-0.1
Rio Barbate	36 11N	5 55W	+0016	+0016	+0045	+0045	-1.9	-1.5	-0.4	+0.1
Punta Camarinal	36 05N	5 48W	-0007	-0007	+0013	+0013	-1.7	-1.4	-0.6	-0.2

GIBRALTAR *Time Zone -0100*

Location	Lat	Long	High Water		Low Water		MHWS	MHWN	MLWN	MLWS
			0000	**0700**	**0100**	**0600**				
GIBRALTAR	36 08N	5 21W	and	and	and	and	1.0	0.7	0.3	0.1
standard port			**1200**	**1900**	**1300**	**1800**				
Tarifa	36 00N	5 36W	-0038	-0038	-0042	-0042	+0.4	+0.3	+0.3	+0.2
Punta Carnero	36 04N	5 26W	-0010	-0010	0000	0000	0.0	+0.1	+0.1	+0.1
Algeciras	36 07N	5 27W	-0010	-0010	-0010	-0010	+0.1	+0.2	+0.1	+0.1

NOTES

ENGLISH CHANNEL AND SOUTH BRITTANY

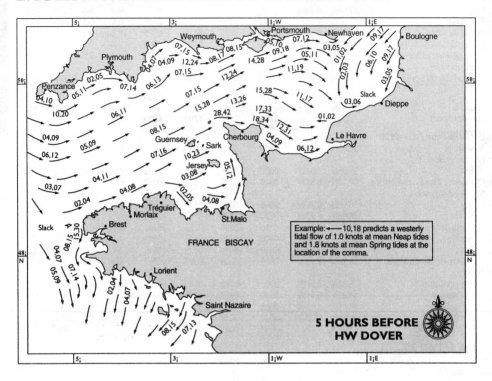

Example: ⟵ 10,18 predicts a westerly tidal flow of 1.0 knots at mean Neap tides and 1.8 knots at mean Spring tides at the location of the comma.

5 HOURS BEFORE HW DOVER

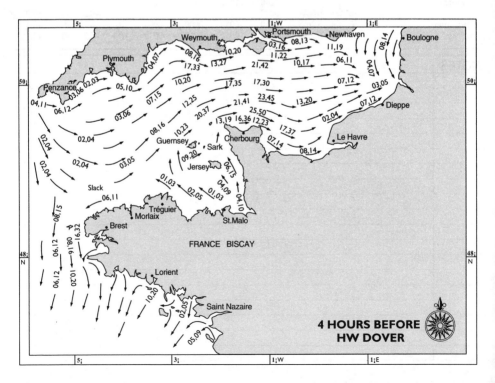

4 HOURS BEFORE HW DOVER

ENGLISH CHANNEL AND SOUTH BRITTANY

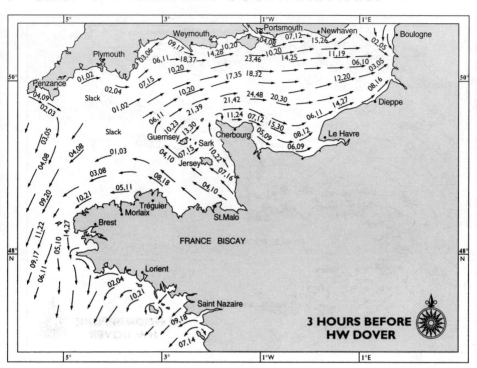

3 HOURS BEFORE HW DOVER

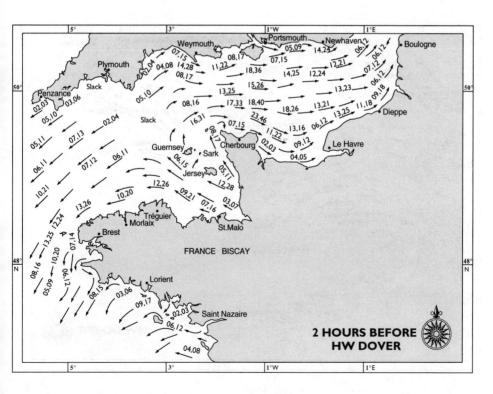

2 HOURS BEFORE HW DOVER

ENGLISH CHANNEL AND SOUTH BRITTANY

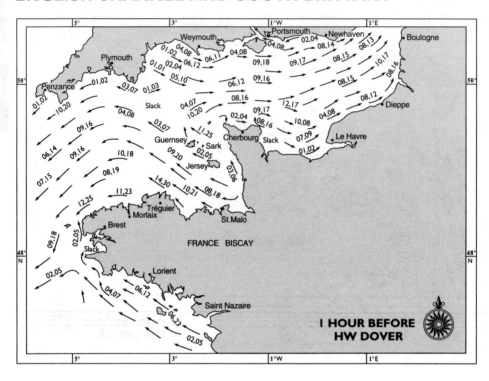

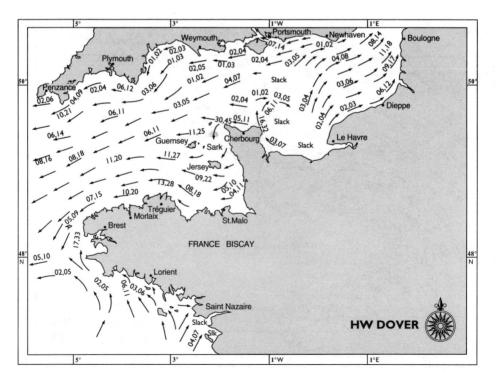

ENGLISH CHANNEL AND SOUTH BRITTANY

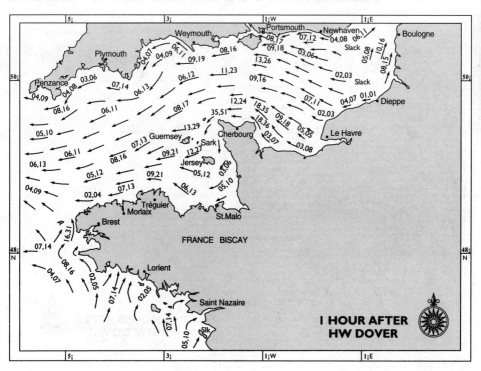

1 HOUR AFTER HW DOVER

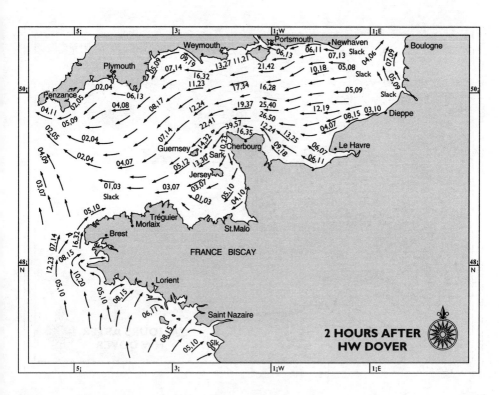

2 HOURS AFTER HW DOVER

ENGLISH CHANNEL AND SOUTH BRITTANY

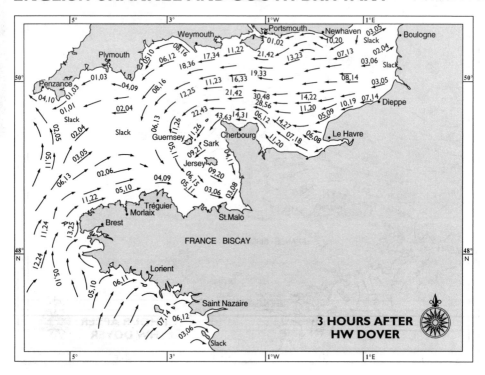

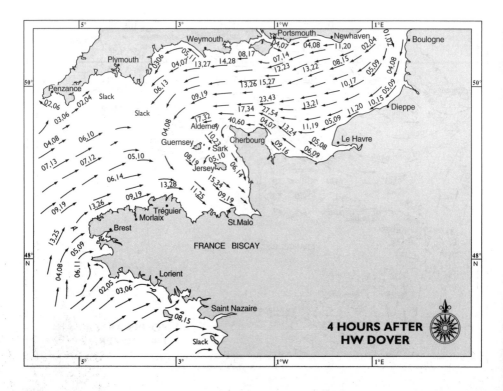

ENGLISH CHANNEL AND SOUTH BRITTANY

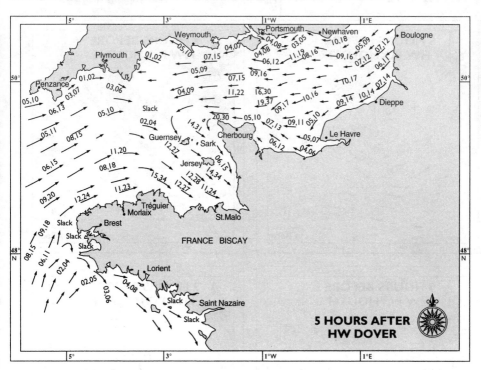

5 HOURS AFTER
HW DOVER

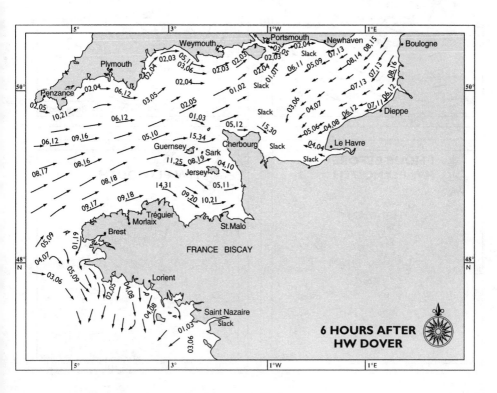

6 HOURS AFTER
HW DOVER

239

PORTLAND

Example:◀──10,18 predicts a westerly tidal flow of 1.0 knots at mean Neap tides and 1.8 knots at mean Spring tides at the location of the comma.

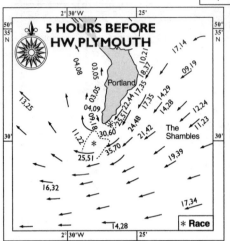

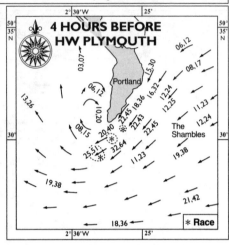

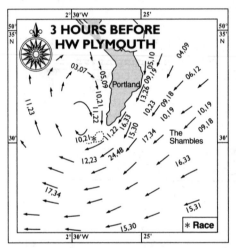

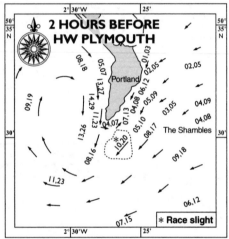

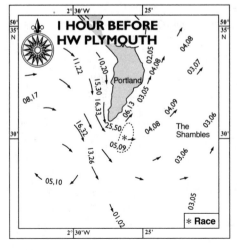

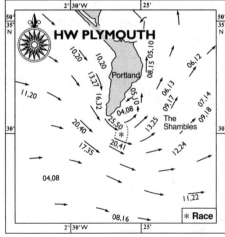

PORTLAND

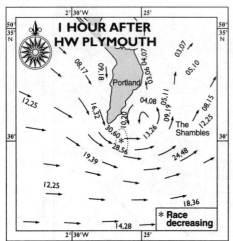

I HOUR AFTER HW PLYMOUTH

* Race decreasing

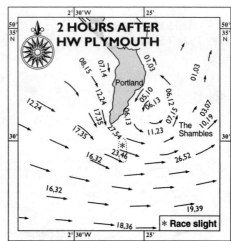

2 HOURS AFTER HW PLYMOUTH

* Race slight

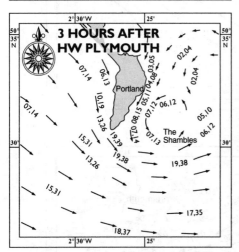

3 HOURS AFTER HW PLYMOUTH

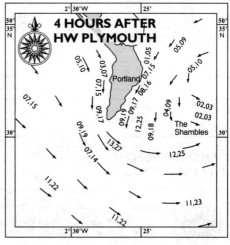

4 HOURS AFTER HW PLYMOUTH

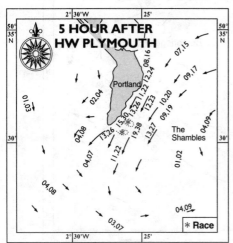

5 HOUR AFTER HW PLYMOUTH

* Race

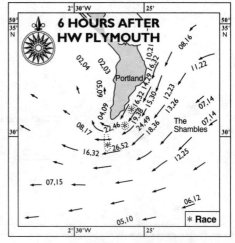

6 HOURS AFTER HW PLYMOUTH

* Race

241

ISLE OF WIGHT

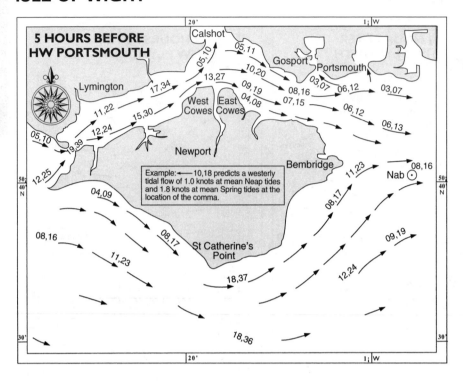

5 HOURS BEFORE HW PORTSMOUTH

Example: ← 10,18 predicts a westerly tidal flow of 1.0 knots at mean Neap tides and 1.8 knots at mean Spring tides at the location of the comma.

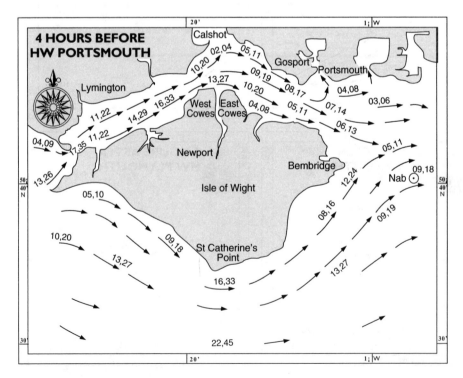

4 HOURS BEFORE HW PORTSMOUTH

ISLE OF WIGHT

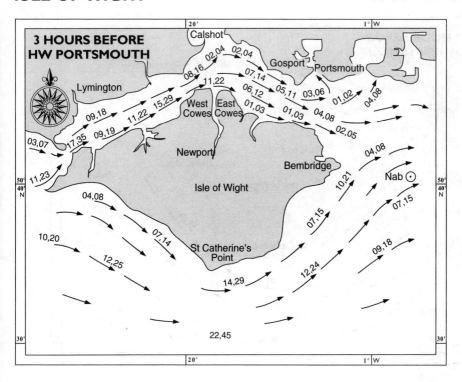

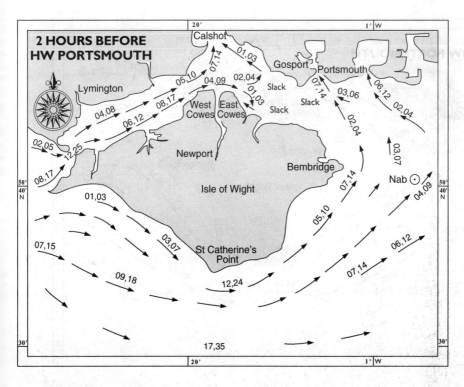

ISLE OF WIGHT

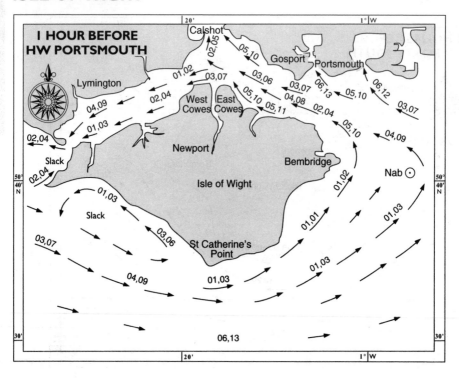

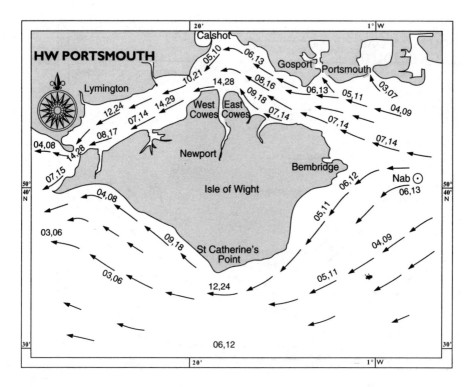

ISLE OF WIGHT

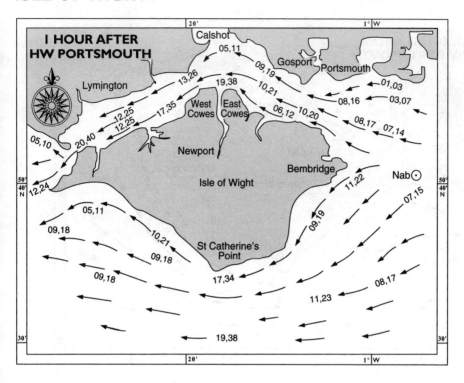

I HOUR AFTER HW PORTSMOUTH

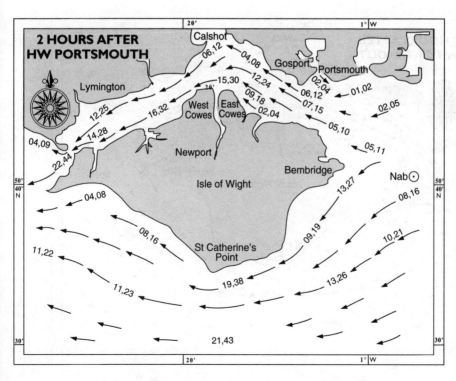

2 HOURS AFTER HW PORTSMOUTH

ISLE OF WIGHT

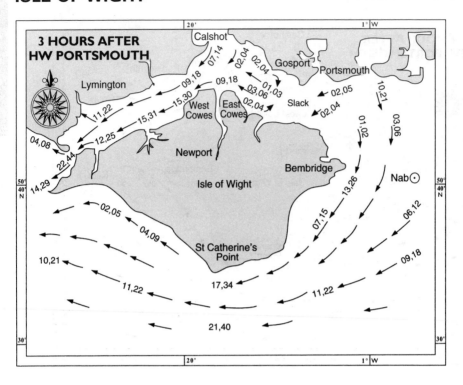

3 HOURS AFTER HW PORTSMOUTH

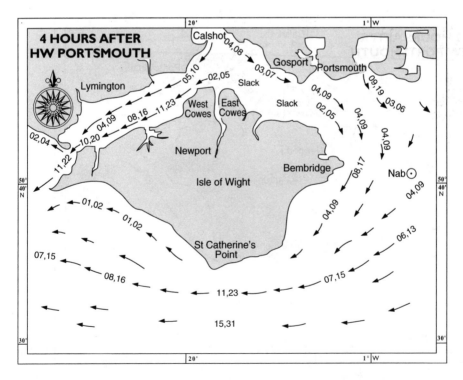

4 HOURS AFTER HW PORTSMOUTH

ISLE OF WIGHT

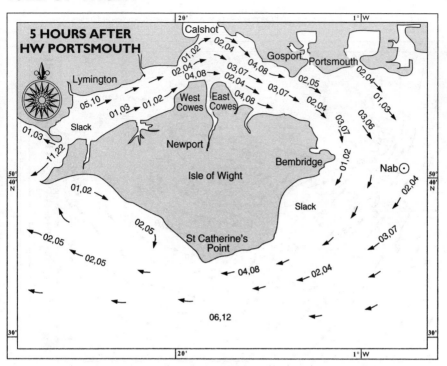

5 HOURS AFTER HW PORTSMOUTH

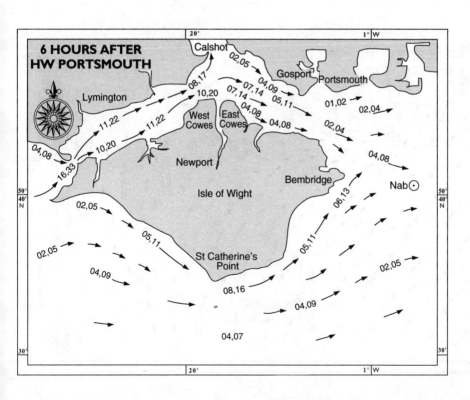

6 HOURS AFTER HW PORTSMOUTH

CHANNEL ISLES

Example:◄—— 10,18 predicts a westerly tidal flow of 1.0 knots at mean Neap tides and 1.8 knots at mean Spring tides at the location of the comma.

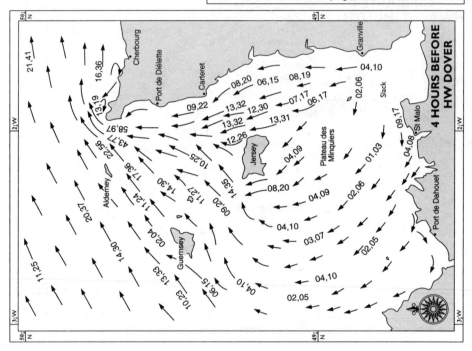

4 HOURS BEFORE HW DOVER

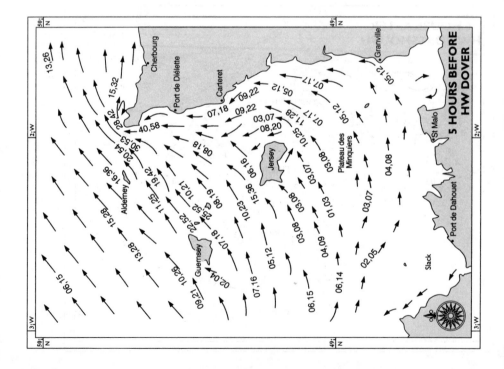

5 HOURS BEFORE HW DOVER

CHANNEL ISLES

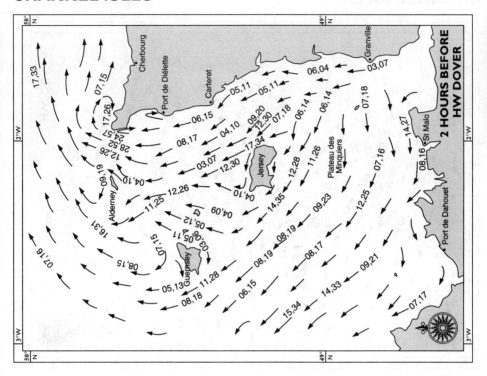

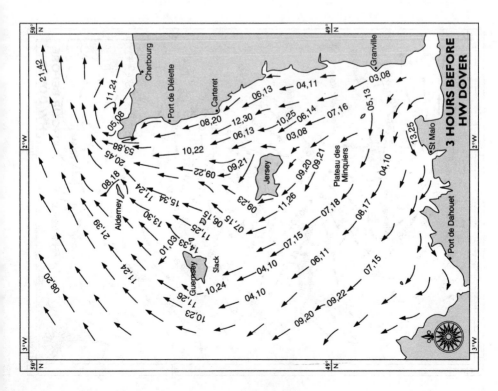

CHANNEL ISLES

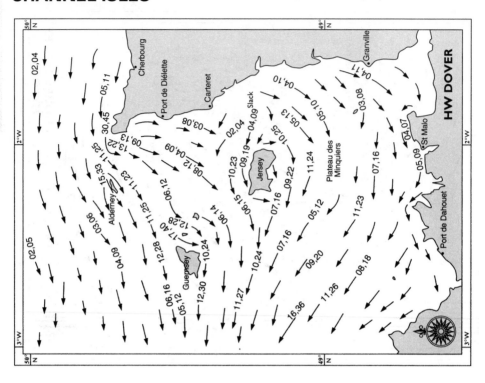

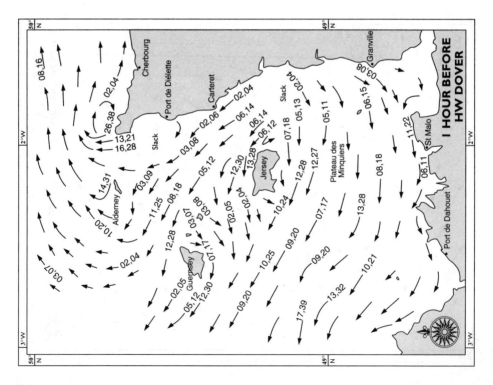

CHANNEL ISLES

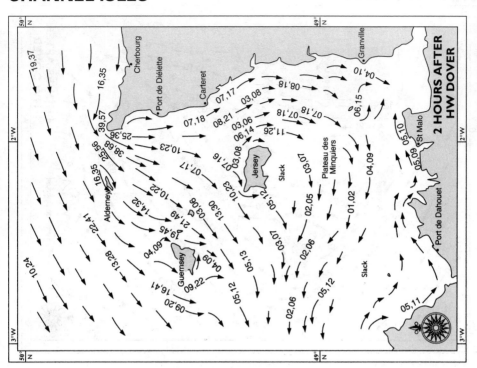

2 HOURS AFTER HW DOVER

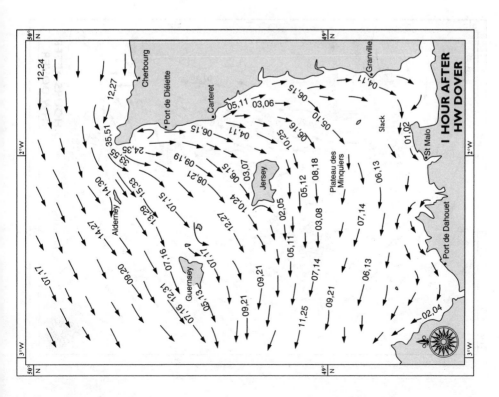

1 HOUR AFTER HW DOVER

CHANNEL ISLES

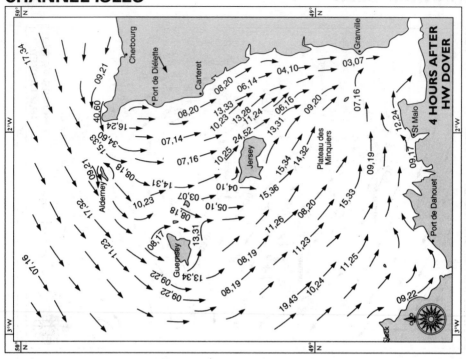

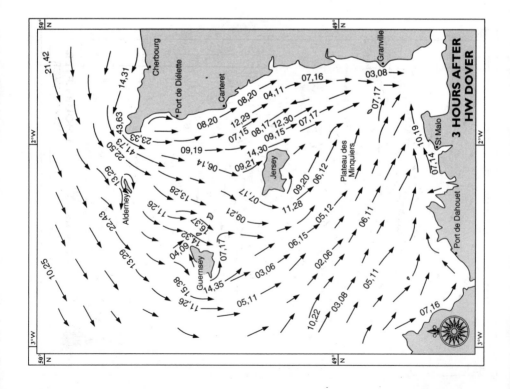

CHANNEL ISLES

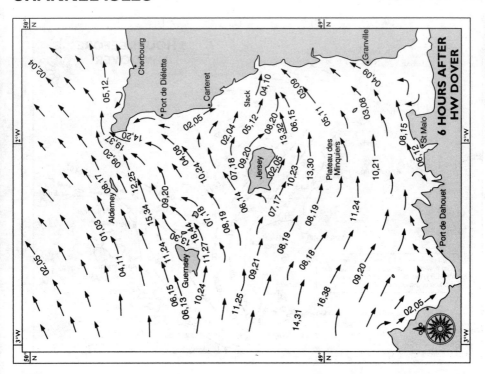

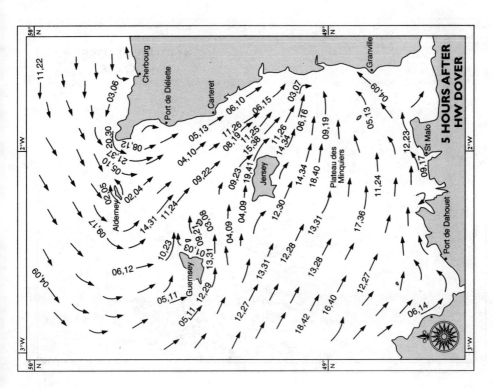

253

NORTH SEA

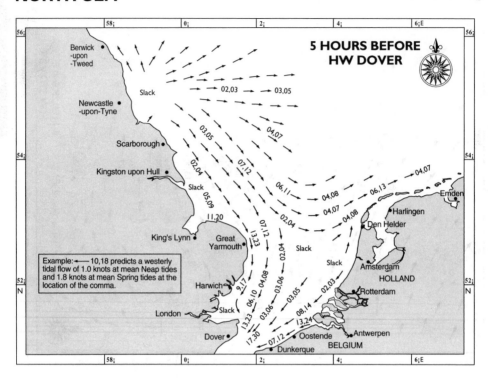

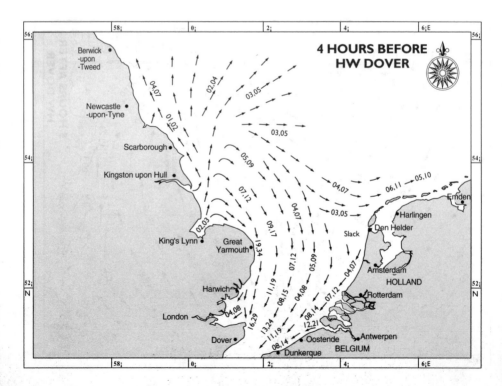

NORTH SEA

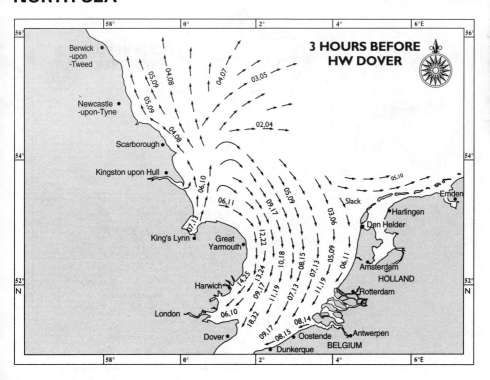

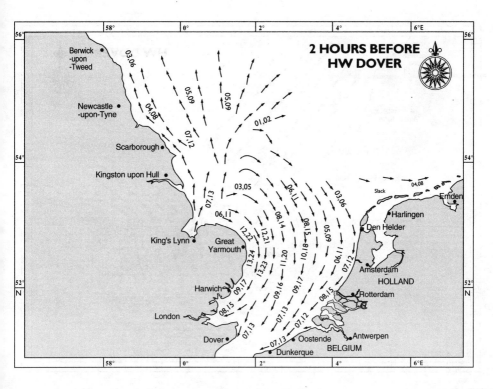

NORTH SEA

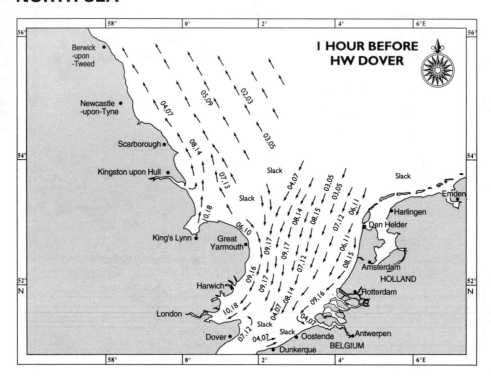

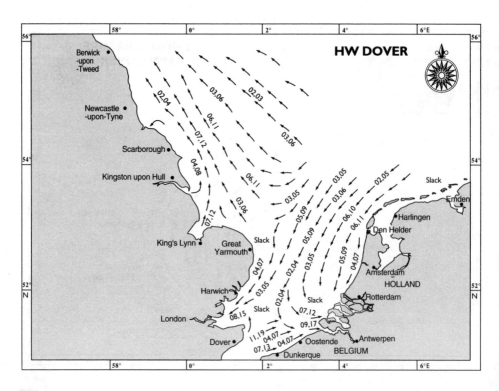

NORTH SEA

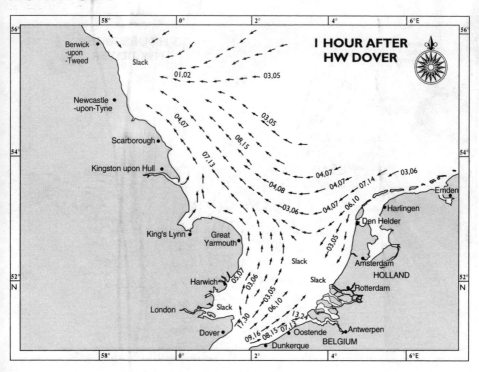

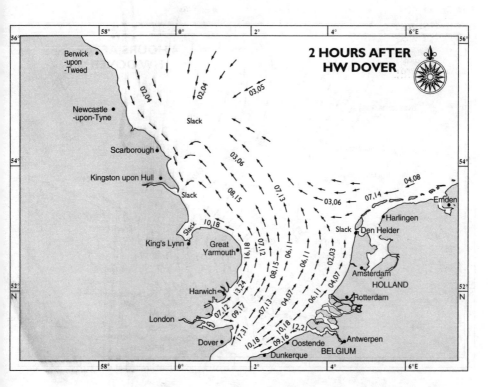

NORTH SEA

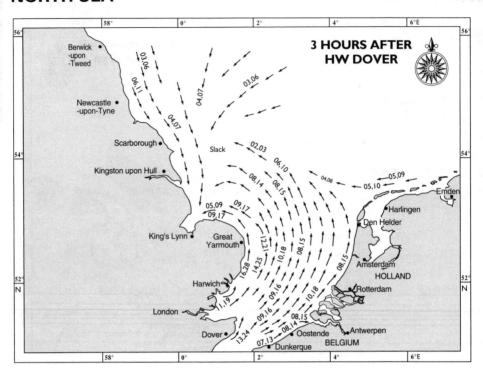

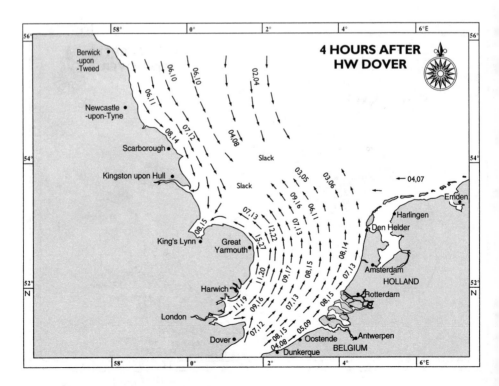

NORTH SEA

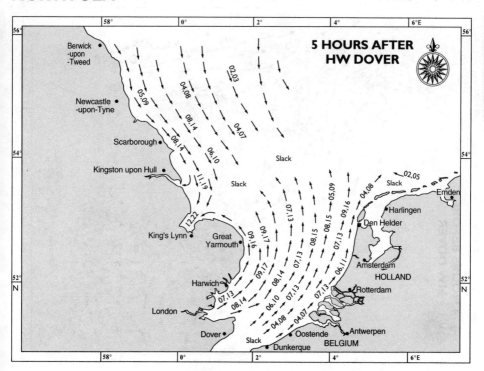

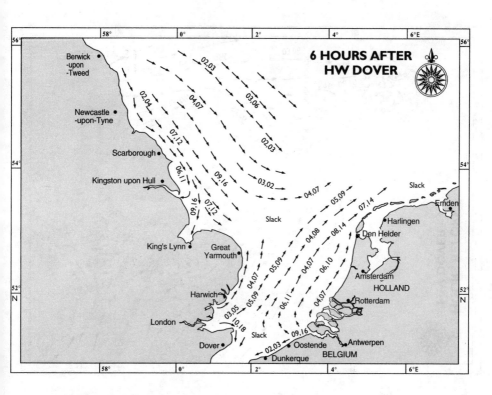

SCOTLAND

Example: ←—10,18 predicts a westerly tidal flow of 1.0 knots at mean Neap tides and 1.8 knots at mean Spring tides at the location of the comma.

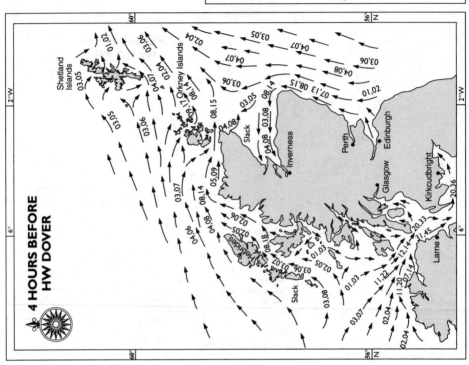

4 HOURS BEFORE HW DOVER

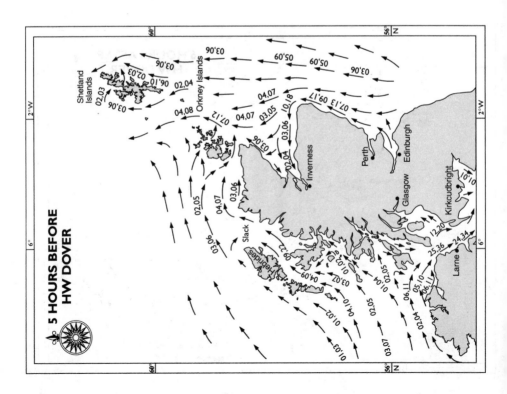

5 HOURS BEFORE HW DOVER

SCOTLAND

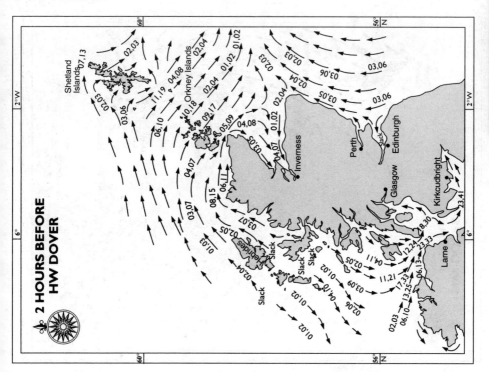

2 HOURS BEFORE HW DOVER

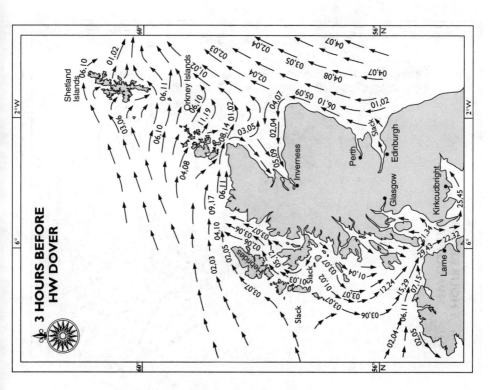

3 HOURS BEFORE HW DOVER

261

SCOTLAND

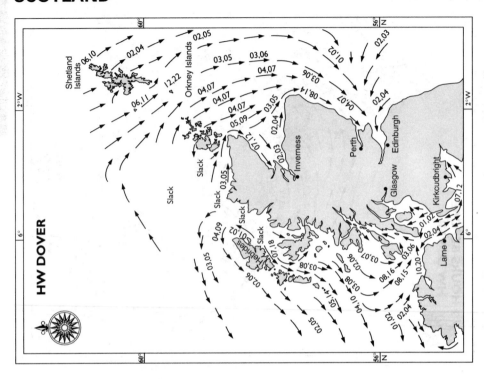

HW DOVER

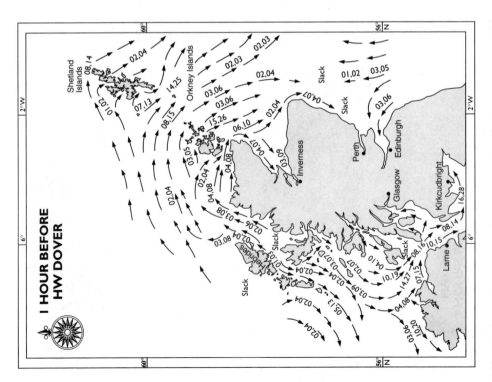

I HOUR BEFORE
HW DOVER

SCOTLAND

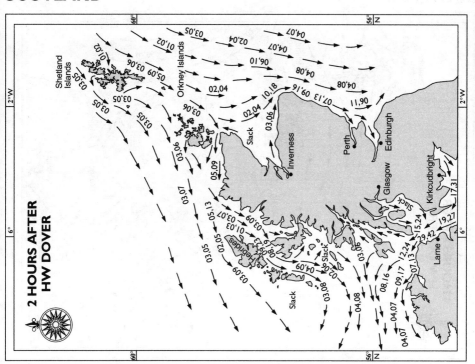

2 HOURS AFTER HW DOVER

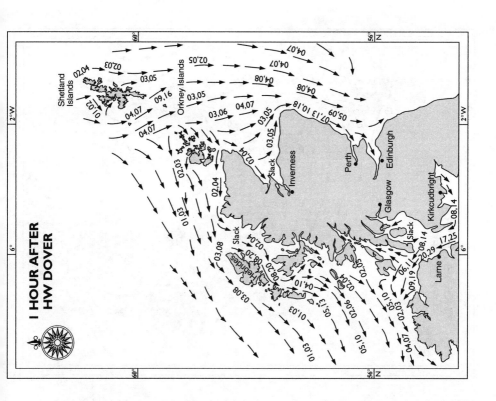

1 HOUR AFTER HW DOVER

SCOTLAND

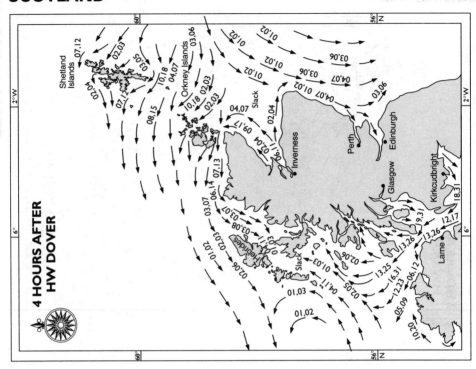

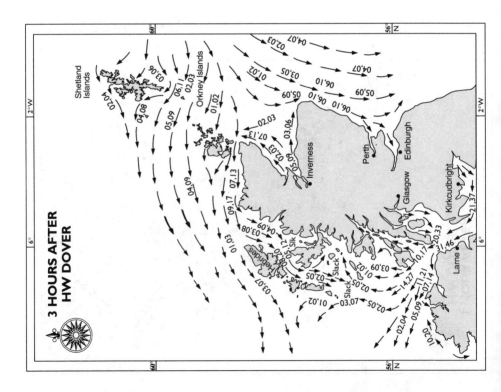

SCOTLAND

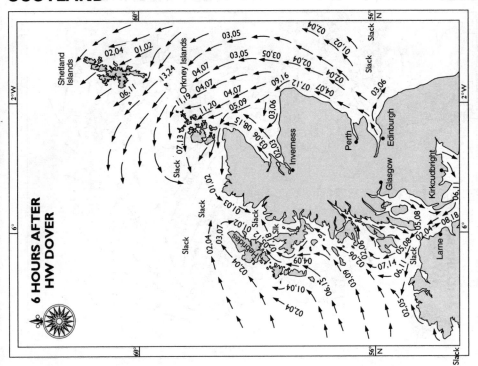

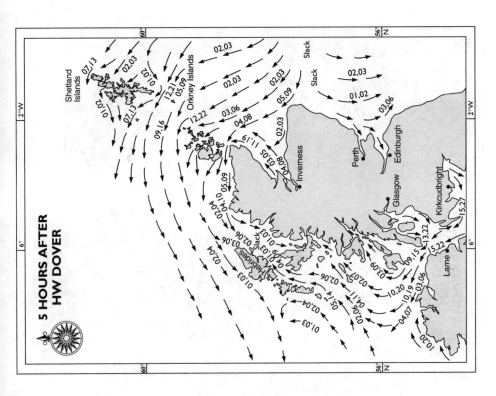

CELTIC SEA, IRISH SEA AND WEST IRELAND

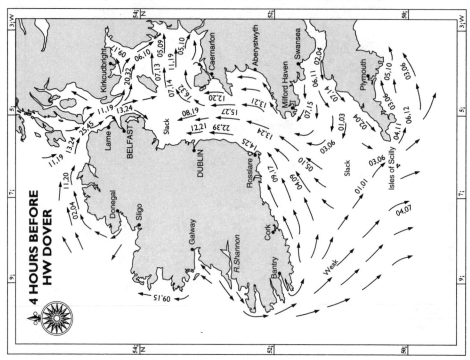

4 HOURS BEFORE HW DOVER

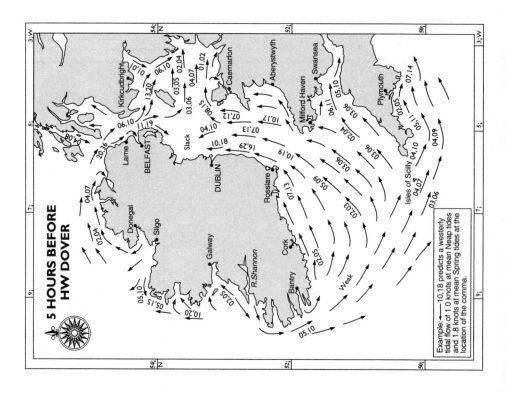

5 HOURS BEFORE HW DOVER

Example: 10,18 predicts a westerly tidal flow of 1.0 knots at mean Neap tides and 1.8 knots at mean Spring tides at the location of the comma.

266

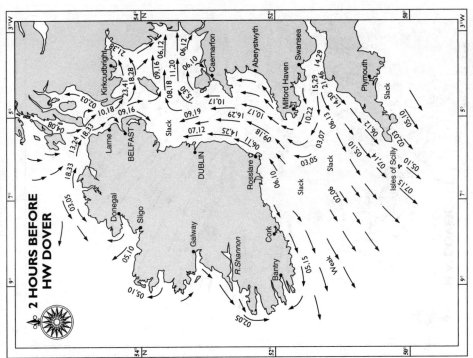

2 HOURS BEFORE HW DOVER

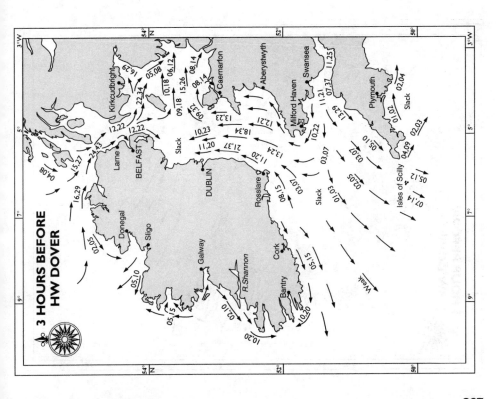

3 HOURS BEFORE HW DOVER

CELTIC SEA, IRISH SEA AND WEST IRELAND

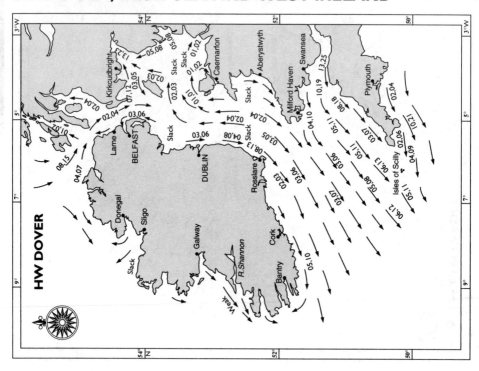

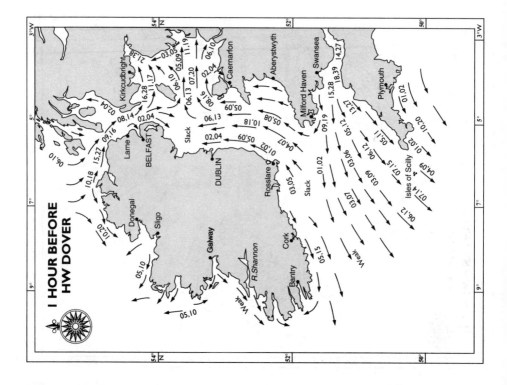

CELTIC SEA, IRISH SEA AND WEST IRELAND

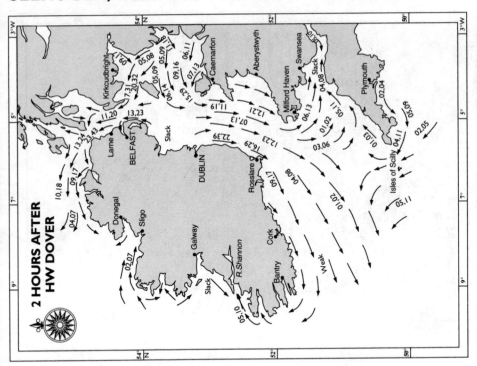

2 HOURS AFTER HW DOVER

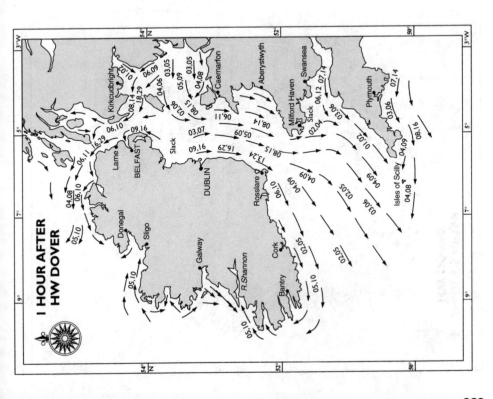

1 HOUR AFTER HW DOVER

CELTIC SEA, IRISH SEA AND WEST IRELAND

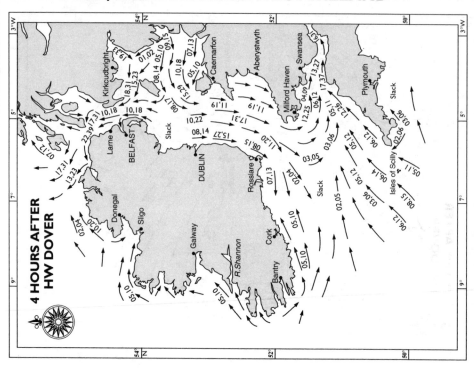

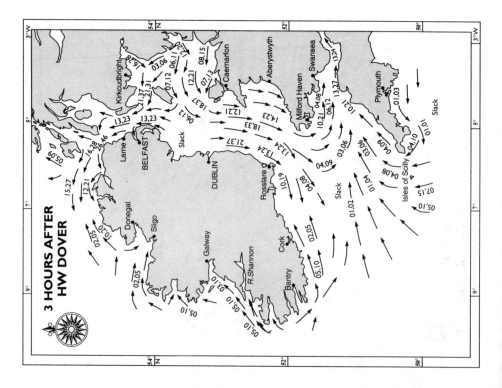

CELTIC SEA, IRISH SEA AND WEST IRELAND

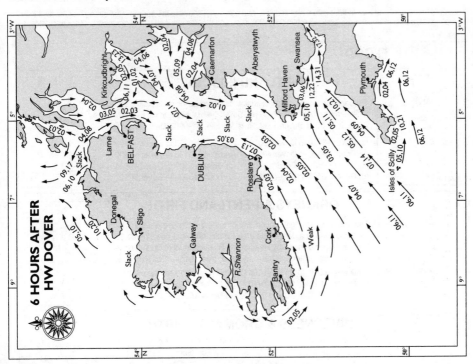

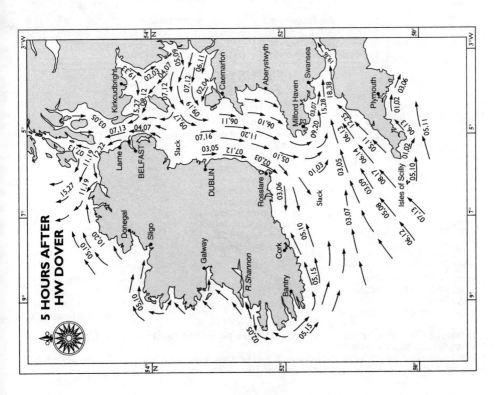

TIDAL GATES - NORTH EAST SCOTLAND

A guide to the time of tide turn at tidal gates, and in straits and estuaries, showing the approximate strength of the tidal flow (spring rates shown - neaps are approximately 60% of these), and the position and timing of races, counter tides etc.

FLOOD	EBB

SHETLAND ISLANDS

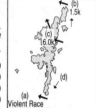

The tidal flow around the Shetland Islands rotates as the cycle progresses. When the flood begins, at −0400 HW Dover, the tidal flow is to the E, at HW Dover it is S, at Dover +0300 it is W, and at −0600 Dover it is N.

(a) Dover −0410 to Dover +0020	(a) Dover +0050 to Dover −0410
(b) Dover −0400 to Dover +0030	(b) Dover +0130 to Dover −0500
(c) Dover −0530 to Dover +0100	(c) Dover +0100 to Dover −0530
(d) Dover −0400 to Dover −0200	(d) Dover +0200 to Dover +0500

ORKNEYS & PENTLAND FIRTH

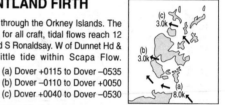

The tide flows strongly around and through the Orkney Islands. The Pentland Firth is a dangerous area for all craft, tidal flows reach 12 knots between Duncansby Head and S Ronaldsay. W of Dunnet Hd & Hoy is less violent. There is little tide within Scapa Flow.

(a) Dover −0500 to Dover +0100	(a) Dover +0115 to Dover −0535
(b) Dover +0500 to Dover −0110	(b) Dover −0110 to Dover +0050
(c) Dover −0530 to Dover +0040	(c) Dover +0040 to Dover −0530

INVERNESS & CROMARTY FIRTHS

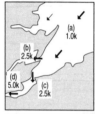

Tidal streams in the Inverness Firth and approaches are not strong, except in the Cromarty Firth Narrows, the Fort George Narrows and the Kessock Road, including off the entrance to the Caledonian Canal.

(a) Dover −0555 to Dover +0030	(a) Dover +0030 to Dover −0555
(b) Dover −0400 to Dover +0115	(b) Dover +0115 to Dover −0400
(c) Dover −0400 to Dover −0220	(c) Dover +0115 to Dover −0440
(d) Dover −0430 to Dover +0100	(d) Dover −0130 to Dover +0545

FIRTHS of FORTH & TAY

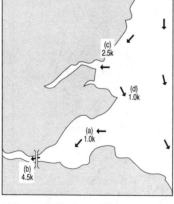

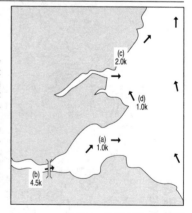

Tidal streams are quite weak in the outer part of the Firth, increasing as the narrows at islands and the bridges are approached.
Apart from the stream of the Tay, which attains 5 knots in most places, the coastwise tidal streams between Fife Ness and Arbroath are weak.

(a) Dover −0225 to Dover +0330	(a) Dover +0330 to Dover −0225
(b) Dover −0200 to Dover +0400	(b) Dover +0400 to Dover −0200
(c) Dover −0210 to Dover +0420	(c) Dover +0420 to Dover −0210
(d) Dover −0110 to Dover +0520	(d) Dover +0520 to Dover −0110

PASSAGES FROM FORTH & TAY

Northbound. Leave before HW (Dover +0400) to be at N Carr at Dover +0600. Bound from Forth to Tay aim to arrive at Abertay By at LW slack (Dover −0200).

Southbound. Leave before LW (Dover -0200) to be at Bass Rk at HW Dover. Similar timings if bound from Tay to Forth, leave late in ebb to pick up early flood off St Andrews to N Carr and into Forth.

TIDAL GATES - NORTH WEST SCOTLAND

These chartlets are designed to help the yachtsman determine accurately the time of tide turn at tidal gates, the approximate maximum strength of the tidal flow, and the position and timing of races, counter tides, etc.

FLOOD	EBB

SOUND OF HARRIS

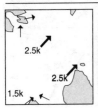

The behaviour of tidal streams in the Sd of Harris varies from day to night, springs to neaps, and winter to summer. The following data applies to daylight, in summer at spring tides in the Cope Channel. Further information can be sought in the Admiralty West of Scotland Pilot.
HW Dover - HW D +0200: SE stream.
HW D +0300 - HW D +0600: Incoming stream from both ends.
HW D -0600 - HW D - 0500: NW stream.
HW D -0500 - HW Dover: Outgoing stream from both ends.
At neaps in summer the stream will run SE for most of the day.
Tide rates shown are the maxima likely to be encountered at any time.

THE LITTLE MINCH

The N going stream on both shores begins at HW Dover +0430 (HW Ullapool -0345), with the strongest flow from mid channel to the Skye coast. There is a W going counter tide E of Vaternish Point.

The S going stream on both shores begins at HW Dover -0130 (HW Ullapool +0240), with the strongest flow from mid channel to the Skye coast. The E going stream in Sound of Scalpay runs at up to 2k.The E going flood and W going ebb in Sound of Scalpay run at up to 2k.

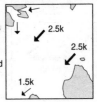

KYLE OF LOCHALSH & KYLERHEA
NOTE: THESE STREAMS ARE SUBJECT TO VARIATION

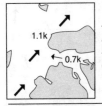

N going stream in Kyle Rhea begins HW Dover +0140 (HW Ullapool +0555) and runs for 6 hours. The E going stream in Kyle Akin begins (Sp) HW Dover +0350 (HW Ullapool -0415). (Nps) HW Dover -0415 (HW Ullapool).

S going stream in Kyle Rhea begins HW Dover -0130 (HW Ullapool) and runs for 6 hours. The W going stream in Kyle Akin begins (Sp) HW Dover -0015 (HW Ullapool +0400). (Nps) HW Dover +0140 (HW Ullapool +0555).

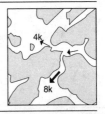

SOUND OF MULL - WEST

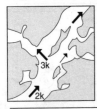

The N going stream off Ardnamurchan begins at HW Dover +0130 (HW Oban -0525). The E going stream in the Sound of Mull begins at HW Dover +0555 (HW Oban -0100).

The S going stream off Ardnamurchan begins at HW Dover -0430 (HW Oban +0100). The W going stream in the Sound of Mull begins at HW Dover -0130 (HW Oban +0400).

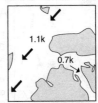

SOUND OF MULL - EAST

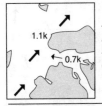

The N going stream in the Firth of Lorne begins at HW Dover -0100 (HW Oban +0430). The W going stream in the Sound of Mull begins at HW Dover +0105 (HW Oban -0550). The ingoing tides at Lochs Feochan, Etive and Creran begin at HW Dover +0300, -0100 & +0030.

The S going stream in the Firth of Lorne begins at HW Dover +0500 (HW Oban -0155). The E going stream in the Sound of Mull begins at HW Dover +0555 (HW Oban -0025). The outgoing tides at Lochs Feochan, Etive and Creran begin at HW Dover -0500, -0520 & -0505.

SOUND OF LUING & DORUS MOR

The N or W going stream begins as follows:
Dorus Mor: HW Dover -0200 (HW Oban +0330). Springs: 8 knots.
Corryvreckan: HW D -0120 (HW O +0410). Sp: 8.5 knots.
Cuan Sound: HW D -0110 (HW O +0420). Sp: 6 knots.
Sound of Jura: HW D -0130 (HW O +0400). Sp: 4 knots.
Sound of Luing: HW D -0100 (HW O +0430). Sp: 7 knots.
The S or E going stream begins as follows:
Dorus Mor: HW Dover +0440 (HW Oban -0215). Springs: 8 knots.
Corryvreckan: HW D +0445 (HW O -0210). Sp: 8.5 knots.
Cuan Sound: HW D +0455 (HW O -0200). Sp: 6 knots.
Sound of Jura: HW D +0450 (HW O -0205). Sp: 4 knots.
Sound of Luing: HW D +0500 (HW O -0155). Sp: 7 knots.

TIDAL GATES - SOUTH WEST SCOTLAND

A guide to the time of tide turn at tidal gates, the approximate maximum strength of the tidal flow (spring rates shown - neaps are approximately 60% of these), and the position and timing of races, counter tides, etc.

FLOOD	EBB

SOUNDS OF ISLAY AND GIGHA

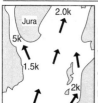

Main flood begins +0015 HW Dover (HW Oban +0545). Streams turn approx 1 hr earlier in Gigha Sd & at Kintyre & Jura shores. S going stream for 9hrs close inshore between Gigha and Machrihanish starting HW Dover (HW Oban -0530).

Main ebb begins HW Dover -0545 (HW Oban -0015). Streams turn 1 hr earlier in Gigha Sd, Kintyre & Jura shores. Overfalls off McArthur's Hd.

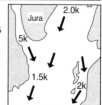

NORTH CHANNEL - NORTH

Main flood begins HW Dover -0600 (HW Greenock +0505). Races off Mull of Kintyre, Altacarry Hd & Fair Hd. Counter tides in bays of Antrim coast., W-going streams in Rathlin Sd, counter tide from Sanda Sd to Machrihanish last 1h30 - 2 hrs.

Main ebb begins HW Dover (HW Greenock -0120). Races off Mull of Kintyre & Altacarry Hd. Counter tides in bays of Antrim coast , counter tide from Macrihanish to Sanda Sd last 1h30 - 2 hrs.

NORTH CHANNEL - SOUTH

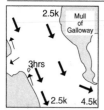

Irish coast - flood begins HW Dover +0610 (HW Belfast -0600). Scottish coast - HW Dover +0430 (HW Greenock +0310). Races off Copeland Is. & Mull of Galloway. Counter tide off Donaghadee and Island Magee last 3 hrs of flood.

Irish coast - ebb begins HW Dover -0015 (HW Belfast). Scottish coast - HW Dover -0130 (HW Greenock -0250). Races off Copeland Is. & Mull of Galloway. Flood begins 2 hrs early close inshore N of Mull of Galloway.

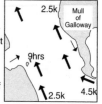

APPROACHES TO STRANGFORD LOUGH

The tide cycle is approx 3 hours later than in the N Channel

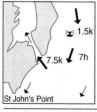

Flood runs for 6 hours from HW Dover -0345 (HW Belfast -0330), with a maximum rate of 7.5 knots at Rue Point. The strong flow flattens the sea in onshore winds and entrance can be made in strong winds.

Ebb runs for 6 hours from HW Dover +0215 (HW Belfast +0230), max rate 7.5k, E of Angus Rk. If entering against ebb use West Channel with care. Smoothest water near Bar Pladdy Buoy when leaving.

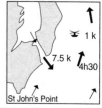

ISLE OF MAN - NORTH

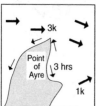

E going stream at Point of Ayre begins HW Dover -0545 (HW Liverpool -0600). Counter tide inside banks E of Point.
In Ramsey Bay the S Going tide runs for 3h from +0530 Dover (+0515 Liverpool).

W going stream at Point of Ayre begins HW Dover +0015 (HW Liverpool). Counter tide inside banks W of Point.
In Ramsey Bay the N going tide runs for 9h from -0330 Dover (-0345 Liverpool).

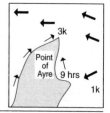

ISLE OF MAN - SOUTH

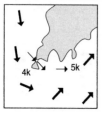

E going stream begins -0600 Dover (Liverpool +0610). Overfalls and race E of Chicken Rock.
Calf Sound: The E going stream begins earlier, at approximately Dover + 0400 (Liverpool +0345).

W going stream begins +0015 Dover (HW Liverpool). Overfalls and race N of Chicken Rock.
Calf Sound:The W going stream begins earlier, at approximately -0130 Dover (-0145 Liverpool).
Note: all times may vary due to weather conditions.

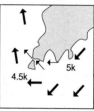

TIDAL GATES - IRISH SEA

A guide to the time of tide turn at tidal gates, the approximate strength of the tidal flow (spring rates shown — neaps are approximately 60% of these), and the position and timing of races, counter tides, etc.

FLOOD	EBB

DUBLIN BAY

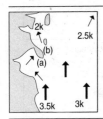

Tide between Rosbeg bank and Howth Hd (a) runs NE from HW Dublin +0300 for 9h30. In Howth Sd (b) the stream is NW going from +0430 to –0130.
New flood and ebb tides begin close to the S shore and N of Baily up to 1h before HW Dublin .

The tide between Rosbeg bank and Howth Hd (a) runs SW from HW Dublin for 3h. In Howth Sd (b) the stream is SE going from –0130 to +0430.
Strengths of steams increase S of Dublin Bay, and decrease N of it.

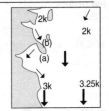

N W ANGLESEY

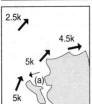

Flood tide close to the coast runs at over 5k springs, and at about 2.5k 7 miles offshore. The brief period of slack water offshore is 1h before HW Dover (1h15 before HW L'pool). Slack water lasts longer in Holyhead Bay.

Ebb tide close to the coast runs at over 5k springs, and at about 2.5k 7 miles offshore. Slack water is 5h after HW Dover (4h45 after HW L'pool). There is no significant counter tide in Holyhead Bay, but the ebb starts first there, giving about 9h W-going tide N of the harbour (a).

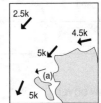

BARDSEY SOUND

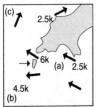

The tide turns to the NW or NE (flood) as follows:
at (a): HW Dover +0300;
at (b): HW D +0500;
at (c): -0545 HW D.
These times are approximate. There is a strong eddy down tide of Bardsey Island and overfalls throughout the area .

The tide turns to the SW or SE (ebb) as follows:
at (a): HW Dover –0300;
at (b): HW D –0100 ;
at (c): at HW D -0030.
These times are approximate. There is a strong eddy down tide of Bardsey Island and overfalls throughout the area.

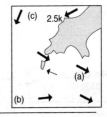

S W WALES

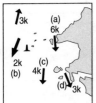

The tide turns to the S or SE (Bristol Channel flood) as follows:
at (a): HW Dover –0200;
at (b) & (c): HW D –0100 ;
at (d): –0300 HW D

The tide turns to the N or NW (Bristol Channel ebb) as follows:
at (a): HW Dover +0400;
at (b) & (c): HW D +0500 ;
at (d): +0300 HW D

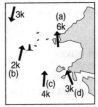

CARNSORE POINT

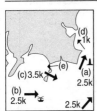

The tide turns to the NE or N (Irish Sea flood) as follows:
at (a): HW Dover +0500; at (b): HW D +0520; at (c): HW D +0600; at (d): –0600 HW D. NE going streams are shorter in duration and weaker than SE going - careful passage planning is essential.

The tide turns to the SW or S as follows:
at (a): –0200 HW D ; at (b): HW D –0020; at (c): –0015 HW D; at (d): –0300 HW Dover. Leaving Rosslare at –0300 HW D a yacht can carry a fair tide for about 8h until HW D +0515 off Hook Head.

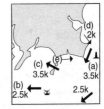

NOTE: The tide turns on St Patrick's Bridge (e) up to 2 hours earlier than in Saltee Sound

CORK COAST

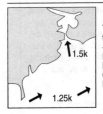

The tide, which flows coastwise, turns to the NE at HW Dover +0045. There is an eddy 5 miles ESE of Old Head of Kinsale at HW Dover +0400. The ingoing Cork Harbour tide begins at HW Dover +0055.

The tide turns SW at HW Dover +0500. The outgoing Cork Harbour tide begins at HW Dover –0540.

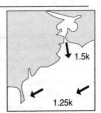

MENAI STRAITS TIDAL GATE

(T) : turning → : < 2k ⟶ : 2-4k ⦀⟶ : 4k +

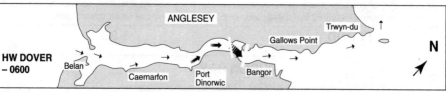

LOCAL LW: Caernarfon: HW Dover –0555. Port Dinorwic: –0620. Menai: –0540. Beaumaris: –0605.

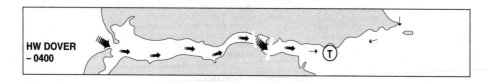

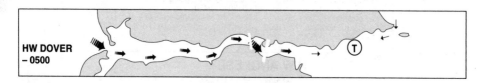

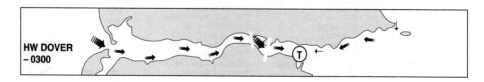

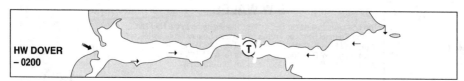

SLACK WATER IN THE SWELLIES: HW Dover –0200 to –0230.

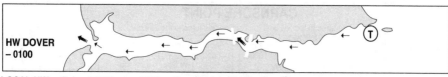

LOCAL HW: Belan: HW Dover –0115. Caernarfon: –0105. Port Dinorwic: –0050.

THE SWELLIES

WESTBOUND: Leave or pass Beaumaris in time to arrive at the Swellies by HW Dover -0230 to -0200. If in doubt about passage speed, leave early; the adverse tide will check your progress. For a first time passage this is useful, as the yachts speed over the ground is reduced. Late arrival will mean a faster passage, but with perhaps less control.

EASTBOUND: Leave or pass Port Dinorwic in time to arrive at Menai Bridge by HW Dover -0230 to -0200. Progress towards the Swellies should be closely monitored, as you are travelling with the last of the flood. Early arrival will mean a fast, perhaps dangerous passage, being late may make it impossible.

MENAI STRAITS TIDAL GATE contd

 (T): turning → : < 2k ⟹ : 2-4k ⟹ : 4k +

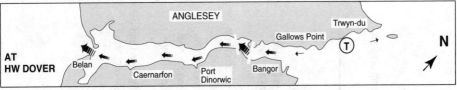

AT
HW DOVER

LOCAL HW TIMES: Menai: Dover – 0005.   Beaumaris: Dover – 0010

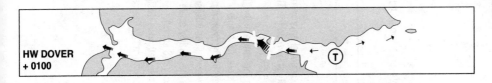

HW DOVER
+ 0100

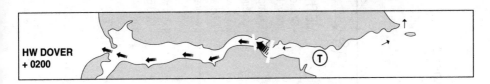

HW DOVER
+ 0200

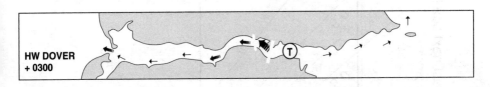

HW DOVER
+ 0300

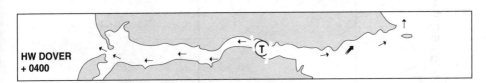

HW DOVER
+ 0400

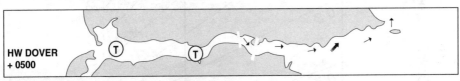

HW DOVER
+ 0500

LOCAL LW TIMES: Belan: Dover + 0520.

CAERNARFON BAR

CAERNARFON BAR is without question highly dangerous in certain conditions. Buoys are located to suit changing channel; positions obtainable from Caernarfon Port Radio - VHF Ch 16; 06, 12: 2h–HW, or when vessel expected. Beware cross track tides near high water. Bar impassable during or after fresh or strong onshore weather. Keep strictly in channel.

| OUTWARD BOUND: Do not leave Belan Narrows after half tide, better as soon as possible after the ebb commences, which gives maximum depth and duration of fair tide if bound S & W. | INWARD BOUND: Locating the bar buoys may be difficult; head for Llanddwyn I. until they are located. Only cross after half tide (HW Dover –0400), which inevitably limits onward passage to max of 3 hours. |

277

TIDAL STREAM RATE INTERPOLATOR

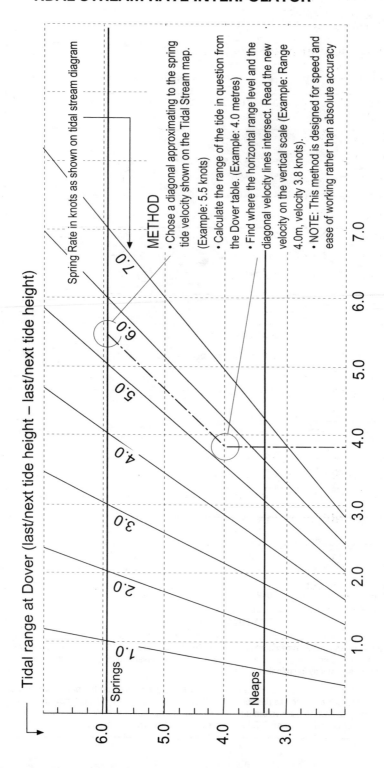

Tidal range at Dover (last/next tide height – last/next tide height)

Spring Rate in knots as shown on tidal stream diagram

METHOD

• Chose a diagonal approximating to the spring tide velocity shown on the Tidal Stream map. (Example: 5.5 knots)

• Calculate the range of the tide in question from the Dover table. (Example: 4.0 metres)

• Find where the horizontal range level and the diagonal velocity lines intersect. Read the new velocity on the vertical scale (Example: Range 4.0m, velocity 3.8 knots).

• NOTE: This method is designed for speed and ease of working rather than absolute accuracy

SECTION 2 - NAVIGATION

CONTENTS

DISTANCES BETWEEN STRATEGIC PORTS

Distances given are the shortest practicable deep-water sea routes whilst abiding by inshore traffic zone regulations

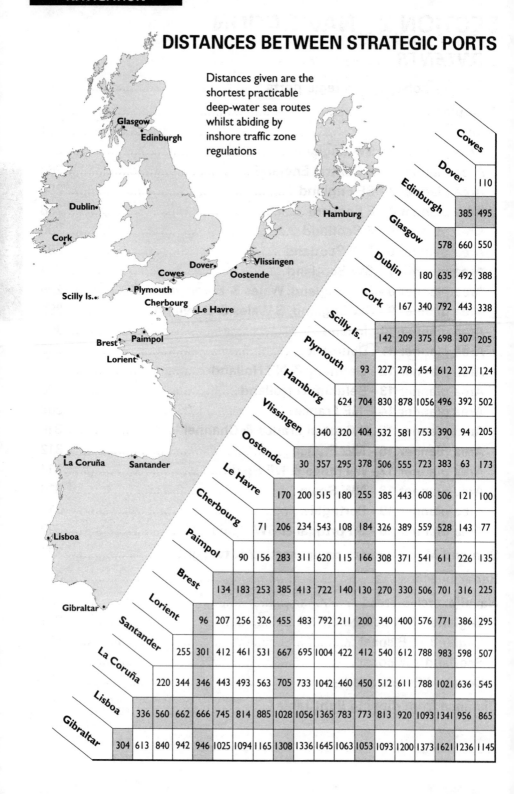

From \ To	Lisboa	La Coruña	Santander	Lorient	Brest	Paimpol	Cherbourg	Le Havre	Oostende	Vlissingen	Hamburg	Plymouth	Scilly Is.	Cork	Dublin	Glasgow	Edinburgh	Dover	Cowes
Dover																			110
Edinburgh																		385	495
Glasgow																	578	660	550
Dublin																180	635	492	388
Cork															167	340	792	443	338
Scilly Is.														142	209	375	698	307	205
Plymouth													93	227	278	454	612	227	124
Hamburg												624	704	830	878	1056	496	392	502
Vlissingen											340	320	404	532	581	753	390	94	205
Oostende										30	357	295	378	506	555	723	383	63	173
Le Havre									170	200	515	180	255	385	443	608	506	121	100
Cherbourg								71	206	234	543	108	184	326	389	559	528	143	77
Paimpol							90	156	283	311	620	115	166	308	371	541	611	226	135
Brest						134	183	253	385	413	722	140	130	270	330	506	701	316	225
Lorient					96	207	256	326	455	483	792	211	200	340	400	576	771	386	295
Santander				255	301	412	461	531	667	695	1004	422	412	540	612	788	983	598	507
La Coruña			220	344	346	443	493	563	705	733	1042	460	450	512	611	788	1021	636	545
Lisboa		336	560	662	666	745	814	885	1028	1056	1365	783	773	813	920	1093	1341	956	865
Gibraltar	304	613	840	942	946	1025	1094	1165	1308	1336	1645	1063	1053	1093	1200	1373	1621	1236	1145

AREA PLANNERS

England, Scotland, Ireland, Wales, France, Belgium, Holland
Germany, Denmark, Spain & Portugal

Ports, waypoints, principal lights, courses and distances

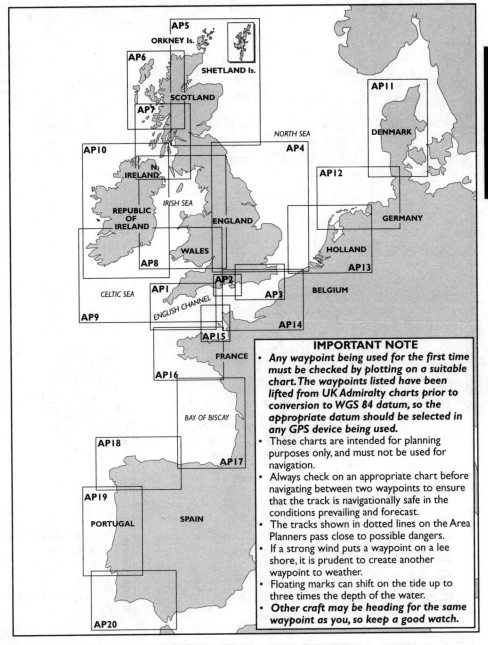

IMPORTANT NOTE

- *Any waypoint being used for the first time must be checked by plotting on a suitable chart. The waypoints listed have been lifted from UK Admiralty charts prior to conversion to WGS 84 datum, so the appropriate datum should be selected in any GPS device being used.*
- These charts are intended for planning purposes only, and must not be used for navigation.
- Always check on an appropriate chart before navigating between two waypoints to ensure that the track is navigationally safe in the conditions prevailing and forecast.
- The tracks shown in dotted lines on the Area Planners pass close to possible dangers.
- If a strong wind puts a waypoint on a lee shore, it is prudent to create another waypoint to weather.
- Floating marks can shift on the tide up to three times the depth of the water.
- *Other craft may be heading for the same waypoint as you, so keep a good watch.*

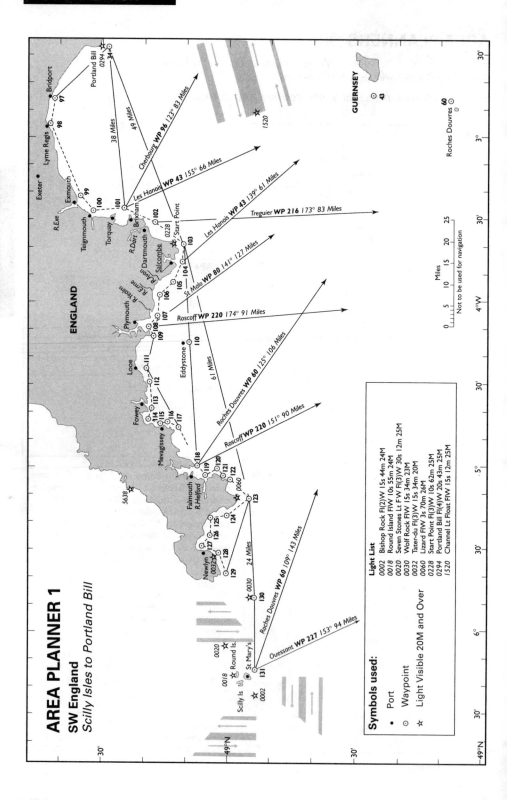

AREA PLANNER 1
SW England
Scilly Isles to Portland Bill

Symbols used:
- • Port
- ⊙ Waypoint
- ☆ Light Visible 20M and Over

Light List

0002	Bishop Rock Fl(2)W 15s 44m 24M
0018	Round Island FlW 10s 55m 24M
0020	Seven Stones Lt. F.W Fl(3)W 30s 12m 25M
0030	Wolf Rock FlW 15s 34m 23M
0032	Tater-du Fl(3)W 15s 34m 20M
0060	Lizard FlW 3s 70m 26M
0228	Start Point Fl(3)W 10s 62m 25M
0294	Portland Bill Fl(4)W 20s 43m 25M
1520	Channel Lt Float FlW 15s 12m 25M

GUERNSEY

Roches Douvres

ENGLAND

Exeter • R.Exe • Exmouth • Lyme Regis • Bridport • Portland Bill
Teignmouth • Torquay • Brixham • Start Point
R.Dart • Dartmouth • Salcombe
R.Erme • R.Yealm • Plymouth
Eddystone
Looe • Fowey • Mevagissey
Falmouth • R.Helford
Newlyn
Scilly Is • St Mary's • Round Is.

Cherbourg **WP 86** 123° 83 Miles
Les Hanois **WP 43** 155° 66 Miles
Les Hanois **WP 43** 139° 61 Miles
Treguier **WP 216** 173° 83 Miles
St Malo **WP 80** 141° 127 Miles
Roscoff **WP 220** 174° 91 Miles
Roches Douvres **WP 60** 125° 106 Miles
Roscoff **WP 220** 151° 90 Miles
Roches Douvres **WP 60** 109° 143 Miles
Ouessant **WP 227** 153° 94 Miles

38 Miles
49 Miles
61 Miles
24 Miles

Miles
0 5 10 15 20 25
Not to be used for navigation

AREA PLANNER 1

WAYPOINTS

England South West - *Scilly Isles to Bridport*

34	Portland Bill - *5M S of*	50°25'·82N	02°27'·30W
43	Guernsey SW - *1·8M W Les Hanois*	49°26'·16N	02°45'·00W
60	Roches Douvres Lt - *2·5M NE*	49°08'·24N	02°45'·96W
80	St Malo - *1·3M NW Grande Jardin Lt. Bn*	48°41'·10N	02°06'·40W
96	Cherbourg - *0·5M N of W ent*	49°40'·95N	01°39'·35W
97	Bridport - *1M S of entrance*	50°41'·50N	02°45'·70W
98	Lyme Regis - *1M SSE on ldg Lts*	50°42'·80N	02°54'·80W
99	River Exe - *0·3M S of E Exe Lt By*	50°35'·67N	03°22'·30W
100	Teignmouth - *1M E of Bar*	50°32'·30N	03°27'·80W
101	Torbay - *1·7M NE of Berry Hd*	50°25'·10N	03°27'·00W
102	Dartmouth - *2M 150° from ent*	50°18'·25N	03°31'·60W
103	Start Point - *2M S of*	50°11'·30N	03°38'·47W
104	Salcombe - *1·5M S of bar*	50°11'·62N	03°46'·60W
105	Bolt Tail - *1·3M SW of R Avon*	50°13'·60N	03°53'·60W
106	River Erme - *1·5M SSW of Battisborough Island*	50°16'·80N	03°58'·50W
107	R Yealm - *1·2M SW of Yealm Hd*	50°17'·30N	04°05'·70W
108	Plymouth - *0·9M S of W end of brkwtr*	50°19'·13N	04°09'·50W
109	Rame Hd - *0·2M S of*	50°18'·15N	04°13'·30W
110	Eddystone - *1M S of*	50°09'·80N	04°15'·85W
111	Looe - *1·5M SE of entrance*	50°19'·80N	04°25'·20W
112	Polperro - *0·7M S of*	50°19'·00N	04°30'·80W
113	Fowey - *1·5M SSW of ent*	50°18'·20N	04°39'·50W
114	Charlestown - *1M SE of*	50°19'·00N	04°44'·10W
115	Mevagissey - *0·8M E of*	50°16'·10N	04°45'·50W
116	Gwineas Lt By - *0·2M E of*	50°14'·40N	04°45'·00W
117	Dodman Pt - *1·3M SSE of*	50°11'·90N	04°47'·00W
118	Falmouth - *0·8M S of St Anthony Hd*	50°07'·64N	05°00'·90W
119	Helford River - *1M E of ent*	50°05'·70N	05°04'·00W
120	Manacles - *0·2M E of*	50°02'·80N	05°01'·50W
121	Coverack - *1M E of*	50°01'·30N	05°04'·30W
122	Black Hd - *0·7M SE of*	49°59'·70N	05°05'·30W
123	Lizard - *2M S of*	49°55'·58N	05°l 2'·07W
124	Porth Mellin - *1·7M W of*	50°00'·80N	05°l 8'·50W
125	Porthleven - *0·4M SW of*	50°04'·50N	05°l 9'·70W
126	Mountamopus By - *0·2M S*	50°04'·40N	05°26'·20W
127	Penzance - *1·5M SE of and for Mousehole*	50°06'·00N	05°30'·00W
128	Tater Du Lt - *1·5M ESE*	50°02'·50N	05°32'·60W
129	Runnel Stone Lt By - *0·3M S*	50°00'·85N	05°40'·30W
130	Wolf Rk - *2M S of*	49°54'·65N	05°48'·50W
131	St Mary's, Scilly - *2M E of St Mary's Sound*	49°54'·00N	06°l 5'·00W
216	Treguier - *4·1M N of Pointe de Chateau*	48°56'·20N	03°14'·30W
220	Roscoff - *6M NNE of ent*	48°49'·10N	03°54'·30W
227	Ushant Creac'h Lt - *3·5M NW*	48°30'·00N	05°11'·30W

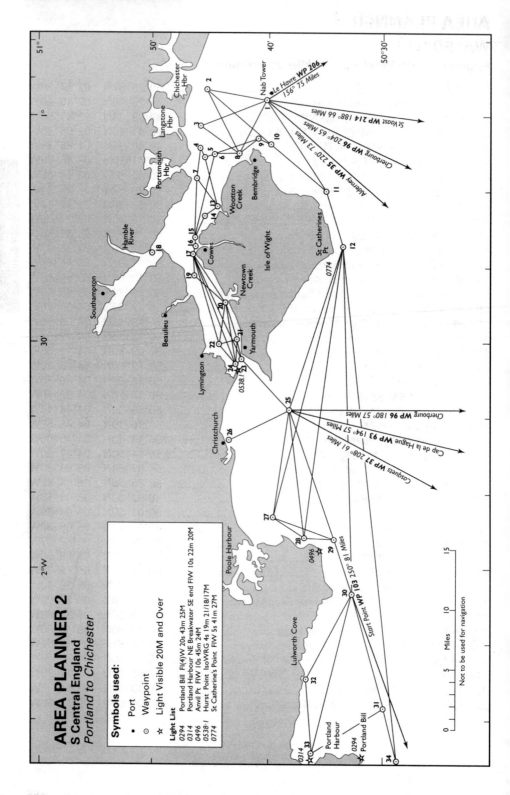

AREA PLANNER 2
S Central England
Portland to Chichester

Symbols used:

- ● Port
- ⊙ Waypoint
- ☆ Light Visible 20M and Over

Light List

0294 Portland Bill Fl(4)W 20s 43m 25M
0314 Portland Harbour NE Breakwater SE end Fl W 10s 22m 20M
0496 Anvil Pt Fl W 10s 45m 24M
0538·1 Hurst Point IsoWRG 4s 19m 21/18/17M
0774 St Catherine's Point Fl W 5s 41m 27M

Not to be used for navigation

Miles

0   5   10   15

AREA PLANNER 2

WAYPOINTS

England South Central - *Portland to Chichester*

1	Nab Tower - *0·5M NW of*	50°40'·38N	00°57'·55W
2	West Pole Bn - *0·3M S of*	50°45'·38N	00°56'·37W
3	Langstone Fairway Buoy - *0·5M S of*	50°45'·78N	01°01'·27W
4	Main Passage - *Dolphin gap off Southsea*	50°45'·98N	01°04'·02W
5	Horse Sand Buoy - *Portsmouth ch*	50°45'·49N	01°05'·18W
6	Forts- *midway between the two*	50°44'·70N	01°05'·00W
7	Gilkicker Point - *0·3M S of*	50°46'·00N	01°08'·40W
8	Bembridge Tide Gauge	50°42'·43N	01°04'·93W
9	Bembridge Ledge Buoy	50°41'·12N	01°02'·72W
10	West Princessa Buoy - *S of Bembridge*	50°40'·12N	01°03'·58W
11	Dunnose Head - *1M off*	50°35'·00N	01°10'·00W
12	St Catherine's Point - *1M S of*	50°33'·52N	01°17'·80W
13	Wootton Beacon	50°44'·51N	01°12'·05W
14	Peel Bank Buoy - *east Solent*	50°45'·58N	01°13'·25W
15	Old Castle Point - *0·3M N of*	50°46'·30N	01°16'·50W
16	Cowes entrance	50°46'·20N	01°17'·85W
17	Egypt Point - *0·4M N of*	50°46'·20N	01°18'·70W
18	Hamble Point Buoy	50°50'·12N	01°18'·58W
19	Beaulieu Spit Beacon - *0·3M off*	50°46'·83N	01°21'·50W
20	Newtown - *0·5M NW of ent*	50°43'·87N	01°25'·20W
21	Yarmouth ent - *0·4M N of*	50°42'·80N	01°30'·00W
22	Lymington, Jack in the basket - *seaward mark*	50°44'·24N	01°30'·48W
23	Hurst Narrows - *midway*	50°42'·20N	01°32'·40W
24	Keyhaven - *0·2M E of entrance*	50°42'·80N	01°32'·80W
25	Fairway Buoy - *Needles channel*	50°38'·20N	01°38'·90W
26	Christchurch - *0·3M E of ent*	50°43'·44N	01°43'·80W
27	Poole No 1 Buoy - *1M E of*	50°38'·332N	01°53'·57W
28	Swanage - *0·7M NE of pier*	50°37'·00N	01°56'·00W
29	Anvil Point - *1·5M SE of*	50°34'·30N	01°56'·00W
30	St Albans Head - *1·5M S of*	50°33'·20N	02°03'·30W
31	East Shambles - *1M SE of*	50°30'·00N	02°18'·90W
32	Lulworth Cove - *0·1M S of ent*	50°36'·87N	02°14'·80W
33	Weymouth - *1M E of ent*	50°36'·60N	02°25'·00W
34	Portland Bill - *5M S of*	50°25'·82N	02°27'·30W
35	Alderney - Bray Harbour - *1M NNE of*	49°45'·00N	02°10'·75W
37	Casquets - *1M W of*	49°43'·38N	02°24'·06W
93	Cap de La Hague - *2M W of*	49°43'·37N	02°00'·00W
96	Cherbourg - *0·5M N of W ent*	49°40'·95N	01°39'·35W
103	Start Point - *2M S of*	50°11'·30N	03°38'·47W
206	Le Havre - *0·5M NE of Le Havre LHA*	49°32'·00N	00°09'·20W
214	St-Vaast-la-Hougue - *3·0 M ENE of entrance*	49°36'·40N	01°11'·00W

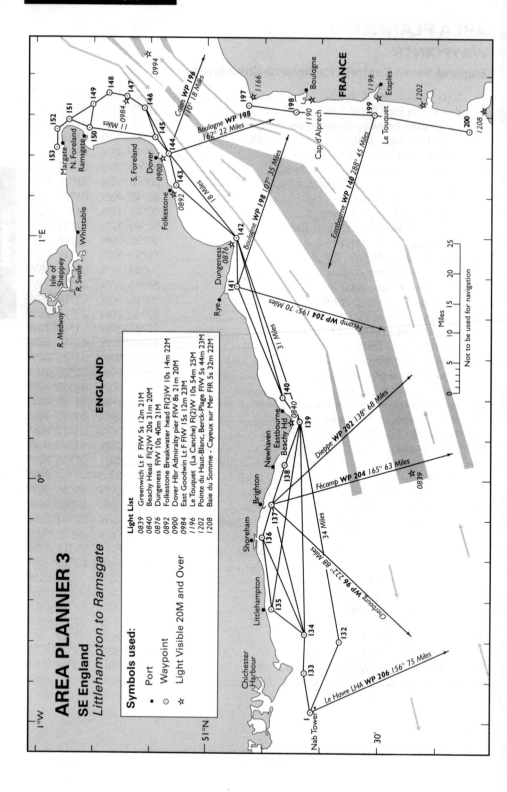

AREA PLANNER 3

SE England
Littlehampton to Ramsgate

Symbols used:

● Port
◎ Waypoint
☆ Light Visible 20M and Over

Light List:

0839	Greenwich Lt F FlW 5s 12m 21M
0840	Beachy Head Fl(2)W 20s 31m 20M
0876	Dungeness FlW 10s 40m 21M
0892	Folkestone Breakwater head Fl(2)W 10s 14m 22M
0900	Dover Hbr Admiralty pier FlW 8s 21m 20M
0984	East Goodwin Lt F FlW 15s 12m 23M
1196	Le Touquet (La Canche) Fl(2)W 10s 54m 25M
1202	Pointe du Haut-Blanc, Berck-Plage FlW 5s 44m 23M
1208	Baie du Somme - Cayeux sur Mer FlR 5s 32m 22M

AREA PLANNER 3
WAYPOINTS
England South East - *Littlehampton to Ramsgate*

#			
1	Nab Tower - *0·5M NW of*	50°40'·38N	00°57'·55W
96	Cherbourg - *0·5M N of W entrance*	49°40'·95N	01°39'·35W
132	Owers SCM- *1·8M SE of*	50°36'·80N	00°40'·60W
133	Boulder Lt by - *0·1M N of*	50°41'·60N	00°49'·03W
134	East Borough Hd Lt By - *0·1M N of*	50°41'·60N	00°39'·00W
135	Littlehampton entrance - *1M 165°of on leading Lts*	50°47'·00N	00°32'·00W
136	Shoreham entrance - *1M S of on leading Lts*	50°48'·50N	00°I 4'·65W
137	Brighton entrance - *1M S of*	50°47'·50N	00°06'·30W
138	Newhaven entrance - *1M S of*	50°45'·50N	00°03'·60E
139	Beachy Hd - *1·5M S of*	50°42'·50N	00°14'·60E
140	Eastbourne - *1·2M SE of Langney Pt*	50°46'·25N	00°21'·10E
141	Rye - *0·1M S of Rye Fairway By*	50°53'·90N	00°48'·13E
142	Dungeness - *1M SE of*	50°54'·00N	00°59'·65E
143	Folkestone - *0·5M SE of breakwater*	51°04'·17N	01°I 2'·35E
144	Dover - *1·2M SE of Western entrance*	51°05'·80N	01°21'·10E
145	South Foreland - *2M E of*	51°08·70N	01°26'·25E
146	South Goodwin Lt By - *0·2M SE of*	51°I 0'·43N	01°32'·59E
147	East Goodwin Lt Float - *0·8M W of*	51°I 3'·23N	01°35'·20E
148	East Goodwin Lt By - *0·2M E of*	51°I 6'·00N	01°35'·92E
149	Goodwin Knoll - *1M SE of*	51°I 8'·84N	01°33'·43E
150	Ramsgate - *1M E of; and for Pegwell Bay*	51°I 9'·47N	01°27'·13E
151	North Foreland - *1M E of*	51°22'·50N	01°28'·70E
152	Foreness Pt - *1M NNE of*	51°24'·46N	01°26'·36E
153	Margate - *0·7M N of*	51°24'·10N	01°22'·50E
197	Cap Gris-Nez - *2·0 M NW of headland*	50°53'·30N	01°32'·50E
198	Boulogne - *2·0 M WNW of entrance*	50°45'·30N	01°31'·50E
199	Étaples - *3·0M W of Le Touquet point*	50°32'·20N	01°30'·80E
200	St Valéry-sur-Somme - *5M WNW Le Hourdel Pt*	50°15'·30N	01°27'·10E
202	Dieppe - *1M NW of entrance*	49°57'·00N	01°04'·00E
204	Fécamp - *1M NW of entrance*	49°46'·70N	00°20'·80E
206	Le Havre - *0·5M NE of Le Havre LHA*	49°32'·00N	00°09'·20W

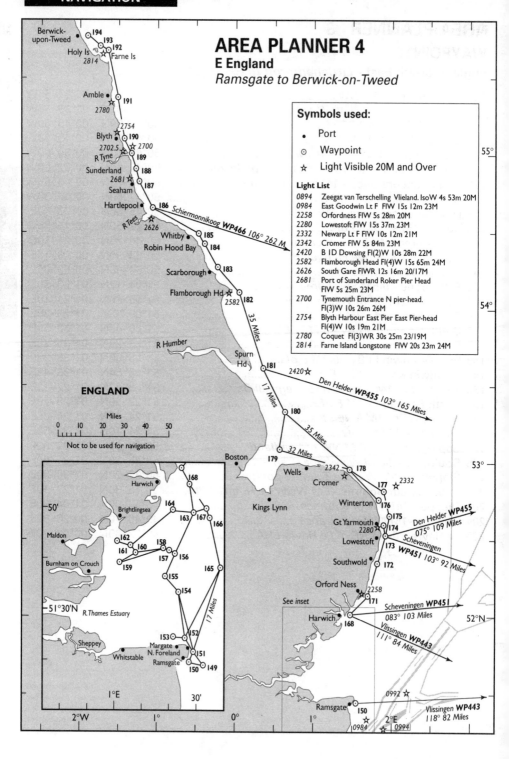

AREA PLANNER 4
E England
Ramsgate to Berwick-on-Tweed

Symbols used:

- • Port
- ⊙ Waypoint
- ☆ Light Visible 20M and Over

Light List

0894	Zeegat van Terschelling Vlieland. IsoW 4s 53m 20M	
0984	East Goodwin Lt F FIW 15s 12m 23M	
2258	Orfordness FIW 5s 28m 20M	
2280	Lowestoft FIW 15s 37m 23M	
2332	Newarp Lt F FIW 10s 12m 21M	
2342	Cromer FIW 5s 84m 23M	
2420	B ID Dowsing Fl(2)W 10s 28m 22M	
2582	Flamborough Head Fl(4)W 15s 65m 24M	
2626	South Gare FIWR 12s 16m 20/17M	
2681	Port of Sunderland Roker Pier Head FIW 5s 25m 23M	
2700	Tynemouth Entrance N pier-head. Fl(3)W 10s 26m 26M	
2754	Blyth Harbour East Pier East Pier-head Fl(4)W 10s 19m 21M	
2780	Coquet Fl(3)WR 30s 25m 23/19M	
2814	Farne Island Longstone FIW 20s 23m 24M	

ENGLAND

Miles

0   10   20   30   40   50

Not to be used for navigation

55°
54°
53°
52°N

288

AREA PLANNER 4
WAYPOINTS
England East - *Ramsgate to Berwick-on-Tweed*

149	Goodwin Knoll - *1M SE of*	51°18'·83N	01°33'·40E
150	Ramsgate -*1M E Pegwell Bay*	51°19'·47N	01°27'·13E
151	North Foreland - *1M E*	51°22'·50N	01°28'·70E
152	Foreness Pt - *1M NNE of*	51°24'·46N	01°26'·36E
153	Margate - *0·7M N of*	51°24'·10N	01°22'·50E
154	Fisherman's Gat - *SE turning waypoint*	51°33'·30N	01°25'·00E
155	Fisherman's Gat - *NW turning waypoint*	51°36'·30N	01°20'·70E
156	Black Deep/Sunk Sand - *turning waypoint*	51°40'·94N	01°25'·00E
157	Barrow No 2 Lt By - *0·3M NE*	51°42'·16N	01°23'·34E
158	Barrow No 3 Lt By - *0·3M N*	51°42'·29N	01°20'·35E
159	Whitaker channel - *for River Crouch (6M)*	51°40'·40N	01°05'·30E
160	Swin Spitway Lt By - *0·1M SSW*	51°41'·83N	01°08'·36E
161	Spitway North - *turning waypt*	51°43'·70N	01°07'·10E
162	Colne,Blackwater - *0·3M W Eagle Lt By*	51°44'·10N	01°03'·43E
163	NE Gunfleet Lt By - *0·5M NW of*	51°50'·25N	01°27'·35E
164	Medusa Lt By - *0·3M SW of*	51°51'·00N	01°20'·00E
165	Kentish Knock Lt By - *0·2M E*	51°38'·50N	01°40'·80E
166	Trinity Lt By - *0·6M N of*	51°49'·65N	01°36'·45E
167	Sunk Lt F - *0·2M SW of*	51°50'·87N	01°34'·80E
168	Cork Lt By - *1M E Harwich Yt ch ent*	51°55'·35N	01°29'·00E
171	Orfordness - *1·5M ESE of*	52°04'·20N	01°37'·00E
172	Southwold - *2M ESE of ent*	52°18'·00N	01°43'·70E
173	Lowestoft - *2·8M E of ent*	52°28'·30N	01°50'·10E
174	Gt Yarmouth - *0·5M WNW of S Corton SCM*	52°32'·07N	01°49'·36E
175	Gt Yarmouth - *4·7M E of ent*	52°34'·33N	01°52'·10E
176	Winterton - *0·5M NE Cockle ECM*	52°44'·40N	01°44'·20E
177	Winterton - *5·2M NE of*	52°46'·90N	01°48'·50E
178	Cromer - *3·0M NNE of Lt*	52°58'·15N	01°21'·20E
179	North Well Lt By - *0·5M NE*	53°03'·35N	00°28'·60E
180	Inner Dowsing Lt By - *0·5M NE of*	53°20'·10N	00°34'·50E
181	Spurn Head - *2·6M E of Spurn Lightship*	53°34'·80N	00°17'·70E
182	Flamborough Head - *2·0 M E*	54°07'·10N	00°01'·10W
183	Scarborough - *1·0M E of ent*	54°16'·87N	00°21'·56W
184	Robin Hood's Bay - *2·6M NE*	54°26'·40N	00°27'·30W
185	Whitby - *1·6M N of ent*	54°31'·10N	00°36'·60W
186	River Tees - *Fairway Buoy*	54°40'·93N	01°06'·38W
187	Seaham - *0·9M E of ent*	54°50'·40N	01°17'·70W
188	Sunderland - *1·7M E of ent*	54°55'·25N	01°18'·10W
189	R Tyne - *1·7 M E by N of ent*	55°01'·15N	01°21'·10W
190	Blyth - *1·5M E of entrance*	55°07'·00N	01°26'·50W
191	Amble - *2·5M NE of ent*	55°21'·85N	01°30'·70W
192	Farne Island - *2·0 M NE of Longstone Lt*	55°40'·00N	01°33'·95W
193	Holy Island - *1·0M NE of Emmanuel Hd*	55°41'·95N	01°45'·50W
194	Berwick-upon-Tweed - *1·5M E of Breakwater*	55°45'·90N	01°56'·30W
443	Breskens/Vlissingen - *1·4M NE Niewe Sluis Lt*	51°25'·50N	03°32'·80E
451	Scheveningen - *0·7M NW harbour ent*	52°07'·00N	04°14'·80E
455	Den Helder - *1·2M S Kijkduin Lt*	52°56'·90N	04°41'·90E
458	Noorderhaaks Is - *3·2M WSW*	52°57'·30N	04°33'·70E
466	Ameland - *2·9M NNW E end*	53°30'·40N	06°00'·00E

Section 2

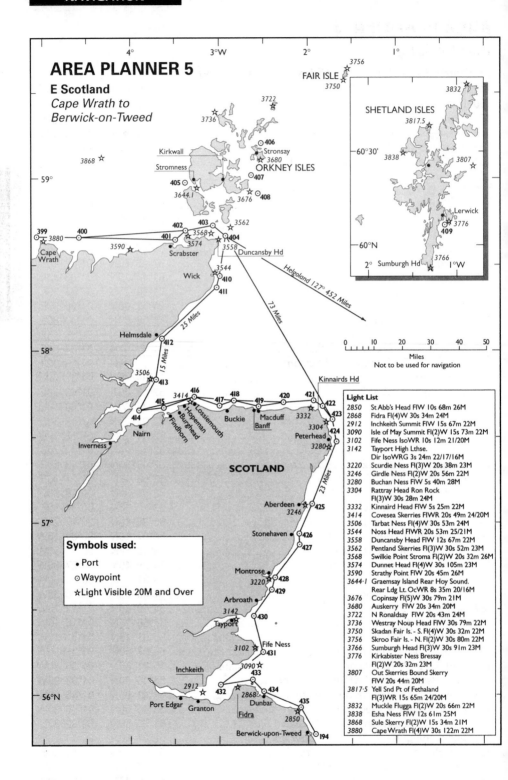

AREA PLANNER 5

E Scotland
Cape Wrath to
Berwick-on-Tweed

FAIR ISLE

SHETLAND ISLES

Lerwick

Sumburgh Hd

Kirkwall
Stronsay
Stromness
ORKNEY ISLES

Cape Wrath
Scrabster
Duncansby Hd
Wick

Helmsdale

Kinnairds Hd

Helsgoland 127° 452 Miles
73 Miles
25 Miles
15 Miles

Lossiemouth
Hopeman
Burghead
Buckie
Macduff
Banff
Findhorn
Nairn
Inverness
Peterhead

SCOTLAND

Aberdeen

Stonehaven

Montrose

Arbroath

Tayport

Fife Ness

Inchkeith

Port Edgar
Granton
Dunbar
Fidra

Berwick-upon-Tweed

Symbols used:

- ● Port
- ⊙ Waypoint
- ☆ Light Visible 20M and Over

0 10 20 30 40 50
Miles
Not to be used for navigation

Light List

2850	St Abb's Head FlW 10s 68m 26M
2868	Fidra Fl(4)W 30s 34m 24M
2912	Inchkeith Summit FlW 15s 67m 22M
3090	Isle of May Summit Fl(2)W 15s 73m 22M
3102	Fife Ness IsoWR 10s 12m 21/20M
3142	Tayport High Lthse.
	Dir IsoWRG 3s 24m 22/17/16M
3220	Scurdie Ness Fl(3)W 20s 38m 23M
3246	Girdle Ness Fl(2)W 20s 56m 22M
3280	Buchan Ness FlW 5s 40m 28M
3304	Rattray Head Ron Rock
	Fl(3)W 30s 28m 24M
3332	Kinnaird Head FlW 5s 25m 22M
3414	Covesea Skerries FlWR 20s 49m 24/20M
3506	Tarbat Ness Fl(4)W 30s 53m 24M
3544	Noss Head FlWR 20s 53m 25/21M
3558	Duncansby Head FlW 12s 67m 22M
3562	Pentland Skerries Fl(3)W 30s 52m 23M
3568	Swilkie Point Stroma Fl(2)W 20s 32m 26M
3574	Dunnet Head Fl(4)W 30s 105m 23M
3590	Strathy Point FlW 20s 45m 26M
3644·1	Graemsay Island Rear Hoy Sound.
	Rear Ldg Lt. OcWR 8s 35m 20/16M
3676	Copinsay Fl(5)W 30s 79m 21M
3680	Auskerry FlW 20s 34m 20M
3722	N Ronaldsay FlW 20s 43m 24M
3736	Westray Noup Head FlW 30s 79m 22M
3750	Skadan Fair Is. - S. Fl(4)W 30s 32m 22M
3756	Skroo Fair Is. - N. Fl(2)W 30s 80m 22M
3766	Sumburgh Head Fl(3)W 30s 91m 23M
3776	Kirkabister Ness Bressay
	Fl(2)W 20s 32m 23M
3807	Out Skerries Bound Skerry
	FlW 20s 44m 20M
3817·5	Yell Snd Pt of Fethaland
	Fl(3)WR 15s 65m 24/20M
3832	Muckle Flugga Fl(2)W 20s 66m 22M
3838	Esha Ness FlW 12s 61m 25M
3868	Sule Skerry Fl(2)W 15s 34m 21M
3880	Cape Wrath Fl(4)W 30s 122m 22M

AREA PLANNER 5

WAYPOINTS

Scotland East - *Cape Wrath to Berwick-upon- Tweed*

194	Berwick-upon - Tweed - *1·5M E*	55°45'·90N	01°56'·30W
399	Cape Wrath - *2M NW of*	58°38'·90N	05°02'·80W
400	Whiten Head - *4·4M N of*	58°39'·20N	04°34'·90W
401	Scrabster - *1·4M NE of Holborn Hd*	58°38'·60N	03°30'·70W
402	Dunnet Head Lt - *1·7M NW of*	58°41'·60N	03°24'·30W
403	Pentl'd Firth - *1·5M NE by N Stroma*	58°43'·00N	03°05'·40W
404	Duncansby Head - *2M NE of*	58°39'·80N	02°58'·40W
405	Stromness - *2·8M NW Graemsay Lt.*	58°57'·10N	03°23'·70W
406	Stronsay - *0·8M NW Ness Lt.*	59°10'·00N	02°35'·80W
407	Kirkwall - *1·5M NW of Mull Hd*	58°59'·40N	02°40'·40W
408	Copinsay Lt - *2·5M E of*	58°54'·10N	02°35'·10W
409	Lerwick - *1·1M SW of Bressay Lt*	60°06'·60N	01°08'·60W
410	Wick - *1·6M E of South Hd*	58°25'·80N	03°01'·00W
411	Scarlet Hd - *2M E by S*	58°21'·90N	03°02'·50W
412	Helmsdale - *1·8M SE of ent*	58°05'·50N	03°36'·80W
413	Tarbat Ness Lt - *2M E of*	57°51'·80N	03°42'·70W
414	Inverness - *0·5 NE of Frwy By*	57°40'·30N	03°53'·30W
415	Findhorn - *2·2M NW of bay*	57°41'·45N	03°40'·00W
416	Lossiemouth - *1·7M N*	57°45'·20N	03°16'·70W
417	Buckie - *2·0M WNW*	57°41'·70N	03°00'·90W
418	Scar Nose - *1·6M N*	57°44'·00N	02°50'·90W
419	Banff - *1·3M N of Meavie Pt*	57°41'·60N	02°31'·40W
420	Troup Head - *1·8M N*	57°43'·50N	02°17'·70W
421	Kinnairds Head - *1·6M N*	57°43'·50N	02°00'·20W
422	Cairnbulg Point Lt - *1·9M NE*	57°42'·20N	01°53'·70W
423	Rattray Head Lt - *1·8M ENE*	57°37'·40N	01°45'·90W
424	Peterhead - *2·1M ESE*	57°29'·30N	01°42'·60W
425	Aberdeen - *2M E by N Girdle Ness*	57°08'·80N	01°59'·00W
426	Stonehaven - *2M E*	56°57'·60N	02°08'·20W
427	Todhead Point Lt - *2·5M E*	56°53'·10N	02°08'·30W
428	Montrose - *2·1M E Scurdie Ness Lt*	56°42'·10N	02°22'·40W
429	Red Head - *1·8M E of*	56°37'·40N	02°25'·30W
430	Tayport - *0·5M E Fairway By*	56°29'·25N	02°37'·24W
431	Fife Ness - *2·8M ESE*	56°15'·95N	02°30'·30W
432	Granton - *0·5M N Inchkeith By*	56°04'·00N	03°00'·00W
433	Bass Rock Lt - *1·5M N*	56°06'·10N	02°38'·40W
434	Dunbar - *1·5M NNE*	56°01'·76N	02°30'·20W
435	St Abb's Head Lt - *1·5M NE*	55°56'·10N	02°06'·40W
450	Hoek van Holland - *1·2M WNW*	51°59'·90N	04°01'·00E

Section 2

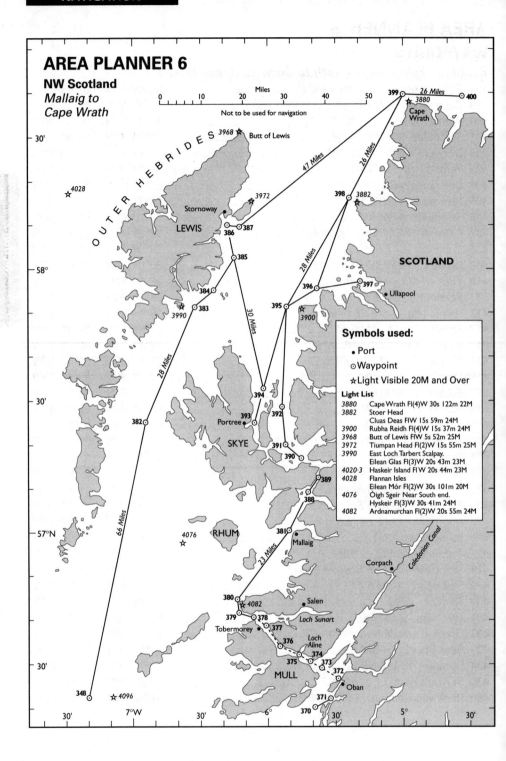

AREA PLANNER 6

NW Scotland
*Mallaig to
Cape Wrath*

Miles

0   10   20   30   40   50

Not to be used for navigation

Symbols used:

● Port

⊙ Waypoint

☆ Light Visible 20M and Over

Light List

3880	Cape Wrath Fl(4)W 30s 122m 22M	
3882	Stoer Head	
	Cluas Deas FlW 15s 59m 24M	
3900	Rubha Reidh Fl(4)W 15s 37m 24M	
3968	Butt of Lewis FlW 5s 52m 25M	
3972	Tiumpan Head Fl(2)W 15s 55m 25M	
3990	East Loch Tarbert Scalpay.	
	Eilean Glas Fl(3)W 20s 43m 23M	
4020·3	Haskeir Island Fl W 20s 44m 23M	
4028	Flannan Isles	
	Eilean Mór Fl(2)W 30s 101m 20M	
4076	Óigh Sgeir Near South end.	
	Hyskeir Fl(3)W 30s 41m 24M	
4082	Ardnamurchan Fl(2)W 20s 55m 24M	

OUTER HEBRIDES

3968 Butt of Lewis

☆ 4028

3972

Stornoway

LEWIS

387
386

385

SCOTLAND

47 Miles

26 Miles

26 Miles

399 3880 400

Cape
Wrath

398 3882

384
383
3990

396 397 ● Ullapool

395 ☆ 3900

28 Miles

30 Miles

382

394

393 392
Portree ●
391
390

SKYE

389
388

4076
☆ RHUM

381 ● Mallaig

23 Miles

28 Miles

66 Miles

Corpach

Caledonian Canal

380 ☆ 4082
379 378
Tobermorey ● 377 ● Salen
376 Loch Sunart
375 374 Loch Aline
373
MULL 372
● Oban
371
348 ☆ 4096 370

7°W   6°   5°
30'   30'   30'   30'   30'

30'

58°

30'

57°N

30'

AREA PLANNER 6

WAYPOINTS

Scotland North West - *Mallaig to Cape Wrath*

348	Skerryvore Lt - *6·8M W by N of*	56°20'·80N	07°18'·80W
370	Sound of Insh - *1M SSW of Insh Island*	56°17'·60N	05°41'·00W
371	Kerrera Sound - *0·7M SSW of Rubha Seanach*	56°21'·70N	05°33'·90W
372	Oban - *0·5M WNW of Maiden Isle*	56°26'·00N	05°30'·30W
373	Between Lady's Rock and Eilean Musdile	56°27'·20N	05°36'·70W
374	Sound of Mull - *1·6M SE of Ardtornish Pt*	56°30'·15N	05°42'·75W
375	Loch Aline - *0·7M S by W of entrance*	56°31'·30N	05°46'·80W
376	Sound of Mull - *1·8M N of Salen*	56°33'·00N	05°56'·30W
377	Tobermory - *0·9M NE of harbour entrance*	56°38'·40N	06°02'·40W
378	Ardmore Point (Mull) - *0·7M N of*	56°40'·00N	06°07'·60W
379	Point of Ardnamurchan - *2·8M S of*	56°40'·90N	06°13'·30W
380	Point of Ardnamurchan - *1·3M W of*	56°43'·60N	06°15'·90W
381	Mallaig - *1·5 miles WNW of harbour entrance*	57°01'·00N	05°52'·10W
382	Neist Point Lt - *4·0M W of*	57°25'·45N	06°54'·50W
383	Sound of Shiant - *2·2M E of Eilean Glas Lt Ho*	57°51'·20N	06°34'·40W
384	Sound of Shiant - *0·3M NW of Shiants Lt By*	57°54'·80N	06°26'·00W
385	Kebock Head - *2·3M E of*	58°02'·40N	06°17'·00W
386	Stornoway - *1·2M SE of harbour entrance*	58°10'·30N	06°20'·60W
387	Chicken Head - *1·2M S of*	58°09'·80N	06°15'·10W
388	Sandaig Islands Lt - *0·6M W by N of*	57°10'·25N	05°43'·20W
389	Kyle Rhea (S appr) - *0·6M W of Glenelg*	57°12'·75N	05°38'·80W
390	Loch Alsh (W appr) - *1·0M NW of entrance*	57°17'·20N	05°46'·10W
391	Crowlin Islands - *1·5 M W of*	57°20'·70N	05°53'·80W
392	Inner Sound - *1·7M E Rubha Ard Ghlaisen*	57°29'·55N	05°55'·50W
393	Portree - *1·8M E of town*	57°25'·00N	06°08'·00W
394	Sd of Raasay - *3·1M SE of Rubha nam Brathairean*	57°33'·30N	06°03'·80W
395	Rubha Reidh - *3·0M W of*	57°51'·60N	05°54'·40W
396	Greenstone Point - *1·6M NW of*	57°56'·60N	05°39'·20W
397	Ullapool - *1·7M NE of Cailleach Head Lt*	57°56'·90N	05°21'·80W
398	Stoerhead Lt - *2M NW of*	58°15'·80N	05°26'·80W
399	Cape Wrath - *2M NW of*	58°38'·90N	05°02'·80W
400	Whiten Head - *4·4M N of*	58°39'·20N	04°34'·90W

Section 2

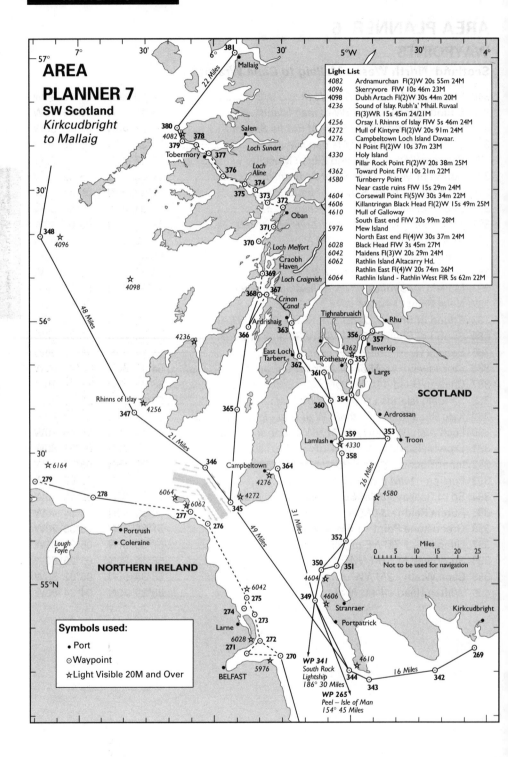

AREA PLANNER 7
SW Scotland
Kirkcudbright to Mallaig

Light List

4082	Ardnamurchan Fl(2)W 20s 55m 24M
4096	Skerryvore FlW 10s 46m 23M
4098	Dubh Artach Fl(2)W 30s 44m 20M
4236	Sound of Islay. Rubh'a' Mháil. Ruvaal Fl(3)WR 15s 45m 24/21M
4256	Orsay I. Rhinns of Islay FlW 5s 46m 24M
4272	Mull of Kintyre Fl(2)W 20s 91m 24M
4276	Campbeltown Loch Island Davaar. N Point Fl(2)W 10s 37m 23M
4330	Holy Island Pillar Rock Point Fl(2)W 20s 38m 25M
4362	Toward Point FlW 10s 21m 22M
4580	Turnberry Point Near castle ruins FlW 15s 29m 24M
4604	Corsewall Point Fl(5)W 30s 34m 22M
4606	Killantringan Black Head Fl(2)W 15s 49m 25M
4610	Mull of Galloway South East end FlW 20s 99m 28M
5976	Mew Island North East end Fl(4)W 30s 37m 24M
6028	Black Head FlW 3s 45m 27M
6042	Maidens Fl(3)W 20s 29m 24M
6062	Rathlin Island Altacarry Hd. Rathlin East Fl(4)W 20s 74m 26M
6064	Rathlin Island - Rathlin West FlR 5s 62m 22M

Symbols used:

- ● Port
- ⊙ Waypoint
- ☆ Light Visible 20M and Over

SCOTLAND

NORTHERN IRELAND

Miles
0   5   10   15   20   25
Not to be used for navigation

WP 341
South Rock
Lightship
186° 30 Miles

WP 265
Peel – Isle of Man
154° 45 Miles

AREA PLANNER 7

WAYPOINTS

Scotland South West - *Kirkcudbright to Mallaig*

265	Peel - *1·0M NW Hbr ent*	54°14'·50N	04°42'·50W
269	Kirkcudbright - *1·5M S Little Ross Lt*	54°44'·50N	04°05'·00W
270	Mew Island Lt - *1·3M ENE*	54°42'·30N	05°29'·90W
271	Belfast - *0·7M ENE No.1 SHM*	54°42'·00N	05°45'·20W
272	Black Head Lt - *1·3M ENE*	54°46'·50N	05°39'·20W
273	Isle of Muck - *1·1M NE*	54°51'·70N	05°41'·85W
274	Larne Lough - *1M N of Barr's Pt*	54°52'·50N	05°46'·80W
275	East Maiden Lt - *1·7M SW*	54°54'·50N	05°45'·50W
276	Torr Head - *0·6M ENE of*	55°12'·20N	06°02'·80W
277	Fair Head - *0·9M N of*	55°14'·60N	06°09'·00W
278	Lough Foyle - *4·8M NNE Inishowen Hd Lt*	55°17'·90N	06°52'·20W
279	Malin Head - *2·0M NNE*	55°25'·00N	07°21'·20W
341	South Rock Lt V - *1·1M E of*	54°24'·30N	05°20'·00W
342	Burrow Head - *2·0 M S of*	54°38'·70N	04°23'·00W
343	Mull of Galloway Lt - *1·7M S of*	54°36'·40N	04°51'·50W
344	Crammag Head Lt - *1·8M SW of*	54°38'·60N	05°00'·00W
345	Mull of Kintyre Lt - *2·5M SW of*	55°16'·90N	05°51'·30W
346	Mull of Kintyre Lt - *10·3M NW of*	55°25'·50N	06°01'·50W
347	Rhinns of Islay Lt - *2·2M SW of*	55°38'·85N	06°33'·50W
348	Skerryvore Lt - *6·8M W by N of*	56°20'·80N	07°18'·80W
349	Killantringan Lt - *4·2M NW of*	54°54'·20N	05°14'·70W
350	Corsewall Pt Lt - *1·8M WNW of*	55°01'·20N	05°12'·20W
351	Stranraer - *1·0M NNW ent to Loch Ryan*	55°02'·40N	05°05'·10W
352	Bennane Head - *1·5M NW of*	55°09'·25N	05°01'·80W
353	Troon - *2·1M W of harbour ent*	55°33'·10N	04°44'·70W
354	Little Cumbrae Island Lt - *0·8M SW of*	55°42'·75N	04°59'·00W
355	Rothesay - *Ent to Rothesay Sound*	55°50'·90N	04°59'·60W
356	Firth of Clyde, Cloch Point Lt - *1·3M WSW of*	55°55'·95N	04°54'·75W
357	R. Clyde, Kempock Point - *0·9M WNW of*	55°58'·10N	04°50'·50W
358	Lamlash - *1·0M SE of S ent*	55°29'·80N	05°03'·60W
359	Lamlash - *1·0M E of N ent*	55°32'·90N	05°03'·00W
360	Isle of Arran - *2·0M NNE of Sannox Bay*	55°41'·60N	05°08'·00W
361	West Kyle - *1·0M E Lamont Shelf IDM*	55°48'·35N	05°11'·80W
362	East Loch Tarbert - *1·0 E of Loch*	55°52'·20N	05°22'·00W
363	Ardrishaig - *1·3 SSE of hbr ent*	55°59'·50N	05°25'·60W
364	Campbeltown - *1·0 NE of Loch ent*	55°26'·40N	05°31'·00W
365	Gigha Island - *1·5M W of Cath Sgeir WCM*	55°39'·70N	05°50'·00W
366	Sound of Jura - *2·5M NW of Island of Danna*	55°58'·80N	05°45'·50W
367	Loch Crinan - *0·6M NW of Ardnoe Point*	56°06'·00N	05°35'·40W
368	Sound of Jura - *2·0M SSW Reisa an t-Sruith I. Lt*	56°06'·00N	05°39'·90W
369	Sound of Luing - *0·5M WSW of Ardluing SHM By*	56°11'·00N	05°39'·40W
370	Sound of Insh - *1M SSW of Insh Island*	56°17'·60N	05°41'·00W
371	Kerrera Sound - *0·7M SSW of Rubha Seanach*	56°21'·70N	05°33'·90W
372	Oban - *0·5M WNW of Maiden Isle*	56°26'·00N	05°30'·30W
373	Between Lady's Rock and Eilean Musdile	56°27'·20N	05°36'·70W
374	Sound of Mull - *1·6M SE of Ardtornish Point*	56°30'·15N	05°42'·75W
375	Loch Aline - *0·7M S by W of ent*	56°31'·30N	05°46'·80W
376	Sound of Mu - *1·8M N of Salen*	56°33'·00N	05°56'·30W
377	Tobermory - *0·9M NE of hbr ent*	56°38'·40N	06°02'·40W
378	Ardmore Pt (Mull) - *0·7M N of*	56°40'·00N	06°07'·60W
379	Pt of Ardnamurchan - *2·8M S*	56°40'·90N	06°13'·30W
380	Pt of Ardnamurchan - *1·3M W*	56°43'·60N	06°15'·90W
381	Mallaig - *1·5M WNW of hbr ent*	57°01'·00N	05°52'·10W

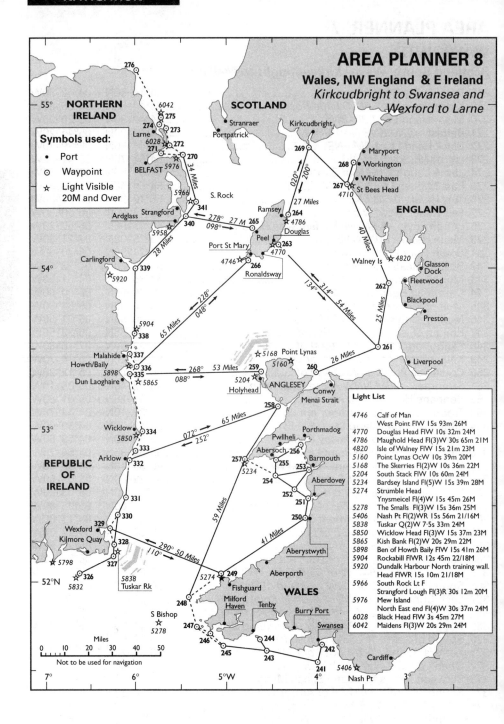

AREA PLANNER 8
Wales, NW England & E Ireland
Kirkcudbright to Swansea and Wexford to Larne

Symbols used:
- • Port
- ⊙ Waypoint
- ☆ Light Visible 20M and Over

Light List

4746	Calf of Man West Point FlW 15s 93m 26M
4770	Douglas Head FlW 10s 32m 24M
4786	Maughold Head Fl(3)W 30s 65m 21M
4820	Isle of Walney FlW 15s 21m 23M
5160	Point Lynas OcW 10s 39m 20M
5168	The Skerries Fl(2)W 10s 36m 22M
5204	South Stack FlW 10s 60m 24M
5234	Bardsey Island Fl(5)W 15s 39m 28M
5274	Strumble Head Ynysmeicel Fl(4)W 15s 45m 26M
5278	The Smalls Fl(3)W 15s 36m 25M
5406	Nash Pt Fl(2)WR 15s 56m 21/16M
5838	Tuskar Q(2)W 7·5s 33m 24M
5850	Wicklow Head Fl(3)W 15s 37m 23M
5865	Kish Bank Fl(2)W 20s 29m 22M
5898	Ben of Howth Baily FlW 15s 41m 26M
5904	Rockabill FlWR 12s 45m 22/18M
5920	Dundalk Harbour North training wall. Head FlWR 15s 10m 21/18M
5966	South Rock Lt F Strangford Lough Fl(3)R 30s 12m 20M
5976	Mew Island North East end Fl(4)W 30s 37m 24M
6028	Black Head FlW 3s 45m 27M
6042	Maidens Fl(3)W 20s 29m 24M

Miles
0 10 20 30 40 50
Not to be used for navigation

AREA PLANNER 8
WAYPOINTS
NW England, Wales & E Ireland - *Kirkcudbright to Swansea*

241	Ledge SCM - *2M S*	51°28'·00N	03°58'·60W
242	Swansea - *1M SE Mumbles Hd*	51°33'·40N	03°57'·00W
243	Caldey Island - *7M SE*	51°32'·20N	04°35'·20W
244	Tenby - *1M SE Caldey Is*	51°37'·20N	04°39'·60W
245	Crow Rock - *1·3M S of*	51°35'·40N	05°03'·50W
246	Milford Haven - *1·1M S St Ann's Hd*	51°39'·70N	05°10'·60W
247	Skokholm Is Lt - *1·6M W of*	51°41'·60N	05°19'·70W
248	South Bishop Is Lt - *3·0M NW of*	51°53'·30N	05°27'·80W
249	Fishguard - *1·5M N Strumble Hd*	52°03'·40N	05°04'·20W
250	Aberystwyth - *1·5M W*	52°24'·40N	04°08'·00W
251	Aberdovey - *1·5M W of hbr bar*	52°31'·70N	04°07'·10W
252	Sarn-y-Bwch WCM - *1·1M W*	52°34'·80N	04°15'·10W
253	Barmouth - *1·2M W of hbr bar*	52°42'·60N	04°05'·60W
254	Causeway WCM - *2M SW*	52°39'·90N	04°28'·00W
255	Abersoch - *1·2M SE St Tudwal's Is Lt*	52°47'·20N	04°26'·80W
256	Porthmadog - *1·1M SW Frwy By*	52°52'·70N	04°12'·50W
257	Bardsey Island light - *4M NNW*	52°48'·60N	04°50'·30W
258	Menai Strait - *1·4M SW Llanddwyn Is*	53°07'·30N	04°26'·80W
259	Holyhead - *1M N of W Bkwtr*	53°21'·00N	04°37'·00W
260	Menai Strait - *1·2M N of Puffin Is*	53°20'·50N	04°01'·50W
261	Liverpool - *0·7M S of Bar Lt V*	53°31'·30N	03°20'·90W
262	Fleetwood - *2M SW Lune Dp By*	53°54'·10N	03°13'·00W
263	Douglas - *1·1M W of Douglas Hd*	54°08'·70N	04°26'·00W
264	Ramsey - *1·3M ENE of S bkwtr*	54°19'·90N	04°20'·20W
265	Peel - *1M NW entrance*	54°14'·50N	04°42'·50W
266	Pt St Mary - *1·2M S of Kallow Pt*	54°02'·90N	04°43'·80W
267	St Bees Head Lt - *2M W of*	54°30'·80N	03°41'·50W
268	Workington - *1M WNW of bkwtr*	54°39'·40N	03°36'·30W
269	Kirkcudbright - *1·5M S Little Ross Lt*	54°44'·50N	04°05'·00W
270	Mew Island Lt - *1·3M ENE*	54°42'·30N	05°29'·90W
271	Belfast - *0·7M ENE No.1 SHM*	54°42'·00N	05°45'·20W
272	Black Head Lt - *1·3M ENE*	54°46'·50N	05°39'·20W
273	Isle of Muck - *1·1M NE*	54°51'·70N	05°41'·85W
274	Larne Lough - *1M N of Barr's pt*	54°52'·50N	05°46'·80W
275	East Maiden Lt - *1·7M SW*	54°54'·50N	05°45'·50W
276	Torr Head - *0·6M ENE of*	55°12'·20N	06°02'·80W
326	Coningbeg Lt - *0·4M N of*	52°02'·80N	06°39'·30W
327	Carnsore Point - *3·2M ESE of*	52°09'·40N	06°16'·40W
328	Greenore Point - *1·8M E of*	52°14'·70N	06°15'·90W
329	Wexford - *1·6M E of entrance*	52°20'·50N	06°19.30'W
330	W Blackwater Pt - *0·4M W of*	52°25'·80N	06°14'·00W
331	Cahore Point - *1·7MSE of*	52°32'·50N	06°09'·90W
332	Arklow - *1·2M E by S*	52°47'·40N	06°06'·40W
333	Mizen Head (E coast) - *1M ESE*	52°51'·00N	06°01'·90W
334	Wicklow - *2·6M E of*	52°58'·90N	05°57'·80W
335	Dun Laoghaire - *2·2M NE of*	53°19'·60N	06°04'·60W
336	Ben of Howth - *1·4M E of*	53°22'·40N	06°00'·50W
337	Malahide - *1·5M E of Bar*	53°27'·00N	06°04'·80W
338	Rockabill Lt - *1·2M WSW*	53°35'·30N	06°02'·00W
339	Carlingford Lough	53°58'·40N	06°00'·00W
340	Strangford Lough	54°18'·40N	05°27'·70W
341	South Rock Lt V - *1·1M E of*	54°24'·30N	05°20'·00W

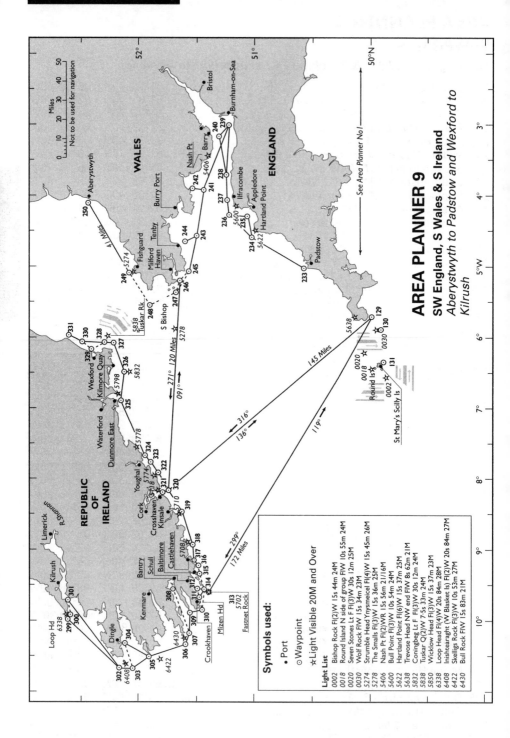

AREA PLANNER 9

SW England, S Wales & S Ireland
Aberystwyth to Padstow and Wexford to Kilrush

Symbols used:

• Port
⊙ Waypoint
★ Light Visible 20M and Over

Light List

0002	Bishop Rock Fl(2)W 15s 44m 24M
0018	Round Island N side of group F(W) 10s 55m 24M
0020	Seven Stones Lt F Fl(3)W 30s 12m 25M
0030	Wolf Rock Fl/W 15s 34m 23M
5278	Strumble Head Ynysmeicel Fl(4)W 15s 45m 26M
5278	The Smalls Fl(3)W 15s 36m 25M
5406	Nash Pt Fl(2)WR 15s 56m 21/16M
5600	Bull Point Fl(3)W 10s 54m 24M
5622	Hartland Point Fl(6)W 15s 37m 25M
5638	Trevose Head NW end FlW 8s 62m 21M
5832	Coningbeg Lt F Fl(3)W 30s 12m 24M
5838	Tuskar Q(2)W 7·5s 33m 24M
5850	Wicklow Hd Fl(3)W 15s 37m 23M
6338	Loop Head Fl(4)W 20s 84m 28M
6408	Inishtearaght (W Blasket Is) Fl(2)W 20s 84m 27M
6422	Skelligs Rock Fl(3)W 10s 53m 27M
6430	Bull Rock FlW 15s 83m 21M

See Area Planner No1

41 Miles

271° 120 Miles

091°

316°

136°

119°

299°

172 Miles

145 Miles

AREA PLANNER 9

WAYPOINTS

SW England, S Wales and S Ireland - *Aberystwyth to Padstow*

129	Runnel Stone Lt By - *0·3M S of*	50°00'·85N	05°40'·30W
130	Wolf Rk Lt - *2M S of*	49°54'·65N	05°48'·50W
131	St Mary's, Scilly - *2M E of St Mary's*	49°54'·00N	06°l 5.00'W
233	Padstow - *2M NW of Stepper Point*	50°35'·70N	04°59'·10W
234	Hartland Point - *2·5M NW of*	51°02'·80N	04°34'·40W
235	River Taw - *1·6M NW Bideford By*	51°06'·20N	04°18'·20W
236	Morte Point - *2·5M NNW of*	51°13'·60N	04°15'·80W
237	Ilfracombe - *1·5M N*	51°14'·20N	04°06'·80W
238	Foreland Point - *1·5 miles N*	51°16'·20N	03°47'·20W
239	Burnham on Sea - *2·6M N*	51°15'·30N	03°07'·80W
240	Barry & R. Severn - *2·9M SSW ent*	51°21'·00N	03°17'·30W
241	Ledge SCM By - *2M S of*	51°28'·00N	03°58'·60W
242	Swansea - *1M SE Mumbles Hd*	51°33'·40N	03°57'·00W
243	Caldey Island - *7 miles SE*	51°32'·20N	04°35'·20W
244	Tenby - *1M SE Caldey Island*	51°37'·20N	04°39'·60W
245	Crow Rock - *1·3M S of*	51°35'·40N	05°03'·50W
246	Milford Haven - *1·1M S St Ann's Hd*	51°39'·70N	05°10'·60W
247	Skokholm Island Lt - *1·6M W of*	51°41'·60N	05°19'·70W
248	South Bishop Is Lt - *3·0M NW*	51°53'·30N	05°27'·80W
249	Fishguard - *1·5M N Strumble Hd*	52°03'·40N	05°04'·20W
250	Aberystwyth - *1·5M W of ent*	52°24'·40N	04°08'·00W
299	Loop Head Lt - *1·6M W of*	52°33'·70N	09°58'·60W
300	Loop Head Lt - *1·4 miles S of*	52°32'·30N	09°55'·80W
301	Kilrush - *0·9M S of Kilcredaun Lt*	52°33'·90N	09°42'·50W
302	Tearaght Island Lt - *2·5M NW*	52°06'·20N	10°42'·50W
303	Great Foze Rock - *1·8M SW*	52°00'·00N	10°43'·20W
304	Dingle - *1·2M S of Reenbeg Point*	52°05'·60N	10°15'·80W
305	Bray Head - *1·4M W of*	51°52'·80N	10°28'·00W
306	The Bull Island Lt - *1·7M SW*	51°34'·30N	10°20'·10W
307	Crow Head - *1·9MS of*	51°32'·90N	10°09'·40W
308	Bantry - *0·8M SW Whiddy Island*	51°40'·00N	09°32'·80W
309	Sheep's Head Lt - *1·5M W of*	51°32'·30N	09°53'·40W
310	Mizen Head Lt (SW) - *2M SSW*	51°25'·00N	09°50'·30W
311	Crookhaven - *1M ESE Streek Hd*	51°27'·80N	09°40'·30W
312	Schull - *1M S of Long Island Lt*	51°29'·20N	09°32'·00W
313	The Fastnet Rock Lt	51°23'·33N	09°36'·16W
314	Cape Clear - *1·6M SW of*	51°24'·20N	09°32'·90W
315	Baltimore - *1·5M Sharbour ent*	51°26'·90N	09°23'·50W
316	Toe Head - *1·5M S of*	51°27'·40N	09°13'·00W
317	Castle Haven - *1M SE of ent*	51°30.30'N	09°09.80'W
318	Galley Head - *1·4M S of*	51°30'·40N	08°57'·20W
319	Old Hd of Kinsale Lt - *1·5M SSE*	51°34'·90N	08°30'·80W
320	Cork Landfall By - *0·4M E of*	51°43'·00N	08°14'·80W
321	Roche's Point Lt - *1·2M S of*	51°46'·40N	08°15'·40W
322	Ballycotton Island Lt - *1·2M S*	51°48'·40N	07°58'·80W
323	Youghal, S - *IM SE Capel Island*	51°52'·40N	07°50'·00W
324	Youghal, SE - *2M SE Blackball PHB*	51°54'·80N	07°45'·60W
325	Waterford - *1·4M SSE Dunmore E*	52°07'·40N	06°58'·80W
326	Coningbeg Lt V - *0·4M N of*	52°02'·80N	06°39'·30W
327	Carnsore Point - *3·2M ESE of*	52°09'·40N	06°16'·40W
328	Greenore Point - *1·8M E of*	52°14'·70N	06°15'·90W
329	Wexford - *1·6M E of entrance*	52°20'·50N	06°19'·30W
330	W Blackwater Pt Mk - *0·4M W*	52°25'·80N	06°14'·00W
331	Cahore Point - *1·7 miles SE of*	52°32'·50N	06°09'·90W

Section 2

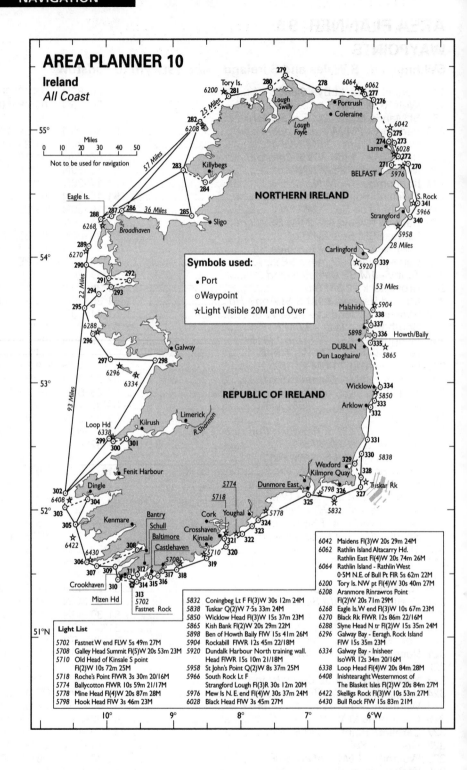

AREA PLANNER 10

Ireland
All Coast

Miles
0 10 20 30 40 50

Not to be used for navigation

Symbols used:
- Port
- ⊙ Waypoint
- ☆ Light Visible 20M and Over

NORTHERN IRELAND

REPUBLIC OF IRELAND

Tory Is.
Lough Swilly
Lough Foyle
Portrush
Coleraine
Larne
BELFAST
S. Rock
Strangford
Carlingford
Killybegs
Sligo
Eagle Is.
Broadhaven
Malahide
Howth/Baily
DUBLIN
Dun Laoghaire/
Galway
Wicklow
Arklow
Limerick
R.Shannon
Loop Hd
Kilrush
Kilrush
Fenit Harbour
Wexford
Kilmore Quay
Tuskar Rk
Dunmore East
Dingle
Cork
Youghal
Bantry
Schull
Baltimore
Castlehaven
Crosshaven
Kinsale
Kenmare
Crookhaven
Mizen Hd
Fastnet Rock

Light List

5702 Fastnet W end FLW 5s 49m 27M
5708 Galley Head Summit Fl(5)W 20s 53m 23M
5710 Old Head of Kinsale S point
  Fl(2)W 10s 72m 25M
5718 Roche's Point FlWR 3s 30m 20/16M
5774 Ballycotton FlWR 10s 59m 21/17M
5778 Mine Head Fl(4)W 20s 87m 28M
5798 Hook Head FlW 3s 46m 23M

5832 Coningbeg Lt F Fl(3)W 30s 12m 24M
5838 Tuskar Q(2)W 7·5s 33m 24M
5850 Wicklow Head Fl(3)W 15s 37m 23M
5865 Kish Bank Fl(2)W 20s 29m 22M
5898 Ben of Howth Baily FlW 15s 41m 26M
5904 Rockabill FlWR 12s 45m 22/18M
5920 Dundalk Harbour North training wall.
  Head FlWR 15s 10m 21/18M
5958 St John's Point Q(2)W 8s 37m 25M
5966 South Rock Lt F
  Strangford Lough Fl(3)R 30s 12m 20M
5976 Mew Is N. E end Fl(4)W 30s 37m 24M
6028 Black Head FlW 3s 45m 27M

6042 Maidens Fl(3)W 20s 29m 24M
6062 Rathlin Island Altacarry Hd.
  Rathlin East Fl(4)W 20s 74m 26M
6064 Rathlin Island - Rathlin West
  0·5M N.E. of Bull Pt FlR 5s 62m 22M
6200 Tory Is. NW pt Fl(4)W 30s 40m 27M
6208 Aranmore Rinrawros Point
  Fl(2)W 20s 71m 29M
6268 Eagle Is. W end Fl(3)W 10s 67m 23M
6270 Black Rk FlWR 12s 86m 22/16M
6288 Slyne Head N tr Fl(2)W 15s 35m 24M
6296 Galway Bay - Eeragh. Rock Island
  FlW 15s 35m 23M
6334 Galway Bay - Inisheer
  IsoWR 12s 34m 20/16M
6338 Loop Head Fl(4)W 20s 84m 28M
6408 Inishtearaght Westernmost of
  The Blasket Isles Fl(2)W 20s 84m 27M
6422 Skelligs Rock Fl(3)W 10s 53m 27M
6430 Bull Rock FlW 15s 83m 21M

AREA PLANNER 10
WAYPOINTS
Ireland

270	Mew Is Lt - *1·3M ENE*	54°42'·30N	05°29'·90W
271	Belfast -		
	0·7M ENE No.1 By	54°42'·00N	05°45'·20W
272	Black Hd Lt -		
	1·3 miles ENE	54°46'·50N	05°39'·20W
273	Isle of Muck - *1·1M NE*	54°51'·70N	05°41'·85W
274	Larne Lough -		
	1M N of Barr's pt	54°52'·50N	05°46'·80W
275	E Maiden Lt - *1·7M SW*	54°54'·50N	05°45'·50W
276	Torr Head - *0·6M ENE of*	55°12'·20N	06°02'·80W
277	Fair Head - *0·9M N of*	55°14'·60N	06°09'·00W
278	L. Foyle		
	4·8M NNE Inishowen Lt	55°17'·90N	06°52'·20W
279	Malin Head - *2M NNE*	55°25'·00N	07°21'·20W
280	Lough Swilly - *1M N of ent*	55°18'·20N	07°34'·30W
281	Tory Island - *1·2M SE of*	55°14'·00N	08°11'·00W
282	Rinrawros Pt Lt,		
	Aran - *1·3M NW*	55°01'·75N	08°35'·40W
283	Rathlin O'Birne Is Lt -		
	1·9M WSW	54°39'·20N	08°52'·90W
284	Killibegs -		
	2·4M WNW S.John's Pt Lt	54°34'·70N	08°31'·80W
285	Sligo -		
	2·7M N of Aughris Hd	54°19'·50N	08°45'·30W
286	The Stags rocks -		
	1·3M N of	54°23'·40N	09°47'·40W
287	Broadhaven -		
	1M N of the bay	54°20'·40N	09°56'·00W
288	Eagle Island - *1·4M NW of*	54°17'·80N	10°07'·40W
289	Black Rock -		
	2·7M NE by N of	54°06'·20N	10°16'·60W
290	Achill Head - *1·4M SW*	53°57'·30N	10°17'·90W
291	Clew Bay -		
	1M SW Achillbeg Is Lt	53°50'·80N	09°57'·90W
292	Westport -		
	1·5M WSW Inishgort Lt	53°49'·00N	09°42'·60W
293	Clew Bay -		
	1·5M NW Roonah Hd	53°46'·90N	09°57'·80W
294	Inishturk Island -		
	1·2M NW	53°43'·60N	10°08'·80W
295	Inishshark Island -		
	1·8M W of	53°36'·50N	10°21'·00W
296	Slyne Head Lt - *1·6M SW*	53°22'·90N	10°16'·00W
297	Rock Is Lt -		
	5·3M NW by W of	53°11'·80N	09°58'·60W
298	Galway -		
	2·3M N Black Hd Lt	53°11'·50N	09°15'·80W
299	Loop Head Lt - *1·6M W of*	52°33'·70N	09°58'·60W
300	Loop Head Lt - *1·4M S of*	52°32'·30N	09°55'·80W
301	Kilrush -		
	9M S Kilcredaun Hd Lt	52°33'·90N	09°42'·50W
302	Tearaght Island Lt -		
	2·5M NW	52°06'·20N	10°42'·50W
303	Great Foze Rk - *1·8M SW*	52°00'·00N	10°43'·20W
304	Dingle -		
	1·2M S of Reenbeg Pt	52°05'·60N	10°15'·80W
305	Bray Head - *1·4M W of*	51°52'·80N	10°28'·00W
306	The Bull Island Lt -		
	1·7M SW	51°34'·30N	10°20'·10W
307	Crow Head - *1·9M S of*	51°32'·90N	10°09'·40W
308	Bantry -		
	0·8M SW Whiddy Is	51°40'·00N	09°32'·80W
309	Sheep's Head Lt -		
	1·5M W of	51°32'·30N	09°53'·40W
310	Mizen Head Lt (SW)-		
	2M SSW	51°25'·00N	09°50'·30W
311	Crookhaven -		
	1M ESE Streek Hd	51°27'·80N	09°40'·30W
312	Schull -		
	M S of Long Is Lt	51°29'·20N	09°32'·00W
313	The Fastnet Rock	51°23'·33N	09°36'·16W
314	Cape Clear - *1·6M SW of*	51°24'·20N	09°32'·90W
315	Baltimore - *1·5M S*	51°26'·90N	09°23'·50W
316	Toe Head - *1·5M S of*	51°27'·40N	09°13'·00W
317	Castle Haven - *1M SE*	51°30'·30N	09°09'·80W
318	Galley Head - *1·4M S of*	51°30'·40N	08°57'·20W
319	Old Hd of Kinsale Lt -		
	1·5M SSE	51°34'·90N	08°30'·80W
320	Cork Landfall By -		
	0·4M E of	51°43'·00N	08°14'·80W
321	Roche's Point Lt -		
	·2M S of	51°46'·40N	08°15'·40W
322	Ballycotton Island Lt -		
	1·2M S	51°48'·40N	07°58'·80W
323	Youghal,		
	IM SE Capel Island	51°52'·40N	07°50'·00W
324	Youghal, SE -		
	2M SE Blackball PHB	51°54'·80N	07°45'·60W
325	Waterford -		
	1·4M SSE Dunmore E	52°07'·40N	06°58'·80W
326	Coningbeg Lt V -		
	0·4M N	52°02'·80N	06°39'·30W
327	Carnsore Point -		
	3·2M ESE	52°09'·40N	06°16'·40W
328	Greenore Point -		
	1·8M E of	52°14'·70N	06°15'·90W
329	Wexford - *1·6M E*	52°20'·50N	06°19'·30W
330	W Blackwater Pt Mk -		
	0·4M W	52°25'·80N	06°14'·00W
331	Cahore Point -		
	1·7 miles SE of	52°32'·50N	06°09'·90W
332	Arklow - *1·2M E by S*	52°47'·40N	06°06'·40W
333	Mizen Head (E coast) -		
	1M ESE	52°51'·00N	06°01'·90W
334	Wicklow - *2·6M E*	52°58'·90N	05°57'·80W
335	Dun Laoghaire - *2·2M NE*	53°19'·60N	06°04'·60W
336	Ben of Howth - *1·4M E of*	53°22'·40N	06°00'·50W
337	Malahide - *1·5M E of Bar*	53°27'·00N	06°04'·80W
338	Rockabill - *1·2M WSW*	53°35'·30N	06°02'·00W
339	Carlingford Lough	53°58'·40N	06°00'·00W
340	Strangford Lough	54°18'·40N	05°27'·70W
341	South Rock Lt V - *1·1M E*	54°24'·30N	05°20'·00W

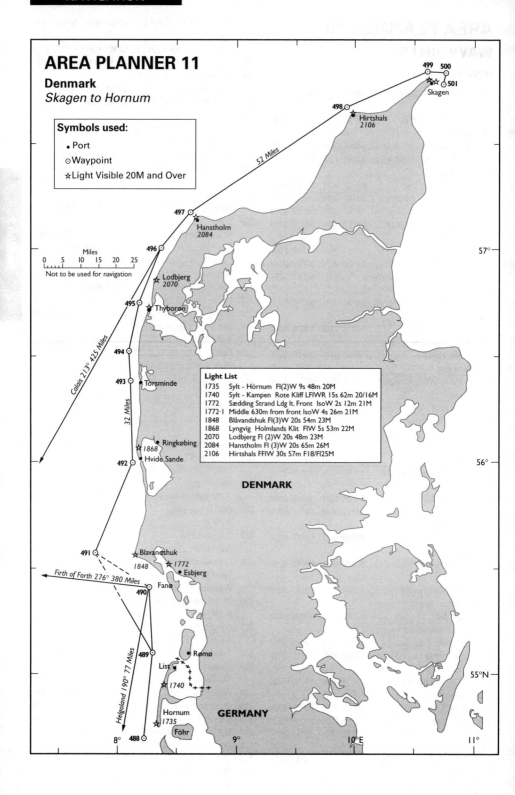

AREA PLANNER 11

Denmark
Skagen to Hornum

Symbols used:
- ● Port
- ⊙ Waypoint
- ☆ Light Visible 20M and Over

499 500
☆☆ ⊙ 501
Skagen

498 ⊙
Hirtshals
2106

52 Miles

497 ⊙
☆ Hanstholm
2084

496 ⊙

Miles
0 5 10 15 20 25
Not to be used for navigation

☆ Lodbjerg
2070

57°

495 ⊙
☆ Thyborøn

Calais 213° 425 Miles

494 ⊙

493 ⊙ ● Torsminde

32 Miles

Light List
1735	Sylt – Hörnum	Fl(2)W 9s 48m 20M
1740	Sylt – Kampen Rote Kliff	LFlWR 15s 62m 20/16M
1772	Sædding Strand Ldg lt. Front	IsoW 2s 12m 21M
1772·1	Middle 630m from front	IsoW 4s 26m 21M
1848	Blåvandshuk	Fl(3)W 20s 54m 23M
1868	Lyngvig Holmlands Klit	FlW 5s 53m 22M
2070	Lodbjerg	Fl (2)W 20s 48m 23M
2084	Hanstholm	Fl (3)W 20s 65m 26M
2106	Hirtshals	FFlW 30s 57m F18/Fl25M

☆ 1868 ● Ringkøbing

492 ⊙ Hvide Sande

DENMARK

56°

491 ⊙ ☆ Blåvandshuk
1848   ☆ 1772
● Esbjerg

Firth of Forth 276° 380 Miles

⊙ Fanø
490

Helgoland 190° 77 Miles

489 ⊙ ● Rømø

List ✚✚
✚✚✚
☆ 1740 ✚ ✚ ✚

55°N

Hornum
☆ 1735
Föhr

GERMANY

8° 488 ⊙

9°   10°E   11°

AREA PLANNER 11
WAYPOINTS

Denmark & NW Germany - *Skagen to Hornum*

488 Hornum - *1·2M W of Holtknobsloch landfall buoy* ...... 54°41'·10N   08°08'·40E
489 Rømø - *0·4M W of Lister Tief landfall buoy* .... 55°05'·40N   08°16'·40E
490 Esbjerg - *0·5M SW of Grådyb landfall buoy* .... 55°24'·30N   08°11'·00E
491 Slugen chan N - *9·6M W by N Blavands Huk Lt* .... 55°35'·40N   07°48'·40E
492 Hvide Sande - *2·7M W of harbour entrance* .... 56°00'·00N   08°02'·50E
493 Torsminde - *2·7 M W of harbour entrance* .... 56°22'·50N   08°02'·30E
494 Bovbjerg lt - *2·6M W* .... 56°30'·80N   08°03'·00E
495 Thyborøn - *0·7M W landfall buoy* .... 56°42'·50N   08°07'·40E
496 Nørre Vorupør Lt - *3·2M W* .... 56°57'·20N   08°16'·40E
497 Hanstholm - *1·0M NW landfall buoy* .... 57°08'·80N   08°33'·70E
498 Hirtshals - *2·3M N by W harbour entrance* .... 57°38'·00N   09°56'·50E
499 Skagen W *Lt - 2·2M N* .... 57°47'·10N   10°35'·70E
500 Skagen *landfall buoy No.1 - 0·7M S* .... 57°46'·40N   10°46'·00E
501 Skagen - *3·3M E Skagen Lt* .... 57°44'·00N   10°43'·50E

Section 2

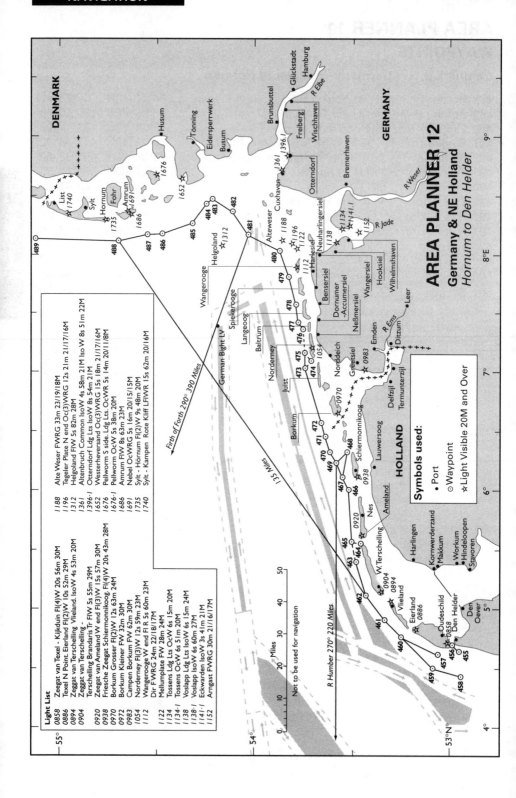

AREA PLANNER 12
Germany & NE Holland
Hornum to Den Helder

DENMARK

GERMANY

HOLLAND

Symbols used:
- ● Port
- ◎ Waypoint
- ✩ Light Visible 20M and Over

Light List

0858	Zeegat van Texel - Kijkduin Fl(4)W 20s 56m 30M
0886	Texel N Point. Eierland Fl(2)W 10s 52m 29M
0894	Zeegat van Terschelling Vlieland. IsoW 4s 53m 20M
0904	Zeegat van Terschelling
	Terschelling Brandaris Tr FlW 5s 55m 29M
0920	Zeegat van Ameland W end Fl(3)W 15s 57m 30M
0938	Friesche Zeegat Schiermonnikoog. Fl(4)W 20s 43m 28M
0970	Borkum Grosser Fl(2)W 12s 63m 24M
0972	Borkum Kleiner FW 32m 30M
0983	Campen Borkum FW 62m 30M
1054	Norderney Fl(3)W 12s 59m 23M
1112	Wangerooge W end Fl R 5s 60m 23M
1122	Dir FWRG 24m 22/18/17M
1134	Mellumplate FW 28m 24M
1134-I	Tossens Ldg Lts OcW 6s 15m 20M
1138	Tossens OcW 6s 51m 20M
1141-I	Voslapp Ldg Lts IsoW 6s 15m 24M
1141-I	Voslapp IsoW 6s 60m 27M
1152	Eckwarden IsoW 3s 41m 21M
	Arngast FWRG 30m 21/16/17M

1188	Alte Weser FWRG 33m 23/19/18M
1196	Tegeler Plate N end Oc(3)WRG 12s 21m 21/17/16M
1312	Helgoland FlW 5s 82m 28M
1361	Altenbruch Common IsoW 4s 58m 21M IsoW 8s 51m 22M
1396-I	Otterndorf Ldg Lts IsoW 8s 54m 21M
1652	Westerheversand Oc(3)WRG 15s 18m 21/17/16M
1676	Pellworm S side. Ldg Lts. OcWR 5s 14m 20/11/8M
1676-I	Pellworm OcW 5s 38m 20M
1686	Amrum FlW 8s 63m 23M
1691	Nebel OcWRG 5s 16m 20/15/15M
1735	Sylt - Hörnum Fl(2)W 9s 48m 20M
1740	Sylt - Kampen Rote Kliff LFlWR 15s 62m 20/16M

Firth of Forth 290° 390 Miles

German Bight LV

135 Miles

R Humber 270° 220 Miles

Not to be used for navigation

Miles
0   10   20   30   40   50

List 1740
Hornum 1735
Sylt
Föhr 1686
Amrum 1691
1676-I
1652
Husum
Tönning
Eidersperrwerk
Busum
Helgoland 1312
Cuxhaven
Otterndorf 1396-I
1361
Freiberg
Wischhaven
Brunsbuttel
Glückstadt
Hamburg
R Elbe
Bremerhaven
R Weser
Alte Weser 1188
1196
R Jade
1134
1141-I
1152
Neuharlingersiel
1138
R Ems
Leer
Emden
Wilhelmshaven
Hooksiel
Wangersiel
Neßmersiel
Accumersiel
Dornumer
Bensersiel
Harlesiel
1112
1122
1054
0983
0970
Greetsiel
Norddeich
Ditzum
Termunterzijl
Delfzijl
Wangerooge
Spiekeroog
Langeoog
Baltrum
Norderney
Juist
Borkum
Memmert
Schiermonnikoog 0938
Lauwersoog
Ameland 0920
Nes
W.Terschelling 0904
Harlingen
Kornwerderzand
Makkum
Workum
Hindeloopen
Stavoren
Vlieland 0894
Eierland 0886
Oudeschild
Den Helder 0858
Den Oever

484 483
482
481
485
486 487
488
489
480
479
478
477
476
475 473 474
472
471
470
469
468
467
466
465
464 463
462
461
460
459
458
457
456 455

54°
53°N
4°   5°   6°   7°   8°E   9°

55°

AREA PLANNER 12
WAYPOINTS
Germany & N Holland - *Hornum to Den Helder*

455 Den Helder - *1·2M SW Kijkduin Lt* .... 52°56'·90N   04°41'·90E
456 Den Helder - *1·1M N by E Kijkduin Lt* .... 52°58'·40N   04°44'·10E
457 Molengat Channel - *N ent* .... 53°03'·00N   04°41'·00E
458 Noorderhaaks I. - *3·2M WSW* .... 52°57'·30N   04°33'·70E
459 Texel - *0·3M W Molengat NCM* .... 53°03'·70N   04°39'·00E
460 Vlieland - *2·8M W of SW end of I.* .... 53°13'·50N   04°46'·60E
461 Vlieland - *W ent to Stortemelk ch* .... 53°19'·10N   04°55'·20E
462 Terschelling - *0·4M NW Otto ECM* .... 53°25'·00N   05°06'·10E
463 Terschelling - *W ent to Westgat buoyed ch* .... 53°27'·80N   05°24'·00E
464 Borndiep Channel - *1·4M WNW Ameland Lt* .... 53°27'·60N   05°35'·60E
465 Ameland Lt - *2·5M N* .... 53°29'·50N   05°37'·40E
466 Ameland - *2·9M NNE of E end* .... 53°30'·40N   06°00'·00E
467 Schiermonnikoog N ent - *Westgat buoyed ch* .... 53°32'·50N   06°08'·40E
468 Schiermonnikoog E ent - *Lauwers buoyed ch* .... 53°33'·20N   06°17'·00E
469 Verkenningston Hubertgat SWM - *0·2M S* .... 53°34'·70N   06°14'·40E
470 Westereems Verkenningston SWM - *0·2M SE* .... 53°36'·80N   06°19'·80E
471 Riffgat SWM - *0·2M SE* .... 53°38'·80N   06°27'·40E
472 Osterems SWM - *0·2M S* .... 53°41'·70N   06°36'·20E
473 Schluchter SWM - *0·2M S* .... 53°44'·60N   07°04'·20E
474 Norderney - *1·5M N by W of W end of I.* .... 53°43'·80N   07°07'·00E
475 Norderney - *Dovetief SWM 0·5M S (frequently moved)* 53°45'·20N   07°09'·80E
476 Baltrum - *1·7M N by E of Baltrum* .... 53°45'·00N   07°22'·40E
477 Langeoog - *0·2M N of Accumer Ee SWM (freq moved)* . 53°46'·90N   07°23'·47E
478 Spiekeroog - *0·2M N Otzumer Balje SWM (freq moved)* 53°48'·31N   07°37'·30E
479 Wangerooge - *0·2M N of Harle SWM* .... 53°49'·48N   07°49'·00E
480 Neue Weser Channel - *3·5M W by S Alte Weser Lt* .... 53°50'·90N   08°01'·90E
481 Elbe Channel - *0·3M W Scharhörnriff N NCM* .... 53°59'·00N   08°10'·70E
482 Busum S Channel - *0·2M W Süderpiep SWM* .... 54°06'·00N   08°21'·60E
483 Busum N Channel - *0·2M W of Norderpiep By* .... 54°11'·50N   08°28'·30E
484 Eidersperrwerk - *0·2M W of Eider SWM* .... 54°14'·60N   08°27'·20E
485 Husum- *0·2M W Hever SWM* .... 54°20'·40N   08°18'·60E
486 Amrun - *0·2M W of Rütergat SWM* .... 54°31'·00N   08°11'·80E
487 Hornum - *0·2M W of Vortrapptief SWM* .... 54°35'·00N   08°11'·80E
488 Hornum - *2M W Holtknobsloch SWM* .... 54°40'·86N   08°07'·06E
489 Rømø - *0·4M W Lister Tief SWM* .... 55°05'·40N   08°16'·10E

Section 2

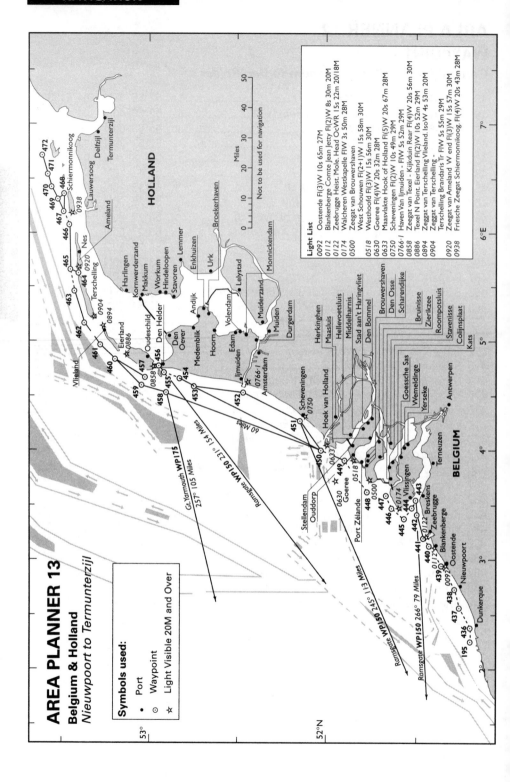

AREA PLANNER 13

Belgium & Holland
Nieuwpoort to Termunterzijl

Symbols used:
- ● Port
- ⊙ Waypoint
- ☆ Light Visible 20M and Over

Light List

0092	Oostende Fl(3)W 10s 65m 27M
0112	Blankenberge Comte Jean Jetty Fl(2)W 8s 30m 20M
0122	Zeebrugge Heist. Mole. Head OcWR 15s 22m 20/18M
0174	Walcheren Westkapelle FlW 3s 50m 28M
0500	Zeegat van Brouwershaven
	West Schouwen Fl(2+1)W 15s 58m 30M
0518	Westhoofd Fl(3)W 15s 56m 30M
0630	Goeree Fl(4)W 20s 32m 28M
0633	Maasvlakte Hook of Holland Fl(5)W 20s 67m 28M
0750	Scheveningen Fl(2)W 10s 49m 29M
0766-I	Haven Van Ijmuiden - FlW 5s 52m 29M
0858	Zeegat van Texel - Kijkduin Rear Fl(4)W 20s 56m 30M
0886	Texel N Point. Eierland Fl(2)W 10s 52m 29M
0894	Zeegat van Terschelling Vlieland. IsoW 4s 53m 20M
0904	Zeegat van Terschelling
	Terschelling Brandaris Tr FlW 5s 55m 29M
0920	Zeegat van Ameland W end Fl(3)W 15s 57m 30M
0938	Friesche Zeegat Schiermonnikoog. Fl(4)W 20s 43m 28M

Not to be used for navigation

HOLLAND

BELGIUM

AREA PLANNER 13
WAYPOINTS
Belgium & NW Holland - *Nieuwport to Termunterzijl*

150	Ramsgate - *1M E of*	51°l 9'·47N	01°27'·13E
175	Gt Yarmouth - *4·7M E*	52°34'·33N	01°52'·10E
195	Dunkerque - Port Est - *2M NW of*	51°05'·00N	02°18'·40E
436	Dunkerque - Port Est - *1·7M NE by E*	51°04'·20N	02°23'·50E
437	Trapegeer SHM - *0·6M N*	051°09'·10N	02°34'·50E
438	Nieuwpoort - *0·9M NW by W*	51°09'·80N	02°41'·80E
439	Oostende - *0·5M NW*	51°14'·70N	02°54'·50E
440	Blankenberge - *0·8M NW*	51°19'·60N	03°05'·60E
441	Zeebrugge - *0·6M NW*	51°22'·30N	03°10'·80E
442	Ft Maisonnueve WCM - *0·3M NE*	51°24'·50N	03°21'·60E
443	Vlissingen - *1·4M NE Niewe Sluis Lt*	51°25'·50N	03°32'·80E
444	Trawl SCM - *0·4M N*	51°26'·70N	03°28'·30E
445	West Kapelle Lt - *4M W by S*	51°31'·30N	03°20'·50E
446	Domburg - *2M NW*	51°35'·60N	03°28'·00E
447	Roompotsluis - *S chnl 5M off*	51°36'·20N	03°33'·20E
448	Geul Van de Banjaard - *N ent*	51°44'·00N	03°33'·00E
449	Haringvlietsluizen - *to S Channel*	51°51'·60N	03°53'·20E
450	Hoek van Holland - *1·2M WNW*	52°00'·10N	04°00'·30E
451	Scheveningen - *0·7M NW*	52°07'·00N	04°14'·80E
452	IJmuiden - *0·7M W by N ent*	52°28'·10N	04°31'·10E
453	Petten WCM - *0·4M W*	52°47'·50N	04°36'·20E
454	Grote Kaap Lt - *0·9M W*	52°52'·90N	04°41'·40E
455	Den Helder - *1·2M SW Kijkduin Lt*	52°56'·90N	04°41'·90E
456	Den Helder - *1·1M N*	52°58'·40N	04°44'·10E
457	Molengat Channel - *N entrance*	53°03'·00N	04°41'·00E
458	Noorderhaaks I. - *3·2M WSW*	52°57'·30N	04°33'·70E
459	Texel - *0·3M W Molengat NCM*	53°03'·70N	04°39'·00E
460	Vlieland - *2·8M W of SW end of I.*	53°13'·50N	04°46'·60E
461	Vlieland - *W ent to Stortemelk chnl*	53°19'·10N	04°55'·20E
462	Terschelling - *0·4M NW Otto ECM*	53°25'·00N	05°06'·10E
463	Terschelling - *W ent*	53°27'·80N	05°24'·00E
464	Borndiep Channel - *1·4M WNW*	53°27'·60N	05°35'·60E
465	Ameland Lt - *2·5M N*	53°29'·50N	05°37'·40E
466	Ameland - *2·9M NNE of E end*	53°30'·40N	06°00'·00E
467	Schiermonnikoog - *N ent*	53°32'·50N	06°08'·40E
468	Schiermonnikoog - *E ent*	53°33'·20N	06°17'·00E
469	Verkenningston Hubertgat By	53°34'·70N	06°14'·40E
470	Westereems Verkenningston By	53°36'·80N	06°19'·80E
471	Riffgat landfall buoy - *0·2M SE*	53°38'·80N	06°27'·40E
472	Osterems landfall By - *0·2M S*	53°41'·70N	06°36'·20E

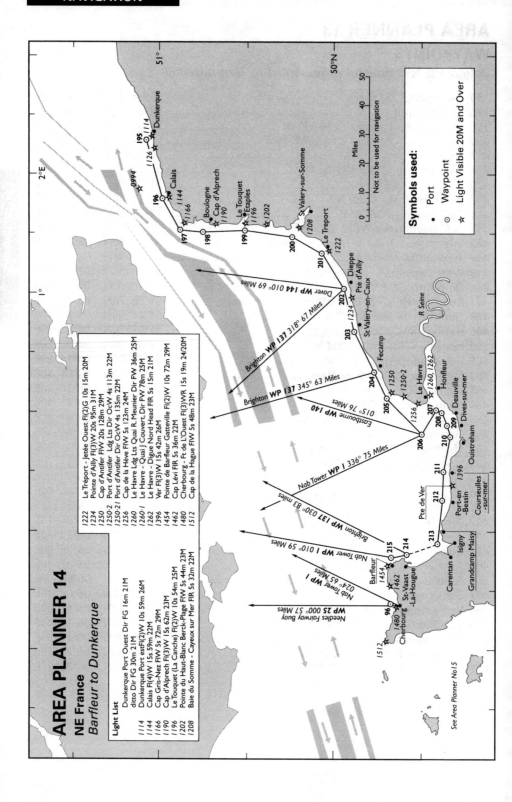

AREA PLANNER 14

NE France
Barfleur to Dunkerque

Light List

	Dunkerque Port Ouest Dir FG 16m 21M
	ditto Dir FG 30m 21M
1114	Calais Fl(4)W 15s 59m 22M
1144	Cap Gris-Nez Fl 5s 72m 29M
1166	Cap d'Alprech Fl(3)W 15s 62m 23M
1190	Le Touquet (La Canche) Fl(2)W 10s 54m 25M
1196	Pointe du Haut-Blanc Berck-Plage Fl W 5s 44m 23M
1202	Baie du Somme - Cayeux sur Mer FlR 5s 32m 22M
1208	

1222	Le Tréport - Jetée Ouest Fl(2)G 10s 15m 20M
1234	Pointe d'Ailly Fl(3)W 20s 95m 31M
1250	Cap d'Antifer FlW 20s 128m 29M
1250-2	Port d'Antifer Ldg Lts Dir OcW 4s 113m 22M
1250-2I	Port d'Antifer Dir OcW 4s 135m 22M
1256	Le Havre Ldg Lts Quai R. Meunier Dir FW 36m 25M
1260	Le Havre - Quai J Couvert, Dir FW 78m 25M
1260-1	Le Havre - Digue Nord Head FlR 4s 15m 21M
1262	
1396	Ver Fl(3)W 15s 42m 26M
1454	Pointe de Barfleur Gatteville Fl(2)W 10s 72m 29M
1462	Cap Lévi FlR 5s 36m 22M
1480	Cherbourg - Ft de L'Ouest Fl(3)WR 15s 19m 24/20M
1512	Cap de la Hague FlW 5s 48m 23M

Symbols used:

- Port
- ⊚ Waypoint
- ☆ Light Visible 20M and Over

Miles

Not to be used for navigation

See Area Planner No15

Places/features labelled on the map:

Dunkerque, Calais, Boulogne, Cap d'Alprech, Le Touquet, Etaples, St Valery-sur-Somme, Le Treport, Dieppe, Pte d'Ailly, St Valery-en-Caux, Fecamp, Cap de la Heve, Le Havre, Honfleur, Deauville, Dives-sur-mer, Ouistreham, Courseulles-sur-mer, Port-en-Bessin, Pte de Ver, Isigny, Grandcamp Maisy, Carentan, St-Vaast-La-Hougue, Barfleur, Cherbourg, R Seine

Waypoint numbers: 95, 195, 196, 197, 198, 199, 200, 201, 202, 203, 204, 205, 206, 207, 208, 209, 210, 211, 212, 213, 214, 215, 96

Light numbers on map: 1114, 1126, 0994, 1144, 1166, 1190, 1196, 1202, 1208, 1222, 1234, 1250, 1250-2, 1256, 1260, 1262, 1396, 1454, 1462, 1480, 1512

Route annotations:
Dover WP 144 010° 69 Miles
Brighton WP 137 318° 67 Miles
Brighton WP 137 345° 63 Miles
Eastbourne WP 140 015° 76 Miles
Nab Tower WP 1 336° 75 Miles
Brighton WP 137 030° 83 miles
Nab Tower WP 1 010° 59 Miles
Nab Tower WP 1 024° 65 Miles
Needles Fairway Buoy WP 25 000° 57 Miles

AREA PLANNER 14

WAYPOINTS

France North - *Barfleur to Dunkerque*

1	Nab Tower - *0·5M NW*	50°40'·38N	00°57'·55W
25	Fairway Buoy - *Needles channel*	50°38'·20N	01°38'·90W
96	Cherbourg - *0·5M N of W ent*	49°40'·95N	01°39'·35W
137	Brighton entrance - *1M S of*	50°47'·50N	00°06'·30W
140	Eastbourne - *1·2M SE Langney Pt*	50°46'·25N	00°21'·10E
141	Rye - *0·1M S of Fairway By*	50°53'·90N	00°48'·13E
144	Dover - *1·2M SE of W ent*	51°05'·80N	01°21'·10E
195	Dunkerque - *2M NW of ent*	51°05'·00N	02°18'·40E
196	Calais - *2M NW of ent*	50°59'·20N	01°47'·70E
197	Cap Gris-Nez - *2M NW*	50°53'·30N	01°32'·50E
198	Boulogne - *2M WNW of ent*	50°45'·30N	01°31'·50E
199	Étaples - *3M W of Le Touquet Pt*	50°32'·20N	01°30'·80E
200	St Valéry-sur-Somme - *5M WNW*	50°15'·30N	01°27'·10E
201	Le Trèport - *2M NW of ent*	50°05'·40N	01°20'·40E
202	Dieppe - *1M NW of ent*	49°57'·00N	01°04'·00E
203	St Valéry-en-Caux - *2M N of ent*	49°54'·50N	00°42'·30E
204	Fécamp - *1M NW of ent*	49°46'·70N	00°20'·80E
205	Cap D'Antifer - *1·8M NW*	49°42'·40N	00°07'·80E
206	Le Havre - *0·5M NE of LHA*	49°32'·00N	00°09'·20W
207	Honfleur - *7·5M W of ent*	49°27'·00N	00°02'·50E
208	Deauville - *3M NNW of ent*	49°24'·50N	00°02'·20E
209	Dives-sur-Mer - *3M NNW*	49°20'·70N	00°07'·00W
210	Ouistreham - *3·6M NNE of ent*	49°21'·00N	00°11'·40W
211	Courseulles-sur-Mer - *3M N*	49°23'·40N	00°27'·00W
212	Port-en-Bessin - *3M NNW*	49°24'·00N	00°43'·60W
213	Grandcamp Maisy - *4M NW*	49°26'·70N	01°06'·30W
214	St-Vaast-la-Hougue - *3M ENE*	49°36'·40N	01°11'·00W
215	Barfleur - *2M NE*	49°42'·00N	01°13'·30W

Section 2

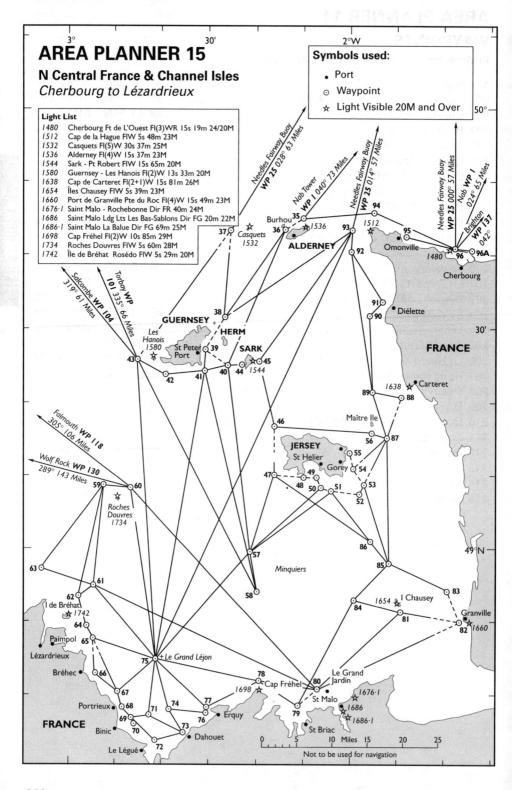

AREA PLANNER 15

N Central France & Channel Isles
Cherbourg to Lézardrieux

Symbols used:
- • Port
- ⊙ Waypoint
- ☆ Light Visible 20M and Over

Light List

1480	Cherbourg Ft de L'Ouest Fl(3)WR 15s 19m 24/20M
1512	Cap de la Hague FlW 5s 48m 23M
1532	Casquets Fl(5)W 30s 37m 25M
1536	Alderney Fl(4)W 15s 37m 23M
1544	Sark - Pt Robert FlW 15s 65m 20M
1580	Guernsey - Les Hanois Fl(2)W 13s 33m 20M
1638	Cap de Carteret Fl(2+1)W 15s 81m 26M
1654	Îles Chausey FlW 5s 39m 23M
1660	Port de Granville Pte du Roc Fl(4)W 15s 49m 23M
1676·1	Saint Malo - Rochebonne Dir FR 40m 24M
1686	Saint Malo Ldg Lts Les Bas-Sablons Dir FG 20m 22M
1686·1	Saint Malo La Balue Dir FG 69m 25M
1698	Cap Fréhel Fl(2)W 10s 85m 29M
1734	Roches Douvres FlW 5s 60m 28M
1742	Île de Bréhat Rosédo FlW 5s 29m 20M

Not to be used for navigation

310

AREA PLANNER 15
WAYPOINTS
France North Central & Channel Islands - *Cherbourg to Lezardrieux*

1   Nab Tower -
    0.5 mile north-west .... 50°40'·38N   00°57'·55W
25 Fairway Buoy -
    Needles channel .... 50°38'·20N   01°38'·90W
35 Alderney - Bray Harbour-
    1M NNE .... 49°45'·00N   02°10'·75W
36 The Swinge -
    turning way point .... 49°43'·50N   02°14'·40W
37 Casquets - *1 mile W of* .... 49°43'·38N   02°24'·06W
38 Guernsey NE -
    1·2m E of Beaucette .... 49°30'·13N   02°28'·30W
39 St Peter Port -
    0·5M E of ent .... 49°27'·40N   02°30'·70W
40 Big Russel - *mid way south* 49°25'·30N   02°26'·00W
41 Guernsey -
    1M SE of St Martin's Pt ..... 49°24'·66N   02°30'·53W
42 Guernsey -
    1·5M S of Pleinmont Pt ..... 49°24'·00N   02°40'·00W
43 Guernsey -
    1·8M W of Les Hanois .... 49°26'·16N   02°45'·00W
44 Sark - *0·3M S of Brecou* .... 49°25'·47N   02°23'·30W
45 Sark -
    1M E of Creux Harbour ..... 49°25'·80N   02°19'·00W
46 Jersey -
    1·75M NW of Grosnez Pt ... 49°16'·60N   02°16'·75W
47 Jersey -
    1M WSW of La Corbiere ... 49°10'·46N   02°16'·32W
48 Jersey -
    0·15M S of Normant Pt ..... 49°09'·80N   02°10'·00W
49 St Helier -
    0·3M S of Breakwater .... 49°09'·97N   02°07'·33W
50 St Helier -
    0·3M S of Demie de Ras .... 49°08'·77N   02°06'·06W
51 SE Jersey -
    1st turning pt going E .... 49°08'·05N   02°03'·35W
52 SE Jersey -
    2nd turning pt to Gorey .... 49°07'·60N   01°57'·90W
53 SE Jersey -
    3rd turning pt to Gorey ..... 49°08'·70N   01°57'·20W
54 Gorey Entrance -
    298°, 1·6 miles .... 49°11'·10N   01°59'·12W
55 St Catherine, Jersey -
    0·5M SE .... 49°13'·10N   02°00'·00W
56 Les Écrehou -
    1·4M S of Maitre Ile Bn ..... 49°15'·70N   01°55'·50W
57 Minquiers NCM -
    0·1M W .... 48°59'·70N   02°20'·65W
58 SW Minquiers WCM -
    0·1M SW .... 48°54'·34N   02°19'·42W
59 Roches Douvres Lt -
    3M W of .... 49°08'·60N   02°52'·10W
60 Roches Douvres Lt -
    2·5M NE .... 49°08'·10N   02°46'·20W
61 Lezardrieux -
    1·5m N La Horaire Bn .... 48°55'·07N   02°55'·15W
62 Lezardrieux Appr -
    1·7M NNE .... 48°53'·60N   02°58'·18W
63 Les Héaux de Brehat -
    3M N of .... 48°57'·60N   03°05'·10W
64 Rade de Brehat -
    2·5M E by S of .... 48°49'·70N   02°56'·00W

65 Paimpol - *1M E of*
    Les Charpentiers Bn .... 48°47'·90N   02°54'·40W
66 Bréhec -
    0·8M E of Le Taureau Mk .. 48°43·60'N   02°54'·00W
67 Ile Harbour Light -
    1M NW of .... 48°40·75'N   02°49'·60W
68 St Quay Portrieux -
    0·2M E of ent .... 48°38'·90N   02°48'·55W
69 La Roselière WCM -
    0·3M S .... 48°37'·25N   02°46'·40W
70 Binic -
    2M 080° from Breakwater . 48°36'·50N   02°45'·85W
71 Caffa ECM By - *0·3M SE* .... 48°37'·68N   02°42'·68W
72 Le Legué Buoy -
    0·2M NW .... 48°34'·52N   02°41'·28W
73 Dahouet - *1M NW of ent* ... 48°35'·50N   02°35'·20W
74 Rohein WCM Bn -
    0·6M SW .... 48°38'·50N   02°38'·40W
75 Grand Léjon Lt Bn -
    0·7M W .... 48°44'·90N   02°40'·80W
76 Erquy-*1M W of* .... 48°38'·10N   02°30'·00W
77 Cap d'Erquy -
    1·0M WNW of .... 48°38'·95N   02°30'·00W
78 Cap Frehel Lt - *1·1M N of* .. 48°42'·50N   02°19'·07W
79 St Briac -
    2M off on approach .... 48°38'·40N   02°10'·90W
80 St Malo - *1·3M NW*
    Le Grande Jardin Bn .... 48°41'·10N   02°06'·40W
81 Iles Chausey -
    1M S of entrance .... 48°51'·10N   01°49'·00W
82 Granville -
    0·7M SW of Granville Lt .... 48°49'·62N   01°37'·55W
83 Iles Chausey -
    0·5M E of Anvers ECM ..... 48°54'·00N   01°40'·00W
84 SE Minquiers ECM -
    1M SE .... 48°53'·20N   01°58'·90W
85 Les Ardentes ECM By -
    0·2M E .... 48°57'·90N   01°51'·15W
86 NE Minquiers ECM -
    0·1M NE .... 49°00'·97N   01°55'·11W
87 Les Écrehou SE -
    0·4M SE of
    Écrevière By .... 49°15'·10N   01°51'·65W
88 Carteret - *1·75M SW* .... 49°20'·90N   01°49'·20W
89 Carteret - *0·3M SW*
    Trois Grunes WCM By ...... 49°21'·65N   01°55'·30W
90 Cap de Flamanville -
    2M W of .... 49°31'·65N   01°56'·30W
91 Diellette -
    1M NW of on transit .... 49°33'·80N   01°53'·00W
92 Cap de La Hague -
    4M SSW of .... 49°40'·54N   02°01'·55W
93 Cap de La Hague -
    2M W of .... 49°43'·37N   02°00'·28W
94 Cap de La Hague -
    1·5M N of
    La Plate Lt .... 49°45'·50N   01°55'·70W
95 Omonville -
    1M E of, in white sec .... 49°42'·55N   01°48'·25W
96 Cherbourg -
    0·5M N of W ent .... 49°40'·95N   01°39'·35W
96a Cherbourg -
    0·5M N of E ent .... 49°40'·87N   01°35'·80W
101 Tor Bay -
    1·7M NE of Berry Hd .... 50°25'·10N   03°27'·00W
104 Salcombe - *1·5M S of bar* . 50°11'·62N   03°46'·60W
118 Falmouth -
    0·8M S of St Anthony Hd .. 50°07'·64N   05°00'·90W
130 Wolf Rk - *2 miles S of* .... 49°54'·65N   05°48'·50W

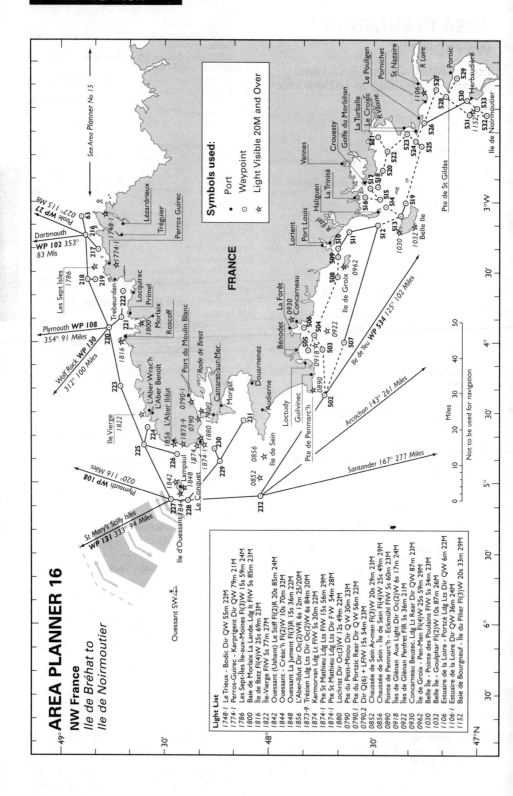

AREA PLANNER 16

WAYPOINTS

France North West & Biscay - *Douarnenez to Ile de Noirmoutier*

27	Poole Fairway Buoy - *1M E*	50°39'·00N	01°53'·20W
63	Les Héaux de Brehat - *3M N*	48°57'·60N	03°05'·10W
102	Dartmouth - *2M 150° from ent*	50°18'·25N	03°31'·60W
108	Plymouth - *0·9M S of W brkwtr*	50°19'·13N	04°09'·50W
130	Wolf Rk - *2MS of*	49°54'·65N	05°48'·50W
131	St Mary's, Scilly - *2M E of St Mary's Sound*	49°54'·00N	06°l 5'·00W
216	Treguier - *4·1M N of Pte de Chateau*	48°56'·20N	03°14'·30W
217	Perros Guirec - *2·3M NNW of Port Blanc*	48°52'·30N	03°20'·20W
218	Ile Bono Light - *4M NW*	48°55'·50N	03°33'·90W
219	Ploumanach - *2·7M E of Les Triagoz*	48°52'·30N	03°34'·60W
220	Roscoff - *6M NNE of ent*	48°49'·10N	03°54'·30W
221	Morlaix & Primel - *2·2M NW Pte de Primel*	48°45'·00N	03°51'·20W
222	Trebeurden - *1·5M S of Le Crapaud*	48°45'·20N	03°40'·50W
223	Pte de Beg-Pol Lt - *4M N*	48°44'·70N	04°20'·80W
224	L'Aber Wrach, L'Aber Benoit - *1M W of Libenter WCM*	48°37'·60N	04°39'·90W
225	Gr Basse de Portsall WCM - *1·6M N of*	48°38'·30N	04°45'·90W
226	Chenal du Four - *3·9M W of L'Aber Ildut ent*	48°28'·30N	04°51'·30W
227	Ushant Creach Lt - *3·5M NW*	48°30'·00N	05°11'·30W
228	Ushant - *4·9M WSW Lampaul*	48°25'·30N	05°12'·30W
229	Vandrée WCM - *4·8M W*	48°15'·30N	04°55'·00W
230	Chenal du Four, *S Ent - 3·5M WSW ent Rade de Brest*	48°17'·20N	04°48'·20W
231	Douarnenez - *1·5M SW Basse Vieille IDM*	48°07'·30N	04°37'·20W
232	Chaussée de Sein WCM - *1·6M SW*	48°02'·90N	05°09.60'W
502	Guilvinec - *5·5M SW hbr ent*	47°44'·30N	04°23'·50W
503	Concarneau appr - *2·3M SW I. aux Moutons Lt*	47°44'·80N	04°03'·90W
504	Concarneau appr - *2·1M ENE I. aux Moutons*	47°47'·50N	03°58'·80W
505	Benodet - *3·0M S by E river mouth*	47°48'·90N	04°05'·40W
506	Concarneau - *2·0M SSW hbr ent*	47°50'·40N	03°56'·50W
507	I de Glenan - *3M S Jument de Glénan Lt By*	47°38'·50N	04°01'·30W
508	Lorient - *3·0M NW by W Pen Men Lt*	47°40'·50N	03°34'·20W
509	Lorient Passe de L'Ouest - *0·5M SW ent*	47°40'·50N	03°25'·70W
510	Lorient S.Chan - *1·5M S by W ent*	47°40'·40N	03°22'·50W
511	R. Etel - *3M SW river mouth*	47°36'·60N	03°15'·70W
512	Quiberon Peninsula - *3·0M W*	47°28'·90N	03°11'·80W
513	Belle I - Le Palais - *1·3M NE hbr ent*	47°21'·60N	03°07'·50W
514	P. de la Teignouse SW ent - *0·7M SW*	47°25'·20N	03°05'·20W
515	P. de la Teignouse NE ent - *0·7M E*	47°26'·90N	03°00'·50W
516	La Trinite-sur-mer - *1·5M S by E ent*	47°32'·70N	02°59'·80W
517	Golfe du Morbihan - *2·2M S Ent ch*	47°31'·00N	02°55'·20W
518	Chimère SCM - *0·5M SW*	47°28'·60N	02°54'·60W
519	Pointe de Kerdonis Lt - *2M NE*	47°20'·20N	03°01'·50W
520	Pointe de S. Jacques Lt - *1·8M S*	47°27'·40N	02°47'·40W
521	R. Vilaine - *0·7M S Les Mâts SCM*	47°28'·50N	02°34'·80W
522	Ile Dumet Lt - *1·5M W*	47°24'·80N	02°39'·30W
523	La Turballe - *2M N Pte du Croisic*	47°19'·80N	02°32'·90W
524	Plateau du Four - *1·6M ESE Le Four Lt*	47°17'·40N	02°35'·80W
525	Plateau du Four - *0·4M S Goué-Vas*	47°14'·60N	02°38'·10W
526	Le Pouliguen *2M W by S of Pt de Penchâteau*	47°15'·00N	02°27'·90W
527	St. Nazaire - *3·5M Pte Aiguillon Lt*	47°11'·40N	02°17'·60W
528	St. Nazaire - *6·1M Pte Aiguillon Lt*	47°09'·00N	02°19'·30W
529	Pornic - *2·1M WSW Pornic hbr ent*	47°05'·70N	02°10'·00W
530	L'Herbaudière - *1·5M N by E hbr ent*	47°03'·10N	02°17'·50W
531	Ile du Pilier Lt - *1·8M W*	47°02'·60N	02°24'·10W
532	Chaussée des Boeufs - *SW ent.*	46°56'·70N	02°24'·10W
533	Ile Noirmoutier - *SW ent Chenal de la Grise*	47°01'·10N	02°20'·80W

Section 2

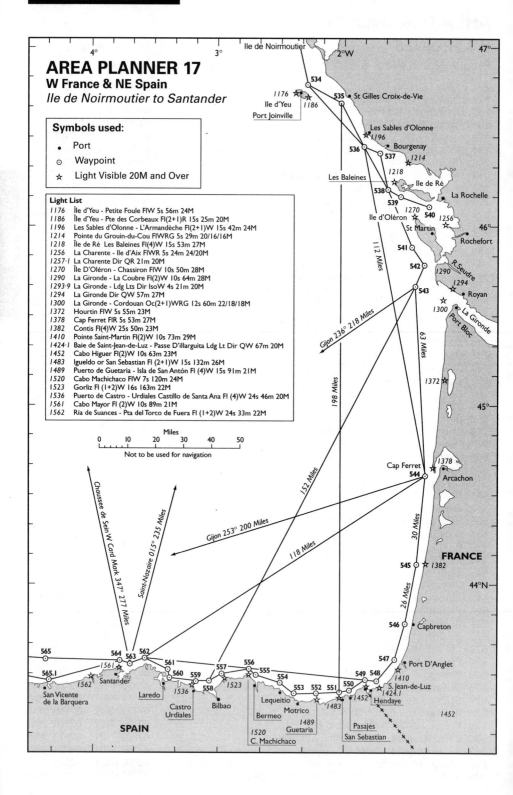

AREA PLANNER 17
W France & NE Spain
Ile de Noirmoutier to Santander

Symbols used:

- • Port
- ⊙ Waypoint
- ☆ Light Visible 20M and Over

Light List
1176 Île d'Yeu - Petite Foule FlW 5s 56m 24M
1186 Île d'Yeu - Pte des Corbeaux Fl(2+1)R 15s 25m 20M
1196 Les Sables d'Olonne - L'Armandèche Fl(2+1)W 15s 42m 24M
1214 Pointe du Grouin-du-Cou FlWRG 5s 29m 20/16/16M
1218 Île de Ré Les Baleines Fl(4)W 15s 53m 27M
1256 La Charente - Ile d'Aix FlWR 5s 24m 24/20M
1257·1 La Charente Dir QR 21m 20M
1270 Île D'Oléron - Chassiron FlW 10s 50m 28M
1290 La Gironde - La Coubre Fl(2)W 10s 64m 28M
1293·9 La Gironde - Ldg Lts Dir IsoW 4s 21m 20M
1294 La Gironde Dir QW 57m 27M
1300 La Gironde - Cordouan Oc(2+1)WRG 12s 60m 22/18/18M
1372 Hourtin FlW 5s 55m 23M
1378 Cap Ferret FlR 5s 53m 27M
1382 Contis Fl(4)W 25s 50m 23M
1410 Pointe Saint-Martin Fl(2)W 10s 73m 29M
1424·1 Baie de Saint-Jean-de-Luz - Passe D'Illarguita Ldg Lt Dir QW 67m 20M
1452 Cabo Higuer Fl(2)W 10s 63m 23M
1483 Igueldo or San Sebastian Fl (2+1)W 15s 132m 26M
1489 Puerto de Guetaria - Isla de San Antón Fl (4)W 15s 91m 21M
1520 Cabo Machichaco FlW 7s 120m 24M
1523 Gorliz Fl (1+2)W 16s 163m 22M
1536 Puerto de Castro - Urdiales Castillo de Santa Ana Fl (4)W 24s 46m 20M
1561 Cabo Mayor Fl (2)W 10s 89m 21M
1562 Ría de Suances - Pta del Torco de Fuera Fl (1+2)W 24s 33m 22M

Miles
0   10   20   30   40   50
Not to be used for navigation

AREA PLANNER 17

WAYPOINTS

France-Biscay & NE Spain - *Ile de Nourmontier to Santander*

534	Ile d'Yeu, Port Joinville - *2·4M N by E harbour ent*	46°46'·00N	02°19'·60W
535	St. Gilles-Croix-da-Vie - *3M SW ent*	46°39'·70N	01°59'·60W
536	Les Sables-d'Olonne - *3·7M SW ent*	46°26'·30N	01°49'·60W
537	Bourgenay - *1·4M SW SWM*	46°24'·40N	01°43'·20W
538	Ile de Ré - *3·0M SW Les Baleines Lt*	46°12'·70N	01°37'·10W
539	La Rochelle appr. chan. - *6·5M NW Pte Chassiron*	46°07'·40N	01°31'·60W
540	La Rochelle Ldg Lts - *6M SW by W harbour ent*	46°06'·00N	01°17'·30W
541	Ile d'Oleron - *3·7M SW Pte Chardonnière*	45°54'·60N	01°26'·70W
542	R. Seudre - *3·0M W Pointe de Gatseau*	45°47'·80N	01°18'·80W
543	R. Gironde-ent chan - *7M SW Pte de la Coubre*	45°38'·20N	01°22'·60W
544	Bassin d'Arcachon - *N ent - 5M SW Cap Ferret Lt*	44°35'·00N	01°19'·80W
545	Contis Lt - *3·5M W*	44°05'·70N	01°23'·80W
546	Capbreton - *1·9M W by N harbour ent*	43°39'·80N	01°29'·50W
547	Port d'Anglet - *1·7M WNW hbr brkwtr*	43°32'·80N	01°33'·70W
548	St Jean-de-Luz - *1·5M NNW harbour ent*	43°25'·50N	01°40'·80W
549	Hendaye - *1·8M N Cabo Higuer Lt*	43°25'·40N	01°47'·70W
550	Pasajes - *2·0M N harbour entrance*	43°22'·30N	01°55'·80W
551	San Sebastian - *2·2M N entrance to bay*	43°21'·80N	01°59'·70W
552	Guetaria - *1·8 M N I. de San Antón*	43°20'·50N	02°11'·80W
553	Motrico - *1·8M NE hbr ent*	43°20'·10N	02°21'·00W
554	Lequeitio - *1·8M NNE hbr ent*	43°23'·60N	02°28'·60W
555	Bermeo - *2·2M NNE*	43°27'·40N	02°41'·40W
556	Cabo Machichaco Lt - *1·9M N*	43°29'·20N	02°45'·10W
557	Cabo Villano Lt - *2·3M N*	43°28'·30N	02°56'·60W
558	Abra de Bilbao - *2·0M N of ent*	43°24'·80N	03°04'·80W
559	Castro Urdiales - *1·9M NW of harbour ent*	43°24'·40N	03°11'·00W
560	Laredo - *2M NW Canto de Laredo*	43°26'·80N	03°22'·50W
561	Punta del Pescador - *1·9M NW*	43°29'·10N	03°24'·20W
562	Cabo Ajo Lt - *2·2M N*	43°32'·90N	03°35'·30W
563	Santander - *1·7M N I. de S. Marina*	43°30'·20N	03°43'·70W
564	Cabo Mayor Lt - *1·7M N*	43°31'·10N	03°47'·40W
565	S Vicente de la Barquera Lt - *9·3M N*	43°33'·00N	04°23'·50W

Section 2

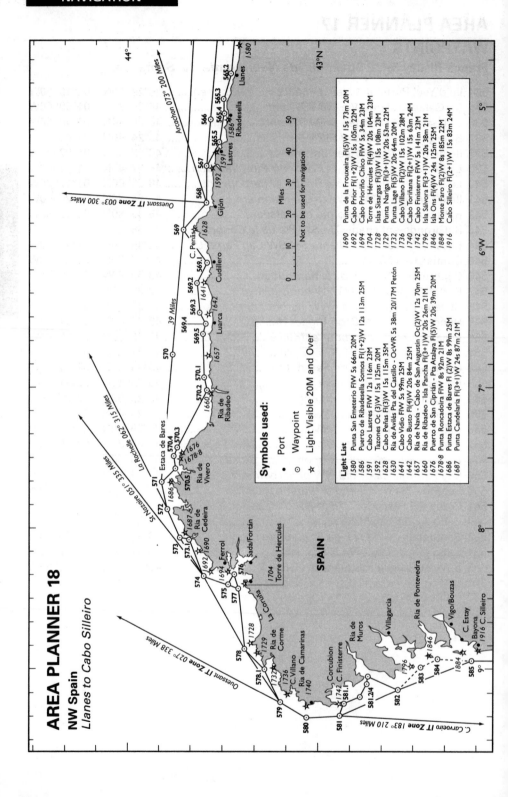

AREA PLANNER 18
NW Spain
Llanes to Cabo Silleiro

Symbols used:

- • Port
- ⊙ Waypoint
- ☆ Light Visible 20M and Over

Light List

1580	Punta San Emeterio Fl/W 5s 66m 20M
1586	Puerto de Ribadesella Somos Fl(1+2)W 12s 113m 25M
1591	Cabo Lastres Fl/W 12s 116m 23M
1592	Tazones Oc (3)W 15s 125m 20M
1628	Cabo Peñas Fl(3)W 15s 115m 35M
1630	Ría de Avilés Pta del Castillo - Oc-WR 5s 38m 20/17M Petón
1641	Cabo Vidio Fl/W 5s 99m 25M
1642	Cabo Busto Fl(4)W 20s 84m 25M
1657	Ría de Navia – Cabo de San Augustín Oc(2)W 12s 70m 25M
1660	Ría de Ribadeo – Isla Pancha Fl(3+1)W 20s 26m 21M
1676	Puerto de San Ciprián – Pta Atalaya Fl(5)W 20s 39m 20M
1678-8	Punta Roncadoira Fl/W 8s 92m 21M
1686	Punta Estaca de Bares Fl (2)W 8s 99m 25M
1687	Punta Candelaria Fl(3+1)W 24s 87m 21M

1690	Punta de la Frouxeira Fl(5)W 15s 73m 20M
1692	Cabo Prior Fl(1+2)W 15s 105m 22M
1694	Cabo Prioriño Chico Fl/W 5s 34m 23M
1704	Torre de Hércules Fl(4)W 20s 104m 23M
1728	Islas Sisargas Fl(3)W 15s 108m 23M
1729	Punta Nariga Fl(3+1)W 20s 53m 22M
1732	Punta Lage Fl(5)W 20s 64m 20M
1736	Cabo Villano Fl(2)W 15s 102m 28M
1740	Punta Toriñana Fl(2+1)W 15s 63m 24M
1742	Cabo Finisterre Fl/W 5s 141m 23M
1796	Isla Sálvora Fl(3+1)W 20s 38m 21M
1846	Isla Ons Fl(4)W 24s 125m 25M
1884	Monte Faro Fl(2)W 8s 185m 22M
1916	Cabo Silleiro Fl(2+1)W 15s 83m 24M

Not to be used for navigation

SPAIN

AREA PLANNER 18

WAYPOINTS

NW Spain - *Llanes to Cabo Silleiro*

565.2	Llanes - *1·5 M N of hbr ent*	43°26'·70N	04°44'·90W
565.3	Cabo de Mar - *1·5 M N of headland*	43°29'·20N	04°55'·70W
566	Punta de Somos Lt - *6·3M N*	43°34'·70N	05°05'·00W
566.1	Ribadesella - *1·5 M N of hbr ent*	43°29'·60N	05°03'·90W
566.2	Lastres - *1·5 M NE of hbr ent*	43°32'·00N	05°14'·33W
567	Tazones Lt - *2·7M N*	43°35'·60N	05°24'·00W
568	Gijon - *1·9M ENE breakwater Lt*	43°35'·00N	05°38'·20W
569	Cabo Peñas Lt - *3·1M N*	43°42'·50N	05°50'·80W
569.1	Cudillero - *1·5 M N of hbr ent*	43°35'·47N	06°08'·86W
569.2	Cabo Vidio - *1·7 M N of light*	43°37'·30N	06°14'·82W
569.3	Cabo Busto - *1·5 M N of light*	43°35'·69N	06°28'·23W
569.4	Luarca - *1·5 M N of hbr ent*	43°34'·54N	06°32'·21W
569.5	Romanellas - *1·5 M N of headland*	43°35'·97N	06°37'·67W
570	Cabo San Augustin Lt - *11·8M N*	43°45'·80N	06°44'·00W
570.1	Cabo S Sebastian - *1·75 M N of light*	43°36'·23N	06°56'·81W
570.2	Ribadeo - *1·75 M N of Ria ent*	43°35'·21N	07°02'·21W
570.3	Los Farallones Is - *1·5 M N of*	43°44'·90N	07°26'·36W
570.4	Pta Roncadoira - *1·8 M N of lt*	43°45'·81N	07°31'·59W
570.5	Vivero - *3·5 M N of Pta de Faro*	43°46'·30N	07°35'·00W
571	Pta de la Estaca de Bares Lt - *2·0M N*	43°49'·30N	07°41'·10W
572	Pta de los Aguillones Lt - *2·5M N*	43°48'·80N	07°52'·10W
573	Pta Candelaria Lt - *2·1M NW*	43°44'·30N	08°04'·70W
573.1	Cedeira - *0·5 M W of Pta Lameda*	43°40'·94N	08°05'·16W
574	Cabo Prior Lt - *3·4M NW*	43°36'·70N	08°21'·50W
575	Cabo Prioriño Chico Lt - *4·4M WNW*	43°29'·40N	08°25'·80W
576	El Ferrol appro - *1·4M SW C. Prioriño Chico Lt*	43°26'·70N	08°21'·80W
577	La Coruña - *3·3M NW Torre de Hercules Lt*	43°25'·10N	08°28'·00W
578	Sisargas Is Lt - *2·9M NW*	43°23'·70N	08°53'·50W
578.1	Corme - *1·8 M W of Pta del Roncundo*	43°16'·57N	09°01'·86W
579	Cabo Villano Lt - *3·6M NW*	43°11'·50N	09°16'·60W
579.1	Camariñas - *1·9 M NW of Pta de la Barca*	43°08'·20N	09°14'·95W
580	Cabo Toriñana Lt - *2·7M W*	43°03'·30N	09°21'·50W
581	Cabo Finisterre Lt - *4M W*	42°52'·80N	09°21'·60W
581.1	Corcubion - *1·5 M S of Cabo Finisterre*	42°51'·50N	09°16'·20W
581.2	Bajo de los Meixidos - *1 M W of*	42°45'·60N	09°14'·10W
581.3	Los Bruyos Is - *2 M SW of*	42°42'·80N	09°10'·30W
581.4	Muros - *1·8 M SSW of Pta Queixal*	42°42'·80N	09°05'·70W
582	Cabo Corrubedo Lt - *4·2M WSW*	42°33'·40N	09°10'·60W
583	Villagarcia - *2·5M S Isla Salvora Lt*	42°25'·50N	09°00'·70W
584	Vigo - NW appr - *5·0M W Pta Couso Lt*	42°18'·60N	08°58'·00W
585	Vigo/Bayona - SW appr - *3·8M NW C Silleiro Lt*	42°08'·70N	08°57'·50W

Section 2

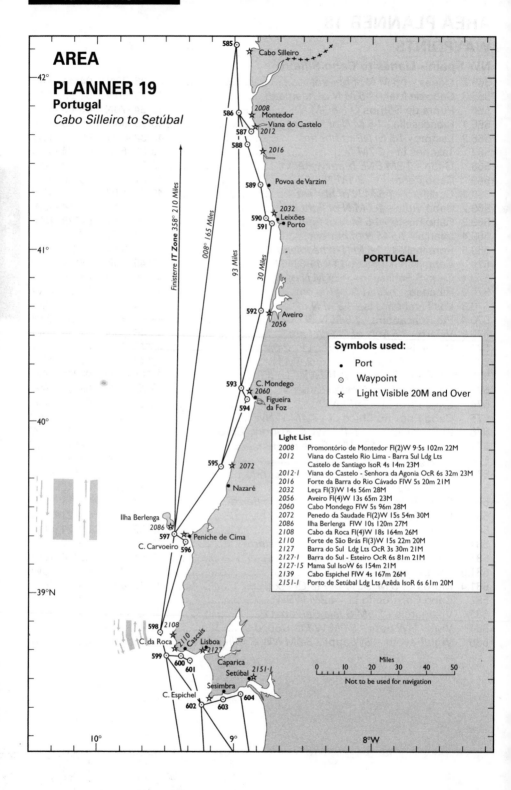

AREA
PLANNER 19
Portugal
Cabo Silleiro to Setúbal

42°
41°
40°
39°N

42°
10°
9°
8°W

585
Cabo Silleiro
586
2008 Montedor
587 Viana do Castelo
2012
588
2016
589 Povoa de Varzim
2032
590 Leixões
591 Porto
592 Aveiro
2056

Finisterre IT Zone 358° 210 Miles
008° 165 Miles
93 Miles
30 Miles

PORTUGAL

593 C. Mondego
2060
594 Figueira
da Foz

595 2072

Nazaré

Ilha Berlenga
2086
597 Peniche de Cima
C. Carvoeiro 596

598 2108
C. da Roca
2110 Cascais
599 Lisboa
600 2127
601
Caparica
Setúbal 2151·1
Sesimbra
C. Espichel
602 603 604

Symbols used:

• Port

⊙ Waypoint

☆ Light Visible 20M and Over

Light List

2008	Promontório de Montedor Fl(2)W 9·5s 102m 22M
2012	Viana do Castelo Rio Lima - Barra Sul Ldg Lts
	Castelo de Santiago IsoR 4s 14m 23M
2012·1	Viana do Castelo - Senhora da Agonia OcR 6s 32m 23M
2016	Forte da Barra do Rio Cávado FlW 5s 20m 21M
2032	Leça Fl(4)W 14s 56m 28M
2056	Aveiro Fl(4)W 13s 65m 23M
2060	Cabo Mondego FlW 5s 96m 28M
2072	Penedo da Saudade Fl(2)W 15s 54m 30M
2086	Ilha Berlenga FlW 10s 120m 27M
2108	Cabo da Roca Fl(4)W 18s 164m 26M
2110	Forte de São Brás Fl(3)W 15s 22m 20M
2127	Barra do Sul Ldg Lts OcR 3s 30m 21M
2127·1	Barra do Sul - Esteiro OcR 6s 81m 21M
2127·15	Mama Sul IsoW 6s 154m 21M
2139	Cabo Espichel FlW 4s 167m 26M
2151·1	Porto de Setúbal Ldg Lts Azêda IsoR 6s 61m 20M

Miles
0 10 20 30 40 50
Not to be used for navigation

AREA PLANNER 19

WAYPOINTS

Portugal - *Cabo Silleiro to Setubal*

585	Vigo/Bayona - SW appro - *3·8M NW C Silleiro Lt*	42°08'·70N	08°57'·50W
586	Montedor Lt - *3·8M W*	41°44'·90N	08°57'·50W
587	Viano do Castelo (Ldg Lts) - *1·2M from breakwater*	41°39'·20N	08°51'·00W
588	Viano do Castelo (Ldg Lts) - *5·5M from breakwater*	41°35'·00N	08°52'·00W
589	Póvoa de Varzim - *1·6M WSW harbour entrance*	41°21'·50N	08°48'·10W
590	Porto de Leixões - *2M W breakwater*	41°10'·20N	08°45'·00W
591	Porto - *1·5M W river mouth*	41°08'·50N	08°42'·80W
592	Aveiro - *2·0M W breakwater*	40°38'·60N	08°48'·20W
593	Cabo Mondego Lt - *3·2M W*	40°11'·30N	08°58'·10W
594	Figueira da Foz - *2·1M W breakwater*	40°08'·60N	08°55'·00W
595	Nazaré - *2·8M W of harbour entrance*	39°35'·40N	09°08'·40W
596	Peniche de Cima - *1·5M SW of harbour entrance*	39°20'·00N	09°23'·84W
597	Cabo Carvoeiro Lt - *3·0M W by N*	39°22'·50N	09°28'·30W
598	Cabo da Roca Lt - *3·5M W*	38°47'·00N	09°34'·20W
599	Cabo Raso Lt - *3·3M SW*	38°40'·40N	09°32'·10W
600	Cascais - *1·5M S S· Marta Lt*	38°40'·00N	09°25'·20W
601	Lisboa (Ldg Lts) - *5·0M SW Gibalta Lt*	38°38'·60N	09°20'·50W
602	Cabo Espichel Lt - *3·2M SW*	38°22'·50N	09°15'·40W
603	Sesimbra (Ldg Lts) - *1·5M S harbour entrance*	38°24'·80N	09°06'·10W
604	Sétubal (Ldg Lts) - *3·5M SW Outão Lt*	38°26'·80N	08°58'·60W

Section 2

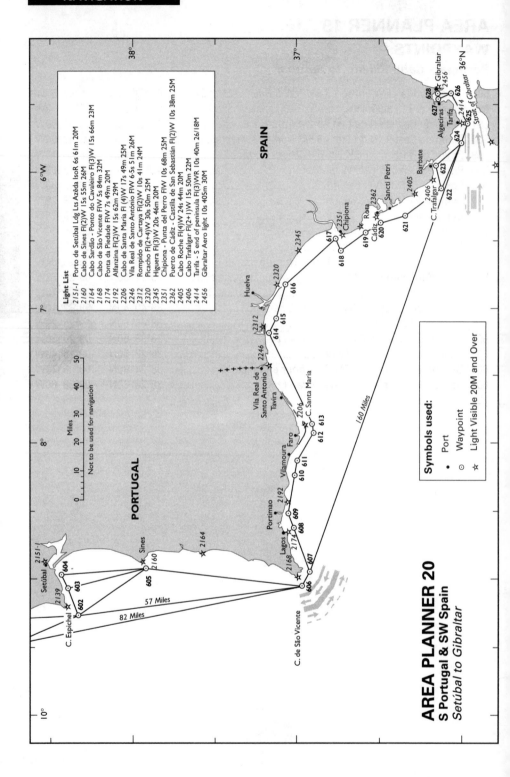

AREA PLANNER 20
S Portugal & SW Spain
Setúbal to Gibraltar

Light List

2151·1	Porto de Setúbal Ldg Lts Azêda IsoR 6s 61m 20M
2160	Cabo de Sines Fl(2)W 15s 55m 26M
2164	Cabo Sardão - Ponto do Cavaleiro Fl(3)W 15s 66m 23M
2168	Cabo de São Vicente FlW 5s 84m 32M
2174	Ponta da Piedade FlW 7s 49m 20M
2192	Alfanzina Fl(2)W 15s 62m 29M
2206	Cabo de Santa Maria Fl (4)W 17s 49m 25M
2246	Vila Real de Santo António FlW 6·5s 51m 26M
2312	Rompido de Carraya Fl(2)W 10s 41m 24M
2320	Picacho Fl(2+4)W 30s 50m 25M
2345	Higuera Fl(3)W 20s 46m 20M
2351	Chipiona - Punta del Perro FlW 10s 68m 25M
2362	Puerto de Cádiz - Castilla de San Sebastián Fl(2)W 10s 38m 25M
2405	Cabo Roche Fl(4)W 24s 44m 20M
2406	Cabo Trafalgar Fl(2+1)W 15s 50m 22M
2414	Tarifa - S end of peninsula Fl(3)WR 10s 40m 26/18M
2456	Gibraltar Aero light 10s 405m 30M

Symbols used:

- • Port
- ⊙ Waypoint
- ☆ Light Visible 20M and Over

Not to be used for navigation

Miles
0 10 20 30 40 50

PORTUGAL

SPAIN

Setúbal
Sines
Lagos
Portimao
Vilamoura
Faro
C. Santa Maria
Tavira
Vila Real de Santo António
Huelva
Chipiona
Rota
Cádiz
Sancti Petri
Barbate
C. Trafalgar
Tarifa
Algeciras
Gibraltar
Strait of Gibraltar

C. Espichel
C. de São Vicente

57 Miles
82 Miles
160 Miles

AREA PLANNER 20
WAYPOINTS
S Portugal & SW Spain - *Setubal to Gibraltar*

602 Cabo Espichel - *3·2M SW* .... 38°22'·50N   09°15'·40W
603 Sesimbra (Ldg Lts) - *1·5M S harbour entrance* .... 38°24'·80N   09°06'·10W
604 Sétubal (Ldg Lts) - *3·5M SW Outão Lt* .... 38°26'·80N   08°58'·60W
605 Sines - *1M W of breakwater* .... 37°56'·30N   08°54'·60W
606 Cabo de São Vicente Lt - *3·0M SW* .... 36°59'·50N   09°02'·50W
607 Pta de Sagres Lt - *2·5M S* .... 36°57'·20N   08°56'·80W
608 Lagos - *1·4M SE Punta da Piedade Lt* .... 37°04'·00N   08°38'·80W
609 Portimão - *2·0M S harbour entrance* .... 37°04'·40N   08°31'·50W
610 Albufeira Lt - *2·6M S* .... 37°02'·60N   08°14'·80W
611 Vilamoura - *1·6M SSW harbour entrance* .... 37°02'·60N   08°08'·20W
612 I. da Barreta - *2·0M SW* .... 36°56'·50N   07°57'·30W
613 Faro/Olhào - *1·0M SSW entrance channel* .... 36°56'·70N   07°52'·60W
614 Santo António - *2·0M S river mouth* .... 37°08'·50N   07°23'·60W
615 Fish Haven off Ria Higuerita - *1·2M S* .... 37°05'·80N   07°20'·00W
616 Huelva - *1M S river mouth* .... 37°05'·60N   06°49'·60W
617 Chipiona/Sanlúcar (Ldg Lts)- *0·5M WSW By* .... 36°45'·70N   06°27'·50W
618 Punta del Perro Lt - *3·2M W* .... 36°44'·80N   06°30'·40W
619 Bahia de Cádiz - *2·2M SSW Punta Candor* .... 36°36'·10N   06°24'·80W
620 Cadiz - *1·6M W by S Castillo de San Sebastián* .... 36°31'·40N   06°20'·80W
621 Sancti Petri - *3M SW chan. entrance* .... 36°21'·00N   06°15'·30W
622 Cabo Trafalgar Lt - *3·6M SW* .... 36°08'·50N   06°05'·20W
623 Barbate - *1·1M S end of breakwater* .... 36°09'·70N   05°55'·40W
624 Punta Paloma Lt - *4·7M SSW* .... 35°59'·50N   05°45'·00W
625 Tarifa - *1·3M S I. de Tarifa Lt* .... 35°58'·80N   05°36'·40W
626 Punta Carnero Lt - *1·8M SE* .... 36°03'·40N   05°24'·00W
627 Algeciras - *1·2M SE end of breakwater* .... 36°08'·20N   05°24'·40W
628 Gibraltar - *0·8M SW E Head pier* .... 36°08'·60N   05°22'·80W

SUN AND MOON TABLES – RISING, SETTING AND TWILIGHTS

Rising and Setting Phenomena
The tables of Sunrise, Sunset and Twilights, Moonrise and Moonset enable the degree of darkness around twilight and throughout the night to be estimated.

Contents of Tables 1, 2 and 3
Table 1 provides Local Mean Times (LMT) for every third day of the year, of morning Nautical Twilight, Sunrise, Sunset and evening Civil Twilight for latitude 50°N and latitude variations (v). Use the left-hand sign in the tabular entry for v for Sunrise, and the right-hand sign for Sunset. The latitude corrections in Table 2 for Sunrise, Sunset and Twilights, enable the LMT for latitudes in the range 30°N to 60°N to be found.

Table 3 gives times of Moonrise and Moonset for each day for latitude 50°N and latitude variations (v). The latitude correction table enables the LMT for latitudes in the range 30°N to 60°N to be found. The tabular values are for the Greenwich Meridian, and are approximately the LMT of the corresponding phenomena for the other meridians. Expressing the longitude in time, the UTC is obtained from:

$$UTC = LMT \, {+west \atop -east} \, longitude$$

For Moonrise and Moonset a further small correction of one minute for every seven degrees of longitude is also required, which is added to the LMT if west, subtracted if east.

At Sunrise and Sunset the upper limb of the Sun is on the horizon at sea level. The Sun's zenith distance is 96° for Civil Twilight and 102° for Nautical Twilight. At Civil Twilight the brightest stars are visible and the horizon is clearly defined. At Nautical Twilight the horizon is not visible.

At Moonrise and Moonset the Moon's upper limb is on the horizon at sea level.

Example (a): The Sun – rising, setting and twilights
Find the UTC of the beginning of morning Nautical Twilight, Sunrise, Sunset and the end of evening Civil Twilight on 22 January 2002 for latitude 36°07'N, longitude 18°20'E.

From Table 1, for 22 January, v = + 30 for the beginning of Nautical Twilight, v = + 51 for Sunrise; v = – 51 for Sunset and v = – 41 for the end of Civil Twilight. From Table 2 the latitude corrections for Nautical Twilight, Sunrise, Sunset and Civil Twilight are – 21 mins, – 38 mins, + 38 mins and + 31 mins respectively. Note that for Sunset, the sign of the correction has to be reversed because v is minus.

Convert longitude from degrees and minutes of arc to whole minutes of time, by multiplying the degrees of longitude by 4 and adding a further correction of 0 mins, 1 min, 2 mins, 3 mins or 4 mins when the minutes of longitude are in the range 0' to 7', 8' to 22', 23' to 37', 38' to 52' or 53' to 59', respectively.

The longitude equivalent in time of 18°20'E is – (18 x 4 + 1) = – 73m.

Remarks	Naut Twilight		Sunrise		Sunset		Civil Twilight	
Tabular value, 22 Jan	06h	31m	07h	46m	16h	37m	17h	13m
Corr'n for latitude		– 21m		– 38m		+ 38m		+ 31m
LMT	06h	10m	07h	08m	17h	15m	17h	44m
Corr'n for longitude	– 1h	13m	– 1h	13m	– 1h	13m	– 1h	13m
UTC of phenomenon	04h	57m	05h	55m	16h	02m	16h	31m

Example (b): The Moon – rising and setting
Find the UTC of Moonrise and Moonset on 24 January 2002 for latitude 36°07'N, longitude 06°30'W. From Table 3 for 24 January, v = – 54 for Moonrise and v = + 51 for Moonset. The latitude correction for Moonrise and Moonset is + 41 mins and – 38 mins, respectively. Note the reversal of the sign of the correction for Moonset, because v is minus.
Using the method in example (a), the longitude equivalent in time of 06°30'W is + 26mins.

Remarks	Moonrise		Moonset	
Tabular value, 24 Jan	12h	25m	03h	18m
Corr'n for latitude		+ 41m		– 38m
LMT	13h	06m	02h	40m
Corr'n for longitude		+ 26m		+ 26m
UTC of phenomenon	13h	32m	03h	06m

These times can be increased by +1min to allow for the effect of longitude on the LMT of the phenomenon. See text at end of Table 3 for the instructions.

TABLE 1   2002 – SUNRISE, SUNSET and TWILIGHTS

Date	Naut Twi	v	Sun-rise	v	Sun-set	Civil Twi	v	Date	Naut Twi	v	Sun-rise	v	Sun-set	Civil Twi	v
	h m		h m		h m	h m			h m		h m		h m	h m	
Jan 1	06 39	+39	07 59	+63	−16 09	16 47	−51	Jul 3	02 08	−114	03 56	−67 +	20 12	20 56	+83
4	06 39	38	07 58	62	16 12	16 50	50	6	02 12	112	03 58	66	20 11	20 54	82
7	06 39	37	07 57	60	16 15	16 53	49	9	02 16	110	04 01	65	20 09	20 52	80
10	06 38	36	07 56	59	16 19	16 57	47	12	02 21	107	04 04	63	20 07	20 49	79
13	06 37	35	07 54	57	16 23	17 01	46	15	02 26	104	04 07	62	20 04	20 46	76
16	06 35	+34	07 52	+56	−16 28	17 05	−44	18	02 31	−100	04 11	−60 +	20 01	20 42	+74
19	06 33	32	07 49	54	16 32	17 09	42	21	02 37	97	04 14	58	19 58	20 39	72
22	06 31	30	07 46	51	16 37	17 13	41	24	02 43	93	04 18	56	19 54	20 34	69
25	06 28	28	07 43	49	16 42	17 18	39	27	02 49	89	04 22	54	19 50	20 30	67
28	06 25	26	07 39	47	16 47	17 22	36	30	02 55	85	04 26	52	19 46	20 25	64
31	06 21	+24	07 35	+44	−16 52	17 27	−34	Aug 2	03 01	−81	04 30	−49 +	19 41	20 20	+61
Feb 3	06 18	22	07 31	42	16 57	17 32	32	5	03 07	78	04 35	47	19 36	20 14	58
6	06 14	20	07 26	39	17 02	17 37	29	8	03 13	74	04 39	44	19 31	20 09	55
9	06 09	17	07 21	36	17 08	17 42	27	11	03 19	70	04 43	42	19 26	20 03	52
12	06 05	15	07 16	34	17 13	17 47	24	14	03 25	66	04 48	39	19 21	19 57	49
15	06 00	+12	07 11	+31	−17 18	17 51	−22	17	03 31	−62	04 52	−36 +	19 15	19 51	+46
18	05 55	10	07 05	28	17 23	17 56	19	20	03 37	58	04 57	33	19 09	19 44	43
21	05 49	7	07 00	25	17 28	18 01	16	23	03 43	55	05 01	31	19 03	19 38	40
24	05 44	4	06 54	22	17 33	18 06	13	26	03 49	51	05 06	28	18 57	19 31	37
27	05 38	+2	06 48	20	17 38	18 11	11	29	03 54	48	05 10	25	18 51	19 25	34
Mar 2	05 32	−1	06 42	+17	−17 43	18 16	−8	Sep 1	04 00	−44	05 15	−22 +	18 45	19 18	+31
5	05 26	4	06 36	14	17 48	18 21	5	4	04 05	41	05 19	19	18 38	19 11	28
8	05 20	7	06 29	11	17 53	18 25	−2	7	04 10	37	05 23	17	18 32	19 05	25
11	05 13	10	06 23	8	17 58	18 30	+1	10	04 15	34	05 28	14	18 25	18 58	22
14	05 07	13	06 16	5	18 03	18 35	4	13	04 21	31	05 32	11	18 19	18 51	19
17	05 00	−16	06 10	+2	−18 08	18 40	+7	16	04 26	−27	05 37	−8 +	18 12	18 44	+16
20	04 53	19	06 03	−1 +	18 13	18 45	10	19	04 31	24	05 41	5	18 05	18 38	13
23	04 46	22	05 57	4	18 17	18 50	13	22	04 35	21	05 46	−2 +	17 59	18 31	10
26	04 39	26	05 50	7	18 22	18 55	16	25	04 40	18	05 50	+1 −	17 52	18 24	7
29	04 32	29	05 44	10	18 27	18 59	19	28	04 45	15	05 55	3	17 46	18 18	4
Apr 1	04 25	−32	05 37	−12 +	18 31	19 04	+22	Oct 1	04 50	−12	06 00	+6	17 39	18 11	+1
4	04 18	36	05 31	15	18 36	19 09	25	4	04 54	9	06 04	9	17 32	18 05	−1
7	04 11	39	05 24	18	18 41	19 14	28	7	04 59	6	06 09	12	17 26	17 58	4
10	04 04	42	05 18	21	18 46	19 19	31	10	05 04	−3	06 14	15	17 20	17 52	7
13	03 57	46	05 12	24	18 50	19 24	34	13	05 08	0	06 18	18	17 13	17 46	10
16	03 49	−50	05 06	−27 +	18 55	19 29	+37	16	05 13	+3	06 23	+21	17 07	17 40	−13
19	03 42	53	05 00	30	19 00	19 34	40	19	05 17	5	06 28	24	17 01	17 34	15
22	03 35	57	04 54	32	19 04	19 40	43	22	05 22	8	06 33	26	16 56	17 29	18
25	03 28	61	04 48	35	19 09	19 45	46	25	05 27	11	06 38	29	16 50	17 23	21
28	03 21	64	04 42	38	19 14	19 50	49	28	05 31	13	06 43	32	16 44	17 18	23
May 1	03 14	−68	04 37	−41 +	19 18	19 55	+53	31	05 36	+16	06 48	+35	16 39	17 13	−26
4	03 07	72	04 32	43	19 23	20 00	56	Nov 3	05 40	18	06 53	37	16 34	17 08	28
7	03 00	76	04 27	46	19 27	20 05	59	6	05 45	20	06 58	40	16 29	17 04	31
10	02 53	80	04 22	48	19 32	20 10	61	9	05 49	23	07 03	43	16 24	16 59	33
13	02 47	84	04 17	51	19 36	20 15	64	12	05 53	25	07 07	45	16 20	16 55	35
16	02 41	−88	04 13	−53 +	19 40	20 20	+67	15	05 58	+27	07 12	+48	16 16	16 52	−38
19	02 35	92	04 09	55	19 45	20 25	70	18	06 02	29	07 17	50	16 13	16 48	40
22	02 29	95	04 06	57	19 49	20 29	72	21	06 06	31	07 22	52	16 09	16 46	42
25	02 24	99	04 02	59	19 52	20 34	75	24	06 10	32	07 26	54	16 06	16 43	43
28	02 19	102	03 59	61	19 56	20 38	77	27	06 13	34	07 31	56	16 04	16 41	45
31	02 14	−106	03 57	−63 +	19 59	20 42	+79	30	06 17	+35	07 35	+58	16 02	16 39	−47
Jun 3	02 10	109	03 55	64	20 02	20 45	81	Dec 3	06 21	37	07 39	59	16 00	16 38	48
6	02 07	111	03 53	66	20 05	20 48	82	6	06 24	38	07 43	61	15 59	16 37	49
9	02 04	114	03 52	67	20 07	20 51	84	9	06 27	39	07 46	62	15 58	16 36	50
12	02 02	116	03 51	68	20 09	20 53	85	12	06 29	39	07 49	63	15 58	16 36	51
15	02 01	−117	03 50	−68 +	20 11	20 55	+85	15	06 32	+40	07 52	+64	15 58	16 37	−52
18	02 00	118	03 50	69	20 12	20 57	86	18	06 34	40	07 54	64	15 59	16 38	52
21	02 00	118	03 51	69	20 13	20 58	86	21	06 36	40	07 56	64	16 00	16 39	52
24	02 01	118	03 51	69	20 13	20 58	86	24	06 37	40	07 57	64	16 02	16 40	52
27	02 03	117	03 53	68	20 13	20 58	85	27	06 38	40	07 58	64	16 04	16 42	52
30	02 05	−116	03 54	−68 +	20 13	20 57	+84	30	06 39	+40	07 59	+63 −	16 07	16 45	−51
Jul 3	02 08	−114	03 56	−67 +	20 12	20 56	+83	Jan 2	06 39	+39	07 59	+62 −	16 09	16 48	−50

Section 2

TABLE 2 2002 – SUNRISE, SUNSET and TWILIGHTS

Corrections to Sunrise and Sunset

v	30°	35°	40°	45°	50°	52°	54°	56°	58°	60°
	m	m	m	m	m	m	m	m	m	m
0	0	0	0	0	0	0	0	0	0	0
2	- 2	- 2	- 1	- 1	0	0	+ 1	+ 1	+ 2	+ 2
4	4	3	2	1	0	+ 1	1	2	3	4
6	6	5	4	2	0	1	2	3	4	6
8	8	6	5	3	0	1	2	4	6	7
10	-10	- 8	- 6	- 3	0	+ 1	+ 3	+ 5	+ 7	+ 9
12	12	10	7	4	0	2	4	6	8	11
14	14	11	8	4	0	2	4	7	10	13
16	16	13	9	5	0	2	5	8	11	15
18	18	14	10	6	0	3	6	9	12	16
20	-20	-16	-12	- 6	0	+ 3	+6	+10	+14	+18
22	22	18	13	7	0	3	7	11	15	20
24	24	19	14	8	0	4	7	12	16	22
26	26	21	15	8	0	4	8	13	18	24
28	28	22	16	9	0	4	9	14	19	26
30	-30	-24	-17	-10	0	+ 4	+ 9	+15	+21	+28
32	32	26	19	10	0	5	10	16	22	30
34	34	27	20	11	0	5	11	17	24	32
36	36	29	21	11	0	5	11	18	25	34
38	38	31	22	12	0	6	12	19	27	36
40	-40	-32	-23	-13	0	+ 6	+13	+20	+28	+38
42	42	34	24	13	0	6	13	21	30	40
44	44	35	26	14	0	7	14	22	31	42
46	46	37	27	15	0	7	15	23	33	44
48	48	39	28	15	0	7	15	24	35	47
50	-50	-40	-29	-16	0	+ 8	+16	+26	+36	+49
52	52	42	30	17	0	8	17	27	38	51
54	54	44	32	17	0	8	17	28	40	54
56	56	45	33	18	0	9	18	29	42	56
58	58	47	34	19	0	9	19	30	43	59
60	-60	-49	-35	-19	0	+ 9	+20	+32	+45	+62
62	62	50	36	20	0	10	20	33	47	64
64	64	52	38	21	0	10	21	34	49	67
66	66	53	39	22	0	10	22	36	51	70
68	68	55	40	22	0	11	23	37	54	74
70	-70	-57	-41	-23	0	+11	+24	+38	+56	+77

If v is negative reverse the sign of the correction

Corrections to Nautical Twilight

v	30°	35°	40°	45°	50°	52°	54°	56°	58°	60°
	m	m	m	m	m	m	m	m	m	m
+40	-40	-31	-22	-12	0	+ 5	+11	+17	+24	+31
30	30	23	16	9	0	4	8	12	17	22
20	20	15	10	5	0	2	5	7	10	13
+10	-10	- 7	- 5	- 2	0	+ 1	+ 2	+ 3	+ 3	+ 4
0	0	+ 1	+ 1	+ 1	0	- 1	- 1	- 2	- 3	- 4
-10	+10	+ 9	+ 7	+ 4	0	- 2	- 4	- 7	-10	-13
20	20	17	13	7	0	3	7	12	17	23
30	30	25	18	10	0	5	11	17	24	33
40	40	33	24	14	0	7	14	23	33	44
50	50	41	30	17	0	- 8	18	29	42	57
-60	+60	+49	+37	+21	0	-10	-22	-36	-52	-73
70	70	58	43	24	0	12	27	44	65	95
80	80	66	49	28	0	15	32	54	83	-136
90	90	75	56	32	0	17	39	67	-116	TAN
100	100	83	63	37	0	20	47	-88	TAN	TAN
-110	+110	+92	+70	+42	0	-24	-59	TAN	TAN	TAN
-120	+120	+101	+78	+47	0	-29	-81	TAN	TAN	TAN

Corrections to Civil Twilight

v	30°	35°	40°	45°	50°	52°	54°	56°	58°	60°
	m	m	m	m	m	m	m	m	m	m
-50	+50	+40	+28	+15	0	- 7	-15	-24	-33	-44
40	40	32	23	12	0	6	12	18	26	34
30	30	24	17	9	0	4	8	13	19	25
20	20	16	11	6	0	3	5	8	12	15
-10	+10	+ 8	+ 5	+ 3	0	-1	- 2	- 4	- 5	- 7
0	0	0	0	0	0	0	+ 1	+ 1	+ 2	+ 2
+10	-10	- 8	- 6	- 4	0	+ 2	4	6	8	11
20	20	16	12	7	0	3	7	11	15	20
30	30	24	18	10	0	5	10	16	22	30
40	40	33	24	13	0	6	13	21	30	41
+50	-50	-41	-30	-17	0	+ 8	+17	+27	+39	+52
60	60	49	36	20	0	10	21	33	48	66
70	70	57	42	24	0	12	25	41	60	84
80	80	66	49	27	0	14	30	49	74	110
83	83	68	50	29	0	14	32	52	80	121
+86	-86	-71	-52	-30	0	+15	+33	+56	+86	+137

The times on the previous page are the local mean times (LMT) of morning nautical twilight, sunrise, sunset and evening civil twilight for latitude 50°N, together with their variations v. The variations are the differences in minutes of time between the time of the phenomenon for latitudes 50°N and 30°N. The sign on the left-handside of v (between sunrise and sunset) applies to sunrise, and the sign on the right-hand side applies to sunset. The LMT of the phenomenon for latitudes between 30°N and 60°N is found by applying the corrections in the tables above to the tabulated times as follows:

Sunrise and sunset: To determine the LMT of sunrise or sunset, take out the tabulated time and v corresponding to the required date. Using v and latitude as arguments in the table of "Corrections to Sunrise and Sunset", extract the correction. This table is for positive v. If v is minus, reverse the sign of the correction. Apply the correction to the tabulated time.

Nautical twilight: To determine the LMT of morning nautical twilight, follow the same method as for sunrise and sunset, but use the table of "Corrections to Nautical Twilight". This table includes both positive and negative values of v. The entry TAN stands for Twilight All Night, because the Sun does not reach an altitude of −12°.

Civil twilight: To determine the LMT of evening civil twilight follow the same method as for nautical twilight, but use the table of "Corrections to Civil Twilight". This table includes both positive and negative values of v.

Convert LMT to UTC by adding the longitude in time if west (+), or subtracting if east (−).

Examples of the use of these tables are given on page 322

TABLE 3 — 2002 – MOONRISE, MOONSET

Day	JANUARY Rise	v	Set	v	MARCH Rise	v	Set	v	MAY Rise	v	Set	v	JULY Rise	v	Set	v
	h m		h m		h m		h m		h m		h m		h m		h m	
1	18 33	-59	09 51	+62	20 41	+6	08 07	+3	24 43	+75	07 34	-75	23 55	+10	10 42	-17
2	19 56	45	10 27	50	22 04	22	08 28	-13	00 43	75	08 31	75	24 10	-3	11 48	-4
3	21 18	30	10 56	35	23 26	38	08 51	29	01 29	70	09 35	68	00 10	3	12 54	+10
4	22 40	-14	11 20	21	24 45	52	09 16	43	02 04	61	10 43	58	00 26	16	14 01	23
5	23 59	+2	11 41	+6	00 45	52	09 45	56	02 31	50	11 51	46	00 43	29	15 10	37
6	25 17	+17	12 01	-9	01 59	+64	10 20	-66	02 53	+38	12 58	-33	01 03	-41	16 21	+50
7	01 17	17	12 22	23	03 06	71	11 04	72	03 11	25	14 04	20	01 28	54	17 32	62
8	02 35	32	12 45	37	04 03	73	11 56	73	03 27	+12	15 10	-6	02 00	65	18 42	71
9	03 51	46	13 11	51	04 50	70	12 55	68	03 43	0	1616	+7	02 42	73	19 46	75
10	05 05	59	13 43	62	05 27	63	13 59	60	03 58	-13	17 23	21	03 37	75	20 41	72
11	06 15	+68	14 23	-70	05 56	+52	15 06	-49	04 15	-26	18 32	+34	04 45	-70	21 24	+63
12	07 16	72	15 12	72	06 19	41	16 13	36	04 35	39	19 43	48	06 02	60	21 57	50
13	08 08	71	16 10	70	06 39	28	17 19	23	04 58	52	20 54	60	07 24	45	22 24	.35
14	08 49	65	17 13	63	06 56	16	18 25	-10	05 28	63	22 03	70	08 47	29	22 46	20
15	09 21	56	18 20	52	07 12	+4	19 30	+3	06 07	72	23 07	75	10 09	-13	23 06	+4
16	09 47	+44	19 27	-40	07 28	-9	20 36	+16	06 57	-75	24 02	+74	11 30	+4	23 25	-11
17	10 09	33	20 33	28	07 45	22	21 43	29	07 59	72	00 02	74	12 51	20	23 45	26
18	10 27	20	21 39	15	08 03	34	22 52	42	09 11	64	00 47	66	14 11	36	24 08	41
19	10 44	+8	22 44	-2	08 25	47	24 01	55	10 30	51	01 22	55	15 31	51	00 08	41
20	11 00	-4	23 50	+11	08 53	58	00 01	55	11 51	35	01 50	41	16 49	64	00 35	55
21	11 17	-17	24 57	+24	09 28	-68	01 11	+65	13 13	-19	02 13	+26	18 01	+73	01 10	-67
22	11 36	29	00 57	24	10 15	73	02 17	72	14 35	-3	02 34	+10	19 03	76	01 53	74
23	11 58	42	02 07	38	11 14	73	03 16	73	15 58	+14	02 53	-5	19 53	73	02 48	76
24	12 25	54	03 18	51	12 25	66	04 05	68	17 22	31	03 14	21	20 31	64	03 51	71
25	13 01	65	04 31	62	13 46	53	04 45	57	18 46	47	03 37	37	21 01	53	05 00	61
26	13 49	-71	05 42	+70	15 12	-38	05 17	+43	20 08	+62	04 04	-52	21 24	+40	06 10	-49
27	14 51	71	06 46	72	16 39	21	05 44	27	21 24	72	04 38	65	21 44	27	07 20	36
28	16 05	64	07 40	67	18 07	-3	06 07	+11	22 30	76	05 21	74	22 00	15	08 28	22
29	17 28	52	08 22	56	19 33	+14	06 28	-5	23 22	74	06 15	76	22 16	+2	09 35	-9
30	18 55	36	08 55	42	20 59	31	06 50	21	24 03	66	07 17	72	22 31	-11	10 40	+5
31	20 20	-20	09 22	+27	22 23	+47	07 14	-37	00 03	+66	08 25	-63	22 47	-24	11 46	+18

Day	FEBRUARY Rise	v	Set	v	APRIL Rise	v	Set	v	JUNE Rise	v	Set	v	AUGUST Rise	v	Set	v
1	21 44	-3	09 45	+11	23 43	+61	07 41	-52	00 33	+55	09 34	-51	23 05	-36	12 54	+32
2	23 05	+13	10 06	-4	24 56	70	08 15	64	00 57	43	10 43	38	23 27	49	14 03	45
3	24 24	28	10 27	19	00 56	70	08 57	72	01 17	30	11 51	25	23 55	61	15 13	58
4	00 24	28	10 49	34	01 58	75	09 47	75	01 34	17	12 57	-12	24 32	70	16 23	68
5	01 42	43	11 14	47	02 50	73	10 45	72	01 49	+5	14 03	+2	00 32	70	17 30	75
6	02 57	+56	11 45	-59	03 30	+66	11 49	-64	02 05	-8	15 09	+15	01 21	-75	18 29	+75
7	04 07	66	12 22	68	04 01	56	12 56	53	02 21	21	16 17	29	02 23	74	19 17	68
8	05 11	72	13 08	72	04 26	45	14 03	41	02 39	34	17 27	42	03 38	65	19 55	56
9	06 05	72	14 02	71	04 46	33	15 10	28	03 01	47	18 39	56	05 01	52	20 25	41
10	06 48	68	15 03	66	05 03	20	16 16	15	03 28	59	19 51	67	06 26	36	20 49	25
11	07 23	+59	16 08	-56	05 20	+8	17 21	-1	04 04	-69	20 58	+74	07 51	-19	21 10	+9
12	07 51	48	17 15	45	05 35	-5	18 28	+12	04 51	75	21 58	75	09 15	-2	21 30	-6
13	08 13	37	18 22	32	05 51	18	19 35	25	05 50	74	22 47	69	10 38	+15	21 50	22
14	08 32	24	19 28	19	06 09	31	20 43	39	07 01	67	23 25	59	12 00	32	22 12	37
15	08 49	+12	20 33	-6	06 30	43	21 53	52	08 18	55	23 55	45	13 21	47	22 38	52
16	09 06	0	21 39	+7	06 55	-55	23 03	+63	09 39	-40	24 19	+30	14 40	+61	23 10	-64
17	09 22	-13	21 45	20	07 27	66	24 10	72	11 00	24	00 19	30	15 53	71	23 50	73
18	09 39	25	23 52	33	08 09	73	00 10	72	12 21	-8	00 40	+15	16 57	76	24 41	76
19	09 59	38	25 02	46	09 03	74	01 11	75	13 41	+8	01 00	0	17 50	75	00 41	76
20	10 24	50	01 02	46	10 09	70	02 03	72	15 03	25	01 19	-16	18 32	68	01 41	75
21	10 54	-61	02 12	+58	11 24	-59	02 45	+50	16 24	+41	01 40	-31	19 04	+57	02 47	-65
22	11 35	69	03 22	68	12 45	45	03 18	50	17 45	56	02 04	46	19 28	45	03 57	54
23	12 28	73	04 28	72	14 09	29	03 45	35	19 03	68	02 34	60	19 49	32	05 07	40
24	13 35	69	05 26	71	15 34	-12	04 08	19	20 13	75	03 13	70	20 06	19	06 16	27
25	14 54	59	06 13	63	17 00	+5	04 29	+3	21 12	75	04 01	76	20 21	+6	07 23	-13
26	16 20	-45	06 50	+50	18 25	+22	04 50	-13	21 58	+70	05 00	-75	20 36	-7	08 29	0
27	17 48	-28	07 20	+35	19 51	39	05 12	29	22 33	60	06 06	68	20 52	19	09 35	+14
28	19 15	-11	07 45	+19	21 15	55	05 38	45	23 00	48	07 16	57	21 09	32	10 41	27
29					22 35	67	06 08	59	23 21	35	08 27	44	21 29	46	11 49	40
30					23 45	+74	06 47	-70	23 39	+23	09 35	-30	21 53	57	12 58	53
31													22 25	-67	14 07	+65

TABLE 3 *(continued)*   **2002 – MOONRISE, MOONSET**

	SEPTEMBER				NOVEMBER			
Day	Rise	v	Set	v	Rise	v	Set	v
	h m		h m		h m		h m	
1	23 07	-75	15 14	+73	01 44	-27	15 35	+18
2	24 02	76	16 15	76	03 08	-10	15 55	+1
3	00 02	76	17 08	73	04 35	+8	16 15	-16
4	01 11	71	17 50	63	06 02	26	16 36	33
5	02 30	59	18 23	49	07 31	44	17 02	49
6	03 55	-44	18 49	+33	08 59	+60	17 34	-64
7	05 22	27	19 12	+17	10 22	73	18 16	75
8	06 49	-9	19 32	0	11 33	79	19 08	79
9	08 16	+9	19 53	-16	12 30	78	20 12	76
10	09 41	26	20 14	32	13 13	70	21 21	67
11	11 06	+43	20 39	-48	13 45	+59	22 33	-55
12	12 28	58	21 09	62	14 09	46	23 44	41
13	13 45	70	21 47	72	14 28	33	24 52	27
14	14 53	76	22 35	77	14 44	20	00 52	27
15	15 50	77	23 33	76	14 59	+6	02 00	-14
16	16 34	+71	24 38	-69	15 13	-7	03 06	0
17	17 08	61	00 38	69	15 28	20	04 12	+14
18	17 34	49	01 47	58	15 44	33	05 19	28
19	17 55	36	02 56	45	16 04	46	06 28	41
20	18 13	23	04 05	31	16 28	58	07 37	55
21	18 28	+10	05 13	-18	16 59	-69	08 47	+67
22	18 43	-2	06 19	-4	17 39	76	09 53	75
23	18 58	15	07 25	+9	18 31	78	10 53	78
24	19 14	28	08 32	23	19 34	74	11 43	75
25	19 32	41	09 39	36	20 46	64	12 23	67
26	19 55	-54	10 47	+50	22 04	-50	12 54	+54
27	20 23	65	11 56	62	23 24	34	13 19	40
28	21 00	73	13 03	72	24 45	17	13 40	24
29	21 48	77	14 06	77	00 45	17	13 59	+9
30	22 49	75	15 00	76	02 07	1	14 18	-8

	OCTOBER				DECEMBER			
1	24 02	-66	15 45	+69	03 31	+17	14 37	-24
2	00 02	66	16 20	57	04 57	34	15 00	41
3	01 23	52	16 49	42	06 25	52	15 28	56
4	02 48	36	17 12	26	07 51	67	16 04	70
5	04 15	18	17 33	+9	09 09	77	16 51	78
6	05 42	-1	17 53	-8	10 15	+79	17 51	-79
7	07 10	+18	18 14	25	11 06	74	19 00	72
8	08 38	35	18 38	41	11 44	64	20 13	61
9	10 05	52	19 06	57	12 12	52	21 27	47
10	11 29	66	19 42	69	12 33	38	22 38	33
11	12 43	+76	20 27	-77	12 51	+25	23 46	-19
12	13 46	78	21 23	78	13 06	+11	24 53	5
13	14 35	74	22 27	73	13 20	-2	00 53	-5
14	15 12	65	23 36	62	13 35	15	01 59	+9
15	15 40	54	24 46	50	13 50	28	03 06	22
16	16 02	+41	00 46	-50	14 08	-41	04 14	+36
17	16 20	28	01 56	36	14 30	54	05 23	50
18	16 36	15	03 03	22	14 59	65	06 33	62
19	16 51	+2	04 10	-9	15 36	74	07 42	73
20	17 05	-11	05 16	+5	16 24	78	08 46	78
21	17 21	-24	06 22	+19	17 25	-76	09 40	+77
22	17 38	37	07 30	32	18 36	67	10 24	70
23	17 59	50	08 38	46	19 53	54	10 58	58
24	18 25	62	09 47	59	21 13	39	11 25	44
25	18 58	72	10 56	70	22 33	23	11 46	29
26	19 41	-77	12 00	+77	23 53	-6	12 05	+13
27	20 37	77	12 56	78	25 13	+11	12 23	-2
28	21 44	71	13 43	73	01 13	11	12 42	18
29	22 45	59	14 21	63	02 35	28	13 02	34
30	24 20	44	14 50	49	03 59	44	13 26	50
31	00 20	-44	15 15	+34	05 23	+60	13 57	-64

Corrections to Moonrise and Moonset

N Lat	30°	35°	40°	45°	50°	52°	54°	56°	58°	60°
v	m	m	m	m	m	m	m	m	m	m
0	0	0	0	0	0	0	0	0	0	0
2	-2	-2	-1	-1	0	0	+1	+1	+1	+2
4	4	3	2	1	0	+1	1	2	3	4
6	6	5	3	2	0	1	2	3	4	5
8	8	6	5	3	0	1	2	4	5	7
10	-10	-8	-6	-3	0	+1	+3	+5	+7	+9
12	12	10	7	4	0	2	4	6	8	11
14	14	11	8	4	0	2	4	7	9	12
16	16	13	9	5	0	2	5	8	11	14
18	18	14	10	6	0	3	5	9	12	16
20	-20	-16	-12	-6	0	+3	+6	+10	+14	+18
22	22	18	13	7	0	3	7	11	15	20
24	24	19	14	8	0	3	7	12	16	22
26	26	21	15	8	0	4	8	13	18	23
28	28	22	16	9	0	4	9	14	19	25
30	-30	-24	-17	-9	0	+4	+9	+15	+21	+27
32	32	26	18	10	0	5	10	16	22	29
34	34	27	20	11	0	5	10	17	23	31
36	36	29	21	11	0	5	11	18	25	33
38	38	31	22	12	0	6	12	19	26	35
40	-40	-32	-23	-13	0	+6	+12	+20	+28	+37
42	42	34	24	13	0	6	13	21	30	39
44	44	35	26	14	0	7	14	22	31	42
46	46	37	27	15	0	7	15	23	33	44
48	48	39	28	15	0	7	15	24	34	46
50	-50	-40	-29	-16	0	+8	+16	+25	+36	+48
52	52	42	30	17	0	8	17	26	38	51
54	54	44	32	17	0	8	17	28	39	53
56	56	45	33	18	0	9	18	29	41	56
58	58	47	34	19	0	9	19	30	43	58
60	-60	-48	-35	-19	0	+9	+20	+31	+45	+61
62	62	50	36	20	0	10	20	33	47	64
64	64	52	38	21	0	10	21	34	49	67
66	66	53	39	22	0	10	22	35	51	70
68	68	55	40	22	0	11	23	37	53	73
70	-70	-57	-41	-23	0	+11	+24	+38	+55	+76
72	72	58	43	24	0	11	24	40	58	80
74	74	60	44	24	0	12	25	41	60	83
76	76	62	45	25	0	12	26	43	62	87
78	78	63	46	26	0	13	27	44	65	91
80	-80	-65	-48	-27	0	+13	+28	+46	+68	+96
82	82	67	49	27	0	13	29	48	70	101
84	84	68	50	28	0	14	30	49	73	106
86	86	70	51	29	0	14	31	51	77	112
88	88	72	53	30	0	15	32	53	80	119
90	-90	-73	-54	-30	0	+15	+33	+55	+84	+127

If *v* is minus reverse the sign of the correction

The daily times of moonrise and moonset given above are the local mean times (LMT) of the phenomena for latitude 50°N, together with their variations *v*. The variations are the differences in minutes between the time of the phenomenon for latitudes 50N° and 30°N. The LMT of the phenomenon for latitudes between 30°N and 60°N is found as follows:

Take out the tabulated time and v corresponding to the required date. Using *v* and latitude as arguments in the table above of "Corrections to Moonrise and Moonset", extract the correction. This table is for positive *v*. If *v* is minus, reverse the sign of the correction. Apply the correction to the tabulated time.

Add a small extra correction of 1m for every 7° of longitude if west. Subtract if east.

Convert LMT to UTC by adding the longitude in time if west, or subtracting if east.

Examples of the use of these tables are given on page 322

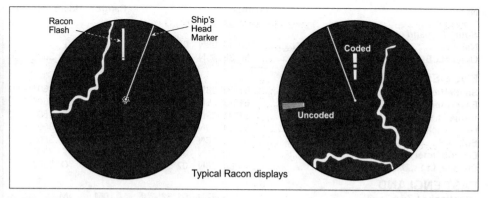

Typical Racon displays

RACONS (RADAR BEACONS)

Description

A Racon is a transponder beacon which, when triggered by a transmission from a vessel's radar, sends back a distinctive signal which appears on the vessel's radar display. Racons are often fitted to major light-vessels, lighthouses and buoys. They are shown on charts by a magenta circle and the word Racon.

In most cases the Racon flash on the radar display is a line extending radially outward from a point slightly beyond the actual position of the Racon, due to the slight delay in the response of the Racon apparatus. Thus the distance to the spot of the Racon flash is a little more than the vessels real distance from the Racon. Some Racons give a flash composed of a Morse identification signal, often with a tail to it, the length of the tail depending on the number of Morse characters.

The typical maximum range of a Racon is 10M, but may be as much as 25M. In practice, picking up a Racon at greater ranges depends on the power and elevation of both the Racon and the boat's radar. With abnormal radio propagation, a spurious Racon flash may be seen at much greater distances than the beacon's normal range, appearing at any random position along the correct bearing on the display. Only rely on a Racon flash if it appears to be consistent, and the boat is believed to be within its quoted range. At short range a Racon sometimes causes unwanted interference on the radar display, and this may be

reduced by adjusting the rain clutter control on the radar receiver.

Radar beacons within the coverage area of this Almanac are listed below.

Details given in the table are:

a.   The name of the beacon.

b.   Latitude and longitude.

c.   Approximate range in nautical miles (M). This to some extent depends on the effective range of the yacht's radar set.

c.   The Morse identification signal. Racons coded 'D' are used to mark new dangers such as wrecks.

d.   The sector within which signals may be received, if not 360°.

Most Racons respond throughout 360°. A few respond only within an angular sector, bearings quoted always being towards the beacon, clockwise from 000° to 359°.

The majority of Racons sweep the frequency range of marine 3cm (X-band) radar emissions. The older type of Racon (swept frequency) take 30 to 90 seconds to sweep the band.

The newer type of Racon (frequency agile) responds immediately to both 3cm and 10cm (S-band) emissions. In order that the Racon response should not obscure wanted echoes, the agile response is switched 'on' and 'off' at a predetermined rate to suit the installation.

Section 4

RACONS – EUROPE (WGS 84 DATUM)

Name	Position	Range	Ident	Sector
SOUTH ENGLAND				
Bishop Rock Lt	49°52'·33N 06°26'·68W	18M	T	254°-215°
Seven Stones Lt F	50°03'·62N 06°04'·34W	15M	O	360°
Wolf Rock Lt	49°56'·72N 05°48'·58W	10M	T	360°
Eddystone Lt	50°10'·85N 04°15'·94W	10M	T	360°
Bridge Lt By	50°39'·63N 01°36'·88W	10M	T	
West Bramble Lt By	50°47'·20N 01°18'·65W	3M	T	360°

Name	Position		Range	Ident	Sector
South England contd					
Nab Lt	50°40'·08N	00°57'·16W	10M	T	360°
Owers Lt By	50°38'·63N	00°41'·22W	10M	O	360°

ENGLISH CHANNEL

Name	Position		Range	Ident	Sector
Sandettié Lt F	51°09'·36N	01°47'·12E	10M	T	360°
East Goodwin Lt F	51°13'·25N	01°36'·38E	10M	T	360°
Varne Lt V	51°01'·29N	01°23'·90E	10M	T	360°
Greenwich Lt V	50°24'·55N	00°00'·14W	10M	M	360°
EC2 Lt By	50°12'·16N	01°12'·57W	10M	T	360°
East Channel Lt By	49°58'·71N	02°28'·95W	10M	T	360°
Channel Lt F	49°54'·36N	02°53'·77W	15M	O	360°

EAST ENGLAND

Name	Position		Range	Ident	Sector
Inter Bank Lt By	51°16'·47N	01°52'·23E	10M	M	
North East Goodwin Lt By	51°20'·30N	01°34'·18E	10M	M	360°
Dover Strait TSS Foxtrot 3 Lt V	51°23'·85N	02°00'·51E	10M	T	360
Thames Reach Lt By No. 1	51°29'·45N	00°52'·57E	10M	T	360
Thames Reach Lt By No. 7	51°30'·10N	00°37'·05E	10M	T	360°
Thames Barrier Pier No. 4 E end*	51°29'·90N	00°02'·24E		T	
Thames Barrier Pier No. 4 W end*	51°29'·89N	00°02'·18E		T	
Thames Barrier Pier No. 5 E end*	51°29'·86N	00°02'·25E		T	
Thames Barrier Pier No. 5 W end*	51°29'·86N	00°02'·19E		T	
Thames Barrier Pier No. 6 E end*	51°29'·82N	00°02'·25E		T	
Thames Barrier Pier No. 6 W end*	51°29'·82N	00°02'19E		T	
Thames Barrier Pier No. 7 E end*	51°29'·78N	00°02'·26E		T	
Thames Barrier Pier No. 7 W end*	51°29'·78N	00°02'·19E		T	
Thames Barrier Pier No. 8 E end*	51°29'·74N	00°02'·26E		T	
Thames Barrier Pier No. 8 W end*	51°29'·74N	00°02'·20E		T	

* Operational only when visibility in Woolwich Reach is 1M or less, or for test purposes or training. Information about Racon operation is included in routine broadcasts on VHF Ch 14.

Name	Position		Range	Ident	Sector
Outer Tongue Lt By	51°30'·69N	01°26'·40E	10M	T	360°
Barrow Lt By No. 3	51°42'·02N	01°20'·24E	10M	M	360°
South Galloper Lt By	51°43'·98N	01°56'·49E	10M	T	360
Sunk Lt F	51°51'·03N	01°34'·89E	10M	T	360°
Harwich Channel No 1 Lt By	51°56'·14N	01°27'·05E	10M	T	360°
Outer Gabbard Lt By	51°57'·83N	02°04'·19E	10M	O	360
North Shipwash Lt By	52°01'·73N	01°38'·27E	10M	M	360°
Orfordness Lt	52°05'·03N	01°34'·44E	18M	T	360°
Cross Sand Lt By	52°37'·03N	01°59'·14E	10M	T	360°
Winterton Old Lt	52°42'·77N	01°41'·70E	10M	T	360°
Smiths Knoll Lt By	52°43'·52N	02°17'·88E	10M	T	360
Newarp Lt V	52°48'·37N	01°56'·69E	10M	O	360°
Cromer Lt	52°55'·48N	01°18'·99E	25M	O	360°
North Haisbro Lt By	53°00'·22N	01°32'·29E	10M	T	360°
North Well Lt By	53°03'·02N	00°27'·90E	10M	T	360°
Dudgeon Lt By	53°16'·62N	01°16'·89E	10M	O	360°
Anglia Field Platform A48/19-B	53°22'·04N	01°38'·97E	15M	Q	360°
Inner Dowsing Lt V	53°19'·52N	00°33'·85E	10M	T	360°
Dowsing Platform B1D	53°33'·68N	00°52'·63E	10M	T	360°
Spurn Lt F	53°33'·56N	00°14'·20E	5M	M	360°
Humber Lt By	53°39'·06N	00°19'·98E	7M	T	360°
Tees Fairway By	54°40'·94N	01°06'·47W		B	360°

EAST AND NORTH SCOTLAND

Name	Position		Range	Ident	Sector
St Abb's Head Lt	55°54'·96N	02°08'·29W	18M	T	360°
Inchkeith Fairway By	56°03'·49N	03°00'·10W	5M	T	360°
Firth of Forth N Channel Lt By	56°02'·80N	03°10'·96W	5M	T	360°
Bell Rock Lt	56°26'·05N	02°23'·07W	18M	M	360
Abertay Lt By	56°27'·39N	02°40'·36W	8M	T	360°

Name	Position		Range	Ident	Sector
Scurdie Ness Lt	56°42'·10N	02°26'·24W	14-16M	T	360
Girdle Ness Lt	57°08'·34N	02°02'·91W	25M	G	360°
Aberdeen Fairway By	57°09'·31N	02°01'·94W	7M	T	360°
Buchan Ness Lt	57°28'·23N	01°46'·51W	14-16M	O	360°
Rattray Head Lt	57°36'·61N	01°49'·03W	15M	M	360°
Kessock Bridge Centre Mark	57°29'·97N	04°13'·81W	6M	K	
Cromarty Firth Fairway By	57°39'·96N	03°54'·19W	5M	M	360°
Tarbat Ness Lt	57°51'·88N	03°46'·76W	14-16M	T	360
Alba Oil Field, Platform Chevron Alba	58°03'·52N	01°04'·88E		C	360°
Saltire Oil Field Platform Saltire Alpha	58°25'·01N	00°19'·93E		Z	360°
Piper Oilfield, Platform Piper Bravo	58°27'·66N	00°14'·98E		N	360°
Duncansby Head Lt	58°38'·65N	03°01'·58W	16M	T	360°
Lother Rock Lt	58°43'·80N	02°58'·68W	10M	M	360°
North Ronaldsay Lt	59°23'·37N	02°23'·03W	14-17M	T	360°
Rumble Rock Bn	60°28'·17N	01°07'·25W	8-10M	O	360°
Gruney Island Lt	60°39'·15N	01°18'·16W	14M	T	360
Ve Skerries Lt	60°22'·36N	01°48'·79W	15M	T	360°
Foinaven Oil Field 204/24	60°18'·90N	04°16'·60W		X	360°
Sule Skerry Lt	59°05'·09N	04°24'·38W	20M	T	360°

WEST SCOTLAND

Name	Position		Range	Ident	Sector
Eilean Glas Lt	57°51'·40N	06°38'·55W	16-18M	T	360°
Ardivachar Pt	57°22'·92N	07°25'·54W	16M	T	360°
Carrach Rocks Lt By	57°17'·20N	05°45'·30W	5M	T	360°
Hyskeir Lt	56°58'·14N	06°40'·87W	14-17M	T	360°
Castlebay South By	56°56'·09N	07°27'·21W	7M	T	360°
Bo Vich Chuan Lt By	56°56'·15N	07°23'·31W	5M	M	360°
Skerryvore Lt	56°19'·36N	07°06'·88W	18M	M	360°
Dubh Sgeir Lt	56°14'·76N	05°40'·20W	5M	M	360

WEST ENGLAND

Name	Position		Range	Ident	Sector
Point of Ayre Lt	54°24'·94N	04°22'·13W	13-15M	M	360°
Halfway Shoal Lt Bn	54°01'·46N	03°11'·88W	10M	B	360°
Lune Deep Lt By	53°55'·81N	03°11'·08W	10M	B	360°
Bar Lt F	53°32'·02N	03°20'·98W	10M	T	360°
West Constable Lt By	53°23'·15N	03°49'·25W	10M	M	
The Skerries Lt	53°25'·27N	04°36'·50W	25M	T	360°
South Bishop Lt	51°51'·14N	05°24'·74W	10M	O	
The Smalls Lt	51°43'·28N	05°40'·19W	25M	T	360°
Watwick Pt Rear Ldg Lt Bn	51°41'·78N	05°09'·25W		Y	On trial
West Blockhouse Front Middle Ldg Lt Bn	51°41'·31N	05°09'·56W		Q	010°-230°
S. Gowan Lt By	51°31'·93N	04°59'·77W	10M	T	360°
West Helwick Lt By W.HWK	51°31'·40N	04°23'·65W	10M	T	360°
Swansea Bar Lt By W. Scar	51°28'·31N	03°55'·57W	10M	T	360°
Cabenda Lt By	51°33'·36N	03°52'·23W		C	
English & Welsh Grounds Lt By	51°27'·13N	02°59'·94W	7M	T	360°
Second Severn Crossing Centre Lt SW	51°34'·45N	02°42'·03W		O	
Breaksea Lt F	51°19'·88N	03°19'·08W	10M	T	360°

NORTHERN IRELAND

Name	Position		Range	Ident	Sector
Hellyhunter Lt By	54°00'·35N	06°02'·06W	5-14M	K	
South Rock Lt F	54°24'·49N	05°22'·02W	13M	T	360°
Mew Island Lt	54°41'·91N	05°30'·81W	14M	O	360°
Belfast Fairway Lt By	54°41'·70N	05°46'·23N		G	
East Maiden Lt	54°55'·73N	05°43'·67W	11-21M	M	360°
Rathlin East Lt	55°18'·06N	06°10'·30W	15-27M	G	089°-003°

IRELAND

Name	Position		Range	Ident	Sector
Bull Rock Lt	51°35'·51N	10°18'·07W	16-27M	N	360°
Fastnet Lt	51°23'·35N	09°36'·19W	18M	G	360°
Cork Lt By	51°42'·92N	08°15'·60W	7M	T	360°

Name	Position		Range	Ident	Sector
Ireland contd					
Hook Head Lt	52°07'·32N	06°55'·85W	10M	K	237°-177°
Coningbeg Lt F	52°02'·40N	06°39'·49W	13M	M	360°
Tuskar Rock Lt	52°12'·19N	06°12'·46W	18M	T	360°
Arklow Lanby	52°39'·52N	05°58'·16W	10M	O	360°
Codling Lanby	53°03'·02N	05°40'·76W	10M	G	360°
Dublin Bay Lt By	53°19'·92N	06°04'·64W		M	
Kish Bank Lt	53°18'·70N	05°55'·44W	15M	T	360°

DENMARK

Name	Position		Range	Ident	Sector
Skagens Rev, Route 'T' Lt By No.1	57°47'·08N	10°45'·93E	10M	T	360°
Skagen Lt	57°44'·11N	10°37'·75E	20M	G	360°
Skagens Rev, Route 'T' Lt By 1A	57°43'·42N	10°53'·51E		N	
Thyboron Approach Lt By	56°42'·54N	08°08'·69E	10M	T	360°
Dan Oil Field Platform DUC-DF-C	55°28'·79N	05°06'·45E		U	
Dagmar Oil Field Platform 'A'	55°34'·48N	04°36'·95E		U	360°
Rolf Oil Field Platform 'A'	55°36'·26N	04°29'·47E		U	
Valdema Oil Field Platform 'A'	55°50'·05N	04°33'·65E		U	
Svend Gas Plaform 'A'	56°10'·66N	04°10'·67E		U	
Harald Gas Field Platform West 'B'	56°20'·59N	04°16'·36E		U	
Gradyb Approach Lt By	55°24'·63N	08°11'·59E	10M	G	360°

GERMANY

Name	Position		Range	Ident	Sector
Westerems Lt By	53°36'·88N	06°19'·38E	8M	T	360°
Borkumriff Lt By	53°47'·44N	06°22'·05E	8M	T	360°
GW/EMS Lt F	54°09'·96N	06°20'·72E	8M	T	360°
Platform GNSC-H-7	54°30'·47N	06°02'·07E		D	
Platform GNSC-B-11	55°27'·72N	04°33'·16E		D	
German Bight Lt V	54°10'·72N	07°27'·53E	8M	T	360°
Weser Lt By	53°54'·25N	07°50'·00E	8M	T	360
Weser 1/Jade 2 Lt By	53°52'·12N	07°47'·35E	8M	T	360
Elbe Lt By	53°59'·95N	08°06'·49E	8M	T	360°

NETHERLANDS

Name	Position		Range	Ident	Sector
Keeten B Lt By	51°36'·35N	03°58'·05E		K	360°
Zuid Vlije Lt By ZV11/SRK 4	51°38'·18N	04°14'·38E		K	360°
Noord Hinder Lt By NHR-SE	51°45'·42N	02°39'·92E	10M	N	360°
Noord Hinder Lt By	52°00'·04N	02°51'·03E		T	
Noord Hinder Noord NHR-N Lt By	52°10'·82N	03°04'·69E		K	
Schouwenbank Lt By	51°44'·94N	03°14'·31E	10M	O	360°
Goeree Lt	51°55'·42N	03°40'·03E	12-15M	T	360°
Maas Centre Lt By (MC)	52°01'·12N	03°53'·46E	10M	M	360°
Scheveningen Approach R&W Lt By	52°09'·00N	04°05'·50E		Z	On trial
Scheveningen Approach Red Lt By	52°10'·80N	04°07'·15E		Q	On trial
Rijn Field Platform P15B	52°18'·37N	03°46'·60E	12-15M	B	030°-270°
IJmuiden (IJM) Lt By	52°28'·44N	04°23'·78E	10M	Y	360°
Horizon P9-6 Platform	52°33'·13N	03°44'·45E		Q	
Helm Veld A Platform	52°52·28N	04°08'·42E		T	
Schulpengat Fairway Lt By SG	52°52'·90N	04°37'·90E		Z	
DW Route Lt By BR/S	52°54'·89N	03°18'·06E		G	
Logger Platform	53°00'·80N	04°12'·91E	12-15M	X	060°-270°
NAM Field Platform K14-FA-1	53°16'·14N	03°37'·58E		7	360°
Vlieland Lanby VL-CENTER	53°26'·93N	04°39'·85E	12-15M	C	360°
Wintershall Platform L8-G	53°34'·85N	04°36'·12E	12-15M	G	000°-340°
Botney Ground BG/S Lt By	53°35'·72N	03°00'·90E		T	
Placid Field Platform PL-K9C-PA	53°39'·14N	03°52'·37E		8	360°
Markham Field Platform J6-A	53°49'·37N	02°56'·65E		M	000°-180°
West Friesland Platform L2-FA-1	53°57'·55N	04°29'·70E		9	
Western Mud Hole, North Platform K4-A	53°45'·05N	03°18'·58E		T	
DW Route Lt By FR/A	54°00'·28N	04°21'·30E		T	
Elf Petroland Platform F15-A	54°12'·91N	04°49'·65E		U	360°

Name	Position		Range	Ident	Sector
DW Route Lt By EF	54°03'·27N	04°59'·70E		T	
DW Route Lt By EF/B	54°06'·59N	05°39'·85E		M	
DW Route Lt By EF/C	54°08'·24N	05°59'·89E		O	
NAM Field Platform F2-A Hanze	54°56'·69N	04°34'·12E		D	
NAM Field Platform F3-OLT	54°51'·19N	04°43'·38E		D	360°

BELGIUM

Name	Position		Range	Ident	Sector
West Hinder Lt	51°23'·31N	02°26'·27E		W	
West Hinder Route Lt By KB	51°21'·03N	02°42'·83E		K	
Wandelaar Lt MOW 0	51°23'·73N	03°02'·83E	10M	S	360°
Bol Van Heist MOW 3	51°23'·37N	03°11'·89E	10M	H	360°

NORTH FRANCE

Name	Position		Range	Ident	Sector
Dyck (Dunkerque Approach) Lt By	51°02'·98N	01°51'·76E		B	360°
Vergoyer Lt By N	50°39'·64N	01°22'·18E	5-8M	C	360°
Bassurelle Lt By	50°32'·74N	00°57'·69E	5-8M	B	360°
Antifer Approach Lt By A5	49°45'·77N	00°17'·50W		K	360°
Le Havre LHA Lanby	49°31'·38N	00°09'·88W	8-10M		360°

CHANNEL ISLANDS

Name	Position		Range	Ident	Sector
Casquets Lt	49°43'·32N	02°22'·62W	25M	T	360°
Platte Fougère Lt	49°30'·82N	02°29'·17W		P	
St Helier Demi de Pas Lt	49°09'·00N	02°06'·15W	10M	T	360°

WEST FRANCE

Name	Position		Range	Ident	Sector
Ouessant NE Lt By	48°45'·78N	05°11'·76W	20M	B	360°
Ouessant SW Lanby	48°31'·15N	05°49'·24W	10M	M	360°
Pointe de Créac'h Lt (Ile Ouessant)	48°27'·55N	05°07'·76W	20M	C	030°-248°
Chausée de Sein Lt By	48°03'·75N	05°07'·79W	10M	O	360°
S. Nazaire Lt By SN1	47°00'·07N	02°39'·84W	3-8M	Z	360°
S. Nazaire La Couronnée	47°07'·59N	02°20'·05W	3-5M		360°
BXA Lanby	45°37'·53N	01°28'·69W		B	360°

NORTH SPAIN

Name	Position		Range	Ident	Sector
Puerto de Pasajes Pilot Look-out	43°20'·10N	01°55'·47W	20M	K	
Punta Barracomuturra Lt Ondarroa	43°19'·53N	02°24'·94W	12M	X	360°
Bilbao Digue de Punta de Lucero Lt	42°22'·67N	03°05'·04W	20M	X	360°
Punta Rabiosa Front Ldg Lt	43°27'·51N	03°46'·43W	10M	K	360°
Punta Mera Front Lt	43°23'·08N	08°21'·17W	18M	M	020°-196
Punta Fiaiteira Lt	43°20'·59N	08°22'·25W	11-21M	X	
Cabo Villano Lt	43°09'·60N	09°12'·70W	35M	M	360°
Toriñana Monte Xastas	43°01'·74N	09°16'·52W	35M	T	360°
Cabo Finisterre Lt	42°52'·93N	09°16'·29W	35M	O	360°
Cap Corrubedo Lt	42°34'·59N	09°05'·39W	8-17M	K	360°
Isla Rua Lt	42°32'·96N	08°56'·38W	10-20M	G	211°-121°
Cabo Estay Front Leg Lt	42°11'·12N	08°48'·89W	22M	B	

PORTUGAL

Name	Position		Range	Ident	Sector
Esteiro Lt	38°41'·95N	09°15'·98W	15M	Q	
Canal do Barreiro Lt By No. 13B IS	38°39'·30N	09°05'·83W	15M	Q	360°
Porto de Setúbal Bn No. 2	38°27'·21N	08°58'·45W	15M	B	360°

SOUTH-WEST SPAIN

Name	Position		Range	Ident	Sector
Huelva (Dique)	37°06'·47N	06°49'·94W	12M	K	360°
Broa de Sanlucar Lt By No. 1	36°45'·82N	06°26'·95W	10M	M	360°
Bajo Salmedina Lt	36°44'·27N	06°28'·64W	10M	M	
Tarifa Lt	36°00'·06N	05°36'·58W	20M	C	360°

Section 4

NAVAL EXERCISE AREAS

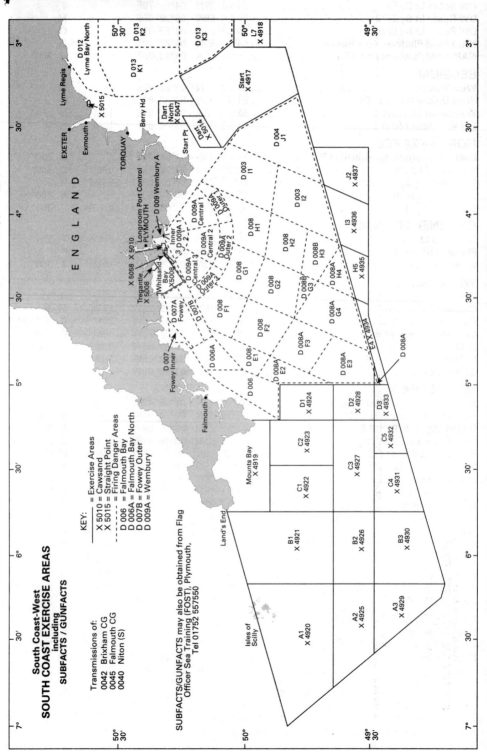

South Coast-West
SOUTH COAST EXERCISE AREAS
including
SUBFACTS / GUNFACTS

Transmissions of:
0042 Brixham CG
0045 Falmouth CG
0040 Niton (S)

KEY:
—— = Exercise Areas
X 5010 = Cawsand
X 5015 = Straight Point
- - - = Firing Danger Areas
D 006 = Falmouth Bay
D 006A = Falmouth Bay North
D 007B = Fowey Outer
D 009A = Wembury

SUBFACTS/GUNFACTS may also be obtained from Flag Officer Sea Training (FOST), Plymouth, Tel 01752 557550

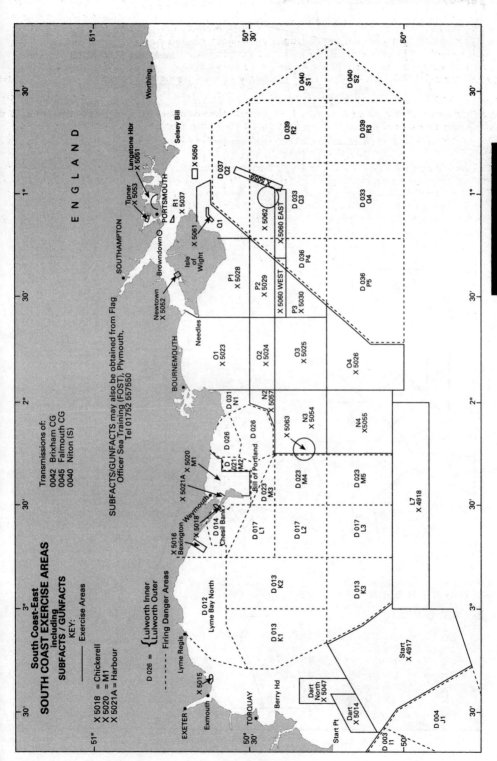

South Coast-East
SOUTH COAST EXERCISE AREAS
including
SUBFACTS / GUNFACTS

KEY:
—— Exercise Areas

X 5018 = Chickerell
X 5020 = M1
X 5021A = Harbour

D 026 = { Lulworth Inner
          Lulworth Outer
—————— Firing Danger Areas

Transmissions of:
0042 Brixham CG
0045 Falmouth CG
0040 Niton (S)

SUBFACTS/GUNFACTS may also be obtained from Flag
Officer Sea Training (FOST), Plymouth.
Tel 01752 557550

ENGLAND

Worthing
Selsey Bill
Langstone Hbr X 5061
Tipner X 5053
PORTSMOUTH
R1 X 5037
Browndown
Q1
X 5061
Newtown X 5062
Isle of Wight
SOUTHAMPTON
Needles
BOURNEMOUTH
Lyme Regis
Lyme Bay North
Berry Hd
TORQUAY
Exmouth
EXETER
Start Pt

D 040 S1
D 040 S2
D 039 R2
D 039 R3
D 037 Q2
X 5050
X 5062
D 033 Q3
D 033 Q4
X 5060 EAST
X 5052
D 036 P4
P1 X 5028
P2 X 5029
X 5060 WEST
D 036 P5
P3 X 5030
O1 X 5023
O2 X 5024
O3 X 5025
O4 X 5026
D 031 N1
N2 X 5057
N3 X 5054
X 5063
N4 X5055
D 026
D 021 M2
D 026
D 023 M2
D 023 M3
Bill of Portland
D 023 M4
D 023 M5
L7 X 4918
X 5016
Bexington
X 5018
X 5021A
X 5020 M1
D 014 Chesil Bank
Weymouth
D 017 L1
D 017 L2
D 017 L3
D 012
D 013 K2
D 013 K3
D 013 K1
Start X 4917
Dart North X 5047
Dart X 5014
D 004 J1
D 003 I1
X 5015

333

Naval Exercise Areas contd

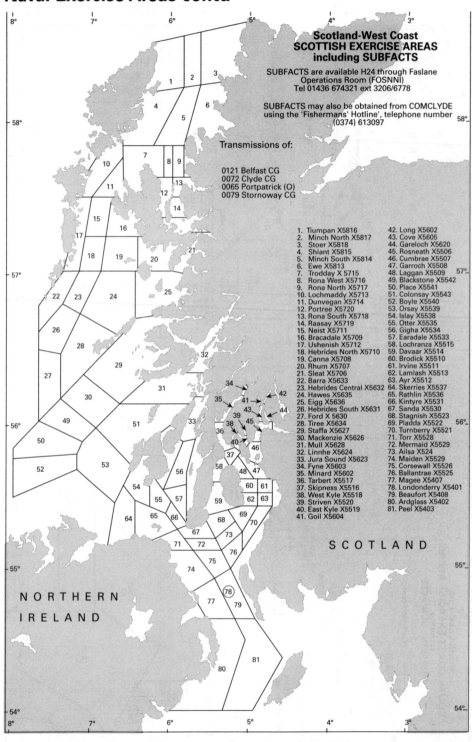

Scotland-West Coast
SCOTTISH EXERCISE AREAS
including SUBFACTS

SUBFACTS are available H24 through Faslane
Operations Room (FOSNNI)
Tel 01436 674321 ext 3206/6778

SUBFACTS may also be obtained from COMCLYDE
using the 'Fishermans' Hotline', telephone number
(0374) 613097

Transmissions of:

0121 Belfast CG
0072 Clyde CG
0065 Portpatrick (O)
0079 Stornoway CG

1. Tiumpan X5816	42. Long X5602
2. Minch North X5817	43. Cove X5605
3. Stoer X5818	44. Gareloch X5620
4. Shiant X5815	45. Rosneath X5506
5. Minch South X5814	46. Cumbrae X5507
6. Ewe X5813	47. Garroch X5508
7. Troddday X 5715	48. Laggan X5509
8. Rona West X5716	49. Blackstone X5542
9. Rona North X5717	50. Place X5541
10. Lochmaddy X5713	51. Colonsay X5543
11. Dunvegan X5714	52. Boyle X5540
12. Portree X5720	53. Orsay X5539
13. Rona South X5718	54. Islay X5538
14. Raasay X5719	55. Otter X5535
15. Neist X5711	56. Gigha X5534
16. Bracadale X5709	57. Earadale X5533
17. Ushenish X5712	58. Lochranza X5515
18. Hebrides North X5710	59. Davaar X5514
19. Canna X5708	60. Brodick X5510
20. Rhum X5707	61. Irvine X5511
21. Sleat X5706	62. Lamlash X5513
22. Barra X5633	63. Ayr X5512
23. Hebrides Central X5632	64. Skerries X5537
24. Hawes X5635	65. Rathlin X5536
25. Eigg X5636	66. Kintyre X5531
26. Hebrides South X5631	67. Sanda X5530
27. Ford X 5630	68. Stagnish X5523
28. Tiree X5634	69. Pladda X5522
29. Staffa X5627	70. Turnberry X5521
30. Mackenzie X5626	71. Torr X5528
31. Mull X5628	72. Mermaid X5529
32. Linnhe X5624	73. Ailsa X524
33. Jura Sound X5623	74. Maiden X5529
34. Fyne X5603	75. Corsewall X5526
35. Minard X5602	76. Ballantrae X5525
36. Tarbert X5517	77. Magee X5407
37. Skipness X5516	78. Londonderry X5401
38. West Kyle X5518	79. Beaufort X5408
39. Striven X5520	80. Ardglass X5402
40. East Kyle X5519	81. Peel X5403
41. Goil X5604	

SCOTLAND

NORTHERN
IRELAND

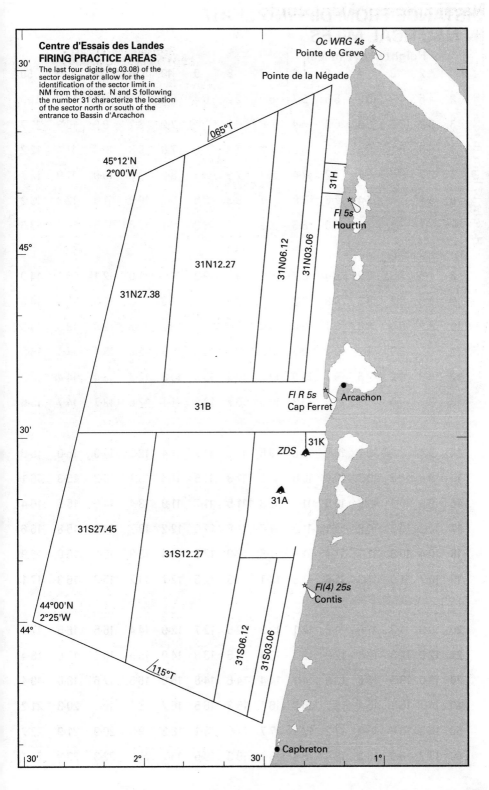

Centre d'Essais des Landes
FIRING PRACTICE AREAS
The last four digits (eg 03.08) of the
sector designator allow for the
identification of the sector limit in
NM from the coast. N and S following
the number 31 characterize the location
of the sector north or south of the
entrance to Bassin d'Arcachon

Oc WRG 4s
Pointe de Grave

Pointe de la Négade

065°T

45°12'N
2°00'W

30'

45°

31H

Fl 5s
Hourtin

31N12.27

31N06.12

31N03.06

31N27.38

31B

Fl R 5s
Cap Ferret

Arcachon

30'

ZDS

31K

31A

31S27.45

31S12.27

Fl(4) 25s
Contis

44°00'N
2°25'W

44°

31S06.12

31S03.06

115°T

● Capbreton

30'

2°

30'

1°

DISTANCE FROM DIPPING LIGHT
IN NAUTICAL MILES

Height of eye in feet

Height of light in metres	2	3	4	5	6	7	8	9	10	20	30	40	50
2	4·6	4·9	5·2	5·5	5·7	6·0	6·2	6·4	6·6	8·1	9·2	10·2	11·0
3	5·2	5·6	5·9	6·2	6·4	6·6	6·8	7·0	7·2	8·7	9·9	10·8	11·7
4	5·8	6·1	6·4	6·7	6·9	7·2	7·4	7·6	7·8	9·3	10·4	11·4	12·2
5	6·3	6·6	6·9	7·2	7·4	7·7	7·9	8·1	8·3	9·8	10·9	11·9	12·7
6	6·7	7·1	7·4	7·6	7·9	8·1	8·3	8·5	8·7	10·2	11·3	12·3	13·2
7	7·1	7·5	7·8	8·0	8·3	8·5	8·7	8·9	9·1	10·6	11·8	12·7	13·6
8	7·5	7·8	8·2	8·4	8·7	8·9	9·1	9·3	9·5	11·0	12·1	13·1	14·0
9	7·8	8·2	8·5	8·8	9·0	9·2	9·5	9·7	9·8	11·3	12·5	13·5	14·3
10	8·2	8·5	8·8	9·1	9·4	9·6	9·8	10·0	10·2	11·7	12·8	13·8	14·6
11	8·5	8·9	9·2	9·4	9·7	9·9	10·1	10·3	10·5	12·0	13·1	14·1	15·0
12	8·8	9·2	9·5	9·7	10·0	10·2	10·4	10·6	10·8	12·3	13·4	14·4	15·3
13	9·1	9·5	9·8	10·0	10·3	10·5	10·7	10·9	11·1	12·6	13·7	14·7	15·6
14	9·4	9·7	10·0	10·3	10·6	10·8	11·0	11·2	11·4	12·9	14·0	15·0	15·8
15	9·6	10·0	10·3	10·6	10·8	11·1	11·3	11·5	11·6	13·1	14·3	15·3	16·1
16	9·9	10·3	10·6	10·8	11·1	11·3	11·5	11·7	11·9	13·4	14·6	15·5	16·4
17	10·2	10·5	10·8	11·1	11·3	11·6	11·8	12·0	12·2	13·7	14·8	15·8	16·6
18	10·4	10·8	11·1	11·4	11·6	11·8	12·0	12·2	12·4	13·9	15·1	16·0	16·9
19	10·7	11·0	11·3	11·6	11·8	12·1	12·3	12·5	12·7	14·2	15·3	16·3	17·1
20	10·9	11·3	11·6	11·8	12·1	12·3	12·5	12·7	12·9	14·4	15·5	16·5	17·3
25	12·0	12·3	12·6	12·9	13·2	13·4	13·6	13·8	14·0	15·5	16·6	17·6	18·4
30	13·0	13·3	13·6	13·9	14·1	14·4	14·6	14·8	15·0	16·5	17·6	18·6	19·4
40	14·7	15·1	15·4	15·7	15·9	16·1	16·3	16·5	16·7	18·2	19·4	20·3	21·2
50	16·3	16·6	16·9	17·2	17·4	17·7	17·9	18·1	18·3	19·8	20·9	21·9	22·7
60	17·7	18·0	18·3	18·6	18·8	19·1	19·3	19·5	19·7	21·2	22·3	23·3	24·1

SECTION 3 - WEATHER

CONTENTS

Section 3

SOURCES OF WEATHER INFORMATION

RADIO BROADCASTING

BBC Radio 4 Shipping forecast

BBC Radio 4 broadcasts shipping forecasts at:

0048 LT[1]	on LW, MW, FM
0535 LT[1]	on LW, MW, FM
1201 LT	on LW only
1754 LT	on LW only
0542 Sun LT[2]	on LW, MW, FM
0556 Sat LT[3]	on LW, MW, FM

[1] Includes weather reports from coastal stations

[2] Long range forecast for mariners

[3] Leisure forecast for UK and parts of Europe

The following frequencies are used:

LW	198 kHz
FM	
England:	92·4-94·6 MHz
Scotland:	92·4-96·1 MHz
	103·5-104·9 MHz
Wales:	92·8-96·0 MHz and
	103·5-104·9 MHz
N Ireland	93·2-96·0 MHz
	103·5-104·9 MHz
Channel Islands:	92·4, 94·6 MHz
MW	
Tyneside:	603 kHz
London and N Ireland:	720 kHz
Redruth:	756 kHz
Enniskillen & Plymouth:	774 kHz;
Aberdeen:	1449 kHz
Carlisle:	1485 kHz

Contents of shipping forecast

The bulletin contains a summary of gale warnings in force; a general synopsis of weather patterns for the next 24 hours with changes expected during that period; and a forecast for each sea area for the next 24 hours, giving wind direction and force, weather and visibility. Sea area **Trafalgar** is included only in the 0048 forecast. Gale warnings are also broadcast at the earliest juncture in Radio 4 programmes after receipt, as well as after the next news bulletin.

The 0048 and 0535 forecast is followed by weather reports from coastal stations. The stations used, and identification letters are shown on the forecast area chart. These reports of actual weather include wind direction and Beaufort force, present weather, visibility, and (if available) sea-level pressure and tendency.

The 1201 and 1754 LT forecasts do not include reports from coastal stations.

On Sundays only, at 0542 LT, a seven day planning outlook is broadcast which includes weather patterns likely to affect UK waters. On Saturdays only, at 0556 LT, a three minutes 'topical leisure' forecast is broadcast.

Shipping forecasts cover large sea areas, and rarely include the detailed variations that may occur near land. The Inshore waters forecast (see below) can be more helpful to yachtsmen on coastal passages.

Inshore waters forecast, BBC Radio 4

A forecast for inshore waters (up to 12M offshore) around the UK and N Ireland, valid until 1800 LT, is broadcast after the 0535 LT and 0048 LT forecasts. It includes a general synopsis, forecasts of wind direction and force, visibility and weather for stretches of inshore waters referenced to well-known places and headlands, clockwise from Berwick-upon-Tweed.

Reports of actual weather at the following stations are broadcast only after the 0048 LT forecast: Boulmer, Bridlington, Sheerness, St Catherine's Point auto, Scilly auto, Milford Haven, Aberporth, Valley, Liverpool (Crosby), Ronaldsway, Larne, Machrihanish auto, Greenock MRCC, Stornoway, Lerwick, Wick auto, Aberdeen and Leuchars.

BBC general (land) forecasts

Land area forecasts may include an outlook period up to 48 hours beyond the shipping forecast, more details of frontal systems and weather along the coasts. The most comprehensive land area forecasts are broadcast by BBC Radio 4.

Land area forecasts – Wind strength

Wind descriptions used in land forecasts, with their Beaufort scale equivalents, are:

Calm:	0	Fresh:	5
Light:	1–3	Strong:	6–7
Moderate:	4	Gale:	8

Land area forecasts – Visibility

The following definitions apply to land forecasts:

Mist:	Visibility between 2000m and 1000m
Fog:	Visibility less than 1000m
Dense fog:	Less than 50m

Weather systems

To obtain the best value from weather forecasts and reports, it is desirable to have some basic understanding of the characteristics and behaviour of different weather which can be expected from the passage of any particular type of weather system.

MISCELLANEOUS SOURCES

HM Coastguard

If requested the following MRCC/MRSCs may be prepared to supply reports of the present weather in their immediate vicinity. Such information only applies to reports of the present weather and do not include forecasts or information concerning other regions.

Falmouth:	☎	01326 317575	📠	01326 318342
Brixham:	☎	01803 882704	📠	01803 882780
Portland:	☎	01305 760439	📠	01305 760452
Solent:	☎	02392 552100	📠	02392 551763
Dover:	☎	01304 210008	📠	01304 202137
Thames:	☎	01255 675518	📠	01255 675249
Yarmouth:	☎	01493 851338	📠	01493 852307
Humber:	☎	01262 672317	📠	01262 606915
Forth:	☎	01333 450666	📠	01333 450725
Aberdeen:	☎	01224 592334	📠	01224 575920
Shetland:	☎	01595 692976	📠	01595 694810
Stornoway:	☎	01851 702013	📠	01851 704387
Clyde:	☎	01475 729988	📠	01475 786955
Belfast:	☎	02891 463933	📠	02891 465886
Liverpool:	☎	0151 931 3341	📠	0151 931 3347
Holyhead:	☎	01407 762051	📠	01497 764373
Milford Haven:	☎	01646 690909	📠	01646 692176
Swansea:	☎	01792 366534	📠	01792 369005

Internet (MetWEB)

A range of meteorological information is available over the Internet including MetFAX marine services, 2 and 3 to 5 day inshore forecasts, shipping forecasts, gale warnings; coastal reports charts and satellite images. Visit the Meteorological Office site at:

www.met-office.gov.uk

More information is available from the MetWEB Helpline ☎ 0845 300 0300 or e-mail:

sales@meto.gov.uk

Press forecasts

The interval between the time of issue and the time at which they are available next day make press forecasts of only limited value to yachtsmen. However, the better papers include a synoptic chart which, in the absence of any other chart, can help to interpret the shipping forecast.

Television forecasts

Some TV forecasts show a synoptic chart which, with the satellite pictures, can be a useful guide to the weather situation.

In the UK Ceefax (BBC) gives the weather index on page 400. inshore waters forecasts on p.409 and 5 day forecasts on p.405. Teletext (ITN) has the weather index on page 151, shipping forecasts on page 157 and inshore waters forecasts on page 158.

Antiope is the equivalent French system. In some remote areas abroad a TV forecast in a bar, cafe or even shop window may be the best or only source of weather information.

Weather Centres and other MET Offices

United Kingdom

London	020 7696 0573
	020 7405 4356
Birmingham	0121 717 0572
Norwich	01603 763898
Newcastle	0191 232 3808
Aberdeen Airport	01224 210575
Kirkwall Airport, Orkney	01856 873802
Sella Ness, Shetland	01806 242069
Glasgow	0141 248 7272
Manchester	0161 4771017
Leeds	0113 2440186
Cardiff	029 2022 5746
Bristol	0117 927 6265
Belfast International Airport	028 9031 2353
Jersey	01534 745550

Republic of Ireland

Central Forecast Office, Dublin (H24)	
	(01) 424655
Dublin Airport Met	(01) 379900 ext 4531
Cork Airport Met (0900–2000)	(021) 965974
Shannon Airport Met (H24)	(061) 61333

Section 3

MAP OF UK SHIPPING FORECAST AREAS

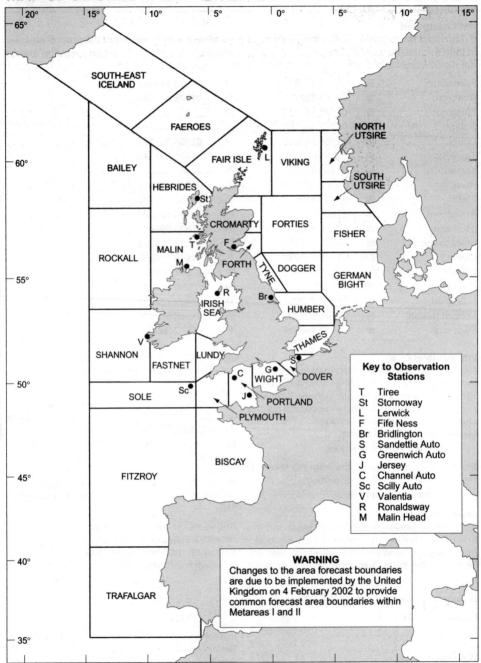

Key to Observation Stations

T	Tiree
St	Stornoway
L	Lerwick
F	Fife Ness
Br	Bridlington
S	Sandettie Auto
G	Greenwich Auto
J	Jersey
C	Channel Auto
Sc	Scilly Auto
V	Valentia
R	Ronaldsway
M	Malin Head

WARNING

Changes to the area forecast boundaries are due to be implemented by the United Kingdom on 4 February 2002 to provide common forecast area boundaries within Metareas I and II

SHIPPING FORECAST RECORD Time/Day/Date ....

GENERAL SYNOPSIS

at .... UTC/BST

System position	Present position at	Movement	Forecast	

Gales	SEA AREA FORECAST	Wind (At first)	(Later)	Weather	Visibility
	VIKING				
	NORTH UTSIRE				
	SOUTH UTSIRE				
	FORTIES				
	CROMARTY				
	FORTH				
	TYNE				
	DOGGER				
	FISHER				
	GERMAN BIGHT				
	HUMBER				
	THAMES				
	DOVER				
	WIGHT				
	PORTLAND				
	PLYMOUTH				
	BISCAY				
	FITZROY				
	TRAFALGAR				
	SOLE				
	LUNDY				
	FASTNET				
	IRISH SEA				
	SHANNON				
	ROCKALL				
	MALIN				
	HEBRIDES				
	BAILEY				
	FAIR ISLE				
	FAEROES				
	S E ICELAND				

COASTAL REPORTS BST at .... UTC	Wind Direction	Force	Weather	Visibility	Pressure	Change	COASTAL REPORTS	Wind Direction	Force	Weather	Visibility	Pressure	Change
Tiree (T)							Greenwich Lt V (G)						
Stornoway (St)							Jersey (J)						
Lerwick (L)							Channel auto (C)						
Fife Ness (F)							Scilly auto (Sc)						
Bridlington (Br)							Valentia (V)						
Sandettie auto (S)							Ronaldsway (R)						
							Malin Head (M)						

IRELAND

Irish Coast Radio Stations

Weather bulletins for the Irish Sea and waters up to 30M off the Irish coast are broadcast on VHF at 0103 0403 0703 1003 1303 1603 1903 2203 (LT) after an initial announcement on Ch 16. Bulletins include gale warnings, synopsis and a 24-hour forecast. The stations and channels are:

Malin Head	Ch 23	**Glen Head**	Ch 24	**Belmullet**	Ch 83
Clifden	Ch 26	**Shannon**	Ch 28	**Valentia**	Ch 24
Bantry	Ch 23	**Cork**	Ch 26	**Mine Head**	Ch 83
Rosslare	Ch 23	**Wicklow Head**	Ch 87	**Dublin**	Ch 83

Valentia Radio broadcasts on MF 1752 kHz forecasts for sea areas Shannon and Fastnet at 0833, 2033 UTC, and on request. Broadcasts are given 1h earlier when DST is in force.

Gale warnings are broadcast on above VHF channels on receipt and repeated at 0033 0633 1233 1833 (LT), after an initial announcement on Ch 16. They are also broadcast by Valentia Radio on 1752 kHz at the end of the next silence period after receipt and at 0303, 0903, 1503 and 2103 (UTC) after an initial announcement on 2182 kHz. Broadcasts are given 1h earlier when DST is in force.

Radio Telefís Éireann (RTE Radio 1) Broadcasting coastal forecasts and gale warnings

RTE Radio 1 on 567 kHz broadcasts a synopsis, detailed forecast and current gale warnings for Irish coastal waters up to 30M offshore and the Irish Sea, a 24 hour outlook, and coastal station reports at 0602, 1253, 1823 (Sat, Sun and Public Holidays) and 1824 (Mon-Fri) 2355 UTC. Broadcasts are given 1 hour earlier when DST is in force.

The main transmitters and FM frequencies are:

East Coast Radio: Kippure 94·9 MHz, Bray Head 96·2 MHz, Wicklow Head 102·9 MHz, Arklow 104·4 MHz.

At: Every H+06 (0700-1800 LT) after the news bulletin. Broadcasts a general forecast, storm warnings and wind strength for area from Dublin Bay to Arklow Head.

South East Radio: Mount Leinster 95·6 MHz, Gorey 96·2 MHz, Wexford 96·4 MHz.

At: 0712 LT (Mon-Fri) and every H+30 (0700-1800 LT) H24 after commercial break. Broadcasts a detailed general forecast and synopsis for coastal waters, including storm warnings if adverse weather conditions are forecast.

WLR FM: Faha Ring 95·1 MHz, Carrickpherish 97·5 MHz.

At every H+03 and 1315 1815 LT broadcasts a general forecast, gale warnings, wind strength for area from Youghal to Kilmore Quay. Tidal information included from Jun-Sep.

Radio Kerry: Mullaghanish 97·0 MHz, Knockanure 97·6 MHz, Kilkieveragh 96·2MHz, Tralee 96·2 MHz.

At: 0004 0104 0704 0804 0835 0910 1004 1107 1204 1330 1404 1507 1607 1704 1740 1904 2204 2104 and 2304, and at 0755 and 1155 LT. Broadcasts a general forecast, synopsis, gale warnings and wind strength for the coastal area from Cork to Shannon.

At: 0755 and 1155 LT a fcst is broadcast including synopsis, visibility, sea state and wind strength for sea areas Fastnet and Shannon. Three Rock 88·5 MHz, Kippure 89·1 MHz, Mount Leinster 89·6 MHz, Mullaghanish 90·0 MHz, Maghera 88·8 MHz, Truskmore 88·2 MHz, Holywell Hill 89·2 MHz, Clermont Carn 95·2 MHz. MW .

Storm warnings

Gale warnings are broadcast by RTE Radio 1 on 567 kHz at the first programme juncture after receipt and with news bulletins; also by RTE 2FM from Athlone 612 kHz, Dublin 1278 kHz and Cork 1278 kHz.

Telephone and Fax

The latest Sea area forecast and gale warnings can be obtained through Weatherdial ☎ on 1550 123 855.

The same information, plus isobaric, swell and wave charts are available by Fax 📠 on 1570 131 838 (H24).

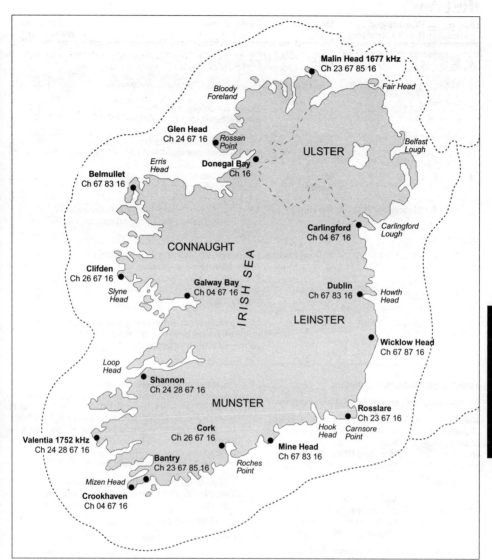

Malin Head 1677 kHz
Ch 23 67 85 16

Fair Head

Bloody
Foreland

Glen Head
Ch 24 67 16

Rossan
Point

ULSTER

Belfast
Lough

Erris
Head

Donegal Bay
Ch 16

Belmullet
Ch 67 83 16

Carlingford
Ch 04 67 16

Carlingford
Lough

CONNAUGHT

IRISH SEA

Clifden
Ch 26 67 16

Slyne
Head

Galway Bay
Ch 04 67 16

Dublin
Ch 67 83 16

Howth
Head

LEINSTER

Wicklow Head
Ch 67 87 16

Loop
Head

Shannon
Ch 24 28 67 16

MUNSTER

Rosslare
Ch 23 67 16

Cork
Ch 26 67 16

Hook
Head

Carnsore
Point

Valentia 1752 kHz
Ch 24 28 67 16

Bantry
Ch 23 67 85 16

Roches
Point

Mine Head
Ch 67 83 16

Mizen Head

Crookhaven
Ch 04 67 16

Section 3

Above chart shows Provinces, headlands sea areas and coastal stations referred to in weather broadcasts. Forecasts for coastal waters cover areas within 30M of the shore. The Irish Sea covers the open waters of the area shown.

Beaufort scale

Force	Wind speed (knots)	(km/h)	(m/sec)	Description	State of sea	Probable wave ht(m)
0	0–1	0–2	0–0·5	Calm	Like a mirror	0
1	1–3	2–6	0·5–1·5	Light air	Ripples like scales are formed	0
2	4–6	7–11	2–3	Light breeze	Small wavelets, still short but more pronounced, not breaking	0·1
3	7–10	13–19	4–5	Gentle breeze	Large wavelets, crests begin to break; a few white horses	0·4
4	11–16	20–30	6–8	Moderate breeze	Small waves growing longer; fairly frequent white horses	1
5	17–21	31–39	8–11	Fresh breeze	Moderate waves, taking more pronounced form; many white horses, perhaps some spray	2
6	22–27	41–50	11–14	Strong breeze	Large waves forming; white foam crests more extensive; probably some spray	3
7	28–33	52–61	14–17	Near gale	Sea heaps up; white foam from breaking waves begins to blow in streaks	4
8	34–40	63–74	17–21	Gale	Moderately high waves of greater length; edge of crests break into spindrift; foam blown in well-marked streaks	5·5

Terms used in weather bulletins

a. Speed of movement of pressure systems

Slowly: Moving at less than 15 knots
Steadily: Moving at 15 to 25 knots
Rather quickly: Moving at 25 to 35 knots
Rapidly: Moving at 35 to 45 knots
Very rapidly: Moving at more than 45 knots

b. Visibility

Good: More than 5 miles
Moderate: 2 – 5 miles
Poor: 1000 metres – 2 miles
Fog: Less than 1000 metres

c. Barometric pressure changes (tendency)
Rising or falling slowly: Pressure change of 0·1 to 1·5 millibars in the preceding 3 hours.

Rising or falling: Pressure change of 1·6 to 3·5 millibars in the preceding 3 hours.

Rising or falling quickly: Pressure change of 3·6 to 6 millibars in the preceding 3 hours.

Rising or falling very rapidly: Pressure change of more than 6 millibars in the preceding 3 hours.

Now rising (or falling): Pressure has been falling (rising) or steady in the preceding 3 hours, but at the time of observation was definitely rising (falling).

d. Gale warnings

A **'Gale'** warning means that winds of at least force 8 (34-40 knots) or gusts reaching 43-51 knots are expected somewhere within the area, but not necessarily over the whole area. **'Severe Gale'** means winds of at least force 9 (41-47 knots) or gusts reaching 52-60 knots. **'Storm'** means winds of force 10 (48-55 knots) or gusts of 61-68 knots. **'Violent Storm'** means winds of force 11 (56-63 kn) or gusts of 69 kn or more; and **'Hurricane Force'** means winds of force 12 (64 knots or more).

Gale warnings remain in force until amended or cancelled ('gales now ceased'). If a gale persists for more than 24 hours the warning is re-issued.

e. Timing of gale warnings

Imminent   Within 6 hrs of time of issue

Soon   Within 6 – 12 hrs of time of issue

Later   More than 12 hrs from time of issue

f. Strong wind warnings

Issued, if possible 6 hrs in advance, when winds F6 or more are expected up to 5M offshore; valid for 12 hrs.

g. Wind

Wind direction: Indicates the direction from which the wind is blowing.

Winds becoming cyclonic: Indicates that there will be considerable changes in wind direction across the path of a depression within the forecast area.

Veering: The changing of the wind in a clockwise direction, i.e. SW to W.

Backing: The changing of the wind in an anti-clockwise direction, i.e. W to SW.

DENMARK

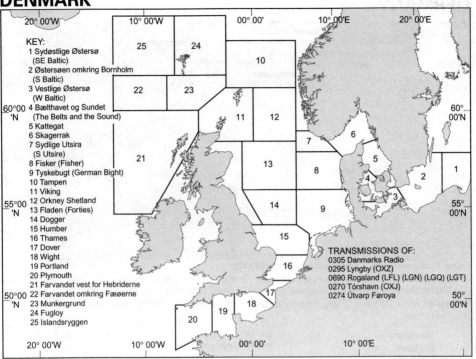

KEY:
1 Sydøstlige Østersø (SE Baltic)
2 Østersøen omkring Bornholm (S Baltic)
3 Vestlige Østersø (W Baltic)
4 Bælthavet og Sundet (The Belts and the Sound)
5 Kattegat
6 Skagerrak
7 Sydlige Utsira (S Utsire)
8 Fisker (Fisher)
9 Tyskebugt (German Bight)
10 Tampen
11 Viking
12 Orkney Shetland
13 Fladen (Forties)
14 Dogger
15 Humber
16 Thames
17 Dover
18 Wight
19 Portland
20 Plymouth
21 Farvandet vest for Hebriderne
22 Farvandet omkring Fæøerne
23 Munkergrund
24 Fugloy
25 Islandsryggen

TRANSMISSIONS OF:
0305 Danmarks Radio
0295 Lyngby (OXZ)
0690 Rogaland (LFL) (LGN) (LGQ) (LGT)
0270 Tórshavn (OXJ)
0274 Útvarp Føroya

The following CRS broadcast in Danish and English gale warnings, synopsis and forecasts on the VHF and MF frequencies shown below.

Blåvand	Ch 23, 1734 kHz	On request
Bovbjerg	Ch 02	On request
Hansholm	Ch 01	On request
Hirtshals	Ch 66	On request
Skagen	Ch 04, 1758 kHz	On request
Als	Ch 07	On request

Radio broadcasts – Danmarks Radio (National Radio)

Broadcasts in Danish storm warnings, synopsis and 12h or 18h forecasts for all Danish Areas (Areas 16 to 20 from 1 Jan to 30 Apr only) and Jylland, Øerne and Bornholm, plus reports from coastal stations at 0445, 0745 1045 1645 and 2145 UTC. Stations and frequencies are:

Kalundborg	243 kHz
West Jutland	92·9 MHz
Kalundborg	1062 kHz
SW Jutland	92·3 MHz
North Jutland	96·6 MHz
South Jutland	97·2 MHz

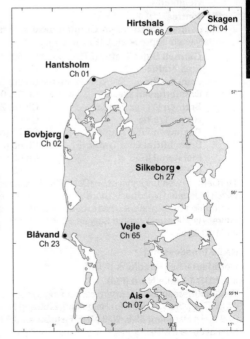

GERMANY

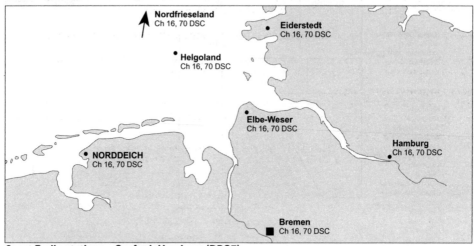

Coast Radio stations – Seefunk Hamburg (DP07)

Seefunk broadcast a weather report, synopsis, 12h forecast and outlook for a further 12h, in German, for Areas B10-B12, N9-N10 and Eastern Boddenwässer at 0645, 0845, 1145, 1545 and 1845 UTC. Broadcasts are given 1 hr earlier when DST is in force. Broadcasts are first announced on Ch 16 before being broadcast on the channel below:

Hamburg	53°33'N 09°58'E	Ch 16 27
Borkum	53°35'N 06°40'E	Ch 16 28
Elber-Weser	53°50'N 08°39'E	Ch 16 01 24
Helgoland	54°11'N 07°53'E	Ch 16 86

Traffic Centres

Traffic Centres broadcast in German local storm warnings, weather messages, visibility and ice reports (when appropriate). (E) = in **English** and German.

German Bight Traffic (E)	Ch 80	Every H+00
Ems Traffic	Ch 15, 18, 20, 21	Every H+50
Jade Traffic	Ch 20, 63	Every H+10
Bremerhaven Weser	Ch 02, 04, 05, 07, 21, 22, 82	Every H+20
Bremen Weser Traffic	Ch 19, 78, 81	Every H+30
Hunte Traffic	Ch 63	Every H+30
Cuxhaven Elbe Traffic (E)	Ch 71 (outer Elbe)	Every H+35
Brunsbüttel Elbe Traffic (E)	Ch 68 (lower Elbe)	Every H+05
Kiel Kanal II	Ch 02 (For East going traffic)	H+15 and H+45
KielKanal III	Ch 03 (For West going traffic)	Every H+20 and H+50

The German weather service (*Der Deutsche Wetterdienst*) provides weather information through a databank which is updated twice daily; more often for weather reports and textual forecasts. SEEWIS (Marine weather information system) allows data to be accessed by telephone/modem and fed into an onboard computer. The address is: German Weather Service, PO Box 30 11 90, 20304 Hamburg. ☎ + 49 (0) 40 31 90 88 11; 🖷 + 49 (0) 40 31 90 88 03.

Radio broadcasting

Norddeutscher Rundfunk (NDR)

a. NDR 1 Welle Nord (FM)

Weather messages in German, comprising synopsis, 12hrs forecast and 24 hrs outlook, are broadcast at 0730 LT (1 May – 30 Sept) for Helgoland, Elbe and North Frisian coast, by the following stations: **Helgoland** 88·9 MHz; **Hamburg** 89·5, 90·3 MHz; **Flensburg** 89·6 MHz; **Heide** 90·5 MHz; **Sylt** 90·9 MHz; Kiel 91·3 MHz; Cuxhaven 98·4 MHz.

b. NDR 4 Hamburg (MW)

Weather messages in German, comprising synopsis, 12hrs forecast and outlook for a further 12 hrs, are broadcast at 0005, 0830 and 2200 LT on 702 & 972 kHz for Areas B10-B14 and N9–N12.

Radio Bremen (RB1) (MW and FM)

Weather messages in German, comprising synopsis, 12hrs forecast and 24 hrs outlook, are broadcast at 0930 and 2300 LT for Areas B11 and N10, by the following stations:

Hansawelle 936, 6190 kHz; **Bremerhaven** 89·3, 92·1, 95·4 100·8 MHz; **Bremen** 88·3, 93·8, 96·7, 101·2 MHz.

Also, about 0930 LT, wind forecast for Weser-Ems area; and synopsis and forecast for next 12hrs in German Bight.

Deutschlandfunk (Köln) (MW)

Weather messages in German, comprising synopsis, 12hrs forecast and 24 hrs outlook, are broadcast at 0105, 0640 and 1105 LT for Areas N9-N12, B6-B14 on 1269 kHz.

Deutschland Radio (Berlin) (LW)

Weather messages in German, comprising synopsis, 12hrs forecast and outlook for a further 12 hrs, are broadcast at 0105, 0640 and 1105 LT for Areas N9-N12, on 177 kHz and 6005 kHz. Gale warnings in German follow the news.

Offenbach (Main) (HF)

The following **English** language radiotelex broadcasts are made on 4583 kHz, 7646 kHz and 10100·8 kHz:

0505 UTC	Wx report for the North Sea and Baltic, 12h fcst and outlook for further 12h
0521 UTC	Wx report, synopsis, 2 day fcst for the Pentlands, Shetlands, Færøer.
1034 UTC	Wx report, synopsis, 2 day fcst for the North Sea.
1059 UTC	Wx report for next few days, synopsis and 2 day fcst for the North Sea and Baltic Sea.
1122 UTC	Wx report, synopsis, 2 dat fcst for the Pentlands, Shetlands, Færøer.
1136 UTC	Wx report, synopsis and 5 day fcst for the Baltic Sea.
1202 UTC	Wx report for the next few days, synopsis, 5 day fcst for the North Sea and Baltic Sea.
1438 UTC	Coastal Wx report, synopsis, 2 day fcst for Nordcap to West Gibraltar
1740 UTC	Synopsis, 12 hrs forecast, 24 hrs outlook for Viking, Forties, Dogger, Fisher and German Bight including station reports for the North Sea and Baltic
2048 UTC	Wx report, synopsis, 2 day fcst for the North Sea.
2113 UTC	Wx report, synopsis, 2 day fcst for the North Sea
2136 UTC	Wx report, synopsis, 2 dat fcst for the Pentlands, Shetlands, Færøer.

In addition to the English language broadcasts there are radio telex broadcasts in German at different times on 147·3 kHz, 11039 kHz and 14467·3 kHz. Details are listed in NP283(1) The ALRS Vol. 3(1).

German Telephone Forecasts

Similar to the British Marinecall; from 1 April – 30 Sept, forecast and outlook are available by dialling 01901160 plus two digits for the following areas:

– 40 = Inland pleasure craft
– 45 = North Frisian Islands and Helgoland
– 46 = R Elbe from Elbe 1/Cuxhaven to Hamburg
– 47 = Weser Estuary and Jade Bay
– 48 = East Frisian Islands and Ems Estuary
– 53 = For inland pleasure craft
– 54 = Denmark
– 55 = Netherlands, IJsselmeer, Schelde, Maas

For year round weather synopsis, forecast and outlook, dial 0190 1169 plus two digits as follows:
– 20 = General information North Sea and Baltic
– 22 = German Bight and SW North Sea – 21 =
– 31 = 5 day bulletin for North Sea and Baltic**

**Containing an outlook and forecasts of wind, sea state, air and water temperature, plus warnings of fog, thunderstorms etc.

The latest wind and storm warnings for individual areas of the North Sea coasts are obtainable by dialling +49·40·3·19·66·28 (H24). If no warning is in operation, a wind forecast for the German Bight is given.

Marine weather is available all year round by telephone as follows (Not available from outside Germany):

01·90·11·69·21 North Sea & Baltic Sea
01·90·11·69·22 German Bight and SW North Sea
01·90·11·69·31 Marineweather reports for North Sea and Baltic Sea
01·90·11·69·59 Current wind strength for the North Sea and Baltic Sea coasts

Section 3

NETHERLANDS

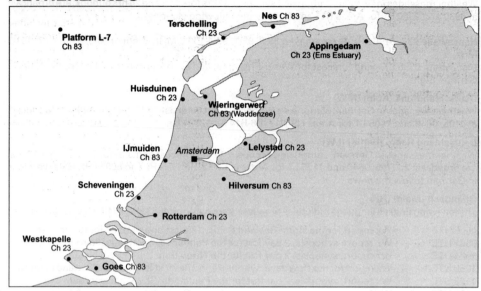

Netherlands Coastguard (IJmuiden)

a. VHF weather broadcasts

Weather messages are broadcast in **English** and Dutch at 0805, 1305, 2305 LT on the VHF channels shown below. Messages include a forecast for Netherlands coastal waters up to 30M offshore (including IJsselmeer). Forecasts are broadcast are announced through DSC 2187·5 kHz and VHF Ch 70 before being broadcast on the scheduled frequency or channel. Gale warnings are broadcast on receipt, and at 0333, 0733, 1133, 1533, 1933 and 2333 UTC.

Goes	Ch 83	Westkapelle	Ch 23	Rotterdam	Ch 23
Scheveningen	Ch 23	Hilversum	Ch 83	IJmuiden	Ch 83
Lelystad	Ch 23	Huisduinen	Ch 23	Wieringerwerf	Ch 83
Platform L7	Ch 83	Terschelling	Ch 23	Nes	Ch 83
Appingedam	Ch 23				

b. MF weather broadcasts

Netherlands Coastguard (IJmuiden) broadcasts weather messages in **English** daily at 0940 and 2140 UTC on 2673 kHz. The messages include a forecast for Netherlands coastal waters up to 30M offshore (including IJsselmeer) and areas Dover, Thames, Humber, German Bight, Dogger, Fisher, Forties and Viking.

Gale warnings are broadcast on receipt, and at 0333, 0733, 1133, 1533, 1933 and 2333 UTC.

BELGIUM

Coast Radio Stations

Oostende Radio broadcasts in English and Dutch strong breeze warnings and a forecast on 2761 kHz and VHF Ch 27 at 0820 and 1720 UTC, valid for sea areas Thames and Dover. Gale warnings are issued *in English* and *Dutch* on receipt and at the end of the next two silent periods.

Antwerpen Radio, on VHF Ch 24, broadcasts gale warnings on receipt at the end of the next two silent periods and every H+03 and H+48. Also strong wind warnings (F6+) on receipt and at every H+05 for the Schelde estuary in English and Dutch.

Radio broadcasting

VRT Radio 1 (Viaamse Radio en Televisie) broadcasts weather messages in Dutch after the news at 0600 0700 0800 0900 1700 2200 LT. The frequencies are 927 kHz, 91·7 MHz, 94·2 MHz, 95·7 MHz and 98·5 MHz. The weather messages include the present situation, forecast for 24 hrs, outlook for the next few days and windspeed; valid for sea areas Humber, Thames, Dover, Wight and Portland.

CHANNEL ISLANDS

Jersey Meteorological Department
An H24 recorded telephone information service is available on ☎ 090 066 50011. Information includes a general situation, 24hr forecast for wind/weather/visibility/sea state/swell/sea temperature and St Helier tide times and heights, plus 2 to 4 day outlooks. The Channel Islands shipping forecast is available on ☎ 0900 665 0022 for an area bounded by latitude 50°N, and the French coast between Cap de la Hague and Ile de Brehat and longitude 03°W.

Radio weather information

Jersey Radio 1659 kHz and Ch 25 82. Storm warnings on receipt and at the end of the next silence period 0307 0907 1507 and 2107 UTC. Weather bulletins consisting of near gale warnings, synopsis, 24h forecast and outlook for next 24 hrs for Channel Islands south of 50°N and East of 03°W and reports from stations at 0645, 0745, 0845 LT (1 May to 31 Aug only), and 1245 1845 and 2245 UTC.

BBC Radio Jersey 1026 kHz and 88·8 MHz. Storm warnings on receipt. Wind information at 0635, 0710, 0735, 0810, 0835, 1710, 1735 and 1835 LT and weather bulletins giving shipping forecast, synopsis, visibility, reports from selected stations, wind direction and force for local waters around Jersey on Mon-Fri at 0635 (Summer only) and 1800 LT and on Sat/Sun at 0735 LT. Tidal information is given on Mon-Fri at 0635, 0710, 0810 1307 1710 1805 1835 LT; on Sats at 0709, 0735 and 0809 LT, and Sun 0708 0735 LT. Shipping movements are broadcast on Mon-Fri at 0733 and 0833 LT.

BBC Radio Guernsey 1116 kHz and 93·2 MHz. Weather bulletins consisting of forecast, synopsis, coastal forecast, storm warnings, wind strength, shipping movements are broadcast for the area of Guernsey, Herm and Sark and local waters at 0807, 1235, and 1710 LT Mon-Fri. Sat/Sun at 0810 LT. During the Summer months coastal reports are included.

Saint Helier Pierheads Ch 18. Continuously broadcasts automatic wind information every 2 minutes, comprising 10 minute mean wind speed, gust and wind direction.

FRANCE

Radio broadcasting

FRANCE INTER (LW) 162 kHz. For all areas: storm warnings, synopsis, 24h fcst and outlook, broadcast in French for Areas 1 to 25, 515, 516, 521-523 and 531-537 (see 5 (13) at 2003 daily. On Sat/Sun at 0654, 2003 LT.

RADIO INTERNATIONALE (RFI) 6175, 15300, 15515, 17570, and 21645 kHz. RFI broadcasts weather messages in French on HF at 1130 UTC daily. Frequencies are: 6175 kHz for North Sea, English Channel and Bay of Biscay; other frequencies are: 15300 kHz, 15515 and 21645 kHz for the North Atlantic, E of 50°W.

RADIO BLEUE (MW). Mainly music, but with Forecasts in French at 0655 LT covering:

English Channel and North Sea	–	**Paris**	864 kHz	**Lille**	1377 kHz
English Channel and East Atlantic	–	**Rennes**	711 kHz	**Brest**	1404 kHz
Bay of Biscay and East Atlantic	–	**Bordeaux**	1206 kHz	**Bayonne**	1494 kHz

LOCAL RADIO (FM)

Radio France Cherbourg 100·7 MHz. Coastal forecast, storm warnings, visibility, wind strength, tidal information, small craft warnings, in French, for the Cherbourg peninsula, broadcast at 0829 LT by:

Cherbourg	100·7 MHz	**St Vaast-la-Hougue**	85·0 MHz;
La Hague	99·8 MHz	**Barneville Carteret**	99·9 MHz.

Recorded forecasts by telephone

a. MÉTÉO (Weather). The BQR (Bulletin Quotidien des Renseignements) is a very informative daily bulletin displayed in Hr Mr offices and YC's. For each French port, under TELEPHONE, Météo is the ☎ of a local Met Office. Auto gives the ☎ for recorded inshore and Coastal forecasts; dial 08·36·68·08·dd (dd is the Département No, shown under each port). To select the inshore (rivage) or Coastal (Côte; out to 20M offshore) bulletin, say "STOP" as your choice is spoken. Inshore bulletins contain 5 day forecasts, local tides, signals, sea temperature, surf conditions, etc. strong wind/gale warnings, general synopsis, 24hrs forecast and outlook.

b. For Offshore bulletins (zones du large) for Channel and North Sea, Atlantic or Mediterranean, dial ☎ 08·36·68·08·08. To select desired offshore area say "STOP" as it is named. Offshore bulletins contain strong wind/gale warnings, the general synopsis and forecast, and the 5 day outlook.

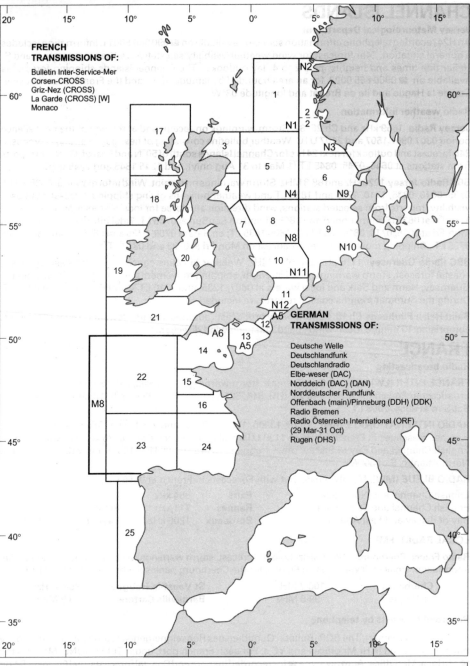

FRENCH
TRANSMISSIONS OF:

Bulletin Inter-Service-Mer
Corsen-CROSS
Griz-Nez (CROSS)
La Garde (CROSS) [W]
Monaco

GERMAN
TRANSMISSIONS OF:

Deutsche Welle
Deutschlandfunk
Deutschlandradio
Elbe-weser (DAC)
Norddeich (DAC) (DAN)
Norddeutscher Rundfunk
Offenbach (main)/Pinneburg (DDH) (DDK)
Radio Bremen
Radio Österreich International (ORF)
(29 Mar-31 Oct)
Rugen (DHS)

FRENCH					GERMAN			
		8	Dogger	17	Ouest Ecosse			
		9	German	18	Nord Irlande			
1	Viking	10	Humber	19	Ouest Irlande	N1	Viking	N10 D Bucht
2	Utsire	11	Thames	20	Med d'Irlande	N2	N Utsire	N11 Humber
3	Cromarty	12	Dover	21	Sud Irlande	N3	S Utsire	N12 Thames
4	Forth	13	Manche Est	22	Sole	N4	Forties	A5 E Eng Ch
5	Forties	14	Manche Ouest	23	Cap Finisterre	N8	Dogger	A6 W Eng Ch
6	Fisher	15	Ouest Bretagne	24	Sud Gascogne	N9	Fisher	M8 Biscay
7	Tyne	16	Nord Gascogne	25	Ouest Portugal			

SPAIN

NORTH AND NORTH WEST SPAIN

Coast Radio Stations

The following CRS broadcast in Spanish gale warnings, synopsis and forecasts for Areas 1-9 at the times and on the VHF or MF frequencies shown below:

Pasages	VHF Ch 27	at 0940 1140 2140 UTC
Machichaco	1707 kHz	at 0903 1233 1733 UTC
Bilbao	VHF Ch 26	at 0940 1140 2140 UTC
Santander	VHF Ch 24	at 0940 1140 2140 UTC
Cabo Peñas	VHF Ch 26	at 0940 1140 2140 UTC
	1677 kHz	at 0803 1203 1703 UTC
Navia	VHF Ch 27	at 0940 1140 2140 UTC
Cabo Ortegal	VHF Ch 02	at 0950 1150 2150 UTC
La Coruña	VHF Ch 26	at 0950 1150 2150 UTC
	1698 kHz	at 0833 1233 1733 UTC
Finisterre	VHF Ch 26	at 0950 1150 2150 UTC
	1764 kHz	at 0803 1203 1703 UTC
Vigo	VHF Ch 20	at 0950 1150 2150 UTC
La Guardia	VHF Ch 82	at 0950 1150 2150 UTC
Tarifa	VHF Ch 81	at 0940 1140 2140 UTC
	1704 kHz	at 0803 1233 1703 UTC

Coastguard MRCC/MRSC

Broadcast in Spanish and English gale warnings on receipt, plus synopsis and forecasts for the Areas, times (UTC) and VHF channels listed below:

Bilbao MRCC	VHF Ch 10	every 4h from 0033 for Areas 2-4.
Santander MRSC	VHF Ch 11	every 4h from 0245 for Areas 2-4.
Gijón MRCC	VHF Ch 10 16	every even H+15 from 0015 to 2215 for Areas 3 & 4.
Coruña MRSC	VHF Ch 12 13 14	every 4h from 0005 for Areas 1-5.
Finisterre MRCC	VHF Ch 11	every 4h from 0233 for Areas 1-5.
Vigo MRSC	VHF Ch 10	every 4h from 0015 for Areas 3-6.

Spanish forecast areas

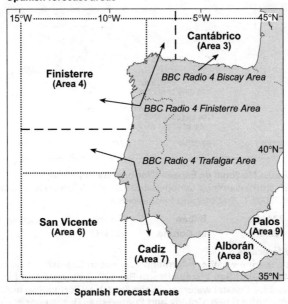

Spanish Forecast Areas

UK Forecast Areas (BBC)

Spanish and Portuguese CRS MSI broadcasts (All times UTC)

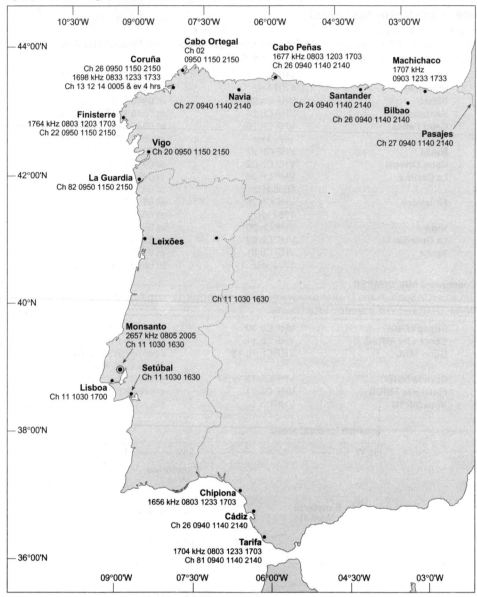

Cabo Ortegal
Ch 02
0950 1150 2150

Coruña
Ch 26 0950 1150 2150
1698 kHz 0833 1233 1733
Ch 13 12 14 0005 & ev 4 hrs

Cabo Peñas
1677 kHz 0803 1203 1703
Ch 26 0940 1140 2140

Machichaco
1707 kHz
0903 1233 1733

Navia
Ch 27 0940 1140 2140

Santander
Ch 24 0940 1140 2140

Bilbao
Ch 26 0940 1140 2140

Finisterre
1764 kHz 0803 1203 1703
Ch 22 0950 1150 2150

Pasajes
Ch 27 0940 1140 2140

Vigo
Ch 20 0950 1150 2150

La Guardia
Ch 82 0950 1150 2150

Leixões

Ch 11 1030 1630

Monsanto
2657 kHz 0805 2005
Ch 11 1030 1630

Setúbal
Ch 11 1030 1630

Lisboa
Ch 11 1030 1700

Chipiona
1656 kHz 0803 1233 1703

Cádiz
Ch 26 0940 1140 2140

Tarifa
1704 kHz 0803 1233 1703
Ch 81 0940 1140 2140

Radio broadcasts – Radio Nacional de España (National Radio)

Broadcasts in Spanish storm warnings, synopsis and 12h or 18h forecasts for Spanish Areas 3 & 4 at 1100, 1400, 1800 and 2200 LT. Stations and frequencies are:

| San Sebastián | 774 kHz | Bilbao | 639 kHz | Santander | 855 kHz |
| Oviedo | 729 kHz | La Coruña | 639 kHz | | |

Recorded telephone forecasts

A recorded telephone marine weather information service in Spanish is available for the Spanish forecast areas 1 to 4, i.e. Gran Sol, Vizcaya (North Biscay), Cantábrico and Finisterre. The service also provides forecasts for Coastal waters from the French to Portuguese borders i.e. Guipuzcoa, Vizcaya, Cantabria, Austurias, Lugo, Coruña and Pontevedra. This service is only available within Spain or for Autolink equipped vessels. Dial ☎ 906 365 372.

PORTUGAL

Coast Radio Stations
The following CRS broadcast *in Portuguese* gale warnings, synopsis and coastal waters forecasts for Portugal, up to 50M offshore for Zona Norte, Zona Centro and Zona Sul.

Leixões	Ch 11	0705 1905 UTC	For Norte and Centro
Lisboa	Ch 11	1030 1730 UTC	For Porto de Lisboa
Setúbal	Ch 11	1030 1630 UTC	For Porto Setúbal

Portuguese forecast areas

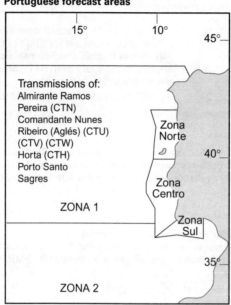

Naval Radio weather broadcasts
Gale warnings are Broadcast in English, on receipt, for the coastal waters of Portugal, including the Azoresand Madeira. The weather bulletins at 0905 and 2105 UTC give gale warnings, a synopsis, a 24h fcst, in Portuguese, for coastal waters of Portugal, up to 50M offshore.
The times and Channels/frequencies are listed below.

Monsanto	MF 2657 kHz	0905 2105 UTC	Gale warnings & fcst for Norte, Centro, Sul, Zona 1 & 2
	VHF Ch 11	1000 1630 UTC	Gale warnings & fcst for Alges

Radio broadcasts – Radiofusão Portuguesa (National Radio) – Programa 1
Broadcasts 24h forecasts for North, Central and South Zones *in Portuguese* at 1100 UTC. Transmitters and frequencies are:

Porto	720 kHz	**Coimbra**	630 kHz	**Lisboa 1**	666 kHz, 95·7 MHz
Miranda do Douro	630 kHz	**Elvas**	720 kHz	**Faro**	720 kHz, 97·6 MHz

Recorded telephone forecasts
Within **Portugal** call ☎ 0601 123, plus 3 digits below:

	Offshore	Inshore
N border-Lisboa	140	123
Lisboa-C St Vincent	141	124
C St Vincent-E border	142	125

For a 9 day general forecast ☎ 0601 123 131. All forecasts are in *Portuguese*.

SOUTH WEST SPAIN

The following CRS broadcast in Spanish gale warnings, synopsis and forecasts for Areas 1-21, in Spanish, at the times and on the VHF or MF frequencies shown below:

Chipiona	1656 kHz	at 0803 1233 1703 UTC
Tarifa	VHF Ch 81	at 0940 1140 2140 UTC
	1704kHz	at 0803 1233 1703 UTC
Cadiz	VHF Ch 26	at 0940 1140 2140 UTC

Coastguard MRCC/MRSC

Broadcast in Spanish and **English** gale warnings on receipt, plus synopsis and forecasts for the Areas, times (UTC) and VHF channels listed below:

Tarifa MRCC   VHF Ch 10 74   every even H+15 for actual wind and visibility at Tarifa, followed by a forecast for Strait of Gibraltar, Cádiz Bay and Alborán, **in English** and Spanish. Fog (visibility) warnings are broadcast every even H+15, and more frequently when the visibility falls below 2M.

Algeciras MRSC   VHF Ch 15, 74   At 0315 0515 0715 1115 1515 1915 2315 UTC

Recorded telephone forecasts

In SW Spain ☎ 906 365 372 for offshore bulletins for forecast areas San Vicente, Cádiz, Alborán, Azores and Canaries; also coastal bulletins from Portugal to Gibraltar, and Canaries. All forecasts are in Spanish. The service is only available within Spain and to Autolink-equipped vessels.

GIBRALTAR

a.   Radio Gibraltar (Gibraltar Broadcasting Corporation)
Broadcasts in **English**: General synopsis, situation, wind direction and strength, visibility and sea state for area up to 50M from Gibraltar. Frequencies are 1458 kHz, 91·3 MHz, 92·6 MHz and 100·5 MHz. Times are:

Mon-Fri:	0610 0930 1030 1230 1300 1530 1715 UTC
Sat:	0930, 1030 1230 1300 UTC
Sun:	1030 1230 UTC

General synopsis, situation, wind direction and strength, sea state, visibility and Sailing forecast, for area up to 50M from Gibraltar.

Mon-Fri:	0630 0730 0830 1130 1740-1755 LT
Sat:	0630 0730 0830 1130 LT
Sun:	0730 0830 1130 LT

b.   British Forces Broadcasting Service (BFBS) Gibraltar
Broadcasts in **English**: Shipping forecast, wind, weather, visbility, sea state, swell, HW & LW times for local waters within 5M of Gibraltar.

Frequencies are: **BFBS 1** – 93·5 and 97·8 MHz FM and **BFBS 2** 89·4 and 99·5 MHGz FM.

BFBS 1 times are:

Mon-Fri:	0745 0845 1130 1715 2345 LT
Sat/Sun:	0845 0945 1230 LT

Mon-Fri: Every H+06 (0700-2400) LT
Sat-Sun: Every H+06 (0700-1000, 1200-1400) LT
Fcst for Gibraltar area; general synopsis, situation, wind direction and strength, sea state, visibility together with HW/LW times.

BFBS 2 times are:

Monday-Fri: 1200 UTC

WEATHER FORECASTS FROM HM COASTGUARD

Weather forecasts are broadcast at regular intervals by all Coastguard Rescue Centres (after initial announcement on Channel 16). Broadcasts are at 4 hourly intervals and also include actual weather. Full details will be found in Coastal Radio Stations section, page 389-393.

WEATHER FORECASTS FROM LOCAL STATIONS

Many local radio stations broadcast local weather reports and forecasts. The information they include varies from present conditions to broadcasting of Small Craft Warnings when Force 6 or more winds are expected. Some of the local radio stations are listed below but it must be remembered that the information is subject to change.

Broadcast times tend to be a little approximate, and are 'clock' times.

STATIONS + TIMES	FREQUENCIES

ISLE of WIGHT RADIO   102.0, 107.0 MHz
Local Inshore Forecast, Tide times
Mon - Fri 0630, 0730, 0830, 1630, 1730, 1830
Sat - Sun 0730, 0830

THE WAVE 105.2 FM   105.2 MHz
Inshore Forecast (Solent) Mon - Fri 0630

BBC RADIO SOLENT   1359, 999 kHz 96.1, 103.8 MHz
Shipping Forecast for southern coastal stations, Portland and Solent Coastguards
Mon -Fri 0645, 0745
Sat 0645, 0745, 0825, 0845
Sun 0645, 0745
Shipping Movements
Mon - Fri 0533, 0645, 0745, 0845
Tide Times
Mon - Fri 0645, 0745, 1745
Gunfacts Mon - Fri 0535, 0635, 0745, Sat - Sun 0633, 0745

WESSEX FM   96.0, 97.2 MHz
Coastal Forecast (Dorset coast)
Mon - Fri 0630, 0730, 0830, 1320, 1630, 1730
Sat - Sun 0730, 0830, 1320

BBC RADIO DEVON   801, 855, 990,1458 kHz 94.8, 95.8, 96.0, 103.4, 104.3 MHz
Shipping Forecast
Mon - Fri 0533, 0633, 0833, 1733
Sat 0605, 0833, 1307

RADIO CORNWALL   630, 657kHz 95.2, 96.0, 103.9 MHz
Tide times, Shipping and Coastal Forecast
Mon - Fri 0655, 0725, 0755, 0825
Sat 0655,0725, 0755, 1305
Sun 0825, 0855, 0925

LANTERN RADIO   96.2 MHz
Inshore Forecast (Bude to Lynmouth)
Daily 0650, 0950, 1250, 1550

PIRATE FM   102.2, 102.8 MHz
Coastal Forecast (Cornwall, Scillies & SW Devon)
Every Hour +00 (0600-2400)

ORCHARD FM   **96.5, 97.1 102.6 MHz**
Coastal Forecast (Avon & Somerset)
Every Hour +00 (0600-0100)

GALAXY 101   **97.2 & 101 MHz**
Coastal Forecast (Ilfracombe to Gower)
Every Hour+50 (0550-1750)

GWR   **1260 kHz** 96.3 MHz
Coastal Forecast (Bristol Channel)
Every Hour +00 & Hour +30 (H24)

THE WAVE, SWANSEA SOUND   **1170 kHz 96.4 MHz**
Coastal forecast
Forecast every Hour +30
Mon - Fri 0630, 0821, 0921
Sat 0730, 0830

RADIO MERSEYSIDE   **1485 kHz, 95.8MHz**
Inshore Waters Forecast
Mon - Fri 0700, 0800, 1200, 1300, 1715, 1745
Sat - Sun 0800, 0900, 1200, 1300, 1800

BBC RADIO LANCASHIRE   **855, 1557 kHz 95.5, 103.9, 104.5 MHz**
Inshore Waters Forecast
Mon - Fri approx 0620, 0650, 0720, 0750, 0820, 0850

THE BAY 96.9 FM   **96.9 MHz**
Coastal Forecast (Morecambe Bay)
Mon - Fri 0630, 0730, 0830, 1630, 1730, 1830,
Sat - Sun 0630, 0730, 0830, 0930, 1630, 1730, 1830,

BBC RADIO CUMBRIA   **95.6, 96.1 MHz**
Coastal Forecast
Mon - Fri 0732, 0832, 1732, 1832
Sat - Sun 0732, 0832

MANX RADIO   **1368 kHz 89, 97.2,103.7 MHz**
Inshore Waters Forecast
0800, 0900, 1300, 1700, 2300
Note: Ronaldsway Met Office give live weather forecasts for this area tel: 0900 6243200

NEVIS RADIO   **96.6,102.3MHz**
Forecast for local waters Daily 0835,1750

SHETLAND Is BROADCASTING Co96.2MHz
Forecast for 150M radius from Bressay Mon - Fri 0705, 0735, 0800, 0835, 0905, 1005, 1105, 1205

NECR 102.1 FM FM   **102M.1 MHz**
Inshore Waters Forecast (Wick to Berwick-upon-Tweed) 0615, 0650, 0750, 0850

BBC RADIO NEWCASTLE   **1458 kHz, 95.4, 96.0, 103.7, 104.4 MHz**
Inshore Forecast (Berwick to Flamborough Hd) Tide Times
Mon - Fri 0655, 0755, 0855, 1155, 1255, 1655, 1755
Sat - Sun 0755, 0855, 0955

RADIO CLEVELAND   **95.0 & 95.8 MHz**
Inshore Forecast (Hartlepool to Flamborough Hd)
Mon - Fri 0705, 0745, 0805, 0845
Sat - Sun 0845

YORKSHIRE COAST RADIO   **96.2, & 103.1 MHz**
Inshore Forecast (Whitby to The Wash), Tide times
Mon - Fri 0730, 0830, 1315, 1630, 1730, 1830
Sat - Sun 0830, 1130

BBC RADIO YORK   **95.5 MHz 1260 kHz (E Coast), 103.7 MHz 666 kHz**
                              (Central), 104.3 MHz (Dales)
Inshore Forecast (Whitby to The Wash)
Mon - Fri 0635, 0735, 0835, 1800
Sat - Sun approx 0630, 0730

BBC RADIO HUMBERSIDE   **95.9 MHz, 1485 kHz**
Coastal Forecast
Daily 0633, 0733, 0833, 1230, 1633, 1733, 1833

THE BEACH   **103.4 MHz**
Inshore Forecast, Tide times (Winterton to Southwold)
Mon-Fri 0903, 1303
Sat 0903

BBC RADIO SUFFOLK   **95.5,103.9 MHz**
Inshore Forecast, Tide Times
Mon - Fri 0617, 0717, 0817, 1305, 1717, 1805
Sat - Sun 0705, 0805, 1305

BBC RADIO ESSEX   **765 kHz 95.3,103.5 MHz**
Inshore Forecast, Tide times
Mon - Fri 0744, 0844, 1744, 1844
Sat 0743, 0843,0740,1206, 1306
Sun 0743, 0843, 0725, 1140, 1756   .

BBC RADIO KENT   **96.7, 97.6, 104.2 MHz**
Shipping Forecast
Mon - Fri 0633, 0733, 0833, 1230
Inshore Forecast, Tide times
Mon - Fri 0633, 0733, 0833, 1230
Shipping, Inshore Forecast, Tide times
Sat 0734, 0835
Sun 0835, 0935

REPUBLIC OF IRELAND

RADIO KERRY   **97.0, 97.6, 96.2 MHz**
Shipping Forecast (Irish Sea Areas) 0755, 1200
Storm Warnings when in force every Hour+00

MWR FM   **96.1,97.1 MHz**
Coastal Forecast (Slyne Head to Fair Head) 0800, 2000

CHANNEL ISLANDS

BBC RADIO GUERNSEY   1116 kHz 93.2 MHz
Shipping Forecast 0630, 0730, 0830
Coastal Forecast Approx every Hour -05 to +05 0600 to 1900

ISLAND FM: 93.7 MHz,104.7 MHz
Coastal Forecast(Channel Islands), Tide Times Every Hour +30

CHANNEL 103FM   103.7 MHz
Local (Jersey) Forecast and Tide times Daily H+03 to H+10 0500 - 2200

BBC RADIO JERSEY   1026 kHz
Inshore Forecast (Channel Is) Daily 0633, 1903

FRANCE

CHANNEL COAST

RADIO FRANCE CHERBOURG   85.0, 99.8, 99.9, 100.7 MHz
Coastal forecasts for the Cherbourg peninsula,
tidal and shipping info in French 0829 LT

RADIO FRANCE ARMORIQUE   101.3, 103.1 MHz
Marine Forecast (Brittany & Channel Is to Noirmoutier) 0829, 1229 & 1829 LT

FOREIGN WEATHER TERMS

English	German	French	Spanish	Dutch
Air mass	Luftmasse	Masse d'air	Massa de aire	Luchtmassa
Anticyclone	Antizyklonisch	Anticyclone	Anticiclón	Hogedrukgebied
Area	Gebiet	Zone	Zona	Gebied
Backing wind	Rückdrehender Wind	Vent reculant	Rolar el viento	Krimpende wind
Barometer	Barometer	Baromètre	Barómetro	Barometer
Breeze	Brise	Brise	Brisa	Bries
Calm	Flaute	Calme	Calma	Kalmte
Centre	Zentrum	Centre	Centro	Centum
Clouds	Wolken	Nuages	Nube	Wolken
Cold	Kalt	Froid	Frio	Koud
Cold front	Kaltfront	Front froid	Frente frio	Kou front
Cyclonic	Zyklonisch	Cyclonique	Ciclonica	Cycloonachtig
Decrease	Abnahme	Affaiblissement	Disminución	Afnemen
Deep	Tief	Profond	Profundo	Diep
Deepening	Vertiefend	Approfondissant	Ahondamiento	Verdiepend
Depression	Sturmtief	Dépression	Depresión	Depressie
Direction	Richtung	Direction	Direción	Richting
Dispersing	Auflösend	Se dispersant	Disipación	Oplossend
Disturbance	Störung	Perturbation	Perturbación	Verstoving
Drizzle	Niesel	Bruine	Lioviena	Motregen
East	Ost	Est	Este	Oosten
Extending	Ausdehnung	S'étendant	Extension	Uitstrekkend
Extensive	Ausgedehnt	Etendu	General	Uitgebreid

English	German	French	Spanish	Dutch
Falling	Fallend	Descendant	Bajando	Dalen
Filling	Auffüllend	Secomblant	Relleno	Vullend
Fog	Nebel	Brouillard	Niebla	Nevel
Fog bank	Nebelbank	Ligne de brouillard	Banco de niebla	Mist bank
Forecast	Vorhersage	Prévision	Previsión	Vooruitzicht
Frequent	Häufig	Fréquent	Frecuenta	Veelvuldig
Fresh	Frisch	Frais	Fresco	Fris
Front	Front	Front	Frente	Front
Gale	Sturm	Coup de vent	Temporal	Storm
Gale warning	Sturmwarnung	Avis de coup de vent	Aviso de temporal	Stormwaarschuwing
Good	Gut	Bon	Bueno	Goed
Gradient	Druckunterschied	Gradient	Gradiente	Gradiatie
Gust, squall	Bö	Rafalle	Ráfaga	Windvlaag
Hail	Hagel	Grêle	Granizo	Hagel
Haze	Diesig	Brume	Calina	Nevel
Heavy	Schwer	Abondant	Abunante	Zwaar
High	Hoch	Anticyclone	Alta presión	Hoog
Increasing	Zunehmend	Augmentant	Aumentar	Toenemend
Isobar	Isobar	Isobare	Isobara	Isobar
Isolated	Vereinzelt	Isolé	Aislado	Verspreid
Lightning	Blitze	Eclair de foudre	Relampago	Bliksem
Local	Örtlich	Locale	Local	Plaatselijk
Low	Tief	Dépression	Baja presión	Laag
Mist	Dunst	Brume légere	Nablina	Mist
Moderate	Mäßig	Modéré	Moderado	Matig
Moderating	Abnehmend	Se modérant	Medianente	Matigend
Moving	Bewegend	Se déplacant	Movimiento	Bewegend
North	Nord	Nord	Septentrional	Noorden
Occluded	Okklusion	Couvert	Okklusie	Bewolkt
Poor	Schlecht	Mauvais	Mal	Slecht
Precipitation	Niederschlag	Précipitation	Precipitación	Neerslag
Pressure	Druck	Pression	Presión	Druk
Rain	Regen	Pluie	lluvia	Regen
Ridge	Hochdruckbrücke	Crête	Cresta	Rug
Rising	Ansteigend	Montant	Subiendo	Stijgen
Rough	Rauh	Agitée	Bravo o alborotado	Ruw
Sea	See	Mer	Mar	Zee
Seaway	Seegang	Haute mer	Alta mar	Zee
Scattered	Vereinzelt	Sporadiques	Difuso	Verspreid
Shower	Schauer	Averse	Aguacero	Bui
Slight	Leicht	Un peu	Leicht	Licht
Slow	Langsam	Lent	Lent	Langzaam
Snow	Schnee	Neige	Nieve	Sneeuw
South	Süd	Sud	Sur	Zuiden
Storm	Sturm	Tempête	Temporal	Storm
Sun	Sonne	Soleil	Sol	Zon
Swell	Schwell	Houle	Mar de fondo	Deining
Thunder	Donner	Tonnerre	Tormenta	Donder
Thunderstorm	Gewitter	Orage	Tronada	Onweer
Trough	Trog, Tiefausläufer	Creux	Seno	Trog
Variable	Umlaufend	Variable	Variable	Veranderlijk
Veering	Rechtdrehend	Virement de vent	Dextrogiro	Ruimende wind
Warm front	Warmfront	Front chaud	Frente calido	Warm front
Weather	Wetter	Temps	Tiempo	Weer
Wind	Wind	Vent	Viento	Wind
Weather report	Wetterbericht	Météo	Previsión meteorologica	Weer bericht

NAVTEX

Introduction

Navtex prints or displays navigational warnings, weather forecasts and other MSI by means of a dedicated aerial and receiver with built-in printer or screen. Navtex is a component of GMDSS.

All messages are in English on a single frequency of 518 kHz, with excellent coverage of Europe. A second frequency, 490 kHz is rapidly becoming available for local language broadcasts. 490 kHz is available from all three UK Navtex transmitters. Interference between stations is avoided by time sharing and by limiting the range of transmitters to about 300M. Three stations cover the UK.

The user programmes the receiver for the station(s) and message category(s) required. Nav warnings (A), Gale warnings (B) and SAR (D) are alway s printed.

Messages

Each message is prefixed by a four-character group. The first character is the code letter of the transmitting station (e.g: S for Niton). The second character is the message category. The third and

fourth are message serial numbers, from 01 to 99. The serial number 00 denotes urgent messages which are always printed. Messages which are corrupt or have already been printed are rejected.

Navtex information applies only to the area for which the transmitting station is responsible, see Area Map on facing page.

Weather information accounts for about 75% of all messages and is particularly valuable when out of range of other sources or if there is a language problem. The areas covered by the 3 UK stations are:

Cullercoats (G) (U)	Faeroes clockwise to Wight
Niton (S) (I)	Thames clockwise to Malin
Niton (K) (A)	The French coast from Cap Gris Nez to Île de Bréhat
Portpatrick (O) (C)	Lundy clockwise to Fair Isle

Inshore forecasts on Navtex will be standardised to cover Inshore Waters out to 12M from the coast for the whole of UK, including Shetland. VHF and MF RT broadcasts will cover waters out to 60M of Shetland.

NAVAREA I (Co-ordinator – UK)

Transmission times (UTC)

O –	**Portpatrick**, UK	0220ⓐ	**0620**	1020	1420	**1820**	2220
C –	**Portpatrick**, UK (490 kHz)		0820ⓐ			2020ⓐ	
G –	**Cullercoats**, UK	0100ⓐ	0500	**0900**	1300	**1700**	**2100**
U –	**Cullercoats**, UK (490 kHz)		0720ⓐ			1920ⓐ	
S –	**Niton**, UK	0300	**0700**	1100	1500	**1900**	2300ⓐ
K –	**Niton**, UK (Note 1)	0140	0540	**0940**	1340	1740	**2140**
I –	**Niton**, UK (490 kHz)		0520ⓐ			1720ⓐ	
A –	**Niton**, UK (490 kHz) (Note 2)	0000	0400	0800	1200	1600	2000
W –	**Valentia**, Eire	0340	**0740**	1140	1540	**1940**	2340
Q –	**Malin Head**, Eire	0240	0640	**1040**	1440	1840	**2240**
P –	**Netherlands CG**, IJmuiden	0230	0630	1030	1430	1830	2230
M –	**Oostende**, Belgium	0200	0600	1000	1400	1800	2200
T –	**Oostende**, Belgium	0310	**0710**	1110	1510	**1910**	2310
L –	**Rogaland**, Norway	**0150**	0550	0950	**1350**	1750	2150

NAVAREA II (Co-ordinator – France)

A –	**Corsen**, Le Stiff, France	**0000**	0400	0800	**1200**	1600	2000
E –	**Corsen**, Le Stiff, France (490 kHz)	0040	0440	**0840**	1240	1640	**2040**
D –	**Coruña**, Spain	**0030**	0430	0830	**1230**	1630	2230
R –	**Lisbon/Monsanto**,Portugal	0250	0650	1050	1450	1850	2250
–	**Lisbon/Monsanto**, Portugal (490 kHz)		Planned				
G –	**Tarifa**, Spain	0100	0500	**0900**	1300	1700	**2100**
I –	**Las Palmas**, Islas Canarias	0120	0520	**0920**	**1320**	**1720**	2120

NAVAREA III (Co-ordinator – Spain)

X –	**Valencia**, Spain	0350	**0750**	1150	1550	**1950**	2350
W –	**La Garde**, (Toulon), France	0340	0740	**1140**	1540	1940	**2340**
S –	**Fort Ste Marguerite**, France (490 kHz)	0300	**0700**	1100	1500	**1900**	2300

Note: 1 In English, for Areas Golf, Hotel and India, south of the Channel median to the French Coast.
2 In French, for Areas Golf, Hotel and India, south of the Channel median to the French Coast.
ⓐ Extended outlook three to four days or inshore waters national three-day outlook.

Navtex areas – UK and NW Europe

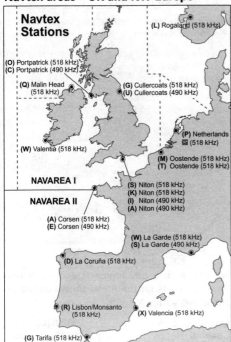

Navtex
Stations

(L) Rogaland (518 kHz)

(O) Portpatrick (518 kHz)
(C) Portpatrick (490 kHz)

(Q) Malin Head
(518 kHz)

(G) Cullercoats (518 kHz)
(U) Cullercoats (490 kHz)

(W) Valentia (518 kHz)

(P) Netherlands
(518 kHz)

(M) Oostende (518 kHz)
(T) Oostende (518 kHz)

NAVAREA I

(S) Niton (518 kHz)
(K) Niton (518 kHz)
(I) Niton (490 kHz)
(A) Niton (490 kHz)

NAVAREA II

(A) Corsen (518 kHz)
(E) Corsen (490 kHz)

(W) La Garde (518 kHz)
(S) La Garde (490 kHz)

(D) La Coruña (518 kHz)

(R) Lisbon/Monsanto
(518 kHz)

(X) Valencia (518 kHz)

(G) Tarifa (518 kHz)

Message categories

A	Navigational warnings
B	Gale warnings
C	Ice reports (unlikely to apply in UK)
D	SAR information and pirate attack warnings
E	Weather forecasts
F	Pilot service messages
H	Loran-C messages
J	Satnav messages
K	Other electronic navaid messages
L	Subfacts and Gunfacts for the UK
V	Amplifying details of nav warnings initially sent under A; plus the weekly oil rig list.
Z	No messages on hand at scheduled time

Stations

The table on the previous page shows Navtex stations in Navareas I to III, and their identity codes and transmission times (UTC). Times of weather messages are shown in **bold**.

Notes: **Oostende (M)** transmits nav warnings for the area bounded by North Foreland and Lowestoft on the UK coast, longitude 03°E and the Belgian/French coasts to Calais. **Oostende (T)** provides nav info for the Belgian coast and weather for sea areas Thames and Dover.

TELEPHONE & FAX

Marinecall

Provides recorded telephone forecasts for 16 inshore areas around the UK. Dial 09068-500 + Area number shown on the Marinecall map (see below). Calls cost 50p per minute at all times.

Forecasts cover the inshore waters out to 12M offshore for up to 48 hrs and include: General situation, any strong wind or gale warnings in force, wind, weather, visibility, sea state, maximum air temperature and sea temperature. The two-day forecasts are followed by forecasts for days three to five. Forecasts are updated at 0700 and 1900 daily. Area 432 (Channel Islands), is updated at 0700, 1300 and 1900 daily.

The local inshore forecast for Shetland is not given by Marinecall, but is available from Lerwick CG on ☎ 01595 692976. Or dial ☎ 09068 500 426 for a Weathercall general land forecast for Caithness, Orkney and Shetland.

Planning forecasts for the following areas are updated at 0800 daily.

450	National inshore 3 to 5-day	992	English Channel 2 to 5-day
991	Southern N Sea 2 to 5-day	954	Irish Sea 2 to-5 day

Coastal reports (Marinecall Select)

For latest weather reports and forecasts from 47 coastal stations dial ☎ 09068 110 010 and follow instructions, keying in the three-digit area number shown below, when requested.

Each of the 16 Marinecall areas contains two to four actual weather reports, which are updated hourly.

The reports include details of wind/gusts, visibility, weather, cloud, temperature, pressure and tendency. After these reports a two day or three – five day forecast for that area is available.

Marinecall and MetFAX areas

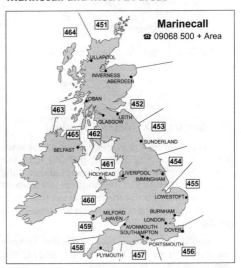

Marinecall
☎ 09068 500 + Area

464 451
ULLAPOOL
INVERNESS
ABERDEEN
OBAN 452
463
LEITH
GLASGOW 453
465 462
SUNDERLAND
BELFAST 454
461
HOLYHEAD LIVERPOOL
IMMINGHAM 455
LOWESTOFT
460
BURNHAM
MILFORD LONDON
HAVEN 459 AVONMOUTH DOVER
SOUTHAMPTON
PORTSMOUTH
458 457 456
PLYMOUTH

Area No	Reports	Area No	Reports
465	Ballycastle Bangor Harbour Malin Head	451	Cape Wrath Wick Lossiemouth
464	Benbecula Aultbea Butt of Lewis	452	Peterhead Aberdeen Fife Ness
463	Oban Tiree	453	Boulmer Tynemouth
462	Machrihanish Prestwick Greenock	454	Bridlington Holbeach
461	Rhyl Crosby Walney Island	455	Walton-on-the-Naze Weybourne Sheerness
460	Aberdaron Aberporth Valley	456	Greenwich Lt V Dover Newhaven
459	Cardiff Mumbles Milford Haven	457	Thorney Island Lee-on-Solent St Catherine's Pt
432	Channel Lt V Guernsey Jersey Bréhat	458	Brixham Plymouth Falmouth St Mary's, Scilly

MetFAX planning forecast areas

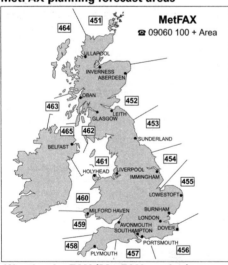

MetFAX
☎ 09060 100 + Area

Weather by FAX (MetFAX marine)

MetFAX Marine provides printed weather forecasts and charts by dialling 09060 100 + the area number shown on the two maps above. Calls cost £1 per minute and the length of call is about three minutes. Do not forget to press the 'Start' button on you fax machine when a connection is made.

For two day forecasts and charts for inshore waters covering the Areas shown above, dial **09060 100 + Area No** required

MetFAX area planners

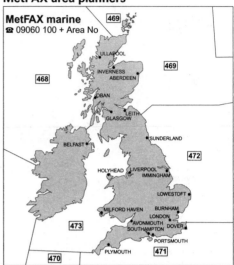

MetFAX marine
☎ 09060 100 + Area No

For two to five day forecasts and 48/72 hour forecast charts for the Areas shown above dial **09060-100 + Area No** of the area required.

English Channel	09060-100 471
Channel Islands	09060-100 466
Southern North Sea	09060-100 472
Irish Sea	09060-100 473
North Sea	09060-100 469
North West Scotland	09060-100 468
Biscay	09060-100 470
National inshore 3-5 day	09060-100 450

For additional fax services dial 09060 100 plus:

24 hr shipping forecast	441
Guide to surface charts	446
Surface analysis chart	444
24 hr surface forecast chart	445
Chart of latest UK weather reports	447
Index to chart of UK weather reports	448
3-5 day UK inshore forecast and charts	450
Users guide to satellite image	498
Satellite image	499
Mediterranean plotted weather reports	474
South Coast tide tables	497
Marine index	401

Note: MetFAX, MetCALL, MetWEB, Marinecall Select and MetFAX Marine are registered trademarks of the Meteorological Office.

Short Message Service (SMS) – introduction

By means of the SMS, the following weather information can be obtained from the Met Office via digital mobile telephones which utilise the Vodafone network:

a. Inshore waters forecasts for seven new areas along the South coast of the UK.

b. Shipping forecasts for sea areas

c. Coastal station weather reports. It is likely that the service will be extended to cover other geographical areas in due course.

How to use SMS

Dial 08700 767 838 on your Vodafone Mobile and follow the recorded main menu. It will prompt you to press:

Key 1   for service information
Key 2   to receive index of products on fax
Key 3   to order a product
Key 4   to connect to customer helpline
Key 0   to return to the main menu

After pressing Key 3, press key 1 for a one-off order or key 2 for a regular order. A regular order ensures that a product, e.g. shipping forecast for sea area around Tyne, is automatically sent to your mobile as it is updated four times during the day.

Then order the product by keying in the appropriate 4 digit code from the list below. The information will duly appear on the screen of your mobile. It can then be read, stored in memory or deleted.

SMS areas

SMS Forecast Areas

ULLAPOOL
INVERNESS
ABERDEEN
OBAN
LEITH
GLASGOW
SUNDERLAND
BELFAST
HOLYHEAD
LIVERPOOL
IMMINGHAM
LOWESTOFT
MILFORD HAVEN
BURNHAM
LONDON
AVONMOUTH
SOUTHAMPTON
DOVER
PORTSMOUTH
PLYMOUTH
4583
4582
4581
4572
4571
4562
4561

SMS Inshore waters forecast areas

Updated at 0530 for the period 0600 to 1200, 1130 for the period 1200 to 1800 and 1630 for the period 1700 to 2300.

4561   North Foreland to Beachy Head
4562   Beachy Head to Selsey Bill
4571   Selsey Bill to Durlston Head
4572   Durlston Head to Lyme Regis
4581   Lyme Regis to Looe
4582   Looe to Padstow
4583   Padstow to Hartland Point

Shipping forecast Sea Areas

Updated at 0001, 0500, 100 and 1700 LT; valid for the same period as the BBC Radio 4 broadcasts.

4411	Viking	4426	Plymouth
4412	North Utsira	4427	Biscay
4413	South Utsira	4428	Finisterre
4414	Forties	4429	Sole
4415	Cromarty	4430	Lundy
4416	Forth	4431	Fastnet
4417	Tyne	4432	Irish Sea
4418	Dogger	4433	Shannon
4419	Fisher	4434	Rockall
4420	German Bight	4435	Malin
4421	Humber	4436	Hebrides
4422	Thames	4437	Bailey
4423	Dover	4438	Fair Isle
4424	Wight	4439	Faeroes
4425	Portland	4440	S E Iceland

Coastal station weather reports

Updated hourly, except places marked * which are updated every 3 hours i.e. 0000, 0300, 0600, etc...

4301	Ballycastle, Bangor Harbour	4313	Channel L/V, Guernsey
4302	Oban, Greenock	4314	Jersey, Brehat
4303	South Uist, Tiree	4315	Thorney Is, Lee-on-Solent
4304	Aultbea, Stornoway	4316	St Catherine's Pt, Greenwich L/V
4305	Machrihanish, Prestwick	4317	Dover, Newhaven
4306	Walney Island, St Bees Head	4318	Walton-on-the-Naze, Sheerness
4307	Rhyl, Crosby	4319	Weybourne Holbeach
4308	Aberdaren, Valley	4320	Bridlington, Donna Nook
4309	Aberporth, Milford Haven	4321	Boulner, Tynemouth
4310	Cardiff Mumbles	4322	Aberdeen, Fife Ness
4311	Falmouth, Scilly-St Mary's	4323	Peterhead, Lossiemouth
4312	Brixham, Plymouth	4324	Sule Skerry, Wick

Charging information and Notes

Charges vary according to the service provided and range from 20p per message on a regular basis to 50p for one-off requests and alerts. Inshore forecasts are charged at 50p per message. Coastal reports and Shipping forecasts are charged at 30p per message. Charges are only made for those messages received.

Registration and pre-set up for these services is via the internet and payment is online via credit card. There is a **MINIMUM** credit card payment of £10.

Section 3

SPEED, TIME AND DISTANCE IN NAUTICAL MILES

Speed in knots

Time in minutes	1	2	3	4	5	6	7	8	9	10	15	20
1	0·0	0·0	0·1	0·1	0·1	0·1	0·1	0·1	0·2	0·2	0·3	0·3
2	0·0	0·1	0·1	0·1	0·2	0·2	0·2	0·3	0·3	0·3	0·5	0·7
3	0·1	0·1	0·2	0·2	0·3	0·3	0·4	0·4	0·5	0·5	0·8	1·0
4	0·1	0·1	0·2	0·3	0·3	0·4	0·5	0·5	0·6	0·7	1·0	1·3
5	0·1	0·2	0·3	0·3	0·4	0·5	0·6	0·7	0·8	0·8	1·3	1·7
6	0·1	0·2	0·3	0·4	0·5	0·6	0·7	0·8	0·9	1·0	1·5	2·0
7	0·1	0·2	0·4	0·5	0·6	0·7	0·8	0·9	1·1	1·2	1·8	2·3
8	0·1	0·3	0·4	0·5	0·7	0·8	0·9	1·1	1·2	1·3	2·0	2·7
9	0·2	0·3	0·5	0·6	0·8	0·9	1·1	1·2	1·4	1·5	2·3	3·0
10	0·2	0·3	0·5	0·7	0·8	1·0	1·2	1·3	1·5	1·7	2·5	3·3
11	0·2	0·4	0·6	0·7	0·9	1·1	1·3	1·5	1·7	1·8	2·8	3·7
12	0·2	0·4	0·6	0·8	1·0	1·2	1·4	1·6	1·8	2·0	3·0	4·0
13	0·2	0·4	0·7	0·9	1·1	1·3	1·5	1·7	2·0	2·2	3·3	4·3
14	0·2	0·5	0·7	0·9	1·2	1·4	1·6	1·9	2·1	2·3	3·5	4·7
15	0·3	0·5	0·8	1·0	1·3	1·5	1·8	2·0	2·3	2·5	3·8	5·0
16	0·3	0·5	0·8	1·1	1·3	1·6	1·9	2·1	2·4	2·7	4·0	5·3
17	0·3	0·6	0·9	1·1	1·4	1·7	2·0	2·3	2·6	2·8	4·3	5·7
18	0·3	0·6	0·9	1·2	1·5	1·8	2·1	2·4	2·7	3·0	4·5	6·0
19	0·3	0·6	1·0	1·3	1·6	1·9	2·2	2·5	2·9	3·2	4·8	6·3
20	0·3	0·7	1·0	1·3	1·7	2·0	2·3	2·7	3·0	3·3	5·0	6·7
21	0·4	0·7	1·1	1·4	1·8	2·1	2·5	2·8	3·2	3·5	5·3	7·0
22	0·4	0·7	1·1	1·5	1·8	2·2	2·6	2·9	3·3	3·7	5·5	7·3
23	0·4	0·8	1·2	1·5	1·9	2·3	2·7	3·1	3·5	3·8	5·8	7·7
24	0·4	0·8	1·2	1·6	2·0	2·4	2·8	3·2	3·6	4·0	6·0	8·0
25	0·4	0·8	1·3	1·7	2·1	2·5	2·9	3·3	3·8	4·2	6·3	8·3
30	0·5	1·0	1·5	2·0	2·5	3·0	3·5	4·0	4·5	5·0	7·5	10·0
35	0·6	1·2	1·8	2·3	2·9	3·5	4·1	4·7	5·3	5·8	8·8	11·7
40	0·7	1·3	2·0	2·7	3·3	4·0	4·7	5·3	6·0	6·7	10·0	13·3
45	0·8	1·5	2·3	3·0	3·8	4·5	5·3	6·0	6·8	7·5	11·3	15·0
50	0·8	1·7	2·5	3·3	4·2	5·0	5·8	6·7	7·5	8·3	12·5	16·7

SECTION 4 - COMMUNICATION

CONTENTS

Section 4

RADIO OPERATION

Avoiding interference

Before transmitting, first listen on the VHF channel. If occupied, wait for a break before transmitting, or choose another. If you cause interference you must comply immediately with any request from a Coastguard or Coast Radio Station to stop transmitting. The request will state how long to desist.

Control of communications

Ship-to-Shore: Except in the case of distress, urgency or safety, communications between ship and shore-based stations are controlled by the latter.

Intership: The ship *called* controls communication. If you call another ship, then it has control. If you are called by a ship, you assume control. If a shore-based station breaks in, both ships must comply with instructions given. A shore-based station has better aerials and equipment and so its transmission and reception areas are greater.

Radio confidentiality

Inevitably you will overhear people's private conversations on VHF. These must not be reproduced, passed on or used for any purpose.

Voice technique

There are two considerations when operating:

What to say – *i.e. voice procedure*

How to say it – *i.e. voice technique*

Clear R/T speech is vital. If a message cannot be understood by the receiving operator it is useless. Anyone can become a good operator by following a few rules: The voice should be pitched at a higher level than for normal conversation. Avoid dropping the voice pitch at the end of a word or phrase. Hold the microphone a few inches in front of the mouth and speak directly into it at a normal level. Speak clearly so that there can be no confusion. Emphasise words with weak syllables; 'Tower', if badly pronounced, could sound like 'tar'. People with strong accents must try to use as understandable a pronunciation as possible. Messages which have to be written down at the receiving station should be sent slowly. This gives time for it to be written down by the receiving operator. Remember, the average reading speed is 250 words a minute, whilst average writing speed is only 20. If the transmitting operator himself writes it down all should be well.

The phonetic alphabet
The syllables to emphasise are underlined

letter	morse	phonetic	spoken as
A	•–	Alfa	AL-fah
B	–•••	Bravo	BRAH-voh
C	–•–•	Charlie	CHAR-lee
D	–••	Delta	DELL-tah
E	•	Echo	ECK-oh
F	••–•	Foxtrot	FOKS-trot
G	––•	Golf	GOLF
H	••••	Hotel	hoh-TELL
I	••	India	IN-dee-ah
J	•–––	Juliett	JEW-lee-ett
K	–•–	Kilo	KEY-loh
L	•–••	Lima	LEE-mah
M	––	Mike	MIKE
N	–•	November	no-VEM-ber
O	–––	Oscar	OSS-car
P	•––•	Papa	pa-PAH
Q	––•–	Quebec	keh-BECK
R	•–•	Romeo	ROW-me-oh
S	•••	Sierra	see-AIR-rah
T	–	Tango	TANG-go
U	••–	Uniform	YOU-nee-form or OO-nee-form
V	•••–	Victor	VIK-tah
W	•––	Whiskey	WISS-key
X	–••–	X-Ray	ECKS-ray
Y	–•––	Yankee	YANG-key
Z	––••	Zulu	ZOO-loo

Difficult words may be spelled phonetically. Operators precede this with 'I spell'. If the word is pronounceable include it before and after it has been spelt. If an operator sends the message 'I will moor alongside the yacht Coila' he would transmit: 'I will moor alongside the yacht Coila – I spell – Charlie Oscar India Lima Alfa – Coila'. When asked for your international callsign – say it is MGLA4 – transmit: 'My callsign is Mike Golf Lima Alfa Four.'

Phonetic numerals
When numerals are transmitted, the following pronunciations make them easier to understand.

no	morse	spoken as	no	morse	spoken as
1	•––––	WUN	2	••–––	TOO
3	•••––	TREE	4	••••–	FOW-ER
5	•••••	FIFE	6	–••••	SIX
7	––•••	SEV-EN	8	–––••	AIT
9	––––•	NIN-ER	0	–––––	ZERO

Numerals are transmitted digit by digit except that multiples of thousands may be spoken as follows.

numeral	spoken as
44	FOW-ER FOW-ER
90	NIN-ER ZERO
136	WUN TREE SIX
500	FIFE ZERO ZERO
1478	WUN FOW-ER SEV-EN AIT
7000	SEV-EN THOU-SAND

Punctuation

Punctuation marks should be used only where their omission would cause confusion.

mark	word	spoken as
.	Decimal	DAY-SEE-MAL
,	Comma	COMMA
.	Stop	STOP

Procedure words or 'prowords'

These are used to shorten transmissions

All after: Used after proword *'say again'* to request repetition of a portion of a message

All before: Used after proword *say again'* to request repetition of a portion of a message

Correct: Reply to repetition of message that was preceded by prowords *'read back for check'* when it has been correctly repeated. Often said twice

Correction: Spoken during the transmission of a message means an error has been made in this transmission. Cancel the last word or group of words. The correct word or group follows.

In figures: Following numeral or group of numerals to be written as figures

In letters: Following numeral or group of numerals to be written as figures as spoken

I say again: I am repeating transmission or portion indicated

I spell: I shall spell the next word or group of letters phonetically

Out: This is the end of working to you

Over: Invitation to reply

Read back: If receiving station is doubtful about accuracy of whole or part of message it may repeat it back to the sending station, preceding the repetition with prowords *'I read back'.*

Say again: Repeat your message or portion referred to ie *'Say again all after', 'Say again address',* etc.

Station calling: Used when a station is uncertain of the calling station's identification

This is: This transmission is from the station. whose callsign or name immediately follows.

Wait: If a called station is unable to accept traffic immediately, it will reply 'WAIT.......MINUTES'. If probable delay exceeds 10 minutes the reason will be given

Word after or Word before: Used after proword *'say again'* to request repetition.

Wrong: Reply to repetition of message preceded by prowords *'read back'* when it has been incorrectly repeated.

Calls, calling and callsigns

Shore-based stations normally identify themselves by using their geographical name followed by the word Radio, e.g. Solent Coastguard, Humber Radio, etc. Vessels normally identify themselves by the name on their licence but the International callsign assigned to the ship may be used in certain cases. If two yachts bear the same name or where some confusion may result, you should give your International callsign when starting communications, and thereafter use your ship's name as callsign.

'All ships' broadcast

Information to be received or used by all who intercept it, eg Gale warnings, navigational warnings, weather forecasts etc, is generally broadcast by Coastguard Radio and addressed 'All stations'. No reply is needed.

Establishing communication with a shore-based station

The initial call is always made on a working channel. Channel 16 should not be used except for distress, urgency or very briefly to establish a working channel.

- Switch to one of the stations working channels, pause to ensure no-one is transmitting
- Are you are close enough to try low power *(1 watt)* first? Possible at ranges up to 10 miles. Otherwise use high power *(25 watts)* with more battery drain. Then give the callsign of the station called *(up to three times only)* and prowords 'This is'
- The callsign of calling station up to three times only
- Indication of number of R/Tcalls you have to make
- Proword 'Over.'

Small faults can drastically reduce your transmitting range. Possibly the aerial for the channel chosen has been optimised for areas east of the station and you are to the west. If approaching the station wait 15 minutes and call again. If the range is opening, either try again in hope, or try another station within range.

Every time you call at high power, you are decreasing battery state and the range your VHF will achieve.

RADIO DATA

RADIO COMMUNICATIONS, SHORT AND MEDIUM RANGE

A SUITABLE RADIO receiver on board will provide weather forecasts and time signals at scheduled times on a number of frequencies in various wavebands. With a maritime receiver you are not limited to the familiar BBC and commercial broadcasts. HM Coastguard transmit navigation warnings, storm warnings and weather messages for shipping in their respective sea areas. Short range radiotelephony (RT) operates on VHF (Very High Frequency) transmission and reception on a number of channels in the marine VHF/RT band. The equipment and procedures are simple, but normally range is limited to about 20 miles from ship to shore, rather less from ship to ship. Interconnection with national telephone systems is possible on certain VHF/RT channels when a yacht is within range of a Coast Radio Station, though there are now no such remaining stations on the mainland of the UK, France or the Netherlands. Mobile telephones are now by far the most common form of ship to shore communication.

Medium range two-way communication operate in the marine medium frequency RT band, the 2MHz 'trawler band'. Single sideband techniques are employed on these medium frequencies and SSB equipment is essential. The effective range depends on the power of the transmitter on board and the sensitivity of the associated receiver; in general this might be upto 200 miles from certain (but not all) Coast Stations.

WAVEBANDS, FREQUENCIES AND CHANNELS

In the Marine VHF/RT band the individual frequencies are separated from their neighbours by exactly 25kHz 'elbow-room' to eliminate mutual interference. For convenience each working frequency is given a channel number; the numbers do not run consecutively because the channels were originally spaced 50kHz apart but it has since been found possible to fit another channel in between each original one and so make fuller use of the waveband. The channels numbered between 19 and 59 have been allocated to a different purpose and one odd channel outside the normal sequence is designated Channel 'M', with a frequency of 157.85MHz.

Each frequency in the MF/RT band and each channel in the VHF/AT band has its specific purpose and may not be used at random for general conversation. Calling on the wrong channel merely wastes time and causes annoyance to other users. Of the 55 channels available in the Marine VHF/RT band, small craft are unlikely to need more than a selected dozen, and some of those may vary with the area in which a boat operates and her usage.

The simplest and cheapest VHF/RT transmitter-receivers operate only in the 'simplex' mode; they can work only on those channels which transmit and receive on the same frequency. Numerically these are Channels 06 (mandatory) 08 to 17 and 67 to 74 and 77. All other channels are for 'duplex' working; the ship transmitter and the ship receiver are on a different one for each and every channel. (Channels 29 to 60 are not used for maritime purposes.)

For full duplex operation a more elaborate and expensive transmitter-receiver with either twin aerials or a special filter is needed, but it does give the ability to interconnect with the shore telephone system and to converse with subscribers who have no knowledge of radio procedures. More common among yachtsmen's VHF/RT's, however, are the semi-duplex operating sets which although involving simplex procedures, allow you to communicate with stations operating duplex systems and to link with shore telephones via some overseas Coast Radio Stations.

Three frequencies are set aside for emergency position indicating radio beacons (EPIRB): 121.5MHz aircraft VHF, 243MHz military UHF and 406MHz Satellite.

MEDIUM RANGE MF/RT

The severely limited line-of-sight range of VHF/RT makes a longer-range system desirable for small craft which need to maintain contact with the shore when out of sight of land or in a coastal area to which VHF cover does not extend. Single sideband MF/RT provides such contact all around the waters of the United Kingdom and Western Europe. A receiver alone gives the ability to hear weather bulletins, storm and navigation warnings for local sea areas broadcast from Radio Stations in the 1.6 to 4.0MHz maritime band.

TWO-WAY MF/RT

An MF single sideband transmitter-receiver makes possible two-way contact between ship and shore over greater distances than by VHF; the actual range depends mainly on the power of the transmitter but might be about 100 miles or more. Not all radio stations are equipped to deal with this traffic but there are sufficient stations adequately spaced around the coast to cover all UK coastal waters.

TRAFFIC LISTS

Coast stations wishing to contact a boat at sea will first attempt to do so by a direct call on Channel 16 which will be heard if a loudspeaker watch is kept and the boat is within range. Failing this, the boat's name will be added to the Traffic List broadcast at (usually) two hour intervals at the times and on the frequencies (channels) shown elsewhere in Coast Radio Stations section, p. 389-393. You have to monitor that frequency at the appropriate time or never know that there is incoming traffic awaiting attention. When such a call is received, the response is to call the station concerned on the working channel.

SILENCE PERIODS

Although there is no official silence period for VHF, it is generally advised that no transmission be made during the silence periods which are enforced for the 2182kHz distress frequency. The periods are the three minutes immediately following the full and half hour.

DISTRESS, URGENCY AND SAFETY

A radio-equipped yacht ought to keep watch on Channel 16 VHF (or 2182kHz MF/RT) at all times when at sea. If we switch on only when we wish to transmit a message, we may fail to hear a distress call from another nearby craft. We will also miss navigation and weather warnings broadcast by Coastguard/Coast radio stations in our own sea area. Traffic on Channel 16 must be severely limited, apart from distress urgency and safety calls, to calling and answering Coastguard/Coast radio stations or other ships before transferring to a working channel.

The distress signal 'MAYDAY' requests immediate assistance to be given to a ship, aircraft or person in grave and imminent danger. This includes a person lost overboard who is not immediately recovered. Anyone hearing the MAYDAY is obliged under the Geneva Convention to give what assistance they can, provided this does not endanger their own crew or vessel.

The urgency signal 'PAN-PAN' prefaces a very urgent message about the safety of a ship or person, or medical advice concerning a serious injury. The safety signal 'SECURITE', is used by coast stations to precede navigation or weather warnings, it might equally be used by ships at sea to report such hazards as a navigation buoy adrift or with its light extinguished.

MEDICAL ADVICE BY RADIO

European countries covered by this Almanac will give medical advice on request. Messages are usually sent via Coastguard or coast radio stations of the country concerned.

UNITED KINGDOM. Yachts should call nearest Coastguard Station by name on VHF Ch 16 using the prefix PAN PAN MEDICO. The Coastguard will nominate Ch 67 for full details and then arrange a priority allocation of a working channel and you will be connected to a doctor on that channel. There is no charge for this call.

As advised, in cases of emergency, call the Coastguard again on Ch 16 to arrange a helicopter or lifeboat. The CG may monitor the call to the doctor and contact the appropriate rescue service. Should you have a casualty who is in grave and imminent danger requiring immediate assistance make a MAYDAY call on VHF Ch 16.

FRANCE. Yachts call nearest coastal radio station using PAN, PAN, repeated three times. 'Radiomedical.... (name of nearest CROSS station)'. French language may well have to be used.

BELGIUM. Yachts call Ostend coast radio station using 'Radio-medical/Ostend': English, French, Dutch or German language may be used.

NETHERLANDS. Yachts call 'Netherlands Coastguard'. English, Dutch, French or German language may be used.

FEDERAL REPUBLIC OF GERMANY. Yachts call nearest coast radio station using 'Funkarzt. . . (name of station)'. English or German language may be used.

REPUBLIC OF IRELAND. Call nearest Coast radio station by name.

ORGANISATION OF THE MARINE VHF BAND

The following table lists all 55 International VHF Channels (Ch 70 is reserved exclusively for Selective-Call Distress and Safety and is no longer used for Ship-to Ship). Note that there are two types of channel, simplex and duplex. On a simplex channel the same frequency is used for both transmission and reception — it is possible to either transmit or receive at any one time, but not do both simultaneously. Duplex channels are used for ship-to-shore communications and have two frequencies on which the ship transmits and the shore receives, the other on which the shore transmits and the ship receives. With full duplex working, it is possible to hold a conversation as one would talk on a land-line telephone. However, most yachts have only one aerial (which both receives and transmits) and thus even when working a duplex channel it is best to adopt the simplex procedure of inviting a reply using the word 'over'.

INTERNATIONAL CHANNELS			
Channel Number	Ship station frequency	Shore station frequency	Function
00	156.000	156.000	H.M. Coastguard - Private
60	156.025	160.625	Public Correspondence and Port Operations (Two-Frequency)
01	156.050	160.650	
61	156.075	160.675	
02	156.100	160.700	
62	156.125	160.725	
03	156.150	160.750	
63	156.175	160.775	
04	156.200	160.800	
64	156.225	160.825	
05	156.250	160.850	
65	156.275	160.875	
06	156.300	—	Inter Ship *only*
66	156.325	160.925	Public Correspondence and Port Operations
07	156.350	160.950	
67	156.375	156.375	Small Boat Safety Channel (British)
08	156.400	—	Inter Ship *only*
68	156.425	156.425	Port Operations *only*
09	156.450	156.450	Inter Ship and Port Operations
69	156.475	156.475	
10	156.500	156.500	
70	156.525	DIGITAL	Selective Call — Distress & Safety
11	156.550	156.550	Port Operations *only*
71	156.575	156.575	

INTERNATIONAL CHANNELS

Channel Number		Ship station frequency	Shore station frequency	Function
12		156.600	156.600	Port Operations *only*
	72	156.625	—	Inter Ship *only*
13		156.650	156.650	Inter Ship and
	73	156.675	156.675	Port Operations
14		156.700	156.700	Port Operations *only*
	74	156.725	156.725	
15		156.750	156.750	Inter Ship and Port Operations
	75	—	—	Guard Band 156.7625 - 156.7875Mhz
16		156.800	156.800	Distress, Urgency & Calling *only*
	76	—	—	Guard Band 156.8125 - 156.8375Mhz
17		156.850	156.850	Inter Ship and Port Operations
	77	156.875	—	Inter Ship *only*
	M		157.850	Marinas secondary working channel
	M2		161.425	Yacht Clubs
18		156.900	161.500	Port Operations *only*
	78	156.925	161.525	Public Corr. and Port Operations
19		156.950	161.550	
	79	156.975	161.575	
20		157.000	161.600	Port Operations *only*
	80	157.025	161.625	Marinas
21		157.050	161.650	
	81	157.075	161.675	Public Corr. and Port Operations
22		157.100	161.700	Port Operations *only*
	82	157.125	161.725	Public Corr. and Port Operations
23		157.150	161.750	Public Correspondence *only*
	83	157.175	161.775	(Two-Frequency)
24		157.200	161.800	
	84	157.225	161.825	Public Corr. and Port Operations
25		157.250	161.850	
	85	157.275	161.875	
26		157.300	161.900	
	86	157.325	161.925	Public Correspondence *only*
27		157.350	161.950	(Two-Frequency)
	87	157.375	161.975	
28		157.400	162.000	
	88	157.425	162.025	

Section 4

371

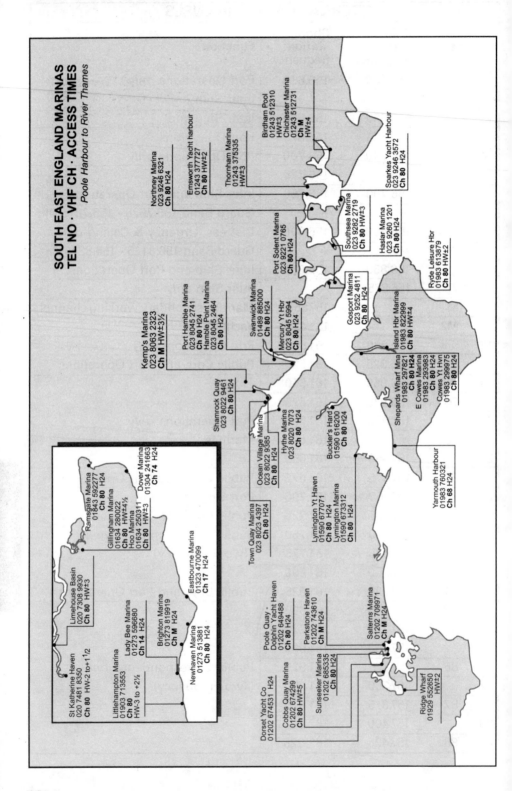

SOUTH EAST ENGLAND MARINAS
TEL NO · VHF CH · ACCESS TIMES
Poole Harbour to River Thames

Northney Marina
023 9246 6321
Ch 80 H24

Emsworth Yacht harbour
01243 377727
Ch 80 HW±2

Thornham Marina
01243 375335
HW±3

Birdham Pool
01243 512310
HW±3
Chichester Marina
01243 512731
Ch M
HW±4

Sparkes Yacht Harbour
023 9246 3572
Ch 80 H24

Southsea Marina
023 9282 2719
Ch 80 HW±3

Haslar Marina
023 9260 1201
Ch 80 H24

Ryde Leisure Hbr
01983 613879
Ch 80 HW±2

Kemp's Marina
023 8063 2323
Ch M HW±3½

Port Hamble Marina
023 8045 2741
Ch 80 H24
Hamble Point Marina
023 8045 2464
Ch 80 H24

Swanwick Marina
01489 885000
Ch 80 H24

Mercury Yt Hbr
023 8045 5994
Ch 80 H24

Port Solent Marina
023 9221 0765
Ch 80 H24

Gosport Marina
023 9252 4811
Ch 80 H24

Island Hbr Marina
01983 822999
Ch 80 HW±4

Shamrock Quay
023 8022 9461
Ch 80 H24

Ocean Village Marina
023 8022 9385
Ch 80 H24

Hythe Marina
023 8020 7073
Ch 80 H24

Buckler's Hard
01590 616200
Ch 80 H24

Shepards Wharf Mna
01983 297821
Ch 80 H24
E Cowes Marina
01983 293983
Ch 80 H24
Cowes Yt Hvn
01983 299975
Ch 80 H24

Yarmouth Harbour
01983 760321
Ch 68 H24

Town Quay Marina
023 8023 4397
Ch 80 H24

Lymington Yt Haven
01590 677071
Ch 80 H24
Lymington Marina
01590 673312
Ch 80 H24

Salterns Marina
01202 709971
Ch M H24

Ridge Wharf
01929 552650
HW±2

St Katherine Haven
020 7481 8350
Ch 80 HW-2 to+1/2

Littlehampton Marina
01903 713553
HW-3 to +2½

Lady Bee Marina
01273 596680
Ch 14 H24

Limehouse Basin
020 7308 9930
Ch 80 HW±3

Brighton Marina
01273 819919
Ch M H24

Ramsgate Marina
01843 592277
Ch 80 H24

Gillingham Marina
01634 280022
Ch 80 HW±4½
Hoo Marina
01634 250311
Ch 80 HW±3

Dover Marina
01304 241663
Ch 74 H24

Eastbourne Marina
01323 470099
Ch 17 H24

Newhaven Marina
01273 513881
Ch 80 H24

Dorset Yacht Co
01202 674531 H24

Cobbs Quay Marina
01202 674299
Ch 80 HW±5

Poole Quay -
Dolphin Yacht Haven
01202 649488
Ch 80 H24

Parkstone Haven
01202 743610
Ch M H24

Sunseeker Marina
01202 685335
Ch 80 H24

372

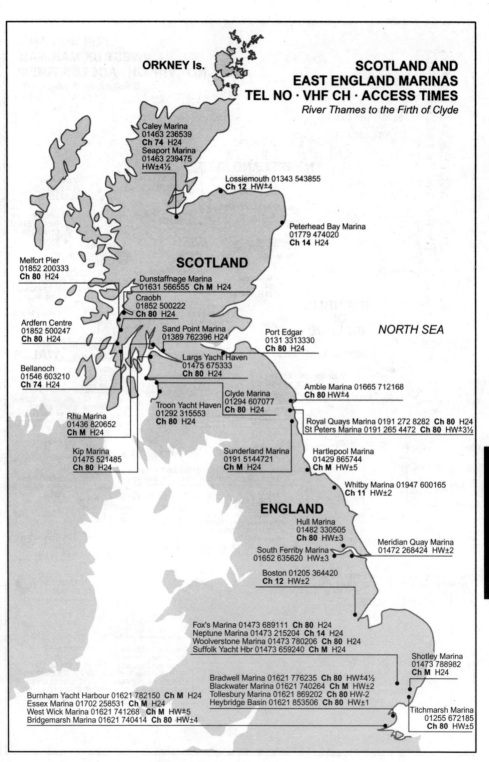

ORKNEY Is.

SCOTLAND AND EAST ENGLAND MARINAS
TEL NO · VHF CH · ACCESS TIMES
River Thames to the Firth of Clyde

Caley Marina
01463 236539
Ch 74 H24
Seaport Marina
01463 239475
HW±4½

Lossiemouth 01343 543855
Ch 12 HW±4

Peterhead Bay Marina
01779 474020
Ch 14 H24

Melfort Pier
01852 200333
Ch 80 H24

SCOTLAND

Dunstaffnage Marina
01631 566555 **Ch M** H24

Craobh
01852 500222
Ch 80 H24

Ardfern Centre
01852 500247
Ch 80 H24

Sand Point Marina
01389 762396 H24

Port Edgar
0131 3313330
Ch 80 H24

NORTH SEA

Bellanoch
01546 603210
Ch 74 H24

Largs Yacht Haven
01475 675333
Ch 80 H24

Amble Marina 01665 712168
Ch 80 HW±4

Rhu Marina
01436 820652
Ch M H24

Troon Yacht Haven
01292 315553
Ch 80 H24

Clyde Marina
01294 607077
Ch 80 H24

Royal Quays Marina 0191 272 8282 **Ch 80** H24
St Peters Marina 0191 265 4472 **Ch 80** HW±3½

Kip Marina
01475 521485
Ch 80 H24

Sunderland Marina
0191 5144721
Ch M H24

Hartlepool Marina
01429 865744
Ch M HW±5

Whitby Marina 01947 600165
Ch 11 HW±2

ENGLAND

Hull Marina
01482 330505
Ch 80 HW±3

Meridian Quay Marina
01472 268424 HW±2

South Ferriby Marina
01652 635620 HW±3

Boston 01205 364420
Ch 12 HW±2

Fox's Marina 01473 689111 **Ch 80** H24
Neptune Marina 01473 215204 **Ch 14** H24
Woolverstone Marina 01473 780206 **Ch 80** H24
Suffolk Yacht Hbr 01473 659240 **Ch M** H24

Shotley Marina
01473 788982
Ch M H24

Bradwell Marina 01621 776235 **Ch 80** HW±4½
Blackwater Marina 01621 740264 **Ch M** HW±2
Tollesbury Marina 01621 869202 **Ch 80** HW-2
Heybridge Basin 01621 853506 **Ch 80** HW±1

Burnham Yacht Harbour 01621 782150 **Ch M** H24
Essex Marina 01702 258531 **Ch M** H24
West Wick Marina 01621 741268 **Ch M** HW±5
Bridgemarsh Marina 01621 740414 **Ch 80** HW±4

Titchmarsh Marina
01255 672185
Ch 80 HW±5

Section 4

373

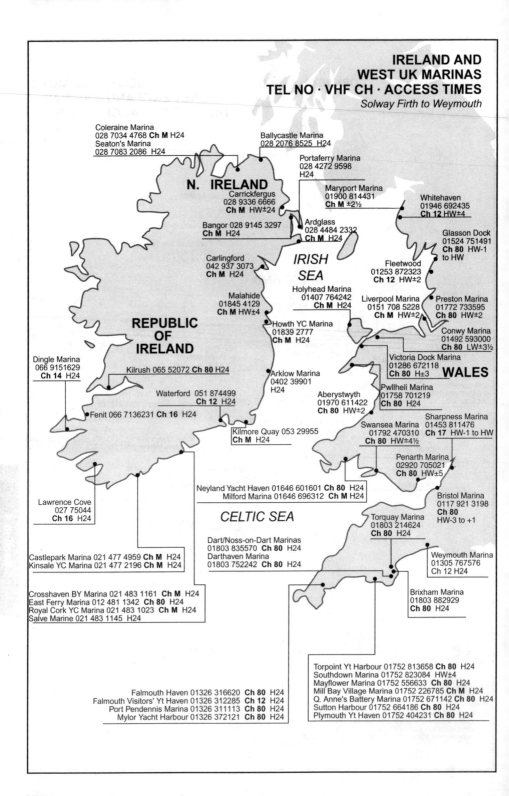

IRELAND AND WEST UK MARINAS
TEL NO · VHF CH · ACCESS TIMES
Solway Firth to Weymouth

Coleraine Marina
028 7034 4768 **Ch M** H24
Seaton's Marina
028 7083 2086 H24

Ballycastle Marina
028 2076 8525 H24

Portaferry Marina
028 4272 9598
H24

N. IRELAND
Carrickfergus
028 9336 6666
Ch M HW±24

Maryport Marina
01900 814431
Ch M ±2½

Whitehaven
01946 692435
Ch 12 HW±4

Bangor 028 9145 3297
Ch M H24

Ardglass
028 4484 2332
Ch M H24

Glasson Dock
01524 751491
Ch 80 HW-1
to HW

Carlingford
042 937 3073
Ch M H24

Fleetwood
01253 872323
Ch 12 HW±2

*IRISH
SEA*

Malahide
01845 4129
Ch M HW±4

Holyhead Marina
01407 764242
Ch M H24

Liverpool Marina
0151 708 5228
Ch M HW±2

Preston Marina
01772 733595
Ch 80 HW±2

**REPUBLIC
OF
IRELAND**

Howth YC Marina
01839 2777
Ch M H24

Conwy Marina
01492 593000
Ch 80 LW±3½

Dingle Marina
066 9151629
Ch 14 H24

Kilrush 065 52072 **Ch 80** H24

Arklow Marina
0402 39901
H24

Victoria Dock Marina
01286 672118
Ch 80 H±3 **WALES**

Waterford 051 874499
Ch 12 H24

Aberystwyth
01970 611422
Ch 80 HW±2

Pwllheli Marina
01758 701219
Ch 80 H24

Fenit 066 7136231 **Ch 16** H24

Sharpness Marina
01453 811476
Ch 17 HW-1 to HW

Kilmore Quay 053 29955
Ch M H24

Swansea Marina 01792 470310
Ch 80 HW±4½

Penarth Marina
02920 705021
Ch 80 HW±5

Lawrence Cove
027 75044
Ch 16 H24

Neyland Yacht Haven 01646 601601 **Ch 80** H24
Milford Marina 01646 696312 **Ch M** H24

CELTIC SEA

Torquay Marina
01803 214624
Ch 80 H24

Bristol Marina
0117 921 3198
Ch 80
HW-3 to +1

Castlepark Marina 021 477 4959 **Ch M** H24
Kinsale YC Marina 021 477 2196 **Ch M** H24

Dart/Noss-on-Dart Marinas
01803 835570 **Ch 80** H24
Darthaven Marina
01803 752242 **Ch 80** H24

Weymouth Marina
01305 767576
Ch 12 H24

Crosshaven BY Marina 021 483 1161 **Ch M** H24
East Ferry Marina 012 481 1342 **Ch 80** H24
Royal Cork YC Marina 021 483 1023 **Ch M** H24
Salve Marine 021 483 1145 H24

Brixham Marina
01803 882929
Ch 80 H24

Torpoint Yt Harbour 01752 813658 **Ch 80** H24
Southdown Marina 01752 823084 HW±4
Mayflower Marina 01752 556633 **Ch 80** H24
Mill Bay Village Marina 01752 226785 **Ch M** H24
Q. Anne's Battery Marina 01752 671142 **Ch 80** H24
Sutton Harbour 01752 664186 **Ch 80** H24
Plymouth Yt Haven 01752 404231 **Ch 80** H24

Falmouth Haven 01326 316620 **Ch 80** H24
Falmouth Visitors' Yt Haven 01326 312285 **Ch 12** H24
Port Pendennis Marina 01326 311113 **Ch 80** H24
Mylor Yacht Harbour 01326 372121 **Ch 80** H24

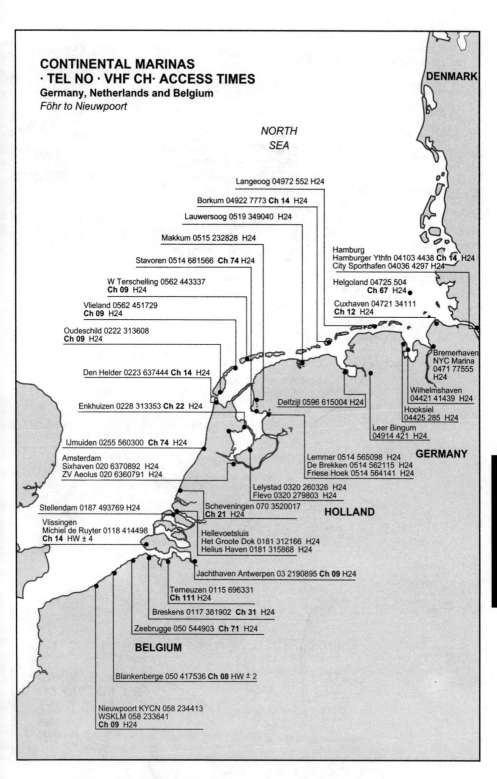

CONTINENTAL MARINAS
· TEL NO · VHF CH· ACCESS TIMES
Germany, Netherlands and Belgium
Föhr to Nieuwpoort

DENMARK

NORTH
SEA

Langeoog 04972 552 H24

Borkum 04922 7773 **Ch 14** H24

Lauwersoog 0519 349040 H24

Makkum 0515 232828 H24

Stavoren 0514 681566 **Ch 74** H24

W Terschelling 0562 443337 **Ch 09** H24

Vlieland 0562 451729 **Ch 09** H24

Oudeschild 0222 313608 **Ch 09** H24

Den Helder 0223 637444 **Ch 14** H24

Enkhuizen 0228 313353 **Ch 22** H24

IJmuiden 0255 560300 **Ch 74** H24

Amsterdam
Sixhaven 020 6370892 H24
ZV Aeolus 020 6360791 H24

Stellendam 0187 493769 H24

Vlissingen
Michiel de Ruyter 0118 414498 **Ch 14** HW ± 4

Hamburg
Hamburger Ythfn 04103 4438 **Ch 14** H24
City Sporthafen 04036 4297 H24

Helgoland 04725 504 **Ch 67** H24

Cuxhaven 04721 34111 **Ch 12** H24

Bremerhaven
NYC Marina
0471 77555 H24

Wilhelmshaven
04421 41439 H24

Hooksiel
04425 285 H24

Leer Bingum
04914 421 H24

Delfzijl 0596 615004 H24

Lemmer 0514 565098 H24
De Brekken 0514 562115 H24
Friese Hoek 0514 564141 H24

GERMANY

Lelystad 0320 260326 H24
Flevo 0320 279803 H24

Scheveningen 070 3520017 **Ch 21** H24

HOLLAND

Hellevoetsluis
Het Groote Dok 0181 312166 H24
Helius Haven 0181 315868 H24

Jachthaven Antwerpen 03 2190895 **Ch 09** H24

Terneuzen 0115 696331 **Ch 111** H24

Breskens 0117 381902 **Ch 31** H24

Zeebrugge 050 544903 **Ch 71** H24

BELGIUM

Blankenberge 050 417536 **Ch 08** HW ± 2

Nieuwpoort KYCN 058 234413
WSKLM 058 233641 **Ch 09** H24

Section 4

375

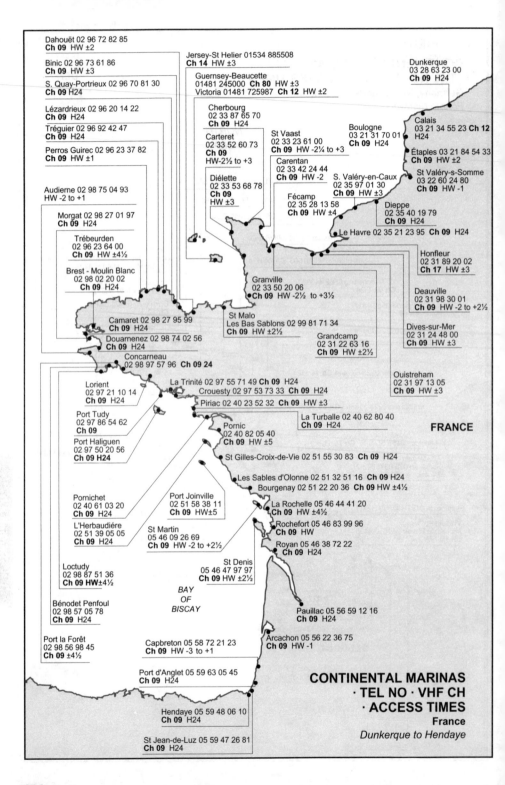

Dahouët 02 96 72 82 85
Ch 09 HW ±2

Binic 02 96 73 61 86
Ch 09 HW ±3

S. Quay-Portrieux 02 96 70 81 30
Ch 09 H24

Lézardrieux 02 96 20 14 22
Ch 09 H24

Tréguier 02 96 92 42 47
Ch 09 H24

Perros Guirec 02 96 23 37 82
Ch 09 HW ±1

Audierne 02 98 75 04 93
HW -2 to +1

Morgat 02 98 27 01 97
Ch 09 H24

Trébeurden
02 96 23 64 00
Ch 09 HW ±4½

Brest - Moulin Blanc
02 98 02 20 02
Ch 09 H24

Camaret 02 98 27 95 99
Ch 09 H24

Douarnenez 02 98 74 02 56
Ch 09 H24

Concarneau
02 98 97 57 96 **Ch 09 24**

Lorient
02 97 21 10 14
Ch 09 H24

Port Tudy
02 97 86 54 62
Ch 09

Port Haliguen
02 97 50 20 56
Ch 09 H24

Pornichet
02 40 61 03 20
Ch 09 H24

L'Herbaudière
02 51 39 05 05
Ch 09 H24

Loctudy
02 98 87 51 36
Ch 09 HW±4½

Bénodet Penfoul
02 98 57 05 78
Ch 09 H24

Port la Forêt
02 98 56 98 45
Ch 09 ±4½

Jersey-St Helier 01534 885508
Ch 14 HW ±3

Guernsey-Beaucette
01481 245000 **Ch 80** HW ±3
Victoria 01481 725987 **Ch 12** HW ±2

Cherbourg
02 33 87 65 70
Ch 09 H24

Carteret
02 33 52 60 73
Ch 09
HW-2½ to +3

Diélette
02 33 53 68 78
Ch 09
HW ±3

Granville
02 33 50 20 06
Ch 09 HW -2½ to +3½

St Malo
Les Bas Sablons 02 99 81 71 34
Ch 09 HW ±2½

La Trinité 02 97 55 71 49 **Ch 09** H24
Crouesty 02 97 53 73 33 **Ch 09** H24
Piriac 02 40 23 52 32 **Ch 09** HW ±3

Pornic
02 40 82 05 40
Ch 09 HW ±5

St Gilles-Croix-de-Vie 02 51 55 30 83 **Ch 09** H24

Les Sables d'Olonne 02 51 32 51 16 **Ch 09** H24
Bourgenay 02 51 22 20 36 **Ch 09** HW ±4½

Port Joinville
02 51 58 38 11
Ch 09 HW±5

St Martin
05 46 09 26 69
Ch 09 HW -2 to +2½

St Denis
05 46 47 97 97
Ch 09 HW ±2½

BAY
OF
BISCAY

St Vaast
02 33 23 61 00
Ch 09 HW -2¼ to +3

Carentan
02 33 42 24 44
Ch 09 HW -2

Fécamp
02 35 28 13 58
Ch 09 HW ±4

Grandcamp
02 31 22 63 16
Ch 09 HW ±2½

La Turballe 02 40 62 80 40
Ch 09 H24

Capbreton 05 58 72 21 23
Ch 09 HW -3 to +1

Port d'Anglet 05 59 63 05 45
Ch 09 H24

Hendaye 05 59 48 06 10
Ch 09 H24

St Jean-de-Luz 05 59 47 26 81
Ch 09 H24

Boulogne
03 21 31 70 01
Ch 09 H24

Dunkerque
03 28 63 23 00
Ch 09 H24

Calais
03 21 34 55 23 **Ch 12**
H24

Étaples 03 21 84 54 33
Ch 09 HW ±2

St Valéry-s-Somme
03 22 60 24 80
Ch 09 HW -1

S. Valéry-en-Caux
02 35 97 01 30
Ch 09 HW ±3

Dieppe
02 35 40 19 79
Ch 09 H24

Le Havre 02 35 21 23 95 **Ch 09** H24

Honfleur
02 31 89 20 02
Ch 17 HW ±3

Deauville
02 31 98 30 01
Ch 09 HW -2 to +2½

Dives-sur-Mer
02 31 24 48 00
Ch 09 HW ±3

Ouistreham
02 31 97 13 05
Ch 09 HW ±3

FRANCE

La Rochelle 05 46 44 41 20
Ch 09 HW ±4½

Rochefort 05 46 83 99 96
Ch 09 HW

Royan 05 46 38 72 22
Ch 09 H24

Pauillac 05 56 59 12 16
Ch 09 H24

Arcachon 05 56 22 36 75
Ch 09 HW -1

**CONTINENTAL MARINAS
· TEL NO · VHF CH
· ACCESS TIMES**
France
Dunkerque to Hendaye

CONTINENTAL MARINAS ·
TEL NO · VHF CH · ACCESS TIMES
Spain and Portugal
Bilbao to Gibraltar

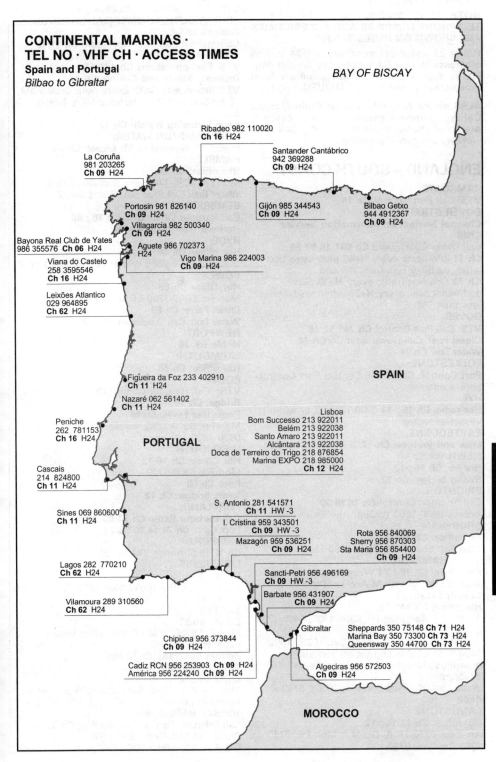

BAY OF BISCAY

Ribadeo 982 110020
Ch 16 H24

La Coruña
981 203265
Ch 09 H24

Santander Cantábrico
942 369288
Ch 09 H24

Portosin 981 826140
Ch 09 H24

Gijón 985 344543
Ch 09 H24

Bilbao Getxo
944 4912367
Ch 09 H24

Villagarcia 982 500340
Ch 09 H24

Bayona Real Club de Yates
986 355576 **Ch 06** H24

Aguete 986 702373
H24

Vigo Marina 986 224003
Ch 09 H24

Viana do Castelo
258 3595546
Ch 16 H24

Leixões Atlantico
029 964895
Ch 62 H24

Figueira da Foz 233 402910
Ch 11 H24

Nazaré 062 561402
Ch 11 H24

SPAIN

Lisboa
Bom Successo 213 922011
Belém 213 922038
Santo Amaro 213 922011
Alcântara 213 922038
Doca de Terreiro do Trigo 218 876854
Marina EXPO 218 985000
Ch 12 H24

Peniche
262 781153
Ch 16 H24

PORTUGAL

Cascais
214 824800
Ch 11 H24

Sines 069 860600
Ch 11 H24

S. Antonio 281 541571
Ch 11 HW -3

I. Cristina 959 343501
Ch 09 HW -3

Mazagón 959 536251
Ch 09 H24

Rota 956 840069
Sherry 956 870303
Sta Maria 956 854400
Ch 09 H24

Lagos 282 770210
Ch 62 H24

Sancti-Petri 956 496169
Ch 09 HW -3

Vilamoura 289 310560
Ch 62 H24

Barbate 956 431907
Ch 09 H24

Chipiona 956 373844
Ch 09 H24

Gibraltar

Sheppards 350 75148 **Ch 71** H24
Marina Bay 350 73300 **Ch 73** H24
Queensway 350 44700 **Ch 73** H24

Cadiz RCN 956 253903 **Ch 09** H24
América 956 224240 **Ch 09** H24

Algeciras 956 572503
Ch 09 H24

MOROCCO

PORT RADIO STATIONS

NOTE THAT MARINA VHF CHANNELS, TELEPHONE NUMBERS AND ACCESS TIMES ARE SHOWN ON PAGES 372-377

Hours of watch are continuous **H24** unless otherwise shown, **HJ** indicate day service only, **HX** no specific hours. Times given are local time except where marked **UT/UTC**.

ALRS means Admiralty List of Radio Signals. Calling channels precede a semi colon **;**, preferred channels are marked *****. *Call on a working channel if possible.*

ENGLAND – SOUTH COAST

RAMSGATE:
VTS: Call Port Control **Ch 14**
DOVER STRAIT:
Channel Navigation Information Service
CNIS:
Call Dover Coastguard **Ch 69* 16 67 80**
Ch 11 Info bcsts every H+40 plus extra bcst when visibility less than 2M and
Ch 79 Gris Nez Traffic every H+10 plus additional bcst every H+25 when visibility less than 2M
DOVER:
VTS: Call Port Control **Ch 74* 12 16**
Diesel Fuel: Call Dover Boat Co **Ch 74**
Water Taxi: **Ch 74**
FOLKESTONE:
Port Control: **Ch 15* 16** Contact Port Control before entering.
RYE:
Hbr radio: **Ch 16 ; 14** 0900-1700 LT or when vessel expected
EASTBOURNE:
Lock and Bridges: **Ch 17**
NEWHAVEN:
Hbr Mr: **Ch 16 ; 12**
Swing bridge: **Ch 12**
BRIGHTON:
Call Brighton Control **Ch 16 M 80 ;**
Access 0800-1800 through the lock
SHOREHAM:
Hbr office: **Ch 14 16**
Mon-Sat: 0800-1830, Sun: 0900-1300
LITTLEHAMPTON:
Hbr office: **Ch 16 ; 71** When vessel expected
Arun Yacht Club: **Ch M** Access HW±3
CHICHESTER:
Hbr office: **Ch 14* 16**
1 Oct - 31 Mar: Mon-Fri: 0900-1300, 1400-1730 LT.
Sat: 0900-1300 LT. 1 Apr-31 Sep: 0900-1300, 1400-1730 LT. Visiting yachts requiring moorings should make arrangements in advance.
Water taxi 0900-1800, mobile 07970 378350
Ch08
LANGSTONE:
Hbr office: **Ch 12 16 ; 12**
Apr-Sep: 0730-1700, Oct-Mar Mon-Fri: 0730-1700 Sat Sun: 0730-1300

PORTSMOUTH:
VTS: Call QHM **Ch 11**, Dockyard craft **Ch 73**
PORTSMOUTH COMMERCIAL HARBOUR:
Queen's HM **Ch 11**
Commercial Port: Call Hbr Radio **Ch 11 13**
SOUTHAMPTON:
VTS: Port operations **Ch 12* 14**
Distress, Safety and Calling: **Ch 16**
VTS Broadcasts **Ch12** Every hour 0600-2200 LT Fri-Sun and Bank Holiday Mon, Easter – 30 Sep
Keep Listening Watch: **Ch 12**
SOUTHAMPTON WATER:
Fuel: Call Wyefuel or **Mr Diesel**: **Ch 08**
HAMBLE:
Hbr office: **Ch 68**
Mon-Fri: 0830-1700, Sat Sun: 0830-1930
Water Taxi: Call Blue Star Boats **Ch 77**
BEMBRIDGE:
Call Harbour Office BHL **Ch 16 ; 80**
Harbour launch **Ch M**
RYDE:
Hbr office: **Ch 80**
Summer 0900-2000 Winter HX. Access HW±2
COWES:
Hbr Office **Ch 69**
Mon-Fri: 0800-1700 LT and by arrangement
Chain Ferry: **Ch 69**
Water Taxi: Call 'Thumper' **Ch 77**
NEWPORT:
Hr Mr: **69 16**
YARMOUTH:
Hbr office: **Ch 68**
POOLE:
VTS: Call Harbour Control **Ch 14**
Bridge: **Ch 14**
Poole Bay Fuels: **Ch M**
Mon-Fri: 0900-1730, weekends in season 0830-1800
WEYMOUTH:
Hbr Office: **Ch 16 12**
Mon-Fri: 0800-1700
Fuel: **Ch 60**
Town Bridge: **Ch 12**
PORTLAND:
Call Harbour Radio **Ch 74 09** (H24)
Port Ops: **Ch 74 14 20 28 71**
BRIDPORT:
Ch 11 16 Summer: 0730-1700
LYME REGIS:
Ch 14 16
Summer: 0800-2000, Winter: 1000-1500. Access HW±2½
EXETER:
Ch 16 ; 06 12
Mon-Fri: 0730-1630 LT and when vessel expected
Retreat Boatyard: **Ch M** HW±3½
TEIGNMOUTH:
Ch 12 16 ; 12
Mon-Fri 0800-1700, Sat 0900-1200 and when vessel expected
TORBAY HARBOURS:
Call Brixham Port or Torquay Port **Ch 12 16**
Ch 16 ; 14 May-Sep: 0800-1700,
Oct-Apr: Mon-Fri: 0900-1800

DARTMOUTH:
Ch 11 09 16 Mon-Fri: 0900-1700 LT, Sat: 0900-1200
Britannia Royal Naval College: Ch 71
SALCOMBE:
Port: Ch 14 0900-1615
Harbour Master Launches: Ch 14
Summer: 0600-2200
Water Taxi: Call Salcombe Harbour Taxi **Ch 12**
Fuel Barge: Ch 06
Winters Marine: Call Lincolme Yard **Ch 72**
Access HW±5
HMS CAMBRIDGE:
Call Wembury Range **Ch 11* 10 16**
When range operating
PLYMOUTH:
Naval: Call Longroom Control **Ch 16 ; 08 11 12
13**
Commercial: Call Longroom Control **Ch 16 ; 14**
Millbay Docks: Ch 16 ; 12 14 Ferry hours only
Sutton Harbour Marina: Ch M 80
Lock: Ch 16 ; 12
LOOE: Ch 16 HX
FOWEY:
Ch 12*; 11 16 0900-1700
Harbour Launch: Call Port Radio **Ch 09** Apr-
Oct
Refueller: Ch 16 10
Summer: 0900-1800, Winter: Mon-Fri: 0900-
1800
PAR:
Hbr office: Ch 16 ; 12 Access HW±2
CHARLESTOWN:
Hbr office: Ch 16 ; 14
Access –2HW+1 only when vessel expected
MEVAGISSEY:
Hbr office: Ch 16 ; 14
Summer: 0900-2100, Winter: 0900-1700
FALMOUTH:
Port Operations Working: Ch 12
Alternative Working: Ch 14
Pollution: Ch 10
Harbour Launch 'Killigrew': Ch 12
Mon-Fri: 0800-1700
Dockmaster: Ch 11
Truro: Ch 12
PENZANCE:
Hbr office: Ch 16 ; 09 12
Mon-Fri: 0800-1630 Sat: 0830-1230. Access –
2HW+1
NEWLYN:
Hbr office: Ch 16 ; 09 12
Mon-Fri: 0800-1700, Sat: 0800-1200
OFF LAND'S END TSS:
Call Falmouth Coastguard **Ch 16 ; 67**
St Mary's, Isles of Scilly: Ch 16 ; 14
Summer 0800-1700, Winter Mon-Fri 0800-1700
Sat 0800-1200

ENGLAND – EAST COAST

BERWICK-UPON-TWEED:
Hbr office: Ch 16 ; 12
WARKWORTH HARBOUR:
Hbr office: Ch 16 ; 14
BLYTH:
Hbr office: Ch 12 16 ; 11

PORT OF TYNE:
VTS: Ch 12 16 ; 11 14
Harbour Launch: Ch 16 ; 06 08 11 12 14
SUNDERLAND:
Port: Ch 16 ; 14
SEAHAM:
Hbr office: Ch 12*; 16 06
Hr Mr Office –2½HW+1½,
Operations Office Mon-Fri: Office hours
TEES:
Port operations: Ch 16 ; 12 14 22 08
Barrage: Ch M
HARTLEPOOL:
Yacht Club: Ch M Office Hours
WHITBY:
Hbr office: Ch 11* 16 ; 12
Bridge: Ch 11* 16 ; 06
Access HW±2
SCARBOROUGH:
Call Scarborough Lighthouse **Ch 16 ; 12**
Access HW±3
BRIDLINGTON:
Hbr office: Ch 16 ; 12* 67 HX. Access HW±3
HUMBER:
VTS Area 1: Ch 14 (Seawards to Clee Ness Lt F)
VTS Area 2: Ch 12
Port: Ch 12 14 16
Navigation and Safety Information: Ch 12
Weather, tides and nav: Ch 12 Every odd H+03
**Listening watch - R Humber & approaches:
Ch 12**
Listening watch - R Ouse: Ch 14
**Listening watch - R Trent (Ouse to Keadby
Br): Ch 08**
**Listening watch - R Trent (Keadby Br to
Gainsborough): Ch 06**
South Ferriby: Ch 74 80
Mon-Fri: 0930-1700, Sat Sun & Holidays: 1030-
1700. Access HW±3
Grimsby: Ch 74 ; 18 74 79
**Immingham Docks: Ch 19 68 ; 17 19 68 69 71
73 74 69 71 73 74**
SOUTH KILLINGHOLME: Ch 19 69 71
NORTH KILLINGHOLME: Ch 19 74
King George Dock: Ch 11 ; 09 11 22
Alexandra Dock: Ch 11 ; 09 11 22
River Hull Port Operations: Ch 22 ; 11 22
Mon-Fri –2HW Hull+1.
Sat 0900-1100 (irrespective of tide)
Albert Dock: Ch 09 ; 09 11 22
New Holland: Ch 11 22
Goole Railway Bridge: Ch 09
Howdendyke: Ch 09
Boothferry bridge: Ch 09
Selby lock: Ch 16 74
Selby railway bridge: Ch 09
Toll Bridge: Ch 09
Outward vessels contact 10 min in advance.
NABURN:
Lock: Ch 16 74 HJ
Burton-upon-Stather: Ch 17
Flixborough: Ch 17
Grove: Ch 17
Keadby: Ch 17
Keadby Lock: Ch 16 74
Gunness: Ch 17

West Stockwith, Torksey and Cromwell locks: Ch 16 74
Gainsborough: Ch 17
BOSTON:
Dock: Ch 16; 11 12
Grand Sluice: Ch 16 74 Only when lock is operating
Denver Sluice: Ch 73 When vessel expected
KING'S LYNN:
Call KLCB Ch 14*; 16 11 12
Mon-Fri: 0800-1730 and –4HW+1
Docks: Call Docks Radio ABP Ch 14* 16; 11 Access –2½HW+1
WISBECH:
Ch 16; 72 –3HW when vessel expected
Sutton Bridge: Ch 09
WELLS-NEXT-THE-SEA:
Hbr office: Ch 12 16
HJ and 3h before HW when vessel expected
GREAT YARMOUTH:
VTS: Ch 12 16
Port: Ch 12 16 ; 09 11 12
Haven Bridge: Ch 12
Norwich Bridges: Ch 12
LOWESTOFT:
Hbr office: Ch 14* 16
Yachts may use bridge openings for commercial ships by arrangement with Hbr Control on Ch 14
Royal Norfolk & Suffolk YC: Ch 80 Access HW±4
Mutford Lock and Road Bridge: Ch 09 14
SOUTHWOLD:
Hr Mr: Ch 12* 16 ; 12 0800-1800 LT
RIVER DEBEN:
Hbr office: Ch 08
Felixstowe Ferry Boatyard: Ch 08 16 ; 08 Access HW±4
Tide Mill Harbour: Ch M 80 Access –2HW+3
HARWICH HARBOUR:
VTS: Ch 71* 14
Calling and Safety: Ch 16
Hbr services: Ch 11
Parkstone Quay: Ch 16 ; 18
RIVER ORWELL:
Ipswich: Ch 14* 16 ; 14* 12
COLCHESTER:
Hbr office: Ch 68* 16 ; 11 14
Mon-Fri: 0900-1700 LT and –3HW+1
Listening Watch: Ch 68
BRIGHTLINGSEA:
Port: Ch 68 0800-2000. Access not LWS
RIVER BLACKWATER:
River Bailiff: Ch 16 0900-1700 Access HW±2
Heybridge Lock: Ch 80 -2HW+1
RIVER CROUCH:
Havengore Bridge: Ch 16 ; 72 Office hours
PORT OF LONDON:
Port Control: Ch 12
(seaward approaches to Sea Reach No 4 Lt buoy)
Port Control: Ch 68
Sea Reach No 4 Lt buoy to Crayford Ness
Port Control: 68 18 20
Below Crayford Ness
Woolwich Radio: Ch 14* 16 22
Above Crayford Ness

Port Control London: Ch 12* 16 18 20
Patrol Launches: Call Thames Patrol Ch 06 12 13 14 16
RIVER THAMES:
Tilbury Docks Lock: Ch 04
Thames Barrier: Ch 14* 16 22
All vessels equipped with VHF intending to navigate in the Thames Barrier Control Zone must report to Woolwich Radio on Ch 14
King George V Dock Lock: Call KG Control Ch 68
West India Dock Lock: Ch 13
Bow Lock: Ch 16 74 0500-2200
Greenwich Yacht Club: Ch M
Thames Lock (Brentford): Ch 74
Summer 0800-1800 Winter 0800-1630
Cadogan Pier: Ch 14 0900-1700
MEDWAY: Ch 74* 16 ; 09 11 22 73
BP Kent, Isle of Grain: Ch 16; 73
While vessels are berthing
Kingsferry Bridge: Ch 10
Whitstable: Ch 09* 12 16
Mon-Fri: 0800-1700 and –3HW+1

SCOTLAND

KIRKCUDBRIGHT: Ch 16 ; 12 HW±2½
STRANRAER: Ch 16 ; 12
GIRVAN: Ch 16 ; 12
Mon-Fri: 0900-1700 LT
AYR: Ch 16 ; 14
TROON: Ch 16 ; 14
Mon-Thu: 0800-2400 LT, Fri: 0800-2300 LT,
IRVINE: Ch 16 ; 12
Mon-Fri: 0800-1600
Irvine Hbr Bridge: Ch 16 0900-1700
CLYDEPORT:
VTS: 12
Port Control: Ch 16 ; 12
QHM Faslane: Ch 13
Greenock Control: Ch 73
Conservancy vessels: Ch 16 ; 11
ARDROSSAN:
Hbr office: Ch 16 ; 12 14
Tarbert, Loch Fyne: Ch 16 14
ROTHESAY, Bute: Ch 16 ; 12
May-Sep: 0600-2100 LT, Oct-Apr: 0600-1900 LT
CRINAN: Ch 16 74
May-Sep: 0800-1200 1230-1600 1620-1800,
Oct: Mon-Sat: 0800-1200 1230-1600, Nov-Apr:
Mon-Fri: 0900-1530. Access summer 0800-1800 Spring/Autumn: Mon-Sat: 0800-1630
Winter: Mon-Fri: 0900-1530
Crinan Boats: Ch 16 ; 12 M
Loch Melfort: Ch 16 ; 12
CAMPBELTOWN: Ch 16 12 14
Mon-Thu: 0845-1645, Fri: 0845-1600
Glensanda Harbour: Ch 14 When vessel expected
OBAN: Ch 16 ; 12
0900-1700. No moorings or alongside berths
Ardoran Marine: Ch 16 Access NOT LW±2
Oban Yachts & Marine Services: Ch 16 80 0800-1700
Tobermory: Ch 16 12 Office Hours, listens only

Craignure Pier, Island of Mull: Ch 31 HX
Gott Bay Pier, Tiree: Ch 31
Arinagour Pier, Isle of Coll: Ch 31
Corpach: Ch 16 74
Summer: 0800-1800, Spring/Autumn: 0800-
1700, Winter: 0945-1600
Salen Jetty Loch Sunart: Ch 16
Mallaig: Ch 16 09 Office hours.
KYLE OF LOCHALSH:
Ch 11 16
Skye Bridge Crossing: Ch 12
Uig: Ch 16 08 HX
Portree Harbour, Isle of Skye: Ch 16 12 HX
Gairloch Harbour: Ch 16 HX
ULLAPOOL:
Ch 14 16 12 H24 fishing season, otherwise
office hours
Lochinver: Ch 09 16 HX
Kinlochbervie: Ch 14 16 HX
STORNOWAY:
Hbr office: Ch 16 12
Loch Maddy, N Uist: Ch 16 12
S Kilda: Call Kilda Radio Ch 16 HJ
Scrabster, Thurso: Ch 16 12 H24
PENTLAND FIRTH:
Call Pentland Coastguard Ch 16
ORKNEY HARBOURS:
Call Orkney Harbour Radio Ch 16 20 09 11
Kirkwall: Ch 16 12
Mon-Fri: 0800-1700 and when vessel
expected
Stromness Harbour: Ch 16 ; 12 Mon-Fri: 0900-
1700
Pierowall (Westray Pier): Ch 16 14 When
vessel expected
FAIR ISLE:
VTS: Call Shetland Coastguard Ch 16
Lerwick, Shetland: Ch 12* 11 16
Scalloway, Shetland: Ch 16 12* 09
Mon-Fri: 0600-1800, Sat: 0600-1230
SULLOM VOE HARBOUR, Shetland:
Distress and Safety: Ch 16
Port Control: Ch 14* 12 20
Traffic information on request: Ch 14 16
Balta Sound Harbour: Ch 16 20
Office hours or as required
Wick: Ch 16 ; 14 When vessel expected
CROMARTY FIRTH, INVERGORDON: Ch 11*
16 13
INVERNESS:
Port: Ch 12
Mon-Fri: 0900-1700 LT and when vessel
expected
Clachaharry Lock: call Clachnaharry Sea
Lock Ch 16 74 HW±4h
HOPEMAN:
Call Burghead Radio Ch 14 0700-1700 and 1H
before vessel expected
LOSSIEMOUTH: Ch 12 16 ; 12
0700-1700 LT
BUCKIE: Ch 12 16 ; 12 H24 on Ch 16
MACDUFF: Ch 16 ; 12
BANFF: Ch 16 14 Access HW ±4
FRASERBROUGH: Ch 16 ; 12
ABERDEEN:
Call Aberdeen Port Control Ch 16 06 11 12* 13

MONTROSE:
Call Port Control Ch 16 ; 12
DUNDEE:
Call Dundee Harbour Radio Ch 16 12
Royal Tay Yacht Club: Ch M
Anstruther: Ch 11 16
PERTH:
Call Perth Harbour Ch 16 09
FORTH PORTS:
Call Forth Navigation Ch 71* ; 12 20
Methil Docks: Ch 16 ; 14 Access –3HW+1
Leith: Ch 16 ; 12
Grangemouth Docks: Ch 16 ; 14
R. Forth Yacht Club: Call Boswall Ch M 80 Access
HW±4
FIRTH OF FORTH:
Eyemouth: Ch 16 ; 12 office hours

W COAST ENGLAND & WALES

ST IVES: Ch 16 14 HX
Hayle Harbour: Ch 18* ; 16 14 0900-1700
PADSTOW:
Hbr office: Ch 16 ; 12
Mon-Fri: 0800-1700 and HW±3
BUDE:
Hbr office: Ch 16 ; 12 When vessel expected
APPLEDORE-BIDEFORD:
Call PV 'Two Rivers' Ch 16 ; 12 Access –2HW
ILFRACOMBE:
Hbr office: Ch 16; 12
Apr-Oct: 0815-1700, when manned, Nov-Mar:
HX. Access HW±2
MINEHEAD:
Hbr office: Ch 16 ; 12 14 HX
WATCHET:
Hbr office: Ch 16 ; 09 12 14 Access from –2HW
BRIDGEWATER:
Hbr office: Ch 16 ; 08
Access –3HW when vessel expected
BRISTOL:
Avonmouth Signal Station:
Call Avonmouth Radio Ch 16
VTS: Ch 12
Port operations: Ch 14
Alternative working: Ch 09 11
BRISTOL:
Hbr office: Ch 16 ; 73 Access –4HW+3½
Portishead Dock: Ch 16 ; 14* 12 Access –
2½HW+1
Royal Portbury Dock Ch 16 12 14 -4¼HW+3½
Royal Edward Dock: Ch 16 ; 14* 12
City Docks: Ch 14 ; 14* 11 Access –3HW+1
Prince Street Bridge: Ch 73
Netham Lock: Ch 73
SHARPNESS:
Call Sharpness Radio Ch 17
Canal operations: Ch 74 Access –6HW+2
NEWPORT:
Port: Ch 16 ; 69 71 Access HW±4
CARDIFF:
Ch 14* 16 ;
Barrage control: Ch 18
Barry Docks: Ch 11* 16 ; 10 Access –4HW+3
Port Talbot: Ch 12 16 ; 12
Neath: Ch 16 ; 77

SWANSEA:
Docks: Ch **14** HJ
Tawe Lock: Ch **18**
Barrage: Ch **18**
Saundersfoot: Ch **16** ; **11**
Summer: 0800-2100, Winter: Mon-Fri: 0800-1800.
Access HW±2½
Monkstone Sailing Club: Ch **M** Access HW±2½
Tenby: Ch **16 80** Access HW±2½
MILFORD HAVEN:
Milford Docks: Call Pierhead Ch **09 12 14 16**
Locking approx HW±3
Pembroke Dock: Ch **13**
Port of Pembroke: Call 'Port of Pembroke' Ch **12**; **68** H24
FISHGUARD: Hbr office: Ch 16 ; 14
ABERAERON: Ch 14* 16 Served by New Quay
Harbourmaster. 0900-1700. Access HW±3
ABERYSTWYTH: Ch 16 ; 14 Access HW±3
ABERDOVEY:
Call Aberdovey Hbr Ch **12 16** ; **12**
0900-1700 LT Access HW±3
BARMOUTH:
Ch **12* 16** ; **12** Apr-Sep: 0900-2200 LT,
Oct-Mar: 0900-1600 LT Access HW±2
Cyngor Dosbarth Dwytor: call Pwllheli
Harbour Master Ch **16** ; **08** 0900-1715. Access −2HW+1½
Abersoch Land & Sea: Ch **M** 0800-1700
PORTHMADOG:
Call Portmadog Hbr Ch **16** ; **12 14**
0900-1700, and when vessel expected.
Access HW±1½
Caernarfon:
Call Caernarvon Hbr Ch **14 16**; **14**
Mon-Fri: 0900-1700 Sat: 0900-1200. Access HW±3
Port Dinorwic Yacht Harbour: Ch **M**
Office Hours. Access −2HW−3½
HOLYHEAD:
Ch **14** ; **16**
Holyhead Sailing Club: Ch **M**
Beaumaris & Menai Bridge: Ch **16** ; **69**
Mon-Fri: 0800-1700
Conwy: Ch **14 16** ; **12***
Apr-Sep: 0900-1800, Oct-Mar: Mon-Fri: 0900-1800. Access −3HW+2.
Raynes Jetty: Ch **16** ; **14**
−4HW only when vessel expected
Llanddulas: Ch **16** ; **14**
Access −4HW only when vessel expected
Mostyn Dock & River Dee Pilots:
Ch **14* 16** ; **14** −2HW or by arrangement
LIVERPOOL PORT OPERATIONS AND INFORMATION:
VTS: Call Mersey Radio Ch **12* 16**
Information broadcasts: Ch **09** at 3h and 2h before HW
Canning Dock: Ch **M**
0900-1700. Access -2HW
Alfred Dock: Ch **22**
Langton Dock: Ch **21**
Gladstone Dock: Ch **05**
MANCHESTER SHIP CANAL

VTS: Call Eastham VTS: Ch **14**
Garston Dock: Ch **20**
Eastham Locks: Ch **07 14**
Stanlow Oil Docks: Ch **14 20**
Weaver Navigation: Ch **73* 14** ; **71**
H24 except 1800-1900 LT
Latchford Locks: Ch **14 20** (Ch **18** Emergency use only)
Irlam Locks: Ch **14** (Ch **18** Emergency use only)
Barton Locks: Ch **14** (Ch **18** Emergency use only)
Modewheel Locks: Ch **14** (Ch **18** Emergency use only)
Blundellsands Sailing Club: Ch **M** Access HW±2
FLEETWOOD:
0400-1100 1600-2300 and when vessel expected
Docks: Ch **12** Access -2HW+1½
Harbour Village: Ch **11 12 16** ;
0900-1700. HW±2
Glasson Dock: Ch **16** ; **69** Access −2HW+1
Heysham: Ch **16** ; **14 74**
Barrow Docks: Ch **16** ; **12**
Ramsden Dock: Ch **16** Access −2½HW
DOUGLAS, Isle of Man:
VTS: Ch **12**
Calling and Port Ops: Ch **16 12**
Castletown, Isle of Man: Ch **16** ; **12** 0830-1700
Port St Mary, Isle of Man: Ch **16** ; **12** HJ and when vessel expected. At other times contact Douglas
Peel, Isle of Man: Ch **16** ; **12**
HJ and when vessel expected. At other times contact Douglas
Ramsey, Isle of Man: Ch **16** ; **12** 0830-1700 and when vessel expected. At other times contact Douglas
WHITEHAVEN:
Ch **16** ; **12**
Access HW±3h
WORKINGTON:
Hbr Radio: Ch **16** ; **11 14** Access −2½HW+2
Silloth Docks: Ch **16** ; **12** Access −2½HW+1

CHANNEL ISLANDS

BRAYE, Alderney:
Port: Ch **16** ; **12 74**
May-Sep: 0800-1800 Oct: 0800-1800 Nov-Apr:
Mon-Fri: 0800-1700. Outside these hours, call
St Peter Port
GUERNSEY:
St Peter Port: Ch **12**
St Sampson: Ch **12** Via St Peter Port Port Control
JERSEY:
St Helier: Ch **14**
Pierheads: Ch **18** Access HW±3
(Note: Do not use Ch **M** in St Helier)
Gorey: Ch **74** HW±3

IRELAND

LONDONDERRY:
Hbr radio: Ch **14* 12**

COLERAINE:
Ch 16 ; 12 Mon-Fri: 0900-1700
Portrush: Ch 16 ; 12 Mon-Fri: 0900-1700, extended Jun-Sep, Sat Sun: 0900-1700, Jun-Sep only
LARNE:
Hr Mr: Ch 16 ; 14
Cloghan Point: Ch 16 ; 10
Carrickfergus: Hbr office: Ch 16 ; 12 14 Access±3
BELFAST:
VTS: Ch 12* 16
Portavogie: Ch 16 ; 12 14 Mon-Fri: 0900-1700
STRANGFORD HARBOUR:
Call Strangford Terminal: Ch 16 ; 12 14 M
Ardglass Harbour: Ch 16 ; 14 12
Killyleagh: Ch 16 ; 12 HX
Kilkeel: Ch 16 ; 12* 14 Mon-Fri: 0900-2000
Warrenpoint: Ch 16 ; 12
Greenore: Ch 16 HJ
Dundalk: Ch 14 Mon-Fri: 0900-1700
Drogheda: Ch 11 Mon-Fri: 0900-1700. HX
HOWTH:
Hr Mr: Ch 16 ; 08 Mon-Fri: 0700-2300 LT Sat/Sun: HX
DUBLIN:
Port: Ch 12* 13
Lifting Bridge: Call Eastlink Ch 12 13
DUN LAOGHAIRE:
Hbr office: Ch 14 16 ; 14
Small craft: Ch M
WICKLOW:
Port: Ch 14*; 16 12
ARKLOW:
Port: Ch 16 HJ
ROSSLARE:
Hbr office: Ch 12* 14 16
Waterford: Ch 16 ; 12 14 HJ and when vessel expected
New Ross: Ch 16 ; 12 14
Youghal: Ch 16 ; 14 Access HW±3
CORK:
VTS: Ch 12 14 16 ; 12 14
Kinsale: Ch 14* 16 ; 06
Office hours and when vessel expected
Bantry: Ch 16 ; 06 11 14
Castletown Bearhaven: Ch 14 16 ; 14
Limerick: Ch 16 ; 12 13
Office hours & when vessel expected
Foynes Harbour: Ch 16 ; 12 13 Office Hours
Aughinish Marine Terminal: Ch 16 ; 12 13
Fenit: Ch M
SHANNON ESTUARY: Ch 16; 12 13
Galway: Ch 16 ; 12 Access –2½HW+1
Rossaveel: Ch 16 ; 12 14 Office Hours
SLIGO:
Hr Mr: Ch 16 ; 12* 14
0900-1700 and when vessel expected
Killybegs: Ch 16 ; 14
Burton Port: Ch 16 ; 14* 06 12

BELGIUM & NETHERLANDS

NIEUWPOORT:
Hbr office: Ch 09 16

OOSTENDE:
Port Control: Ch 09
Lock: Ch 14
ZEEBRUGGE:
Port Entrance: Ch 71
Port Control: Ch 71
Emergencies: Ch 67
Locks: Ch 68
WESTERSCHELDE:
VTS: See VTS Chart No 3. Reporting, in English or Dutch, is compulsory within the VTS Schelde and Estuaries area for all Inward-Bound and Outward-Bound vessels. Vessels must maintain a continuous listening watch on the VHF channel for the appropriate Traffic Area including vessels at anchor. Each Traffic Area is marked by buoys and the appropriate Traffic Centre must be called on the relevant channel when a vessel enters the area
WANDELAAR TRAFFIC AREA:
VTS Tfc Centre: Ch 65
Outward bound vessels report when between buoys A1 bis and Scheur 2.
Radar: Ch 04
Emergency: Ch 67
ZEEBRUGGE TRAFFIC AREA:
VTS Tfc Centre: Ch 69
Report when inward/outward bound and within Zeebrugge Hr.
Radar: Ch 04
Harbour: Ch 19
Emergency: Ch 67
Radar Control Zeebrugge: Ch 19
STEENBANK TRAFFIC AREA:
VTS Tfc Centre: Ch 64
Emergency: Ch 67
VTS Tfc Centre: Ch 14
Radar: Ch 21
Emergency: Ch 67
TERNEUZEN TRAFFIC AREA:
VTS Tfc Centre: Ch 03
Emergency: Ch 67
GENT/TERNEUZEN TRAFFIC AREA:
VTS Tfc Centre: Ch 11
Emergency: Ch 67
HANSWEERT TRAFFIC AREA:
VTS Tfc Centre: Ch 65
Emergency Reporting In and Out: Ch 67
Centrale Hansweert, In: Ch 65
Centrale Zandvliet, Out: Ch 12
Centrale Vlissingen: Ch 14
ANTWERPEN TRAFFIC AREA:
VTS: Tfc Centre: Ch 12
Radar Waarde: Ch 19
Radar Saeftinge: Ch 21
Radar Zandvliet: Ch 04
Radar Kruischans: Ch 66
Emergency Reporting: In and Out: Ch 67
Information by Vlissingen: Ch 14
In Dutch and English every H+50
Information by Terneuzen: Ch 11
In Dutch and English every H+00 Ch 11
Information by Zeebrugge: Ch 69
In Dutch and English every H+10
Information by Zandvliet: Ch 12
In Dutch and English every H+00

COMMUNICATIONS

Information by Antwerpen: Ch 16
Traffic lists and navigation warnings between H+05 and H+10
VLISSINGEN:
Call Flushing Port Control **Ch 09**
Locks: Ch 18
Bridge: Ch 18
TERNEUZEN:
Hr office: Ch 11 14
Locks: Ch 69
Westsluis and Middensuis: Ch 06
Oostsluis: Ch 18
Gent: Ch 05 11
Hansweert Locks: Ch 22
ANTWERPEN:
Calling and safety: Ch 74
VTS Centre: Ch 18
Bridges: Ch 62
Dock Mr: Ch 63
Radar: Ch 02 60
Boudewijnsluis & Van Cauwelaertsluis: Ch 08 11
Royerssluis & Kattendijksluis: Ch 22
Kallosluis: Ch 03 08
Zandvlietsluis and Barendrechtsluis: Ch 06 79
Winthamsluis: Ch 68
OOSTERSCHELDE:
Call Roompotsluis **Ch 18** Lock operating times: Mon and Thu: 0000-2200 LT, Tue and Sun: 0600-0000 LT, Wed: H24, Fri and Sat: 0600-2200 LT. Vessels should report to the locks as follows: S bound: after passing Tholen Hr: N bound: after passing Bath Br.
Roompot: Ch 31
Ouddorp Coastguard: Ch 74
Wemeldinge: Ch 68
Zeelandbrug: Ch 18
Krammer: Ch 22
Kreekraksluizen: Ch 20 Vessels should report to the locks as follows: S bound: after Tholen Hr; N bound: after Bath bridge
Harlingvliet-Sluizen: Ch 20 Operating times Mon/Thu: H24 Fri: 0000-2200 Sat-Sun 0800-2000
HOEK VAN HOLLAND ROADSTEAD:
VTS: Call Maasmond Entrance **Ch 03** See VTS chart No 4. Yachts should follow a track close W of a line joining buoys MV, MVN and Indusbank N. Before crossing, report vessel's name, position and course. Whilst crossing, maintain continuous listening watch
NIEUWE WATERWEG:
HCC Central Traffic Control **Ch 11 14** See VTS Charts No 4. Report to and keep a continuous listening watch on the appropriate Traffic Centres
OUDE MAAS: Ch 13 19
Bridges and Locks: Ch 18
Brienenoordbrug: Ch 20
Sluis W eurt: Ch 18
Prins Bernhardsluis: Ch 18
Sluis S. Andries: Ch 20
DORDRECHT:
Port: Ch 19 Maintain a listening watch
Sector Heerjansdam: Ch 04
Information: Call Post Dordrecht **Ch 71**
Bruggen: Ch 19
Alblasserdamse brug: Ch 22

Papendrechtse brug: Ch 19
Merwedesluis en Verkeersbrug: Ch 18
Algera sluis en Stuw: Ch 22
Julianasluis: Ch 18
Grote Sluis Vianen and Andel Wilhelminasluis: Ch 22
SCHEVENINGEN:
Traffic Centre: Ch 21
Port: Ch 14
IJMUIDEN:
Traffic Centre: Ch 07 West of IJmuiden Light buoy
Port Control: Ch 61 From IJmuiden Lt by to the North Sea Locks
NORDZEEKANAAL:
VTS: Ch 61
From IJmuiden Lt By to the IJmuiden Sluices
Noordzeesluizen: Call Sluis IJmuiden **Ch 22**
Noordzeekanaal: Ch 03 From Ijmuiden Sluices to km 11·2
Zijkanaal C Sluice: Call Sluis IJmuiden **Ch 68**
AMSTERDAM:
Port Control: Ch 04
Port Information: Ch 14
Beverwijk: Ch 71
Wilhelminasluis: Ch 20
Westerkeersluis: Ch 22
Haarlem: Ch 18
Oranjesluisen: Ch 18
Enkhuizen or Krabbersgat: Ch 22
Lock operates weekdays 0300-2300, Sun and holidays 0800-2000
DEN HELDER: Ch 14
VTS: All vessels equipped with VHF to report when entering/leaving the area, berthing/unberthing, anchoring/weighing or entering/leaving Koopvaardersschutsluis stating vessel's name, type, position, destination and special details
Port Control: Ch 14
Moormanbrug Bridge: Ch 18
Koopvaarders Lock: Ch 22
Den Oever: Ch 20
Kornwerderzand: Ch 18
Eierland Coastguard: Ch 05 0800-2330
Harlingen: Ch 11 Mon 0000-Sat 2200
Terschelling: Call Brandaris VTS **Ch 02**
All vessels must report when entering/leaving the area and thereafter keep a continuous listening watch
Waddenzee Central Reporting - Incidents: Ch 04
Waddenzee Central Reporting - SAR Rescue: Ch 16
AMELAND:
Coastguard: Ch 05 0800-2330 LT
EEMSHAVEN:
Hbr office: Ch 14
Radar: Ch 19
DELFZIJL:
Hbr office: Ch 14 Radar assistance given when visibility falls below 2000m
Information: Ch 14 Every H+10
Locks: Ch 11 Mon-Sat: H24, Sun & holidays on request
Weiwerder Bridge: Ch 11
Heemskes and Handelshaven Bridges: Ch 14

Mon-Sat: 0600-1400
Farmsumerhaven: Ch 14

GERMANY

IMPORTANT: *Before navigating German waterways, all vessels must report to waterway authorities.*

DIE EMS VTS: Call Ems Traffic **Ch 15 16 18 20 21** Ems Traffic broadcasts every H+50 on Ch 15 18 20 and 21 in German. All vessels must report to waterway authorities, and keep a continuous watch on the appropriate channel
Emden Locks: Ch 13 16
Oldersum Lock: Ch 13 May-Sep Mon-Fri 0700-2000 Sat & Sun 0800-2000, Oct-Apr Mon-Thur 0700-1530 Fri 0700-1400
Leer Road Bridge: Ch 15
Leer Lock: Ch 13 16
Weener Bridge: Ch 15
Weener Lock: Ch 13 16 1 Apr- 31 Oct only: Mon-Thu 0700-1600 Fri: 0700-sunset Sat & Sun: sunrise-sunset
Papenburg Lock: Ch 13 16
Leysiel Lock: Ch 17
BORKUM:
Port: Ch 14 16 All year Mon-Fri: 0700-2200, Sep-Apr Sat & Sun: 0700-1700, May-Aug Sat: 0800-1200 1500-2100 Sun: 0700-1100 1400-2000. All vessels report arrival/departure.
Norddeich: Ch 28* 17
Mon: 0730-1900, Tue-Fri: 0700-1300 1330-1900, Sat & Sun: 0800-1200 1230-1730
Nordeney: Ch 17 Mon: 0700-1200 1230-1730, Tues: 0900-1200 1230-1900, Wed-Sun: 0700-1200 1230-1900
Langeoog: Ch 17 0700-1700
Benersiel: Ch 17 Oct-Mar Mon-Fri: 0700-1230 1330-1700, Apr-Sep Mon-Fri: 0700-1900 Sat & Sun: 0700-1100 1300-1700
Harlesiel: lock Ch 17 0700-2100
Wangerooge: Ch 17 0700-1700
INNER DEUTSCHE BUCHT (GERMAN BIGHT):
VTS: Eastern part: Ch 80 16
VTS: Western part: Ch 79 16
DIE JADE:
VTS: Ch 20 63 16
Information bcsts: Ch 20 63 every H+10
WILHEMSHAVEN:
Port: Ch 11 16
Naval Port: Ch 11 16
Lock: Ch 13 16
Bridges: Ch 11
VAREL Lock: Ch 13 HW±2
DIE WESER AND DIE HUNTE:
Bremerhaven Weser Tfc: Ch 02 04 05 07 16 21 22 82
Bremen Weser Traffic: Ch 16 19 78 81
Hunte Traffic:
VTS: Ch 16 63
Information in German: Ch 02 04 05 07 21 22 82 every H+20 by Bremerhaven Weser Traffic
Information in German: Ch 19 78 81 H+30 by Bremen Weser Traffic

Information in German: Ch 63 H+30 by Hunte Traffic
BREMERHAVEN:
Port: Ch 12 16
Locks: Ch 12
Bremerhaven Weser:
Port: Ch 14 16
Brake Lock: Ch 10
Elsfleth-Ohrt Railway Bridge: Ch 73
Hunte Lock: Ch 73
Hunte lifting bridge: Ch 73
Oldenburg:
Railway Bridge: Ch 73
H24 except Sun and public holidays 0030-0630
Lock: Ch 20 Mon-Sat: 0500-2100 Sun: 0900-1200
Cäcilien Bridge: Ch 73
Oslebshausen Lock: Ch 12
BREMEN:
Port: Ch 03 16
Lock: Ch 20 Mon-Sat: 0600-2200, Sun: Oct-Apr 0800-1100 May-Sep: 0800-1100 1730-1930
DIE ELBE:
VTS: Ch 71* 16
Brunsbüttel Elbe Traffic: Ch 68* 16
CUXHAVEN ELBE:
Cuxhaven Elbe Port: Ch 12* 16
Cuxhaven Port and Lock: Ch 69
BRUNSBÜTTEL ELBE PORT:
Port: Ch 12* 16
Oste Bridge: Ch 16 69
Apr-Sep the bridge is opened on request Ch 69. Oct-Mar request through Ch 03 or 16 Belum Radar or Ch 21 Cuxhaven Radar
Geversdorf Bridge: Ch 69 ; The bridge opens on request for small craft Apr-Sep: 1930-0730 and every H+00 and H+30
Obendorf Bridge: Ch 69 Oct-Mar H24, Apr-Sep 1930-0730. The bridge is opened on request by telephone 04772 86 10 11
Stör Llock: Ch 09 16 The bridge is opened on request
Glückstadt Lock: Ch 11 0700-1600 and during HW
Stadersand Elbe Port: Ch 12* 16
Este Lock: Ch 10 16
Este Bridge: Ch 11 Opened on request
HAMBURG:
VTS: Ch 74* 13 14 16
Port Traffic: Ch 73* 13 14 16
Elbe Port: Ch 12* 16
Rethe Bridge: Ch 13* 16
Kattwyk Bridge: Ch 13* 16
Harburg Lock: Ch 13* 16
Tiefstack Lock: Ch 11
NORD-OSTSEE KANAL:
KIEL KANAL: Ch 02
VTS Canal 1 Ch 09
VTS Canal 2 Ch 02
Brieholz: Ch 73
Ostermoor: Ch 73
Friedrichskoog: Ch 10 Access HW±2h
Büsum Port: Ch 11 16

Eider Lock: Ch 14 16
Husum Port: Ch 11 16
Information bcsts: Ch 11 every H+00, Access –4HW+2
Pellworm Port: Ch 11 0700-1700
Wyk Port: Ch 11 16
List Port: Ch 11 0800-1200 1600-1800
HELGOLAND:
Port: Ch 16 67
May-Aug: Mon-Thu: 0700-1200 1300-2000
Fri-Sat: 0700-2000 Sun: 0700-1200
Sep-Apr: Mon-Thu: 0700-1200 1300-1600 Fri: 0700-1200

DENMARK

Rømø Havn: Ch 16 ; 10 12 13 HX
Esbjerg: Ch 16 ; 12 13 14
Hvide Sande: Ch 16 ; 12 13 HX
Torsminde: Ch 16 ; 12 13 0300-1300, 1400-2400
THYBORØN: Ch 16 ; 12 13
Hanstholm Havn: Ch 16 ; 12 13 HX
Torup Strand: Ch 16 ; 12 13 HX
Hirtshals Havn: Ch 16 ; 14 HX
Skagen: Ch 16 12 13

FRANCE

DUNKERQUE
Port: Ch 73
CALAIS:
Port: Call Calais Port Traffic Ch 16 ; 12
Ecluse Carnot: Ch 12 16 HX
CROSS GRIS NEZ:
VTS: Ch 13* 79 16
Distress and Safety: Ch 13 79 Calling and working
Information: Call Gris Nez Traffic Ch 13 79 H+10. Occasional when visibility less than 2M H+25
SAR Coordination: Ch 68* 15 67 73
BOULOGNE:
Call Control Tower, Boulogne Port Ch 12
Le Touquet: Ch 09 ; 77 Access –2HW+1
Étaples-Sur-Mer: Ch 09 Access HW±2
Le Treport: Ch 16 ; 12 72 Access HW±3
DIEPPE:
Port: Ch 12 16 ; 12*
(Ch 12 Office Hours, Ch 16 H24)
S VALÉRY-EN-CAUX: lock Ch 09 Day: HW±2, Night: HW±½
Fécamp: Ch 16 ; 10 12 Access –3HW+1
Gayant Lock (Bassin Freycinet):
Call Bureau du Port Ch 16
Bérigny Lock: Call Ecluse Bérigny Ch 09
LE HAVRE:
Port de Commerce: Control Tower: Ch 16; 12 20 22
Port Operations: Ch 67 69
Antifer Port: Ch 22* 14
LA SEINE:
VTS: Ch 73 15 16 68
Call Radar Ch 13 73 82 Honfleur when entering and then Rouen control Centre while on passage

Honfleur: Port: Ch 17 73 16
Access –2HW Le Havre+4
Locks and Bridges: Ch 16 17 H24.
Access –2HW Le Havre+4
Tancarville: Ch 16 HX
Lock: Ch 18 HX
Port Jérome: Call PR Ch 16 ; 73
ROUEN:
Port: Ch 73* 16 68
ROUEN TO PARIS LOCKS: Ch 18
Send ETA by VHF to next lock 30 mins in advance throughout the passage
Poses-Amfreville:
Ch 18
Notre-Dame-de-la-Garenne: Ch 22
Mericourt: Ch 18
Andrésy: Ch 22
Bougival: Ch 22
Chatou: Ch 18
Suresnes: Ch 22
Paris-Arsenal: Ch 09
Deauville-Trouville: Ch 09 0800-1730 LT
CAEN-OUISTREHAM:
Port: Ch 68* 16
Lock: Ch 12 68 Access –2HW+3
Canal de Caen: Ch 68 Keep listening watch
Courseulles-sur-Mer: Ch 09 HW±3
Port-en-Bessin: Ch 18 HW±2
CHERBOURG: Call Le Homet Ch 16; 12 H24.
Lock: Ch 06 Access HW$\pm\frac{3}{4}$
JOBOURG TRAFFIC SERVICE:
Calling/working: Ch 13* 16 80
Information in French and English on Ch 80 at H+20 and H+50
CROSS JOBOURG:
Distress and Safety: Call CROSS Jobourg Ch 16 70
SAR Coordination: Ch 68* 15 67 73
GRANVILLE:
Hbr office: Ch 12 -2½HW±3½
ST MALO:
Hbr office: Ch 12 16; 12
Plouer-sur-Rance Marina: Ch 13
DAHOUËT:
Fishing Port: 16 LT and –2HW+1. Out of season 0830-1215 1400-1715 LT (except Sat afternoon and Sun)
LE LÉGUÉ, SAINT BRIEUC:
Call Légué Port Ch 16 ; 12
–1½/2HW+1½ and –1HW+1½ depending on height of tide
Pontrieux Lock: Ch 12 Access –2HW+1
Morlaix Marina: Ch 16 ; 09 HW±2, lock – 1½HW+1
ROSCOFF-BLOSCON:
Port: Ch 16 ; 12
0830-1200 1330-1800 LT
Marina: Ch 09 0800-1200 1330-1730 LT
CORSEN-OUESSANT:
Calling and Working: 13* 79
DSC: Ch 70
Distress and Safety: Ch 16
Keep a listening watch on Ch 16 when sailing within a 35M radius centred on Ile d'Ouessant (Le Stiff Radar Tr 48°28'·6N 05°03'·1W)

Vigie d'Ouessant: Call Le Stiff **Ch 16**
Vigie de Saint-Mathieu: Ch 16
Cap de la Chevre (Semaphore): **Ch 16** HJ
Vigie du Raz (Pointe du Raz semaphore): **Ch 16**
Information bcsts: in French and English Ch 79 Every H+10 and H+40
SAR: Call CROSS Corsen or Ouessant **Ch 68* 15 67 73** Distress and safety
LE CONQUET:
Port: Ch 16 ; 08
Season 0830-1200 1330-1800 LT, out of season HX
BREST:
VTS: Ch 16
Port de Commerce: Ch 16; 12*
A compulsory reporting system exists for vessels over 25m LOA
Military Port: Ch 74
CAMARET-SUR-MER: Ch 09, out of season: 0830-1200 1330-1730 LT
DOUARNENEZ:
Hbr office: Ch 16 ; 12
0800-1200 1330-1730 LT
SAINT GUÉNOLE: Ch 12 HJ
LE GUILVINEC:
Port: Ch 12 HX
LOCTUDY:
Hbr office: Ch 12 (Portable VHF)
Mon-Fri: 0630-1200 1400-1900 LT. Sat: 0800-1200 LT
CONCARNEAU:
Port: Ch 16 ; 12
LORIENT:
Hbr office: Call Vigie Port Louis **Ch 16 ; 12**
ÉTEL CROSS:
Calling and working Ch 13 80
Search and Rescue: Ch 15 67 68 73
Information: Ch 16 ; 79 80
Urgent navigational messages bcst on receipt and then every 2h. Non-urgent navigational messages bcst 0433 and 2133 after weather forecasts.
La Loire Signal Station: Call Chemoulin **Ch 16**
Reporting System: Ch 12* 16 ; 12* 06 14 67 69
Compulsory for all commercial vessels
SAINT-NAZAIRE:
PORT: Ch 12* 16; 06 14 67 69
Tidal Information: Ch 73 Tidal information between Saint-Nazaire and Nantes automatically broadcast at H+00, H+15, H+30 and H+45
DONGES:
Port: Ch 12 16 69
Nantes Port: Ch 12* 16 ; 12* 06 14 67 69
LES SABLES D'OLONNE:
Lock: Ch 12
Harbour Master Mon-Fri: 0800-1800 LT, lock HW±2 or HW±1½ depending on tide
LA ROCHELLE
Port: Ch 12* 16 ; 12*
ROCHEFORT:
Hr office: Ch 16 ; 12
0800-1200 1400-1800LT

Tonnay-Charente: Ch 16 ; 12 HX
LA GIRONDE:
VTS: Ch 12
Compulsory for all vessels in the area from BXA Lt buoy to Bordeaux
Radar: Ch 12 ; 16
Tidal Information: Ch 17
Height of water between Le Verdon and Bordeaux bcst automatically every 5 min
Le Verdon:
HM and Radar: Ch 12
PAUILLIC:
Hbr office: Ch 12
BLAYE:
Port: Ch 12
Ambès: Ch 12
BORDEAUX:
Hbr office: Ch 16 ; 12
SOULAC CROSS:
Distress and Safety: Ch 16 70
Calling and Working: Ch 13* 79
SAR Coordination: Ch 68* 15 67 73
Information: Ch 79
Urgent navigational information is bcst on receipt and then every 2h. Non-urgent navigational information is bcst at 0433 and 2133 LT after the weather forecast.
Bayonne: Ch 12

SPAIN

PASAJES:
Call Pasajes Prácticos **Ch 16 ; 14* 11 12 13**
BILBAO:
VTS: Ch 12* 16 05
Signal Station: Ch 16 ; 12 13 HX
SANTANDER:
Port: Ch 16 ; 06 12 14
Pilot Office: Ch 16 ; 12* 09 14
REQUEJADA, SUANCES:
Pilots: Ch 12 16 When vessel expected
Gijón: Ch 16 ; 14* 11 12
Avilés: Ch 12 ; 06 09 14 16
Pilot Office: Ch 16 ; 14* 11 12
Ribadeo Pilots: Ch 16
PUERTO DE SAN CIPRIÄN:
Pilots and Port: Ch 14 16
EL FERROL DEL CAUDILLO:
Ch 14*(H24) 16 ; 10 11 12 13 14
LA CORUÑA:
Port: Ch 16 12 HX
CORCUBIÓN:
Pilots: Ch 16
FINISTERRE:
VTS: Ch 11 74 16
Ch 11 16 (H24)
Voluntary reporting for non-Spanish vessels
VILLAGARCIA DE AROSA:
Port: Ch 16 ; 12
Marin: Call Marin Pilots **Ch 16 ; 12** When vessel expected
VIGO:
VTS: Call Vigo Traffic (H24) **Ch 16 10**
Port: Call Vigo Prácticos **Ch 16 ; 14** HX

Section 4

PORTUGAL

Caminha: Call Postradcaminha **Ch 16 ; 11**
Mon-Fri 0900-1200 1400-1700
VIANA DO CASTELO:
Call Capimarviana **Ch 16 ; 11**
Mon-Fri 0900-1200 1400-1700
PÓVOA DE VARZIM:
Call Capimarvarzim **Ch 16 ; 11**
Mon-Fri 0900-1200 1400-1700
Vila Do Conde: Call Capimarconde **Ch 16 ; 11**
Mon-Fri 0900-1200 1400-1700
LEIXÕES: Call Postradleixões **Ch 16 ; 11 13 19 60**
Distress and Safety: Ch 16
Intership: Ch 06 08
Marinas: Ch 62
Radar Station: Ch 12 16 ; 01 04 09 10 11 12 14 18 20 61 63 67 68 69 71 79 80 84
Controls all radar, navigational, tidal and berthing information for Leixões
Posto Central: Ch 12 ; 18 67 68 0730-1900
Serviços Maritimos: Ch 12 ; 18 67 68 0700-2400
Bascule Bridge: Call Pónte Movel **Ch 12 ; 18 67 68**
Douro: Call Capimardouro **Ch 16 ; 11**
Mon-Fri 0900-1200 1400-1700
Aveiro: Call Capimaraveiro **Ch 16 ; 11**
Mon-Fri 0900-1200 1400-1700
Figueira da Foz: Call Capimarfoz **Ch 16 ; 11**
Mon-Fri 0900-1200 1400-1700
Nazaré: Call Capimarnazare **Ch 16 ; 11**
Mon-Fri 0900-1200 1400-1700
Peniche: Call Postradpeniche **Ch 16 ; 11**
LISBOA: Call Port Control Lisboa **Ch 12 16 ; 12**
Calling: Ch 16
Listening: Ch 12 13 61
Working: Ch 64
Listening watch When near to Forte de S Julao, on entering or leaving, vessels should report on Ch 12 or 16. When navigating between the harbour approach and the harbour, maintain continuous listening watch on Ch 13
Information: Ch 11 In Portuguese at 1030 and 1630
LISBOA DOCKS: Call Docopesca **Ch 03 12** 0100 Mon-0100 Sat
Doca de Alcântara Lock: Ch 12 ; 05
0700 0815 0915 1015 1115 1315 1500 1630 1800
Sesimbra: Call Delegmarsesimbra **Ch 16 ; 11**
Mon-Fri 0900-1200 1400-1700
Setúbal: Call Postradsetúbal **Ch 16 ; 11 13**
Sines: Call Capimarsines **Ch 16 ; 11 13**

Lagos: Call Capimarlagos **Ch 16; 11**
Mon-Fri 0900-1200 1400-1700
Portimão: Call Postradportimão **Ch 16; 11**
Mon-Fri 0900-1200 1400-1700
Vilamoura: Call Vilamouraradio **Ch 16 20 62**
0830-1830 (2130 in summer)
Faro: Call Postradfaro **Ch 16 ; 11**
OLHÃO: Call Capimarolhão **Ch 16 ; 11**
VILA REAL DE SANTO ANTÓNIO:
Call Capimarreal **Ch 16 ; 11**
Mon-Fri 0900-1200 1400-1700

SPAIN

EL ROMPIDO:
Marina: Ch 09 16 HX
PUNTA UMBRÍA:
Marina: Ch 09 16 HX
Bridge: Call Huelva Pilots **Ch 16 ; 14* 06 11 12**
HUELVA:
Port: Call Huelva Barra Prácticos for Bar or Huelva Puerto Prácticos for Harbour **Ch 14 16 06 11 12**
RÍO GUADALQUIVIR:
Call Obras Puerto Sevilla **Ch 12**
CÁDIZ:
Call Cádiz Prácticos
Ch 14 16* 11 12

STRAIT OF GIBRALTAR
TARIFA:
VTS: Call Tarifa Traffic **Ch 10 16**
(also Ch 67 by mutual arrangement)
DSC Ch 70
Information: Ch 10 16
Urgent messages will be bcst at any time on Ch 10 and Ch 16. Routine messages will be bcst every even H+15 on Ch 10
ALGECIRAS:
Port: Call Algeciros Prácticos **Ch 16 ; 09 12 13** HX
Real Club Nautico de Algeciras: Ch 09 16 HX
Algeciras Iberia: Call Sea Land Iberia **Ch 16 ; 09** HX

GIBRALTAR

GIBRALTAR: Ch 06* 12* 13 14 16
Ch 12 is the Gibraltar Bay Working Channel
Lloyds Gibraltar Radio: Ch 12* 08 16 14
Queen's Harbour Master: Ch 08
Mon-Thu: 0800-1630 LT Fri: 0800-1600 LT

VHF COAST RADIO STATIONS
UNITED KINGDOM
Coast Radio in the UK is operated by HM Coastguard who broadcast weather and navigation information on Ch 10, 23, 67, 73, 84, 86 after an initial announcement on Ch 16 and who receive urgent and safety messages only on Ch 67 via Ch 16. All Centres have operational A1 DSC. Navigation Warnings, Gale Warnings and Inshore Forecasts are broadcast as follows:
Stations additionally broadcasting Gunfacts and Subfacts are indicated by *.
Weather bulletin times are shown in bold.

FALMOUTH COASTGUARD (MRCC)   50°09'N 05°03'W. ☎ 01326 317575.   📠 01326 318342.
Area from Marsland Mouth to Dodman Pt. *DSC MMSI 002320014, 2187·5 kHz, Ch 70. MF 2226 kHz*:*
0140 0540 **0940** 1340 1740 and **2140** UTC.

BRIXHAM COASTGUARD (MRSC)   50°24'N 03°31'W. ☎ 01803 882704.   📠 01803 882780.
Area from Dodman Pt to Topsham. *DSC MMSI 002320013, Ch 70*. MF 2182 kHz:*
0050 0450 **0850** 1250 1650 **2050** UTC

PORTLAND COASTGUARD (MRSC)   50°36'N 02°27'W. ☎ 01305 760439.   📠 01305 760452.
Area from Topsham to Chewton Bunney. *DSC MMSI 002320012, Ch 70*:*
0220 0620 **1020** 1420 1820 and **2220** UTC

SOLENT COASTGUARD (MRSC)   50°48'N 01°12'W. ☎ 023 9255 2100.   📠 023 9255 1763.
Area from Chewton Bunney to Beachy Head. *DSC MMSI 002320011, Ch 70. Call Ch 67 (H24) for safety traffic*. MF 1641 kHz:*
0040 0440 **0840** 1240 1640 **2040** UTC

DOVER COASTGUARD (MRCC)   50°08'N 01°12'E. ☎ 01304 210008.   📠 01304 202137.
Area from Beachy Head to Reculver Towers. *DSC MMSI 002320010, Ch 70. MF 2182 kHz:*
Operates Channel Navigation Information Service (CNIS) which broadcasts navigation and traffic info on Ch 11 every H+40 (and H+55 in bad vis). *Monitor Ch 69 for safety info.*
0105 0505 **0905** 1305 1705 **2105**

THAMES COASTGUARD (MRSC)   51°51'N 01°17'E. ☎ 01255 675518.   📠 01255 675249.
Area from Reculver Towers to Southwold. *DSC MMSI 002320009, Ch 70, MF 2182 kHz:*
0010 0410 **0810** 1210 1610 and **2010** UTC

YARMOUTH COASTGUARD (MRCC)   52°37'N 01°43'E. ☎ 01493 851338.   📠 01493 852307.
Area from Southwold to Haile Sand Fort. *DSC MMSI 002320008, Ch 70. MF 1869 kHz:*
0040 0440 **0840** 1240 1640 and **2040** UTC

HUMBER COASTGUARD (MRSC)   54°06'N 00°11'W. ☎ 01262 672317.   📠 01262 606915.
Area from Haile Sand Ft to Scottish border. *DSC MMSI 002320007, 2187·5 kHz, Ch 70. MF 2226 kHz:*
0340 0740 1140 1540 1940 and 2340 UTC

FORTH COASTGUARD (MRSC)   56°17'N 02°35'W. ☎ 01333 450666.   📠 01333 450725.
Area from English border to Doonie Point. *DSC MMSI 002320005, Ch 70:*
0205 0605 **1005** 1405 1805 and **2205** UTC

ABERDEEN COASTGUARD (MRCC)   57°08'N 02°05'W. ☎ 01224 592334.   📠 01224 575920.
Area from Doonie Pt to C. Wrath.*DSC MMSI 00230004, 2187·5 kHz, Ch 70. MF 2226 kHz:*
0320 **0720** 1120 1520 **1920** and 2320 UTC

SHETLAND COASTGUARD (MRSC)   60°09'N 01°08'W. ☎ 01595 692976.   📠 01595 694810.
Area covers Shetland, Orkney and Fair Isle. *DSC MMSI 002320001, 2187·5 kHz, Ch70. MF 1770 kHz:*
0105 0505 **0905** 1305 1705 **2105** UTC

STORNOWAY COASTGUARD (MRSC)   58°12'N 06°22'W. ☎ 01851 702013.   📠 01851 704387.
Area from Cape Wrath to Ardnamurchan Pt. *DSC MMSI 002320024, 2187·5 kHz, Ch 70. MF 1743 kHz:*
0110 0510 **0910** 1310 1710 **2110** UTC

CLYDE COASTGUARD (MRCC)   55°58'N 04°48'W. ☎ 01475 729988.   📠 01475 786955.
Area from Ardnamurchan Pt to Mull of Galloway. *DSC MMSI 002320022, 2187·5 kHz, Ch 70. MF 1883 kHz*:*
0020 0420 **0820** 1220 1620 **2020**

BELFAST COASTGUARD (MRSC)   54°40'N 05°40'W. ☎ 02891 463933.   📠 02891 465886.
Area covers Northern Ireland. *DSC MMSI 002320021, Ch 70*:*
0305 **0705** 1105 1505 **1905** and 2305 UTC

LIVERPOOL COASTGUARD (MRSC) 53°30'N 03°03'W. ☎ 0151 931 3341 🖷 0151 931 3347
Area from Mull of Galloway to Queensferry. *DSC MMSI 002320019, Ch 70:*
0210 0610 **1010** 1410 1810 and **2210** UT

HOLYHEAD COASTGUARD (MRSC) 53°19'N 04°38'W. ☎ 01407 762051 🖷 01407 764373
Area from Queensferry to Friog *DSC MMSI 002320018, Ch 70 2187·5 kHz:*
0235 **0635** 1035 1435 **1835** and 2235 UTC

MILFORD HAVEN COASTGUARD (MRSC) 51°41'N 05°10'W. ☎ 01646 690909. 🖷 01646 692176.
Area from Friog to River Towy. *DSC MMSI 002320017, 2187·5 kHz, Ch 70.* MF 1767 kHz:
0335 **0735** 1135 1535 **1935** and 2335 UTC

SWANSEA COASTGUARD (MRCC) 51°34'N 03°58'W. ☎ 01792 366534. 🖷 01792 369005.
Area from River Towy to Marsland Mouth. *DSC MMSI 002320016, Ch 70:*
0005 0405 **0805** 1205 1605 and **2005** UTC

CHANNEL ISLANDS

ST PETER PORT RADIO 49°27'·00N 02°32'00W. ☎: 01481 720672. 🖷: 01534 714177
Area covers Northern Channel Is; Alderney Radio monitors Ch 16 HJ. *DSC MMSI 002320064 Ch 70,*
Ch 20, MF 1764 kHz:
0133 0533 0933 1333 1733 and 2133 UTC

JERSEY RADIO 49°10'·85N 02°14'30W. ☎: 01534 741121. 🖷: 01534 499089
Area covers the Channel Islands Southern area.*DSC MMSI 002320060, Ch 70*
On VHF Ch 25 82, MF 1658 kHz:
0645 0433 0745 0845 1245 1633 1845 2033 2245 2033 UTC

IRELAND

Coast Radio is provided by the Dept of the Marine, Leeson Lane, Dublin 2, Eire. ☎ +353 (0)1 785444;
ext 670 for enquiries. Broadcasts are made on a working channel/frequency following a preliminary
announcement on Ch 16 and 2182 kHz. Ch 67 is used for Safety messages only.
VHF calls to an Irish Coast radio station should be made on a working channel. Only use Ch 16 in case
of difficulty, or in emergency.

NW and SE Ireland

Stations broadcast at 0033, 0433, 0833, 1233, 1633 and 2033 UTC on VHF Channels listed. Navigational
warnings and Traffic Lists are broadcast at every odd H+03 (except 0303 0703).

Clifden Radio	53°30'N 09°56'W VHF 26	
Belmullet Radio	54°16'N 10°03'W VHF 83	
Donegal Bay	VHF 16	
Glen Head Radio	54°44'N 08°43'W VHF 24	
MALIN HEAD RADIO	55°22'N 07°21'W VHF 23, 85	☎ +353 (0) 77 70103, MF 1677 kHz
MMSI 002500100 DSC: 2187·5 kHz		
Carlingford Radio	VHF 04 16 67	
Dublin Radio	53°23'N 06°04'W VHF 83	
Wicklow Head Radio	52°58'N 06°00'W VHF 87	
Rosslare Radio	52°15'N 06°20'W VHF 23	
Mine Head Radio	52°00'N 07°35'W VHF 83	

SW Ireland

Stations broadcast at 0233, 0633, 1033, 1433, 1833 and 2233 UTC on VHF Channels listed.
Navigational warnings and Traffic Lists are broadcast at every odd H+33 (not 0133 0533).

Cork Radio	51°51'N 08°29'W VHF 26	
Crookhaven Radio	VHF 04, 67, 16	
Bantry Radio	51°38'N 10°00'W VHF 23, 85	
VALENTIA RADIO	51°56'N 10°21'W VHF 24, 28 ☎ + 353 (0) 667 6109 MF 1752 kHz	
MMSI 002500200, DSC: 2187·5 kHz		
Shannon Radio	52°31'N 09°36'W VHF 24, 28	
Galway Bay Radio	VHF 04, 67, 16	

GERMANY

MRCC Coastguard Radio Stations

North Sea Coastguard Radio MRCC stations are remotely controlled from Bremen (MMSI 00211240). All monitor Ch 16 H24. Initial call on Ch 16 using the name of the local station as callsign. There are no MF facilities. All stations operate DSC on VHF Ch 70 (H24). No stations accept public correspondence calls.

Bremen MRCC Radio 53°05'N 08°48'E	VHF Ch 16	DSC Ch 70
Norddeich Radio 53°34'N 07°06'E	VHF Ch 16	DSC Ch 70
Helgoland Radio 54°11'N 07°53'E	VHF Ch 16	DSC Ch 70
Elbe-Weser Radio 53°50'N 08°39'E	VHF Ch 16	DSC Ch 70
Hamburg Radio 53°33'N 09°58'E	VHF Ch 16	DSC Ch 70
Eiderstedt Radio 54°20'N 08°47'E	VHF Ch 16	DSC Ch 70
Nordfriesland Radio 54°55'N 08°18'E	VHF Ch 16	DSC Ch 70

Navigation Warnings: On VHF Ch 16.

Vital warnings for the North Sea and Baltic. On receipt and repeated at every H+00 and H+30 until cancelled.

German Coast Radio Stations DPO7 – Seefunk (Hamburg) (MMSI 002113100)

Hamburg 53°33'N 09°58'E	VHF Ch 16 27	DSC Ch 70
Borkum 53°35'N 06°40'E	VHF Ch 16 28	DSC Ch 70
Elbe Weser 53°50'N 08°39'E	VHF Ch 16 01 24	DSC Ch 70
Helgoland 54°11'N 07°53'E	VHF Ch 16 86	DSC Ch 70

Traffic Lists: Ch 16 every H+30

HOLLAND

Netherlands Coastguard Radio monitors Ch 16 and 2182 kHz for Distress, Urgency, Safety traffic and operates DSC on 2187·5 kHz and Ch 70 (MMSI 002442000). No stations accept public correspondence calls.

IJMUIDEN RADIO 52°06'N 04°16'E ☎ (0) 255 545345 MMSI 002442000

Westkapelle	Ch 23	Goes	Ch 83	Rotterdam	Ch 23
Scheveningen	Ch 23	Haarlem	Ch 83	Huisduinen	Ch 23
Wieringerwerf	Ch 83	Platform L-7	Ch 83	Terschelling	Ch 23
Nes	Ch 83	Appingedam	Ch 23	Lelystad	Ch 23
IJmuiden	Ch 83	Hilversum	Ch 83		

Navigational Warnings:

On VHF Ch 23:	At 0333 0733 1133 1533 1933 2333 UTC
On MF 2673 kHz:	At 0333 0733 1133 1533 1933 2333 UTC

BELGIUM

ANTWERPEN RADIO 51°17'N 04°20'E MMSI 002050485, DSC Ch 70, VHF 24 87

Traffic Lists: Ch 24 every H+05.

Navigation Warnings: Ch 24 on receipt and every H+03 and H+48, in English and Dutch for the Schelde.

OOSTENDE RADIO 51°06'N 03°21'E MMSI 002050480, 2187·5 kHz (H24) DSC Ch 70

Ch 28 & 78	near French border
Ch 27, 28 & 85	off Oostende
Ch 27, 87 & 88	off Zeebrugge)
MF 2817 kHz	for foreign vessels
MF 3632 kHz	for foreign vessels

Traffic Lists:Ch 27 every H+20 and 2761 kHz every even H+20 (UTC).

Navigation Warnings: Ch 27 and 2761 kHz on receipt, after next two silence periods and on 2761 kHz at: 0233 0633 1033 1433 1833 2233 UTC, in English and Dutch.

Fog Warnings for the Schelde: 2761 kHz on receipt and after next silence period, in English and Dutch.

Section 4

FRANCE

Five Centres Régionaux Opérationnels de Surveillance et de Sauvetage (CROSS) cover the Channel and Atlantic coasts. A CROSS is equivalent to an MRCC and a sous-CROSS an MRSC. CROSS provides a permanent, H24, all weather operational presence along the French coast and liaises with foreign CGs.

CROSS Étel specialises in providing medical advice and responds to alerts from Cospas/Sarsat satellites.

CROSS can be contacted by R/T, by ☎, through Coast radio stations, via the National Gendarmerie or Affaires Maritimes, or via a Semaphore station.

In addition to their safety and SAR functions, CROSS stations using, for example, the call sign *Corsen Traffic* monitor Traffic Separation Schemes in the Dover Strait, off Casquets and off Ouessant, they also broadcast navigational warnings and weather forecasts.

All centres keep watch on VHF Ch 16 and Ch 70 (DSC), and broadcast gale warnings and weather forecasts and local navigational warnings;

CROSS stations

All stations co-ordinate SAR on VHF Ch 15 67 68 73. *DSC Ch 70*

CROSS Gris-Nez 50°52'N 01°35'E   Belgian Border to Cap d'Antifer,
☎ 03·21·87·21·87   📠 03·21·87·78s·55   *MMSI 002275100, DSC Ch 70 MF 2187·5 kHz*
On VHF Ch 79: From: Dunkerque, Gris-Nez, Saint-Frieux, and L'Ailly every H+10
On MF 1659 kHz: Gris-Nez at 0833 2033 UTC

CROSS Jobourg 49°41'N 01°54'W   Cap de la Hague to the Pointe Penmarc'h
MMSI 002275200, ☎ 02·33·52·72·13   📠 02·33·52·71·72
On VHF Ch 80: From: Antifer, Ver-sur-Mer, Gatteville, Jobourg, Granville and Roche Douvres every H+20/H+50. On MF 1650 kHz: Gris-Nez at 0915 2115 LT

CROSS Corsen 48°24'N 04°47'W   Mont St Michel to Pointe de Penmarc'h, **MMSI 002275300,**
☎ 02·98·89·31·31   📠 02·98·89·65·75
On MF 2677 kHz: From CROSS Corsen at 0735 1935 LT

CROSS Étel 47°39'N 03°12'W   Pointe de Penmarc'h to l'Anse de l'Aiguillon
MMSI 002275000, ☎ 02·97·55·35·35   📠 02·97·55·49·34
On VHF Ch 80: From: Penmarc'h 0703 1533 1903 LT, Ile de Groix at 0715 1545 1915 LT. Belle-Ile at 0733 1603 1933 LT, Saint-Nazaire at 0745 1615 1945 LT, Ile d'Yeu at 0803 1633 2003 LT, and Les Sable d'Olonne at 0815 1645 2015 LT.

CROSS Soulac 45°31'N 01°07'W   L'Anse de l'Aiguillon to the French border, *MMSI 002275010,* From: 0700 to 2200 LT.   Night service is provided by CROSS Etel MRCC.
☎ 05·56·09·82·00   📠 05·56·09·79·73 On VHF Ch 79 From: Chassiron at 0703 1903 LT, Soulac at 0715 1915 LT, Cap Ferrat at 0733 1933 LT, Contis at 0745 1945 LT, and Biarritz at 0803 2003 LT.

SPAIN

Call initially on Ch 16 (H24) using the callsign of the remotely controlled station which will switch you to a working channel. Dedicated Autolink channels are in brackets; before calling verify that the Autolink channel is not in use.
Traffic lists are broadcast only on MF, every odd H+33, 0333-2333 UTC, except 2133.

NORTH SPAIN

Stations are remotely controlled by Bilbao Comms Centre.

Pasajes Radio 43°17'N 01°55'W VHF 27 Navigation warnings: VHF Ch 27 on receipt, after next silence period and at 0803 1503 UTC, *in Spanish.*

Machichaco Radio 43°27'N 02°45'W (no VHF) MF: Transmits 1707, 2182 kHz (H24); receives on 2132, 2045, 2048, 2182 (H24).Traffic lists: 1707 kHz. Every odd H+33
Navigation warnings: 1707 kHz. Urgent warnings on receipt, after next silence period at 0833 and 2033 UTC in Spanish and at 0033 0433 0833 1233 1633 and 2033 UTC *in English and Spanish.*

Bilbao VHF 26 Navigation warnings: VHF 26 at 0933 and 1533 UTC, *in Spanish.*

N Spain contd

Santander VHF 24 Navigation warnings: VHF 24 at 0803 1503 UTC, *in Spanish.*

Cabo Peñas VHF 26, MF 1677 kHz Navigation warnings: VHF 26 at 0903 and 1603 UTC, *in Spanish.*

Navia VHF 27 Navigation warnings: VHF 27 at 0833 and 1533 UTC, *in Spanish.*

PORTUGAL

Stations are remotely controlled from Lisboa. All monitor Ch 16 H24)

Arga Radio 41°48'N 08°41'W	VHF 25 28 83
Arestal Radio 40°46'N 08°21'W	VHF 24 26 85
Montejunto Radio 39°10'N 09°03'W	VHF 23 27 87

LISBOA RADIO 38°44'N 09°14'W VHF 23 25 26 27 28 MF: Transmits on 2182, 2578, 2640, 2691, 2781, 3607, 2778, 2693 kHz. Receives on 2182 (kHz) (H24)
Traffic lists: 2693 kHz every even H+05, following announcement on 2182 kHz.

Atalaia Radio 38°10'N 08°38'W	VHF 24 26 85
Picos Radio 37°18'N 08°39'W	VHF 23 27 85
Estoi Radio 37°10'N 07°50'W	VHF 24 28 86

SOUTH WEST SPAIN

Stations are remotely controlled from Malaga. All monitor Ch 16 H24

Chipiona Radio 36°42'N 06°25'W, No VHF MF: Transmits 1656, 2182 kHz (H24); receives on 2081 2182
Traffic lists: 1656 kHz every odd H+33 (except 0133 & 2133). Navigation warnings: 1656 kHz.
Urgent warnings on receipt, and at 0803 2003 UTC, *in Spanish.*

Cádiz Radio 36°21'N 06°17'W VHF 26 Navigation warnings: Ch 26 on receipt, after next silence period, and at 0903 1603 UTC, *in Spanish.*

Tarifa Radio 36°03'N 05°33'W VHF 81 MF 1704 kHz MF: Transmits kHz 1704 2182 (H24). Receives 2129 2182 (H24), 2045 2048 2610 3290 (Autolink).
Traffic lists: 1704 kHz. Navigation warnings: VHF 81 at 0833 and 1533 UTC. 1704 kHz on receipt, at 0803 1503 UTC, *in Spanish.*

NOTES	

Section 4

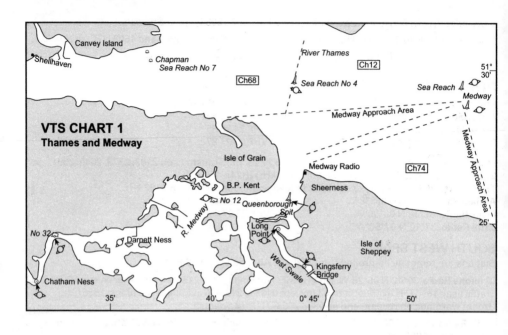

VTS CHART 1
Thames and Medway

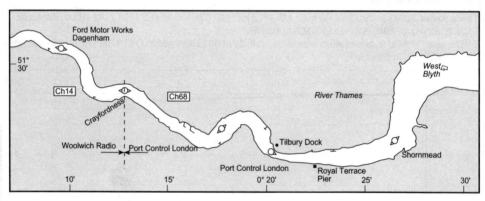

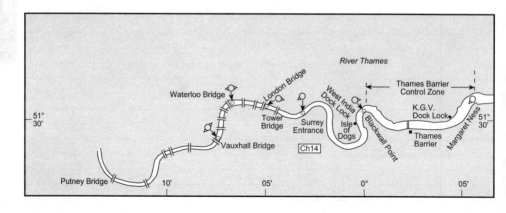

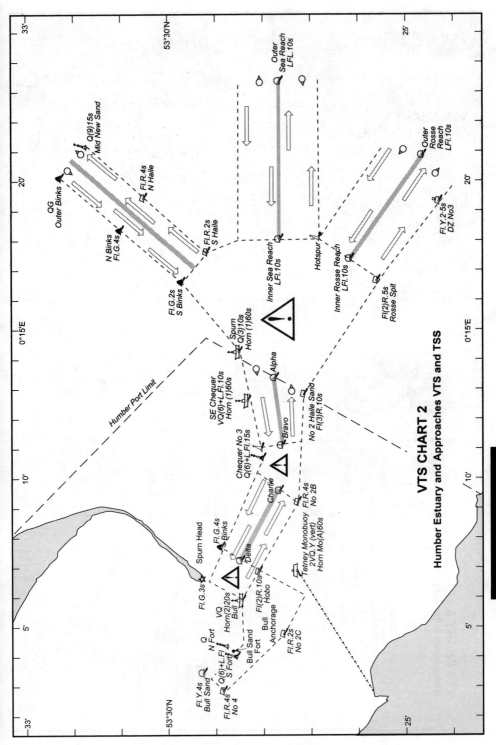

VTS CHART 2

Humber Estuary and Approaches VTS and TSS

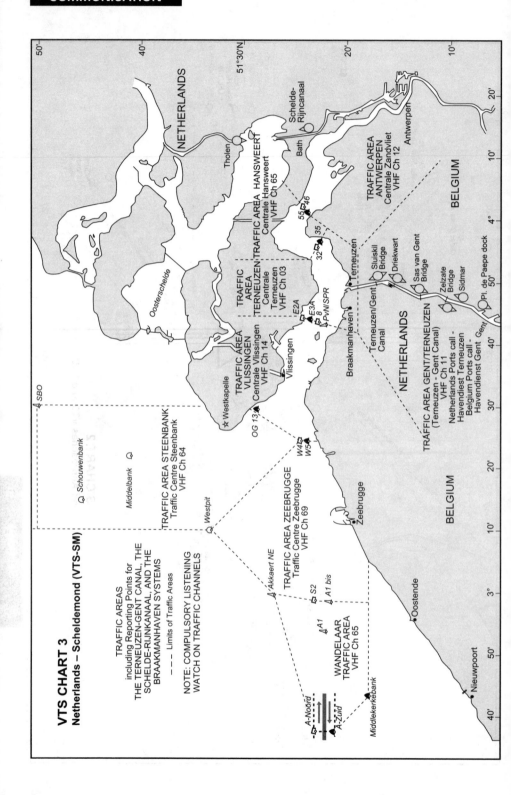

VTS CHART 3
Netherlands – Scheldemond (VTS-SM)

TRAFFIC AREAS
including Reporting Points for
THE TERNEUZEN-GENT CANAL, THE
SCHELDE-RIJNKANAAL, AND THE
BRAAKMANHAVEN SYSTEMS

– – – Limits of Traffic Areas

NOTE: COMPULSORY LISTENING
WATCH ON TRAFFIC CHANNELS

WANDELAAR
TRAFFIC AREA
VHF Ch 65

TRAFFIC AREA ZEEBRUGGE
Traffic Centre Zeebrugge
VHF Ch 69

TRAFFIC AREA STEENBANK
Traffic Centre Steenbank
VHF Ch 64

TRAFFIC AREA
VLISSINGEN
Centrale Vlissingen
VHF Ch 14

TRAFFIC
AREA
TERNEUZEN
Centrale
Terneuzen
VHF Ch 03

TRAFFIC AREA HANSWEERT
Centrale Hansweert
VHF Ch 65

TRAFFIC AREA
ANTWERPEN
Centrale Zandvliet
VHF Ch 12

TRAFFIC AREA GENT/TERNEUZEN
(Terneuzen - Gent Canal)
VHF Ch 11
Netherlands Ports call -
Havendienst Terneuzen
Belgium Ports call -
Havendienst Gent Gent

NETHERLANDS

BELGIUM

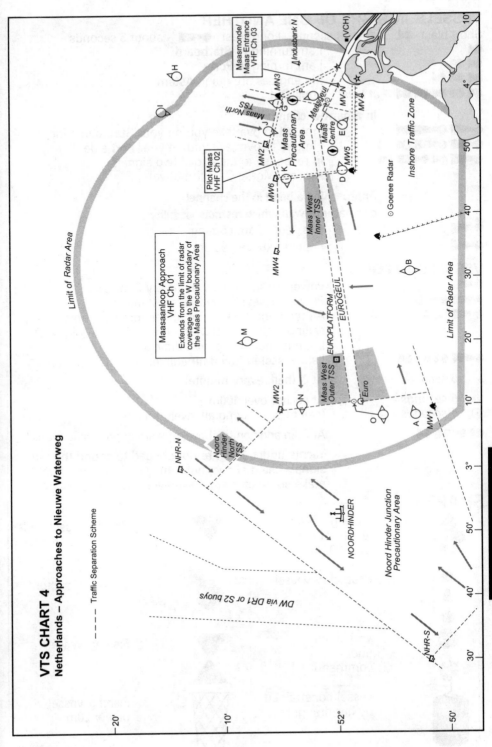

VTS CHART 4
Netherlands – Approaches to Nieuwe Waterweg

– – – – – Traffic Separation Scheme

Limit of Radar Area

Maasmonde/
Maas Entrance
VHF Ch 03

Maas North TSS

Pilot Maas
VHF Ch 02

Maasaanloop Approach
VHF Ch 01
Extends from the limit of radar
coverage to the W boundary of
the Maas Precautionary Area

Maas
Precautionary
Area

*Maas West
Inner TSS*

*Maas West
Outer TSS*

EUROPLATFORM
EUROGEUL
EUROGEUL

Euro

Noord
Hinder
North
TSS

NOORDHINDER

Noord Hinder Junction
Precautionary Area

DW via DR1 or S2 buoys

Inshore Traffic Zone

○ Goeree Radar

Limit of Radar Area

Indusbank N

(VCH)

MN3
MN2
MV-N
MV5
MV6
MW6
MW4
MW2
MW1
NHR-N
NHR-S

Maas
Centre

Maasgeul

SOUNDS

VESSELS IN SIGHT OF ONE ANOTHER

Short blast ◖◗ - about I second, Long blast ◖━ - about 5 seconds

◖◗ I am turning to **Starboard**
◖◗ ◖◗ I am turning to **Port**
◖◗ ◖◗ ◖◗ My engines are going **Astern**
◖◗ ◖◗ ◖◗ ◖◗ ◖◗ - *at least* **Look Out**

In a narrow channel

◖━ ◖━ ◖◗ I intend to overtake you on your **Starboard** side
◖━ ◖━ ◖◗ ◖◗ I intend to overtake you on your **Port** side
◖━ ◖◗ ◖━ ◖◗ In response to the above two signals -
Agreed (Morse C - affirmative)

Approaching a bend in the channel
or a harbour wall which restricts visibility

◖━ Look out - I am coming
◖━ Reply to above - so am I

VESSELS IN FOG

◖━ Power vessel under way (every 2 mins)
◖━ ◖━ Power vessel stopped (every 2 mins)
◖━ ◖◗ ◖◗ All the lame ducks - not under command, restricted,
sailing, fishing or towing - (every 2 mins)(Morse D -
I am manoeuvring with difficulty)
◖━ ◖◗ ◖◗ ◖◗ Last vessel in tow (immediately after tug signal)
🔔 5 seconds At ⚓ (bell, every minute)
🔔 5 seconds + At anchor over 100m
🔔 5 seconds (bell forward, gong aft, every minute)
◖◗ ◖━ ◖◗ At ⚓, in addition to above, to warn approaching vessel

Yachts under 12m are not obliged to sound the fog
signals listed above, but if they do not, they *must*
make some efficient noise every two minutes

SHAPES

Shape	Description	Shape	Description
◆	Towing vessel - length of tow over 200m	▼	Sailing vessel under sail *and* power
● ◆ ●	Restricted vessel	●	Vessel at anchor
● ●	Vessel not under command	▼▲	Fishing vessel
⬛	Vessel constrained by her draught	⧖	Fishing vessel below 20m

SECTION 5 - SAFETY

CONTENTS

Section 5

HOW TO MAKE A DISTRESS CALL.

1. Turn on Power and Radio.
2. Select VHF Channel 16.
3. Turn to **HIGH POWER (25W)**.
4. Switch off DUAL WATCH.
5. Hold down the button on the mike.
6. Then say slowly and clearly:
7. **MAYDAY, MAYDAY, MAYDAY**
8. This is.....................................(Repeat your boat name 3 times)
9. **MAYDAY**...........(Repeat boat's name again)
10. My position is...................

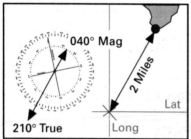

Use the chart
compass rose
to convert
Magnetic to True,
or give a
**Lat and Long
position**

Say if you are not sure – don't guess!

11. ***Tell them what is wrong:***
    the number of people (including you), if you have fired flares, if you are abandoning, etc. If there is time, repeat your position.
    I require immediate assistance
12. **Over** - This means: please reply.
13. **Release the button on the mike and listen.**
14. Only if you can't hear clearly, adjust the *SQUELCH* and/or *VOLUME*.

    If there is no reply, check the radio and repeat the message.

MAYDAY RELAY

1. **If you hear a MAYDAY CALL, write it down.**
2. If it is practical, give assistance.
3. If the MAYDAY is not answered pass it on like this:
4. Select VHF CH 16
5. Turn to HIGH POWER (25W)
6. Switch off DUAL WATCH
7. Hold down the button on the mike
8. Then say this slowly and clearly
   MAYDAY RELAY, MAYDAY RELAY, MAYDAY RELAY
9. **This is**......................(repeat your boat name 3 times)
10. **Repeat the MAYDAY message**
11. **Over** - This means : please reply
12. **Release the button and listen.**

MEDICAL HELP

1. **CH 16, High power, Dual watch off.**
2. **PAN PAN MEDICO** (repeat 3 times).
3. **ALL STATIONS** (repeat 3 times).
4. **This is** ....(repeat 3 times).
5. **Over.**

   Next message should contain:
   Yacht's name, callsign, nationality.
   Yacht's position and nearest harbour.
   Patient's details, symptoms and advice wanted.
   The medication you have onboard.

HELICOPTER RESCUE

1. **COMMUNICATE ON (CH 16) VHF.**
2. Use flares or smoke when helicopter is seen or heard.
3. Pilot may ask you to drop sails and motor an **EXACT COURSE**.
4. You may be asked to stream tender astern with casualty in.
5. Brief crew early (too noisy later).
6. **HELM MUST KEEP ON COURSE** and not be distracted.
7. Weighted line lowered.
8. Let it touch boat or water first (to earth any static charge).
9. Take in slack line only.
10. **PULL IN AS DIRECTED.**
11. **DO NOT TIE IT ON.**
12. **DO AS YOU ARE TOLD.**

FIRST AID

ESSENTIAL INFORMATION:

First ensure your own own safety and that of the vessel.

GETTING HELP

The recognition of signs of serious injury is not usually difficult and it is always better to ask advice if not sure. This is available by making a **MEDICO PAN-PAN** call by R/T or VHF radio, which will normally be processed by a coast radio station and/or the Coastguard. You will be connected to a local doctor or hospital for advice, and if assistance is required, it will be co-ordinated by the Coastguard. See Distress Communications Section.

FIRST STEPS

A - AIRWAY - NOT BREATHING: Know how to achieve and maintain an airway in all unconscious patients, by:

(1) Clearing any seaweed, excess saliva, vomit, false teeth, etc. from mouth and nose.

(2) Lifting the chin to prevent choking by tongue and soft palate falling back.

B - BREATHING - Sealing mouth with own mouth and pinching nose, then blow slowly and gently until the casualty's chest rises. 10 inflations should improve colour, then continue after 2-4 seconds another 10 ventilations, then re-assess. You can use mouth to nose ventilation if the casualty's mouth cannot be opened enough to breath into. The best position for maintaining spontaneous breathing after restarting is in the semi-prone or coma position. The casualty is rolled carefully on his side keeping head and neck in line.

C - CIRCULATION - HEART NOT BEATING: You can revive an unconscious or possibly near dead patient by external cardiac massage, if there is no pulse. The best place to find pulse is in the neck beside Trachea (Windpipe).

The patient must be lying on a firm surface. First ventilate 1 - 2 breaths. Then apply cardiac massage by pressure over the lower third of the sternum (breastbone) The heel of one hand should be placed two fingers width above the lower extremity of the sternum, and the heel of the other hand placed on top, with the fingers interlocked, keeping the elbows straight. Press down firmly on the sternum using just enough force to depress it (4.5cm), then release keeping hands in place. Continue by pressing firmly over the sternum with both hands, one on top of the other, with intermittent mouth to mouth respiration. The rate should be 80 compresses per minute, and the ratio of breaths to pressure should be 2:15. This should be continued until either colour improves, breathing starts or a pulse becomes palpable in the neck. Then place the patient in the recovery position.

BLEEDING: Know how to deal with severe haemorrhage.

EXTERNAL BLEEDING:- 1: Remove any loose foreign bodies from wounds. 2: Press a folded handkerchief or soft pad directly on to wound, adding more padding if this becomes soaked. 3: If possible raise bleeding part. 4: If pressure is used to control bleeding check colour and temperature of parts distal to pressure pad to ensure adequate blood supply, releasing pressure frequently.

INTERNAL BLEEDING: Apparent when blood appears from the mouth or rectum, or suspected when a person collapses with pallor, sweating and a fast pulse.

All that can be done is to place the victim in the semi-prone position and prevent heat loss by covering with a blanket or sleeping bag. Supervision is necessary. *ADVICE SHOULD BE SOUGHT AS SOON AS POSSIBLE BY RADIO* (Make VHF **MEDICO PAN-PAN** call).

LIVES CAN BE SAVED in all cases of injury by attending to the **A**IRWAY, **B**REATHING, **C**IRCULATION AND CONSCIOUS LEVEL, of injured crew and doing this in an organised method, using a check list prevents less important factors taking precedent. Always keep checking on anyone who has had an injury or been in the water.

GENERAL MEDICAL INFORMATION

ARREST - of heart's action can be caused by near drowning, by blood loss and by illness such as heart attack. It is not hard to recognise as the victim is obviously near death and a pulse cannot be found.

Refer to resuscitation above and perform external cardiac massage with patient on a firm surface such as deck or cabin sole, and with mouth to mouth resuscitation in a ratio of roughly 2 breaths to 15 chest pressings. Start with 2 breaths of expired air.

BREATHING - In conscious patients, problems can be caused by pain from injured ribs or chest infection. Help is given by pain killing tablets and/or antibiotics. Crew members with asthma will usually have their own medication and should be kept propped up. Keep checking. In an unconscious patient the airway must be cleared, the jaw tipped up and mouth to mouth breathing started if necessary, or if the patient is able to breath by himself he must be placed in the semi-prone position and carefully watched in case the airway gets blocked by his tongue or by vomit or saliva.

CIRCULATION: Problems of central (the heart/pump) and peripheral (blood vessels/distribution) should be tackled as follows:

(1) Central: Failure of the Heart's Action - dealt with by External Cardiac Massage (see above)

(2) Peripheral: Attempt to stop haemorrhage by method described above (see Bleeding)

BROKEN BONES - principles are immobilisation and observation of circulation to the part beyond the probable fracture.

Skull: suspect fracture in severe blows to the head, especially if the patient is unconscious.

Priorities are (a) airway clearance and maintenance and cardiac massage if required (b) pressure if scalp bleeding is severe (c) monitoring of conscious or unconscious state (d) remember the possibility of neck injuries, keep neck and shoulders in line.

Spine: possible in falls from a height. Priority is always airway clearance and maintenance, *DO NOT USE EXCESSIVE CHIN TILT*, but if possible try to roll or lift patient from danger with head and back in a straight line - for example on a board large enough to stretch from head to buttocks with a rolled towel around the neck to minimise movement. The head should be held steady at all times in line with body in horizontal and vertical planes. *THIS IS ESSENTIAL TO PROTECT THE SPINAL CORD.*

Ribs: are often fractured in crush injuries and falls and do not take precedent over skull or spine injuries. If they appear to be the only injury then pain relief is essential to allow free movement of the chest for efficient breathing. Consider internal bleeding if patient becomes pale, clammy and collapsed. Possible internal damage if he becomes breathless.

Upper Limbs: can be splinted to the trunk whether the fracture is closed or if bone is protruding. The bone should be immobilised at the joint above and below the fracture and padding should be inserted below any bandage or strapping. This should not be too tight and the part of the limb beyond should be checked regularly for changes in colour and temperature and for swelling which can restrict the blood flow. If this happens the bindings must be loosened. If the bone is protruding cut clothing away and if possible cover with sterile gauze. Pain killers and in the case of open fracture, antibiotics should be given as soon as possible.

Lower Limbs: Immobilise at point above and below fracture if possible. Check circulation in limb. Give pain relief or antibiotic cover for open fractures. The other limb, or an oar, is a suitable splint. Strapping should be added and distal circulation monitored.

BURNS - best treatment is immediate immersion of affected part in clean, cold sea water for at least 10 minutes. Severe burns will swell a lot so any tight clothing or jewellery should be cut open or removed. The swelling around the burn is fluid from the body which is then lost from the circulation so the victim can be shocked and dehydrated and fluid replacement is essential.

Burned tissue is easily infected and should not be handled, removed or blisters pricked. If clothing is stuck it should be left. Sunburn is a form of burn and can result in severe dehydration and shock.

BRUISES - can cause a lot of pain under a finger or toenail. These can be treated safely by flaming the end of a piece of wire (such as a paper clip) and burning through the nail, just enough to release the blood.

COLD INJURY - hypothermia should be suspected after any accidental immersion. Treat, whether apparent or not, by gradual re-warming. Shelter, dry clothes, gentle warmth from another person or handwarm heat source in a sleeping bag will help. *RESUSCITATION MAY BE REQUIRED.* Continual observation is essential.

CHOKING - can be relieved by a sharp blow to the back preferably in the head down position. Alternatively grasp the victim from behind and pull clasped hands into the upper abdomen.

COLLAPSE - can complicate injuries involving loss of blood, pain and loss of fluid. If the patient is unconscious then airway clearance, resuscitation and treatment of blood loss, then maintenance in the semi-prone position is paramount. Heat loss should be prevented but no active heating should be used. If the patient is conscious, loosen tight clothes and elevate the lower limbs. Fluids should be given (if conscious) frequently in small amounts.

CUTS - if deep, remove any foreign body and treat bleeding with compression. Clean and dry cut. Bring the edges together using Steristrips (or adhesive tape) to hold them closed, starting in mid-cut and working to ends. Reinforce middle strips to prevent bursting.

DROWNING - Try all the resuscitation techniques in the introduction, according to need.

A - Airway: clearance and maintenance

B - Breathing: by mouth to mouth or mouth to nose

C - Circulation: External Cardiac Massage may be required.

If successful, remember to monitor level of consciousness and check airway. Maintain semi-prone position and keep under observation. Hypothermia: usually complicates cold water immersion. Remove wet clothes and put patient in a dry sleeping bag with either a handwarm hot water bottle or a warm dry person. Look after patient out of wind, chill and rain and warm the cabin if possible. It can help to raise lower limbs and wrap towel round abdomen. Remember to watch for deterioration during warming.

DIARRHOEA - should be treated by oral fluids only; no solid food for 24/48 hours.

EYE INJURIES - Foreign body(ies) -

(a) Try to flush out with plenty of clean water.

(b) Try pulling upper lid over lower then releasing to remove foreign body from under upper lid. (c) Raise upper, then lower lid, asking casualty to look all around. The upper lid can be turned back on itself over a matchstick. The speck can usually be seen and removed with a Q-tip or clean handkerchief.

If the foreign body cannot be removed it may have penetrated the eye and no further attempts should be made to remove it. The eye should be covered and both eyes rested. If pain persists after the speck is removed there may be a concealed abrasion and the eyes should be rested and Chloromycetin eye drops or a solution of 1 teaspoonful salt to 1 pint of boiled cooled water inserted.

Lost contact lenses can be sometimes be lodged under upper lid in upper outer part of eye. It is possible to see them by turning back the lid and massaging them back into position through the lid.

403

FISH HOOKS - can penetrate the skin and may have to be pushed right through until the barb can be cut off with pliers and the hook withdrawn.

HEART ATTACK - though often hard to be sure, the following treatment should at least do no harm. First get the patient to lie down preferably on his side. Give strongest available pain killers and observe carefully for maintenance of clear airway and resuscitation should it be necessary.

HYPOTHERMIA - nearly always complicates cold water immersion and should be considered even when not apparent. If conscious the victim may be confused and appear drunk, seeming lethargic and remote from what is going on. Shivering fits may or may not occur and poor colour, vomiting or faintness can develop. The treatment is mentioned under Cold Injury above and consists of gradual rewarming by removal from wet and cold, replacement of wet clothing and if conscious rewarming in a warm sleeping bag. Priority must be given to attention to airway and the semi-prone position if the victim is unconscious.

INTERNAL INJURIES - may occur in any of the accidents which cause broken bones and bleeding and should be suspected when the patient seems unduly distressed, collapsed or blood appears from the body openings. The abdomen may appear rigid.

The priorities are airway clearance and maintenance and the adoption of the semi-prone position with careful observation to ensure prompt treatment of respiratory or cardiac arrest. The victim should be covered to prevent heat loss.

JOINTS - can be strained and sprained on decks and winches. The treatment is rest and time, but supporting crepe bandages can be comforting.

SEASICKNESS - is best avoided by starting treatment such as Stugeron or your favourite at least 12 hours before sailing. All these drugs may cause drowsiness. Alcohol must be avoided and hangovers predispose to seasickness.

ALL SEASICK CREW ON DECK SHOULD WEAR A HARNESS and should not be allowed to vomit over the side. Oral rehydration with very small amounts of rehydration fluids should be started, and fresh air and the ability to see the horizon can help.

The danger of cold should not be ignored. Stemetil anti-sickness suppositories can be useful.

SWALLOWING - Accidentally swallowed objects can usually be left to nature. Dangerous objects such as watch batteries and open safety pins should be treated as emergencies.

STINGS - from jellyfish are treated by oral antihistamines.

TOOTHACHE - caused by abscess and accompanied by swelling can be treated with antibiotics and painkillers. You can buy (OTC) dental kits.

VOMITING - Attempts should be made at rehydration using small amounts of fluid, preferably oral rehydration packs.

The information in the above list should give a casualty the best possibility of recovering until help arrives.

NOTE: It is so far unknown to contract AIDS from saliva, for although the virus may be present, the concentration is low. Intact skin is believed to be a secure protection from the virus present in blood and the risk in dealing with an unknown person is still very small.

First Aid for Cruising Yachtsmen, published by the RYA, offers more comprehensive coverage of this subject.

FIRST AID KIT

Items marked Rx require a prescription from a General Practitioner, who will have his own preferences and opinion on the need for a prescription: These are mainly for guidance.

ANALGESICS - for pain relief

Paracetamol (Panadol) tabs 500mg. Dose; 2 tabs 4-6 hours for medium to moderate pain. Dihydrocodeine tabs (Rx). Dose: 1 tab 4-6 hourly for moderate to severe pain. Cause constipation with long term use. Can be used at night for cough or in the treatment of diarrhoea. Pharmacists will discuss other (OTC) painkillers which are used for moderate pain.

ANTACIDS - for heartburn and indigestion. Gaviscon tabs. Dose; 2 tabs chewed and swallowed 3/4 times daily.

ANTIBIOTICS - for infections

Amoxycillin capsules 250mg (Rx). Dose; 2 caps three times daily. Check for allergy, otherwise safe. Oxytetracycline tablets 250mg (Rx) For infection if allergic to Penicillin. Dose; 1 tab four times daily. *NOT FOR CHILDREN OR PREGNANT WOMEN.*

DIARRHOEALS - Imodium capsules after each loose stool. Up to 6 per day in conjunction with oral rehydration and avoiding solid food.

ANTIEMETICS - for seasickness. Prevention - Stugeron or other proprietory preparation. Stemetil suppositories (Rx) along with oral rehydration in severe cases.

ANTIHISTAMINES - for stings, bites and hay fever. Newer Antihistamine - Loratadine, 1 tablet daily is less likely to cause drowsiness. Piriton tablets 4mg - cause drowsiness

ANTISEPTICS - Savlon, TCP, Dettol etc.

DRESSINGS - Melolin Sterile Squares 10cm x 10cm. Put shiny side to wound, can be cut up and secured with Elastoplast or Micropore Tape. Crepe bandages - assorted widths for dressings, sprains or for securing splints. Steristrips for wound closure.

EYE DROPS - for sticky, gritty or red eyes. Chloromycetin drops (Rx).

ORAL REHYDRATION - for vomiting and diarrhoea. Rehidrat or Diarolyte Powders in sachets with instructions. Start with small amounts then give freely to replace lost fluid in vomiting, diarrhoea, burns and sunburn.

UK VHF DIRECTION FINDING SERVICE

Remotely controlled continuosly by an HM Coastguard Maritime Rescue Co-ordination Centre (MRCC) or Maritime Rescue Sub-Centre (MRSC), this equipment is for emergency use only. It is not a free navigational service and should only be used 'one stage down' from real distress and it is in all yachtsmen's interests not to abuse the service.

Watch is kept on Ch 16 and after making contact invariably Ch 67 is used for the VHF-DF procedure. Note that the bearing obtained is from the station.

VHF-DF stations are identified by the prefix 'RG' on all charts in this manner.

STATION	CONTROLLED BY	POSITION	
Barra	MRSC Stornoway	57°00'·81N	07°30'·42W
Bawdsey	MRSC Thames	51°59'·55N	01°24'·59E
Berry Head	MRSC Brixham	50°23'·97N	03°29'·05W
Boniface	MRSC Solent	50°36'·21N	01°12'·03W
Compass Head	MRSC Shetland	59°52'·05N	01°16'·30W
Crosslaw	MRSC Forth	55°54'·50N	02°12'·20W
Dunnet Head	MRSC Pentland	58°40'·31N	03°22'·52W
Easington	MRSC Humber	53°39'·13N	00°05'·95E
Fairlight	MRCC Dover	50°52'·19N	00°38'·83E
Fife Ness	MRSC Forth	56°16'·78N	02°35'·25W
Flamborough	MRSC Humber	54°07'·08N	00°05'·12W
Great Ormes Head	MRSC Holyhead	53°19'·98N	03°51'·11W
Grove Point	MRSC Portland	50°32'·93N	02°25'·20W
Hartland	MRCC Swansea	51°01'·20N	04°31'·32W
Hartlepool	MRSC Tyne/Tees	54°41'·79N	01°10'·47W
Hengistbury Head	MRSC Portland	50°42'·95N	01°45'·64W
Inverbervie	MRCC Aberdeen	56°51'·10N	02°15'·65W
Kilchiaran	MRCC Clyde	55°45'·90N	06°27'·19W
Lands End	MRCC Falmouth	50°08'·13N	05°38'·19W
Landgon Battery	MRCC Dover	51°07'·93N	01°20'·69E
Law Hill	MRCC Clyde	55°41'·76N	04°50'·46W
Newhaven	MRSC Solent	50°46'·90N	00°03'·13E
Newton	MRSC Tyne/Tees	55°31'·01N	01°37'·10W
North Foreland	MRCC Dover	51°22'·50N	01°26'·82E
Rame Head	MRSC Brixham	50°18'·99N	04°13'·10W
Rhiw	MRSC Holyhead	52°49'·98N	04°37'·69W
Rodel	MRSC Stornoway	57°44'·90N	06°57'·41W
St Ann's Head	MRSC Milford Haven	51°40'·97N	05°10'·52W
St Mary's, Isles of Scilly	MRCC Falmouth	49°55'·70N	06°18'·17W
Sandwick	MRSC Stornoway	58°12'·65N	06°21'·27W
Selsey	MRSC Solent	50°43'·82N	00°48'·20W
Shoeburyness	MRSC Thames	51°31'·34N	00°46'·69E
Snaefell	MRSC Liverpool	54°15'·84N	04°27'·66W
Thrumster	MRSC Pentland	58°28'·70N	03°03'·00W
Tiree	MRSC Oban	56°30'·62N	06°57'·68W
Trevose Head	MRCC Falmouth	50°32'·91N	05°01'·89W
Trimingham	MRCC Yarmouth	52°54'·57N	01°20'·60E
Tynemouth	MRSC Tyne/Tees	55°01'·08N	01°24'·90W
Walney Island	MRSC Liverpool	54°06'·61N	03°16'·00W
Whitby	MRSC Humber	54°29'·40N	00°36'·25W
Wideford Hill	MRSC Pentland	58°59'·29N	03°01'·40W
Windyhead	MRCC Aberdeen	57°38'·90N	02°14'·50W

CHANNEL ISLANDS

Guernsey	Ship transmits on Ch 16 (Distress only)	49°26'·27N	02°35'·77W
Jersey	or Ch 67 (Guernsey) or Ch 82 (Jersey)	49°10'·85N	02°14'·30W

IRELAND

Orlock Point	MRSC Belfast	54°40'·42N	05°34'·97W
West Torr	MRSC Belfast	55°11'·90N	06°05'·60W

Section 5

VHF DIRECTION FINDING SERVICES

Compass Head
Wideford Hill
Dunnett Head
Thrumster
Sandwick
Rodel
Windyhead
Barra
Inverbervie
Tiree
Fife Ness
Kilchiaran
Crosslaw
Law Hill
Newton
Tynemouth
West Torr
Hartlepool
Orlock Head
Whitby
Snaefell
Flamborough
Walney Island
Easington
Great Ormes Head
Rhiw
Trimingham
52°N
Bawdsey
St Ann's Head
Shoeburyness
North Foreland
Langdon Battery
Fairlight
Hartland
Selsey Bill
Dunkerque
Hengistbury Head
Sangatte
Trevose Head
Newhaven
Gris-Nez
Rame Head
Grove Point
Boniface
Boulogne
Berry Head
Land's End
Levy
Ault
Homet
Barfleur
Dieppe
St Mary's
Lizard
La Hague
Saint-Vaast
Fécamp
Guernsey
Jobourg
La Hève
Roches-Douvres
Carteret
Villerville
Ploumanach
Jersey
Port-en-Bessin
Batz
Bréhat
Le Roc
Brignogan
Grouin
Créach
Saint-Cast
Saint-Mathieu
Toulinguet
Cap de la Chèvre
S-Quay-Portrieux
Pointe du Raz
Beg-Meil
Penmarc'h
Étel
Beg Melen
Saint-Julien
Port Louis
Piriac
Le Talut
Chemoulin
Taillefer
Saint-Sauveur

United Kingdom	Ch 16 (Distress only) Ch 67	
Guernsey	Ch 16 (Distress) Ch 67	
Jersey	Ch 16 (Distress) Ch 82	
France	Ch 16 11 67	

Les Baleines
Chassiron
La Coubre
Pointe de Grave
Cap Ferret
Messanges
Socoa

FRENCH VHF DIRECTION FINDING SERVICE

This service is for EMERGENCY USE ONLY. Each VHF direction-finding station is remotely control-led either by a Regional Operational Centre for Surveillance and Rescue (CROSS)', Signal Station or Naval Lookout Station. See associated diagram. CROSS Stations watch on Ch 16 or 11; (if a mari-time rescue operation is already underway on Ch 11, then Ch 67 is used).
Signal Stations and Lookout Stations keep a priority watch on Ch 16. Also available are 7 additional frequencies retained in memory (scanner sweeping) from amongst the following channels:

1-29	:	156.050 MHz-1 57.450 MHz	52	:	155.625 MHz
36	:	162.400MHz	55	:	155.775MHz
39	:	162.550MHz	56	:	155.825MHz
48	:	121.500 MHz	60-88	:	156.025 MHz-157.425 MHz
50	:	155.525 MHz			

Ship transmits on Ch 16 (distress only) or Ch 11 in order that the station can determine its bearing. Ship's bearing from the station is transmitted on Ch 16 (distress only) or Ch 11

STATION	HOURS	CONTROLLED BY	POSITION	
Ault	HJ	Controlled by Sig Stn	50°06'·50N	01°27'·50E
Barfleur	H24	Controlled by Sig Stn	49°41'·90N	01°15'·90W
Batz	HJ	Controlled by Sig Stn	48°44'·80N	04°00'·60W
Beg-Meil	HJ	Controlled by Sig Stn	47°51'·30N	03°58'·40W
Beg Melen	HJ	Controlled by Sig Stn	47°39'·20N	03°30'·10W
Boulogne	HJ	Controlled by Sig Stn	50°44'·00N	01°36'·00E
Bréhat	HJ	Controlled by Sig Sin	48°51'·30N	03°00'·10W
Brignogan	H24	Controlled by Sig Stn	48°40'·60N	04°19'·70W
Cap de La Chèvre	HJ	Controlled by Sig Stn	48°10'·20N	04°33'·00W
Cap Ferret	HJ	Controlled by Sig Stn	44°37'·50N	01°15'·00W
Carteret	HJ	Controlled by Sig Stn	49°22'·40N	01°48'·30W
Chassiron	HJ	Controlled by Sig Stn	46°02'·80N	01°24'·50W
Chemoulin	H24	Controlled by Sig Stn	47°14'·10N	02°17'·80W
Créach (Ouessant)	H24	Controlled by CROSS Corsen	48°27'·60N	05°07'·80W
Créach (Ouessant)	HJ	Controlled by Sig Stn	48°27'·60N	05°07'·70W
Dieppe	HJ	Controlled by Sig Stn	49°56'·00N	01°05'·20E
Dunkerque	H24	Controlled by Sig Stn	51°03'·40N	02°20'·40E
Étel	H24	Controlled by CROSS	47°39'·80N	03°12'·00W
Fécamp	H24	Controlled by Sig Stn	49°46'·10N	00°22'·20E
Gris-Nez	H24	Controlled by CROSS	50°52'·20N	01°35'·00E
Grouin (Cancale)	HJ	Controlled by Sig Stn	48°42'·60N	01°50'·60W
Homet	H24	Controlled by Lookout Stn	49°39'·50N	01°37'·90W
Jobourg	H24	Controlled by CROSS	49°41'·15N	01°54'·50W
La Coubre	H24	Controlled by Sig Stn	45°41'·90N	01°13'·40W
La Hague	HJ	Controlled by Sig Stn	49°43'·60N	01°56'·30W
La Hève	H24	Controlled by Sig Stn	49°30'·60N	00°04'·20E
Le Roc	HJ	Controlled by Sig Stn	48°50'·10N	01°36'·90W
Le Talut	HJ	Controlled by Sig Stn	47°17'·70N	03°13'·00W
Les Baleines	HJ	Controlled by Sig Stn	46°14'·60N	01°33'·70W
Levy	HJ	Controlled by Sig Sin	49°41'·70N	01°28'·20W
Messanges	HJ	Controlled by Sig Stn	43°48'·80N	01°23'·90W
Penmarc'h	H24	Controlled by Sig Stn	47°47'·90N	04°22'·40W
Piriac	HJ	Controlled by Sig Stn	47°22'·50N	02°33'·40W
Ploumanach	H24	Controlled by Sig Stn	48°49'·50N	03°28'·20W
Pointe de Grave	HJ	Controlled by Sig Stn	45°34'·30N	01°03'·90W
Pointe du Raz	H24	Controlled by Sig Stn	48°02'·30N	04°43·80W
Port-en-Bessin	H24	Controlled by Sig Stn	49°21'·10N	00°46'·30W
Port-Louis	H24	Controlled by Lookout Stn	47°42'·60N	03°21'·80W
Roches-Douvres	H24	Controlled by CROSS Jobourg	49°06'·39N	02°48'·80W
Saint-Cast	HJ	Controlled by Sig Stn	48°38'·60N	02°14'·70W
Saint-Julien	HJ	Controlled by Sig Stn	47°29'·70N	03°07'·50W
Saint-Mathieu	H24	Controlled by Lookout Stn	48°19'·80N	04°46'·20W
Saint-Quay-Portrieux	H24	Controlled by Sig Stn	48°39'·30N	02°49'·50W
Saint-Sauveur	HJ	Controlled by Sig Stn	46°41'·70N	02°18'·80W
Saint-Vaast	HJ	Controlled by Sig Stn	49°34'·50N	01°16'·50W
Sangatte	H24	Controlled by Sig Stn	50°57'·10N	01°46'·39E
Socoa	H24	Controlled by Sig Stn	43°23'·30N	01°41'·10W
Taillefer	HJ	Controlled by Sig Stn	47°21'·80N	03°09'·00W
Toulinguet (Camaret)	HJ	Controlled by Sig Stn	48°16'·80N	04°37'·50W
Villerville	HJ	Controlled by Sig Stn	49°23'·20N	00°06'·50E

GMDSS

Introduction

The Global Maritime Distress and Safety System (GMDSS) is an improved maritime distress and safety communications system adopted by the International Maritime Organisation (IMO).

Before the advent of GMDSS, maritime distress and safety relied heavily on ships and Coast radio stations keeping continuous watch on the three main international distress frequencies: 500 kHz (Morse) and R/T on 2182 kHz and VHF Ch 16. When out of range of Coast radio stations, only ships in the vicinity of a distress incident could render assistance.

GMDSS was introduced in Feb 1992 and became operational in most respects on 1 Feb 1999. The speed with which the various elements of GMDSS are put in place varies from sea area to sea area according to national policies. The Coastguard will cease its dedicated headset VHF Distress Watch on 31 Jan 2005.

It is important to note that ceasing the dedicated distress watch does not dispense with the capability to monitor the VHF Distress Channel since the channel is still needed to talk to a distressed vessel after the GMDSS DSC electronic alert. It is also still required to maintain communications with other ships assisting in the distress situation. Therefore, after 31 January 2005 HM Coastguard will keep a loudspeaker watch on the VHF Distress Channel.

Recommended reading:

ALRS, Vol 5. (UK Hydrographic Office).

GMDSS for small craft. (Clemmetsen/Fernhurst).

VHF DSC Handbook. (Fletcher/Reed's Publications).

Objective

The objective of GMDSS is to alert SAR authorities ashore and ships in the vicinity to a distress incident by means of a combination of satellite and terrestrial communication, and navigation systems. As a result a coordinated SAR operation can be mounted rapidly and reliably anywhere in the world. GMDSS also provides urgency and safety communications, and promulgates Marine Safety Information (MSI).

Regardless of the sea areas in which they operate, vessels complying with GMDSS must be able to perform certain functions:

- transmit ship-to-shore distress alerts by two independent means;

- transmit ship-to-ship distress alerts;

- transmit and receive safety information, e.g. navigation and weather warnings;

- transmit signals for locating incidents;

- receive shore-to-ship distress alerts;

- receive ship-to-ship distress alerts;

- transmit and receive communications for SAR co-ordination.

GMDSS regulations apply to all ships over 300 tons engaged in international voyages, but they affect all seagoing craft. Although not obligatory for yachts, some features of GMDSS are already of interest and, as equipment becomes more affordable, yachtsmen may decide to fit GMDSS voluntarily. This will become an increasing necessity as the present system for sending and receiving distress calls is run down.

Distress alerting

GMDSS requires participating ships to be able to send distress alerts by two out of three independent means. These are:

1 Digital Selective Calling (DSC) using VHF Ch 70, MF 2187.5 kHz, or HF distress and alerting frequencies in the 4, 6, 8, 12 and 16 MHz bands.   •

2 EPIRBs (406 MHz/i 21.5 MHz; float-free or manually operated) using the Cospas/Sarsat satellite system; or the Inmarsat system in the 1.6 GHz band. Both types transmit distress messages which include the position and identification of the vessel in distress.

3 Inmarsat, via ship terminals.

Communications

GMDSS uses both terrestrial and satellite based communications. Terrestrial communications, ie VHF, MF and HF, are employed in Digital Selective Calling (see below). Satellite communications come in the form of INMARSAT and Cospas/Sarsat.

Digital Selective Calling

DSC is a fundamental part of GMDSS. It is so called because information is sent by a burst of digital code; selective because it is addressed to another DSC radio-telephone.

Under GMDSS, every vessel and relevant shore stations has a 9-digit identification number, known as an MMSI (Maritime Mobile Service Identity) that is used for identification in all DSC messages.

DSC is used to transmit distress alerts from ships, and to receive distress acknowledgments from ships or shore stations. DSC can also be used for relay purposes and for Urgency, Safety and Routine calling and answering.

In practice, a DSC distress call sent on VHF might work roughly as follows:

Yachtsman presses the distress button; the set automatically switches to Ch 70 and transmits a coded distress message before reverting to Ch 16.

Any ship will reply directly by voice on Ch 16. But a CRS would send a distress acknowledgment on Ch 70 (automatically turning off the distress transmission), before replying on Ch 16. If a distress acknowledgment is not received from a CRS, the call will automatically be repeated about every four minutes.

Inmarsat

Inmarsat (International Maritime Satellite System), via four geostationary satellites, provides near-global communications except in the polar regions above about 70°N and 70°S.

Additionally, 1.6 GHz satellite EPIRBs, operating through Inmarsat, can also be used for alerting as an alternative to 406 MHz EPIRBs which use Cospas/Sarsat.

Cospas/Sarsat

The US/Russian Cospas/Sarsat satellites complement the various other Satcom systems. They not only detect an emergency signal transmitted by an EPIRB, but also locate it to a high degree of accuracy.

There are four Cospas/Sarsat satellites operating in low polar orbits. In addition to these, there are four GEOSAR geostationary earth orbit satellites capable of receiving alerts from 406 MHz beacons.

Sea Areas

For the purposes of GMDSS, the world's sea areas are divided into four categories in each of which ships must carry certain types of radio equipment. The UK has declared its coastal waters to be an A1 area, but intends to continue guarding VHF Channel 16 until 01 Feb 2005. VHF DSC is fully operational at all UK Coastguard radio stations.

In 1995 France declared the English Channel to be an A1 area. As most UK yachtsmen will operate in an A1 area, a VHF radio and a Navtex receiver will initially meet GMDSS requirements. As suitable VHF DSC sets become available (and affordable) it will make sense to re-equip with DSC equipment.

The types of areas are:

A1 an area within RT coverage of at least one VHF Coast or Coastguard radio station in which continuous alerting via DSC is available. Range: roughly 40 miles from the CRS/CG.

A2 an area, excluding sea area Al, within RT coverage of at least one MF CRS/CG in which continuous DSC alerting is available. Range: roughly 100-150 miles from the CRS/CG.

A3 an area, excluding sea areas Al and A2, within coverage of an Inmarsat satellite between 70°N and 70°S in which continuous alerting is available.

A4 an area outside sea areas Al, A2 and A3. In practice this means the polar regions.

Maritime Safety Information (MSI)

MSI refers to the vital meteorological, navigational and SAR messages which, traditionally, have been broadcast to vessels at sea by CRSs in Morse and by RT on VHF and MF.

GMDSS broadcasts MSI in English by two independent but complementary means, Navtex and SafetyNet:

Navtex on MF (518kHz) covers coastal/offshore waters out to about 300 miles from transmitters. SafetyNet uses the Inmarsat satellites to cover beyond MF range. The Enhanced Group Call (EGC) service is a part of SafetyNet which enables MSI to be sent selectively by Inmarsat-C satellites to groups of users in any of the 4 oceans.

MSI is prepared/coordinated by the nations which control the 16 Navareas used for Nav and Met warnings. The UK controls Navarea 1, which covers the Atlantic between 48°27N and 71°N, out to 40°W.

GLOSSARY OF FOREIGN TERMS

English	German	French	Spanish	Dutch
Ashore				
Ashore	An Land	A terre	A tierra	Aan land
Airport	Flughafen	Aéroport	Aeropuerto	Vliegveld
Bank	Bank	Banque	Banco	Bank
Boathoist	Bootskran	Travelift	Travelift	Botenlift
Boatyard	Bootswerft	Chantier naval	Astilleros	Jachtwerf
Bureau de change	Wechselstelle	Bureau de change	Cambio	Geldwisselkantoor
Bus	Bus	Autobus	Autobús	Bus
Chandlery	Yachtausrüster	Shipchandler	Efectos navales	Scheepswinkel
Chemist	Apotheke	Pharmacie	Farmacia	Apotheek
Dentist	Zahnarzt	Dentiste	Dentista	Tandarts
Doctor	Arzt	Médecin	Médico	Dokter
Engineer	Motorenservice	Ingénieur/mécanique	Mecánico	Ingenieur
Ferry	Fähre	Ferry/transbordeur	Ferry	Veer/Pont
Garage	Autowerkstatt	Station service	Garage	Garage
Harbour	Hafen	Port	Puerto	Haven
Hospital	Krankenhaus	Hôpital	Hospital	Ziekenhuis
Mast crane	Mastenkran	Grue	Grúa	Masten kraan
Post office	Postamt	Bureau de poste/PTT	Correos	Postkantoor
Railway station	Bahnhof	Gare de chemin de fer	Estación de ferrocanil	Station
Sailmaker	Segelmacher	Voilier	Velero	Zeilmaker
Shops	Geschäfte	Boutiques	Tiendas	Winkels
Slip	Slip	Cale	Varadero	Helling
Supermarket	Supermarkt	Supermarché	Supermercado	Supermarkt
Taxi	Taxi	Taxi	Taxis	Taxi
Village	Ort	Village	Pueblo	Dorp
Yacht club	Yachtclub	Club nautique	Club náutico	Jacht club
Navigation				
Abeam	Querab	A côté	Por el través	Naast
Ahead	Voraus	Avant	Avante	Voor
Astern	Achteraus	Arrière	Atrás	Achter
Bearing	Peilung	Cap	Maración	Peiling
Buoy	Tonne	Bouée	Boya	Boei
Binoculars	Fernglas	Jumelles	Prismáticos	Verrekijker
Channel	Kanal	Chenal	Canal	Kanaal
Chart	Seekarte	Carte	Carta náutica	Zeekaart
Compass	Kompass	Compas	Compás	Kompas
Compass course	Kompass Kurs	Cap du compas	Rumbo de aguja	Kompas koers
Current	Strömung	Courant	Coriente	Stroom
Dead reckoning	Koppelnavigation	Estime	Estimación	Gegist bestek
Degree	Grad	Degré	Grado	Graden
Deviation	Deviation	Déviation	Desvio	Deviatie
Distance	Entfernung	Distance	Distancia	Afstand
Downstream	Flußabwärts	En aval	Río abajo	Stroom afwaards
East	Ost	Est	Este	Oost
Ebb	Ebbe	Jusant	Marea menguante	Eb

English	German	French	Spanish	Dutch
Echosounder	Echolot	Sondeur	Sonda	Dieptemeter
Estimated position	Gegißte Position	Point estimé	Posición estimado	Gegiste positie
Fathom	Faden	Une brasse	Braza	Vadem
Feet	Fuß	Pieds	Pie	Voet
Flood	Flut	Flot	Flujo de marea	Vloed
GPS	GPS	GPS	GPS	GPS
Handbearing compass	Handpeilkompass	Compas de relèvement	Compás de marcaciones	Handpeil kompas
Harbour guide	Hafenhandbuch	Guide du port	Guia del Puerto	Havengids
High water	Hochwasser	Peine mer	Altamer	Hoog water
Latitude	Geographische Breite	Latitude	Latitud	Breedte
Leading lights	Feuer in Linie	Alignement	Luz de enfilación	Geleide lichten
Leeway	Abdrift	Dérive	Hacia sotavento	Drift
Lighthouse	Leuchtturm	Phare	Faro	Vuurtoren
List of lights	Leuchtfeuer Verzeichnis	Liste des feux	Listude de Luces	Lichtenlijst
Log	Logge	Loch	Corredera	Log
Longitude	Geographische Länge	Longitude	Longitud	Lengte
Low water	Niedrigwasser	Basse mer	Bajamar	Laag water
Metre	Meter	Mètre	Metro	Meter
Minute	Minute	Minute	Minuto	Minuut
Nautical almanac	Nautischer Almanach	Almanach nautique	Almanaque náutico	Almanak
Nautical mile	Seemeile	Mille nautique	Milla marina	Zeemijl
Neap tide	Nipptide	Morte-eau	Marea muerta	Dood tij
North	Nord	Nord	Norte	Noord
Pilot	Lotse	Pilote	Práctico	Loods/Gids
Pilotage book	Handbuch	Instructions nautiques	Derrotero	Vaarwijzer
RDF	Funkpeiler	Radio gonio	Radio-gonió	Radio richtingzoeker
Radar	Radar	Radar	Radar	Radar
Radio receiver	Radio, Empfänger	Récepteur radio	Receptor de radio	Radio ontvanger
Radio transmitter	Sender	Emetteur radio	Radio-transmisor	Radio zender
River outlet	Flußmündung	Embouchure	Embocadura	Riviermond
South	Süd	Sud	Sud, Sur	Zuid
Spring tide	Springtide	Vive-eau	Marea viva	Springtij/springvloed
Tide	Tide, Gezeit	Marée	Marea	Getijde
Tide tables	Tidenkalender	Annuaire des marées	Anuario de mareas	Getijdetafel
True course	Wahrer Kurs	Vrai cap	Rumbo	Ware Koers
Upstream	Flußaufwärts	En amont	Río arriba	Stroom opwaards
VHF	UKW	VHF	VHF	Marifoon
Variation	Mißweisung	Variation	Variación	Variatie
Waypoint	Wegpunkt	Point de rapport	Waypoint	Waypoint/Route punt
West	West	Ouest	Oeste	West

Officialdom

English	German	French	Spanish	Dutch
Certificate of registry	Schiffszertifikat	Acte de franchisation	Documentos de matrícuia	Zeebrief
Check in	Einklarieren	Enregistrement	Registrar	Check-in
Customs	Zoll	Douanes	Aduana	Douane
Declare	Verzollen	Déclarer	Declarar	Aangeven
Harbour master	Hafenmeister	Capitaine du port	Capitán del puerto	Havenmeester
Insurance	Versicherung	Assurance	Seguro	Verzekering
Insurance certificate	Versicherungspolice	Certificat d'assurance	Certificado deseguro	Verzekeringsbewijs

English	German	French	Spanish	Dutch
Passport	Paß	Passeport	Pasaporte	Paspoort
Police	Polizei	Police	Policía	Politie
Pratique	Verkehrserlaubnis	Pratique	Prático	Verlof tot ontscheping
Register	Register	Liste de passagers	Lista de tripulantes/rol	Register
Ship's log	Logbuch	Livre de bord	Cuaderno de bitácora	Logboek
Ship's papers	Schiffspapiere	Papiers de bateau	Documentos del barco	Scheepspapieren
Surveyor	Gutachter	Expert maritime	Inspector	Opzichter

Safety/Distress

English	German	French	Spanish	Dutch
Assistance	Hilfeleistung	Assistance	Asistencia	Assistentie
Bandage	Verband	Pansement	Vendas	Verband
Burns	Verbrennung	Brûlures	Quemadura	Brand wond
Capsize	Kentern	Chavirage	Volcó	Omslaan
Coastguard	Küstenwache	Garde de côte	Guarda costas	Kust wacht
Dismasted	Mastbruch	Démâtè	Desarbolar	Mastbreuk
Distress	Seenot	Détresse	Pena	Nood
Distress flares	Signalraketen	Fusées de détresse	Bengalas	Nood signaal
Doctor	Doktor	Médecin	Médico	Doktor/Arts
EPIRB	EPIRB	Balise	Baliza	EPIRB
Emergency	Notfall	Urgence	Emergencias	Noodgeval
Exhaustion	Erschöpfung	Epuisement	Agotamiento	Uitputting
Fever	Fieber	Fièvre	Fiebre	Koorts
Fire extinguisher	Feuerlöscher	Extincteur	Extintor	Brand blusser
First aid	Erste Hilfe	Premier secours	Primeros auxillos	Eerste hulp
Fracture	Fraktur	Cassure	Fractura	Breuk
Grounded	Aufgelaufen	Echoué	Encallado	Vastgelopen
Harness	Lifebelt	Harnais	Arnés de seguridad	Harnas/Tuig
Headache	Kopfschmerz	Mal à la tête	Dolor de cabeza	Hoofdpijn
Heart attack	Herzanfall	Crise cardiaque	Ataque corazón	Hartaanval
Helicopter	Hubschrauber	Hélicoptère	Helicóptero	Helikopter
Hospital	Krankenhaus	Hôpital	Hospital	Ziekenhuis
Illness	Krankheit, Übelkeit	Maladie	Enfermo	Ziekte
Injury	Verletzung	Blessure	Lesión	Verwonding
Jackstay	Strecktau	Contre-étai	Violín	Veiligheidstag
Lifeboat	Rettungsboot	Canot de sauvetage	Lancha de salvamento	Reddingsboot
Liferaft	Rettungsinsel	Radeau de sauvetage	Balsa salvavidas	Reddingsvlot
Lifejacket	Schwimmweste	Gilet de sauvetage	Chaleco salvavidas	Reddingsvest
Man overboard	Mann über Bord	Homme à la mer	Hombre al agua	Man over boord
Pulse	Puls	Poux	Pulso	Hartslag
Rest	Ruhen	Repos	Reposo	Rust
Seacock	Seeventil	Vanne	Grifos de fondo	Afsluiter
Seasickness	Seekrankheit	Mal de mer	Mareo	Zeeziekte
Seaworthy	Seetüchtig	Marin	Marinero	Zeewaardig
Shock	Schock	Choc	Choque	Shock
Sinking	Sinken	En train de couler	Hundiendo	Zinken
Sleep	Schlaf	Sommeil	Sueño	Slaap
Tow line	Schleppleine	Filin de remorque	Cabo	Sleeplijn
Unconscious	Bewußtlos	Inconscient	Inconsciente	Buiten bewustzijn
Wound	Wunde	Blessure	Herida	Wond

INDEX

Section 5

415

NOTES

CORRECTIONS

Any necessary corrections will be published on a monthly basis by *Practical Boat Owner* Magazine and on the web site www.ybw.com.

Data in this almanac is corrected up to Edition 36/2001 of the *Admiralty Notices to Mariners*.